Showing Why Math Matters

Rockswold teaches algebra and trigonometry in context, answering the question, "Why am I learning this?"

Creating a Social Network

Although it may not be obvious, math is essential for social networks to operate properly. Matrices are used to keep track of relationships between people on Facebook, Twitter, or Spotify. Also, a matrix can be used to describe links to and from websites on the Internet. (See the Chapter 9 Opener on page 700, Example 2 on page 755, and Example 9 on page 762.)

Starting Up Your Own Company

If you are starting up a small business, you might be interested in a payment startup called Square that allows businesses to swipe credit cards on iPhones and Android devices. Square's dramatic growth during recent years can be analyzed with the aid of a linear inequality. (See the Introduction to Section 2.3 on page 104 and Example 3 on pages 107-108.)

Getting the Jitters?

The side effects of caffeine include either headaches or the jitters. However, with the aid of a system of linear inequalities, we can identify the levels of caffeine intake where neither side effect occurs. (See the Introduction to Section 9.2 on page 719.)

Determining a Margin of Error

Whether a person is being shot out of a cannon or manufacturing an iPhone, the concept of a margin of error is essential. To determine accurate margins of error, we need the concept of an absolute value inequality. (See the Introduction to Section 2.5 on page 134 and Example 7 on page 140.)

Modeling Half-Life of a Facebook Link

A typical Facebook link experiences half of its engagements, or hits, during the first 3 hours. By using exponential functions we can estimate how many hits a Facebook link might experience in a given period of time. (See the Chapter 5 Opener on page 348 and Example 12 in Section 5.3 on pages 390-391.)

Classifying Tornados

The intensity of a tornado is often classified using the Fujita scale: the greater the wind speed of a tornado, the greater its Fujita number. To use this scale we need the concept of a piecewise-constant function. (See the discussion in Section 2.4 on page 121.)

Diminishing Returns and Overfishing

If there are only a few fishing boats in a large body of water, each boat might catch its limit. However, as the number of boats increases, there is a point of diminishing returns, where each boat starts to catch fewer and fewer fish. We can analyze this situation with a piecewise-polynomial function. (See Example 7 in Section 4.2 on pages 250-251.)

Understanding Size in Biology

Larger animals tend to have slower heart rates and larger birds tend to have bigger wings. To understand size and physical characteristics in nature, we need to study power functions. (See the discussion and Example 10 in Section 4.8 on pages 326-328.)

Gary Rockswold
with Terry A. Krieger and Jessica C. Rockswold

Trigonometry with Modeling and Visualization

Second Custom Edition for Oregon State University – Math 112

Taken from:
Algebra and Trigonometry with Modeling and Visualization, Fifth Edition
by Gary Rockswold with Terry A. Krieger and Jessica C. Rockswold

Cover Art: Courtesy of Pearson Learning Solutions.

Taken from:

Algebra and Trigonometry with Modeling and Visualization, Fifth Edition
by Gary K. Rockswold with Terry A. Krieger and Jessica C. Rockswold
Copyright © 2014, 2010, 2006 by Pearson Education, Inc.
Published by Pearson
Upper Saddle River, New Jersey 07458

This special edition published in cooperation with Pearson Learning Solutions.

All trademarks, service marks, registered trademarks, and registered service marks are the property of their respective owners and are used herein for identification purposes only.

Pearson Learning Solutions, 501 Boylston Street, Suite 900, Boston, MA 02116
A Pearson Education Company
www.pearsoned.com

Printed in the United States of America

2 3 4 5 6 7 8 9 10 VOZN 17 16 15 14 13

000200010271795844

AG

ISBN 10: 1-269-43824-7
ISBN 13: 978-1-269-43824-7

In memory of a kind man who said to me,

"Have joy wherever you go."

Marvin, 1914–2010

Foreword

In today's dynamic society, students need to understand mathematics regardless of their major. However, at every level, students continue to have difficulty learning and retaining mathematics. In order to both learn and retain mathematics, students must see a connection between the concepts and their real-life experiences. *Algebra and Trigonometry with Modeling and Visualization,* Fifth Edition, addresses these issues by appropriately connecting applications, modeling, and visualization to mathematical concepts and skills. This text consistently gives meaning to the equations and demonstrates that mathematics *is* relevant. It allows students to learn mathematics in the context of their experiences. Students learn mathematics more fully when concepts are presented not only symbolically but also visually. By complementing a symbolic approach with an emphasis on visual presentations, this text allows students to absorb information faster and more intuitively.

The concept of a function is the unifying theme in this text with an emphasis on the rule of four (verbal, graphical, numerical, and symbolic representations). A flexible approach allows instructors to strike their own balance of skills, rule of four, applications, modeling, and technology. Rather than reviewing all of the necessary intermediate algebra skills in the first chapter, this text integrates required math skills seamlessly by referring students "just in time" to Chapter R, "Basic Concepts from Algebra and Geometry." Instructors are free to assign supplemental homework from this chapter. Students also have additional opportunities to review their skills in the MyMathLab® course when needed. Here personalized homework and quizzes are readily available on a wide variety of review topics.

Students frequently do not realize that mathematics is transforming our society. To communicate this fact, the author has established a website at www.garyrockswold.net. Here, several resources are available, including a number of invited addresses given by the author. These presentations are accessible to students and allow them to understand the big picture of how mathematics influences everyone's life.

Contents

9 Systems of Equations and Inequalities *700*

Preface

Changes to the Fifth Edition

The Fifth Edition has an exciting new look that makes mathematics more visual and easier for students to understand. The following changes are the result of suggestions made by students, instructors, and reviewers.

- Several features have been added that allow graphs and tables to be labeled in a way that explains topics visually with fewer words.
- Hundreds of new real-world applications that relate to students' lives have been added.
- Approximately 1000 examples and exercises have been replaced or modified to better meet student needs.
- Real-world data has been added and updated to be more current and meaningful to students.
- Chapter 1 has been streamlined from five to four sections at the request of reviewers. As a result, the first two chapters can be covered more efficiently. Also at the request of reviewers, the definition of increasing and decreasing has been modified.
- Chapter 2 has been reorganized so that it begins with equations of lines in Section 2.1. Now additional modeling with linear functions occurs in Section 2.4.
- Chapter 3 includes new visual presentations and explanations for quadratic equations, quadratic inequalities, and transformations of graphs. Rules for the order of transformations have also been included.
- Chapter 4 includes a new subsection covering radical functions and their transformations. Several visuals have been added to help students understand polynomial behavior and graphs of rational functions.
- Chapter 5 has increased emphasis on transformations of exponential and logarithmic functions. It includes more visual explanations of logarithms.
- Chapter 6 has new visuals to explain angular velocity and transformations of sinusoidal graphs. Additional material covering other inverse trigonometric functions has also been added.
- Chapter 7 has improved clarity for students when they verify identities, simplify expressions, find reference angles, and solve trigonometric equations.
- Chapter 8 has additional examples for solving triangles using the law of sines and the law of cosines. New visuals have been added to the topic of vectors to help students understand this important concept better.
- Chapter 9 has a new subsection on social networks and matrices. Several application topics that relate to students' lives, such as the Internet, have been included.
- Chapter 10 has several new visuals that help students understand conic sections.
- Chapter 11 has an increased emphasis on explaining the distinction between sequences and series. More explanation of conditional probability is also given.
- Appendix D is new and explains how percentages, constant percent change, and exponential functions are related. These topics are important to students in their everyday lives.

Features

NEW!

■ **See the Concept**

This new and exciting feature allows students to make important connections by walking them through detailed visualizations. Students use graphs, tables, and diagrams to learn new concepts in a concise and efficient way. This feature also promotes multiple learning styles and deepens every student's understanding of mathematics. (See pages 32, 109, 233, 290, and 373.)

NEW!

■ **Comment Boxes**

This new feature allows graphs, tables, and symbolic explanations to be labeled in such a way that a *concept is easier to understand.* The explanation is now tied closely to a graph, table, or equation. (See pages 26, 73, 214, 271, and 294.)

■ **Chapter and Section Introductions**

Many algebra and trigonometry students have little or no understanding of mathematics beyond basic computation. To motivate students, chapter and section introductions explain some of the reasons for studying mathematics. (See pages 1, 67, 134, and 232.)

■ **Now Try**

This feature occurs after each example. It suggests a similar exercise students can work to see if they understand the concept presented in the example. (See pages 17, 74, and 106.)

■ **Getting Started**

This feature occurs in selected examples that require multistep solutions. Getting Started helps students develop an overall problem-solving strategy before they begin writing a detailed solution. (See pages 6, 71, and 390.)

■ **Algebra and Geometry Review Notes**

Throughout the text, Algebra and Geometry Review Notes, located in the margins, direct students "just in time" to Chapter R, where important topics in algebra and geometry are reviewed. Instructors can use this chapter for extra review or refer students to it as needed. This feature *frees* instructors from having to frequently review material from intermediate algebra and geometry. (See pages 97 and 160.) In addition, quizzes and personalized homework on review skills are now embedded in MyMathLab.

■ **Calculator Help Notes**

The Calculator Help Notes in the margins direct students "just in time" to Appendix A, "Using the Graphing Calculator." This appendix shows students the keystrokes necessary to complete specific examples from the text. This feature *frees* instructors from having to teach the specifics of the graphing calculator and gives students a convenient reference written specifically for this text. (See pages 6, 20, and 93.)

■ **Class Discussion**

This feature, included in most sections, poses a question that can be used for either classroom discussion or homework. (See pages 47, 157, and 236.)

■ **Making Connections**

This feature, which occurs throughout the text, shows students how concepts covered previously are related to new concepts being presented. (See pages 29, 94, 110, 136, and 175.)

■ **Putting It All Together**

This helpful feature at the end of each section summarizes techniques and reinforces the mathematical concepts presented in the section. It is given in an easy-to-follow grid. (See pages 98–99, 331–332, and 392–393.)

■ **Checking Basic Concepts**

This feature, included after every two sections, provides a small set of exercises that can be used as mixed review. These exercises require about 15 or 20 minutes to complete and can be used for collaborative learning exercises if time permits. (See pages 104, 133, and 188.)

■ **Exercise Sets**

The exercise sets are the heart of any mathematics text, and this text includes a large variety of instructive exercises. Each set of exercises covers skill building, mathematical concepts, and applications. Graphical interpretation and tables of data are often used to extend students' understanding of mathematical concepts. The exercise sets are graded carefully and categorized according to topic, making it easy for an instructor to select appropriate assignments. (See pages 80–85 and 183–188.)

■ **Chapter Summaries**

Chapter summaries are presented in an easy-to-read grid. They allow students to quickly review key concepts from the chapter. (See pages 224–227 and 337–341.)

■ **Chapter Review Exercises**

This exercise set contains both skill-building and applied exercises. These exercises stress different techniques for solving problems and provide students with the review necessary to pass a chapter test. (See pages 63–66 and 341–345.)

■ **Extended and Discovery Exercises**

Extended and Discovery Exercises occur at the end of selected sections and at the end of every chapter. These exercises are usually more complex and challenging than the rest of the exercises and often require extension of a topic presented or exploration of a new topic. They can be used for either collaborative learning or extra homework assignments. (See pages 65–66, 230, and 344–345.)

■ **Cumulative Review Exercises**

These comprehensive exercise sets, which occur after every two chapters, give students an opportunity to review previous material. (See pages 152–154 and 345–347.)

Instructor Supplements

ANNOTATED INSTRUCTOR'S EDITION

- Includes sample homework assignments indicated by problem numbers underlined in blue within each end-of-section exercise set.
- Sample homework assignments assignable in MyMathLab.
- Includes Teaching Examples, an extra set of examples for instructors to present in class, doubling the number of examples available for instructors. Solutions and Power Point Slides are available for these.
- Includes Teaching Tips, helpful ideas about presenting topics or teaching from the text
- Includes all the answers to the exercise sets, usually right on the page where the exercise appears

ISBN: 0-321-83679-0 / 978-0-321-83679-3

INSTRUCTOR'S SOLUTIONS MANUAL

- By David Atwood, *Rochester Community and Technical College*
- Provides complete solutions to all text exercises, excluding Writing about Mathematics

ISBN: 0-321-82619-1 / 978-0-321-82619-0

INSTRUCTOR'S TESTING MANUAL (DOWNLOAD ONLY)

- By David Atwood, *Rochester Community and Technical College*
- Provides prepared tests for each chapter of the text, as well as answers
- Available in MyMathLab or downloadable from Pearson Education's online catalog.

TESTGEN® (DOWNLOAD ONLY)

- Enables instructors to build, edit, print, and administer tests using a computerized bank of questions that cover all the objectives of the text
- Using algorithmically based questions, allows instructors to create multiple but equivalent versions of the same question or test with the click of a button
- Lets instructors modify test bank questions or add new questions
- Provides printable or online tests
- Available in MyMathLab or downloadable from Pearson Education's online catalog

INSIDER'S GUIDE

- Includes resources to help faculty with course preparation and classroom management
- Provides helpful teaching tips correlated to the sections of text, as well as general teaching advice

ISBN: 0-321-57717-5 / 978-0-321-57717-7

POWERPOINT PRESENTATION (DOWNLOAD ONLY)

- Classroom presentation software correlated specifically to this textbook sequence
- Available for download within MyMathLab or from Pearson Education's online catalog

Student Supplements

STUDENT'S SOLUTIONS MANUAL

- By David Atwood, *Rochester Community and Technical College*
- Provides complete solutions to all odd-numbered text exercises, excluding Writing about Mathematics and Extended and Discovery Exercises

ISBN: 0-321-83307-4 / 978-0-321-83307-5

Technology Resources

MyMathLab®   MyMathLab Online Course (access code required)

MyMathLab delivers **proven results** in helping individual students succeed.

- MyMathLab has a consistently positive impact on the quality of learning in higher education math instruction. MyMathLab can be successfully implemented in any environment—lab-based, hybrid, fully online, traditional—and demonstrates the quantifiable difference that integrated usage has on student retention, subsequent success, and overall achievement.

- MyMathLab's comprehensive online gradebook automatically tracks your students' results on tests, quizzes, homework, and in the study plan. You can use the gradebook to quickly intervene if your students have trouble or to provide positive feedback on a job well done. The data within MyMathLab is easily exported to a variety of spreadsheet programs, such as Microsoft Excel. You can determine which points of data you want to export and then analyze the results to determine success.

MyMathLab provides **engaging experiences** that personalize, stimulate, and measure learning for each student.

- **Exercises:** The homework and practice exercises in MyMathLab are correlated to the exercises in the textbook, and they regenerate algorithmically to give students unlimited opportunity for practice and mastery. The software offers immediate, helpful feedback when students enter incorrect answers.

- **Multimedia Learning Aids:** Exercises include guided solutions, sample problems, videos, and eText clips for extra help at point-of-use.

- **Expert Tutoring:** Although many students describe the whole of MyMathLab as "like having your own personal tutor," students using MyMathLab do have access to live tutoring from Pearson, from qualified math and statistics instructors.

And, MyMathLab comes from a **trusted partner** with educational expertise and an eye on the future.

- Knowing that you are using a Pearson product means knowing that you are using quality content. That means that our eTexts are accurate and our assessment tools work. Whether you are just getting started with MyMathLab, or have a question along the way, we're here to help you learn about our technologies and how to incorporate them into your course.

Rockswold's MyMathLab course engages students and keeps them thinking.

- Author designated preassigned homework assignments are provided.

- Integrated Review provides optional quizzes throughout the course that test prerequisite knowledge. After taking each quiz, students receive a personalized, just-in-time review assignment to help them refresh forgotten skills.

- Interactive figures are available, enabling users to manipulate figures to bring hard-to-convey math concepts to life.

- Section-Lecture Videos provide lectures for each section of the text to help students review important concepts and procedures 24/7. Assignable questions are available to check students' video comprehension.

To learn more about how MyMathLab combines proven learning applications with powerful assessment, visit www.mymathlab.com or contact your Pearson representative.

MyMathLab Ready to Go Course (access code required)

These new Ready to Go courses provide students with all the same great MyMathLab features, but make it easier for instructors to get started. Each course includes pre-assigned homework and quizzes to make creating a course even simpler.

Ask your Pearson representative about the details for this particular course or to see a copy of this course.

MyMathLab Plus/MyLabsPlus

MyLabsPlus combines proven results and engaging experiences from MyMathLab with convenient management tools and a dedicated services team. Designed to support growing math and statistics programs, it includes additional features such as

- **Batch Enrollment:** Your school can create the login name and password for every student and instructor, so everyone can be ready to start class on the first day. Automation of this process is also possible through integration with your school's Student Information System.
- **Login from your campus portal:** You and your students can link directly from your campus portal into your MyLabsPlus courses. A Pearson service team works with your institution to create a single sign-on experience for instructors and students.
- **Advanced Reporting:** MyLabsPlus's advanced reporting allows instructors to review and analyze students' strengths and weaknesses by tracking their performance on tests, assignments, and tutorials. Administrators can review grades and assignments across all courses on your MyLabsPlus campus for a broad overview of program performance.
- **24/7 Support:** Students and instructors receive 24/7 support, 365 days a year, by email or online chat.

MyLabsPlus is available to qualified adopters. For more information, visit our website at www.mylabsplus.com or contact your Pearson representative.

MathXL® MathXL Online Course (access code required)

MathXL is the homework and assessment engine that runs MyMathLab. (MyMathLab is MathXL plus a learning management system.)

With MathXL, instructors can
- Create, edit, and assign online homework and tests using algorithmically generated exercises correlated at the objective level to the textbook.
- Create and assign their own online exercises and import TestGen tests for added flexibility.
- Maintain records of all student work tracked in MathXL's online gradebook.

With MathXL, students can:
- Take chapter tests in MathXL and receive personalized study plans and/or personalized homework assignments based on their test results.
- Use the study plan and/or the homework to link directly to tutorial exercises for the objectives they need to study.
- Access supplemental animations and video clips directly from selected exercises.

MathXL is available to qualified adopters. For more information, visit our website at www.mathxl.com or contact your Pearson representative.

Acknowledgments

Many individuals contributed to the development of this textbook. I would like to thank the following reviewers, whose comments and suggestions were invaluable in preparing this edition of the text.

Dawit Aberra	*Fort Valley State University*
Dr. Josephine D. Davis	*Fort Valley State University*
Christy Dittmar	*Austin Community College*
Chi Giang	*Westchester Community College*
Christian Mason	*Virginia Commonwealth University*
Val Mohanakumar	*Hillsborough Community College*
Nancy Pevey	*Pellissippi State Community College*
Carolynn Reed	*Austin Community College*
Tracy Romesser	*Erie Community College North*
Jeffrey Saikali	*San Diego Miramar College*
Meredith Watts	*Massachusetts Bay Community College*
Cathleen Zucco-Teveloff	*Rowan University*

I would like to welcome Terry Krieger and Jessica Rockswold to the team for the fifth edition. They have provided invaluable help with developing new applications, visualizations, examples, and exercises. Terry and Jessica have contributed at all levels in the development of this new and exciting edition.

I would like to thank Paul Lorczak, Lynn Baker, Namyong Lee at Minnesota State University, Mankato, Mark Rockswold at Denver Community College, and David Atwood at Rochester Community and Technical College for their superb work with proofreading and accuracy checking.

Without the excellent cooperation from the professional staff at Pearson, this project would have been impossible. They are, without a doubt, the best. Thanks go to Greg Tobin for his support of this project. Particular recognition is due Anne Kelly and Christine O'Brien, who gave advice, support, assistance, and encouragement. The outstanding contributions of Sheila Spinney, Judith Garber, Heather Scott, Peggy Sue Lucas, Justine Goulart, and Joe Vetere are much appreciated. The outstanding work of Kathy Diamond was instrumental to the success of this project.

Thanks go to Wendy Rockswold, who gave invaluable assistance and encouragement throughout the project. She also supplied several of the photographs found throughout the text.

A special thank you goes to the many students and instructors who used the first four editions of this text. Their suggestions were insightful. Please feel free to contact me at either *gary.rockswold@mnsu.edu* or *www.garyrockswold.net* with your comments. Your opinion is important.

Gary Rockswold

6 Trigonometric Functions

Industrial robots comprise a multi-billion-dollar industry in the United States. Robots paint our automobiles, recognize voices, and even perform surgery that is more precise and less invasive than traditional techniques. In the future, robots will affect our quality of life by being able to assist the elderly, handle hazardous material, and help repair over 2 million miles of underground piping in our deteriorating infrastructure. Spectacular advances in microelectronic mechanical systems (MEMS) may make it possible for tiny robots to repair human tissue at the cellular level.

The trigonometry that has played a key role in the design of robots goes back to the 19th century. Some of the most important results in robotics have come from mathematicians and their interactions with engineers. Trigonometry is also used in applications involving monthly average temperatures, tidal currents, the Global Positioning System, electricity, highways, orbits of satellites, phases of the moon, and even music. In this chapter, we discuss the six basic trigonometric functions and many of their applications.

> It is not enough to have a good mind; the main thing is to use it well.
> —René Descartes

Source: National Science Foundation, *The Interplay between Mathematics and Robotics: Summary of a Workshop.*

6.1 Angles and Their Measure

- Learn basic concepts about angles
- Apply degree measure to problems
- Apply radian measure to problems
- Calculate arc length
- Calculate the area of a sector

Introduction

In 2007 at the French Open, Venus Williams hit the fastest serve recorded in a women's tour main-draw match, reaching 128 miles per hour. Much of the speed gained in a serve comes from flexing the wrist and rotating the shoulder joint. These rotations create *angular speed*, which transfers *linear speed* to the tennis ball. Trigonometry can be used to understand how fast it is possible to hit a tennis ball.   (***Source:*** J. Cooper and R. Glassow, *Kinesiology.*)

Angles

An **angle** is formed by rotating a ray about its endpoint. The starting position of the ray is called the **initial side**, and the final position of the ray is the **terminal side**. If the rotation of the ray is counterclockwise, the angle has *positive measure*; if the rotation is clockwise, the angle has *negative measure.* For simplicity we will refer to an angle as being **positive** or **negative**. The endpoint of the ray is called the **vertex** of the angle. See Figures 6.1 and 6.2, where the Greek letter θ (theta) has been used to denote an angle.

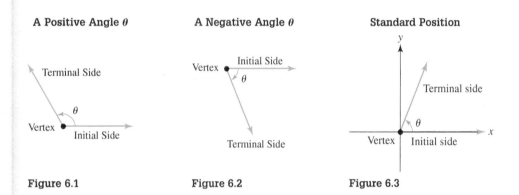

A Positive Angle θ

A Negative Angle θ

Standard Position

Figure 6.1

Figure 6.2

Figure 6.3

If the vertex is positioned so that it corresponds to the origin in the *xy*-plane and the initial side coincides with the positive *x*-axis, then the angle is in **standard position**, as shown in Figure 6.3.

There are two common systems for measuring the size of an angle: *degree measure* and *radian measure.*

Degree Measure

In **degree measure**, one complete rotation of a ray about its endpoint contains 360 degrees. One degree, denoted 1°, represents $\frac{1}{360}$ of a complete rotation. Figure 6.4 shows some examples of angles with their degree measure.

Degree Measure

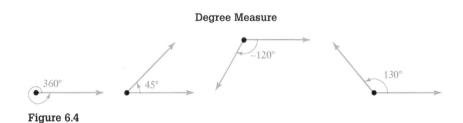

Figure 6.4

A **right angle** has measure 90°, and a **straight angle** has measure 180°. The measure of an **acute angle** is greater than 0° but less than 90°, whereas the measure of an **obtuse angle** is greater than 90° but less than 180°. Examples are shown in Figure 6.5.

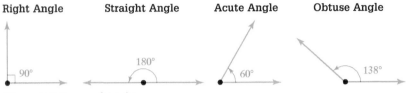

Figure 6.5 Types of Angles

We will use the Greek letters α (alpha), β (beta), γ (gamma) and θ (theta) to denote angles. For simplicity, we sometimes refer to an angle θ having measure 45° as a 45° angle, or an angle of 45°. This may be expressed as $\theta = 45°$. Two angles with the same initial and terminal sides are **coterminal angles**. Examples of coterminal angles are shown in Figure 6.6.

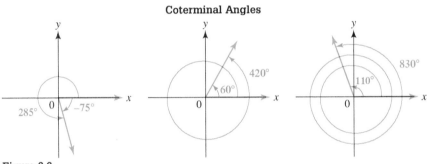

Figure 6.6

EXAMPLE 1   Finding coterminal angles

Find three angles coterminal with $\theta = 45°$, where θ is in standard position. Sketch these angles in standard position.

SOLUTION We can find coterminal angles by either adding multiples of 360° to θ or subtracting multiples of 360° from θ.

i. $45° + 360° = 405°$ **ii.** $45° + 2(360°) = 765°$ **iii.** $45° - 360° = -315°$

The angles 405°, 765°, and −315° are all coterminal with a 45° angle. These three angles and θ are sketched in Figure 6.7. Note that other angles are also possible.

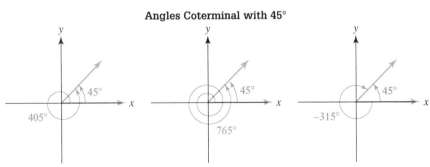

Figure 6.7

Now Try Exercise 13

Two positive angles are **complementary angles** if their sum is 90° and **supplementary angles** if their sum is 180°. For example, $\alpha = 35°$ and $\beta = 55°$ are complementary angles, whereas $\alpha = 60°$ and $\beta = 120°$ are supplementary angles. See Figures 6.8 and 6.9.

Complementary Angles   **Supplementary Angles**

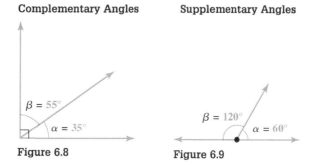

Figure 6.8   **Figure 6.9**

Fractions of a degree may be measured using **minutes** and **seconds**. One minute, written $1'$, equals $\frac{1}{60}$ of a degree, and one second, written $1''$, equals $\frac{1}{60}$ of a minute or $\frac{1}{3600}$ of a degree. The measurement $25°45'30''$ represents 25 degrees, 45 minutes, 30 seconds. Expressed in decimal degrees, this measurement is as follows.

Converting to Decimal Degrees

$$25°45'30'' = 25° + \left(\frac{45}{60}\right)^° + \left(\frac{30}{3600}\right)^° = 25.758\overline{3}°$$

$$1' = \frac{1}{60}° \qquad\qquad 1'' = \frac{1}{3600}°$$

We can convert decimal degrees to degrees, minutes, and seconds as illustrated in the next example.

EXAMPLE 2 Converting to degrees, minutes, and seconds

Convert 32.41° to degrees, minutes, and seconds.

SOLUTION

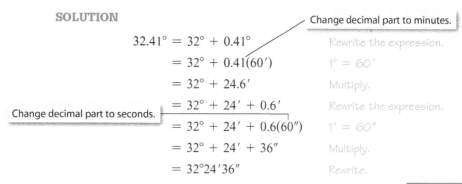

$32.41° = 32° + 0.41°$	Rewrite the expression.
$= 32° + 0.41(60')$	$1° = 60'$
$= 32° + 24.6'$	Multiply.
$= 32° + 24' + 0.6'$	Rewrite the expression.
$= 32° + 24' + 0.6(60'')$	$1' = 60''$
$= 32° + 24' + 36''$	Multiply.
$= 32°24'36''$	Rewrite.

Change decimal part to minutes.
Change decimal part to seconds.

Now Try Exercise 27

In the next example, we find complementary and supplementary angles using degree measure.

EXAMPLE 3 Finding complementary and supplementary angles

Find angles that are complementary and supplementary to $\alpha = 34°19'42''$.

SOLUTION If angle β is complementary to α, then $\beta = 90° - \alpha$.

$$\beta = 90° - 34°19'42''$$
$$= 89°59'60'' - 34°19'42'' \qquad 90° = 89°59'60''$$
$$= 55°40'18''$$

An angle supplementary to $\alpha = 34°19'42''$ is given by $\gamma = 180° - \alpha$.

$$\gamma = 180° - 34°19'42''$$

$$= 179°59'60'' - 34°19'42'' \qquad 180° = 179°59'60''$$

$$= 145°40'18''$$

> **Now Try Exercise 31**

NOTE Some calculators are capable of performing arithmetic using degrees, minutes, and seconds, as shown in Figures 6.10 and 6.11. (See the ANGLE menu.)

Converting to Degrees, Minutes, and Seconds

Results from Examples 2 and 3

```
32.41▶DMS
          32°24'36"
```

```
90°−34°19'42"▶DM
S
          55°40'18"
180°−34°19'42"▶D
MS
         145°40'18"
```

Figure 6.10 Degree Mode   **Figure 6.11** Degree Mode

Radian Measure

One Radian

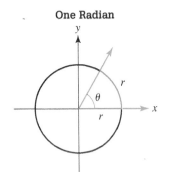

Figure 6.12

A second system of angle measure is based on *radians*. Radians are a common unit of measurement that often make formulas simpler and easier to use. Two examples are the formulas for arc length and area of a sector, which are introduced later in this section.

Angle θ in Figure 6.12 has a measure of one radian. The vertex of θ is located at the center of the circle, and its initial and terminal sides intercept an arc whose length is equal to the *radius r* of the circle.

> **RADIAN MEASURE**
>
> An angle that has its vertex at the center of a circle and intercepts an arc on the circle equal in length to the radius of the circle has a measure of **one radian**.

One Revolution Contains
$2\pi \approx 6.28$ Radians

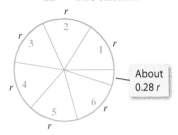

About 0.28 r

Figure 6.13

The circumference of a circle is $C = 2\pi r$. If we mark off distances of r along the circumference of a circle, it will appear as in Figure 6.13, where $2\pi \approx 6.28$ distances of r are shown. Therefore one rotation contains $2\pi \approx 6.28$ radians, and so 360° is equivalent to 2π radians. Radian measure can be compared to degree measure using proportions. Since 180° is equivalent to π radians, it follows that

$$\frac{\text{Radian measure}}{\text{Degree measure}} = \frac{\pi}{180°}.$$

Solving for radian measure results in

$$\text{Radian measure} = \text{Degree measure} \times \frac{\pi}{180°},$$

and solving for degree measure results in

$$\text{Degree measure} = \text{Radian measure} \times \frac{180°}{\pi}.$$

The following statements summarize the preceding discussion.

CONVERTING BETWEEN DEGREES AND RADIANS

To convert *degrees to radians*, multiply a degree measure by $\frac{\pi}{180°}$.

To convert *radians to degrees*, multiply a radian measure by $\frac{180°}{\pi}$.

NOTE One radian is equivalent to approximately 57.3°, because $1 \times \frac{180°}{\pi} \approx 57.3°$.

EXAMPLE 4 Converting degrees to radians

Convert each degree measure to radian measure.
(a) 90°   **(b)** 225°

SOLUTION
(a) To convert degrees to radians, multiply by $\frac{\pi}{180°}$.

$$90° \times \frac{\pi}{180°} = \frac{\pi}{2} \text{ radians}$$

Thus 90° is equivalent to $\frac{\pi}{2}$ radians.

(b) $225° \times \frac{\pi}{180°} = \frac{5\pi}{4}$ radians

Now Try Exercise 39

Table 6.1 shows some equivalent measures in degrees and radians.

Degree and Radian Measure

Degrees	0°	30°	45°	60°	90°	180°	360°
Radians	0	$\frac{\pi}{6}$	$\frac{\pi}{4}$	$\frac{\pi}{3}$	$\frac{\pi}{2}$	π	2π

Table 6.1

EXAMPLE 5 Converting radians to degrees

Convert each radian measure to degree measure.
(a) $\frac{4\pi}{3}$ **(b)** $\frac{5\pi}{6}$

Converting to Radians

```
90°
          1.570796327
225°
          3.926990817
```

Figure 6.14 Radian Mode

SOLUTION
(a) To convert radians to degrees, multiply by $\frac{180°}{\pi}$.

$$\frac{4\pi}{3} \times \frac{180°}{\pi} = 240°$$

Thus $\frac{4\pi}{3}$ radians is equivalent to 240°.

(b) $\frac{5\pi}{6} \times \frac{180°}{\pi} = 150°$

Now Try Exercise 43

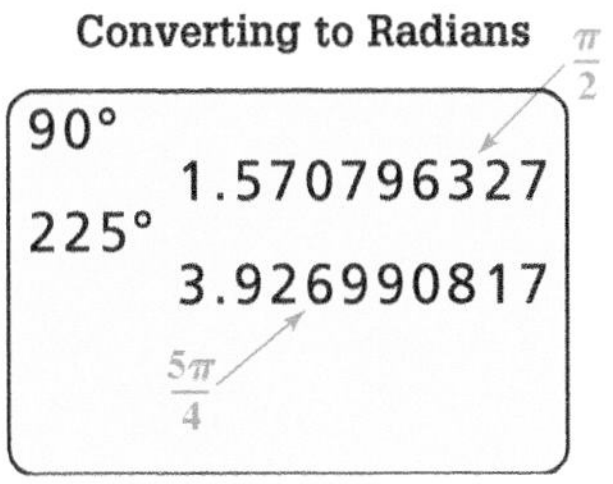

Converting to Degrees

```
(4π/3)ʳ
              240
(5π/6)ʳ
              150
```

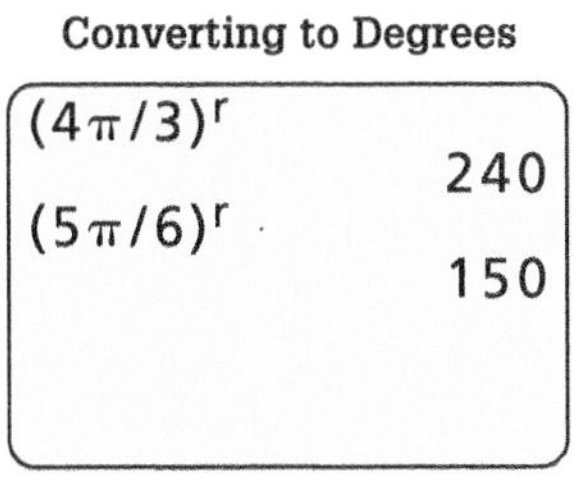

Figure 6.15 Degree Mode

NOTE Some calculators can convert degrees to radians and radians to degrees, as shown in Figures 6.14 and 6.15, respectively. When converting from degrees to radians, many calculators give only decimal approximations rather than exact values. For example, $\frac{\pi}{2}$ may be expressed as 1.570796327.

Arc Length $s = r\theta$

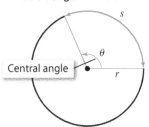

Figure 6.16

Arc Length

From geometry we know that the arc length s on a circle is proportional to the measure of the **central angle** θ. See Figure 6.16. A central angle of 2π radians corresponds to an arc length that equals the circumference $C = 2\pi r$. Using proportions yields

$$\frac{s}{\theta} = \frac{2\pi r}{2\pi},$$

which simplifies to $s = r\theta$.

ARC LENGTH

The **arc length** s intercepted on a circle of radius r by a central angle of θ *radians* is given by

$$s = r\theta.$$

NOTE   Angle θ *must* be in radian measure to use the arc length formula $s = r\theta$.

EXAMPLE 6   Finding arc length

A circle has a radius of 25 inches. Find the length of an arc intercepted by a central angle of 45°.

SOLUTION   First convert 45° to *radian* measure.

Calculating Arc Length

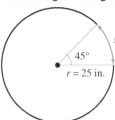

Figure 6.17

$$45° \times \frac{\pi}{180°} = \frac{\pi}{4}$$

The arc length s is given by   Must be radian measure

$$s = r\theta = 25\left(\frac{\pi}{4}\right) = 6.25\pi \text{ inches.}$$

The arc length s shown in Figure 6.17 is $6.25\pi \approx 19.6$ inches.

Now Try Exercise 47

EXAMPLE 7   Finding distance between cities

Albuquerque, New Mexico, and Glasgow, Montana, have the same longitude of 106°37′ W. The latitude of Albuquerque is 35°03′ N, and the latitude of Glasgow is 48°13′ N. If the *average* radius of Earth is approximately 3955 miles, estimate the distance between Albuquerque and Glasgow. See Figure 6.18.   (***Source:*** J. Williams, *The Weather Almanac.*)

Distance between Cities

Glasgow
Albuquerque

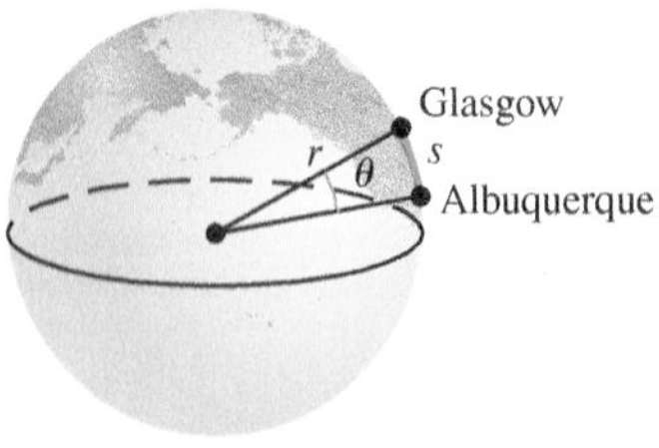

Figure 6.18 (not to scale)

SOLUTION   This distance can be estimated using the arc length formula. Start by converting $\theta = 48°13′ - 35°03′ = 13°10′$ to radian measure.

$$\left[13° + \left(\frac{10}{60}\right)^°\right] \times \frac{\pi}{180°} \approx 0.2298 \text{ radian}$$

The distance between Albuquerque and Glasgow is approximated by

$$s = r\theta \approx 3955(0.2298) \approx 909 \text{ miles.}$$

Must be radian measure

Now Try Exercise 81

Flexing the Wrist in Tennis

Figure 6.19

Rotation and Angular Speed The human joint that can be flexed the fastest is the wrist, which can rotate through 90°, or $\frac{\pi}{2}$ radians, in 0.045 second while holding a tennis racket. See Figure 6.19. **Angular speed** ω (omega) measures the speed of rotation and is defined by

$$\omega = \frac{\theta}{t}, \quad \text{Angular speed}$$

where θ is the angle of rotation and t is time. The angular speed ω of a human wrist holding a tennis racket is

$$\frac{\theta}{t} = \frac{\pi/2}{0.045} \approx 34.9 \text{ rad/sec},$$

or about 35 radians per second. The **linear speed** v at which the tip of the racket travels as a result of flexing the wrist is given by

$$v = r\omega, \quad \text{Linear speed}$$

where r is the radius (distance) from the tip of the racket to the wrist joint and ω is in radians per unit of time. If $r = 2$ feet, then the speed at the tip of the racket is

$$v = r\omega \approx (2)(35) = 70 \text{ ft/sec},$$

or about 48 miles per hour. In a tennis serve the arm flexes at the elbow and rotates at the shoulder, so the final speed of the racket is considerably faster. (***Source:*** J. Cooper and R. Glassow, *Kinesiology.*)

EXAMPLE 8 Finding the speed of a GPS satellite

GPS Satellite Coverage

Figure 6.20

Each of the 24 satellites used in the Global Positioning System is located 16,526 miles from the *center* of Earth and has a nearly circular orbit with a period of 12 hours. See Figure 6.20. (***Source:*** Y. Zhao, *Vehicle Location and Navigation Systems.*)
(a) Find the angular speed of a satellite.
(b) Estimate the linear speed of a satellite.

SOLUTION
(a) A GPS satellite circles Earth once (2π radians) every 12 hours. Its angular speed is

$$\omega = \frac{2\pi}{t} = \frac{2\pi}{12} = \frac{\pi}{6} \approx 0.5236 \text{ rad/hr}.$$

(b) Its linear speed is $v = r\omega = (16,526)(0.5236) \approx 8653$ miles per hour.

Now Try Exercise 79

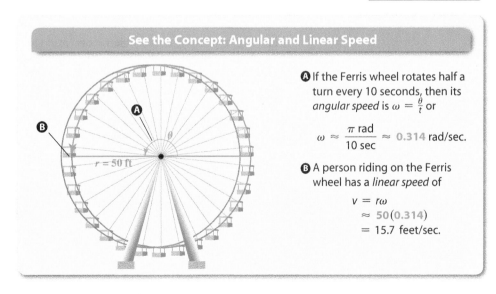

See the Concept: Angular and Linear Speed

Ⓐ If the Ferris wheel rotates half a turn every 10 seconds, then its *angular speed* is $\omega = \frac{\theta}{t}$ or

$$\omega \approx \frac{\pi \text{ rad}}{10 \text{ sec}} \approx 0.314 \text{ rad/sec}.$$

Ⓑ A person riding on the Ferris wheel has a *linear speed* of

$$v = r\omega$$
$$\approx 50(0.314)$$
$$= 15.7 \text{ feet/sec}.$$

$r = 50 \text{ ft}$

A shoulder can rotate at about 25 radians per second. Estimate how much this rotation increases the speed of a racket if the total length of the (straight) arm and racket is 4 feet.

Sector of a Circle

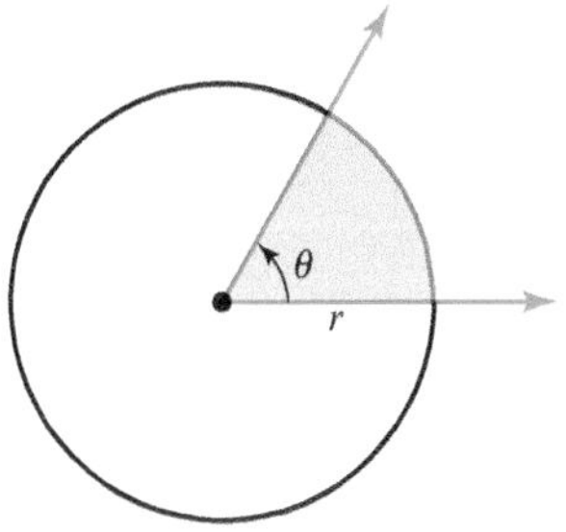

Figure 6.21

Area of a Sector

The **sector of a circle** is the portion of the interior of a circle intercepted by a central angle. The shaded region in Figure 6.21 shows a sector of a circle with radius r and central angle θ. The area of a sector is proportional to the measure of the central angle. If the central angle is 2π radians, then the area of the sector is the entire interior of the circle, which has an area of πr^2. Using proportions yields

$$\frac{\text{area of a sector}}{\theta} = \frac{\pi r^2}{2\pi}.$$

Solving the equation for the area of the sector results in

$$\text{area of a sector} = \frac{1}{2}r^2\theta.$$

AREA OF A SECTOR

The **area of a sector** A of a circle of radius r and central angle θ in *radians* is given by

$$A = \frac{1}{2}r^2\theta.$$

NOTE Angle θ *must* be in radian measure to use the area formula $A = \frac{1}{2}r^2\theta$.

EXAMPLE 9 Finding the area of a sector

A circle has a radius of 6 inches. Find the area of the sector if its central angle is 60°.

SOLUTION Since 60° is equivalent to $\frac{\pi}{3}$ radians, the area of the sector is given by

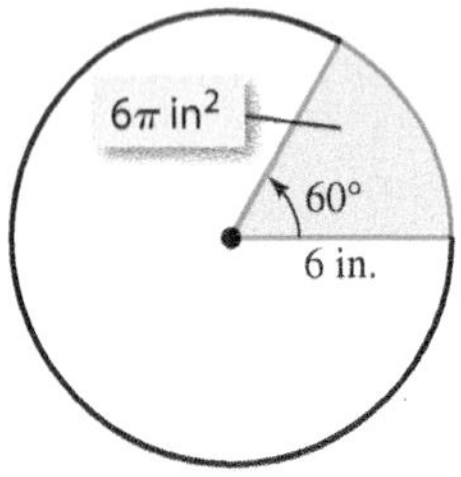

$$A = \frac{1}{2}r^2\theta = \frac{1}{2}(6)^2\left(\frac{\pi}{3}\right) = 6\pi \text{ square inches.}$$

Must be radian measure

This region of $6\pi \approx 18.8$ square inches is illustrated in Figure 6.22.

Calculating Area

6π in^2

60°

6 in.

Figure 6.22

Now Try Exercise 63

An Application Consider the robotic arm shown in Figure 6.23. The *work space* of the robotic arm is the shaded region and corresponds to the places that the hand can reach either by rotating or by changing the length of the arm. (***Source:*** W. Stadler, *Analytical Robotics and Mechatronics.*)

Work Space of a Robotic Arm

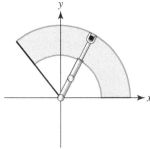

Figure 6.23

EXAMPLE 10 Finding the area of the work space for a robotic arm

Suppose that a robotic arm similar to the one in Figure 6.23 can rotate between $\theta = 10°$ and $\theta = 130°$. If the length of the robotic arm can vary between 5 inches and 20 inches, find the area of its work space.

SOLUTION The work space can be thought of as a large sector having radius $r_1 = 20$ inches with a small sector of radius $r_2 = 5$ inches removed. The arm can rotate through $130° - 10° = 120°$, or $\frac{2\pi}{3}$ radians. See Figure 6.24. The area A of the work space is computed as follows.

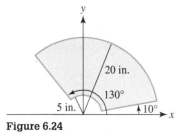

Figure 6.24

$$A = \frac{1}{2}r_1{}^2\theta - \frac{1}{2}r_2{}^2\theta \qquad \text{Area of large sector minus area of small sector}$$

$$= \frac{1}{2}\theta\left(r_1{}^2 - r_2{}^2\right) \qquad \text{Factor out } \tfrac{1}{2}\theta.$$

$$= \frac{1}{2}\left(\frac{2\pi}{3}\right)(20^2 - 5^2) \qquad \text{Substitute.}$$

$$= 125\pi \qquad \text{Simplify.}$$

The work space is $125\pi \approx 392.7$ square inches.

Now Try Exercise 71

6.1 Putting It All Together

Some concepts involving angles are summarized in the following table.

CONCEPT	EXPLANATION OR FORMULA	EXAMPLES
Degree measure	One complete rotation contains 360°.	A right angle contains 90°. A straight angle contains 180°. An acute angle α satisfies $0° < \alpha < 90°$. An obtuse angle β satisfies $90° < \beta < 180°$.
Radian measure	One complete rotation contains 2π radians.	2π radians is equivalent to 360°. π radians is equivalent to 180°. $\frac{\pi}{2}$ radians is equivalent to 90°. $\frac{\pi}{3}$ radians is equivalent to 60°. $\frac{\pi}{4}$ radian is equivalent to 45°. $\frac{\pi}{6}$ radian is equivalent to 30°.
Arc length	$s = r\theta$, where θ is in *radians*	If $r = 12$ feet and $\theta = 90°$, then $s = (12)\frac{\pi}{2} = 6\pi \approx 18.8$ feet.
Area of a sector	$A = \frac{1}{2}r^2\theta$, where θ is in *radians*	If $r = 6$ inches and $\theta = 45°$, then $A = \frac{1}{2}(6)^2\left(\frac{\pi}{4}\right) = 4.5\pi \approx 14.1$ square inches.
Angular speed	$\omega = \frac{\theta}{t}$, where θ is the angle of rotation and t is time	If $\theta = 5$ radians and $t = 0.1$ second, then $\omega = \frac{5}{0.1} = 50$ radians per second.
Linear speed of a rotating object	$v = r\omega$, where r is the radius and ω is the angular speed in *radians* per unit of time	If $r = 3$ feet and $\omega = 5$ radians per second, then $v = (3)(5) = 15$ feet per second.

6.1 Exercises

Angles

Exercises 1 and 2: Sketch the following angles in standard position.

1. (a) $45°$ (b) $-150°$
   (c) $\frac{\pi}{3}$ (d) $-\frac{3\pi}{4}$

2. (a) $-90°$ (b) $225°$
   (c) $-\frac{2\pi}{3}$ (d) $\frac{\pi}{6}$

Exercises 3–10: Sketch an angle θ in standard position that satisfies the conditions. Assume α is in standard position.

3. Acute   4. Obtuse

5. A positive straight angle   6. Complementary to $60°$

7. Positive and the terminal side lies in quadrant III

8. Negative and the terminal side lies in quadrant IV

9. Negative and coterminal with $\alpha = 90°$

10. Positive and coterminal with $\alpha = -135°$

11. What fraction of a complete revolution is each of the following angles?
    (a) $90°$ (b) $30°$ (c) $\frac{\pi}{3}$ (d) $\frac{\pi}{4}$

12. What angle is its own complement? What angle is its own supplement?

Degree Measure

Exercises 13–20: Find a positive angle and a negative angle that are coterminal with the given angle.

13. $150°$

14. $65°$

15. $-72°$

16. $-330°$

17. $\frac{\pi}{2}$

18. $\frac{5\pi}{6}$

19. $-\frac{\pi}{5}$

20. $-\frac{2\pi}{3}$

Exercises 21–24: Express the angle in decimal degrees.

21. $125°15'$ 22. $15°30'$

23. $108°45'36''$ 24. $256°06'12''$

Exercises 25–28: Convert the given angle to degrees, minutes, and seconds.

25. $125.3°$ 26. $15.25°$

27. $51.36°$ 28. $22.46°$

Exercises 29–34: Find the complementary angle α and the supplementary angle β to θ.

29. $\theta = 55.9°$ 30. $\theta = 71.5°$

31. $\theta = 85°23'45''$ 32. $\theta = 5°45'30''$

33. $\theta = 23°40'35''$ 34. $\theta = 67°25'10''$

Radian Measure

Exercises 35–38: Use the figure to determine the radian measure of angle θ. Then approximate the degree measure of θ to the nearest tenth of a degree.

35.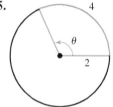

36.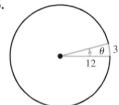

37.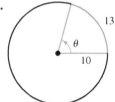

38.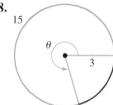

Exercises 39–42: Convert each angle from degree measure to radian measure. Round to the nearest hundredth of a radian when appropriate.

39. (a) $45°$ (b) $135°$ (c) $-120°$ (d) $-210°$

40. (a) $105°$ (b) $245°$ (c) $-255°$ (d) $-80°$

41. (a) $37°$ (b) $123.4°$ (c) $-92°25'$ (d) $230°17'$

42. (a) $56°$ (b) $88.7°$ (c) $122°15'$ (d) $-7°48'$

Exercises 43–46: Convert each angle from radian measure to degree measure. Round to the nearest hundredth of a degree when appropriate.

43. (a) $\frac{\pi}{6}$ (b) $\frac{\pi}{15}$ (c) $-\frac{5\pi}{3}$ (d) $-\frac{7\pi}{6}$

44. (a) $-\frac{\pi}{12}$ (b) $-\frac{5\pi}{2}$ (c) $\frac{17\pi}{15}$ (d) $\frac{5\pi}{6}$

45. (a) $\frac{\pi}{4}$ (b) $\frac{\pi}{7}$ (c) 3.1   (d) $-\frac{5}{2}$

46. (a) $\frac{7\pi}{2}$ (b) $\frac{2\pi}{5}$ (c) -4.1 (d) $-\frac{2}{3}$

Arc Length

Exercises 47–52: Use the formula $s = r\theta$ to determine the missing value in the figure.

47.

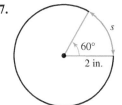

48.

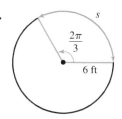

49.

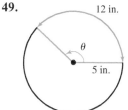

50.

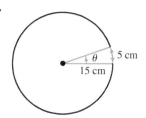

51.

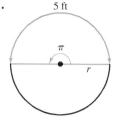

52.

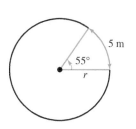

Exercises 53–58: Find the length of the arc intercepted by a central angle θ in a circle of radius r.

53. $r = 3$ m, $\theta = \frac{\pi}{12}$ **54.** $r = 7.3$ mm, $\theta = \frac{7\pi}{4}$

55. $r = 12$ ft, $\theta = 15°$ **56.** $r = 5$ cm, $\theta = 240°$

57. $r = 2$ mi, $\theta = 1°45'$ **58.** $r = 3$ mi, $\theta = 4°15'09''$

*Exercises 59–62: **Clocks** A minute hand on a clock is 4 inches long. Determine how far the tip of the minute hand travels between the given times. Find the linear speed of the tip.*

59. 10:15 A.M., 10:30 A.M.   **60.** 1:00 P.M., 1:40 P.M.

61. 3:00 P.M., 4:15 P.M.   **62.** 11:00 A.M., 1:25 P.M.

Area of a Sector

Exercises 63–66: Find the area of the shaded sector.

63.

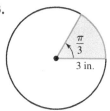

64.

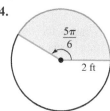

65.

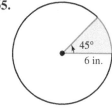

66.

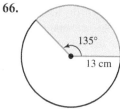

Exercises 67–70: Find the area of the sector of a circle having radius r and central angle θ.

67. $r = 13.1$ cm, $\theta = \frac{\pi}{15}$ **68.** $r = 7.3$ m, $\theta = \frac{5\pi}{4}$

69. $r = 1.5$ ft, $\theta = 30°$ **70.** $r = 5.5$ in., $\theta = 225°$

*Exercises 71–74: **Robotics** (Refer to Example 10.) Find the area of the work space for a robotic arm that can rotate between angles θ_1 and θ_2 and can change its length from r_1 to r_2. See the figure.*

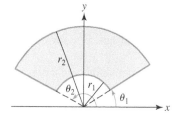

71. $\theta_1 = -45°$, $\theta_2 = 90°$, $r_1 = 6$ in., $r_2 = 26$ in.

72. $\theta_1 = -60°$, $\theta_2 = 60°$, $r_1 = 0.5$ ft, $r_2 = 2.5$ ft

73. $\theta_1 = 15°$, $\theta_2 = 195°$, $r_1 = 21$ cm, $r_2 = 95$ cm

74. $\theta_1 = 43°$, $\theta_2 = 178°$, $r_1 = 0.4$ m, $r_2 = 1.8$ m

Applications

75. Bicycle Tire A bicycle has a tire 26 inches in diameter that is rotating at 15 radians per second. Approximate the speed of the bicycle in feet per second.

76. Skateboard Wheel The wheels on a skateboard have a diameter of 2.25 inches. If a skateboarder is traveling downhill at 15 miles per hour, determine the angular velocity of the wheels in radians per second.

77. Ferris Wheel A large Ferris wheel has a diameter of 140 feet. It completes 1 revolution every 420 seconds.
(a) Find the angular velocity in radians per second.

(b) What is the linear speed of a person who is riding this Ferris wheel?

78. Location of the North Star Presently the North Star, Polaris, is located near the true North Pole. However, because Earth is inclined 23.5°, Earth precesses like a spinning top and the direction of the celestial North Pole traces out a circular path once every 26,000 years, as shown in the figure. Calculate the angle in seconds that the celestial North Pole moves each year, as viewed from the center *C* of this circular path. (*Source:* M. Zeilik et al., *Introductory Astronomy and Astrophysics.*)

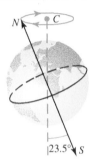

79. Fan Speed The blades of a fan have a 30-inch diameter and rotate at 500 revolutions per minute.
(a) Find the angular velocity of a fan blade.

(b) Estimate the linear speed at the tip of a fan blade.

80. Earth's Rotation Earth rotates 1 complete revolution every 24 hours and has an *equatorial* radius of about 3963 miles.
(a) Find the angular velocity of a person standing at the equator in radians per hour.

(b) Estimate the linear speed in miles per hour at the equator due to Earth's rotation.

81. Distance between Cities (Refer to Example 7.) Daytona Beach, Florida, and Akron, Ohio, have nearly the same longitude of 81° W. The latitude of Daytona Beach is 29°11′, and the latitude of Akron is 40°55′. Approximate the distance between these two cities if the *average* radius of Earth is 3955 miles.

82. Nautical Miles Nautical miles are used by ships and airplanes. They are different from statute miles, which equal 5280 feet. A nautical mile is defined to be the arc length along the equator intercepted by a central angle *AOB* of 1 minute, as illustrated in the figure at the top of the next column. If the *equatorial* radius of Earth is 3963 statute miles, use the arc length formula to approximate the number of statute miles in 1 nautical mile. Round your answer to two decimal places.

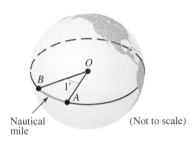

Nautical mile   (Not to scale)

83. Tennis Serve (See the discussion before Example 8.) Suppose that a tennis player rotates her wrist 85° in 0.05 second. If the tennis racket is 28 inches in length, estimate the speed of the tip of the racket in feet per second.

84. Club Speed in Golf The shoulder joint can rotate at about 25 radians per second. Assuming that a golfer's arm is straight and the distance from the shoulder to the club head is 5 feet, estimate the linear speed of the club head from shoulder rotation. (*Source:* J. Cooper and R. Glassow, *Kinesiology.*)

85. Pulleys Approximate how many inches the weight in the figure will rise if *r* = 11 inches and the pulley is rotated through an angle of 75.3°.

11 in.

86. Pulleys Use the figure in Exercise 85 to estimate the angle *θ* through which the pulley should be rotated to raise the weight 5 inches.

87. Bicycle Chain Drive The figure shows the chain drive of a bicycle. The radius of the sprocket wheel that the pedals are attached to is 3.75 inches, and the radius of the other sprocket wheel is 1.5 inches.
(a) Determine the number of revolutions that the bicycle tire rotates when the pedals are rotated one revolution.

(b) If the bicycle has a tire with a 26-inch diameter, determine how fast the bicycle travels in feet per second when the pedals turn through two revolutions per second.

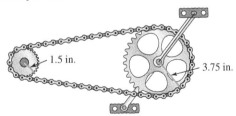

1.5 in.   3.75 in.

88. **Wind Speed** One of the most common ways to measure wind speed is with a *three-cup anemometer*, as shown in the figure. The cups catch the wind and cause the vertical shaft to rotate. At lower wind speeds the cups move at approximately the same speed as the wind. If the cups are rotating 5 times per second with a radius of 6 inches, estimate the wind speed in miles per hour. (*Source:* J. Navarra, *Atmosphere, Weather and Climate.*)

89. **Velocity of Planets** The average distance D in millions of miles from the sun and the orbital period P in years are given for various planets. Assuming that the orbits are circular, approximate the average orbital velocity in miles per hour for each planet. Discuss the effect that average distance from the sun has on orbital velocity. (*Source:* C. Ronan, *The Natural History of the Universe.*)
    (a) Venus: $D = 67.2$, $P = 0.615$
    (b) Earth: $D = 92.9$, $P = 1$
    (c) Jupiter: $D = 483.6$, $P = 11.86$
    (d) Neptune: $D = 2794$, $P = 164.8$

90. **Speed of a Propeller** When a 90-horsepower outboard motor is at full throttle, its propeller makes 5000 revolutions per minute. Find the angular velocity of the propeller in radians per second. What is the linear speed in inches per second of a point at the tip of the propeller if its diameter is 10 inches?

91. **Surveying** The *subtense bar method* is a technique used in surveying to measure distances. A green subtense bar is shown in the figure connecting points P and Q. If the distance d from the surveyor to the bar is large, then there is little difference between the length of the subtense bar, which is usually 2 meters, and that of the red arc connecting P and Q. Similarly, there is little difference between d and the radius r of the arc intercepted by the subtense bar. If θ is measured to be $0.835°$, approximate d using the arc length formula. (*Source:* I. Mueller and K. Ramsayer, *Introduction to Surveying.*)

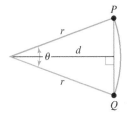

92. **Diameter of the Moon** (Refer to Exercise 91.) The distance to the moon is approximately 238,900 miles. Use the arc length formula to estimate the diameter d of the moon if angle θ in the figure at the top of the next column is measured to be $0.517°$.

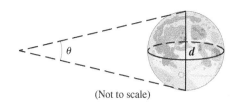
(Not to scale)

93. **Solar Power Plant** A 150-megawatt solar power plant requires approximately 475,000 square meters of land to collect the required amount of energy from sunlight. (*Source:* C. Winter, *Solar Power Plants.*)
    (a) If this land area is circular, approximate its radius.
    (b) If this land area is a sector of a circle with $\theta = 70°$, approximate its radius.

94. **Measuring the Circumference of Earth** The first accurate estimate of the distance around Earth was made by the Greek astronomer Eratosthenes (276–195 B.C.), who noted that the noontime position of the sun at the summer solstice differed by $7°12'$ from the city of Syene to the city of Alexander. See the figure. The distance between these two cities is 496 miles. Use the arc length formula to estimate the radius of Earth. Then find the circumference of Earth. (*Source:* M. Zeilik et. al., *Introductory Astronomy and Astrophysics.*)

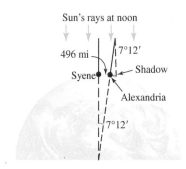

Sun's rays at noon

496 mi

$7°12'$

Syene

Shadow

Alexandria

$7°12'$

Writing about Mathematics

95. Give definitions for 1 degree and 1 radian. Compare these two units of angle measure. Which unit of measure do you prefer? Explain why.

96. Suppose a central angle θ of a circle remains fixed. Describe what happens to the arc length intercepted by θ and the area of the corresponding sector as the radius r doubles and triples.

Extended and Discovery Exercises

1. **Arc Length Formula** Modify the arc length formula $s = r\theta$ so that angle θ can be given in degrees rather than radians. Which of the two formulas is simpler?

2. **Area of a Sector Formula** Modify the area formula $A = \frac{1}{2}r^2\theta$ so that angle θ can be given in degrees rather than radians. Which of the two formulas is simpler?

6.2 Right Triangle Trigonometry

- Learn basic concepts about trigonometric functions
- Apply right triangle trigonometry
- Understand complementary angles and cofunctions

Introduction

A right triangle is a basic geometric shape that occurs in many applications such as astronomy, surveying, construction, highway design, GPS, weather, and aerial photography. Trigonometric functions are used to *solve* triangles. **Solving a triangle** involves finding the measure of each side and angle in the triangle. Like other functions that we have encountered previously, the six trigonometric functions can be used to model data and a variety of physical phenomena.

Basic Concepts of Trigonometric Functions

The **standard labeling** used to designate vertices, angles, and sides of a triangle ABC is shown in Figure 6.25.

Standard Labeling of a Triangle

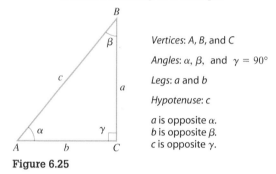

Vertices: *A*, *B*, and *C*

Angles: α, β, and $\gamma = 90°$

Legs: *a* and *b*

Hypotenuse: *c*

a is opposite α.
b is opposite β.
c is opposite γ.

Figure 6.25

Many important ideas in trigonometry depend on the properties of similar triangles. **Similar triangles** have congruent corresponding angles, but similar triangles are not necessarily the same size. Similar triangles are shown in Figures 6.26 and 6.27. Corresponding sides of similar triangles are proportional.

Similar Triangles

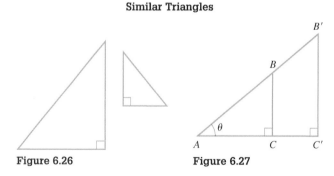

Figure 6.26   **Figure 6.27**

Geometry Review
To review similar triangles, see Chapter R (page R-5).

The Sine Function The right triangles ABC and $AB'C'$ shown in Figure 6.27 are similar triangles. By the properties of similar triangles, the following ratios are equal.

$$\frac{BC}{AB} = \frac{B'C'}{AB'}$$

That is, the ratio of the length of the side opposite angle θ to the length of the hypotenuse is constant for a given angle θ and does not depend on the size of the right triangle. If the measure of θ changes, then the ratio of the length of the side opposite θ to the length of the hypotenuse also changes. This concept can be used to define a new function called the *sine function*. That is, if θ is an acute angle in a right triangle, as shown in Figure 6.28, then we define the sine of θ as

Sine function ⎯⎯⎯ $\sin \theta = \dfrac{\text{side opposite}}{\text{hypotenuse}},$ ⎯ Length of the leg opposite angle θ
⎯ Length of the hypotenuse

where $\sin \theta$ denotes the sine function with input θ. The three letters "sin" are used to denote the sine function, much like "log" was used to denote the common logarithmic function.

CLASS DISCUSSION

Is it possible that $\sin \theta > 1$ for some acute angle θ? Explain your reasoning.

Sides of a Right Triangle

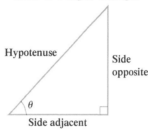

Figure 6.28

EXAMPLE 1 Evaluating the sine function

Find $\sin 30°$. Support your answer by using a calculator.

SOLUTION Since the sine function depends only on the measure of θ, we can choose any size right triangle to evaluate $\sin \theta$. For convenience, let the length of the hypotenuse equal 2, as shown in Figure 6.29. From geometry we know that the length of the shortest leg in a 30°–60° right triangle is half the hypotenuse. Thus the side opposite equals 1 and

$$\sin 30° = \frac{\text{side opposite}}{\text{hypotenuse}} = \frac{1}{2}.$$

This result is supported in Figure 6.30, where the sine function has been evaluated at 30° using a calculator set in degree mode.

30°–60° Right Triangle

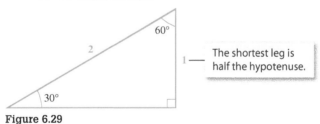

Figure 6.29

Evaluating sin 30°

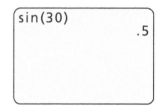

Figure 6.30 Degree Mode

Now Try Exercise 7

The Cosine Function Using Figures 6.27 and 6.28, we can define other trigonometric functions. Since

$$\frac{AC}{AB} = \frac{AC'}{AB'},$$

the ratio of the side adjacent (next) to θ to the hypotenuse is constant for a fixed angle θ and does not depend on the size of the right triangle. We define the *cosine function* to be

Cosine function ⎯⎯⎯ $\cos \theta = \dfrac{\text{side adjacent}}{\text{hypotenuse}}.$ ⎯ Length of the leg next to angle θ
⎯ Length of the hypotenuse

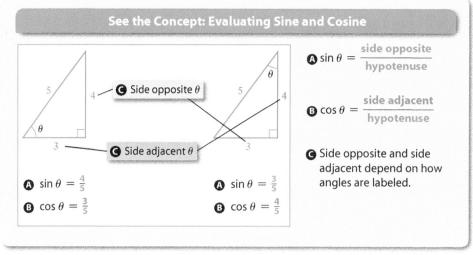

The Six Trigonometric Functions   The six trigonometric functions of angle θ are called **sine**, **cosine**, **tangent**, **cosecant**, **secant**, and **cotangent**. The customary abbreviation for each trigonometric function is shown below.

RIGHT TRIANGLE-BASED DEFINITIONS OF TRIGONOMETRIC FUNCTIONS

Let θ be an acute angle in a right triangle. Then the six trigonometric functions of θ may be evaluated as follows.

$$\sin \theta = \frac{\text{side opposite}}{\text{hypotenuse}} \qquad \cos \theta = \frac{\text{side adjacent}}{\text{hypotenuse}} \qquad \tan \theta = \frac{\text{side opposite}}{\text{side adjacent}}$$

$$\csc \theta = \frac{\text{hypotenuse}}{\text{side opposite}} \qquad \sec \theta = \frac{\text{hypotenuse}}{\text{side adjacent}} \qquad \cot \theta = \frac{\text{side adjacent}}{\text{side opposite}}$$

The next example illustrates how to evaluate the trigonometric functions.

EXAMPLE 2   Evaluating trigonometric functions

Consider the right triangle shown in Figure 6.31. Find the six trigonometric functions of θ.

SOLUTION   In triangle *ABC*, the side opposite angle θ is $a = 8$ and the hypotenuse is $c = 17$. To find the adjacent side b, we apply the Pythagorean theorem.

$$c^2 = a^2 + b^2 \qquad \textit{Pythagorean theorem}$$
$$b^2 = c^2 - a^2 \qquad \textit{Solve for } b^2.$$
$$b^2 = 17^2 - 8^2 \qquad \textit{Let } c = 17 \text{ and } a = 8.$$
$$b^2 = 225 \qquad \textit{Simplify.}$$
$$b = 15 \qquad \textit{Solve for } b, \text{ where } b > 0.$$

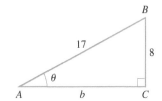

Figure 6.31

Algebra Review
To review the Pythagorean theorem, see Chapter R (page R-2).

Thus the six trigonometric functions of θ are as follows.

$$\sin \theta = \frac{\text{side opposite}}{\text{hypotenuse}} = \frac{8}{17} \qquad \csc \theta = \frac{\text{hypotenuse}}{\text{side opposite}} = \frac{17}{8}$$

$$\cos \theta = \frac{\text{side adjacent}}{\text{hypotenuse}} = \frac{15}{17} \qquad \sec \theta = \frac{\text{hypotenuse}}{\text{side adjacent}} = \frac{17}{15}$$

$$\tan \theta = \frac{\text{side opposite}}{\text{side adjacent}} = \frac{8}{15} \qquad \cot \theta = \frac{\text{side adjacent}}{\text{side opposite}} = \frac{15}{8}$$

Now Try Exercise 19

If an object is located above the horizontal, then the acute angle between the horizontal and the line of sight *XY* is called the **angle of elevation**. See Figure 6.32. If an object is located below the horizontal, then the acute angle between the horizontal and the line of sight *XY* is called the **angle of depression**. See Figure 6.33.

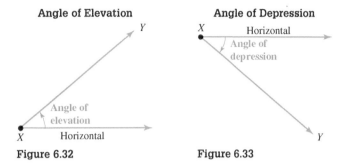

Figure 6.32   **Figure 6.33**

An Application Trigonometry allows people to determine distances without measuring them directly. For example, the altitude of the cloud base is important at airports. Although it is not practical to measure this altitude directly, trigonometry can indirectly determine this height at nighttime. In Figure 6.34 a bright spotlight is directed vertically upward. It creates a bright spot on the cloud base. From a known horizontal distance *d* from the spotlight, the angle of elevation θ is measured. The side adjacent to θ is *d*, and the side opposite θ is *h*, where *h* represents the height of the cloud base. It follows that

θ can be measured. $\qquad \tan \theta = \dfrac{\text{side opposite}}{\text{side adjacent}} = \dfrac{h}{d}.$ *h* is the only unknown.

d can be measured.

Finding the Height of the Cloud Base

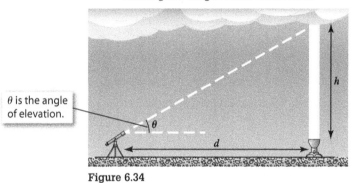

θ is the angle of elevation.

Figure 6.34

EXAMPLE 3 Determining the height of the cloud base

Suppose that $\theta = 55°$ and $d = 1150$ feet in Figure 6.34. Estimate the height of the cloud base. (Neglect the height of the telescope and spotlight in Figure 6.34.)

SOLUTION Solve the equation $\tan \theta = \dfrac{h}{d}$ for *h* and then substitute values for θ and *d*.

$$\tan \theta = \frac{h}{d}$$

$$h = d \tan \theta \qquad \text{Multiply by } d; \text{ rewrite.}$$

$$= 1150 \tan 55° \qquad \text{Substitute for } d \text{ and } \theta.$$

$$\approx 1150 \,(1.4281) \qquad \text{Approximate } \tan 55°.$$

$$\approx 1642 \text{ feet} \qquad \text{Multiply.}$$

Thus the cloud base is about 1642 feet high. See Figure 6.35.

Approximating tan 55°

```
tan(55)
         1.428148007
```

Figure 6.35 Degree Mode

Now Try Exercise 59

Solving a Triangle We can use trigonometric functions to find unknown sides of a right triangle. This process, sometimes referred to as *solving a triangle*, is demonstrated in the next example.

EXAMPLE 4   Solving a triangle

Find the lengths of the unknown sides a and c for the right triangle shown in Figure 6.36. Round each value to the nearest hundredth.

SOLUTION We are given angle $\theta = 40°$ and side $b = 35$, which is adjacent to angle θ. Side a is opposite angle θ. Because the tangent function involves the opposite and adjacent sides, we use it to find side a.

$$\tan 40° = \frac{a}{35} \qquad \text{tan } \theta = \frac{\text{side opposite}}{\text{side adjacent}}$$

$$35 \tan 40° = a \qquad \text{Multiply by 35.}$$

$$a \approx 29.37 \qquad \text{Rewrite; approximate (if desired).}$$

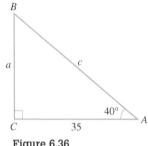

Figure 6.36

To find the length of hypotenuse c, we could use the Pythagorean theorem. However, we use $\cos \theta$ instead, which involves the adjacent side and the hypotenuse.

$$\cos 40° = \frac{35}{c} \qquad \cos \theta = \frac{\text{side adjacent}}{\text{hypotenuse}}$$

$$c \cos 40° = 35 \qquad \text{Multiply by } c.$$

$$c = \frac{35}{\cos 40°} \qquad \text{Divide by cos 40°.}$$

$$c \approx 45.69 \qquad \text{Approximate (if desired).}$$

Now Try Exercise 39

Finding Exact Values In most applications, calculators are used to approximate values of the trigonometric functions. However, with the aid of geometry we can determine exact values for the trigonometric functions of some special angles such as 30°, 45°, and 60°.

EXAMPLE 5   Evaluating trigonometric functions by hand

Evaluate the six trigonometric functions of $\theta = 45°$.

SOLUTION Begin by drawing a right triangle with a 45° angle, as shown in Figure 6.37. The lengths of the legs in this triangle are equal. Since the size of the right triangle does *not* affect the values of the trigonometric functions, let the lengths of both legs equal 1. Using the Pythagorean theorem, we can find the length of the hypotenuse as follows.

$$c^2 = a^2 + b^2 \qquad \text{Pythagorean theorem}$$

$$c^2 = 1^2 + 1^2 \qquad a = b = 1$$

$$c^2 = 2 \qquad \text{Simplify.}$$

$$c = \sqrt{2} \qquad \text{Solve for } c, \text{ where } c > 0.$$

A 45°–45° Right Triangle

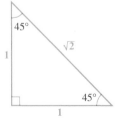

Figure 6.37

The hypotenuse has length $\sqrt{2}$. Evaluating the six trigonometric functions gives the following.

$$\sin 45° = \frac{\text{side opposite}}{\text{hypotenuse}} = \frac{1}{\sqrt{2}} \qquad \csc 45° = \frac{\text{hypotenuse}}{\text{side opposite}} = \frac{\sqrt{2}}{1} = \sqrt{2}$$

$$\cos 45° = \frac{\text{side adjacent}}{\text{hypotenuse}} = \frac{1}{\sqrt{2}} \qquad \sec 45° = \frac{\text{hypotenuse}}{\text{side adjacent}} = \frac{\sqrt{2}}{1} = \sqrt{2}$$

$$\tan 45° = \frac{\text{side opposite}}{\text{side adjacent}} = \frac{1}{1} = 1 \qquad \cot 45° = \frac{\text{side adjacent}}{\text{side opposite}} = \frac{1}{1} = 1$$

Now Try Exercise 23

Reciprocal Trigonometric Functions In Example 5, we saw that $\sin 45° = \frac{1}{\sqrt{2}}$ and $\csc 45° = \frac{\sqrt{2}}{1}$. Because

$$\sin\theta = \frac{\text{side opposite}}{\text{hypotenuse}} \qquad \text{and} \qquad \csc\theta = \frac{\text{hypotenuse}}{\text{side opposite}},$$

> $\sin\theta$ and $\csc\theta$ are reciprocals.

it follows that $\csc\theta = \frac{1}{\sin\theta}$ in general. In a similar manner,

> $\cos\theta$ and $\sec\theta$ are reciprocals.

$$\sec\theta = \frac{1}{\cos\theta} \qquad \text{and} \qquad \cot\theta = \frac{1}{\tan\theta}.$$

> $\tan\theta$ and $\cot\theta$ are reciprocals.

For example, if $\tan\theta = \frac{2}{3}$, then $\cot\theta = \frac{3}{2}$.

Calculators Most calculators have keys to evaluate the sine, cosine, and tangent functions but do not have keys to evaluate the cosecant, secant, and cotangent functions. These three functions may be evaluated by using the following *reciprocal identities*.

Reciprocal Identities

$$\csc\theta = \frac{1}{\sin\theta}, \qquad \sec\theta = \frac{1}{\cos\theta}, \qquad \cot\theta = \frac{1}{\tan\theta}$$

Results from Example 5 are supported in Figure 6.38, where these reciprocal identities have been applied to evaluate $\csc 45°$, $\sec 45°$, and $\cot 45°$.

NOTE Do not use the $\sin^{-1}$, $\cos^{-1}$, and $\tan^{-1}$ calculator keys to evaluate reciprocals. They represent inverse functions, which will be discussed in Section 6.6. You may want to use the x^{-1} key to evaluate reciprocals instead.

Using the right triangles shown in Figures 6.37 and 6.39, we can evaluate the six trigonometric functions at 30°, 45°, and 60° without the aid of a calculator. See Table 6.2.

Reciprocal Identities:
csc 45°, sec 45°, and cot 45°

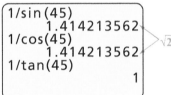

Figure 6.38 Degree Mode

A 30°–60° Right Triangle

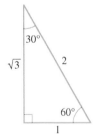

Figure 6.39

Some Exact Values of Trigonometric Functions

θ	$\sin\theta$	$\cos\theta$	$\tan\theta$	$\csc\theta$	$\sec\theta$	$\cot\theta$
30°	$\frac{1}{2}$	$\frac{\sqrt{3}}{2}$	$\frac{1}{\sqrt{3}}$	2	$\frac{2}{\sqrt{3}}$	$\sqrt{3}$
45°	$\frac{1}{\sqrt{2}}$	$\frac{1}{\sqrt{2}}$	1	$\sqrt{2}$	$\sqrt{2}$	1
60°	$\frac{\sqrt{3}}{2}$	$\frac{1}{2}$	$\sqrt{3}$	$\frac{2}{\sqrt{3}}$	2	$\frac{1}{\sqrt{3}}$

Table 6.2

> If you can sketch Figures 6.37 and 6.39, you will be able to find the values in Table 6.2 without memorizing them.

Algebra Review
To review rationalizing the denominator, see Chapter R (page R-47).

NOTE If we rationalize the denominators in Table 6.2, then

$$\frac{1}{\sqrt{2}} = \frac{1}{\sqrt{2}} \cdot \frac{\sqrt{2}}{\sqrt{2}} = \frac{\sqrt{2}}{2}.$$

Similarly, $\frac{1}{\sqrt{3}} = \frac{\sqrt{3}}{3}$ and $\frac{2}{\sqrt{3}} = \frac{2\sqrt{3}}{3}$.

Applications of Right Triangle Trigonometry

For centuries astronomers wanted to know how far it was to the stars. Not until 1838 did the astronomer Friedrich Bessel determine the distance to a star called 61 Cygni. He used a *parallax method* that relied on the measurement of very small angles. See Figure 6.40. As Earth revolves around the sun, the observed parallax of 61 Cygni is $\theta \approx 0.0000811°$. Because stars are so distant, parallax angles are very small. (*Sources:* H. Freebury, *A History of Mathematics;* M. Zeilik et al., *Introductory Astronomy and Astrophysics.*)

EXAMPLE 6 Calculating the distance to a star

One of the nearest stars to Earth is Alpha Centauri, which has a parallax of $\theta \approx 0.000212°$. (*Source:* M. Zeilik et al.)

(a) Find the distance to Alpha Centauri if the Earth–Sun distance is 93,000,000 miles.

(b) A light-year, defined to be the distance that light travels in 1 year, equals about 5.9 trillion miles. Find the distance to Alpha Centauri in light-years.

Parallax of a Star

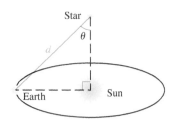

Figure 6.40 (not to scale)

SOLUTION

(a) Let d represent the distance between Earth and Alpha Centauri. From Figure 6.40 it can be seen that

$$\sin\theta = \frac{93,000,000}{d}, \quad \text{or} \quad d = \frac{93,000,000}{\sin\theta}.$$

Substituting for θ gives the following result.

$$d = \frac{93,000,000}{\sin 0.000212°} \approx 2.51 \times 10^{13} \text{ miles}$$

(b) This distance equals $\dfrac{2.51 \times 10^{13}}{5.9 \times 10^{12}} \approx 4.3$ light-years.

One light-year

Now Try Exercise 75

Applications from Surveying Water is often an obstacle to surveyors in the field when measuring distances between two points. For example, to measure the distance between points P and Q in Figure 6.41 a baseline PR, perpendicular to PQ, is determined. Angle PRQ is then measured. Right triangle trigonometry can be used to determine the length of PQ. (*Source:* P. Kissam, *Surveying Practice.*)

Figure 6.41

EXAMPLE 7 Finding distance

Suppose in Figure 6.41 the length of PR is 94.75 feet and angle PRQ has measure 41.6°. Estimate the distance between points P and Q.

SOLUTION Let angle PRQ be θ. Since $\tan\theta = \frac{PQ}{PR}$, it follows that

$$PQ = PR \tan\theta = 94.75 \tan 41.6° \approx 84.12 \text{ feet.}$$

Now Try Exercise 69

EXAMPLE 8 Finding the height of a tree

From a point A on level ground, the angle of elevation to the top of a tree is 38°. From a point B that is 46 feet farther from the tree the angle of elevation is 22°. See Figure 6.42. Find the height h of the tree to the nearest tenth of a foot.

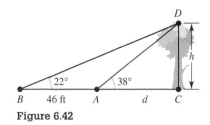

Figure 6.42

SOLUTION From triangles ACD and BCD,

$$\tan 38° = \frac{h}{d}, \qquad \text{or} \qquad h = d \tan 38°, \qquad \text{and}$$

$$\tan 22° = \frac{h}{d + 46}, \qquad \text{or} \qquad h = (d + 46) \tan 22°.$$

We can set the two expressions for h equal to each other and solve for d.

$$d \tan 38° = (d + 46) \tan 22° \qquad \text{Set expressions for } h \text{ equal.}$$

$$d \tan 38° = d \tan 22° + 46 \tan 22° \qquad \text{Distributive property}$$

$$d \tan 38° - d \tan 22° = 46 \tan 22° \qquad \text{Subtract } d \tan 22°.$$

$$d \,(\tan 38° - \tan 22°) = 46 \tan 22° \qquad \text{Factor out } d.$$

$$d = \frac{46 \tan 22°}{\tan 38° - \tan 22°} \qquad \text{Solve for } d.$$

From above, $h = d \tan 38°$, so the height of the tree is

$$h = \left(\frac{46 \tan 22°}{\tan 38° - \tan 22°} \right) \tan 38° \approx 38.5 \text{ feet.} \qquad h = d \tan 38°$$

Expression for d

Now Try Exercise 71

Highway Design Next we derive a formula that is used in the design of highways.

EXAMPLE 9 Deriving a formula for the design of highway curves

One common type of highway curve is a *simple horizontal curve*. It consists of two straight segments of highway connected by a portion of a circular arc with radius r, as shown in Figure 6.43. The distance d is called the *external distance*. (*Source:* F. Mannering and W. Kilareski, *Principles of Highway Engineering and Traffic Analysis.*)

(a) Derive a formula for d that involves r and θ.

(b) Find d for a curve with a 750-foot radius and $\theta = 36°$.

A Simple Horizontal Curve

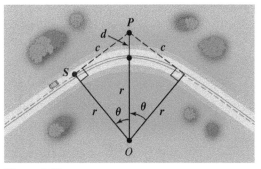

Figure 6.43

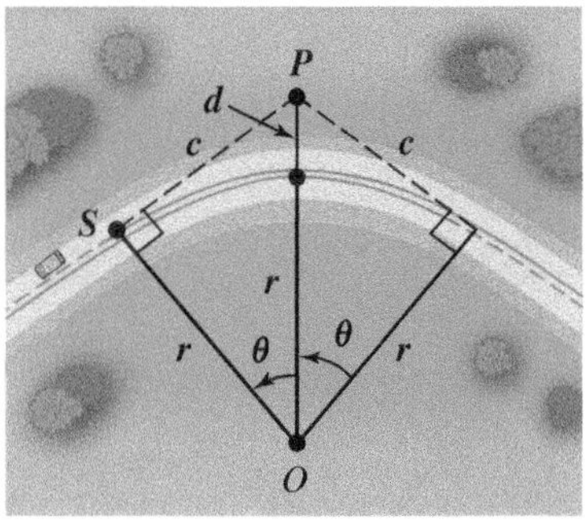

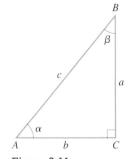

Figure 6.43 (Repeated)

SOLUTION

(a)
$$\cos\theta = \frac{r}{r+d} \qquad \text{Use triangle } OSP.$$

$$(r+d)\cos\theta = r \qquad \text{Multiply by } r+d.$$

$$r+d = \frac{r}{\cos\theta} \qquad \text{Divide by } \cos\theta.$$

$$d = \frac{r}{\cos\theta} - r \qquad \text{Subtract } r.$$

$$d = r\left(\frac{1}{\cos\theta} - 1\right) \qquad \text{Factor out } r.$$

(b) $d = 750\left(\dfrac{1}{\cos 36°} - 1\right) \approx 177$ feet

> **Now Try Exercise 83**

Complementary Angles and Cofunctions

Complementary Angles
$\alpha + \beta = 90°$

In Figure 6.44, α and β are complementary angles since their measures sum to 90°. The six trigonometric functions for α and β can be expressed as follows.

Figure 6.44

Cofunction Values ($\alpha + \beta = 90°$)

$$\sin\alpha = \frac{a}{c} = \cos\beta \qquad \cos\alpha = \frac{b}{c} = \sin\beta$$

$$\tan\alpha = \frac{a}{b} = \cot\beta \qquad \cot\alpha = \frac{b}{a} = \tan\beta$$

$$\sec\alpha = \frac{c}{b} = \csc\beta \qquad \csc\alpha = \frac{c}{a} = \sec\beta$$

Notice that the value of a trigonometric function for α equals the value of the trigonometric cofunction for β. For example, $\sin\alpha = \cos\beta$ and $\sin\beta = \cos\alpha$. This is how cofunctions were named. In 1620 Edmund Gunter combined the words "complement" and "sine" to obtain *co*sine. Similarly, the cosecant and cotangent functions are the "complementary functions" of the secant and tangent functions, respectively, and their names were shortened to *co*secant and *co*tangent.

COFUNCTION FORMULAS

$$\sin\theta = \cos(90° - \theta) \qquad \cos\theta = \sin(90° - \theta)$$

$$\tan\theta = \cot(90° - \theta) \qquad \cot\theta = \tan(90° - \theta)$$

$$\sec\theta = \csc(90° - \theta) \qquad \csc\theta = \sec(90° - \theta)$$

EXAMPLE 10 Evaluating functions using complementary angles

Write an equivalent expression using a cofunction. Then evaluate the expression using a calculator.
(a) $\cot 23°$ **(b)** $\sec 70°$ **(c)** $\cos 12°$

SOLUTION
(a) The complementary angle of 23° is 90° − 23° = 67°. Thus

$$\cot 23° = \tan 67° \approx 2.3559.$$

(b) $\sec 70° = \csc(90° - 70°) = \csc 20° = \dfrac{1}{\sin 20°} \approx 2.9238$

(c) $\cos 12° = \sin(90° - 12°) = \sin 78° \approx 0.9781$

> **Now Try Exercise 55**

6.2 Putting It All Together

$\mathbf{T}$he following table summarizes some properties of right triangle trigonometry.

CONCEPT	FORMULAS AND FIGURES	
Trigonometric functions	Let θ be an acute angle in a right triangle *ABC*. $\sin\theta = \dfrac{\text{side opposite}}{\text{hypotenuse}}$ $\csc\theta = \dfrac{\text{hypotenuse}}{\text{side opposite}}$ $\cos\theta = \dfrac{\text{side adjacent}}{\text{hypotenuse}}$ $\sec\theta = \dfrac{\text{hypotenuse}}{\text{side adjacent}}$ $\tan\theta = \dfrac{\text{side opposite}}{\text{side adjacent}}$ $\cot\theta = \dfrac{\text{side adjacent}}{\text{side opposite}}$	
Cofunction formulas	Let α and β be complementary angles. $\sin\alpha = \cos(90° - \alpha) = \cos\beta$ $\tan\alpha = \cot(90° - \alpha) = \cot\beta$ $\sec\alpha = \csc(90° - \alpha) = \csc\beta$	

6.2 Exercises

Sketching Triangles

Exercises 1–6: Sketch a right triangle with the following properties. Label the measure of each angle and side.

1. Acute angles of 30° and 60° and a hypotenuse with length 2

2. Acute angle of 45° and a leg with length 1

3. Acute angle of 45° and a hypotenuse with length 1

4. Acute angle of 60° and a hypotenuse with length 1

5. Isosceles and a hypotenuse with length 4

6. Acute angle of 60° and the shorter leg with length 3

Evaluating Trigonometric Functions

Exercises 7–12: (Refer to Example 1.) Use a 30°–60° right triangle to find the exact value of the trigonometric expression.

7. $\sin 60°$ 8. $\tan 30°$

9. $\cos 30°$ 10. $\cot 30°$

11. $\sec 60°$ 12. $\csc 60°$

Exercises 13–18: Use a 45°–45° right triangle to find the exact value of the trigonometric expression.

13. $\tan 45°$ 14. $\sec 45°$

15. $\cot 45°$ 16. $\csc 45°$

17. $\sin 45°$ 18. $\cos 45°$

Exercises 19–22: Find the six trigonometric functions of θ.

19.
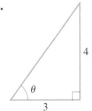

20.
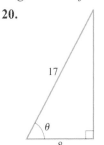

21.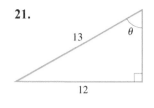

22.

Exercises 23–32: Find the six trigonometric functions of the given angle. Approximate to three decimal places when appropriate.

23. 60°

24. 45°

25. 25°

26. 30°

27. 5°35′

28. 85°35′33″

29. 13°45′30″

30. 45°44′

31. 1.05°

32. 0.161°

Exercises 33–38: Let θ be an acute angle. Find the unknown trigonometric value, using the given information.

33. sec θ if cos θ = $\frac{1}{3}$

34. cot θ if tan θ = 5

35. csc θ if sin θ = $\frac{12}{13}$

36. sin θ if csc θ = $\frac{5}{4}$

37. tan θ if cot θ = $\frac{7}{24}$

38. cos θ if sec θ = $\frac{7}{5}$

Solving Triangles

Exercises 39–46: Find the lengths of the unknown sides in the right triangle. Round values to the nearest hundredth.

39.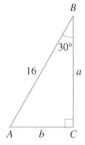

40.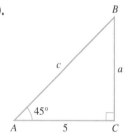

41.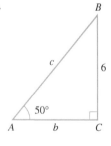

42.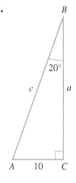

43.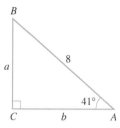

44.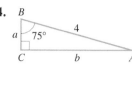

45.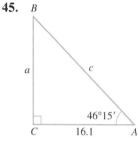

46.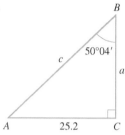

Exercises 47–50: Find the exact length of each side labeled with a variable in the figure.

47.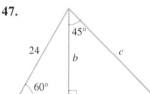

48.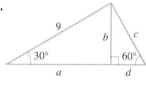

49.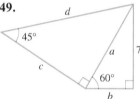

50.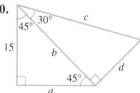

Exercises 51–54: Complete the following for right triangle ABC having the standard labeling shown in Figure 6.25. Approximate the answer to the nearest hundredth.

51. Find *a* if *b* = 12 and α = 60°.

52. Find *b* if *c* = 23 and β = 45°.

53. Find *c* if *a* = 100 and β = 53°43′.

54. Find *a* if *b* = 64 and α = 78°15′.

Cofunctions

Exercises 55–58: (Refer to Example 10.) Write an equivalent expression using a cofunction. Approximate the expression to four decimal places using a calculator.

55. (a) sin 70°   **(b)** cos 40°

56. (a) cot 23°   **(b)** tan 48°

57. (a) csc 49°   **(b)** sec 63°

58. (a) cot 87°   **(b)** sec 72°

Applications

59. Height of the Cloud Base (Refer to Example 3 and Figure 6.34.) From a distance of 1500 feet from the spotlight, the angle of elevation θ equals 37°30′. Find the height of the cloud base.

60. Height of a Tree One hundred feet from the trunk of a tree on level ground, the angle of elevation of the top of the tree is 35°. Find the height of the tree to the nearest foot.

61. Length of a Shadow The angle of elevation of the sun is 34°. Find the length of a shadow cast by a person who is 5 feet 3 inches tall. Round your answer to the nearest tenth of a foot.

62. Height of a Tower The shadow of a vertical tower is 40.6 meters long when the angle of elevation of the sun is 34.6°. Find the height of the tower.

63. Angle of Depression of a Floodlight A company safety committee recommended that a floodlight be mounted in a parking lot as shown in the figure, so as to illuminate the employee exit. Find *h* to the nearest tenth of a foot.

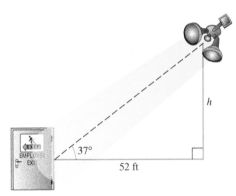

64. Aerial Photography An aerial photograph is taken directly above a building. The length of the building's shadow is 48 feet when the angle of elevation of the sun is 35.3°. Estimate the height of the building.

65. Angle of Depression An airplane is flying near a football stadium at 12,000 feet above level ground. The angle of depression from the airplane to the stadium is 13°. How far horizontally must the airplane fly to be directly over the football stadium? Round your answer to the nearest thousand feet.

66. Angle of Depression An airplane is flying 10,500 feet above the level ground. The angle of depression from the plane to the base of a tree is 13°50′. How far horizontally must the plane fly to be directly over the tree?

67. Height of a Building From a window 30 feet above the street, the angle of elevation to the top of the building across the street is 50° and the angle of depression to the base of this building is 20°. See the figure. Find the height of the building across the street.

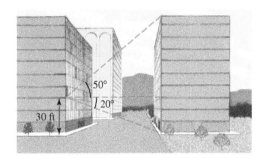

68. Height of a Building The angle of elevation from the top of a small building to the top of a nearby taller building is 46°40′, while the angle of depression to the bottom is 14°10′. If the smaller building is 28.0 meters high, find the height *x* of the taller building.

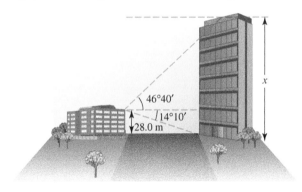

69. Surveying (Refer to Example 7 and Figure 6.41.) Find the distance from *P* to *Q* if *PR* is 85.62 feet and angle *PQR* is 23.76°.

70. Weather Tower A 410-foot weather tower used to measure wind speed has a guy wire attached to it 175 feet above the ground. The angle between the wire and the vertical tower is 57°, as shown in the figure. Approximate the length of the guy wire. (*Source:* Brookhaven National Laboratory.)

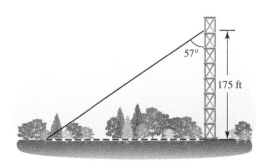

71. Height of a Mountain (Refer to Example 8.) From a point *A* the angle of elevation of Mount Kilimanjaro in Africa is 13.7°, and from a point *B*, directly behind *A*, the angle of elevation is 10.4°. See the figure. If the distance between *A* and *B* is 5 miles, approximate the height of Mount Kilimanjaro to the nearest hundred feet.

72. Height of Mt. Whitney The angle of elevation from Lone Pine to the top of Mt. Whitney is 10°50′. Exactly 9.3 kilometers from Lone Pine along a straight, level road toward Mt. Whitney, the angle of elevation is 22°40′. Find the height of the top of Mt. Whitney *above* the level of the road to the nearest hundredth of a kilometer.

73. Height of a Pyramid The angle of elevation from a point on the ground to the top of a pyramid is 35°30′. The angle of elevation from a point 135 feet farther back to the top of the pyramid is 21°10′. Find the height of the pyramid to the nearest foot.

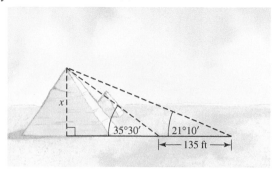

74. Height of an Antenna An antenna is on top of the center of a house. The angle of elevation from a point on the ground 28.0 meters from the center of the house to the top of the antenna is 27°10′, and the angle of elevation to the bottom of the antenna is 18°10′. Find the height of the antenna.

75. Distance to Nearby Stars (Refer to Example 6 and Figure 6.40.) The table lists the parallax *θ* in degrees for some nearby stars. Approximate the distance from Earth to each star in miles and in light-years.

Star	θ (degrees)
Barnard's Star	1.52×10^{-4}
Sirius	1.05×10^{-4}
61 Cygni	8.11×10^{-5}
Procyon	7.97×10^{-5}

Source: M. Zeilik et al., *Introductory Astronomy and Astrophysics.*

76. Parallax and Distance (Refer to Exercise 75.) When the parallax *θ* is equal in measure to 1 second, a star is said to have a distance from Earth of 1 parsec. If the distance between Earth and the sun is 93,000,000 miles, approximate the number of miles in 1 parsec. How many light-years is this? (*Source:* M. Zeilik et al.)

77. Observing Mercury The planet Mercury is closer to the sun than Earth. For this reason it can only be observed low in the horizon around sunset or sunrise. See the figure, where angle *θ* is called the *elongation*. Because Mercury's orbit is not circular, the elongation varies between 18° and 28°. Approximate the minimum and maximum distances between Mercury and the sun. (*Source:* M. Zeilik et al.)

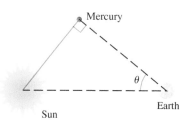

78. Observing Venus (Refer to Exercise 77.) The orbit of Venus is nearly circular with an elongation of 48°. Estimate the distance between Venus and the sun.

79. Orbital Height of a GPS Satellite The figure illustrates a satellite in the Global Positioning System (GPS) orbiting over the equator, where $r = 3963$ miles and $\theta = 76.1°$. Use $d = r\left(\frac{1}{\cos\theta} - 1\right)$ from Example 9 to determine the altitude of the GPS satellite above Earth's surface to the nearest mile. (*Source:* Y. Zhao, *Vehicle Location and Navigation Systems.*)

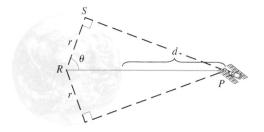

80. Heights of Lunar Mountains The lunar mountain peak Huygens has a height of 21,000 feet. The shadow of Huygens on a photograph was 2.8 mm, and the nearby mountain Bradley had a shadow of 1.8 mm on the same photograph. Use similar triangles to calculate the height of Bradley to the nearest hundred feet. (*Source:* T. Webb, *Celestial Objects for Common Telescopes.*)

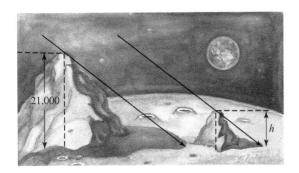

81. Highway Curve Design Highway curves are sometimes banked so that the outside of the curve is slightly elevated or inclined above the inside of the curve, as shown in the figure. This inclination is called the *superelevation*. Both the curve's radius and the super-elevation must be correct for a given speed limit. The relationship among a car's velocity v in feet per second, the safe radius r of the curve in feet, and the superelevation θ in degrees is given by $r = \frac{v^2}{4.5 + 32.2 \tan\theta}$. (*Source:* F. Mannering and W. Kilareski *Principles of Highway Engineering and Traffic Analysis.*)

(a) A curve has a speed limit of 66 feet per second (45 mi/hr) and a superelevation of $\theta = 3°$. Approximate the safe radius r.

(b) Find r if $\theta = 5°$ and $v = 66$.

(c) Make a conjecture about how increasing θ affects the safe radius r. Verify your conjecture by making a table for r, starting at $\theta = 0$ and incrementing by 1. Let $v = 66$.

82. Highway Design (Refer to Exercise 81.) A highway curve has a radius of $r = 1150$ feet and a superelevation of $\theta = 2.1°$. What should be the speed limit (in miles per hour) for this curve?

83. Highway Design (Refer to Example 9 and Figure 6.43.) Find the external distance d for a highway curve with $r = 625$ feet and $\theta = 54°$.

84. Highway Design (Refer to Example 9.) A simple horizontal curve is shown in the figure at the top of the next column. The points P and S mark the beginning

and end of the curve. Let Q be the point of intersection where the two straight sections of highway leading into the curve would meet if extended. The radius of the curve is r, and the angle θ denotes how many degrees the curve turns. If $r = 765$ feet and $\theta = 83°$, find the distance between P and Q. (*Source:* F. Mannering and W. Kilareski.)

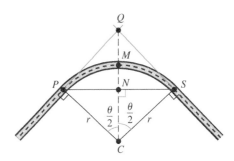

85. Area of an Equilateral Triangle Find the area of the equilateral triangle shown in the figure in terms of s.

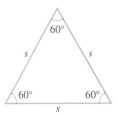

86. Area of a Hexagon Write the area of the hexagon shown in the figure in terms of x. Assume that the six triangles that comprise the hexagon are equilateral and congruent.

Writing about Mathematics

87. Most calculators have built-in keys to compute the sine, cosine, and tangent functions but not the secant, cosecant, and cotangent functions. Is it possible to evaluate all of the trigonometric functions with this type of calculator? Explain and include examples.

88. The sine function is defined in terms of right triangles as $\sin\theta = \frac{\text{side opposite}}{\text{hypotenuse}}$. Suppose that a fixed angle θ occurs in two right triangles. If the hypotenuse in the first triangle has twice the length of the hypotenuse in the second triangle, what can be said about the sides opposite in each triangle? How does the value $\sin\theta$ compare in each triangle? Explain.

CHECKING BASIC CONCEPTS FOR SECTIONS 6.1 AND 6.2

1. Find the radian measure of each angle.
   (a) 45°   (b) 75°

2. Find the degree measure of each angle.
   (a) $\frac{\pi}{6}$ (b) $\frac{5\pi}{4}$

3. Find the arc length intercepted by a central angle of $\theta = 30°$ in a circle with radius $r = 12$ inches. Calculate the area of the sector determined by r and θ.

4. Evaluate the six trigonometric functions of $\theta = 60°$ by hand. Support your results by using a calculator.

5. Use the right triangle in the figure to find the six trigonometric functions of θ.

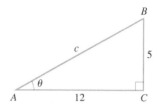

6. If $\alpha = 63°$ and $a = 9$ in right triangle ABC, approximate the length of the hypotenuse to the nearest tenth.

6.3 The Sine and Cosine Functions and Their Graphs

- **Define the sine and cosine functions for any angle**
- **Define the sine and cosine functions for any real number by using the unit circle and the wrapping function**
- **Represent the sine and cosine functions**
- **Use the sine and cosine functions in applications**
- **Model with the sine function (optional)**

Introduction

The sine and cosine functions are used not only in applications involving right triangles but also to model phenomena involving rotation and periodic motion. Extending the domains of the trigonometric functions from acute angles to angles of any measure will allow us to model a wide variety of phenomena such as biorhythms, weather, tides, electricity, robotic arms, and the design of highways.

Definitions

Robotics is a rapidly growing field that requires extensive mathematics. One basic problem in designing a robotic arm is determining the location of the robot's hand. Suppose we have a robotic arm that rotates at the shoulder and is controlled by changing the angle θ and the length of the arm r, as illustrated in Figure 6.45. We would like to find a relation between the xy-coordinates of the hand and the values for r and θ. (**Source:** W. Stadler, *Analytical Robotics and Mechatronics.*)

Notice that for a fixed angle θ, if the length of the arm is changed from r_1 to r_2, triangle ABC in Figure 6.46 and triangle DEF in Figure 6.47 are similar triangles. Thus the following ratios are equal and depend only on the measure of θ.

$$\frac{x_1}{r_1} = \frac{x_2}{r_2} \qquad \text{and} \qquad \frac{y_1}{r_1} = \frac{y_2}{r_2}$$

> Because the triangles are similar, these ratios are equal.

Robotic Arm at Angle θ

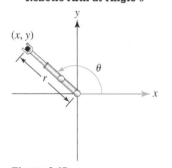

Figure 6.45

Similar Triangles

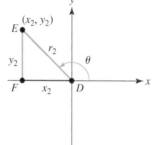

Figure 6.46

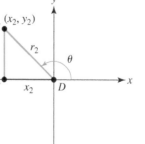

Figure 6.47

Defining $\sin \theta$ and $\cos \theta$

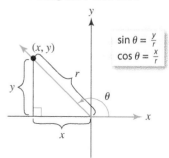

$\sin \theta = \frac{y}{r}$
$\cos \theta = \frac{x}{r}$

Figure 6.48

In Figure 6.48 the Pythagorean theorem gives $r^2 = x^2 + y^2$. Since $r > 0$, it follows that $r = \sqrt{x^2 + y^2}$. The ratios $\frac{y}{r}$ and $\frac{x}{r}$ depend only on θ and can be used to define the *sine* and *cosine* functions of *any* angle θ.

THE SINE AND COSINE FUNCTIONS OF ANY ANGLE θ

Let angle θ be in standard position with the point (x, y) lying on the angle's terminal side. If $r = \sqrt{x^2 + y^2}$, then

$$\sin\theta = \frac{y}{r} \quad \text{and} \quad \cos\theta = \frac{x}{r} \ (r \neq 0).$$

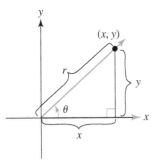

Figure 6.49

Although the terminal side of θ in Figure 6.48 is shown in the second quadrant, these definitions are valid for any angle θ having a terminal side in any of the four quadrants.

MAKING CONNECTIONS

Right Triangle Trigonometry   If $0° < \theta < 90°$, then x corresponds to the length of the adjacent side, y corresponds to the length of the opposite side, and r corresponds to the length of the hypotenuse. See Figure 6.49. These new definitions for sine and cosine are consistent with the definitions presented in Section 6.2, when θ is an acute angle.

EXAMPLE 1   Evaluating sine and cosine for coterminal angles

Suppose a robotic hand is located at the point $(15, -8)$, where all units are in inches.
(a) Find the length of the arm.
(b) Let α satisfy $0° \leq \alpha < 360°$ and represent the angle between the positive x-axis and the robotic arm. Find $\sin\alpha$ and $\cos\alpha$.
(c) Let β satisfy $-360° \leq \beta < 0°$ and represent the angle between the positive x-axis and the robotic arm. Find $\sin\beta$ and $\cos\beta$. How do the values for $\sin\beta$ and $\cos\beta$ compare with the values for $\sin\alpha$ and $\cos\alpha$?

SOLUTION
(a) Let $x = 15, y = -8$, and $r = \sqrt{x^2 + y^2}$. Thus $r = \sqrt{15^2 + (-8)^2} = 17$ and the length of the arm is 17 inches. See Figure 6.50.
(b) Let $x = 15, y = -8$, and $r = 17$. Then

$$\sin\alpha = \frac{y}{r} = -\frac{8}{17} \quad \text{and} \quad \cos\alpha = \frac{15}{17}.$$

(c) In Figure 6.51, β satisfies $-360° \leq \beta < 0°$. Since the values of x, y, and r do *not* change, the trigonometric values for β are the *same* as those for α in part (b).

Coterminal Angles Have Equal Sine and Cosine Values

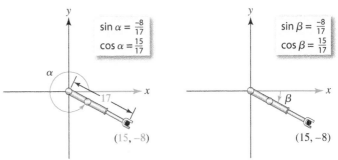

$$\sin\alpha = \frac{-8}{17}$$
$$\cos\alpha = \frac{15}{17}$$

$$\sin\beta = \frac{-8}{17}$$
$$\cos\beta = \frac{15}{17}$$

Figure 6.50   **Figure 6.51**

Now Try Exercise 1

**Coterminal Angles Have
Equal Trigonometric Values**

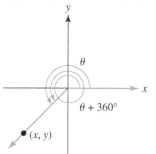

Figure 6.52

Sine and Cosine of Coterminal Angles The results of Example 1 can be generalized. If α and β are *coterminal* angles, then

$$\sin \alpha = \sin \beta \qquad \text{and} \qquad \cos \alpha = \cos \beta.$$

The angles θ and $\theta + 360°$ are coterminal for any θ. Their terminal sides pass through the same point (x, y), as shown in Figure 6.52. Therefore for all θ, $\sin \theta = \sin(\theta + 360°)$ and $\cos \theta = \cos(\theta + 360°)$. In general, if n is any integer, then

$$\sin \theta = \sin(\theta + n \cdot 360°) \qquad \text{and} \qquad \cos \theta = \cos(\theta + n \cdot 360°).$$

As a result, we say that the sine and cosine functions are **periodic** with **period 360°** (or 2π radians). For example,

$$\sin 90° = \sin(90° + 360°) = \sin(90° - 2 \cdot 360°).$$

See Figure 6.53.

Sine Has Period 360°

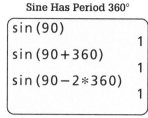

Figure 6.53 Degree Mode

Evaluating Sine and Cosine by Hand If an angle is a multiple of 30° or 45°, exact evaluation of the sine function or cosine function is possible by hand. The next example illustrates an angle for which the sine and cosine functions can be evaluated exactly by hand.

EXAMPLE 2 Finding values of sin θ and cos θ

Find sin 120° and cos 120°. Support your answer using a calculator.

Finding Exact Values

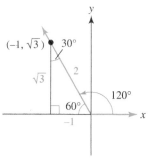

Figure 6.54

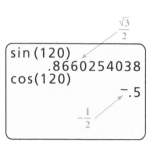

Figure 6.55 Degree Mode

SOLUTION When evaluating the sine or cosine function by hand, we can select any positive value for r and it does not change the resulting values for $\sin \theta$ and $\cos \theta$. For convenience, we let $r = 2$, as shown in Figure 6.54. The length of the shortest leg in a 30°–60° right triangle is half the hypotenuse. Since the terminal side of θ is in the second quadrant, $x < 0$ and so $x = -1$. Next we find y.

$$x^2 + y^2 = r^2 \qquad \text{Pythagorean theorem}$$
$$y^2 = r^2 - x^2 \qquad \text{Subtract } x^2.$$
$$y^2 = 2^2 - (-1)^2 \qquad \text{Let } r = 2 \text{ and } x = -1.$$
$$y = \pm\sqrt{3} \qquad \text{Square root property}$$

Since the terminal side of θ is in the second quadrant, $y > 0$ and so $y = \sqrt{3}$. Thus

$$\sin 120° = \frac{y}{r} = \frac{\sqrt{3}}{2} \approx 0.8660 \qquad \text{and}$$

$$\cos 120° = \frac{x}{r} = -\frac{1}{2} = -0.5.$$

These results are supported in Figure 6.55.

Now Try Exercise 13

NOTE When evaluating trigonometric functions by hand as in Example 2, *always* draw the perpendicular line segment from a point on the terminal side to the x-axis, *not* the y-axis.

The values of the sine and cosine functions for the **quadrantal angles** 0°, 90°, 180°, and 270° are shown in Table 6.3. Try to verify these values.

Quadrantal Angles

	0°	90°	180°	270°
sin θ	0	1	0	−1
cos θ	1	0	−1	0

Terminal sides of these angles lie on the *x*- or *y*-axis.

Table 6.3

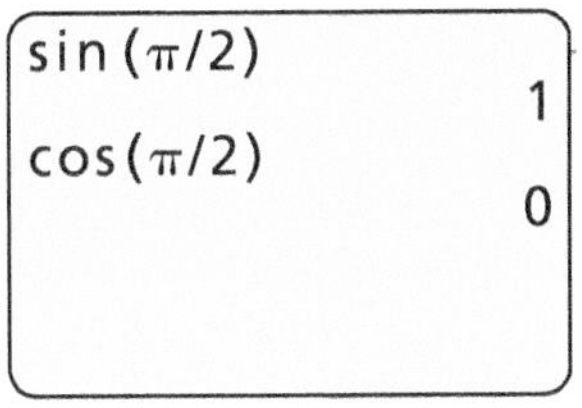

sin (π/2)   1

cos (π/2)   0

Figure 6.56 Radian Mode

NOTE If the terminal side of an angle θ in standard position lies on the *y*-axis, then $\sin\theta = \pm 1$ and $\cos\theta = 0$; if it lies on the *x*-axis, $\sin\theta = 0$ and $\cos\theta = \pm 1$.

Evaluation in Radian Mode Trigonometric functions can also be evaluated using radian mode. See Figure 6.56. Since 90° is equivalent to $\frac{\pi}{2}$ radians, it follows that

$$\sin\frac{\pi}{2} = 1 \quad \text{and} \quad \cos\frac{\pi}{2} = 0.$$

EXAMPLE 3 Finding values of sin *t* and cos *t*

Find the exact values of $\sin\left(-\frac{3\pi}{4}\right)$ and $\cos\left(-\frac{3\pi}{4}\right)$.

SOLUTION

Getting Started Because there is no degree symbol, it is assumed that $-\frac{3\pi}{4}$ is measured in radians. Its terminal side lies in quadrant III, as shown in Figure 6.57. ▶

From a point on the terminal side, draw a perpendicular line segment to the *x*-axis, forming a 45°–45° right triangle. Label the resulting triangle conveniently so that the length of each leg equals 1. (Each side is labeled −1, because the terminal side lies in quadrant III.) By the Pythagorean theorem, the hypotenuse is $\sqrt{2}$. Thus $x = -1$, $y = -1$, and $r = \sqrt{2}$. It follows that

$$\sin\left(-\frac{3\pi}{4}\right) = \frac{y}{r} = -\frac{1}{\sqrt{2}} \quad \text{and} \quad \cos\left(-\frac{3\pi}{4}\right) = \frac{x}{r} = -\frac{1}{\sqrt{2}}.$$

NOTE If we rationalize the denominator, each result becomes $-\frac{\sqrt{2}}{2}$.

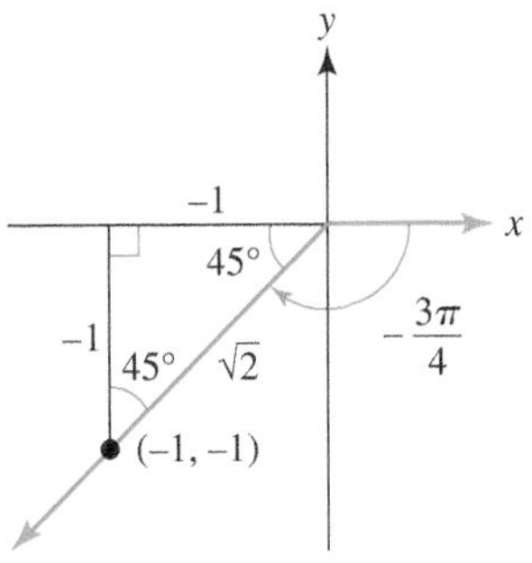

Now Try Exercise 27

Finding Exact Values

Figure 6.57

An Application from Highway Design *Grade*, or slope, is a measure of steepness and indicates whether a highway is uphill or downhill. A 5% grade indicates that a road is increasing 5 vertical feet for each 100-foot increase in horizontal distance. *Grade resistance R* is the gravitational force acting on a vehicle and is given by

$$R = W\sin\theta,$$

where W is the weight of the vehicle and θ is the angle associated with the grade. See Figure 6.58. For an uphill grade $\theta > 0$, and for a downhill grade $\theta < 0$. (*Source:* F. Mannering and W. Kilareski, *Principles of Highway Engineering and Traffic Analysis.*)

Uphill and Downhill Grade

Figure 6.58

EXAMPLE 4 Calculating the grade resistance

A downhill highway grade is modeled by the line $y = -0.06x$ in the fourth quadrant.
(a) Find the grade of the road.
(b) Determine the grade resistance for a 3000-pound car. Interpret the result.

SOLUTION

(a) The slope of the line is -0.06, so when x *increases* by 100 feet, y *decreases* by 6 feet. See Figure 6.59. Thus this road has a grade of -6%.

A Grade of -6%

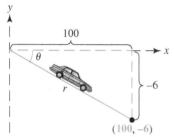

Figure 6.59 (Not to scale)

(b) Because $R = W \sin\theta$, we must find $\sin\theta$. From Figure 6.59 we see that the point $(100, -6)$ lies on the terminal side of θ. Since

$$r = \sqrt{100^2 + (-6)^2} = \sqrt{10{,}036},$$

it follows that

$$\sin\theta = \frac{y}{r} = \frac{-6}{\sqrt{10{,}036}}.$$

The grade resistance is

$$R = W\sin\theta = 3000\left(\frac{-6}{\sqrt{10{,}036}}\right) \approx -179.7 \text{ lb}.$$

On this stretch of highway, gravity pulls a 3000-pound vehicle *downhill* with a force of about 180 pounds. Note that a downhill grade results in a negative grade resistance.

Now Try Exercise 89

The Unit Circle

Unit Circle ($r = 1$)

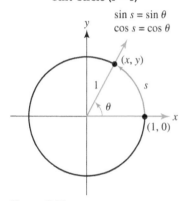

Figure 6.60

Trigonometric functions were first defined for angles. As applications became more diverse, real numbers were included in the domains of the six trigonometric functions. Real numbers were needed to represent quantities such as time and distance. To extend the domains of the sine and cosine functions to include all real numbers, we will introduce the unit circle.

The **unit circle** has radius 1 and equation $x^2 + y^2 = 1$. Let (x, y) be a point on the unit circle, and let s be the arc length along the unit circle from the point $(1, 0)$ to the point (x, y) determined by a counterclockwise rotation. See Figure 6.60. Since $r = 1$, the arc length formula $s = r\theta$ reduces to $s = \theta$. That is, the real number s representing arc length is numerically equal to the radian measure of θ. Thus if s is a real number and θ is an angle measured in radians, as shown in Figure 6.60, we define

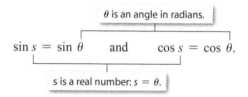

If $s < 0$, then the red arc in Figure 6.60 is wrapped around the unit circle in a *clockwise* direction and θ has negative measure. This discussion suggests how trigonometric functions of a real number are evaluated.

TRIGONOMETRIC FUNCTIONS OF REAL NUMBERS

The value of a trigonometric function for the real number s is equal to its value for s radians.

NOTE To evaluate a trigonometric function of a real number s with a calculator, use *radian* mode.

EXAMPLE 5   Approximating the sine and cosine of a real number

Use a calculator to approximate sin 1.78 and cos 1.78.

SOLUTION To approximate the sine and cosine of the real number 1.78, use *radian* mode. As shown in Figure 6.61, sin 1.78 ≈ 0.978 and cos 1.78 ≈ −0.208.

Sine and Cosine of a Real Number

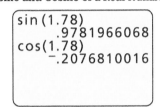

Figure 6.61 Radian Mode

Now Try Exercise 33

Trigonometic Functions and the Unit Circle The following See the Concept illustrates that if the terminal side of an angle θ intersects the *unit circle* at (x, y), then this point can also be written as $(\cos \theta, \sin \theta)$ since on the unit circle $x = \cos \theta$ and $y = \sin \theta$. Because trigonometric functions can be defined using the unit circle, they are also referred to as **circular functions.**

See the Concept: Circular Functions

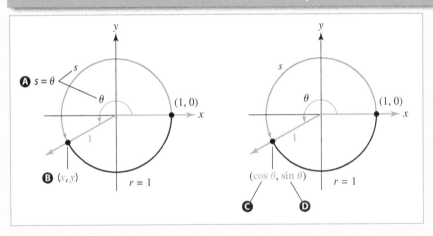

Ⓐ $s = \theta$ because $s = r\theta$ and $r = 1$.
(s is arc length; θ is in radians)

Ⓑ The terminal side of θ intersects the unit circle at (x, y).

Ⓒ $\cos \theta = \frac{x}{r}$ and $r = 1$, so $x = \cos \theta$.

Ⓓ $\sin \theta = \frac{y}{r}$ and $r = 1$, so $y = \sin \theta$.

EXAMPLE 6   Evaluating circular functions

Use Figure 6.62 to find sin θ and cos θ.

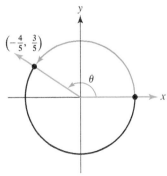

Figure 6.62

SOLUTION The terminal side of angle θ intersects the unit circle at the point $\left(-\frac{4}{5}, \frac{3}{5}\right)$. Because this point is in the form $(\cos\theta, \sin\theta)$ it follows that

$$\cos\theta = -\frac{4}{5} \quad \text{and} \quad \sin\theta = \frac{3}{5}.$$

Now Try Exercise 37

A Trigonometric Identity The unit circle is described by $x^2 + y^2 = 1$. Because $x = \cos\theta$ and $y = \sin\theta$, we have

$$(\cos\theta)^2 + (\sin\theta)^2 = 1,$$

or equivalently,

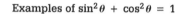

$$\sin^2\theta + \cos^2\theta = 1.$$

Trigonometric identity (True for all values of θ)

This equation is an example of a **trigonometric identity**. An identity is true for all meaningful values of the variable. In Figures 6.63 and 6.64 this identity is evaluated for different values of θ. In every case the result is 1, regardless of whether θ is measured in degrees or radians.

Examples of $\sin^2\theta + \cos^2\theta = 1$

(sin(80))²+(cos(
80))²
1
(sin(⁻12))²+(cos
(⁻12))²
1
Figure 6.63 Degree Mode

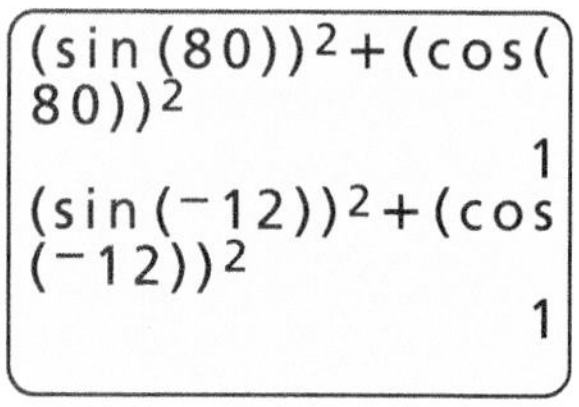

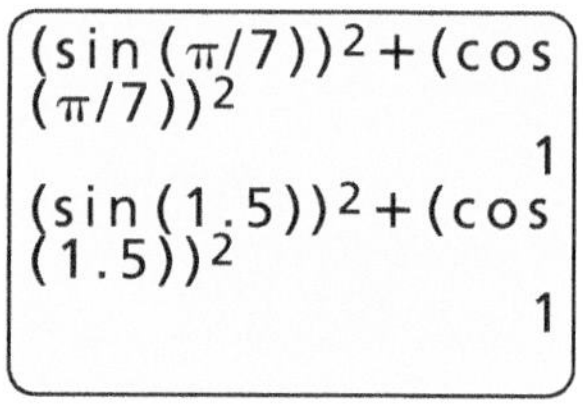

(sin(π/7))²+(cos
(π/7))²
1
(sin(1.5))²+(cos
(1.5))²
1
Figure 6.64 Radian Mode

The Wrapping Function (Optional)

Evaluating the Wrapping Function Trigonometric functions of real numbers can be defined more formally *without angles* by using a wrapping function. To define the **wrapping function** W on the unit circle, let the input s be any real number. The following See the Concept shows that given any positive real number input s, the wrapping function outputs a point (x, y) on the unit circle. That is, $W(s) = (x, y)$. See Figure 6.65.

See the Concept: Evaluating the Wrapping Function

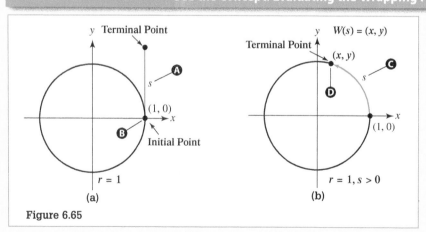

y
Terminal Point
A
s
(1, 0)
x
B
Initial Point
r = 1
(a)
y
W(s) = (x, y)
Terminal Point
(x, y)
C
s
D
x
(1, 0)
r = 1, s > 0
(b)
Figure 6.65

A Cut a "string" having length s.

B Place one end of the "string" at the initial point (1, 0).

C Wrap the "string" counterclockwise around the unit circle if $s > 0$.

D If the "string" stops at the terminal point (x, y), then $W(s) = (x, y)$.

If s is negative, the string has length $|s|$ and is wrapped clockwise. Note that the initial point is always (1, 0).

NOTE   The wrapping function is different from other functions that we have encountered because its output is a *point* on the unit circle.

EXAMPLE 7   Evaluating the wrapping function

For each real number s, evaluate $W(s)$.

(a) 2π (b) π (c) $-\dfrac{\pi}{2}$ (d) $-\dfrac{\pi}{4}$

SOLUTION

(a) Because the radius of the unit circle is 1, the circumference C of the unit circle is $C = 2\pi r = 2\pi$. If a string of length $s = 2\pi$ is wrapped counterclockwise around the unit circle, it will make one complete revolution and the terminal point will coincide with the initial point $(1, 0)$. Thus $W(2\pi) = (1, 0)$. See Figure 6.66.

(b) Half the circumference of the unit circle is π. The string wraps halfway around the unit circle, and the terminal point is $(-1, 0)$. Thus $W(\pi) = (-1, 0)$. See Figure 6.67.

(c) Because s is *negative*, the string wraps *clockwise* around the unit circle, as shown in Figure 6.68. A length of $\frac{\pi}{2}$ represents a fourth of the circumference of the unit circle, so the terminal point is $(0, -1)$ and $W\left(-\frac{\pi}{2}\right) = (0, -1)$.

(d) A distance of $\frac{\pi}{4}$ represents an eighth of the circumference of the unit circle. Thus the terminal point lies on the line $y = -x$, as shown in Figure 6.69. The 45°–45° right triangle formed has a hypotenuse with length 1 and legs both with length a.

Evaluating $W(2\pi)$

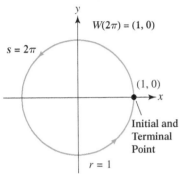

Figure 6.66

$$a^2 + a^2 = 1 \qquad \text{Pythagorean theorem: } a = b$$

$$2a^2 = 1 \qquad \text{Add like terms.}$$

$$a^2 = \frac{1}{2} \qquad \text{Divide by 2.}$$

$$a = \pm\frac{1}{\sqrt{2}} \qquad \text{Square root property}$$

Because the terminal point is located in quadrant IV, the x-coordinate is $\frac{1}{\sqrt{2}}$ and the y-coordinate is $-\frac{1}{\sqrt{2}}$. Thus $W\left(-\frac{\pi}{4}\right) = \left(\frac{1}{\sqrt{2}}, -\frac{1}{\sqrt{2}}\right)$.

Evaluating the Wrapping Function

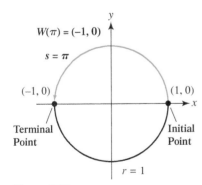

Figure 6.67

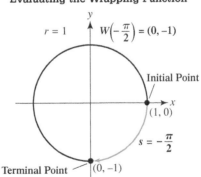

Figure 6.68

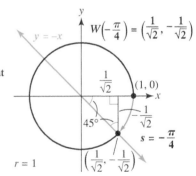

Figure 6.69

Now Try Exercises 51, 53, 55, and 59

NOTE   The concept of string is used only to help you visualize the wrapping function. Instead, you could visualize moving a distance s around the unit circle.

Evaluating the Sine and Cosine with the Wrapping Function   The wrapping function on the unit circle can be used to define the sine and cosine functions for any real number s by letting

$$\sin s = y \qquad \text{and} \qquad \cos s = x,$$

where $W(s) = (x, y)$. The next example illustrates how to apply this definition.

EXAMPLE 8   Evaluating the sine and cosine functions

Find $\sin s$ and $\cos s$ for each real number s.

(a) 2π **(b)** π **(c)** $-\dfrac{\pi}{2}$ **(d)** $-\dfrac{\pi}{4}$

SOLUTION

Getting Started First note that the values for s are the same as those used in Example 7. Thus if $W(s) = (x, y)$, we need only apply the fact that $\sin s = y$ and $\cos s = x$. ▶

(a) $W(2\pi) = (1, 0)$ by Example 7(a), so $\sin 2\pi = 0$ and $\cos 2\pi = 1$.

(b) $W(\pi) = (-1, 0)$ by Example 7(b), so $\sin \pi = 0$ and $\cos \pi = -1$.

(c) $W\left(-\dfrac{\pi}{2}\right) = (0, -1)$ by Example 7(c), so $\sin\left(-\dfrac{\pi}{2}\right) = -1$ and $\cos\left(-\dfrac{\pi}{2}\right) = 0$.

(d) $W\left(-\dfrac{\pi}{4}\right) = \left(\dfrac{1}{\sqrt{2}}, -\dfrac{1}{\sqrt{2}}\right)$ by Example 7(d), so $\sin\left(-\dfrac{\pi}{4}\right) = -\dfrac{1}{\sqrt{2}}$ and $\cos\left(-\dfrac{\pi}{4}\right) = \dfrac{1}{\sqrt{2}}$.

Now Try Exercises 67, 69, 71, and 75

NOTE The results obtained by using the wrapping function to evaluate trigonometric functions are equivalent to those arrived at by the other methods presented earlier.

Representations of the Sine and Cosine Functions

Like other functions that we have studied, the sine and cosine functions also have symbolic, numerical, and graphical representations. Both functions are nonlinear.

The Sine Function A *symbolic representation* of the sine function is $f(t) = \sin t$. The domain of the sine function is all real numbers. There is no simple formula that can be used to evaluate the sine function. Instead, we generally rely on other methods for its evaluation.

A *numerical representation* of $f(t) = \sin t$ is shown in Table 6.4. Since outputs from the sine function correspond to a y-coordinate on the unit circle, the range of the sine function is $-1 \le y \le 1$.

Evaluating the Sine Function

t	0	$\dfrac{\pi}{4}$	$\dfrac{\pi}{2}$	$\dfrac{3\pi}{4}$	π	$\dfrac{5\pi}{4}$	$\dfrac{3\pi}{2}$	$\dfrac{7\pi}{4}$	2π
$\sin t$	0	$\dfrac{1}{\sqrt{2}}$	1	$\dfrac{1}{\sqrt{2}}$	0	$-\dfrac{1}{\sqrt{2}}$	-1	$-\dfrac{1}{\sqrt{2}}$	0

Table 6.4

Increases: $\left(0, \dfrac{\pi}{2}\right)$ Decreases: $\left(\dfrac{\pi}{2}, \dfrac{3\pi}{2}\right)$ Increases: $\left(\dfrac{3\pi}{2}, 2\pi\right)$

A *graphical representation* of $f(t) = \sin t$ is shown in the following See the Concept. The points from Table 6.4 have been plotted on the graph.

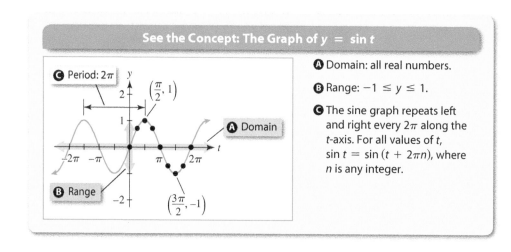

See the Concept: The Graph of $y = \sin t$

Ⓒ Period: 2π

$\left(\dfrac{\pi}{2}, 1\right)$

$\left(\dfrac{3\pi}{2}, -1\right)$

Ⓑ Range

Ⓐ Domain: all real numbers.

Ⓑ Range: $-1 \le y \le 1$.

Ⓒ The sine graph repeats left and right every 2π along the t-axis. For all values of t, $\sin t = \sin(t + 2\pi n)$, where n is any integer.

Unit Circle ($r = 1$)

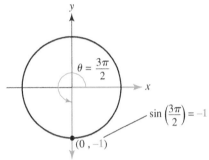

Figure 6.70

The Unit Circle and the Sine Graph   The graph of the sine function may be easier to understand if we use a unit circle. If a point P on the unit circle starts at $(1, 0)$ and rotates counterclockwise, then the y-coordinate of P corresponds to $\sin\theta$. Refer to Figure 6.70. As a result, $\sin\theta$ first increases from 0 to 1, then decreases from 1 to -1, and finally increases from -1 to 0 (see Table 6.4), where P completes one rotation and returns to the point $(1, 0)$. If P continues to rotate, it passes through the same points a second time, and so the sine function has period 2π, or $360°$.

EXAMPLE 9   Evaluating the sine function

Evaluate $f(t) = \sin t$ at $t = \frac{3\pi}{2}$ by hand.

SOLUTION An angle θ of $\frac{3\pi}{2}$ radians in standard position has a terminal side that intersects the unit circle at the point $(0, -1)$. See Figure 6.71. Therefore $\sin\left(\frac{3\pi}{2}\right) = -1$.

$$\theta = \frac{3\pi}{2}$$

$$\sin\left(\frac{3\pi}{2}\right) = -1$$

$(0, -1)$

Figure 6.71

Now Try Exercise 41

The Cosine Function The cosine function, is *represented symbolically* by $f(t) = \cos t$. Its domain is all real numbers and its range is $-1 \le y \le 1$.

A *numerical representation* of $f(t) = \cos t$ is shown in Table 6.5.

Evaluating the Cosine Function

t	0	$\frac{\pi}{4}$	$\frac{\pi}{2}$	$\frac{3\pi}{4}$	π	$\frac{5\pi}{4}$	$\frac{3\pi}{2}$	$\frac{7\pi}{4}$	2π
$\cos t$	1	$\frac{1}{\sqrt{2}}$	0	$-\frac{1}{\sqrt{2}}$	-1	$-\frac{1}{\sqrt{2}}$	0	$\frac{1}{\sqrt{2}}$	1

Table 6.5   Decreases: $(0, \pi)$ Increases: $(\pi, 2\pi)$

A *graphical representation* of $f(t) = \cos t$ is shown in the following See the Concept. The points from Table 6.5 have been plotted on the graph.

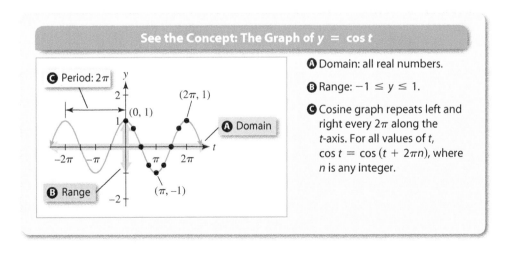

See the Concept: The Graph of $y = \cos t$

Ⓐ Domain: all real numbers.

Ⓑ Range: $-1 \le y \le 1$.

Ⓒ Cosine graph repeats left and right every 2π along the t-axis. For all values of t, $\cos t = \cos(t + 2\pi n)$, where n is any integer.

If a point P on the unit circle in Figure 6.70 on the preceding page starts at $(1, 0)$ and rotates counterclockwise, then the x-coordinate of P corresponds to $\cos\theta$. Explain how this relates to the graph of the cosine function.

EXAMPLE 10   Evaluating the cosine function

Evaluate $f(t) = \cos t$ at $t = \frac{5\pi}{6}$ by hand.

SOLUTION   An angle of $\frac{5\pi}{6}$ radians in standard position has a terminal side that intersects the unit circle in the second quadrant. See Figure 6.72. To find the point of intersection (x, y), notice that the hypotenuse of the 30°–60° right triangle has length 1 and the shorter leg has length $y = \frac{1}{2}$. We can determine x symbolically.

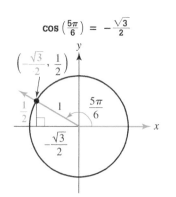

$$\cos\left(\frac{5\pi}{6}\right) = -\frac{\sqrt{3}}{2}$$

Figure 6.72

$$x^2 + y^2 = 1 \qquad \text{Equation of the unit circle}$$

$$x^2 + \left(\frac{1}{2}\right)^2 = 1 \qquad y = \tfrac{1}{2}$$

$$x^2 = \frac{3}{4} \qquad \text{Solve for } x^2.$$

$$x = \pm\frac{\sqrt{3}}{2} \qquad \text{Square root property}$$

The point (x, y) is in the second quadrant, so choose $x = -\frac{\sqrt{3}}{2}$. Because $\cos t = x$, it follows that $\cos\frac{5\pi}{6} = -\frac{\sqrt{3}}{2} \approx -0.8660$.

Now Try Exercise 43

Applications of the Sine and Cosine Functions

Periodic graphs that are similar in shape to the graphs of the sine and cosine functions are **sinusoidal**. Of all the periodic graphs, sinusoidal graphs are the most important in applications because they occur in nearly every aspect of physical science.

Because the moon orbits Earth, we observe different phases of the moon during the period of a month. In Figure 6.73, angle θ is called the *phase angle*. The *phase F* of the moon is computed by

$$F(\theta) = \frac{1}{2}(1 - \cos\theta)$$

and gives the fraction of the moon's face that is illuminated by the sun. (***Source:*** P. Duffet-Smith, *Practical Astronomy with Your Calculator.*)

Phase Angle θ

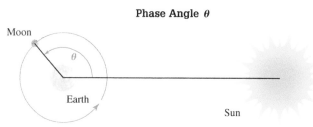

Figure 6.73 (Not to scale)

EXAMPLE 11   Modeling the phases of the moon

Let $F(\theta) = \frac{1}{2}(1 - \cos\theta)$.
(a) A graph of F is shown in Figure 6.74. Discuss how the graph relates to the phases of the moon.
(b) Evaluate $F(0)$, $F\left(\frac{\pi}{2}\right)$, $F(\pi)$, and $F\left(\frac{3\pi}{2}\right)$. Interpret each result.

Phases of the Moon

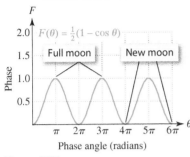

Figure 6.74

SOLUTION
(a) The phases of the moon are periodic and have a period of 2π. Each peak represents a full moon, and each valley represents a new moon.
(b) $F(0) = \frac{1}{2}(1 - \cos 0) = \frac{1}{2}(1 - 1) = 0$. When $\theta = 0$, the moon is located between Earth and the sun. Since $F = 0$, the face of the moon is not visible, which corresponds to a *new moon*.

$F\left(\frac{\pi}{2}\right) = \frac{1}{2}\left(1 - \cos\frac{\pi}{2}\right) = \frac{1}{2}(1 - 0) = \frac{1}{2}$. When $\theta = \frac{\pi}{2}$, $F = \frac{1}{2}$. Thus half the face of the moon is visible. This phase is called the *first quarter*.

$F(\pi) = \frac{1}{2}(1 - \cos\pi) = \frac{1}{2}(1 - (-1)) = 1$. When $\theta = \pi$, Earth is between the moon and the sun. Since $F = 1$, the face of the moon is completely visible, which corresponds to a *full moon*.

$F\left(\frac{3\pi}{2}\right) = \frac{1}{2}\left(1 - \cos\frac{3\pi}{2}\right) = \frac{1}{2}(1 - 0) = \frac{1}{2}$. When $\theta = \frac{3\pi}{2}$, $F = \frac{1}{2}$. Thus half the face of the moon is visible. This phase is called the *last quarter*.

> **Now Try Exercise 91**

An Application from Electricity   Common household current is called *alternating current* (AC) because the voltage and current change direction 120 times per second. Sinusoidal curves are often used to model the voltage in a common household electrical outlet, as demonstrated in the next example.

EXAMPLE 12   Analyzing household current

The voltage V in a household outlet can be modeled by $V(t) = 160\sin(120\pi t)$, where t represents time in seconds.
(a) A graph of $y = V(t)$ is shown in Figure 6.75. Describe the voltage.
(b) Evaluate $V\left(\frac{1}{240}\right)$ and interpret the result.
(c) One way to estimate the "average" voltage in a circuit is to use the **root mean square** voltage, which equals the maximum voltage divided by $\sqrt{2}$. Find this "average" or root mean square voltage.

Voltage in a Circuit

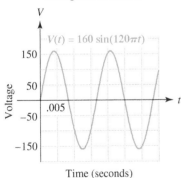

Figure 6.75

SOLUTION
(a) The graph of V in Figure 6.75 is sinusoidal and varies between -160 volts and 160 volts, corresponding to the fact that the current is changing direction in a household outlet. When the graph is above the t-axis the current flows one direction, and when it is below the t-axis the current flows in the opposite direction.
(b) $V\left(\frac{1}{240}\right) = 160\sin\frac{\pi}{2} = 160(1) = 160$. After $\frac{1}{240} \approx 0.004$ second, the voltage is 160 volts. Figure 6.75 supports this result.
(c) The maximum voltage is 160 volts. The "average" voltage is $\frac{160}{\sqrt{2}} \approx 113$ volts. Common household electricity is often rated at 110–120 volts.

> **Now Try Exercise 95**

NOTE   In Example 12, the input to the function V is time, not an angle. This example illustrates why it is necessary to extend the domain of trigonometric functions to include all real numbers.

Modeling with the Sine Function (Optional)

The study of *biological clocks* is a fascinating field. Many living organisms undergo regular biological rhythms, or circadian rhythms. (See Exercises 93 and 94.) A simple example is a flower that opens during daylight and closes at nighttime. One amazing result is that flowers often continue to open and close even when they are placed in continual darkness. (*Source:* F. Brown et al., *The Biological Clock.*)

EXAMPLE 13 Modeling biological rhythms

Some types of water plants are *luminescent*—they radiate a type of "cold" light that is similar to the light emitted from a firefly. A sample of a luminescent plant (*Gonyaulax polyedra*) was put into continual dim light. The luminescence was measured at 6-hour intervals, and the data in Table 6.6 summarize the results. Noon corresponds to $t = 0$ and the y-units of luminescence are arbitrary.

Luminescence of a Plant

t (hour)	0	6	12	18	24	30	36	42	48
y (luminescence)	1	4	7	4	1	4	7	4	1

Table 6.6 *Source:* E. Bünning, *The Physiological Clock.*

(a) Make a scatterplot of the data in $[-6, 54, 6]$ by $[0, 8, 1]$. Interpret the data.
(b) Graph the data and $f(t) = 3 \sin (0.27t - 1.7) + 4$. How well does f model the data?
(c) Estimate the luminescence when $t = 33$.

SOLUTION

(a) A scatterplot of the data is shown in Figure 6.76. Luminescence appears to be periodic, increasing and decreasing at regular intervals even though the lighting was always dim. The plant was most luminescent during times that correspond to midnight: $t = 12$ and 36. It was least luminescent at times corresponding to noon: $t = 0, 24,$ and 48.

(b) Let $Y_1 = 3 \sin (.27X - 1.7) + 4$; the data are graphed in Figure 6.77. The graph of f models the periodic data quite well.

A Scatterplot

$[-6, 54, 6]$ by $[0, 8, 1]$

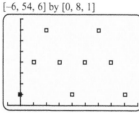

Figure 6.76

A Sinusoidal Model

$[-6, 54, 6]$ by $[0, 8, 1]$

$y_1 = 3 \sin (0.27t - 1.7) + 4$

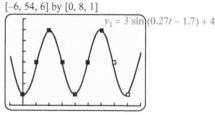

Figure 6.77

(c) Evaluate $f(t)$ at $t = 33$ using radian mode.

$$f(33) = 3 \sin (0.27(33) - 1.7) + 4 \approx 6.4$$

The luminescence was about 6.4 after 33 hours, or at 9 P.M.

Calculator Help

To make a scatterplot and graph an equation, see Appendix A (pages AP-3 and AP-6).

Now Try Exercise 101

6.3 Putting It All Together

In this section we extended the domains of the sine and cosine functions to include any angle θ and any real number t. Both of these functions are nonlinear functions, and their ranges include values satisfying $-1 \leq y \leq 1$. Some concepts about the sine and cosine functions are summarized in the following table.

CONCEPT	FORMULAS AND FIGURES
Sine and cosine of any angle θ.	$\sin \theta = \dfrac{y}{r}$ and $\cos \theta = \dfrac{x}{r}$, where $r = \sqrt{x^2 + y^2}$
The unit circle and the sine and cosine functions	$x^2 + y^2 = 1 \quad (r = 1)$ *Evaluation:* $\sin t = y$, $\cos t = x$ *Period:* 2π or $360°$ $\sin(t + 2\pi n) = \sin t$ $\cos(t + 2\pi n) = \cos t$
Graph of the sine function	**The Sine Function** *Domain:* $-\infty < t < \infty$ *Range:* $-1 \leq y \leq 1$
Graph of the cosine function	**The Cosine Function** *Domain:* $-\infty < t < \infty$ *Range:* $-1 \leq y \leq 1$

6.3 Exercises

Basic Concepts

Exercises 1–4: The xy-coordinates of the hand for a robotic arm are shown in the figure.

(a) Find the length of the arm.
(b) Find the sine and cosine functions for the angle θ.

1.   **2.**

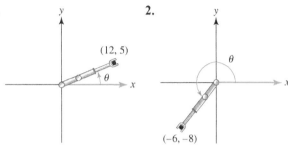

3.   **4.**

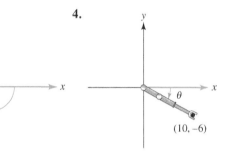

Exercises 5–8: Find sin θ and cos θ.

5.   **6.**

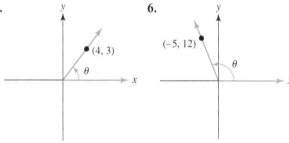

7.   **8.**

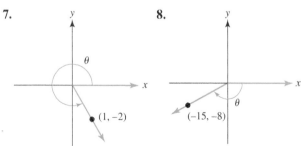

Exercises 9–12: The terminal side of an angle θ in standard position lies on the line in the given quadrant. Find the sine and cosine functions of θ. (Hint: Find a point (x, y) lying on the terminal side of θ.)

9. $y = 2x$,   Quadrant I

10. $y = -\frac{1}{2}x$,   Quadrant II

11. $y = -3x$,   Quadrant IV

12. $y = \frac{3}{4}x$,   Quadrant III

Evaluating Sine and Cosine

Exercises 13–28: (Refer to Examples 2 and 3.) Find the sine and cosine functions by hand for the given angle. Then support your answer using a calculator.

13. $45°$	**14.** $150°$
15. $-30°$	**16.** $-180°$
17. $225°$	**18.** $510°$
19. $-420°$	**20.** $-225°$
21. $\frac{\pi}{3}$	**22.** $\frac{5\pi}{4}$
23. $-\frac{\pi}{2}$	**24.** -2π
25. $\frac{7\pi}{6}$	**26.** $\frac{4\pi}{3}$
27. $-\frac{9\pi}{4}$	**28.** $-\frac{19\pi}{6}$

Exercises 29–36: Approximate the sine and cosine of each angle to four decimal places.

29. $93.2°$	**30.** $-43°$
31. $123°50'$	**32.** $12°40'45''$
33. -4	**34.** 1.56
35. $\frac{11\pi}{7}$	**36.** $-\frac{7\pi}{5}$

The Unit Circle

Exercises 37–40: Each figure at the top of the next page shows angle θ in standard position with its terminal side intersecting the unit circle. Evaluate sin θ and cos θ.

37.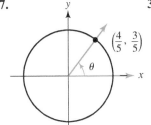

38.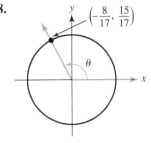

39.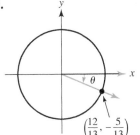

40.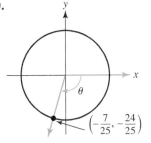

Exercises 41–50: (Refer to Examples 9 and 10.) Use a unit circle to evaluate sin t and cos t by hand.

41. $t = \frac{\pi}{2}$ **42.** $t = \pi$

43. $t = \frac{7\pi}{6}$ **44.** $t = -\frac{\pi}{4}$

45. $t = -\frac{3\pi}{4}$ **46.** $t = \frac{5\pi}{3}$

47. $t = \frac{5\pi}{2}$ **48.** $t = \frac{11\pi}{6}$

49. $t = -\frac{\pi}{3}$ **50.** $t = -\frac{3\pi}{2}$

The Wrapping Function

Exercises 51–66: (Refer to Example 7.) For each number s, evaluate W(s).

51. 3π **52.** 4π

53. -2π **54.** -5π

55. $\frac{3\pi}{2}$ **56.** $\frac{7\pi}{2}$

57. $-\frac{5\pi}{2}$ **58.** $-\frac{9\pi}{2}$

59. $\frac{5\pi}{4}$ **60.** $\frac{7\pi}{4}$

61. $-\frac{5\pi}{4}$ **62.** $-\frac{3\pi}{4}$

63. $\frac{11\pi}{6}$ **64.** $\frac{7\pi}{3}$

65. $-\frac{7\pi}{3}$ **66.** $-\frac{5\pi}{6}$

Exercises 67–82: (Refer to Example 8 and Exercises 51–66.) Use the wrapping function to evaluate sin s and cos s for each real number s.

67. 3π **68.** 4π

69. -2π **70.** -5π

71. $\frac{3\pi}{2}$ **72.** $\frac{7\pi}{2}$

73. $-\frac{5\pi}{2}$ **74.** $-\frac{9\pi}{2}$

75. $\frac{5\pi}{4}$ **76.** $\frac{7\pi}{4}$

77. $-\frac{5\pi}{4}$ **78.** $-\frac{3\pi}{4}$

79. $\frac{11\pi}{6}$ **80.** $\frac{7\pi}{3}$

81. $-\frac{7\pi}{3}$ **82.** $-\frac{5\pi}{6}$

Graphs of Trigonometric Functions

83. Sketch a graph of $y = \sin t$ for $-2\pi \le t \le 2\pi$.

84. Sketch a graph of $y = \cos t$ for $-2\pi \le t \le 2\pi$.

Exercises 85–88: Graph the function f in the viewing rectangle $[-2\pi, 2\pi, \pi/2]$ by $[-4, 4, 1]$. Identify the range of f and then evaluate $f\left(\frac{3\pi}{2}\right)$.

85. **(a)** $f(t) = 3 \sin t$ **(b)** $f(t) = \sin(3t)$

86. **(a)** $f(t) = 2 \cos t$ **(b)** $f(t) = \cos(2t)$

87. **(a)** $f(t) = 2 \cos(t) + 1$ **(b)** $f(t) = \cos(2t) - 1$

88. **(a)** $f(t) = 3 \sin(t) + 1$ **(b)** $f(t) = \sin(3t) - 1$

Applications

89. **Highway Grade** (Refer to Example 4.) Suppose an uphill grade of a highway can be modeled by the line $y = 0.03x$ in the first quadrant.
   (a) Find the grade of the hill.

   (b) Determine the grade resistance for a gravel truck weighing 25,000 pounds.

90. **Highway Grade** (Refer to Example 4.) A downhill graph is modeled by the line $y = -0.04x$ in the fourth quadrant.
   (a) Find the grade of the road.

   (b) Determine the grade resistance for a 6000-pound pickup truck. Interpret the result.

91. **Phases of the Moon** (Refer to Example 11.) Find all phase angles θ that correspond to the first quarter phase of the moon. Assume that θ can be any angle measured in radians.

92. **Phases of the Moon** (Refer to Example 11.) Find all phase angles θ that correspond to a full moon and all phase angles that correspond to a new moon. Assume that θ can be any angle measured in radians.

93. Circadian Rhythm A human body has an internal clock called *circadian rhythm* that helps determine when a person is awake and has the most energy. If a person's energy levels are determined by a scale of 0 to 100, then the function

$$C(x) = 50 - 40 \sin\left(\frac{\pi}{12}x\right),$$

where x is hours past midnight, describes a typical circadian rhythm. (*Source:* Hozumi.net)

(a) Graph $y = C(x)$ for $0 \le x \le 24$.

(b) When is a typical person's energy the greatest?

(c) When is a typical person's energy the least?

94. Circadian Rhythm Disorder (Refer to Exercise 93.) Some people experience a disorder of their circadian rhythm. An example is given by

$$C(x) = 40 + 30 \cos\left(\frac{\pi}{12}x\right),$$

where x is hours past midnight.

(a) Graph $y = C(x)$ for $0 \le x \le 24$.

(b) With this disorder, when is a person's energy the greatest?

(c) With this disorder, when is is the person's energy the least?

95. Voltage (Refer to Example 12.) Electric ranges and ovens often use a higher voltage than that found in normal household outlets. This voltage can be modeled by $V(t) = 310 \sin(120\pi t)$, where t represents time in seconds.

(a) A graph of $y = V(t)$ is shown in the given figure. Describe the voltage in the circuit.

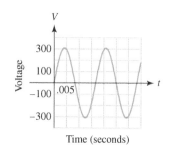

Time (seconds)

(b) Evaluate $V\left(\frac{1}{120}\right)$ and interpret the result.

(c) Approximate the root mean square voltage.

96. Amperage (Refer to Example 12.) The amperage I in an electrical circuit after t seconds is modeled by $I(t) = 10 \cos(120\pi t)$.

(a) Find the range of I.

(b) Evaluate $I\left(\frac{1}{60}\right)$ and interpret the result.

97. Braking Distance and Grade The braking distance D in feet required for a typical automobile on dry pavement to change its velocity from V_1 to V_2 can be estimated using the equation

$$D = \frac{1.05\left(V_1^2 - V_2^2\right)}{27 + 64.4 \sin\theta}.$$

In this equation, θ represents the angle of the grade of the highway and velocity is measured in feet per second. See Figure 6.58. (*Source:* F. Mannering and W. Kelareski, *Principles of Highway Engineering and Traffic Analysis.*)

(a) Compute the number of feet required to slow a car from 88 feet per second (60 mi/hr) to 44 feet per second (30 mi/hr) while it is traveling uphill with $\theta = 3°$.

(b) Repeat part (a) with $\theta = -3°$.

(c) How is braking distance affected by θ? Does this result agree with your driving experience?

98. Braking Distance (Refer to Exercise 97.) An automobile is traveling at 88 feet per second (60 mi/hr) on a highway with $\theta = -4°$. The driver sees a stalled truck in the road and applies the brakes 250 feet from the vehicle. Assuming that a collision cannot be avoided, how fast is the car traveling when it collides with the truck?

99. Highway Design When an automobile travels along a circular curve with radius r, trees and buildings situated on the inside of the curve can obstruct the driver's vision. See the figure. To ensure a safe stopping distance S, the *minimum* distance d that should be cleared on the inside of a highway curve is given by the equation $d = r\left(1 - \cos\frac{\beta}{2}\right)$, where β in radians is determined by $\beta = \frac{S}{r}$. (*Source:* F. Mannering and W. Kelareski.)

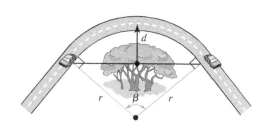

(a) At 45 miles per hour, $S = 390$ feet. If $r = 600$ feet, approximate d.

(b) At 60 miles per hour, $S = 620$ feet. Approximate d for the same curve.

(c) Discuss how the speed limit affects the amount of land that should be cleared on the inside of the curve.

100. Dead Reckoning Suppose an airplane flies the path shown in the figure, where distance is measured in hundreds of miles. Approximate the final coordinates of the airplane if its initial coordinates are $(0, 0)$.

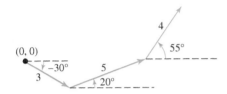

101. Modeling Biological Rhythms (Refer to Example 13.) The table shows the time y in the afternoon when a typical flying squirrel becomes active during month x.

x (month)	1	2	3	4
y (P.M.)	4:30	5:15	5:45	6:30

x (month)	5	6	7	8
y (P.M.)	7:00	7:30	7:45	7:30

x (month)	9	10	11	12
y (P.M.)	6:45	6:15	5:00	4:15

Source: J. Harker, *The Physiology of Diurnal Rhythms.*

(a) Make a scatterplot of the data. (*Hint:* Represent 4:30 P.M. by 4.5.)

(b) The formula $f(x) = 1.9 \sin (0.42x - 1.2) + 5.7$ models the time of sunset, where x represents the month. Graph f and the data together. Interpret the graph.

102. Modeling Biological Rhythms (Refer to Example 13.) The table lists the luminescence y of a plant after t hours, where $t = 0$ corresponds to midnight.

t	0	6	12	18	24	30	36	42	48
y	10	6	2	6	10	6	2	6	10

(a) Graph the data and $L(t) = 4 \cos (0.27t) + 6$. How well does the function model the data?

(b) Estimate the luminescence when $t = 15$.

(c) Use the midpoint formula to complete part (b). Are your answers the same? Why?

Writing about Mathematics

103. Discuss whether the sine and cosine functions are linear or nonlinear functions. Use graphical and numerical representations to justify your reasoning.

104. Describe two ways to define the sine and cosine functions. Give examples.

Extended and Discovery Exercises

1. Graph $f(t) = \sin t$ and $g(t) = \cos t$ in the same viewing rectangle. Then translate the graph of f to the left $\frac{\pi}{2}$ units by graphing $y = f\left(t + \frac{\pi}{2}\right)$. How does this translated graph compare to the graph of g?

2. (Continuation of Exercise 1) Translate the graph of $g(t) = \cos t$ to the right $\frac{3\pi}{2}$ units by graphing the function given by $y = g\left(t - \frac{3\pi}{2}\right)$. How does this translated graph compare to the graph of $f(t) = \sin t$?

6.4 Other Trigonometric Functions and Their Graphs

- Learn definitions and basic identities
- Define the other trigonometric functions for any angle and any real number
- Represent other trigonometric functions
- Solve applications

Introduction

Unlike the sine function, the tangent and cotangent functions did not originate with astronomy. Rather, they were developed as part of surveying land, finding heights of objects, and determining time. The cotangent function was computed as early as 1500 B.C. in Egypt, where sundials were used to determine time. Depending on the position of the sun in the sky, a vertical stick casts shadows of different lengths. See Figure 6.78. This is a simple device for evaluating the cotangent function.   (**Source:** NCTM, *Historical Topics for the Mathematics Classroom, Thirty-first Yearbook.*)

Modeling Shadow Length

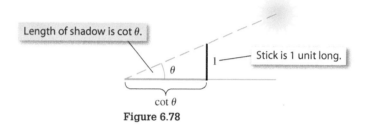

Length of shadow is $\cot \theta$.

Stick is 1 unit long.

$\cot \theta$

Figure 6.78

Definitions

Using Figure 6.79, the other trigonometric functions may be defined for any angle θ in a manner similar to the way sine and cosine functions were defined.

Finding Trig Functions of θ

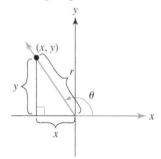

Figure 6.79

TRIGONOMETRIC FUNCTIONS OF ANY ANGLE θ

Let (x, y) be a point other than the origin on the terminal side of an angle θ in standard position. If $r = \sqrt{x^2 + y^2}$, then the six trigonometric functions are as follows.

$$\sin \theta = \frac{y}{r} \qquad\qquad \csc \theta = \frac{r}{y} \ (y \neq 0)$$

$$\cos \theta = \frac{x}{r} \qquad\qquad \sec \theta = \frac{r}{x} \ (x \neq 0)$$

$$\tan \theta = \frac{y}{x} \ (x \neq 0) \qquad \cot \theta = \frac{x}{y} \ (y \neq 0)$$

The domains of both the sine and the cosine functions include all angles. However, the cotangent and cosecant functions are undefined when $y = 0$, which corresponds to angles whose terminal sides lie on the *x-axis*. Examples include $0°$, $\pm 180°$, and $\pm 360°$. The domains of the cotangent and cosecant functions are as follows where n is an integer.

Domain of Cotangent and Cosecant

$$D = \{\theta \,|\, \theta \neq 180° \cdot n\} \qquad \text{or} \qquad D = \{t \,|\, t \neq \pi n\}$$

Degrees

Radians or real numbers

Similarly, the tangent and secant functions are undefined whenever $x = 0$. This corresponds to angles whose terminal sides lie on the *y-axis*. Examples include $\pm 90°$, $\pm 270°$, and $\pm 450°$. The domains of the tangent and secant functions are as follows, where n is an integer.

Domain of Tangent and Secant

$$D = \{\theta \mid \theta \neq 90° + 180° \cdot n\} \qquad \text{or} \qquad D = \left\{t \mid t \neq \tfrac{\pi}{2} + \pi n\right\}$$

Degrees

Radians or real numbers

In some situations we can evaluate the six trigonometric functions without a calculator, as illustrated in the next example.

EXAMPLE 1 Finding values of trigonometric functions

The point $(5, -12)$ is located on the terminal side of an angle θ in standard position. Find the six trigonometric functions of θ.

SOLUTION There are many coterminal angles that have the point $(5, -12)$ located on their terminal sides. However, the *trigonometric values for coterminal angles are equal*. In Figure 6.80 one possibility for θ is shown. Begin by calculating r.

$$r = \sqrt{x^2 + y^2} = \sqrt{5^2 + (-12)^2} = 13$$

Since $x = 5$, $y = -12$, and $r = 13$, the values of the six trigonometric functions are as follows.

$$\sin \theta = \frac{y}{r} = -\frac{12}{13} \qquad \csc \theta = \frac{r}{y} = -\frac{13}{12}$$

$$\cos \theta = \frac{x}{r} = \frac{5}{13} \qquad \sec \theta = \frac{r}{x} = \frac{13}{5}$$

$$\tan \theta = \frac{y}{x} = -\frac{12}{5} \qquad \cot \theta = \frac{x}{y} = -\frac{5}{12}$$

Now Try Exercise 1

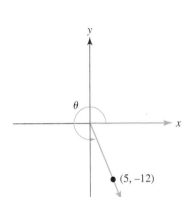

Figure 6.80

NOTE If an angle is a multiple of 30° or 45° $\left(\tfrac{\pi}{6} \text{ or } \tfrac{\pi}{4} \text{ radians}\right)$, then we can determine its six trigonometric functions by hand.

EXAMPLE 2 Evaluating the trigonometric functions

Find the six trigonometric functions for each angle by hand.
(a) 330°   **(b)** $-\frac{5\pi}{4}$

SOLUTION

Getting Started First sketch the given angle in standard position and draw a perpendicular line segment from the terminal side to the *x*-axis. Choose or calculate values for x, y, or r. Use these values to determine each trigonometric function. ▶

(a) An angle of 330° is sketched in Figure 6.81 on the next page, with a perpendicular line segment drawn to the *x*-axis. A 30°–60° right triangle is formed. See also Figure 6.82 on the next page. From Figure 6.81 we can see that $x = \sqrt{3}$, $y = -1$, and $r = 2$.

Finding *x*, *y*, and *r* for 330°

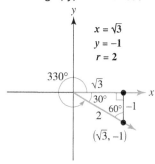

Figure 6.81

A 30°–60° Right Triangle

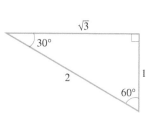

Figure 6.82

$$\sin 330° = \frac{y}{r} = -\frac{1}{2} \qquad \csc 330° = \frac{r}{y} = -\frac{2}{1} = -2$$

$$\cos 330° = \frac{x}{r} = \frac{\sqrt{3}}{2} \qquad \sec 330° = \frac{r}{x} = \frac{2}{\sqrt{3}}$$

$$\tan 330° = \frac{y}{x} = -\frac{1}{\sqrt{3}} \qquad \cot 330° = \frac{x}{y} = \frac{\sqrt{3}}{-1} = -\sqrt{3}$$

(b) An angle of $-\frac{5\pi}{4}$ (radians) is sketched in Figure 6.83, with a perpendicular line segment drawn to the *x*-axis. A 45°–45° right triangle is formed. See also Figure 6.84. From Figure 6.83 we can see that $x = -1, y = 1,$ and $r = \sqrt{2}$.

Finding *x*, *y*, and *r* for $-\frac{5\pi}{4}$

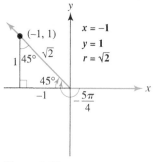

Figure 6.83

A 45°–45° Right Triangle

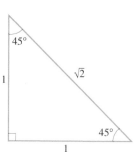

Figure 6.84

$$\sin\left(-\frac{5\pi}{4}\right) = \frac{y}{r} = \frac{1}{\sqrt{2}} \qquad \csc\left(-\frac{5\pi}{4}\right) = \frac{r}{y} = \frac{\sqrt{2}}{1} = \sqrt{2}$$

$$\cos\left(-\frac{5\pi}{4}\right) = \frac{x}{r} = -\frac{1}{\sqrt{2}} \qquad \sec\left(-\frac{5\pi}{4}\right) = \frac{r}{x} = -\frac{\sqrt{2}}{1} = -\sqrt{2}$$

$$\tan\left(-\frac{5\pi}{4}\right) = \frac{y}{x} = -\frac{1}{1} = -1 \qquad \cot\left(-\frac{5\pi}{4}\right) = \frac{x}{y} = -\frac{1}{1} = -1$$

Now Try Exercises 7 and 17

Some Basic Trigonometric Identities

Since $\sin \theta = \frac{y}{r}$ and $\csc \theta = \frac{r}{y}$, it follows that $\sin \theta$ and $\csc \theta$ are reciprocals. This may be expressed using either of the *reciprocal identities*,

$$\sin\theta = \frac{1}{\csc\theta} \qquad \text{or} \qquad \csc\theta = \frac{1}{\sin\theta}.$$

For angle θ in Example 1, it was shown that $\sin \theta = -\frac{12}{13}$. It follows that

$$\csc \theta = \frac{1}{-12/13} = -\frac{13}{12}.$$

Identities are equations that are true for all meaningful values a variable. Reciprocal identities also hold for $\tan \theta$ and $\cot \theta$ as well as $\cos \theta$ and $\sec \theta$.

RECIPROCAL IDENTITIES

$$\sin \theta = \frac{1}{\csc \theta} \qquad \cos \theta = \frac{1}{\sec \theta} \qquad \tan \theta = \frac{1}{\cot \theta}$$

$$\csc \theta = \frac{1}{\sin \theta} \qquad \sec \theta = \frac{1}{\cos \theta} \qquad \cot \theta = \frac{1}{\tan \theta}$$

The expressions $\cot \theta$ and $\tan \theta$ can be written in terms of $\sin \theta$ and $\cos \theta$. For example,

$$\cot \theta = \frac{x}{y} = \frac{x/r}{y/r} = \frac{\cos \theta}{\sin \theta}.$$

A *quotient identity* can be obtained for $\tan \theta$ similarly.

QUOTIENT IDENTITIES

$$\tan \theta = \frac{\sin \theta}{\cos \theta} \qquad \cot \theta = \frac{\cos \theta}{\sin \theta}$$

EXAMPLE 3   Using identities

If $\sin \theta = \frac{3}{5}$ and $\cos \theta = -\frac{4}{5}$, find the other four trigonometric functions of θ.

SOLUTION   To find the other four trigonometric functions, apply the quotient and reciprocal identities.

Quotient identities

$$\tan \theta = \frac{\sin \theta}{\cos \theta} = \frac{3/5}{-4/5} = -\frac{3}{4}$$

$$\cot \theta = \frac{\cos \theta}{\sin \theta} = \frac{-4/5}{3/5} = -\frac{4}{3}$$

Reciprocal identities

$$\sec \theta = \frac{1}{\cos \theta} = \frac{1}{-4/5} = -\frac{5}{4}$$

$$\csc \theta = \frac{1}{\sin \theta} = \frac{1}{3/5} = \frac{5}{3}$$

Now Try Exercise 29

In Section 6.3 we showed that $\sin^2 \theta + \cos^2 \theta = 1$ for all real numbers (or angles) θ. In the next example, we apply this identity to find the values of the trigonometric functions.

EXAMPLE 4 Applying the identity $\sin^2\theta + \cos^2\theta = 1$

If $\sin\theta = \frac{4}{5}$ and $\cos\theta < 0$, find the values of the other five trigonometric functions.

SOLUTION The identity $\sin^2\theta + \cos^2\theta = 1$ can be used to determine $\cos\theta$.

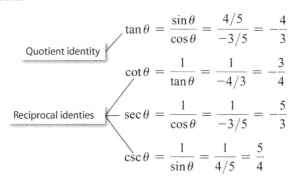

$$\sin^2\theta + \cos^2\theta = 1 \qquad \text{Identity}$$

Solve for $\cos\theta$

$$\cos^2\theta = 1 - \sin^2\theta \qquad \text{Subtract } \sin^2\theta.$$

$$\cos\theta = \pm\sqrt{1 - \sin^2\theta} \qquad \text{Square root property}$$

$$\cos\theta = \pm\sqrt{1 - \left(\frac{4}{5}\right)^2} \qquad \text{Let } \sin\theta = \frac{4}{5}.$$

$$\cos\theta = \pm\sqrt{\frac{9}{25}} \qquad \text{Simplify.}$$

$$\cos\theta = -\frac{3}{5} \qquad \cos\theta < 0$$

Now we can use $\sin\theta = \frac{4}{5}$ and $\cos\theta = -\frac{3}{5}$ to determine the other four trigonometric functions.

Quotient identity

$$\tan\theta = \frac{\sin\theta}{\cos\theta} = \frac{4/5}{-3/5} = -\frac{4}{3}$$

$$\cot\theta = \frac{1}{\tan\theta} = \frac{1}{-4/3} = -\frac{3}{4}$$

Reciprocal identies

$$\sec\theta = \frac{1}{\cos\theta} = \frac{1}{-3/5} = -\frac{5}{3}$$

$$\csc\theta = \frac{1}{\sin\theta} = \frac{1}{4/5} = \frac{5}{4}$$

Now Try Exercise 35

Unit Circle (r = 1)

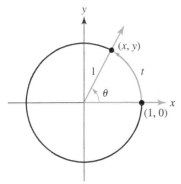

Figure 6.85

Unit Circle Evaluation Suppose the terminal side of an angle θ in standard position intersects the unit circle at the point (x, y). See Figure 6.85. In this case $r = 1$ and the definitions of the six trigonometric functions become as follows.

$$\sin\theta = y \qquad \cos\theta = x \qquad \tan\theta = \frac{y}{x}$$

$$\csc\theta = \frac{1}{y} \qquad \sec\theta = \frac{1}{x} \qquad \cot\theta = \frac{x}{y}$$

As with the sine and cosine functions, evaluating the other trigonometric functions for a real number t is equivalent to evaluating these functions for t radians.

The Wrapping Function (Optional)

The six trigonometric functions can be evaluated for real numbers by using the wrapping function presented in Section 6.3. For any real number s, if $W(s) = (x, y)$, then the six trigonometric functions can be defined as follows.

$$\sin s = y \qquad \cos s = x \qquad \tan s = \frac{y}{x}$$

$$\csc s = \frac{1}{y} \qquad \sec s = \frac{1}{x} \qquad \cot s = \frac{x}{y}$$

The next example illustrates how the wrapping function can be used to evaluate the six trigonometric functions.

EXAMPLE 5 Applying the wrapping function

For $s = -5\pi$, evaluate $W(s)$. If possible, find the six trigonometric functions of s.

SOLUTION The circumference of the unit circle is 2π. A string of length 5π wraps (clockwise) around the unit circle two and a half times. Because the initial point is always $(1, 0)$, the terminal point is $(-1, 0)$, as shown in Figure 6.86. Thus $W(-5\pi) = (-1, 0)$.

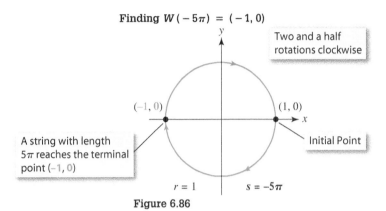

Finding $W(-5\pi) = (-1, 0)$

Two and a half rotations clockwise

A string with length 5π reaches the terminal point $(-1, 0)$

Initial Point

$r = 1$ $s = -5\pi$

Figure 6.86

The six trigonometric functions can be evaluated by using $x = -1$ and $y = 0$. Note that the cosecant and cotangent are undefined because $y = 0$.

$$\sin(-5\pi) = y = 0 \qquad\qquad \csc(-5\pi) = \frac{1}{y} \text{ (undefined)}$$

$$\cos(-5\pi) = x = -1 \qquad \sec(-5\pi) = \frac{1}{x} = \frac{1}{-1} = -1$$

$$\tan(-5\pi) = \frac{y}{x} = \frac{0}{-1} = 0 \qquad \cot(-5\pi) = \frac{x}{y} \text{ (undefined)}$$

Now Try Exercise 39

Representations of Other Trigonometric Functions

Like $\sin t$ and $\cos t$, the other four trigonometric functions cannot be evaluated with simple formulas. However, these functions do have numerical and graphical representations. We begin by discussing the tangent function.

The Tangent Function Figure 6.87 shows angle θ in *standard position* with its terminal side passing through the point (x, y). The slope of this terminal side is

$$m = \frac{y - 0}{x - 0} = \frac{y}{x} = \tan\theta.$$

It can be shown that the slope of the terminal side of θ equals $\tan \theta$, regardless of the quadrant containing θ. See Figure 6.88.

$$\tan\theta = \frac{y}{x} = m$$

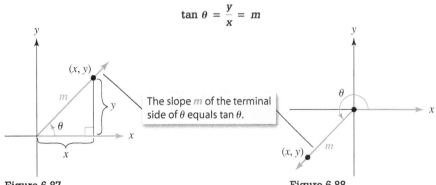

(x, y)

m

y

The slope m of the terminal side of θ equals $\tan \theta$.

θ

x

θ

(x, y)

m

Figure 6.87   **Figure 6.88**

The following See the Concept uses the fact that $m = \tan \theta$ to derive the graph of $y = \tan \theta$.

See the Concept: The Graph of $y = \tan \theta$.

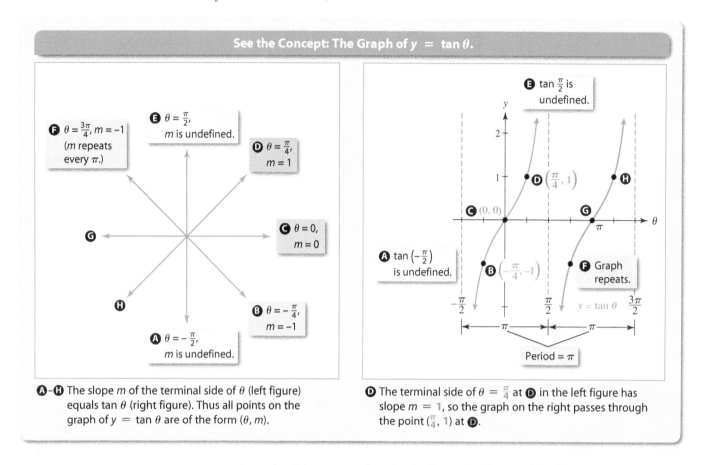

A–H The slope m of the terminal side of θ (left figure) equals $\tan \theta$ (right figure). Thus all points on the graph of $y = \tan \theta$ are of the form (θ, m).

D The terminal side of $\theta = \frac{\pi}{4}$ at **D** in the left figure has slope $m = 1$, so the graph on the right passes through the point $(\frac{\pi}{4}, 1)$ at **D**.

A graph of the tangent function is shown in Figure 6.89 with period π and vertical asymptotes at $t = \pm\frac{\pi}{2}, \pm\frac{3\pi}{2}, \pm\frac{5\pi}{2}, \ldots$. The domain of the tangent function is $D = \{t \mid t \neq \frac{\pi}{2} + \pi n\}$. The domain excludes x-values where vertical asymptotes occur.

The Tangent Function

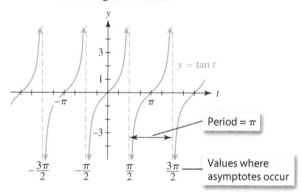

Figure 6.89

A *numerical representation* of $f(t) = \tan t$ for selected (real number) values of t satisfying $-\frac{\pi}{2} \le t \le \frac{\pi}{2}$ is shown in Table 6.7. (A dash indicates that $\tan t$ is undefined.)

A Table of Values for the Tangent Function

t	$-\frac{\pi}{2}$	$-\frac{\pi}{3}$	$-\frac{\pi}{4}$	$-\frac{\pi}{6}$	0	$\frac{\pi}{6}$	$\frac{\pi}{4}$	$\frac{\pi}{3}$	$\frac{\pi}{2}$
$\tan t$	—	$-\sqrt{3}$	-1	$-\frac{1}{\sqrt{3}}$	0	$\frac{1}{\sqrt{3}}$	1	$\sqrt{3}$	—

Table 6.7

EXAMPLE 6 Evaluating the tangent function

Evaluate $f(t) = \tan t$ at $t = -\frac{\pi}{4}$ by hand.

SOLUTION If angle $-\frac{\pi}{4}$ is in standard position, the terminal side intersects the unit circle at the point $\left(\frac{1}{\sqrt{2}}, -\frac{1}{\sqrt{2}}\right)$. See Figure 6.90. Therefore

$$\tan\left(-\frac{\pi}{4}\right) = \frac{y}{x} = \frac{-1/\sqrt{2}}{1/\sqrt{2}} = -1.$$

Note that the 45°–45° right triangle in Figure 6.91 can be used as an aid in determining the length of the sides of the triangle in Figure 6.90. Also note that the slope of the terminal side of the angle is -1 and equals $\tan\left(-\frac{\pi}{4}\right)$.

Now Try Exercise 51

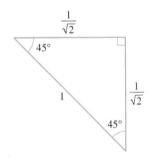

Figure 6.90

The Cosecant Function The cosecant function can also be evaluated by hand. For example, if $t = \frac{7\pi}{6}$, then the terminal side of $\theta = \frac{7\pi}{6}$ intersects the unit circle at the point $\left(-\frac{\sqrt{3}}{2}, -\frac{1}{2}\right)$. See Figure 6.92. It follows that

$$\csc\frac{7\pi}{6} = \frac{1}{y} = \frac{1}{-1/2} = -2.$$

Note that the 30°–60° right triangle in Figure 6.93 can be used as an aid in determining the length of the sides of the triangle in Figure 6.92.

A *numerical representation* of $f(t) = \csc t$ is shown in Table 6.8 for selected values of t satisfying $-\pi \le t \le \pi$. Note that $\csc t = \frac{1}{\sin t}$. (A dash indicates that $\csc t$ is undefined.)

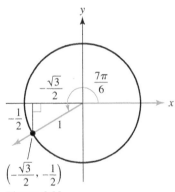

Figure 6.91

t	$-\pi$	$-\frac{3\pi}{4}$	$-\frac{\pi}{2}$	$-\frac{\pi}{4}$	0	$\frac{\pi}{4}$	$\frac{\pi}{2}$	$\frac{3\pi}{4}$	π
$\csc t$	—	$-\sqrt{2}$	-1	$-\sqrt{2}$	—	$\sqrt{2}$	1	$\sqrt{2}$	—

Table 6.8

A graph of $\csc t$ is given in Figure 6.94. The domain of the cosecant function is $D = \{t \mid t \ne \pi n\}$, where n is an integer and vertical asymptotes occur whenever $t = \pi n$. The period of the cosecant function equals 2π.

Since $\csc t = \frac{1}{\sin t}$, we can sketch the graph of $y = \csc t$ by using the graph of $y = \sin t$ as an aid. See Figure 6.95. When $\sin t = 0$, $\csc t$ is undefined and a vertical asymptote occurs on the graph of $\csc t$. When $\sin t = \pm 1$, $\csc t = \pm 1$. Whenever $\sin t$ increases, $\csc t$ decreases, and whenever $\sin t$ decreases, $\csc t$ increases. Because $|\sin t| \le 1$ for all t, it follows that $|\csc t| \ge 1$ for all $t \ne \pi n$.

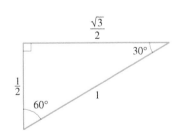

Figure 6.92

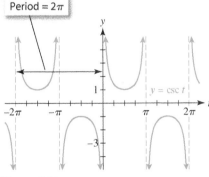

Figure 6.94

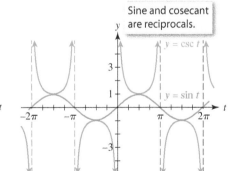

Figure 6.95

The Cosecant Function

The Sine and Cosecant Functions

Figure 6.93

The Cotangent Function A graph of $y = \cot t$ is shown in Figure 6.96 on the next page. Its period is π, and its domain is $D = \{t \mid t \ne \pi n\}$, where n is an integer. Vertical asymptotes occur at $t = \pi n$.

The Cotangent Function

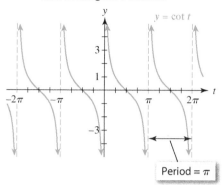

Figure 6.96

Friendly Windows in Degree Mode (Optional) Trigonometric functions may be represented graphically in either radian or degree mode. If a friendly window is selected using degree mode, a trigonometric function may be accurately graphed in connected mode. Graphs of the cosecant and cotangent functions are shown in Figures 6.97 and 6.98.

Friendly window

The Cosecant Function
$[-352.5°, 352.5°, 90°]$ by $[-4, 4, 1]$

The Cotangent Function
$[-352.5°, 352.5°, 90°]$ by $[-4, 4, 1]$

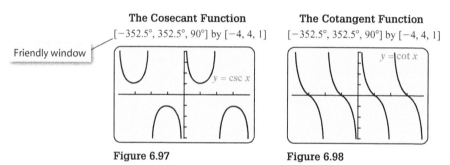

$y = \csc x$

$y = \cot x$

Figure 6.97   Figure 6.98

The Secant Function A graph of $y = \sec t$ is shown in Figure 6.99. Its period is 2π, and its domain is $D = \{t \mid t \neq \frac{\pi}{2} + \pi n\}$, where n is an integer. Vertical asymptotes occur at $t = \frac{\pi}{2} + \pi n$. The graph of the cosine function may be used as an aid in graphing the secant function, since the zeros of $y = \cos t$ correspond to the vertical asymptotes on the graph of $y = \sec t$. See Figure 6.100.

The Secant Function   **The Cosine and Secant Functions**

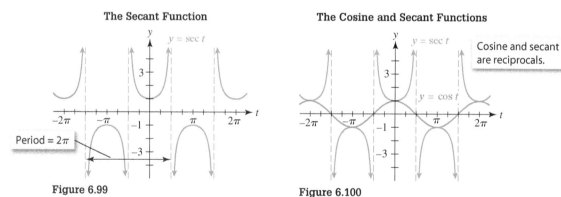

Cosine and secant are reciprocals.

Period = 2π

Figure 6.99   Figure 6.100

The next two examples illustrate how to evaluate the six trigonometric functions first by hand and then with a calculator.

EXAMPLE 7 Evaluating the trigonometric functions

If $\theta = \frac{3\pi}{2}$, find the six trigonometric functions of θ.

SOLUTION If $\theta = \frac{3\pi}{2}$ is in standard position, then its terminal side intersects the unit circle at the point $(0, -1)$. See Figure 6.101. Thus $x = 0$ and $y = -1$. The values of the six trigonometric functions are as follows.

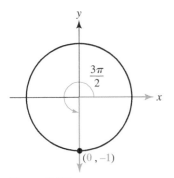

Figure 6.101

$$\sin\frac{3\pi}{2} = y = -1$$

$$\cos\frac{3\pi}{2} = x = 0$$

$$\tan\frac{3\pi}{2} = \frac{y}{x} \text{ is undefined, since } x = 0$$

$$\csc\frac{3\pi}{2} = \frac{1}{y} = \frac{1}{-1} = -1$$

$$\sec\frac{3\pi}{2} = \frac{1}{x} \text{ is undefined, since } x = 0$$

$$\cot\frac{3\pi}{2} = \frac{x}{y} = \frac{0}{-1} = 0$$

Now Try Exercise 57

EXAMPLE 8 Using a calculator to evaluate trigonometric functions

Find values of the six trigonometric functions of θ.
(a) $\theta = 102.6°$ **(b)** $\theta = 2.56$

SOLUTION

(a) Most calculators do not have special keys for secant, cosecant, and cotangent. To evaluate these functions, we use the reciprocal identities. For example, to find sec(102.6°), evaluate $1/\cos(102.6°)$. The values of the trigonometric functions are shown in Figures 6.102 and 6.103.

(b) Since there is no degree symbol, use radian mode. With the aid of a calculator, the values of the six trigonometric functions are approximated as follows.

$$\sin 2.56 \approx 0.5494 \qquad \cos 2.56 \approx -0.8356 \qquad \tan 2.56 \approx -0.6574$$

$$\csc 2.56 \approx 1.8203 \qquad \sec 2.56 \approx -1.1968 \qquad \cot 2.56 \approx -1.5210$$

Now Try Exercises 63 and 67

```
sin(102.6)
           .9759167619
cos(102.6)
          -.2181432414
tan(102.6)
          -4.473742829
```

Figure 6.102 Degree Mode

Applying Reciprocal Identities

```
1/sin(102.6)
           1.024677553
1/cos(102.6)
          -4.584143857
1/tan(102.6)
          -.2235264829
```

Figure 6.103 Degree Mode

Applications of Trigonometric Functions

Highway Design A *sag curve* occurs when a highway goes downhill and then uphill. Improperly designed sag curves can be dangerous at night because a vehicle's headlights point downward and may not illuminate the uphill portion of the highway, as illustrated in Figure 6.104. The minimum safe length L for a typical sag curve with a 40-mile-per-hour speed limit is given by the following.

$$L = \frac{2700}{h + 3\tan\alpha}$$

> The tangent function is often used when designing highways.

The variable h represents the height of the headlights above the road surface, and α represents a small (upward) angle associated with the vertical alignment of the headlight, shown in Figure 6.104. (***Source:*** F. Mannering and W. Kilareski, *Principles of Highway Engineering and Traffic Analysis.*)

Designing a Safe Sag Curve

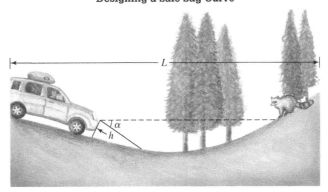

Figure 6.104 (Not to scale)

EXAMPLE 9 Designing a sag curve

Calculate L for a car with headlights 2.5 feet above the ground and $\alpha = 1°$. Repeat the calculations for a truck with headlights 4 feet above the ground and $\alpha = 2°$.

SOLUTION For the car, let $h = 2.5$ and $\alpha = 1°$.

$$L = \frac{2700}{2.5 + 3 \tan 1°} \approx 1058 \text{ feet} \qquad L = \frac{2700}{h + 3 \tan \alpha}$$

For the truck, let $h = 4$ and $\alpha = 2°$.

$$L = \frac{2700}{4 + 3 \tan 2°} \approx 658 \text{ feet} \qquad L = \frac{2700}{h + 3 \tan \alpha}$$

(Since both cars and trucks use the same highways, engineers typically use the larger of the two distances to design a safe sag curve.)

Now Try Exercise 89

Bending of Starlight When a stick is put partially into a glass of water, it appears to bend at the surface of the water. A similar phenomenon occurs when starlight enters Earth's atmosphere. To an observer on the ground, a star's apparent position α is different from its true position. This phenomenon is referred to as *atmospheric refraction*. See Figure 6.105 below. The amount that starlight is bent is given by angle θ measured in seconds, where $\theta = 57.3 \tan \alpha$ with $0° \le \alpha \le 45°$. (*Source:* W. Schlosser, *Challenges of Astronomy.*)

Atmospheric Refraction

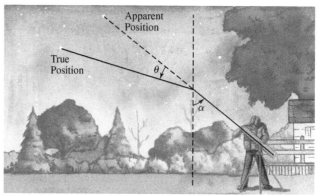

Figure 6.105 (Not to scale)

EXAMPLE 10 Calculating refraction of starlight

Use Figure 6.105 and the formula $\theta = 57.3 \tan \alpha$ to calculate θ when $\alpha = 32°35'21''$.

SOLUTION $\theta = 57.3 \tan (32°35'21'') \approx 36.6''$. The star is actually 36.6'' lower in the sky than it appears.

Now Try Exercise 91

Sun Traveling Through the Atmosphere

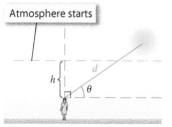

Figure 6.106 (Not to scale)

Time of Day and Sun Tanning The shortest path through Earth's atmosphere for the sun's rays occurs when the sun is directly overhead. As the sun moves lower in the horizon, sunlight travels through more atmosphere. See Figure 6.106, where $d = h \csc \theta$. *Explain why.* If the angle of elevation of the sun is θ, then the path length d of sunlight through the atmosphere increases by a factor of $\csc \theta$ from its noontime value of h. (Because of the curvature of Earth, this model is not accurate when $\theta < 20°$ and the sun is positioned near the horizon. See Exercise 95.) When sunlight passes through more atmosphere, less ultraviolet light reaches Earth's surface. This is one reason why some experts recommend sun tanning either earlier or later in the day. (*Source:* C. Winter, *Solar Power Plants.*)

EXAMPLE 11   Measuring the intensity of the sun

Assuming that the sun is directly overhead at noon, calculate the percent increase between the atmospheric distance that sunlight passes through at noon and at 10:00 A.M.

SOLUTION From Figure 6.106, $\theta = 90°$ at noon and $d = h \csc \theta$. The apparent position of the sun changes 360° in the sky in 24 hours, or 15° per hour. Therefore 2 hours earlier $\theta = 60°$. At noon,

$$d = h \csc 90° = \frac{h}{\sin 90°} = \frac{h}{1} = h$$

Apply reciprocal identity.

and at 10:00 A.M.,

$$d = h \csc 60° = \frac{h}{\sin 60°} = \frac{h}{\sqrt{3}/2} \approx 1.15h.$$

This means that sunlight travels through about 15% more atmosphere at 10:00 A.M. than at noon.

Now Try Exercise 93

Putting It All Together

The following table summarizes the domain, range, and period of each trigonometric function. In this table n is an integer and t is a real number.

FUNCTION	DOMAIN	RANGE	PERIOD
$\sin t$	$-\infty < t < \infty$	$-1 \leq \sin t \leq 1$	2π
$\cos t$	$-\infty < t < \infty$	$-1 \leq \cos t \leq 1$	2π
$\tan t$	$t \neq \frac{\pi}{2} + \pi n$	$-\infty < \tan t < \infty$	π
$\cot t$	$t \neq \pi n$	$-\infty < \cot t < \infty$	π
$\sec t$	$t \neq \frac{\pi}{2} + \pi n$	$\left| \sec t \right| \geq 1$	2π
$\csc t$	$t \neq \pi n$	$\left| \csc t \right| \geq 1$	2π

GRAPHS OF TRIGONOMETRIC FUNCTIONS

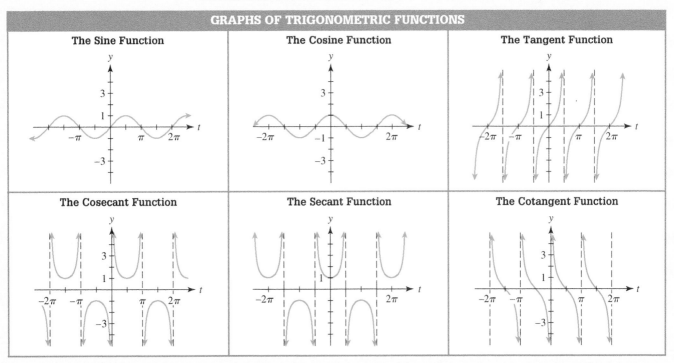

The Sine Function · The Cosine Function · The Tangent Function · The Cosecant Function · The Secant Function · The Cotangent Function

continued on next page

EVALUATING TRIGONOMETRIC FUNCTIONS

The following figure can be used to evaluate the trigonometric functions for certain angles. For example, if $\theta = 120°$ (or $\frac{2\pi}{3}$ radians) is in standard position, then its terminal side intersects the unit circle at the point $\left(-\frac{1}{2}, \frac{\sqrt{3}}{2}\right)$. It follows that $\cos 120° = -\frac{1}{2}$ and $\sin 120° = \frac{\sqrt{3}}{2}$. Other trigonometric values can also be found using these values. Note that $\frac{\sqrt{2}}{2} = \frac{1}{\sqrt{2}}$.

The Unit Circle and Special Angles

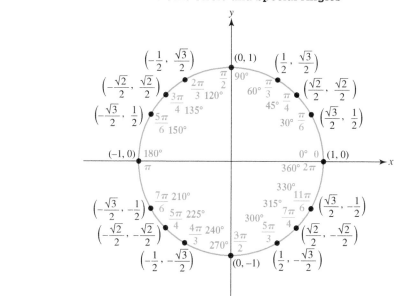

6.4 Exercises

Basic Concepts

Exercises 1–4: Find the six trigonometric functions of θ.

1.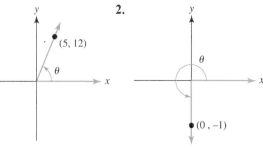
2.
3.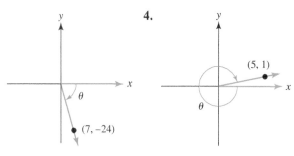
4.

Exercises 5–24: Find the six trigonometric functions of the given angle by hand.

5. 90°
6. 135°
7. −45°
8. −180°
9. π
10. $\frac{3\pi}{4}$
11. $-\frac{\pi}{3}$
12. $-\frac{5\pi}{6}$
13. $-\frac{\pi}{2}$
14. $\frac{3\pi}{2}$
15. 360°
16. 60°
17. $\frac{\pi}{6}$
18. $-\frac{2\pi}{3}$
19. $\frac{4\pi}{3}$
20. $\frac{2\pi}{3}$
21. −225°
22. −315°
23. $-\frac{13\pi}{6}$
24. $-\frac{7\pi}{6}$

Exercises 25–28: The terminal side of an angle θ lies on the line in the given quadrant. Find the six trigonometric functions of θ. How does the slope of the line compare to tan θ?

25. $y = -4x$, Quadrant II   **26.** $y = \frac{1}{2}x$, Quadrant I

27. $y = 6x$, Quadrant III   **28.** $y = -\frac{2}{3}x$, Quadrant IV

Identities

Exercises 29–38: Determine the values of the trigonometric functions of θ by using the given information.

29. $\sin\theta = \frac{3}{5}$ and $\cos\theta = \frac{4}{5}$

30. $\sin\theta = -\frac{7}{25}$ and $\cos\theta = \frac{24}{25}$

31. $\csc\theta = -\frac{17}{15}$ and $\sec\theta = -\frac{17}{8}$

32. $\csc\theta = 2$ and $\sec\theta = -\frac{2}{\sqrt{3}}$

33. $\tan\theta = \frac{5}{12}$ and $\cos\theta = \frac{12}{13}$ (*Hint:* $\sin\theta = \tan\theta\cos\theta$.)

34. $\sin\theta = \frac{3}{5}$ and $\cot\theta = -\frac{4}{3}$

35. $\sin\theta = -\frac{3}{5}$ and $\cos\theta > 0$

36. $\sin\theta = -\frac{12}{13}$ and $\cos\theta < 0$

37. $\cos\theta = -\frac{4}{5}$ and $\sin\theta < 0$

38. $\cos\theta = \frac{7}{25}$ and $\sin\theta > 0$

Wrapping Function

Exercises 39–46: Use the wrapping function to determine the six trigonometric functions of the given number.

39. -7π **40.** 4π

41. $\frac{7\pi}{2}$ **42.** $-\frac{3\pi}{2}$

43. $-\frac{3\pi}{4}$ **44.** $\frac{7\pi}{4}$

45. $\frac{7\pi}{6}$ **46.** $-\frac{11\pi}{6}$

Unit Circle Evaluation

Exercises 47–50: The figure shows angle θ in standard position with its terminal side intersecting the unit circle. Evaluate the six trigonometric functions of θ.

47.   **48.**

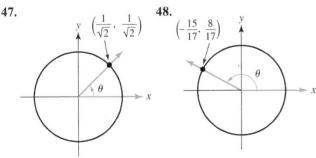

49.   **50.**

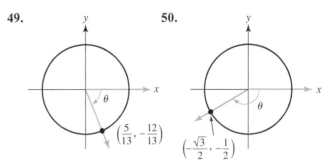

Exercises 51–56: Evaluate the trigonometric function by using the unit circle.

51. $\tan\left(-\frac{5\pi}{4}\right)$ **52.** $\tan\left(-\frac{7\pi}{4}\right)$

53. $\csc\frac{\pi}{6}$ **54.** $\csc\frac{7\pi}{6}$

55. $\sec\frac{\pi}{6}$ **56.** $\cot\frac{7\pi}{4}$

Exercises 57–62: Evaluate the six trigonometric functions of the given number by using the unit circle.

57. $\frac{9\pi}{2}$ **58.** $-\frac{9\pi}{4}$ **59.** $-\pi$

60. 7π **61.** $\frac{4\pi}{3}$ **62.** $\frac{5\pi}{6}$

Approximations

Exercises 63–70: Approximate to four decimal places.

63. **(a)** $\sin 93.2°$ **(b)** $\csc 93.2°$

64. **(a)** $\cos(-43°)$ **(b)** $\sec(-43°)$

65. **(a)** $\tan 234°33'$ **(b)** $\cot 234°33'$

66. **(a)** $\sec 123°44'25''$ **(b)** $\cos 123°44'25''$

67. **(a)** $\cot(-4)$ **(b)** $\tan(-4)$

68. **(a)** $\csc 1.56$ **(b)** $\sin 1.56$

69. **(a)** $\cos\left(\frac{11\pi}{7}\right)$ **(b)** $\sec\left(\frac{11\pi}{7}\right)$

70. **(a)** $\tan\left(\frac{7\pi}{5}\right)$ **(b)** $\cot\left(\frac{7\pi}{5}\right)$

Exercises 71–74: **Average Rate of Change** *Approximate, to the nearest thousandth, the average rate of change of f from 0 to $\frac{\pi}{4}$.*

71. $f(x) = \sin x$ **72.** $f(x) = \cos x$

73. $f(x) = \tan\frac{1}{2}x$ **74.** $f(x) = \sin 2x$

Graphs

Exercises 75–80: Graph $y = f(t)$. Discuss the symmetry of the graph.

75. $f(t) = \sin t$ **76.** $f(t) = \cos t$

77. $f(t) = \tan t$ **78.** $f(t) = \cot t$

79. $f(t) = \sec t$ **80.** $f(t) = \csc t$

Exercises 81–86: Use the graph of f to identify its domain, range, and period.

81. $f(t) = \sin t$

82. $f(t) = \cos t$

83. $f(t) = \tan t$

84. $f(t) = \cot t$

85. $f(t) = \sec t$

86. $f(t) = \csc t$

Applications

87. Shadow Length The introduction showed how shadows can be used to compute the cotangent function.
  (a) Graph $f(t) = \cot t$ for $0 \le t \le \pi$.

  (b) Let $t = 0$ correspond to sunrise, $t = \frac{\pi}{2}$ to noon, and $t = \pi$ to sunset. Explain how the graph of f models the length of a shadow cast by a vertical stick with length 1.

88. Shadow Length (Refer to Figure 6.78.) Calculate the shadow length of a 2-foot stick when the angle of elevation of the sun is $\theta = 27°31'$.

89. Highway Design (Refer to Example 9.) Calculate the minimum length L of a typical sag curve on a highway with a 40-mile-per-hour speed limit for a car with headlights 2 feet above the ground and alignment set at $\alpha = 1.5°$.

90. Highway Design Repeat Exercise 89 for a truck with headlights 3.5 feet above the ground and alignment set at $\alpha = 2.5°$.

91. Refraction (Refer to Example 10.) Use the formula $\theta = 57.3 \tan \alpha$ to calculate the refraction θ in seconds when $\alpha = 17°23'43''$. Use an identity to rewrite the formula in terms of $\sin \alpha$ and $\cos \alpha$.

92. Refraction (Refer to Example 10.) Use the formula $\theta = 57.3 \tan \alpha$ to calculate the refraction θ in seconds when $\alpha = 5°15'50''$. Use an identity to rewrite the formula in terms of $\cot \alpha$.

93. Intensity of the Sun (Refer to Example 11.) If the sun is directly overhead at noon, calculate the percent increase between the atmospheric distance that sunlight must pass through at noon and at 3:00 P.M.

94. Intensity of the Sun (Refer to Example 11.) If the sun is directly overhead at 1:00 P.M., calculate the percent increase between the atmospheric distance that sunlight must pass through at 1:00 P.M. and at 2:30 P.M.

95. Intensity of the Sun (Refer to Example 11.) The formula $y_1 = \csc \theta = \frac{1}{\sin \theta}$, presented in Example 11 to calculate the path length of sunlight through the atmosphere relative to the path length at noon, is not accurate when the sun's elevation is less than 20°. A more accurate formula for small values of θ is given by

$$y_2 = \frac{1}{\sin \theta + 0.5(6° + \theta)^{-1.64}},$$

where θ is measured in degrees. Make a table of y_1 and y_2 starting at $\theta = 2°$ and incrementing by 1°. How do the values of y_1 and y_2 compare as θ increases? (**Source:** C. Winter, *Solar Power Plants.*)

96. GPS Satellite Communication Artificial satellites that orbit Earth often use VHF signals to communicate with the ground. Because VHF signals travel in straight lines, a satellite orbiting Earth can communicate with a fixed location on the ground only during certain times. The height h in miles of an orbit with communication time T is given by

$$h = 3955 \left(\sec \left(\pi T / P \right) - 1 \right),$$

where P is the period for the satellite to orbit Earth. Suppose a GPS satellite orbit has a period of $P = 12$ hours and can communicate with a person at the North Pole for $T = 5.08$ hours during each orbit. Approximate the height h of its orbit. (**Sources:** W. Schlosser, *Challenges of Astronomy.*)

Exercises 97 and 98: **Projectile Flight** *If a projectile is fired with an initial velocity of v feet per second at an angle θ with the horizontal, it will follow a parabolic path described by $y = \frac{-16x^2}{v^2 (\cos \theta)^2} + x \tan \theta$. See the figure.*

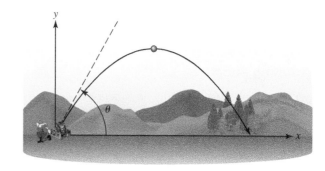

97. If $v = 750$ and $\theta = 30°$, graph the path of the projectile.
  (a) Approximate the coordinates when the maximum height occurs.

  (b) Assuming the ground is flat, find the total horizontal distance traveled by the projectile graphically.

98. If $v = 500$ and $\theta = 45°$, graph the path of the projectile.
  (a) Determine the maximum height graphically.

  (b) Assume that the projectile is fired from the base of a hill that rises with a constant slope of $\frac{1}{4}$. Approximate graphically the total horizontal distance traveled by the projectile.

Writing about Mathematics

99. Discuss whether any of the six trigonometric functions are linear functions. Justify your reasoning.

100. If α and β are coterminal angles, what can be said about the six trigonometric functions of α and β? Explain your answer using an example.

Extended and Discovery Exercise

1. The figure shows the unit circle and an acute angle θ in standard position. Explain why the trigonometric functions $\sin \theta$, $\cos \theta$, $\tan \theta$, and $\sec \theta$ are equal to the lengths of the line segments shown.

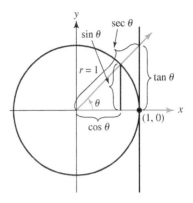

CHECKING BASIC CONCEPTS FOR SECTIONS 6.3 AND 6.4

1. Find the six trigonometric functions of θ if θ is in standard position and its terminal side passes through the point $(-7, 6)$.

2. Evaluate $\sin 45°$ by hand. Check your results with a calculator.

3. Sketch a graph of the sine, cosine, and tangent functions.

4. Evaluate the six trigonometric functions by hand at the given real number. Support your results using a calculator.
  (a) $-\pi$ **(b)** $\frac{3\pi}{4}$ **(c)** $\frac{7\pi}{6}$

6.5 Graphing Trigonometric Functions

- **Learn basic transformations of trigonometric graphs**
- **Graph trigonometric functions by hand**
- **Understand simple harmonic motion**
- **Model real data with trigonometric functions (optional)**

Introduction

Trigonometric graphs can be used to model periodic data. For example, monthly average temperatures and precipitation are usually periodic. They can vary dramatically during a twelve-month period, but tend to be periodic from one year to the next. Tides are also periodic. By performing basic transformations of graphs we can model a variety of phenomena. See Example 8.

Transformations of Trigonometric Graphs

We begin by discussing how the constants a and b affect the graphs of

$$y = a \sin bx \quad \text{and} \quad y = a \cos bx.$$

The Constant a and Amplitude The constant a controls the *amplitude* of a sinusoidal wave. If $y = 3 \sin x$, then the amplitude is $|a| = 3$. The graph of $f(x) = \sin x$ oscillates between -1 and 1, whereas the graph of $g(x) = 3 \sin x$ oscillates between -3 and 3. These concepts are shown in See the Concept and Figure 6.107 on the next page. When the constant a is negative, the graphs are reflected across the x-axis. See Figure 6.108.

> **CLASS DISCUSSION**
>
> Predict how the graph of the given equation will compare with the graph of $f(x) = \cos x$. Check your prediction by graphing both f and the equation.
>
>   **i.** $y = 2 \cos x$ **ii.** $y = -\frac{1}{2} \cos x$ **iii.** $y = -3 \cos x$

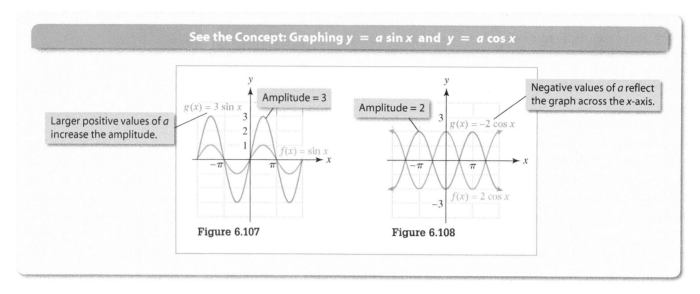

See the Concept: Graphing $y = a \sin x$ **and** $y = a \cos x$

Larger positive values of a increase the amplitude.

Amplitude = 3

$g(x) = 3 \sin x$

$f(x) = \sin x$

Figure 6.107

Amplitude = 2

$g(x) = -2 \cos x$

$f(x) = 2 \cos x$

Negative values of a reflect the graph across the x-axis.

Figure 6.108

The Constant b and Oscillations The constant b controls the number of oscillations in each interval of length 2π. For example, if $b = 2$, then there are two complete oscillations in every interval of length 2π. As a result, the graph repeats every π units and the period of both $y = \sin 2x$ and $y = \cos 2x$ is π. The *period P* of a sinusoidal graph can be computed by using the formula

$$P = \frac{2\pi}{b}, \qquad \textit{Period formula}$$

where $b > 0$. See Figures 6.109 and 6.110.

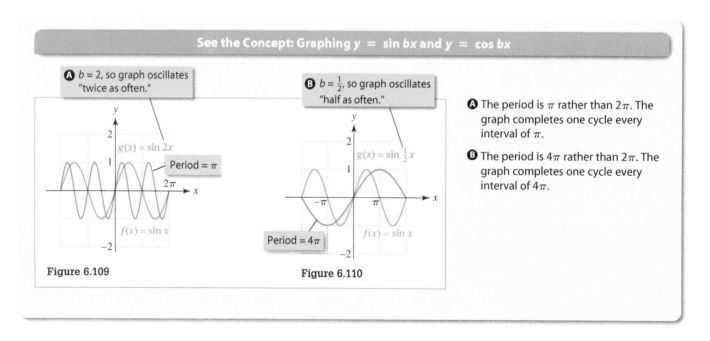

See the Concept: Graphing $y = \sin bx$ **and** $y = \cos bx$

Ⓐ $b = 2$, so graph oscillates "twice as often."

$g(x) = \sin 2x$

Period = π

$f(x) = \sin x$

Figure 6.109

Ⓑ $b = \frac{1}{2}$, so graph oscillates "half as often."

$g(x) = \sin \frac{1}{2} x$

$f(x) = \sin x$

Period = 4π

Figure 6.110

Ⓐ The period is π rather than 2π. The graph completes one cycle every interval of π.

Ⓑ The period is 4π rather than 2π. The graph completes one cycle every interval of 4π.

Stretching and Shrinking The preceding discussion can be understood in terms of stretching and shrinking. When $a > 1$, the graph of $y = a \sin x$ is *stretched* vertically compared to $y = \sin x$. When $0 < a < 1$, the graph of $y = a \sin x$ is vertically *shrunk* compared to $y = \sin x$. Similarly, when $b > 1$, the graph of $y = \sin bx$ is horizontally *shrunk* compared to the graph of $y = \sin x$. When $0 < b < 1$, the graph of $y = \sin bx$ is horizontally *stretched* compared to the graph of $y = \sin x$. Similar statements can be made for the graph of $y = a \cos x$ and $y = \cos bx$.

EXAMPLE 1   Sketching graphs of trigonometric functions

Sketch a graph of each equation. Identify the period and amplitude.

(a) $y = 3 \cos \dfrac{1}{2}x$ **(b)** $y = -2 \sin 3x$

SOLUTION

(a) The graph of $y = 3 \cos \frac{1}{2}x$ is similar to that of $y = \cos x$, except that its period P is

$$P = \frac{2\pi}{b} = \frac{2\pi}{1/2} = 4\pi$$

rather than 2π and its amplitude is 3 rather than 1. A graph of $y = 3 \cos \frac{1}{2}x$ is shown in Figure 6.111, and a graph $y = \cos x$ is shown in Figure 6.112 for comparison.

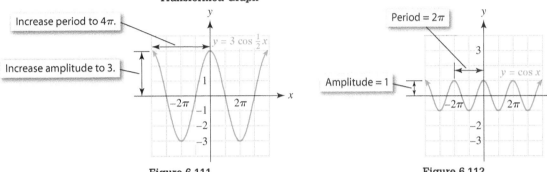

Figure 6.111   Figure 6.112

(b) The graph of $y = \sin x$ is shown in Figure 6.113. By comparison, the graph of $y = \sin 3x$, shown in Figure 6.114 has period

$$P = \frac{2\pi}{b} = \frac{2\pi}{3}.$$

It oscillates three times every interval of length 2π, whereas the graph of $y = \sin x$ oscillates once every interval of length 2π. The graph of $y = -2 \sin 3x$ is similar to the graph of $y = \sin 3x$, except that its amplitude is 2 rather than 1 and its graph is reflected across the x-axis. Figure 6.115 shows the required graph of $y = -2 \sin 3x$.

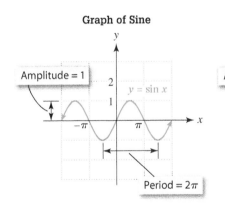

Figure 6.113   Figure 6.114

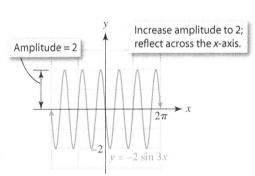

Figure 6.115

Now Try Exercises 1 and 3

Vertical and Horizontal Shifts Trigonometric graphs can be shifted vertically or horizontally. For example, to shift the graph of $f(x) = \sin x$ upward 1 unit, graph $g(x) = \sin(x) + 1$, as shown in Figure 6.116 on the next page. Similarly, to shift the graph of $f(x) = \sin x$ right $\frac{\pi}{2}$ units, graph the equation $g(x) = \sin\left(x - \frac{\pi}{2}\right)$, as shown in Figure 6.117 on the next page. A horizontal shift of a trigonometric graph is called a *phase shift*.

Vertical Shift: 1

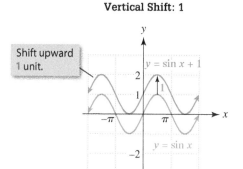

Figure 6.116

Phase Shift: $\frac{\pi}{2}$

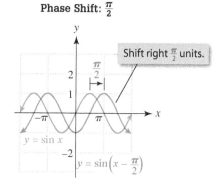

Figure 6.117

EXAMPLE 2 Transforming sinusoidal graphs

Explain how the graph of f can be obtained from the graph of either the sine or the cosine function. Then graph f.

(a) $f(x) = 3 \cos(2x) + 1$ **(b)** $f(x) = -2 \sin\left(x - \frac{\pi}{2}\right)$

SOLUTION

(a) The graph of f can be obtained from the graph of the cosine function by performing the following steps: shorten the period to π, increase the amplitude to 3, and shift the graph upward 1 unit. These three steps are shown in Figures 6.118–6.120.

Shorten Period

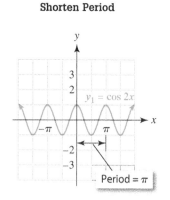

Figure 6.118

Increase Amplitude

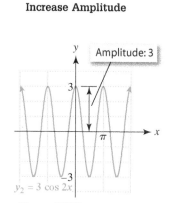

Figure 6.119

Shift Upward

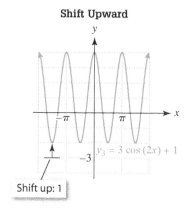

Figure 6.120

(b) The graph of f can be obtained from the graph of the sine function by shifting the graph right $\frac{\pi}{2}$ units and increasing the amplitude to 2. The negative sign will cause the graph to be reflected across the x-axis. These steps are shown in Figures 6.121–6.123.

Shift Right

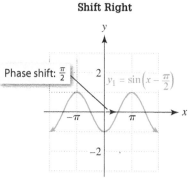

Figure 6.121

Increase Amplitude

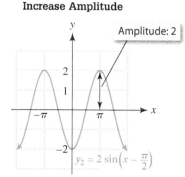

Figure 6.122

Reflect Graph

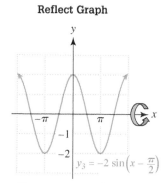

Figure 6.123

Now Try Exercises 7 and 9

The preceding discussion is summarized in the following box.

AMPLITUDE, PERIOD, PHASE SHIFT, AND VERTICAL SHIFT

The **amplitude**, **period**, **phase shift**, and **vertical shift** for the graphs of

$$y = a \sin (b(x - c)) + d \quad \text{and} \quad y = a \cos (b(x - c)) + d$$

with $b > 0$ may be determined as follows.

$$\text{Amplitude} = |a|, \quad \text{Period} = \frac{2\pi}{b}, \quad \text{Phase shift} = c, \quad \text{Vertical shift} = d$$

The vertical shift is $|d|$ units upward when $d > 0$ and $|d|$ units downward when $d < 0$.

The following See the Concept illustrates how to transform the sine graph.

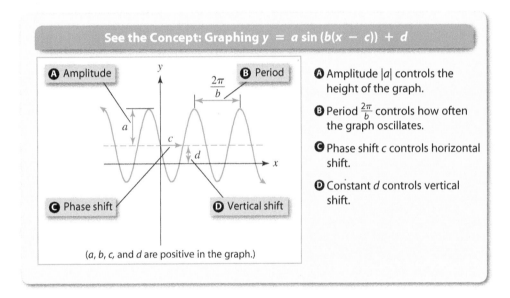

See the Concept: Graphing $y = a \sin (b(x - c)) + d$

Ⓐ Amplitude Ⓑ Period Ⓒ Phase shift Ⓓ Vertical shift

Ⓐ Amplitude $|a|$ controls the height of the graph.

Ⓑ Period $\frac{2\pi}{b}$ controls how often the graph oscillates.

Ⓒ Phase shift c controls horizontal shift.

Ⓓ Constant d controls vertical shift.

(a, b, c, and d are positive in the graph.)

EXAMPLE 3 Identifying amplitude, period, phase shift, and vertical shift

For the graph of each equation, identify the amplitude, period, phase shift, and vertical shift.

(a) $y = 7 \sin \left(4\left(x + \frac{\pi}{3} \right) \right) + 2$ **(b)** $y = -3 \cos (5x - 3) - 6$

SOLUTION

(a) For the graph of $y = 7 \sin (4 (x - (-\frac{\pi}{3}))) + 2$, the amplitude is 7, and the period is

$$P = \frac{2\pi}{b} = \frac{2\pi}{4} = \frac{\pi}{2}.$$

The phase shift is $-\frac{\pi}{3}$, and the vertical shift is 2.

(b) Start by applying the distributive property to rewrite the equation as

$$y = -3 \cos \left(5\left(x - \frac{3}{5} \right) \right) - 6.$$

The amplitude is 3, and the period is $P = \frac{2\pi}{b} = \frac{2\pi}{5}$. The phase shift is $\frac{3}{5}$, and the vertical shift is -6.

Now Try Exercises 13 and 17

Graphing Trigonometric Functions by Hand

Transformations can be used to graph trigonometric functions by hand, as was shown in the previous subsection. A second technique for graphing sinusoidal functions by hand is to first locate five **key points**. These key points are labeled for the graph of $y = \sin x$ in Figure 6.124. Notice that they are equally spaced along the interval $[0, 2\pi]$ on the x-axis.

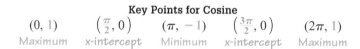

Key Points for Sine

$(0, 0)$ $\left(\frac{\pi}{2}, 1\right)$ $(\pi, 0)$ $\left(\frac{3\pi}{2}, -1\right)$ $(2\pi, 0)$

x-intercept   Maximum   x-intercept   Minimum   x-intercept

Five key points on the graph of $y = \cos x$ are shown in Figure 6.125.

Key Points for Cosine

$(0, 1)$ $\left(\frac{\pi}{2}, 0\right)$ $(\pi, -1)$ $\left(\frac{3\pi}{2}, 0\right)$ $(2\pi, 1)$

Maximum   x-intercept   Minimum   x-intercept   Maximum

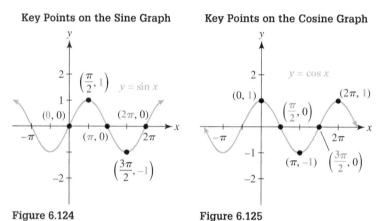

Key Points on the Sine Graph   **Key Points on the Cosine Graph**

Figure 6.124   **Figure 6.125**

One way to sketch a sinusoidal graph by hand is to find the *transformed* key points. You can use these points and the fact that the graph is periodic to make a sketch.

EXAMPLE 4   Sketching a sinusoidal graph by hand

Graphing with Key Points

$y = 3 \sin 2x$ $\left(\frac{\pi}{4}, 3\right)$ $\left(\frac{\pi}{2}, 0\right)$

$\left(\frac{3\pi}{4}, -3\right)$ $(\pi, 0)$

Figure 6.126

Find the amplitude, period, and phase shift of the graph of $f(x) = 3 \sin 2x$. Sketch a graph of f by hand on the interval $[-2\pi, 2\pi]$.

SOLUTION If $f(x) = 3 \sin 2x$, then the amplitude is 3 and the period is π. There is no phase or vertical shift. The graph of f passes through the point $(0, 0)$ and completes one oscillation in π units. Thus the graph passes through the point $(\pi, 0)$. An amplitude of 3 will change the maximum and minimum y-values to 3 and -3, respectively. The transformed key points for sine are equally spaced on the graph of f.

$(0, 0)$ $\left(\frac{\pi}{4}, 3\right)$ $\left(\frac{\pi}{2}, 0\right)$ $\left(\frac{3\pi}{4}, -3\right)$ $(\pi, 0)$

x-intercept   Maximum   x-intercept   Minimum   x-intercept

These points and the graph of f are plotted in Figure 6.126.

Now Try Exercise 33

EXAMPLE 5   Sketching a graph by hand

Graph $y = 2 \cos (4x + \pi)$ by hand.

SOLUTION First write the equation in the form $y = a \cos (b(x - c))$ by factoring out 4.

$$y = 2 \cos\left(4\left(x + \tfrac{\pi}{4}\right)\right)$$

Graphing with Key Points

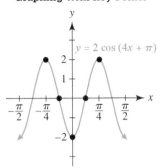

Figure 6.127

The amplitude is 2, and the period is $\frac{2\pi}{4} = \frac{\pi}{2}$. The graph is translated $\frac{\pi}{4}$ unit to the left compared to the graph of $y = 2 \cos 4x$. Because the graph is translated $\frac{\pi}{4}$ unit to the left, start the x-values in the key points at $0 - \frac{\pi}{4} = -\frac{\pi}{4}$. The first period ends at $-\frac{\pi}{4} + \frac{\pi}{2} = \frac{\pi}{4}$. The key points for this cosine graph are as follows.

$$\left(-\frac{\pi}{4}, 2\right) \quad \left(-\frac{\pi}{8}, 0\right) \quad (0, -2) \quad \left(\frac{\pi}{8}, 0\right) \quad \left(\frac{\pi}{4}, 2\right)$$

Maximum   x-intercept   Minimum   x-intercept   Maximum

Plot these key points to complete one period of the graph. The graph can be extended to show two periods, ranging from $-\frac{\pi}{2}$ to $\frac{\pi}{2}$, as shown in Figure 6.127.

Now Try Exercise 45

CLASS DISCUSSION

How would you modify the graph in Figure 6.127 to obtain the graph of

$$y = 2 \cos (4x + \pi) - 1?$$

What are the key points for this graph?

Graphs of Other Trigonometric Functions The periods of the tangent and cotangent functions are π. As a result, the graphs of $y = \tan(b(x - c))$ and $y = \cot(b(x - c))$ have a period of $P = \frac{\pi}{b}$ and a phase shift of c. Since the ranges of the tangent and cotangent functions include all real numbers, their graphs do not have an amplitude. Graphs of the secant and cosecant functions are done in Exercises 65–70.

EXAMPLE 6 Graphing other trigonometric functions

Find the period and phase shift for the graph of f. Graph f on the interval $[-2\pi, 2\pi]$. Identify where asymptotes occur in the graph.

(a) $f(x) = \tan \frac{1}{2}x$ **(b)** $f(x) = \cot \left(x + \frac{\pi}{2}\right) + 1$

SOLUTION

(a) If $f(x) = \tan \frac{1}{2}x$, then $b = \frac{1}{2}$ and $c = 0$. The period is $P = \frac{\pi}{b} = 2\pi$, and there is no phase shift. Graph $y = \tan \frac{1}{2}x$, as shown in Figure 6.128. On the interval $[-2\pi, 2\pi]$, vertical asymptotes occur at $x = \pm\pi$. The graph of f is horizontally stretched compared to the graph of the tangent function.

(b) If $f(x) = \cot \left(x + \frac{\pi}{2}\right) + 1$, then $b = 1$ and $c = -\frac{\pi}{2}$. The period is π, the phase shift is $-\frac{\pi}{2}$, and the graph is shifted upward 1 unit. Vertical asymptotes occur at $x = \pm\frac{\pi}{2}$ and $x = \pm\frac{3\pi}{2}$. The graph of $y = \cot \left(x + \frac{\pi}{2}\right) + 1$ is shown in Figure 6.129.

Increase Period to 2π

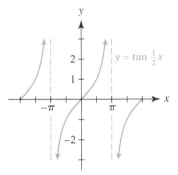

Figure 6.128

Shift Left $\frac{\pi}{2}$; Shift Up 1

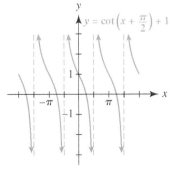

Figure 6.129

Now Try Exercises 57 and 63

Simple Harmonic Motion

Harmonic motion occurs frequently in nature and physical science. A particle or object undergoing small oscillations about a point of stable equilibrium executes simple harmonic motion. For example, if a string on a guitar is plucked gently, any point on the string will vibrate back and forth about its natural position of equilibrium. If a pendulum on a clock is pulled to one side, the pendulum will swing back and forth about its stable, vertical position. A small weight on a spring will bounce up and down when displaced from its natural length. All of these situations are examples of simple harmonic motion.

When an object undergoes simple harmonic motion, its distance or displacement from its stable or natural position can be modeled by either of the following equations.

Modeling Simple Harmonic Motion

$$s(t) = a \sin bt \qquad \text{or} \qquad s(t) = a \cos bt$$

In these equations, $s(t)$ represents the displacement being experienced at time t. To better understand this, consider the spring and weight shown in Figure 6.130. If $s = 0$ corresponds to the spring's natural length, then $s = -2$ indicates that the spring is stretched 2 units beyond its natural length and $s = 2$ indicates that the spring is compressed 2 units. When a spring is stretched and let go, it will oscillate up and down. If the displacement s is plotted after t seconds, a sinusoidal graph results, as shown in Figure 6.131.

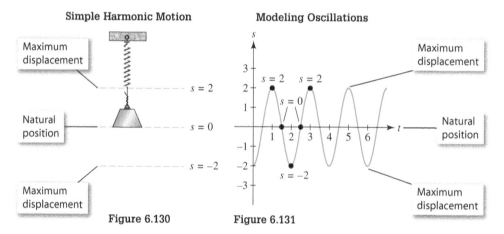

Figure 6.130   Figure 6.131

The amplitude of each oscillation equals $|a|$, and the period P is given by $\frac{2\pi}{b}$. The number of oscillations per unit time is the **frequency**. The frequency F equals the reciprocal of the period P. That is, $F = \frac{1}{P}$. Since $P = \frac{2\pi}{b}$, it follows that $F = \frac{b}{2\pi}$, or equivalently, $b = 2\pi F$. Substituting for b in the formulas for $s(t)$ results in the following equations.

Simple Harmonic Motion with Frequency F

$$s(t) = a \sin(2\pi F t) \qquad \text{or} \qquad s(t) = a \cos(2\pi F t)$$

EXAMPLE 7   Modeling simple harmonic motion

Suppose that the weight and spring in Figure 6.130 have a period of 0.4 second. Initially, the weight is lifted 3 inches above its natural length and then let go.
(a) Find an equation $s(t) = a \cos bt$ that models the displacement s of the weight.
(b) Find s after 0.92 second. Is the weight moving upward or downward at this time?

SOLUTION
(a) Let $s(t) = a \cos(2\pi F t)$. The spring is initially compressed 3 inches, so the amplitude is 3. Let $a = 3$. The period is $P = 0.4$, so the frequency is

$$F = \frac{1}{P} = \frac{1}{0.4} = 2.5.$$

This indicates that the weight and spring oscillate up and down 2.5 times per second. It follows that $b = 2\pi F = 5\pi$ and $s(t) = 3 \cos(5\pi t)$. Note that the initial position is $s(0) = 3$ inches.

(b) After 0.92 second, the displacement is

$$s(0.92) = 3 \cos(5\pi(0.92)) \approx -0.927. \qquad \text{Use radian mode.}$$

The weight is about 0.93 inch *below* its natural position after 0.92 second.

   The weight initially moves downward and oscillates with a period of 0.4 second. During the time intervals $(0, 0.2)$, $(0.4, 0.6)$, and $(0.8, 1.0)$ the weight is moving downward, and during the intervals $(0.2, 0.4)$, $(0.6, 0.8)$, and $(1.0, 1.2)$ the weight is moving upward. Thus the weight is moving *downward* when $t = 0.92$.

Now Try Exercise 71

Models Involving Trigonometric Functions (Optional)

Modeling Temperature   The monthly *average* temperatures for Prince George, Canada, are shown in Table 6.9, where the months have been assigned the standard numbers.

Monthly Average Temperatures

Month	1	2	3	4	5	6	7	8	9	10	11	12
Temperature (°F)	15	19	28	41	50	55	59	57	50	41	28	19

Source: A. Miller and J. Thompson, *Elements of Meteorology.*

Table 6.9

   Since the data are periodic, they are plotted over a 2-year period in Figure 6.132. For example, both $x = 1$ and $x = 13$ correspond to January. Notice that the scatterplot suggests that a sinusoidal graph might model these data.

   Data of the type shown in Figure 6.132 sometimes can be modeled by

$$f(x) = a \sin(b(x - c)) + d, \qquad \text{Modeling equation}$$

where a, b, c, and d are constants. To estimate values for these constants, we will perform transformations on the graph of $y = \sin x$.

   The addition of a constant d causes a vertical shift to the graph of f. The monthly average temperatures at Prince George vary from 15°F to 59°F. The average of these two temperatures is 37°F. If we let $d = 37$ and graph $y = \sin(x) + 37$, the resulting graph is as shown in Figure 6.133. Compared to the graph of the sine function, this graph is shifted upward 37 units. (Be sure to use radian mode.)

Plot Data for Two Years
[0, 25, 2] by [−5, 70, 10]

Amplitude Is Too Small
[0, 25, 2] by [−5, 70, 10]

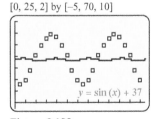

Oscillates Too Often
[0, 25, 2] by [−5, 70, 10]

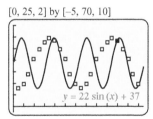

Figure 6.132   **Figure 6.133**   **Figure 6.134**

   From Figure 6.133 it is apparent that the amplitude of the oscillations in the graph of $y = \sin(x) + 37$ is too small to model the data. The monthly average temperatures have a range of $59°F - 15°F = 44°F$. If we let $a = \frac{44}{2} = 22$, the peaks and valleys on the graph of $y = 22 \sin(x) + 37$ will model the data better. See Figure 6.134.

   In Figure 6.134 the oscillations are too frequent, which indicates that the period is too small. Since the temperature cycles every 12 months, the period is $P = \frac{2\pi}{b} = 12$. Thus

$$b = \frac{2\pi}{P} = \frac{2\pi}{12} = \frac{\pi}{6} \approx 0.524.$$

The graph of $y = 22 \sin\left(\frac{\pi}{6}x\right) + 37$ is shown in Figure 6.135.

Needs to Be Shifted Right

[0, 25, 2] by [−5, 70, 10]

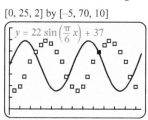

Figure 6.135

CLASS DISCUSSION

Is the value of $c = 4$ the only phase shift that can be used to model the temperature data? Explain your reasoning.

We can obtain a reasonable fit by shifting the graph horizontally to the right. The maximum of $y = 22 \sin\left(\frac{\pi}{6}x\right) + 37$ is at $x = 3$, which corresponds to March. We would like this maximum to occur in July ($x = 7$), so we translate the graph $7 - 3 = 4$ units to the right by replacing x with $x - 4$ to obtain

$$y = 22 \sin\left(\frac{\pi}{6}(x - 4)\right) + 37.$$

This equation is graphed in Figure 6.136. The phase shift is $c = 4$.

Final Model

[0, 25, 2] by [−5, 70, 10]

About right?

Figure 6.136

Sine Regression Linear and nonlinear regression were introduced in previous chapters. **Sine regression** can also be performed, using a sinusoidal function of the form

$$f(x) = a \sin(bx + c) + d.$$

Sine regression may be performed on a 2-year interval of the temperature data in Table 6.9. See Figures 6.137 and 6.138.

Calculator Help

To find an equation of least-squares fit, see Appendix A (page AP-9).

Select Sine Regression

```
EDIT CALC TESTS
7↑QuartReg
8:LinReg(a+bx)
9:LnReg
0:ExpReg
A:PwrReg
B:Logistic
C:SinReg
```

Figure 6.137

Regression Equation

```
SinReg
y=a*sin(bx+c)+d
a=21.7399239
b=.5207209998
c=−2.06480837
d=38.38287503
```

Figure 6.138

NOTE Sine regression gives the modeling function in the form $y = a \sin(bx + c) + d$, whereas our modeling function is in the form $f(x) = a \sin(b(x - c)) + d$. These forms have the same values for a, b, and d, but with sine regression c does not represent the phase shift. However, they are equivalent forms. If we factor out $b \approx 0.5207$ in the regression equation shown in Figure 6.138, we obtain $y \approx 21.74 \sin(0.5207(x - 3.965)) + 38.38$, which is approximately equal to our modeling equation.

Summary of Modeling Sinusoidal Data If the data appear to be sinusoidal with maximum Max, minimum Min, and period P, then the following method can be used to find values for a, b, and d for either $f(x) = a \sin(b(x - c)) + d$ or $f(x) = a \cos(b(x - c)) + d$.

$$a = \frac{\text{Max} - \text{Min}}{2}, \qquad b = \frac{2\pi}{P}, \qquad \text{and} \qquad d = \frac{\text{Max} + \text{Min}}{2},$$

If necessary, the phase shift c can be determined by shifting the graph a distance $|c|$ either left or right to fit the data. If the shift is to the right, $c > 0$, and if it is to the left, $c < 0$.

Modeling Tides Tides, which usually occur once or twice a day, represent the largest collective motion of water on Earth. We model tides in the next example.

EXAMPLE 8 Modeling tides

Figure 6.139 shows a function f that models the tides in feet at Clearwater Beach, Florida, x hours after midnight starting on August 26, 1998.   (*Source: Tide and Current Predictor.*)
(a) Find the time between high tides.
(b) What is the difference in water levels between high tide and low tide?
(c) Determine a, b, c, and d so that $f(x) = a \cos(b(x - c)) + d$ models the data. Graph f and the data in the same viewing rectangle.

Tides at Clearwater Beach

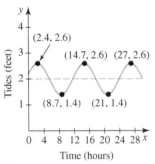

Figure 6.139

SOLUTION
(a) A high tide corresponds to a peak on the graph. The time between peaks is 12.3 hours, since $14.7 - 2.4 = 12.3$ and $27 - 14.7 = 12.3$, which is the period P.
(b) High tides were 2.6 feet, and low tides were 1.4 feet. The difference is 1.2 feet, which is twice the amplitude.
(c) *Amplitude* The amplitude of f is given by

$$a = \frac{\text{Max} - \text{Min}}{2} = \frac{2.6 - 1.4}{2} = 0.6.$$

Period Since the period is $P = 12.3$ hours, the value of b is

$$b = \frac{2\pi}{P} = \frac{2\pi}{12.3} \approx 0.511.$$

Vertical Shift The average of high tide and low tide is

$$d = \frac{\text{Max} + \text{Min}}{2} = \frac{2.6 + 1.4}{2} = 2.$$

Phase Shift Finally, a peak occurs at about 2.4 hours after midnight. Since midnight corresponds to $x = 0$ and the cosine function has a peak at $x = 0$, we translate the graph of f right 2.4 units by letting $c = 2.4$. Thus

$$f(x) = 0.6 \cos(0.511(x - 2.4)) + 2.$$

Graphs of f and the data are shown in Figure 6.140.

Final Model
[0, 28, 2] by [0, 4, 1]

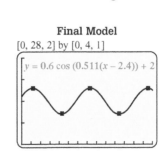

Figure 6.140

Now Try Exercise 93

6.5 Putting It All Together

Some concepts about trigonometric models are summarized in the following table.

CONCEPT	EXPLANATION	EXAMPLES
Sinusoidal Model $$f(x) = a \sin(b(x - c)) + d$$ or $$f(x) = a \cos(b(x - c)) + d$$ with $b > 0$	Amplitude $= |a|$ Period $= \dfrac{2\pi}{b}$ Phase shift $= c$ Vertical shift $= d$, upward if $d > 0$ and downward if $d < 0$ If $b = 2\pi F$, then F represents the frequency.	Let $f(x) = 3 \sin(2(x - \pi)) - 1$. Amplitude $= 3$ Period $= \dfrac{2\pi}{2} = \pi$ Phase shift $= \pi$ Vertical shift downward 1 unit The frequency is $F = \dfrac{b}{2\pi} = \dfrac{1}{\pi}$, which is approximately 0.32 oscillation per unit of time.
Simple Harmonic Motion $$s(t) = a \sin bt$$ or $$s(t) = a \cos bt$$	An object that oscillates about a stable equilibrium point undergoes simple harmonic motion.	A pendulum on a clock A weight on a spring

6.5 Exercises

Graphs of Trigonometric Functions

Exercises 1–6: Sketch a graph of the equation on the interval $[-4\pi, 4\pi]$. Identify the period and amplitude.

1. $y = 3 \sin \frac{1}{2}x$

2. $y = 2 \cos \frac{1}{3}x$

3. $y = -2 \cos 3x$

4. $y = -3 \sin 2x$

5. $y = \frac{1}{2} \sin \pi x$

6. $y = -\frac{3}{2} \cos \frac{\pi}{2}x$

Exercises 7–12: (Refer to Example 2.) Explain how the graph of f can be obtained from the graph of either the sine or the cosine function. Then sketch a graph of f on the interval $[-2\pi, 2\pi]$.

7. $y = 3 \sin(2x) - 1$

8. $y = -2 \cos(3x) + 1$

9. $y = -2 \cos\left(x + \frac{\pi}{2}\right)$

10. $y = -\frac{1}{2} \sin(x + \pi)$

11. $y = \frac{1}{2} \cos(\pi x - 1)$

12. $y = \sin\left(\frac{2}{3}x\right) + 2$

Exercises 13–18: For the graph of the equation, identify the amplitude, period, phase shift, and vertical shift. Do not graph the equation.

13. $y = 3 \sin\left(4\left(x - \frac{\pi}{4}\right)\right) - 4$

14. $y = -5 \sin\left(\frac{1}{2}(x - \pi)\right) + 7$

15. $y = -4 \cos\left(\frac{\pi}{2}(x - 1)\right) + 6$

16. $y = \frac{4}{5} \cos\left(\pi x + \frac{\pi}{3}\right) - \frac{2}{3}$

17. $y = 20 \cos\left(\frac{2}{3}x + \pi\right) + 2$

18. $y = \frac{2}{3} \sin(6x + 3\pi) - \frac{5}{2}$

Exercises 19 and 20: A graph of the equation $y = a \sin bx$ is shown, where b is a positive constant. Estimate the values for a and b.

19.

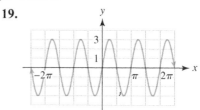

20.

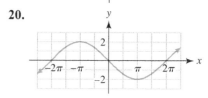

Exercises 21 and 22: The graph of a trigonometric function represented by $f(x) = a \sin(b(x - c))$ is shown, where a, b, and c are nonnegative. State the amplitude, period, and phase shift.

21. 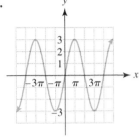   **22.**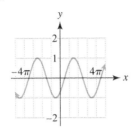

Exercises 23–28: Match the function f with its graph (a–f). Do not use a calculator.

23. $f(t) = 2 \sin\left(\frac{1}{2}t\right)$ **24.** $f(t) = -\sin(2t)$

25. $f(t) = 3 \cos(\pi t)$ **26.** $f(t) = 2 \sin\left(t - \frac{\pi}{4}\right)$

27. $f(t) = \cos\left(t + \frac{\pi}{2}\right)$ **28.** $f(t) = -3 \cos t$

a. 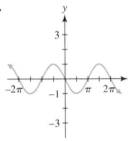   **b.**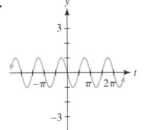

c. 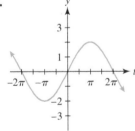   **d.**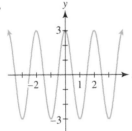

e. 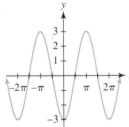   **f.**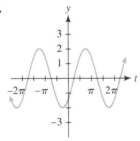

Exercises 29 and 30: Find an equation $y = a \sin(b(x - c))$ for the graph shown in the exercise. Assume that a, b, and c are nonnegative.

29. Exercise 21   **30.** Exercise 22

Exercises 31–48: Find the amplitude, period, and phase shift of f. Then graph f by hand on the interval $[-2\pi, 2\pi]$.

31. $f(t) = 2 \sin t$ **32.** $f(x) = -3 \sin x$

33. $f(x) = \sin \frac{1}{2}x$ **34.** $f(t) = \cos 2t$

35. $f(x) = 1 + \sin x$ **36.** $f(x) = -2 + 2 \cos x$

37. $f(t) = \cos(\pi t) + 2$ **38.** $f(t) = 2 \sin\left(t - \frac{\pi}{2}\right)$

39. $f(t) = -\sin(2(t + \pi))$ **40.** $f(t) = -3 \cos \frac{1}{2}t$

41. $f(x) = -\cos\left(x - \frac{\pi}{2}\right)$ **42.** $f(x) = -2 \cos(x + \pi)$

43. $f(x) = -\frac{1}{2} \sin 2x$ **44.** $f(x) = 3 \sin 4x$

45. $f(x) = 2 \cos\left(2x + \frac{\pi}{2}\right) - 1$

46. $f(x) = -\frac{1}{2} \sin(3x + \pi) + 2$

47. $f(t) = \cos\left(2\left(t - \frac{\pi}{2}\right)\right)$ **48.** $f(t) = 3 \sin\left(\frac{1}{2}(t - \pi)\right)$

Exercises 49–56: Graph f in $[-2\pi, 2\pi, \pi/2]$ by $[-4, 4, 1]$. State the amplitude, period, and phase shift.

49. $f(t) = 2 \sin(2t)$

50. $f(t) = -3 \sin(t - \pi)$

51. $f(t) = \frac{1}{2} \cos\left(3\left(t + \frac{\pi}{3}\right)\right)$

52. $f(t) = 1.5 \cos\left(\frac{1}{2}\left(t + \frac{\pi}{2}\right)\right)$

53. $f(t) = -2.5 \cos\left(2t + \frac{\pi}{2}\right)$

54. $f(t) = -2.5 \sin\left(\pi t + \frac{\pi}{2}\right) - 1$

55. $f(x) = -2 \cos\left(2\pi x + \frac{\pi}{4}\right) + 1$

56. $f(x) = \frac{3}{4} \sin(\pi x + \pi) - 2$

Exercises 57–64: (Refer to Example 6.) Find the period and phase shift for the graph of f. Graph f on the interval $[-2\pi, 2\pi]$. Identify where asymptotes occur in the graph.

57. $f(t) = \tan 2t$ **58.** $f(t) = \tan \frac{1}{2}t$

59. $f(t) = \tan\left(t - \frac{\pi}{2}\right)$ **60.** $f(t) = \cot\left(\frac{1}{3}\left(t - \frac{\pi}{2}\right)\right)$

61. $f(t) = -\cot 2t$ **62.** $f(t) = -\cot\left(t + \frac{\pi}{2}\right)$

63. $f(x) = \cot\left(2\left(x - \frac{\pi}{4}\right)\right) - 1$

64. $f(x) = \tan\left(\frac{1}{2}x - \frac{\pi}{2}\right)$

Exercises 65–70: Use the directions for Exercises 57–64 to graph f.

65. $f(t) = \sec \frac{1}{2}t$ **66.** $f(t) = \sec\left(2\left(t - \frac{\pi}{2}\right)\right)$

67. $f(t) = \csc(t - \pi)$ **68.** $f(t) = -\csc 2t$

69. $f(x) = \sec\left(\frac{1}{3}\left(x - \frac{\pi}{6}\right)\right)$ **70.** $f(x) = \csc(\pi(x - 1))$

Simple Harmonic Motion

Exercises 71–74: **Springs** *(Refer to Example 7.) Suppose that a weight on a spring has an initial position of s(0) and a period of P.*

(a) *Find a function s given by* $s(t) = a \cos(2\pi Ft)$ *that models the displacement of the weight.*

(b) *Evaluate s(1). Is the weight moving upward, downward, or neither when t = 1?*

71. $s(0) = 2$ inches, $P = 0.5$ second

72. $s(0) = 5$ inches, $P = 1.5$ seconds

73. $s(0) = -3$ inches, $P = 0.8$ second

74. $s(0) = -4$ inches, $P = 1.2$ seconds

⌨ *Exercises 75–78:* **Music** *A note on the piano has the given frequency F. Suppose the maximum displacement at the center of the piano wire is given by s(0). Find constants a and b so that* $s(t) = a \cos bt$ *models this displacement. Graph s(t) in* $[0, 0.05, 0.01]$ *by* $[-0.3, 0.3, 0.1]$*.*

75. $F = 27.5, s(0) = 0.21$ **76.** $F = 110, s(0) = 0.11$

77. $F = 55, s(0) = 0.14$ **78.** $F = 220, s(0) = 0.06$

Applications

79. Flower Opening for Sunlight Flowers tend to open in the daylight and close in the dark. The percent P of flowers open during a 24-hour period can be modeled by $P(x) = a \sin(bx) + d$, where x is hours past 6 A.M.

(a) Suppose that for P the maximum is 90%, the minimum is 10%, and the period is 24 hours. Determine $P(x)$.

(b) When are the most flowers open?

(c) When are the fewest flowers open?

80. Body Temperature A typical body temperature in degrees Fahrenheit over a 24-hour period can be modeled by the sinusoidal function

$$T(x) = a \sin(bx) + d,$$

where x is hours past 6 A.M.

(a) Suppose that for T the maximum temperature is 99.2°F, the minimum temperature is 98.0°F, and the period is 24 hours. Determine $T(x)$.

(b) When is this person's temperature highest?

(c) When is this person's temperature lowest?

81. Average Temperatures The graph models the monthly average temperature y in degrees Fahrenheit for a city in Canada, where x is the month.

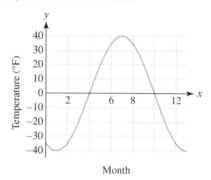

Month

(a) Find the maximum and minimum monthly average temperatures.

(b) Find the amplitude and period. Interpret the results.

(c) Explain what the x-intercepts represent.

82. Average Temperatures The graph in Exercise 81 is given by $y = 40 \cos\left(\frac{\pi}{6}(x - 7)\right)$. Modify this equation to model the following situations.

(a) The maximum monthly average temperature is 50°F and the minimum is −50°F.

(b) The maximum monthly average temperature is 60°F and the minimum is −20°F.

(c) The maximum monthly average temperature occurs in August and the minimum occurs in February.

83. Average Temperatures The monthly average temperatures in degrees Fahrenheit at Mould Bay, Canada, may be modeled by $f(x) = 34 \sin\left(\frac{\pi}{6}(x - 4.3)\right)$, where x is the month and $x = 1$ corresponds to January. (*Source:* A. Miller and J. Thompson, *Elements of Meteorology.*)

(a) Find the amplitude, period, and phase shift.

(b) Approximate the average temperature during May and December.

(c) Estimate the *yearly* average temperature at Mould Bay.

84. Average Temperatures The monthly average temperatures in degrees Fahrenheit at Austin, Texas, are given by $f(x) = 17.5 \sin\left(\frac{\pi}{6}(x - 4)\right) + 67.5$, where x is the month and $x = 1$ corresponds to January. (*Source:* A. Miller and J. Thompson, *Elements of Meteorology.*)

(a) Find the amplitude, period, phase shift, and vertical shift.

(b) Determine the maximum and minimum monthly average temperature and the months when they occur.

(c) Make a conjecture as to how the *yearly* average temperature might be related to $f(x)$.

85. Modeling Temperatures The monthly average temperatures in Vancouver, Canada, are shown in the table.

Month	1	2	3	4	5	6
Temperature (°F)	36	39	43	48	55	59

Month	7	8	9	10	11	12
Temperature (°F)	64	63	57	50	43	39

Source: A. Miller and J. Thompson, *Elements of Meteorology.*

(a) Plot these monthly average temperatures over a 24-month period by letting $x = 1$ and $x = 13$ correspond to January.

(b) Find the constants a, b, c, and d so that the function $f(x) = a \sin(b(x - c)) + d$ models the data.

(c) Graph f together with the data.

86. Modeling Temperatures The monthly average temperatures in Chicago, Illinois, are shown in the table.

Month	1	2	3	4	5	6
Temperature (°F)	25	28	36	48	61	72

Month	7	8	9	10	11	12
Temperature (°F)	74	75	66	55	39	28

Source: A. Miller and J. Thompson, *Elements of Meteorology.*

(a) Plot these monthly average temperatures over a 24-month period by letting $x = 1$ and $x = 13$ correspond to January.

(b) Find the constants a, b, c, and d so that the function $f(x) = a \sin(b(x - c)) + d$ models the data.

(c) Graph f and the data together.

87. Modeling Temperatures The monthly average high temperatures in Augusta, Georgia, are shown in the table.

Month	1	2	3	4	5	6
Temperature (°F)	58	60	68	77	82	90

Month	7	8	9	10	11	12
Temperature (°F)	92	91	83	77	68	60

Source: J. Williams, *The Weather Almanac.*

(a) Use $f(x) = a \cos(b(x - c)) + d$ to model these data.

(b) Are different values for c possible? Explain.

88. Modeling Temperatures The maximum monthly average temperature in Anchorage, Alaska, is 57°F and the minimum is 12°F.

Month	1	2	3	4	5	6
Temperature (°F)	12	18	23	36	46	55

Month	7	8	9	10	11	12
Temperature (°F)	57	55	48	36	23	16

Source: A. Miller and J. Thompson, *Elements of Meteorology.*

(a) Using only these two temperatures, determine $f(x) = a \cos(b(x - c)) + d$ so that $f(x)$ models the monthly average temperatures in Anchorage.

(b) Graph f and the actual data in the table over a 2-year period.

89. Daylight Hours The graph models the daylight hours at 60°N latitude, where $x = 1$ corresponds to January 1, $x = 2$ to February 1, and so on.

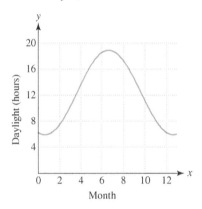

(a) Estimate the maximum number of daylight hours. When does this occur?

(b) Estimate the minimum number of daylight hours. When does this occur?

(c) Interpret the amplitude and period.

90. Daylight Hours The graph in Exercise 89 is given by $y = 6.5 \sin\left(\frac{\pi}{6}(x - 3.65)\right) + 12.4$. Modify this equation to model the following situations.

(a) At 50°N latitude, the maximum daylight is about 16.3 hours and the minimum is about 8.3 hours.

(b) The daylight hours at 60°S latitude

(c) The daylight hours at the equator

91. Average Precipitation The graph models the monthly average precipitation in inches at Mount Adams, Washington, over a 3-year period, where x is the month.

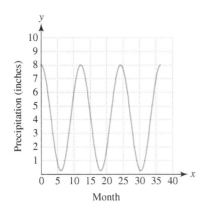

Month

(a) Find the maximum and minimum monthly average precipitation.

(b) Find the amplitude and interpret the result.

(c) Use $f(x) = a \cos(b(x - c)) + d$ to model the given graph.

92. Daylight Hours San Antonio, Texas, has a latitude of 29.5°N. The table lists the number of daylight hours on the first day of each month in San Antonio.

Month	1	2	3	4	5	6
Daylight (hr)	10.2	10.7	11.5	12.5	13.3	13.9

Month	7	8	9	10	11	12
Daylight (hr)	14.1	13.6	12.7	11.9	11.0	10.4

Source: J. Williams, The Weather Almanac.

(a) Plot the data over a 2-year period.

(b) Use $f(x) = a \cos(b(x - c)) + d$ to model these data.

(c) Estimate the daylight hours on February 15.

93. Average Precipitation Suppose that the monthly average precipitation at a particular location varies sinusoidally between a maximum of 6 inches in January and a minimum of 2 inches in July. Let $t = 1$ correspond to January and $t = 12$ correspond to December.
(a) Use $f(t) = a \cos(b(t - c)) + d$ to model these conditions.

(b) Evaluate $f(1)$ and $f(7)$.

94. Modeling Tidal Currents Tides cause ocean currents to flow into and out of harbors and canals. The table at the top of the next column shows the speed of the ocean current at Cape Cod Canal in bogo-knots (bk) x hours after midnight on August 26, 1998. (Note that to change bogo-knots to knots, take the square root of the absolute value of the number of bogo-knots.)

Time (hr)	3.7	6.75	9.8
Current (bk)	−18	0	18

Time (hr)	13.0	16.1	22.2
Current (bk)	0	−18	18

Source: Tide and Current Predictor.

(a) Use $f(x) = a \cos(b(x - c)) + d$ to model the data.

(b) Graph f and the data in $[0, 24, 4]$ by $[-20, 20, 5]$. Interpret the graph.

95. Modeling Ocean Temperature The following table lists the monthly average ocean temperatures in degrees Fahrenheit at Veracruz, Mexico.

Month	1	2	3	4	5	6
Temperature (°F)	72	73	74	78	81	83

Month	7	8	9	10	11	12
Temperature (°F)	84	85	84	82	78	74

Source: J. Williams, The Weather Almanac.

(a) Make a scatterplot of the data over a 2-year period.

(b) Use $f(x) = a \sin(b(x - c)) + d$ to model the data.

96. Ocean Temperatures The water temperature in degrees Fahrenheit at St. Petersburg, Florida, can be modeled by $f(x) = 12.4 \sin\left(\frac{\pi}{6}(x - 4.2)\right) + 75$. Modify this formula to model the following situations.
(a) The monthly average water temperatures vary between 60°F and 90°F.

(b) The monthly average water temperatures vary between 50°F and 70°F.

97. Interpreting a Model Graph $y = 20 + 15 \sin \frac{\pi t}{12}$ for $0 \le t \le 12$. Let y represent the outdoor temperature in degrees Celsius at time t in hours, where $t = 0$ corresponds to 9 A.M. Interpret the graph.

98. Carbon Dioxide Levels in Hawaii At Mauna Loa, Hawaii, atmospheric carbon dioxide levels in parts per million (ppm) have been measured regularly since 1958. The equation

$$L(x) = 0.022x^2 + 0.55x + 316 + 3.5 \sin(2\pi x)$$

may be used to model these levels, where x is the year and $x = 0$ corresponds to 1960.
(a) Graph L in $[20, 35, 5]$ by $[320, 370, 10]$ and interpret the graph.

(b) The function L is represented by the sum of a quadratic function and a sine function. How does each function affect the shape of the graph? Discuss reasons for each function. (*Source:* A. Nilsson, *Greenhouse Earth.*)

99. Music and the Sine Function A *pure tone* can be modeled by a sine wave. Pure tones typically sound dull and uninteresting. An example of a pure tone is the sound heard when a tuning fork is lightly struck. The pure tone of the first A-note above middle C can be modeled by $f(t) = \sin(880\pi t)$. (***Source:*** J. Pierce, *The Science of Musical Sound.*)

(a) In $[0, 1/100, 1/880]$ by $[-1.5, 1.5, 0.5]$, graph the function f.

(b) Find the period P of this tone.

(c) Frequency gives the number of vibrations or cycles per second in a sinusoidal graph. The human ear can hear frequencies from 16.4 to 16,000 cycles per second. Frequency F may be determined using the equation $f = \frac{1}{P}$, where P is the period. Find the frequency of this A-note.

100. Music (Continuation of Exercise 99.) Middle C has a frequency of 261.6 cycles per second and can be modeled by $g(t) = \sin(523.2\pi t)$. (***Source:*** J. Pierce, *The Science of Musical Sound.*)

(a) Estimate the period of middle C.

(b) Graph f from Exercise 99 and g in the window $[0, 1/100, 1/880]$ by $[-1.5, 1.5, 0.5]$. Compare their graphs.

Sine Regression

Exercises 101–104: **Modeling Data** *Use regression to find a formula $f(x) = a \sin(bx + c) + d$ that models the real data given in the previous exercise. Graph the data and f together.*

101. Exercise 85 **102.** Exercise 86

103. Exercise 87 **104.** Exercise 88

Writing about Mathematics

105. Discuss how the constants a, b, c, and d affect the graph of $y = a \sin(b(x - c)) + d$. Give an example.

106. Discuss some types of real data that could be modeled by $y = a \cos(b(x - c)) + d$. Give an example.

6.6 Inverse Trigonometric Functions

- **Define and use the inverse sine function**
- **Define and use the inverse cosine function**
- **Define and use the inverse tangent function**
- **Solve triangles and equations**
- **Define and use other inverse trigonometric functions**

Introduction

In construction it is sometimes necessary to determine angles. For example, the pitch, or slope, of a roof frequently is expressed as the ratio $\frac{k}{12}$, where k represents a k-foot rise for every 12 feet of run in horizontal distance. See Figure 6.141. A typical roof pitch for homes is $\frac{6}{12}$. To correctly cut the rafters, a carpenter needs to know the measure of angle θ. This problem can be solved easily using inverse trigonometric functions. See Exercise 89.

Simple Roof Truss

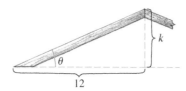

Figure 6.141

The Inverse Sine Function

A numerical representation of the sine function is shown in Table 6.10.

Sine Function

x	0	$\frac{\pi}{6}$	$\frac{\pi}{4}$	$\frac{\pi}{3}$	$\frac{\pi}{2}$	$\frac{2\pi}{3}$	$\frac{3\pi}{4}$	$\frac{5\pi}{6}$	π
$\sin x$	0	$\frac{1}{2}$	$\frac{1}{\sqrt{2}}$	$\frac{\sqrt{3}}{2}$	1	$\frac{\sqrt{3}}{2}$	$\frac{1}{\sqrt{2}}$	$\frac{1}{2}$	0

Table 6.10

$f(0) = 0$ and $f(\pi) = 0$
(not one-to-one)

Notice that different inputs do not always result in different outputs. Therefore the sine function is *not* one-to-one and so an inverse function does *not* exist. By the horizontal line test the sine function is not one-to-one. See Figure 6.142 on the next page, where a horizontal line intersects the sine graph infinitely many times.

If we restrict the domain of $f(x) = \sin x$ to $-\frac{\pi}{2} \le x \le \frac{\pi}{2}$, as shown in Figure 6.143, the graph of $y = \sin x$ is one-to-one, since a horizontal line intersects it at most once. On this restricted domain, the sine function has a unique inverse called the *inverse sine function*.

Fails Horizontal Line Test **Restricting the Domain of Sine**
(no inverse exists) **(inverse exists)**

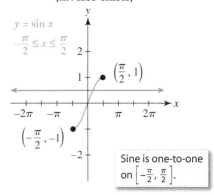

Figure 6.142 Figure 6.143

INVERSE SINE FUNCTION

The **inverse sine function**, denoted $\sin^{-1} x$ or arcsin x, is defined as follows. For $-1 \le x \le 1$ and y in the interval $\left[-\frac{\pi}{2}, \frac{\pi}{2}\right]$,

$$y = \sin^{-1} x \quad \text{or} \quad y = \arcsin x \quad \text{means} \quad x = \sin y.$$

NOTE When evaluating the inverse sine function, it may be helpful to think of $\sin^{-1} x$ as an *angle* θ, where $\sin \theta = x$ and θ satisfies $-\frac{\pi}{2} \le \theta \le \frac{\pi}{2}$.

The next example illustrates how to evaluate the inverse sine function.

EXAMPLE 1 Evaluating the inverse sine function

Evaluate each of the following by hand and then support your results with a calculator.
(a) $\sin^{-1} 1$ **(b)** $\arcsin\left(-\frac{1}{2}\right)$

SOLUTION
(a) The expression $\sin^{-1} 1$ represents the angle (or real number) θ whose sine equals 1 and that satisfies $-\frac{\pi}{2} \le \theta \le \frac{\pi}{2}$. Thus $\theta = \sin^{-1} 1 = \frac{\pi}{2} \approx 1.57$. In degrees, $\sin^{-1} 1 = 90°$.
(b) The expression $\arcsin\left(-\frac{1}{2}\right)$ represents the angle (or real number) θ whose sine equals $-\frac{1}{2}$ and that satisfies $-\frac{\pi}{2} \le \theta \le \frac{\pi}{2}$. Thus $\theta = \arcsin\left(-\frac{1}{2}\right) = -\frac{\pi}{6} \approx -0.52$. In degrees, $\sin^{-1}\left(-\frac{1}{2}\right) = -30°$. Figures 6.144 and 6.145 support these results in both radian mode and degree mode.

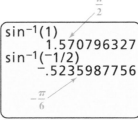

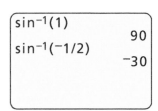

Figure 6.144 Radian Mode Figure 6.145 Degree Mode

Now Try Exercise 13

Domain, Range, and Inverse Properties Functions and their inverses interchange domains and ranges. The range of the sine function is $-1 \le y \le 1$. Therefore the domain of the inverse sine function is $-1 \le x \le 1$. Since the domain of the sine function has been restricted to $-\frac{\pi}{2} \le x \le \frac{\pi}{2}$, the range of the inverse sine function is $-\frac{\pi}{2} \le y \le \frac{\pi}{2}$. That is, $\sin^{-1} x$ outputs angles (numbers) only in the interval $\left[-\frac{\pi}{2}, \frac{\pi}{2}\right]$. The following are properties of the inverse sine function.

$$\sin^{-1}(\sin x) = x \quad \text{for} \quad -\frac{\pi}{2} \le x \le \frac{\pi}{2}$$
$$\sin(\sin^{-1} x) = x \quad \text{for} \quad -1 \le x \le 1$$

Inverse properties

NOTE $\sin^{-1} 2$ is undefined because $-1 \le \sin x \le 1$ for all angles (or numbers) x.

MAKING CONNECTIONS

Notation and Inverse Functions In Section 5.2, we learned that $f^{-1}(x) \neq \frac{1}{f(x)}$. The same is true for the inverse sine function: $\sin^{-1} x \neq \frac{1}{\sin x}$. For example, $\sin^{-1} 1 = \frac{\pi}{2} \approx 1.57$ and $\frac{1}{\sin 1} \approx 1.19$. Note that $(\sin x)^{-1} = \frac{1}{\sin x}$.

EXAMPLE 2 Finding representations of the inverse sine function

Represent the inverse sine function verbally, numerically, graphically, and symbolically.

SOLUTION

Verbal Representation To compute $\sin^{-1} x$ for $-1 \le x \le 1$, determine the angle (or real number) θ such that $\sin \theta = x$ and $-\frac{\pi}{2} \le \theta \le \frac{\pi}{2}$.

Numerical Representation Table 6.11 shows a numerical representation of $\sin x$ on the interval $\left[-\frac{\pi}{2}, \frac{\pi}{2}\right]$. It follows that a numerical representation of $\sin^{-1} x$ is as shown in Table 6.12. Notice that if $\sin a = b$, then $\sin^{-1} b = a$, provided $-\frac{\pi}{2} \le a \le \frac{\pi}{2}$.

Sine Function on $\left[-\frac{\pi}{2}, \frac{\pi}{2}\right]$

x	$-\frac{\pi}{2}$	$-\frac{\pi}{3}$	$-\frac{\pi}{4}$	$-\frac{\pi}{6}$	0	$\frac{\pi}{6}$	$\frac{\pi}{4}$	$\frac{\pi}{3}$	$\frac{\pi}{2}$
$\sin x$	-1	$-\frac{\sqrt{3}}{2}$	$-\frac{1}{\sqrt{2}}$	$-\frac{1}{2}$	0	$\frac{1}{2}$	$\frac{1}{\sqrt{2}}$	$\frac{\sqrt{3}}{2}$	1

Table 6.11

Inverse Sine Function on $[-1, 1]$

x	-1	$-\frac{\sqrt{3}}{2}$	$-\frac{1}{\sqrt{2}}$	$-\frac{1}{2}$	0	$\frac{1}{2}$	$\frac{1}{\sqrt{2}}$	$\frac{\sqrt{3}}{2}$	1
$\sin^{-1} x$	$-\frac{\pi}{2}$	$-\frac{\pi}{3}$	$-\frac{\pi}{4}$	$-\frac{\pi}{6}$	0	$\frac{\pi}{6}$	$\frac{\pi}{4}$	$\frac{\pi}{3}$	$\frac{\pi}{2}$

Table 6.12

Interchange domain and range.

Inverse Sine Function

Reflect $y = \sin x$ across $y = x$.

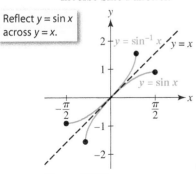

Figure 6.146

Graphical Representation The graph of $y = \sin^{-1} x$ can be found by reflecting the graph of $y = \sin x$ for $-\frac{\pi}{2} \le x \le \frac{\pi}{2}$ across the line $y = x$, as shown in Figure 6.146. See also Putting It All Together at the end of this section.

Symbolic Representation A symbolic representation of the inverse sine function can be written as either $f(x) = \sin^{-1} x$ or $f(x) = \arcsin x$. There is no simple formula that can be used to evaluate $\sin^{-1} x$.

Now Try Exercise 31

An Application In track and field, when an athlete throws the shot, the distance that the shot travels depends on the angle θ that the initial direction of the shot makes with the horizontal. Angle θ in Figure 6.147 is called the *projection angle*. The optimal projection angle θ, which results in maximum distance for the shot, may be calculated by

$$\theta = \sin^{-1} \sqrt{\frac{v^2}{2v^2 + 64.4h}},$$

where v is the initial speed in feet per second of the shot and h is the height in feet of the shot when it is released. (***Source:*** J. Cooper and R. Glassow, *Kinesiology.*)

Throwing the Shot with Projection Angle θ

Figure 6.147

> **CLASS DISCUSSION**
>
> If a cannonball is shot from ground level, what is the optimal projection angle? Does this angle depend on v?

EXAMPLE 3 Finding the optimal projection angle for a shot-putter

Suppose that an athlete releases a shot 8 feet above the ground with velocity v. Give a numerical representation of the optimum projection angle θ. Interpret the results.

SOLUTION Make a table for $Y_1 = \sin^{-1} (\sqrt{(X{\wedge}2/(2X{\wedge}2 + 64.4 * 8)))}$, as shown in Figure 6.148. We can see that the faster a person throws the shot, the greater the optimal projection angle θ becomes. For example, if a shot is thrown at 25 feet per second, then $\theta \approx 36.5°$, whereas if the shot is thrown at 50 feet per second, then $\theta \approx 42.3°$.

Now Try Exercise 91

Optimal Projection Angle

X	Y₁	
20	33.469	
25	36.515	
30	38.571	
35	39.997	
40	41.014	
45	41.76	
50	42.32	

X=25

Figure 6.148 Degree Mode

The Inverse Cosine Function

By the horizontal line test, the cosine function is not one-to-one, as illustrated in Figure 6.149. If we restrict the domain of $f(x) = \cos x$ to $0 \le x \le \pi$, then the resulting function is one-to-one and has an inverse function. See Figure 6.150. This inverse function is called the *inverse cosine function*.

Fails Horizontal Line Test
(no inverse exists)

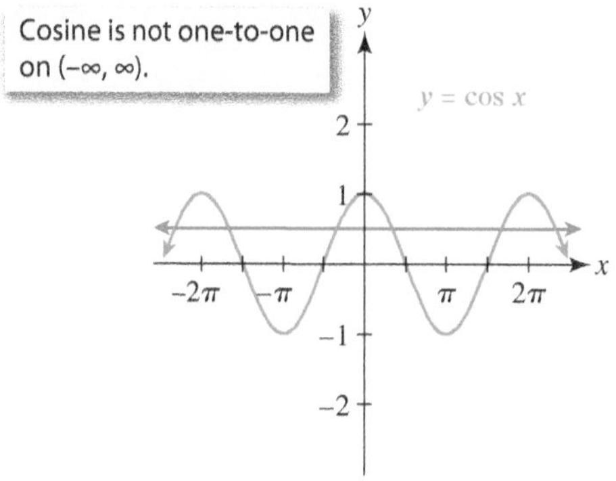

Cosine is not one-to-one on $(-\infty, \infty)$.

$y = \cos x$

Figure 6.149

Restricting the Domain of Cosine
(inverse exists)

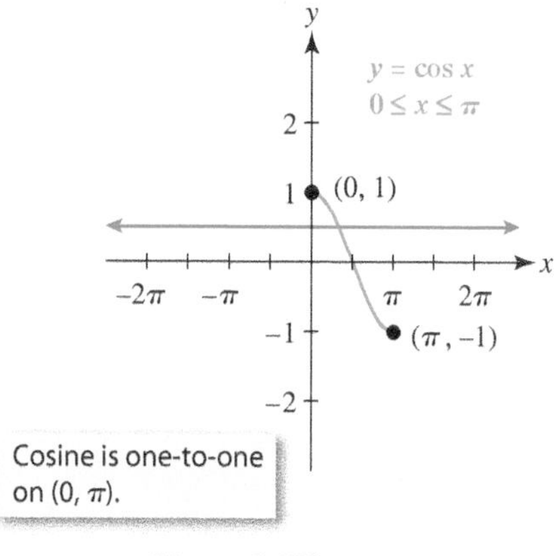

$y = \cos x$
$0 \le x \le \pi$

$(0, 1)$

$(\pi, -1)$

Cosine is one-to-one on $(0, \pi)$.

Figure 6.150

> ### INVERSE COSINE FUNCTION
>
> The **inverse cosine function**, denoted $\cos^{-1} x$ or arccos x, is defined as follows. For $-1 \le x \le 1$ and y in the interval $[0, \pi]$,
>
> $$y = \cos^{-1} x \quad \text{or} \quad y = \arccos x \qquad \text{means} \qquad x = \cos y.$$

EXAMPLE 4 Evaluating the inverse cosine function

Evaluate each of the following.
(a) $\cos^{-1} 1$ **(b)** $\arccos(-0.75)$

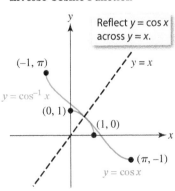

cos⁻¹(⁻.75)
          2.418858406
Ans*180/π
          138.5903779

Change to degrees

Figure 6.151 Radian Mode

SOLUTION
(a) The expression $\cos^{-1} 1$ represents the angle (or real number) θ whose cosine equals 1 and that satisfies $0 \le \theta \le \pi$. Thus $\theta = \cos^{-1} 1 = 0$, or $0°$.
(b) A calculator is often necessary to evaluate inverse trigonometric functions approximately. In Figure 6.151, $\cos^{-1}(-0.75) \approx 2.42$ radians, or about $138.6°$.

> **Now Try Exercises 15 and 19(c)**

The following are properties of the inverse cosine function.

$$\cos^{-1}(\cos x) = x \quad \text{for} \quad 0 \le x \le \pi$$

$$\cos(\cos^{-1} x) = x \quad \text{for} \quad -1 \le x \le 1$$

Inverse properties

EXAMPLE 5 Finding representations of the inverse cosine function

Represent the inverse cosine function verbally, numerically, graphically, and symbolically.

SOLUTION
Verbal Representation To compute $\cos^{-1} x$ for $-1 \le x \le 1$, determine the angle θ (or real number) such that $\cos \theta = x$ and $0 \le \theta \le \pi$.

Numerical Representation A numerical representation of $\cos x$ on the interval $[0, \pi]$ is shown in Table 6.13. A numerical representation of $\cos^{-1} x$ is shown in Table 6.14. Notice that if $\cos a = b$, then $\cos^{-1} b = a$, provided that $0 \le a \le \pi$.

Cosine Function on $[0, \pi]$

x	0	$\frac{\pi}{6}$	$\frac{\pi}{4}$	$\frac{\pi}{3}$	$\frac{\pi}{2}$	$\frac{2\pi}{3}$	$\frac{3\pi}{4}$	$\frac{5\pi}{6}$	π
$\cos x$	1	$\frac{\sqrt{3}}{2}$	$\frac{1}{\sqrt{2}}$	$\frac{1}{2}$	0	$-\frac{1}{2}$	$-\frac{1}{\sqrt{2}}$	$-\frac{\sqrt{3}}{2}$	-1

Table 6.13

Inverse Cosine Function on $[-1, 1]$

x	-1	$-\frac{\sqrt{3}}{2}$	$-\frac{1}{\sqrt{2}}$	$-\frac{1}{2}$	0	$\frac{1}{2}$	$\frac{1}{\sqrt{2}}$	$\frac{\sqrt{3}}{2}$	1
$\cos^{-1} x$	π	$\frac{5\pi}{6}$	$\frac{3\pi}{4}$	$\frac{2\pi}{3}$	$\frac{\pi}{2}$	$\frac{\pi}{3}$	$\frac{\pi}{4}$	$\frac{\pi}{6}$	0

Table 6.14

Interchange domain and range.

Graphical Representation The graph of $y = \cos^{-1} x$ can be found by reflecting the graph of $y = \cos x$ for $0 \le x \le \pi$ across the line $y = x$, as shown in Figure 6.152. See also Putting It All Together at the end of this section.

Symbolic Representation A symbolic representation of the inverse cosine function can be written as either $f(x) = \cos^{-1} x$ or $f(x) = \arccos x$. There is no simple formula that can be used to evaluate $\cos^{-1} x$.

> **Now Try Exercise 33**

Inverse Cosine Function

Reflect $y = \cos x$ across $y = x$.

$(-1, \pi)$

$y = x$

$y = \cos^{-1} x$

$(0, 1)$

$(1, 0)$

$(\pi, -1)$

$y = \cos x$

Figure 6.152

Explain the results in Figure 6.153.

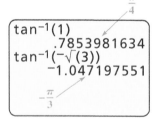

Figure 6.153 Degree Mode

The Inverse Tangent Function

By the horizontal line test, the tangent function is not one-to-one on $(-\infty, \infty)$, as shown in Figure 6.154. If we restrict the domain of $f(x) = \tan x$ to $-\frac{\pi}{2} < x < \frac{\pi}{2}$, then the resulting function is one-to-one and has an inverse function. See Figure 6.155. This inverse function is called the *inverse tangent function.*

Fails Horizontal Line Test
(no inverse exists)

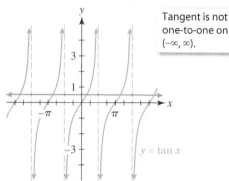

Figure 6.154

Restricting the Domain of Tangent
(inverse exists)

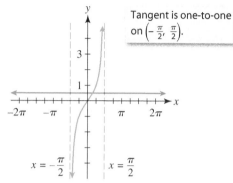

Figure 6.155

INVERSE TANGENT FUNCTION

The **inverse tangent function,** denoted $\tan^{-1} x$ or arctan x, is defined as follows. For y in the interval $\left(-\frac{\pi}{2}, \frac{\pi}{2} \right)$,

$$y = \tan^{-1} x \quad \text{or} \quad y = \arctan x \quad \text{means} \quad x = \tan y.$$

The following are properties of the inverse tangent function.

$$\tan^{-1}(\tan x) = x \quad \text{for} \quad -\frac{\pi}{2} < x < \frac{\pi}{2}$$

$$\tan(\tan^{-1} x) = x \quad \text{for all real numbers } x$$

Inverse properties

EXAMPLE 6 Evaluating the inverse tangent function

Evaluate each of the following. Support your answer using a calculator.
(a) $\tan^{-1} 1$ **(b)** arctan $\left(-\sqrt{3} \right)$

SOLUTION

(a) The expression $\tan^{-1} 1$ represents the angle (or real number) θ whose tangent equals 1 and that satisfies $-\frac{\pi}{2} < \theta < \frac{\pi}{2}$. Thus $\theta = \tan^{-1}(1) = \frac{\pi}{4} \approx 0.7854$. See Figure 6.156. In degrees, $\tan^{-1}(1) = 45°$.

(b) The expression arctan $\left(-\sqrt{3} \right)$ represents the angle (or real number) θ whose tangent is $-\sqrt{3}$ and that satisfies $-\frac{\pi}{2} < \theta < \frac{\pi}{2}$. Thus $\theta = \arctan \left(-\sqrt{3} \right) = -\frac{\pi}{3} \approx -1.047$. Support is shown in Figure 6.156. In degrees, arctan $\left(-\sqrt{3} \right) = -60°$.

Now Try Exercises 17 and 19(b)

```
        π
        ─
        4
tan⁻¹(1)
        .7853981634
tan⁻¹(⁻√(3))
        ⁻1.047197551
   π
 ─ ─
   3
```

Figure 6.156 Radian Mode

EXAMPLE 7 Evaluating inverse trigonometric functions

Let θ be an acute angle. Write $\cos \theta$ in terms of x, if $\theta = \sin^{-1} x$.

SOLUTION

Getting Started First sketch a right triangle so that one of its angles is θ. Because $\theta = \sin^{-1} x$, it follows that $\sin \theta = x$. Label the sides of the triangle so that $\sin \theta = \frac{x}{1}$. Use the triangle to find $\cos \theta$. ▶

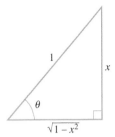

Figure 6.157

Figure 6.157 shows angle θ with $\sin\theta = \frac{x}{1}$. By the Pythagorean theorem, the other leg has length $\sqrt{1-x^2}$. Because $\cos\theta$ equals the side adjacent divided by the hypotenuse, we have $\cos\theta = \sqrt{1-x^2}$.

Now Try Exercise 35

NOTE Properties and graphs of the inverse sine, inverse cosine, and inverse tangent functions are given in Putting It All Together at the end of this section.

An Application The next example applies the inverse tangent function to robotics.

EXAMPLE 8 Using robots to spray paint

In industry it is common to use robots to spray paint. The robotic arm in Figure 6.158 is being used to paint a flat surface. Because the spray gun must move at a constant speed v, parallel to the surface being painted, the angle of the arm θ_1 and the angle of the spray gun θ_2 must be continually adjusted. Using Figure 6.158, it can be shown that

$$\theta_1 = \arctan\frac{h}{vt} \quad \text{and} \quad \theta_2 = 90° - \theta_1,$$

where $t > 0$ is time in seconds. (Try to verify this.) Let $v = 3$ inches per second and $h = 24$ inches. Determine the degree measure of θ_1 and θ_2 after 10 seconds. (*Source:* W. Stadler, *Analytical Robotics and Mechatronics.*)

Robotic Arm Painting

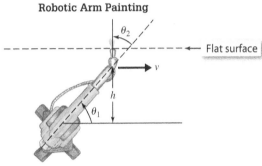

Figure 6.158

CLASS DISCUSSION

Give verbal, numerical, and graphical representations of $y = \tan^{-1} x$.

SOLUTION Substitute $h = 24$ and $v = 3$. When $t = 10$, $\theta_1 = \arctan\frac{24}{3(10)} \approx 38.7°$ and $\theta_2 = 90° - \theta_1 \approx 51.3°$.

Now Try Exercise 95

Solving Triangles and Equations

Figure 6.159 shows *standard labeling* used to denote the vertices, sides, and angles of a right triangle. The next example illustrates the process of finding the measures of the angles and sides in a triangle, called *solving a triangle.*

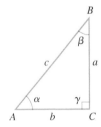

Figure 6.159

EXAMPLE 9 Solving a right triangle

Solve triangle ABC in Figure 6.160 if $a = 5$ and $c = 13$. Round values to the nearest tenth.

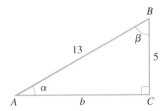

Figure 6.160

SOLUTION We are given $a = 5$, $c = 13$, and $\gamma = 90°$. We must find b, α, and β. We begin by finding b using the Pythagorean theorem.

$$a^2 + b^2 = c^2 \qquad \text{Pythagorean theorem}$$
$$b^2 = c^2 - a^2 \qquad \text{Subtract } a^2.$$
$$b^2 = 13^2 - 5^2 \qquad \text{Substitute.}$$
$$b^2 = 144 \qquad \text{Simplify.}$$

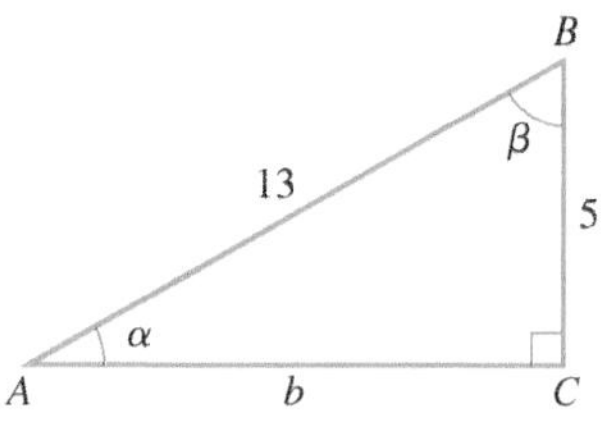

B

13

5

β

α

A   b   C

Figure 6.160 (Repeated)

Thus $b = 12$ in Figure 6.160 because $b^2 = 144$. We can find angle α as follows.

$$\sin \alpha = \frac{5}{13} \qquad \sin \alpha = \frac{side\ opposite}{hypotenuse}$$

$$\alpha = \sin^{-1}\frac{5}{13} \qquad Solve\ for\ \alpha.$$

$$\alpha \approx 22.6° \qquad Approximate.$$

Since β is complementary to α, $\beta \approx 90° - 22.6° = 67.4°$. 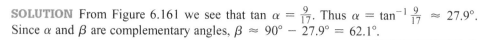 **Now Try Exercise 47**

NOTE There is more than one way to solve the triangle in Example 9. We could have let $\alpha = \tan^{-1}\frac{5}{12} \approx 22.6°$ and $\beta = \cos^{-1}\frac{5}{13} \approx 67.4°$. There are other possibilities.

EXAMPLE 10 Finding angles in a triangle

Approximate the degree measure of the angles α and β shown in Figure 6.161.

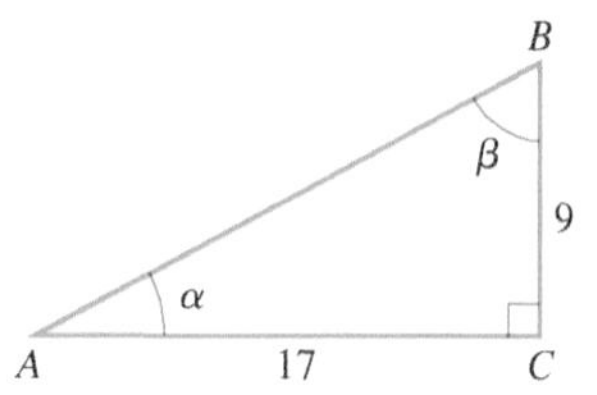

SOLUTION From Figure 6.161 we see that $\tan \alpha = \frac{9}{17}$. Thus $\alpha = \tan^{-1}\frac{9}{17} \approx 27.9°$. Since α and β are complementary angles, $\beta \approx 90° - 27.9° = 62.1°$.

Now Try Exercise 45

B

β

9

α

A   17   C

Figure 6.161

An Application Grade resistance is the force F that causes a car to roll down a hill. It can be calculated by $F = W \sin \theta$, where θ represents the angle of the grade and W represents the weight of the vehicle. See Figure 6.162.

Uphill and Downhill Grade

Figure 6.162

EXAMPLE 11 Calculating highway grade

Find the angle θ for which a 3000-pound car has grade resistance of 500 pounds.

SOLUTION Solve the equation $F = W \sin \theta$ for θ.

$$F = W \sin \theta \qquad Given\ equation$$

$$500 = 3000 \sin \theta \qquad Let\ W = 3000\ and\ F = 500.$$

$$\sin \theta = \frac{1}{6} \qquad Solve\ for\ \sin\ \theta.$$

$$\theta = \sin^{-1}\frac{1}{6} \qquad Property\ of\ inverse\ sine$$

$$\theta \approx 9.6° \qquad Approximate.$$

Thus if a road is inclined at approximately 9.6°, a 3000-pound car would experience a force of 500 pounds pulling downhill.

Now Try Exercise 85

Solving an Equation There are a wide variety of trigonometric equations. In the next example, we solve one basic type of equation. In Chapter 7, we will solve more types of trigonometric equations.

EXAMPLE 12   Solving a trigonometric equation

Solve $9\cos^2\theta = 4$, where θ is an acute angle.

SOLUTION Begin by dividing each side of the equation by 9.

$$9\cos^2\theta = 4 \qquad \textit{Given equation}$$

$$\cos^2\theta = \frac{4}{9} \qquad \textit{Divide by 9.}$$

$$\cos\theta = \pm\frac{2}{3} \qquad \textit{Square root property}$$

Because θ is an acute angle, $\cos\theta$ must be positive. Thus $\cos\theta = \frac{2}{3}$, and the solution to the equation is $\theta = \cos^{-1}\frac{2}{3} \approx 48.2°$.

Now Try Exercise 61

Other Trigonometric Inverse Functions

Definitions and Graphs The cotangent, secant, and cosecant functions are not one-to-one functions. However, by restricting their domains, inverse trigonometric functions can be defined. The following box gives common definitions for these functions; some texts use slightly different definitions.

OTHER INVERSE TRIGONOMETRIC FUNCTIONS

Inverse Cotangent For $0 < y < \pi$,

$$y = \cot^{-1}x \quad \text{or} \quad y = \text{arccot } x \quad \text{means that} \quad x = \cot y.$$

Inverse Secant For $0 \le y \le \pi$ with $y \ne \frac{\pi}{2}$ and $|x| \ge 1$,

$$y = \sec^{-1}x \quad \text{or} \quad y = \text{arcsec } x \quad \text{means that} \quad x = \sec y$$

Inverse Cosecant For $-\frac{\pi}{2} \le y \le \frac{\pi}{2}$ with $y \ne 0$ and $|x| \ge 1$,

$$y = \csc^{-1}x \quad \text{or} \quad y = \text{arccsc } x \quad \text{means that} \quad x = \csc y.$$

The graphs of the functions $y = \cot^{-1}x$, $y = \sec^{-1}x$, and $y = \csc^{-1}x$ are shown in Figures 6.163–6.165. These inverse graphs can be found by reflecting the graphs of $y = \cot x$, $y = \sec x$, and $y = \csc x$ across the line $y = x$ on a restricted interval.

Inverse Cotangent

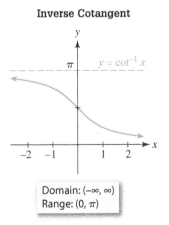

Domain: $(-\infty, \infty)$
Range: $(0, \pi)$

Figure 6.163

Inverse Secant

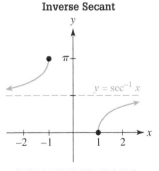

Domain: $(-\infty, -1] \cup [1, \infty)$
Range: $\left[0, \frac{\pi}{2}\right) \cup \left(\frac{\pi}{2}, \pi\right]$

Figure 6.164

Inverse Cosecant

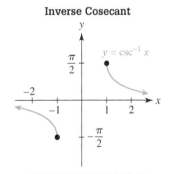

Domain: $(-\infty, -1] \cup [1, \infty)$
Range: $\left[-\frac{\pi}{2}, 0\right) \cup \left(0, \frac{\pi}{2}\right]$

Figure 6.165

Evaluating Other Inverse Functions Most calculators do not have keys for $\sec^{-1} x$, $\csc^{-1} x$, or $\cot^{-1} x$. However, we can evaluate these functions by using the functions $\cos^{-1} x$, $\sin^{-1} x$, and $\tan^{-1} x$.

For example, $y = \sec^{-1} x$ can be rewritten in terms of the inverse cosine function as follows.

$$y = \sec^{-1} x \qquad \text{Inverse secant, } |x| \geq 1$$

$$\sec y = x \qquad \text{Definition of inverse secant}$$

$$\frac{1}{\cos y} = x \qquad \text{Reciprocal identity}$$

$$\cos y = \frac{1}{x} \qquad \text{Invert each side, } x \neq 0.$$

$$\cos^{-1}(\cos y) = \cos^{-1} \frac{1}{x} \qquad \text{Take inverse cosine.}$$

$$y = \cos^{-1} \frac{1}{x} \qquad \text{Inverse properties}$$

Thus to evaluate $y = \sec^{-1} x$, we can evaluate $y = \cos^{-1} \frac{1}{x}$. The following box shows how to evaluate $\sec^{-1} x$, $\csc^{-1} x$, and $\cot^{-1} x$.

EVALUATING OTHER INVERSE TRIGONOMETRIC FUNCTIONS

Inverse Secant $\sec^{-1} x = \cos^{-1} \frac{1}{x}$ for $|x| \geq 1$.

Inverse Cosecant $\csc^{-1} x = \sin^{-1} \frac{1}{x}$ for $|x| \geq 1$.

Inverse Cotangent *Method I:* $\cot^{-1} x = \frac{\pi}{2} - \tan^{-1} x$

$\qquad\qquad\qquad$ *Method II:* $\cot^{-1} x = \tan^{-1} \frac{1}{x}$ if $x > 0$

$\qquad\qquad\qquad\qquad\qquad$ $\cot^{-1} x = \frac{\pi}{2}$ if $x = 0$

$\qquad\qquad\qquad\qquad\qquad$ $\cot^{-1} x = \pi + \tan^{-1} \frac{1}{x}$ if $x < 0$

In the next example, we evaluate other inverse trigonometric functions.

EXAMPLE 13 Evaluating other inverse functions

Find each of the following in radians. Approximate to the nearest thousandth when appropriate.

(a) $\sec^{-1} 2$ **(b)** $\csc^{-1}(-1)$ **(c)** $\cot^{-1} 6$

SOLUTION

(a) $\sec^{-1} 2 = \cos^{-1} \frac{1}{2} = \frac{\pi}{3}$

(b) $\csc^{-1}(-1) = \sin^{-1}\left(\frac{1}{-1}\right) = \sin^{-1}(-1) = -\frac{\pi}{2}$

(c) $\cot^{-1} 6 = \frac{\pi}{2} - \tan^{-1} 6 \approx \frac{\pi}{2} - 1.406 \approx 0.165$

Now Try Exercises 71, 73, and 81

6.6 Putting It All Together

$\mathbf{T}$he six trigonometric functions are not one-to-one functions. However, by *restricting* their domains to appropriate intervals, inverse trigonometric functions can be defined. The following table summarizes some properties of three important inverse trigonometric functions.

FUNCTION	EXPLANATION	EXAMPLES AND GRAPHS
Inverse sine	*Description:* $f(x) = \sin^{-1} x$ or $f(x) = \arcsin x$ computes the angle or number in $\left[-\frac{\pi}{2}, \frac{\pi}{2}\right]$ whose sine equals x, where $-1 \leq x \leq 1$. *Domain:* $\{x \mid -1 \leq x \leq 1\}$ *Range:* $\left\{y \mid -\frac{\pi}{2} \leq y \leq \frac{\pi}{2}\right\}$ *Inverse Properties:* $\sin^{-1}(\sin x) = x$ for $-\frac{\pi}{2} \leq x \leq \frac{\pi}{2}$ $\sin(\sin^{-1} x) = x$ for $-1 \leq x \leq 1$	$\sin^{-1} 1 = 90°$, or $\frac{\pi}{2}$ $\arcsin\left(-\frac{1}{2}\right) = -30°$, or $-\frac{\pi}{6}$ $\sin^{-1} 0 = 0°$, or 0 $\sin^{-1} 4$ is undefined. $\sin^{-1} 0.3 \approx 17.5°$, or 0.305
Inverse cosine	*Description:* $f(x) = \cos^{-1} x$ or $f(x) = \arccos x$ computes the angle or number in $[0, \pi]$ whose cosine equals x, where $-1 \leq x \leq 1$. *Domain:* $\{x \mid -1 \leq x \leq 1\}$ *Range:* $\{y \mid 0 \leq y \leq \pi\}$ *Inverse Properties:* $\cos^{-1}(\cos x) = x$ for $0 \leq x \leq \pi$ $\cos(\cos^{-1} x) = x$ for $-1 \leq x \leq 1$	$\cos^{-1} 1 = 0°$, or 0 $\arccos\left(-\frac{1}{2}\right) = 120°$, or $\frac{2\pi}{3}$ $\cos^{-1} 0 = 90°$, or $\frac{\pi}{2}$ $\cos^{-1}(-5)$ is undefined. $\cos^{-1} 0.8 \approx 36.9°$, or 0.644
Inverse tangent	*Description:* $f(x) = \tan^{-1} x$ or $f(x) = \arctan x$ computes the angle or number in $\left(-\frac{\pi}{2}, \frac{\pi}{2}\right)$ whose tangent equals x, where x is any real number. *Domain:* $\{x \mid -\infty < x < \infty\}$ (all real numbers) *Range:* $\left\{y \mid -\frac{\pi}{2} < y < \frac{\pi}{2}\right\}$ *Inverse Properties:* $\tan^{-1}(\tan x) = x$ for $-\frac{\pi}{2} < x < \frac{\pi}{2}$ $\tan(\tan^{-1} x) = x$ for all real numbers x *Horizontal Asymptotes:* $y = -\frac{\pi}{2}, y = \frac{\pi}{2}$	$\tan^{-1} 1 = 45°$, or $\frac{\pi}{4}$ $\tan^{-1} 0 = 0°$, or 0 $\tan^{-1} 8 \approx 82.9°$, or 1.446 $\arctan(-1) = -45°$, or $-\frac{\pi}{4}$

6.6 Exercises

Review of Inverses

1. For a function f to have an inverse, f must be _____.

2. A function is one-to-one if different inputs always result in _____ outputs.

3. If $f(\pi) = -1$, then $f^{-1}(-1) =$ _____.

4. If $f(c) = d$, then $f^{-1}(d) =$ _____.

5. If $f^{-1}(0) = 1$, then $f(1) =$ _____.

6. If $f^{-1}(b) = a$, then $f(a) =$ _____.

Inverse Trigonometric Functions

7. Since $\sin \frac{\pi}{2} = 1$ and $\frac{\pi}{2}$ is in the interval $\left[-\frac{\pi}{2}, \frac{\pi}{2}\right]$, $\sin^{-1} 1 =$ _____.

8. Since $\cos \frac{\pi}{3} = \frac{1}{2}$ and $\frac{\pi}{3}$ is in the interval $[0, \pi]$, $\cos^{-1} \frac{1}{2} =$ _____.

9. Since $\tan\left(-\frac{\pi}{4}\right) = -1$ and $-\frac{\pi}{4}$ is in the interval $\left(-\frac{\pi}{2}, \frac{\pi}{2}\right)$, $\tan^{-1}(-1) =$ _____.

10. Since $\sin\left(-\frac{\pi}{6}\right) = -\frac{1}{2}$ and $-\frac{\pi}{6}$ is in the interval $\left[-\frac{\pi}{2}, \frac{\pi}{2}\right]$, $\sin^{-1}\left(-\frac{1}{2}\right) =$ _____.

11. Since $\cos\left(\frac{2\pi}{3}\right) = -\frac{1}{2}$ and $\frac{2\pi}{3}$ is in the interval $[0, \pi]$, $\cos^{-1}\left(-\frac{1}{2}\right) =$ _____.

12. Since $\tan\left(\frac{\pi}{3}\right) = \sqrt{3}$ and $\frac{\pi}{3}$ is in the interval $\left(-\frac{\pi}{2}, \frac{\pi}{2}\right)$, $\tan^{-1}\sqrt{3} =$ _____.

Exercises 13–18: Evaluate each of the following, if possible. Give results in both radians and degrees.

13. (a) $\sin^{-1} 1$ (b) $\arcsin 4$

    (c) $\arcsin\left(-\frac{\sqrt{3}}{2}\right)$

14. (a) $\arcsin \frac{1}{2}$ (b) $\sin^{-1}(-2)$

    (c) $\sin^{-1}(-1)$

15. (a) $\cos^{-1} 0$ (b) $\arccos(-1)$

    (c) $\cos^{-1} \frac{1}{2}$

16. (a) $\arccos \frac{\sqrt{3}}{2}$ (b) $\cos^{-1}\left(-\frac{1}{2}\right)$

    (c) $\arccos 1$

17. (a) $\tan^{-1} 1$ (b) $\arctan(-1)$

    (c) $\tan^{-1} \sqrt{3}$

18. (a) $\arctan(-\sqrt{3})$ (b) $\tan^{-1} 0$

    (c) $\tan^{-1}\left(-\frac{1}{\sqrt{3}}\right)$

Exercises 19 and 20: If possible, approximate the following to a hundredth of a radian and a tenth of a degree.

19. (a) $\sin^{-1} 1.5$ (b) $\tan^{-1} 10$

    (c) $\arccos(-0.25)$

20. (a) $\cos^{-1}(-3)$ (b) $\arcsin(-0.54)$

    (c) $\arctan(-2.5)$

Exercises 21 and 22: Evaluate each expression using the figure to obtain either α or β.

21. (a) $\tan^{-1} \frac{4}{3}$

    (b) $\sin^{-1} \frac{3}{5}$

    (c) $\arccos \frac{3}{5}$

22. (a) $\arcsin \frac{12}{13}$

    (b) $\cos^{-1} \frac{5}{13}$

    (c) $\tan^{-1} \frac{5}{12}$

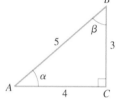

Exercises 23–28: Evaluate each expression.

23. $\sin(\sin^{-1} 1)$ 24. $\sin^{-1}\left(\sin \frac{\pi}{4}\right)$

25. $\cos^{-1}\left(\cos \frac{5\pi}{4}\right)$ 26. $\cos(\cos^{-1}(-3))$

27. $\tan(\tan^{-1}(-3))$ 28. $\tan^{-1}\left(\tan \frac{\pi}{5}\right)$

Exercises 29 and 30: Evaluate the expression in degree mode. Make a generalization about the result and then test your conjecture.

29. (a) $\sin^{-1} \frac{3}{5} + \cos^{-1} \frac{3}{5}$ (b) $\sin^{-1} \frac{1}{3} + \cos^{-1} \frac{1}{3}$

    (c) $\sin^{-1} \frac{2}{7} + \cos^{-1} \frac{2}{7}$

30. (a) $\tan^{-1} \frac{3}{4} + \tan^{-1} \frac{4}{3}$ (b) $\tan^{-1} \frac{5}{12} + \tan^{-1} \frac{12}{5}$

    (c) $\tan^{-1} \frac{1}{4} + \tan^{-1} 4$

Exercises 31–34: Represent the given $f(x)$ verbally, numerically, and graphically.

31. $f(x) = \sin^{-1} 2x$ 32. $f(x) = \sin^{-1} \frac{1}{2}x$

33. $f(x) = \cos^{-1} \frac{1}{2}x$ 34. $f(x) = \cos^{-1} 2x$

Evaluating Inverses with Variables

Exercises 35–38: (Refer to Example 7.) Evaluate the indicated trigonometric function of θ, where θ is an acute angle determined by an inverse trigonometric function. (Hint: Make a sketch of a right triangle containing angle θ.)

35. $\tan \theta$, if $\theta = \sin^{-1} x$

36. $\sin \theta$, if $\theta = \tan^{-1} \dfrac{x}{\sqrt{1 - x^2}}$

37. $\cos \theta$, if $\theta = \sin^{-1} \dfrac{x}{\sqrt{1 + x^2}}$

38. $\tan \theta$, if $\theta = \cos^{-1} \dfrac{1}{x}$

Exercises 39–44: (Refer to Example 7.) Write the expression as an algebraic expression of u if $0 < u < 1$.

39. $\sin (\cos^{-1} u)$

40. $\cos (\sin^{-1} u)$

41. $\tan (\cos^{-1} u)$

42. $\sin (\tan^{-1} u)$

43. $\cot \left(\tan^{-1} \dfrac{1}{u} \right)$

44. $\sec (\sin^{-1} u)$

Solving Triangles

Exercises 45–50: (Refer to Example 9.) Solve the triangle.

45.

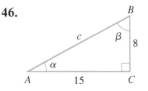

46.

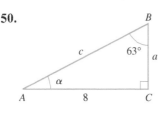

47.

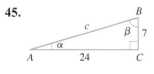

48.

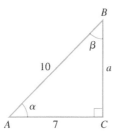

49.

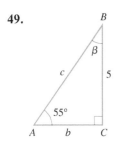

50.

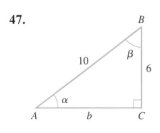

Solving Trigonometric Equations

Exercises 51–56: Solve the trigonometric equation for θ, where $0° \le \theta \le 90°$.

51. $\sin \theta = 1$

52. $\cos \theta = \dfrac{1}{2}$

53. $\tan \theta = 1$

54. $\sin \theta = \dfrac{\sqrt{3}}{2}$

55. $\cos \theta = 0$

56. $\tan \theta = \dfrac{1}{\sqrt{3}}$

Exercises 57–62: Solve the equation for θ, where θ is an acute angle. Approximate θ to the nearest tenth of a degree.

57. $2 \cos \theta = \dfrac{1}{4}$

58. $3 \sin \theta = \dfrac{4}{5}$

59. $\tan \theta - 1 = 5$

60. $4 \cos \theta + 1 = 6$

61. $\sin^2 \theta = 0.87$

62. $\tan^3 \theta - 2 = 1.65$

Exercises 63–70: Solve the equation for t, where t is a real number in the given interval. Approximate t to three decimal places.

63. $\tan t = -\dfrac{1}{5}, \left(-\dfrac{\pi}{2}, \dfrac{\pi}{2} \right)$

64. $\sin t = -\dfrac{1}{3}, \left[-\dfrac{\pi}{2}, \dfrac{\pi}{2} \right]$

65. $\cos t = 0.452, [0, \pi]$

66. $\tan t = 5.67, \left(-\dfrac{\pi}{2}, \dfrac{\pi}{2} \right)$

67. $2 \sin t = -0.557, \left[-\dfrac{\pi}{2}, \dfrac{\pi}{2} \right]$

68. $3 \cos t + 1 = 0.333, [0, \pi]$

69. $\cos^2 t = \dfrac{1}{25}, [0, \pi]$

70. $\sin^2 t = \dfrac{1}{16}, \left[-\dfrac{\pi}{2}, \dfrac{\pi}{2} \right]$

Exercises 71–82: Find each of the following in radians. Approximate to the nearest thousandth when appropriate.

71. $\sec^{-1} (-1)$

72. $\sec^{-1} \sqrt{2}$

73. $\csc^{-1} (-\sqrt{2})$

74. $\csc^{-1} \dfrac{2\sqrt{3}}{3}$

75. $\cot^{-1} (-1)$

76. $\cot^{-1} 0$

77. $\sec^{-1} 3$

78. $\sec^{-1} (-4)$

79. $\csc^{-1} 5.1$

80. $\csc^{-1} (-3)$

81. $\cot^{-1} 1.5$

82. $\cot^{-1} (-7.1)$

Applications

83. Angle of Elevation Find the angle of elevation θ of the top of a 50-foot tree at a distance of 85 feet. See the figure.

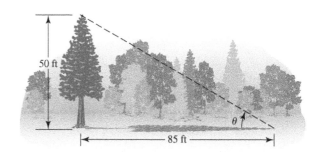

84. Angle of Elevation A 28-foot building casts a 40-foot shadow on level ground. Find the angle of elevation θ of the sun to the nearest tenth of a degree. See the figure.

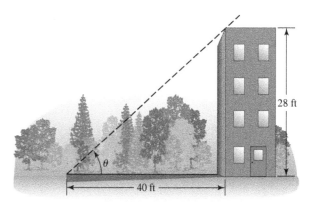

85. Grade Resistance (Refer to Example 11.) Approximate θ to the nearest tenth of a degree for the given grade resistance F and vehicle weight W. Use the equation $F = W \sin \theta$.

(a) $F = 400$ lb, $W = 5000$ lb

(b) $F = 130$ lb, $W = 3500$ lb

(c) $F = -200$ lb, $W = 4000$ lb

86. Robotics Approximate the angle θ if the robotic hand is located at the following points, where $-90° < \theta < 90°$. See the figure.

(a) $(5, 11)$ (b) $(1, -3)$

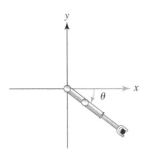

87. Designing Steps Steps are being attached to a deck as shown in the figure. The bottom of the steps should land 10 feet from the deck. If the deck is 4 feet above the ground, estimate angle θ between the ground and the side board of the step.

88. Designing Steps (Refer to Exercise 87.) If the length of the side boards for the steps is 4 feet and the deck is 2 feet above the ground, find angle θ.

89. Roof Pitch The pitch, or slope, of a roof may be expressed in the form $k/12$, where k represents a k-foot rise for every 12 feet of run in horizontal distance. Determine angle θ in Figure 6.141 for each pitch.

(a) $\frac{3}{12}$ (b) $\frac{4}{12}$ (c) $\frac{6}{12}$ (d) $\frac{12}{12}$

90. Phases of the Moon (See Example 11 in Section 6.3.) Find the phase angle θ for the given phase F. Assume that $0° \le \theta \le 180°$ and use $F(\theta) = \frac{1}{2}(1 - \cos \theta)$.

(a) $F = \frac{1}{4}$ (b) $F = \frac{3}{4}$

91. Shot Put (Refer to Example 3.) Suppose that a shot is released 7 feet above the ground with a velocity of 43 feet per second. Find the optimal projection angle.

92. Shot-Putting on the Moon Repeat Exercise 91 with $v = 50$ feet per second if the shot is thrown on the moon and the optimal projection angle is given by

$$\theta = \sin^{-1} \sqrt{\frac{v^2}{2v^2 + 10.2h}}.$$

93. Calculating Daylight Hours The ability to calculate the number of daylight hours H at any location is important for estimating potential solar energy production. The value of H on the longest day can be calculated using the formula

$$\cos(0.1309 \, H) = -0.4336 \tan L,$$

where L is the latitude. Using *radian* mode, calculate the greatest number of daylight hours H during the year for the various cities and their latitudes. (*Source:* C. Winter, *Solar Power Plants.*)

(a) Akron, Ohio; $L = 40°55'$

(b) Corpus Christi, Texas; $L = 27°46'$

(c) Richmond, Virginia; $L = 37°30'$

94. Shortest Day (Refer to Exercise 93.) The value of H on the shortest day can be calculated using the formula

$$\cos(0.1309 \, H) = 0.4336 \tan L.$$

Find the least number of daylight hours at the following locations. (*Source:* C. Winter, *Solar Power Plants.*)

(a) Anchorage, Alaska; $L = 61°10'$

(b) Atlantic City, New Jersey; $L = 39°27'$

(c) Honolulu, Hawaii; $L = 21°20'$

95. Robotics (Refer to Example 8.) Let $v = 5$ inches per second and $h = 18$. Determine the degree measure of θ_1 and θ_2 after 5 seconds.

96. Snell's Law When a ray of light enters water, it is bent. This change in direction can be calculated using Snell's law. See the figure. The angles θ_1 and θ_2 are related by the equation $n_1 \sin \theta_1 = n_2 \sin \theta_2$, where n_1 and n_2 are constants called *indexes of refraction*. For air $n_1 = 1$, and for water $n_2 = 1.33$. If a ray of light enters the water with $\theta_1 = 40°$, estimate θ_2. (*Source:* R. Weidner and R. Sells, *Elementary Classical Physics*, Vol. 2.)

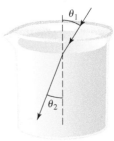

97. Landscaping Formula A shrub is planted in a 100-foot-wide space between buildings measuring 75 feet and 150 feet tall. The location of the shrub determines how much sun it receives each day. Show that if θ is the angle in the figure and x is the distance of the shrub from the taller building, then the value of θ (in radians) is given by the equation

$$\theta = \pi - \arctan\left(\frac{75}{100-x}\right) - \arctan\left(\frac{150}{x}\right).$$

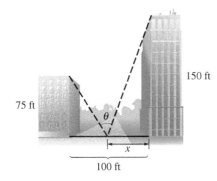

98. Communications Satellite Coverage The figure shows a stationary communications satellite positioned 20,000 miles above the equator. What percent of the equator can be seen from the satellite? The diameter of Earth is 7927 miles at the equator.

Writing about Mathematics

99. Explain verbally what each expression computes. Give examples.
  (a) $\sin^{-1} x$ **(b)** $\cos^{-1} x$ **(c)** $\tan^{-1} x$

100. Explain why
$$\sin^{-1}\left(\sin\frac{\pi}{2}\right) = \frac{\pi}{2} \quad \text{but} \quad \sin^{-1}\left(\sin\frac{5\pi}{2}\right) \neq \frac{5\pi}{2}.$$
Give a similar example using $\cos x$ and $\cos^{-1} x$.

EXTENDED AND DISCOVERY EXERCISE

1. Movie Screen A 10-foot-high movie screen is mounted on a vertical wall so that the bottom of the screen is 6 feet above a horizontal floor. A person sits on a level floor x feet from the screen. If eye level is 3 feet above the floor, then angle θ shown in the figure can be expressed as

$$\theta = \tan^{-1}\left(\frac{10x}{x^2 + 39}\right).$$

Graph θ in [0, 50, 10] by [0, 50, 10] using degree mode. Determine where a person should sit to maximize θ.

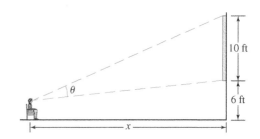

CHECKING BASIC CONCEPTS FOR SECTIONS 6.5 AND 6.6

1. Graph $f(t) = 3 \sin\left(2\left(t - \frac{\pi}{4}\right)\right)$ for $-\pi \le t \le \pi$. State the amplitude, period, and phase shift.

2. The accompanying table contains data that can be modeled by $f(t) = a \cos(bt)$. Find values for a and b.

t	0	0.5	1.0	1.5	2.0	2.5	3.0
$f(t)$	2	0	−2	0	2	0	−2

3. Evaluate the following, expressing your answer in degrees.
  (a) $\sin^{-1} 0$ **(b)** $\cos^{-1}(-1)$

  (c) $\tan^{-1}(-1)$ **(d)** $\sin^{-1}\frac{1}{2}$
  (e) $\tan^{-1}\sqrt{3}$ **(f)** $\cos^{-1}\frac{1}{2}$

4. Solve a right triangle if $a = 30$ and $b = 40$.

5. Use a calculator to solve each equation, where t is in the indicated interval.
  (a) $\sin t = 0.55$, $\left[-\frac{\pi}{2}, \frac{\pi}{2}\right]$
  (b) $\cos t = -0.35$, $[0, \pi]$
  (c) $\tan t = -2.9$, $\left(-\frac{\pi}{2}, \frac{\pi}{2}\right)$

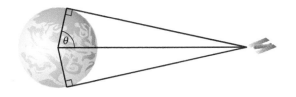

6 | Summary

CONCEPT	EXPLANATION AND EXAMPLES

Section 6.1 Angles and Their Measure

Angle Measure

Degree measure: $360° =$ one revolution
$1° = 60'$ (minutes)
$1' = 60''$ (seconds)

Radian measure: 2π radians $=$ one revolution

radian measure $\times \frac{180°}{\pi} =$ degree measure

degree measure $\times \frac{\pi}{180°} =$ radian measure

Arc Length

$s = r\theta$, where θ is in *radians*

Example: The arc length intercepted by a central angle of $120°$ with a radius of 5 inches is

$$s = 5\left(\frac{2\pi}{3}\right) = \frac{10\pi}{3} \approx 10.47 \text{ inches.}$$

Area of Sector

$A = \frac{1}{2}r^2\theta$, where θ is in *radians*

Example: The area of the sector determined by a central angle of $45°$ with a radius of 10 inches is

$$A = \frac{1}{2}\left(10^2\right)\left(\frac{\pi}{4}\right) = \frac{25\pi}{2} \approx 39.27 \text{ square inches.}$$

Section 6.2 Right Triangle Trigonometry

Trigonometric Functions (Right Triangles)

$\sin\theta = \dfrac{\text{side opposite}}{\text{hypotenuse}}$ $\csc\theta = \dfrac{\text{hypotenuse}}{\text{side opposite}}$

$\cos\theta = \dfrac{\text{side adjacent}}{\text{hypotenuse}}$ $\sec\theta = \dfrac{\text{hypotenuse}}{\text{side adjacent}}$

$\tan\theta = \dfrac{\text{side opposite}}{\text{side adjacent}}$ $\cot\theta = \dfrac{\text{side adjacent}}{\text{side opposite}}$

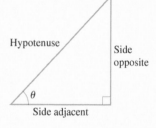

Example: The six trigonometric functions of θ in the figure are as follows.

$\sin\theta = \frac{11}{61}$ $\csc\theta = \frac{61}{11}$

$\cos\theta = \frac{60}{61}$ $\sec\theta = \frac{61}{60}$

$\tan\theta = \frac{11}{60}$ $\cot\theta = \frac{60}{11}$

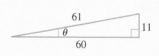

Cofunction Formulas

Let α and β be complementary angles.

$\sin\alpha = \cos(90° - \alpha) = \cos\beta$

$\tan\alpha = \cot(90° - \alpha) = \cot\beta$

$\sec\alpha = \csc(90° - \alpha) = \csc\beta$

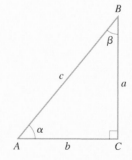

CONCEPT	EXPLANATION AND EXAMPLES

Section 6.3 The Sine and Cosine Functions and Their Graphs

Sine and Cosine

If angle θ is in standard position and its terminal side passes through the point (x, y), then

$$\sin\theta = \frac{y}{r} \quad \text{and} \quad \cos\theta = \frac{x}{r},$$

where $r = \sqrt{x^2 + y^2}$. In the figure to the right, $x = 3$, $y = -4$, and $r = \sqrt{3^2 + (-4)^2} = 5$.

$$\sin\theta = -\frac{4}{5} \quad \text{and} \quad \cos\theta = \frac{3}{5}$$

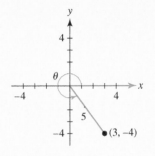

Unit Circle

If the terminal side of an angle t intersects the unit circle at the point (x, y), then $\sin t = y$ and $\cos t = x$. The domains of the sine and cosine functions include all real numbers, and their ranges include all real numbers y, such that $-1 \le y \le 1$.

In the figure, $x = -\frac{1}{2}$ and $y = \frac{\sqrt{3}}{2}$. Thus

$$\sin t = \frac{\sqrt{3}}{2} \quad \text{and} \quad \cos t = -\frac{1}{2}.$$

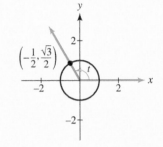

Section 6.4 Other Trigonometric Functions and Their Graphs

Trigonometric Functions

The domains, ranges, periods, and graphs of the six trigonometric functions are discussed in Putting It All Together in Section 6.4.

If angle θ is in standard position and its terminal side passes through the point (x, y), then it follows that

$$\tan\theta = \frac{y}{x}, \quad \cot\theta = \frac{x}{y}, \quad \sec\theta = \frac{r}{x}, \quad \text{and} \quad \csc\theta = \frac{r}{y}, \text{ where } r = \sqrt{x^2 + y^2}.$$

In the figure, $x = -2$, $y = 3$, and $r = \sqrt{(-2)^2 + 3^2} = \sqrt{13}$.

$$\tan\theta = -\frac{3}{2} \qquad \cot\theta = -\frac{2}{3}$$

$$\sec\theta = -\frac{\sqrt{13}}{2} \qquad \csc\theta = \frac{\sqrt{13}}{3}$$

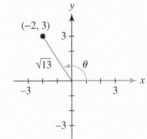

Unit Circle

If the terminal side of an angle t intersects the unit circle at the point (x, y), then

$$\tan t = \frac{y}{x}, \quad \cot t = \frac{x}{y}, \quad \sec t = \frac{1}{x}, \quad \text{and} \quad \csc t = \frac{1}{y}.$$

In the figure, $x = 0$ and $y = 1$. Thus

$\tan t$ is undefined; $\quad \cot t = 0$;

$\sec t$ is undefined; $\quad \csc t = 1$.

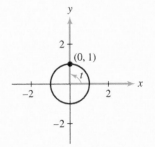

CONCEPT	EXPLANATION AND EXAMPLES

Section 6.5 Graphing Trigonometric Functions

Modeling with Sine and Cosine Functions

$f(x) = a \sin(b(x - c)) + d$ or $f(x) = a \cos(b(x - c)) + d$

Amplitude $= |a|$ Period $= \dfrac{2\pi}{b}, b > 0$

Phase shift $= c$ Vertical shift $= d$

Simple Harmonic Motion

Can be modeled by $s(t) = a \sin bt$ or $s(t) = a \cos bt$

If $b = 2\pi F$, then F represents the frequency of the sinusoidal graph.

Example: If a spring is initially compressed 3 inches and oscillates 4 times per second, then $a = 3$, $b = 2\pi F = 8\pi$, and its motion can be modeled by $s(t) = 3 \cos(8\pi t)$.

Section 6.6 Inverse Trigonometric Functions

Inverse Sine Function

$\theta = \sin^{-1} x$ implies that $\sin \theta = x$ and either $-\dfrac{\pi}{2} \leq \theta \leq \dfrac{\pi}{2}$ or $-90° \leq \theta \leq 90°$. $\sin^{-1} x$ is also denoted arcsin x.

Example: $\sin^{-1} 1 = \dfrac{\pi}{2}$, $\sin^{-1}\left(-\dfrac{1}{2}\right) = -30°$,   arcsin $0 = 0°$

Inverse Cosine Function

$\theta = \cos^{-1} x$ implies that $\cos \theta = x$ and either $0 \leq \theta \leq \pi$ or $0° \leq \theta \leq 180°$. $\cos^{-1} x$ is also denoted arccos x.

Example: $\cos^{-1} 1 = 0$, $\cos^{-1}(-1) = 180°$,   arccos $\dfrac{1}{2} = 60°$

Inverse Tangent Function

$\theta = \tan^{-1} x$ implies that $\tan \theta = x$ and either $-\dfrac{\pi}{2} < \theta < \dfrac{\pi}{2}$ or $-90° < \theta < 90°$. $\tan^{-1} x$ is also denoted arctan x.

Example: $\tan^{-1} 1 = \dfrac{\pi}{4}$, $\tan^{-1}(-1) = -45°$,   arctan $\sqrt{3} = 60°$

Solving Triangles

Inverse trigonometric functions can be used to solve equations and find angles in triangles.

Example: In triangle ABC, inverse trigonometric functions can be used to find α and β.

$\alpha = \sin^{-1}\dfrac{3}{5} \approx 36.9°$

$\alpha = \tan^{-1}\dfrac{3}{4} \approx 36.9°$

$\beta = \cos^{-1}\dfrac{3}{5} \approx 53.1°$

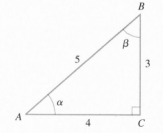

6 Review Exercises

1. Sketch the following angles in standard position.
   (a) 60°   (b) $-\frac{5\pi}{6}$

2. Find the complementary angle and the supplementary angle to $\theta = 61°40'$.

3. Convert each angle from radians to degrees.
   (a) $\frac{\pi}{3}$ (b) $\frac{\pi}{36}$ (c) $-\frac{5\pi}{6}$ (d) $-\frac{7\pi}{4}$

4. Convert each angle from degrees to radians.
   (a) 30°   (b) 165°   (c) −90°   (d) −105°

5. Find the length of the arc intercepted by a central angle $\theta = 60°$ and a radius $r = 6$ feet.

6. Find the area of the sector of a circle having a radius $r = 5$ inches and a central angle $\theta = 150°$.

Exercises 7–12: Find the exact value of each trigonometric expression by hand.

7. $\sin 30°$ 8. $\tan 45°$

9. $\cot 60°$ 10. $\cos 60°$

11. $\sec \frac{\pi}{4}$ 12. $\csc \frac{\pi}{6}$

13. Find the six trigonometric functions of θ.

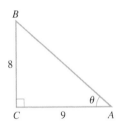

14. Solve triangle ABC.

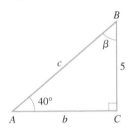

15. Find $\csc \theta$ if $\sin \theta = \frac{1}{3}$.

16. Find $\cot \theta$ if $\sin \theta = \frac{5}{13}$ and $\cos \theta = -\frac{12}{13}$.

Exercises 17 and 18: Approximate the six trigonometric functions of θ to three decimal places.

17. $\theta = 25°$ 18. $\theta = -\frac{6\pi}{7}$

Exercises 19 and 20: Find the six trigonometric functions of angle θ.

19.

20.

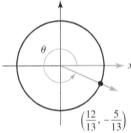

Exercises 21 and 22: The figure shows angle θ in standard position with its terminal side intersecting the unit circle. Find the six trigonometric functions of θ.

21.

22.

Exercises 23–26: (Wrapping function) Evaluate the function f at the given value of t.

23. $f(t) = \sin t, t = -\frac{\pi}{2}$ 24. $f(t) = \cos t, t = \pi$

25. $f(t) = \tan t, t = -3\pi$ 26. $f(t) = \csc t, t = \frac{\pi}{2}$

27. Find the other trigonometric functions of θ if $\sin \theta = -\frac{4}{5}$ and $\cos \theta = \frac{3}{5}$.

28. Convert $65°45'36''$ to decimal degrees.

Exercises 29–32: Graph f for $-2\pi \le t \le 2\pi$. State the amplitude, period, and phase shift.

29. $f(t) = 3 \cos 2t$ 30. $f(t) = -2 \sin(2t + \pi)$

31. $f(t) = -3 \sin\left(\frac{1}{2}(t - \pi)\right) + 1$

32. $f(t) = \frac{1}{2} \cos\left(\frac{\pi}{2}(t - 1)\right) - 2$

Exercises 33 and 34: A graph of $y = a \cos bx$ is shown, where b is a positive constant. Estimate the values for a and b.

33.

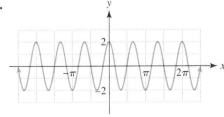

34.

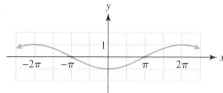

Exercises 35 and 36: Graph f for $-2\pi \le t \le 2\pi$. State the period and phase shift.

35. $f(t) = \cot 2t$ **36.** $f(t) = \sec 2t$

Exercises 37 and 38: If possible, evaluate each of the following in both radians and degrees.

37. (a) $\sin^{-1}(-1)$ **(b)** $\arccos \frac{1}{2}$ **(c)** $\tan^{-1} 1$

38. (a) $\arcsin 3$ **(b)** $\cos^{-1} 0$ **(c)** $\arctan\left(-\sqrt{3}\right)$

39. Approximate the following to a hundredth of a radian and a tenth of a degree.
  (a) $\sin^{-1}(-0.6)$ **(b)** $\tan^{-1} 5$ **(c)** $\arccos 0.12$

40. Evaluate each expression.
  (a) $\sin(\sin^{-1} 0.5)$ **(b)** $\tan^{-1}(\tan 45°)$

Exercises 41 and 42: Solve the right triangle ABC.

41.   **42.**

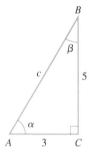
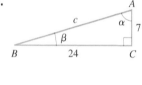

Exercises 43 and 44: Solve the equation for θ, where $0° \le \theta \le 90°$.

43. $\tan \theta = \frac{1}{\sqrt{3}}$ **44.** $\cos \theta = 1$

Exercises 45 and 46: Solve the equation for θ, where θ is an acute angle. Approximate θ to the nearest tenth of a degree.

45. $\cos \theta = \frac{1}{5}$ **46.** $3 \sin \theta = \frac{15}{13}$

Exercises 47 and 48: Solve the equation for t, where t is a real number located in the indicated interval. Approximate t to four decimal places.

47. $\tan t = -\frac{3}{4}, \left(-\frac{\pi}{2}, \frac{\pi}{2}\right)$ **48.** $\sin t = -\frac{3}{5}, \left[-\frac{\pi}{2}, \frac{\pi}{2}\right]$

Applications

49. Ferris Wheel   A Ferris wheel has a diameter of 50 feet and completes 1 revolution every 50 seconds.
  (a) Find the angular velocity of the Ferris wheel in radians per second.

  (b) What is the linear speed in feet per second of a person who is riding this Ferris wheel?

50. Fan Speed   The blades of a fan have a 25-inch diameter and rotate at 400 revolutions per minute.
  (a) Find the angular velocity of a fan blade.

  (b) Estimate the linear speed in inches per second at the tip of a fan blade.

51. Height of a Tree   Eighty feet from the trunk of a tree on level ground, the angle of elevation of the top of the tree is 48°. Estimate the height of the tree to the nearest foot.

52. Angle of Elevation   Find the angle of elevation of the top of a 35-foot building at a horizontal distance of 52 feet.

53. Grade Resistance   Approximate θ to the nearest tenth of a degree for the given grade resistance F and vehicle weight W, where $F = W \sin \theta$.
  (a) $F = 350$ lb, $W = 6000$ lb

  (b) $F = 160$ lb, $W = 4500$ lb

54. Highway Grade   (Refer to Exercise 53.) Suppose an uphill grade of a highway can be modeled by the line $y = 0.05x$.
  (a) Find the grade of the hill.

  (b) Determine the grade resistance for a gravel truck that weighs 30,000 pounds.

55. Distance Between Cities   Cheyenne, Wyoming, and Colorado Springs, Colorado, have nearly the same longitude of 104°45′W. The latitude of Cheyenne is 41°09′, and the latitude of Colorado Springs is 38°49′. Approximate the distance between these two cities if the average radius of Earth is 3955 miles. (**Source:** J. Williams, *The Weather Almanac.*)

56. Safe Distance for a Tree   From a distance of 45 feet from the base of a tree, the angle of elevation to the top of the tree is 57°, as shown in the figure. A building is located 52 feet from the base of the tree. Determine if the tree could fall in a storm and damage the building.

57. Modeling Temperatures The monthly average low temperatures in Green Bay, Wisconsin, are shown in the table.

Month	1	2	3	4	5	6
Temperature (°F)	6	10	22	35	45	52

Month	7	8	9	10	11	12
Temperature (°F)	58	56	48	38	26	11

Source: A. Miller and J. Thompson, *Elements of Meteorology.*

(a) Plot the monthly average temperature over a 24-month period by letting $x = 1$ and $x = 13$ correspond to January.

(b) Use $f(x) = a \cos(b(x - c)) + d$ to model the data.

(c) Graph f together with the data.

58. Phases of the Moon If the phase angle of the moon is θ, then the phase F of the moon is given by

$$F = \frac{1}{2}(1 - \cos\theta).$$

Solve this equation for θ.

Extended and Discovery Exercises

1. Surveying The first fundamental problem of surveying is to determine the coordinates of a point Q given the coordinates of a point P, the distance between P and Q, and the bearing θ from P to Q. See the figure. (*Source:* I. Mueller and K. Ramsayer, *Introduction to Surveying.*)

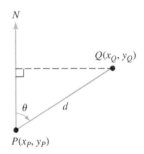

(a) Find a formula for the coordinates (x_Q, y_Q) of the point Q given θ, the coordinates (x_P, y_P) of P, and the distance d between P and Q.

(b) Use your formula to find the coordinates (x_Q, y_Q) if $(x_P, y_P) = (152, 186)$, $\theta = 23.2°$, and $d = 208$ feet.

2. Highway Grade (Refer to Example 4, Section 6.3.) Complete the table at the top of the next column for the trigonometric values of θ to five decimal places.
(a) How do $\sin\theta$ and $\tan\theta$ compare for small values of θ?

θ	$\sin\theta$	$\tan\theta$
0°		
1°		
2°		
3°		
4°		

(b) Highway grades are usually small. Give an approximation to the grade resistance given by $F = W \sin\theta$ that uses the tangent function instead of the sine function.

(c) A stretch of highway has a 4-foot vertical rise for every 100 feet of horizontal run. Use your approximation to estimate the grade resistance for a 3000-pound car.

(d) Compare your result to the exact answer using $F = W \sin\theta$.
(*Source:* F. Mannering and W. Kilareski, *Principles of Highway Engineering and Traffic Analysis.*)

3. Average Temperature The maximum monthly average temperature in Buenos Aires, Argentina, is 74°F and the minimum monthly average temperature is 49°F.
(a) Using these two temperatures and the fact that the highest monthly average temperature occurs in January, find values for a, b, c, and d so that

$$f(x) = a \cos(b(x - c)) + d$$

models the monthly average temperature.

(b) On the same coordinate axes, graph f for a 2-year period together with the actual data values found in the table. Are your results as good as you expected? Explain.

(c) Buenos Aires is located in the Southern Hemisphere. Discuss the effect that this has on the graph of f compared to a city in the Northern Hemisphere.

Month	1	2	3	4	5	6
Temperature (°F)	74	73	69	61	55	50

Month	7	8	9	10	11	12
Temperature (°F)	49	51	55	60	66	71

Source: A. Miller and J. Thompson, *Elements of Meteorology.*

1. Write 125,000 in scientific notation and 4.67×10^{-3} in standard notation.

2. Find the midpoint of the line segment connecting the points $(-3, 2)$ and $(-1, 6)$.

3. Graph $y = g(x)$ by hand.
   (a) $g(x) = 2^x$ **(b)** $g(x) = |x + 2|$

   (c) $g(x) = \dfrac{1}{x + 1}$ **(d)** $g(x) = \sqrt{x - 2}$

Exercises 4 and 5: Complete the following.
   (a) Determine the domain of f.
   (b) Evaluate f(−1) and f(2a).

4. $f(x) = \sqrt{4 - x}$ 5. $f(x) = \dfrac{x - 2}{4x^2 - 16}$

6. The graph of a linear function f is shown.
   (a) Identify the slope, y-intercept, and x-intercept.

   (b) Write a formula for $f(x)$.

   (c) Evaluate $f(-2)$ symbolically and graphically.

   (d) Find any zeros of f.

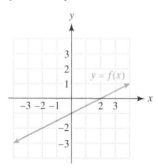

7. Find the average rate of change of $f(x) = 10^x$ from $x = 1$ to $x = 2$.

8. Find the difference quotient for $f(x) = 3x^2$.

9. Write the slope-intercept form of a line that passes through $(2, -3)$ and is parallel to the line $2x + 3y = 6$.

10. Determine the x- and y-intercepts on the graph of the equation $-2x + 5y = 20$.

11. *Solve each equation.*
    (a) $|4 - 5x| = 8$ **(b)** $2e^x - 1 = 27$

    (c) $x^3 - 3x^2 + 2x = 0$ **(d)** $\sqrt{2x - 1} = x - 2$

    (e) $x^2 - x - 2 = 0$ **(f)** $\log_2(x + 1) = 16$

12. Graph f. Is f continuous on its domain? Evaluate $f(1)$.

$$f(x) = \begin{cases} 1 - x & \text{if} \quad -4 \le x \le -1 \\ -2x & \text{if} \quad -1 < x < 2 \\ \frac{1}{2}x^2 & \text{if} \quad 2 \le x \le 4 \end{cases}$$

13. Solve the inequality. Write the solution set in interval notation.
    (a) $-3(2 - x) < 4 - (2x + 1)$

    (b) $-3 \le 4 - 3x < 6$ **(c)** $|4x - 3| \ge 9$

    (d) $x^2 - 5x + 4 \le 0$ **(e)** $t^3 - t > 0$

14. Write $f(x) = -2x^2 + 6x - 1$ in the vertex form given by $f(x) = a(x - h)^2 + k$.

15. Solve $2x^2 + 4x = 1$ by completing the square.

16. Use the given graph of $y = f(x)$ to sketch a graph of each expression.
    (a) $y = f(x - 1) + 2$ **(b)** $y = \frac{1}{2}f(x)$

    (c) $y = -f(-x)$ **(d)** $y = f(2x)$

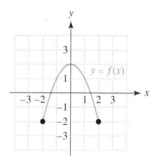

17. Use the graph of f to estimate each of the following.
    (a) Where f is increasing or decreasing

    (b) The zeros of f

    (c) The coordinates of any turning points

    (d) Any local extrema

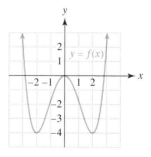

18. Write the complete factored form for the polynomial given by $f(x) = 2x^3 + x^2 - 8x - 4$.

19. Divide each expression.

(a) $\dfrac{5a^4 - 2a^2 + 4}{2a^2}$ (b) $\dfrac{x^3 - 3x^2 + x + 1}{x^2 + 1}$

20. Find all zeros, real or imaginary, of

$$f(x) = x^3 - x^2 + 4x - 4,$$

given that one zero is $2i$.

21. State the domain of $f(x) = \frac{2x + 5}{3x - 7}$. Find any vertical or horizontal asymptotes.

22. Write $x^{2/3}$ in radical notation. Evaluate the expression for $x = 27$.

23. Use the tables to evaluate each expression, if possible.

x	0	1	2	3	4
$f(x)$	4	3	2	1	0

x	0	1	2	3	4
$g(x)$	0	4	3	2	1

(a) $(f + g)(2)$ (b) $(g/f)(4)$

(c) $(f \circ g)(3)$ (d) $(f^{-1} \circ g)(1)$

24. Use the graphs of f and g to complete the following.

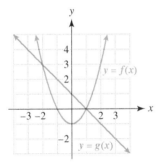

(a) $(f - g)(-1)$ (b) $(fg)(2)$

(c) $(g \circ f)(0)$ (d) $(g^{-1} \circ f)(2)$

25. Let $f(x) = x^2 + 3x - 2$ and $g(x) = x - 2$. Find the following.

(a) $(f + g)(2)$ (b) $(g \circ f)(1)$

(c) $(f - g)(x)$ (d) $(f \circ g)(x)$

26. Find $f^{-1}(x)$ if $f(x) = 2\sqrt[3]{x + 1}$.

27. Use the graph of $y = Ca^x$ to determine values for C and a.

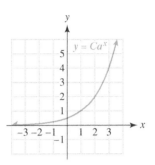

28. Five hundred dollars is deposited in an account that pays 5% annual interest compounded monthly. Find the amount in the account after 10 years.

29. Simplify each logarithm by hand.

(a) $\log 100$ (b) $\log_2 16$

(c) $\ln \dfrac{1}{e^2}$ (d) $\log 4 + \log 25$

30. Write $3 \log x - 4 \log y + \frac{1}{2} \log z$ as a logarithm of a single expression.

31. Approximate $\log_3 125$ to three decimal places.

32. Solve each equation.

(a) $3(2)^{-2x} + 4 = 100$

(b) $2 \log_3 3x = 4$

33. Convert $150°$ to radians.

34. Convert $\frac{5\pi}{4}$ radians to degrees.

35. Find the length of the arc intercepted by a central angle of $15°$ in a circle with a radius of 3 feet.

36. Find the six trigonometric functions of θ.

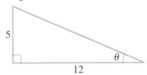

37. Find the length of a in the figure.

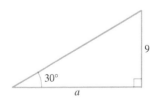

38. Approximate $\sec(1.24)$ to the nearest hundredth.

39. Find the six trigonometric functions of θ.

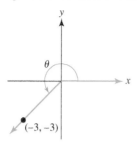

40. Find the exact values of the six trigonometric functions of $\theta = \frac{7\pi}{6}$.

41. Find the exact values of the six trigonometric functions of θ if $\cos\theta = \frac{5}{13}$ and $\sin\theta < 0$.

42. State the amplitude, period, phase shift, and vertical shift for the graph of $f(x) = 5\sin\left(\frac{\pi}{2}(x-1)\right) - 2$.

43. Sketch a graph of f on the interval $[-2\pi, 2\pi]$.
(a) $f(x) = 2\sin 3x$

(b) $f(x) = \sec x$

(c) $f(x) = -2\cos\left(2x + \frac{\pi}{2}\right) + 1$

44. Evaluate $\sin^{-1}\left(-\frac{1}{2}\right)$.

45. Solve the right triangle.

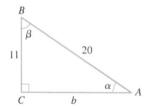

46. Solve $2\cos\theta = -1$ if $0 \le \theta \le 180°$.

Applications

47. Inverse Variation The force of gravity F varies inversely with the square of the distance d from the *center* of Earth. If a person weighs 150 pounds on the surface of Earth ($d = 4000$ miles), how much would this person weigh at a distance of 10,000 miles from the center of Earth?

48. Working Together Suppose one person can mow a large lawn in 4 hours and another person can mow the same lawn in 6 hours. How long will it take to mow the lawn if they work together?

49. Inverse Function The function given by the formula $f(x) = \frac{5}{9}(x - 32)$ converts degrees Fahrenheit to degrees Celsius.
(a) Find $f^{-1}(x)$.

(b) What does f^{-1} compute?

50. Volume of a Balloon The radius r in inches of a spherical balloon after t seconds is given by $r = \sqrt{t}$.
(a) Is the radius increasing or decreasing?

(b) Write a formula for a function V that calculates the volume of the sphere after t seconds.

(c) Evaluate $V(4)$ and interpret the result.

51. Bacteria Growth There are initially 200,000 bacteria per milliliter in a sample. The number of bacteria grows exponentially and reaches 300,000 per milliliter after 3 hours.
(a) Use the formula $N(t) = N_0 e^{kt}$ to model the concentration of bacteria after t hours.

(b) Evaluate $N(5)$ and interpret the result.

(c) After how long did the concentration reach 500,000 per milliliter?

52. Length of a Shadow If the angle of elevation of the sun is 43°, find the length of the shadow cast by a person who is 6 feet tall. Round your answer to the nearest tenth of a foot.

53. Modeling Temperature The monthly average high temperatures in New Orleans are shown in the table. Model these data by using a function of the form

$$f(x) = a\sin(b(x - c)) + d.$$

Month	1	2	3	4	5	6
Temperature (°F)	61	65	70	78	85	89

Month	7	8	9	10	11	12
Temperature (°F)	90	89	88	80	70	63

Source: J. Williams, *The Weather Almanac.*

54. Angle of Elevation A 52-foot building cast a 63-foot shadow. Estimate the angle of elevation of the sun to the nearest tenth of a degree.

7 Trigonometric Identities and Equations

Music is the pleasure the human mind experiences from counting without being aware that it is counting.
—Gottfried Leibniz

Music is both art and science. Although Pythagoras is usually associated with the Pythagorean theorem, in 500 B.C. he also discovered the mathematical ratios that governed pitch and motion. These discoveries marked the beginning of the science of musical sound. In 1862, the psychologist and scientist Hermann von Helmholtz published his classic work that opened a new direction for music using mathematics and technology. Then in 1957, Max Mathews created complex musical sounds with a computer. Mathematics has been essential in the development and reproduction of music.

The communications industry also uses the mathematics of sound. For example, each number on a touch-tone phone has a unique sound that is a combination of two different tones. These unique tones are easily distinguished when transmitted as cellular phone signals. Trigonometric functions play an important role in clear, reliable communication systems.

This chapter introduces the concept of verifying an identity. Identities are important because they allow us to write trigonometric expressions in simpler and more convenient forms.

Source: J. Pierce, *The Science of Musical Sound.*

7.1 Fundamental Identities

- Learn and apply the reciprocal and quotient identities
- Learn and apply the Pythagorean identities
- Learn and apply the negative-angle identities

Introduction

Trigonometric expressions can often be written in more than one way. For example, in Section 6.4 we discussed that $\cot \theta$ is equivalent to $\frac{\cos \theta}{\sin \theta}$. The equation

$$\cot \theta = \frac{\cos \theta}{\sin \theta} \qquad \textit{Trigonometric identity}$$

is a *trigonometric identity*. This identity is true for every value of θ, provided $\sin \theta \neq 0$. Trigonometric identities are used to help solve equations and model physical phenomena such as light intensity and temperature variations. (See Example 11 and Exercises 85 and 89.) They are also used in calculus. We begin our discussion with the reciprocal and quotient identities.

Reciprocal and Quotient Identities

In Section 6.4, the following definitions were presented for the trigonometric functions of any angle θ. See Figure 7.1.

Visualizing Trigonometric Functions

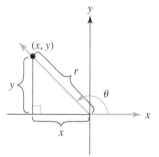

Figure 7.1

TRIGONOMETRIC FUNCTIONS OF ANY ANGLE θ

Let (x, y) be a point other than the origin on the terminal side of an angle θ in standard position. If $r = \sqrt{x^2 + y^2}$, then the six trigonometric functions are as follows.

$$\sin \theta = \frac{y}{r} \qquad\qquad \csc \theta = \frac{r}{y} \, (y \neq 0)$$

$$\cos \theta = \frac{x}{r} \qquad\qquad \sec \theta = \frac{r}{x} \, (x \neq 0)$$

$$\tan \theta = \frac{y}{x} \, (x \neq 0) \qquad \cot \theta = \frac{x}{y} \, (y \neq 0)$$

NOTE The definitions of trigonometric functions of angle θ are valid whether angle θ is measured in radians or degrees.

These definitions allow us to write several identities. For example,

$$\cos \theta = \frac{x}{r} = \frac{1}{r/x} = \frac{1}{\sec \theta} \quad \text{and} \quad \sec \theta = \frac{r}{x} = \frac{1}{x/r} = \frac{1}{\cos \theta}.$$

These identities are examples of *reciprocal identities*. Each of the six trigonometric functions can be written as the reciprocal of another trigonometric function.

RECIPROCAL IDENTITIES

$$\sin \theta = \frac{1}{\csc \theta} \qquad \cos \theta = \frac{1}{\sec \theta} \qquad \tan \theta = \frac{1}{\cot \theta}$$

$$\csc \theta = \frac{1}{\sin \theta} \qquad \sec \theta = \frac{1}{\cos \theta} \qquad \cot \theta = \frac{1}{\tan \theta}$$

In the next example, we use reciprocal identities to write a trigonometric expression in a more simplified form.

EXAMPLE 1 Applying reciprocal identities

Use reciprocal identities to rewrite

$$\frac{1}{\csc^2\theta} + \frac{1}{\sec^2\theta}$$

in terms of $\sin\theta$ and $\cos\theta$ and then simplify if possible.

SOLUTION

Getting Started First note that $\csc^2\theta = (\csc\theta)^2$ and $\sec^2\theta = (\sec\theta)^2$. The reciprocal identities $\sin\theta = \frac{1}{\csc\theta}$ and $\cos\theta = \frac{1}{\sec\theta}$ can be used to rewrite the given identity as follows. ▶

$$\frac{1}{\csc^2\theta} + \frac{1}{\sec^2\theta} = \left(\frac{1}{\csc\theta}\right)^2 + \left(\frac{1}{\sec\theta}\right)^2 \qquad \text{Rewrite: } \frac{1}{x^2} = \left(\frac{1}{x}\right)^2.$$

$$= (\sin\theta)^2 + (\cos\theta)^2 \qquad \text{Reciprocal identities}$$

$$= \sin^2\theta + \cos^2\theta \qquad \text{Rewrite.}$$

$$= 1 \qquad \text{Identity}$$

(The identity $\sin^2\theta + \cos^2\theta = 1$ was introduced in Section 6.3. We discuss this identity in more depth later in this section.)

Now Try Exercise 13

NOTE When writing the square of $\sin\theta$, it is common to write $\sin^2\theta$ instead of $(\sin\theta)^2$. This is also true for the other trigonometric functions.

By using reciprocal identities it is possible to write $\csc\theta$ and $\sec\theta$ in terms of $\sin\theta$ and $\cos\theta$, respectively. It is also possible to write the other two trigonometric functions, $\tan\theta$ and $\cot\theta$, in terms of $\sin\theta$ and $\cos\theta$.

$$\tan\theta = \frac{y}{x} = \frac{y/r}{x/r} = \frac{\sin\theta}{\cos\theta} \qquad \text{and} \qquad \cot\theta = \frac{x}{y} = \frac{x/r}{y/r} = \frac{\cos\theta}{\sin\theta}$$

These identities are called the *quotient identities*.

QUOTIENT IDENTITIES

$$\tan\theta = \frac{\sin\theta}{\cos\theta} \qquad \cot\theta = \frac{\cos\theta}{\sin\theta}$$

NOTE The reciprocal and quotient identities are valid not only for angles but also for any real number t. For example, $\tan t = \frac{\sin t}{\cos t}$ for all real numbers t such that $\cos t \neq 0$.

Evaluating Trigonometric Functions If $\sin\theta$ and $\cos\theta$ are known, the reciprocal and quotient identities can be used to find the other four trigonometric functions of θ, as illustrated in the next example.

EXAMPLE 2 Using reciprocal and quotient identities

If $\sin\theta = \frac{7}{25}$ and $\cos\theta = -\frac{24}{25}$, find the other four trigonometric functions of θ.

SOLUTION We can use identities to find $\tan\theta$, $\cot\theta$, $\sec\theta$, and $\csc\theta$.

$$\tan\theta = \frac{\sin\theta}{\cos\theta} = \frac{7/25}{-24/25} = -\frac{7}{24}, \qquad \cot\theta = \frac{\cos\theta}{\sin\theta} = \frac{-24/25}{7/25} = -\frac{24}{7},$$

$$\sec\theta = \frac{1}{\cos\theta} = \frac{1}{-24/25} = -\frac{25}{24}, \qquad \text{and} \qquad \csc\theta = \frac{1}{\sin\theta} = \frac{1}{7/25} = \frac{25}{7}$$

Now Try Exercise 15

NOTE If the value of a trigonometric function of θ is 0, the reciprocal and quotient identities will reveal that two of the remaining five trigonometric functions are undefined at θ. For example, if $\sin \theta = 0$ then both $\csc \theta = \frac{1}{\sin \theta}$ and $\cot \theta = \frac{\cos \theta}{\sin \theta}$ are undefined.

EXAMPLE 3 Using identities to find trigonometric values

If $\tan \theta = -\frac{8}{15}$ and $\cos \theta = -\frac{15}{17}$, find the other four trigonometric functions of θ.

SOLUTION Using the reciprocal identities, we can find $\cot \theta$ and $\sec \theta$.

$$\cot \theta = \frac{1}{\tan \theta} = \frac{1}{-8/15} = -\frac{15}{8} \quad \text{and} \quad \sec \theta = \frac{1}{\cos \theta} = \frac{1}{-15/17} = -\frac{17}{15}$$

To find $\sin \theta$, consider the following.

$$\tan \theta \cos \theta = \frac{\sin \theta}{\cos \theta} \cdot \cos \theta = \sin \theta$$

Thus

$$\sin \theta = \tan \theta \cos \theta = \left(-\frac{8}{15}\right)\left(-\frac{15}{17}\right) = \frac{8}{17}$$

and, using a reciprocal identity, we find

$$\csc \theta = \frac{1}{\sin \theta} = \frac{1}{8/17} = \frac{17}{8}.$$

Now Try Exercise 17

Pythagorean Identities

In Section 6.3, the unit circle (shown in Figure 7.2) was used to define the sine and cosine functions.

$$\sin \theta = y \quad \text{and} \quad \cos \theta = x$$

An equation for the unit circle is given by $x^2 + y^2 = 1$. By substitution, it follows that

$$(\cos \theta)^2 + (\sin \theta)^2 = 1,$$

or equivalently, $\cos^2 \theta + \sin^2 \theta = 1$. This identity can be supported graphically and numerically by letting

$$Y_1 = (\cos (X))^{\wedge}2 + (\sin (X))^{\wedge}2,$$

as shown in Figures 7.3 and 7.4. The graph of Y_1 is the horizontal line $y = 1$. Either radian or degree mode may be used. Notice that regardless of the value of x, $Y_1 = 1$.

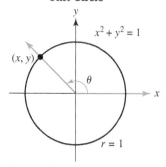

Unit Circle

$x^2 + y^2 = 1$

(x, y)

θ

$r = 1$

Figure 7.2

$[-352.5, 352.5, 90]$ by $[-2, 2, 1]$

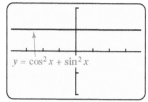

$y = \cos^2 x + \sin^2 x$

Figure 7.3 Degree Mode

X	Y₁	
0	1	
30	1	
60	1	
90	1	
120	1	
150	1	
180	1	
X=0		

Figure 7.4 Degree Mode

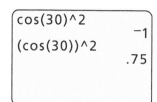

```
cos(30)^2
                    -1
(cos(30))^2
                  .75
```

Figure 7.5 Degree Mode

NOTE On some older graphing calculators, $\cos^2 x$ must be entered as $(\cos (X))^{\wedge}2$, rather than $\cos (X)^{\wedge}2$, since $\cos (X)^{\wedge}2$, may be interpreted as $\cos (x^2)$. See Figure 7.5.

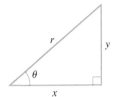

Figure 7.6

CLASS DISCUSSION

Use the triangle in Figure 7.6 to justify the Pythagorean identity

$$1 + \tan^2 \theta = \sec^2 \theta.$$

Deriving the Pythagorean Identities Using the right triangle shown in Figure 7.6, we also can derive the Pythagorean identity $\cos^2 \theta + \sin^2 \theta = 1$ geometrically when θ is acute.

$$x^2 + y^2 = r^2 \qquad \text{Pythagorean theorem}$$

$$\frac{x^2}{r^2} + \frac{y^2}{r^2} = \frac{r^2}{r^2} \qquad \text{Divide each side by } r^2.$$

$$\left(\frac{x}{r}\right)^2 + \left(\frac{y}{r}\right)^2 = 1 \qquad \text{Properties of exponents}$$

$$\cos^2 \theta + \sin^2 \theta = 1 \qquad \cos \theta = \tfrac{x}{r}, \sin \theta = \tfrac{y}{r}$$

For this reason, $\sin^2 \theta + \cos^2 \theta = 1$ is an example of a Pythagorean identity. Another Pythagorean identity can be derived as follows.

$$\sin^2 \theta + \cos^2 \theta = 1$$

$$\frac{\sin^2 \theta}{\cos^2 \theta} + \frac{\cos^2 \theta}{\cos^2 \theta} = \frac{1}{\cos^2 \theta} \qquad \text{Divide each side by } \cos^2 \theta.$$

$$\tan^2 \theta + 1 = \sec^2 \theta \qquad \tan \theta = \tfrac{\sin \theta}{\cos \theta}, \sec \theta = \tfrac{1}{\cos \theta}$$

In a similar manner, a third Pythagorean identity can be found.

$$\sin^2 \theta + \cos^2 \theta = 1$$

$$\frac{\sin^2 \theta}{\sin^2 \theta} + \frac{\cos^2 \theta}{\sin^2 \theta} = \frac{1}{\sin^2 \theta} \qquad \text{Divide each side by } \sin^2 \theta.$$

$$1 + \cot^2 \theta = \csc^2 \theta \qquad \cot \theta = \tfrac{\cos \theta}{\sin \theta}, \csc \theta = \tfrac{1}{\sin \theta}$$

This discussion is summarized in the following box.

PYTHAGOREAN IDENTITIES

$$\sin^2 \theta + \cos^2 \theta = 1 \qquad 1 + \tan^2 \theta = \sec^2 \theta \qquad 1 + \cot^2 \theta = \csc^2 \theta$$

In the next example, we use a reciprocal, quotient, and Pythagorean identity to simplify a trigonometric expression.

EXAMPLE 4 Applying identities to an expression

Simplify the expression $1 + \sin^2 \theta \sec^2 \theta$.

SOLUTION Begin by applying a reciprocal identity.

$$1 + \sin^2 \theta \sec^2 \theta = 1 + \sin^2 \theta \cdot \frac{1}{\cos^2 \theta} \qquad \text{Reciprocal identity: } \sec \theta = \tfrac{1}{\cos \theta}$$

$$= 1 + \frac{\sin^2 \theta}{\cos^2 \theta} \qquad \text{Multiply.}$$

$$= 1 + \left(\frac{\sin \theta}{\cos \theta}\right)^2 \qquad \text{Properties of exponents}$$

$$= 1 + \tan^2 \theta \qquad \text{Quotient identity}$$

$$= \sec^2 \theta \qquad \text{Pythagorean identity: } 1 + \tan^2 \theta = \sec^2 \theta$$

Now Try Exercise 35

An Application The next example illustrates the use of identities in electronics.

EXAMPLE 5 Applying a Pythagorean identity to radios

Inductor L, Capacitor C

Figure 7.7

Tuners in radios select a radio station by adjusting the frequency. These tuners may contain an inductor L and a capacitor C, as illustrated in Figure 7.7. The energy stored in the inductor at time t is given by $L(t) = k \sin^2(2\pi Ft)$, and the energy stored in the capacitor is given by $C(t) = k \cos^2(2\pi Ft)$, where F is the frequency of the radio station and k is a constant. The total energy E in the circuit is given by $E(t) = L(t) + C(t)$. Show that E is a constant function. (*Source:* R. Weidner and R. Sells, *Elementary Classical Physics,* Vol. 2.)

SOLUTION

$$
\begin{aligned}
E(t) &= L(t) + C(t) && \text{Given equation} \\
&= k \sin^2(2\pi Ft) + k \cos^2(2\pi Ft) && \text{Substitute.} \\
&= k\left(\sin^2(2\pi Ft) + \cos^2(2\pi Ft)\right) && \text{Factor out } k. \\
&= k(1) && \sin^2\theta + \cos^2\theta = 1 \, (\theta = 2\pi Ft) \\
&= k && k \text{ is constant.}
\end{aligned}
$$

Now Try Exercise 87

Angle θ in Quadrant II

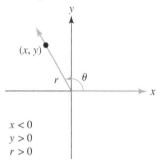

$x < 0$
$y > 0$
$r > 0$

Figure 7.8

Quadrants and Signs of Trigonometric Functions If an angle θ is in standard position and its terminal side lies in quadrant II, as shown in Figure 7.8, then we say that θ is *contained in quadrant II*, or θ is a *second quadrant angle*. Similar statements can be made for angles whose terminal sides lie in other quadrants.

If an angle θ is contained in a particular quadrant, then any point (x, y) on the terminal side of θ with $r = \sqrt{x^2 + y^2} > 0$ also lies in that quadrant. For example, the point (x, y) on the terminal side of angle θ in Figure 7.8 lies in quadrant II because θ is a second quadrant angle.

Since each of the six trigonometric functions can be defined in terms of x, y, and r, with $r > 0$, we can determine whether a trigonometric function of θ is positive or negative by simply considering the quadrant containing θ. For example, for angle θ in Figure 7.8, $\sin\theta = \frac{y}{r}$ is positive because both y and r are positive in quadrant II. Similarly, $\tan\theta = \frac{y}{x}$ is negative because x is negative and y is positive in quadrant II.

Figure 7.9 in the following See the Concept shows whether trigonometric functions of θ are positive or negative as determined by the quadrant containing θ.

See the Concept: Trigonometric Functions by Quadrant

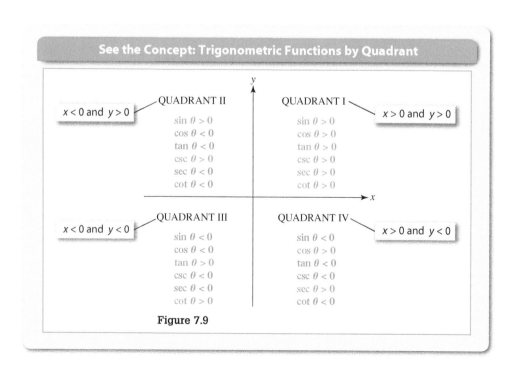

Figure 7.9

EXAMPLE 6   Finding the quadrant containing an angle

If $\sin\theta > 0$ and $\cos\theta < 0$, find the quadrant that contains θ. Support your results graphically and numerically.

SOLUTION   If $\sin\theta > 0$ and $\cos\theta < 0$, then any point (x, y) on the terminal side of θ must satisfy $y > 0$ and $x < 0$. Thus θ is contained in quadrant II.

Graphical Support   The graphs of $Y_1 = \sin(X)$ and $Y_2 = \cos(X)$ are shown in Figure 7.10. Notice that when $\theta = 135°$ (a second quadrant angle), the graph of $\sin\theta$ is above the x-axis and the graph of $\cos\theta$ is below the x-axis.

Numerical Support   In Figure 7.11, angles in quadrant II have positive sine values listed under Y_1 and negative cosine values listed under Y_2.

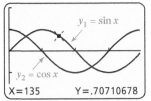

$[0, 352.5, 90]$ by $[-2, 2, 1]$

Figure 7.10 Degree Mode

Second Quadrant Angles

X	Y1	Y2
90	1	0
105	.96593	-.2588
120	.86603	-.5
135	.70711	-.7071
150	.5	-.866
165	.25882	-.9659
180	0	-1

X=90

Figure 7.11 Degree Mode

Now Try Exercise 49

Evaluating Trigonometric Functions   If a trigonometric function of θ is known and the quadrant containing θ is also known, then we can find the other five trigonometric functions of θ, as illustrated in the next example.

EXAMPLE 7   Using identities to find trigonometric values

If $\sin\theta = -\frac{3}{5}$ and θ is a third quadrant angle, find the values of the other trigonometric functions.

SOLUTION

Getting Started   If we can find $\cos\theta$, then we can determine the other four trigonometric functions by using reciprocal and quotient identities. To determine $\cos\theta$, we can use the identity $\sin^2\theta + \cos^2\theta = 1$ and the fact that θ is a third quadrant angle. ▶

$$\sin^2\theta + \cos^2\theta = 1 \qquad \text{Pythagorean identity}$$
$$\cos^2\theta = 1 - \sin^2\theta \qquad \text{Subtract } \sin^2\theta.$$
$$\cos\theta = \pm\sqrt{1 - \sin^2\theta} \qquad \text{Square root property}$$
$$\cos\theta = \pm\sqrt{1 - (-3/5)^2} \qquad \text{Substitute for } \sin\theta.$$
$$\cos\theta = \pm\frac{4}{5} \qquad \text{Simplify.}$$

In quadrant III, $x < 0$, and so $\cos\theta = -\frac{4}{5}$. The other four trigonometric functions of θ can be found by letting $\sin\theta = -\frac{3}{5}$ and $\cos\theta = -\frac{4}{5}$ and applying identities.

$$\tan\theta = \frac{\sin\theta}{\cos\theta} = \frac{-3/5}{-4/5} = \frac{3}{4}, \qquad\qquad \cot\theta = \frac{\cos\theta}{\sin\theta} = \frac{-4/5}{-3/5} = \frac{4}{3},$$

$$\sec\theta = \frac{1}{\cos\theta} = \frac{1}{-4/5} = -\frac{5}{4}, \qquad \text{and} \qquad \csc\theta = \frac{1}{\sin\theta} = \frac{1}{-3/5} = -\frac{5}{3}.$$

Now Try Exercise 63

EXAMPLE 8 Using identities to find trigonometric values

If $\tan\theta = -\frac{7}{3}$ and $\sin\theta > 0$, find the values of the other trigonometric functions.

SOLUTION Since $\tan\theta = -\frac{7}{3}$, it follows that $\cot\theta = -\frac{3}{7}$. Next we find $\sec\theta$.

$$\sec^2\theta = 1 + \tan^2\theta \qquad \textit{Pythagorean identity}$$
$$\sec\theta = \pm\sqrt{1 + \tan^2\theta} \qquad \textit{Square root property}$$
$$= \pm\sqrt{1 + (-7/3)^2} \qquad \textit{Substitute for } \tan\theta.$$
$$= \pm\frac{\sqrt{58}}{3} \qquad \textit{Simplify.}$$

Since $\tan\theta < 0$ and $\sin\theta > 0$, θ is a second quadrant angle. It follows that

$$\sec\theta = -\frac{\sqrt{58}}{3} \quad \text{and} \quad \cos\theta = -\frac{3}{\sqrt{58}}.$$

Multiplying both sides of the identity $\tan\theta = \frac{\sin\theta}{\cos\theta}$ by $\cos\theta$ gives $\sin\theta = \tan\theta\cos\theta$. Thus

$$\sin\theta = \left(-\frac{7}{3}\right)\left(-\frac{3}{\sqrt{58}}\right) = \frac{7}{\sqrt{58}} \quad \text{and} \quad \csc\theta = \frac{1}{\sin\theta} = \frac{\sqrt{58}}{7}.$$

Now Try Exercise 57

We can also express any trigonometric function in terms of any other trigonometric function. This fact is demonstrated in the next example.

EXAMPLE 9 Expressing one function in terms of another

Write $\cos x$ and $\cot x$ in terms of $\sin x$, if $\sec x < 0$.

SOLUTION We can write $\cos x$ in terms of $\sin x$ by applying a Pythagorean identity. Note that $\sec x < 0$ implies that $\cos x < 0$ because $\cos x = \frac{1}{\sec x}$ by a reciprocal identity.

$$\sin^2 x + \cos^2 x = 1 \qquad \textit{Pythagorean identity}$$
$$\cos^2 x = 1 - \sin^2 x \qquad \textit{Subtract } \sin^2 x.$$
$$\cos x = \pm\sqrt{1 - \sin^2 x} \qquad \textit{Square root property}$$

Because $\cos x < 0$, we let $\cos x = -\sqrt{1 - \sin^2 x}$. Now we can write $\cot x$ in terms of $\sin x$ by using a quotient identity.

$$\cot x = \frac{\cos x}{\sin x} \qquad \textit{Quotient identity}$$
$$= -\frac{\sqrt{1 - \sin^2 x}}{\sin x} \qquad \textit{Substitute for } \cos x.$$

Now Try Exercise 67

EXAMPLE 10 Using identities to find trigonometric expressions

If $\sin\theta = x$ and θ is a fourth quadrant angle, find an expression for $\sec\theta$ in terms of x. Approximate $\sec\theta$ if $\sin\theta = -0.7813$.

SOLUTION We begin by writing $\sec\theta$ in terms of $\sin\theta$.

$$\sin^2\theta + \cos^2\theta = 1 \qquad \textit{Pythagorean identity}$$
$$\cos^2\theta = 1 - \sin^2\theta \qquad \textit{Subtract } \sin^2\theta.$$
$$\cos\theta = \pm\sqrt{1 - \sin^2\theta} \qquad \textit{Square root property}$$
$$\sec\theta = \pm\frac{1}{\sqrt{1 - \sin^2\theta}} \qquad \textit{sec }\theta = \frac{1}{\cos\theta}$$

Since $\sin\theta = x$ and angle θ is in quadrant IV, where $\sec\theta > 0$,

$$\sec\theta = \frac{1}{\sqrt{1-x^2}}. \qquad \sin\theta = x;\ \sec\theta > 0$$

Since $\sin\theta = x$, let $x = -0.7813$. Then

$$\sec\theta = \frac{1}{\sqrt{1-(-0.7813)^2}} \approx 1.602.$$

Now Try Exercise 73

Negative-Angle Identities

In Section 4.1, we discussed odd and even functions. The graphs of odd functions are symmetric with respect to the origin, and the graphs of even functions are symmetric with respect to the y-axis. The graphs of all six trigonometric functions have symmetry, as shown in Figures 7.12–7.17.

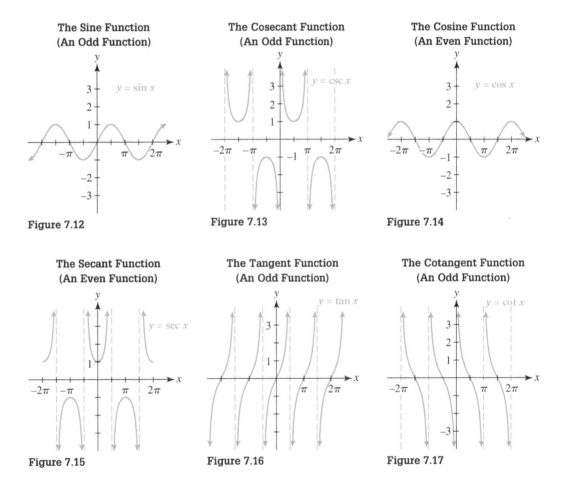

The Sine Function (An Odd Function)

Figure 7.12

The Cosecant Function (An Odd Function)

Figure 7.13

The Cosine Function (An Even Function)

Figure 7.14

The Secant Function (An Even Function)

Figure 7.15

The Tangent Function (An Odd Function)

Figure 7.16

The Cotangent Function (An Odd Function)

Figure 7.17

The cosine and secant functions are even functions, and the other four trigonometric functions are odd functions. For even functions the sign of the input does not affect the output, whereas for odd functions changing the sign of the input changes the sign of the output. That is, for all x in the domain of an even function f or an odd function g,

Even Function		Odd Function
$f(-x) = f(x)$	and	$g(-x) = -g(x)$.

These results can be expressed using the negative-angle identities.

NEGATIVE-ANGLE IDENTITIES

$$\sin(-\theta) = -\sin\theta \qquad \cos(-\theta) = \cos\theta \qquad \tan(-\theta) = -\tan\theta$$

$$\csc(-\theta) = -\csc\theta \qquad \sec(-\theta) = \sec\theta \qquad \cot(-\theta) = -\cot\theta$$

Negative-angle identities are often used to simplify expressions. For example, the expression $\cos(-x) + \sin(-x)$ can be simplified to $\cos x - \sin x$.

An Application In the next example, we see how the symmetry of a trigonometric function can be used to model temperature.

EXAMPLE 11 Modeling Temperature

The monthly average high temperatures in degrees Fahrenheit at Chattanooga, Tennessee, can be modeled by

$$f(x) = 21\cos\left(\frac{\pi x}{6}\right) + 70,$$

where x is the month with $x = -6$ corresponding to January, $x = 0$ to July, and $x = 5$ to December. (**Source:** J. Williams, *The Weather Almanac.*)

(a) Graph f in $[-6, 6, 1]$ by $[40, 100, 10]$. Interpret any symmetry in the graph.

(b) Make a table of f and discuss whether f is an even or odd function.

(c) Express any symmetry symbolically.

SOLUTION

(a) Graph $Y_1 = 21\cos(\pi X/6) + 70$, as shown in Figure 7.18 using radian mode. The graph is symmetric with respect to the y-axis. This type of symmetry implies that the monthly average high temperatures x months before July and x months after July are equal. For example, April ($x = -3$), which is 3 months before July, and October ($x = 3$), which is 3 months after July, have the same average high temperature of 70°.

(b) A table of Y_1 is shown in Figure 7.19. Notice that f is an even function since the sign of the input does not affect the output.

(c) Symbolically, this symmetry can be expressed as $f(-x) = f(x)$.

Now Try Exercise 89

$[-6, 6, 1]$ by $[40, 100, 10]$

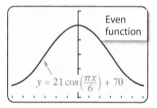

$y = 21\cos\left(\frac{\pi x}{6}\right) + 70$

Even function

Figure 7.18 Radian Mode

X	Y1
-3	70
-2	80.5
-1	88.187
0	91
1	88.187
2	80.5
3	70

X=0

Even function

Figure 7.19 Radian Mode

7.1 Putting It All Together

This section discussed the reciprocal identities, the quotient identities, the Pythagorean identities, and the negative-angle identities. Collectively, they are called fundamental identities.

IDENTITY	GENERAL FORM		
Reciprocal	$\sin\theta = \dfrac{1}{\csc\theta}$	$\cos\theta = \dfrac{1}{\sec\theta}$	$\tan\theta = \dfrac{1}{\cot\theta}$
	$\csc\theta = \dfrac{1}{\sin\theta}$	$\sec\theta = \dfrac{1}{\cos\theta}$	$\cot\theta = \dfrac{1}{\tan\theta}$
Quotient	$\tan\theta = \dfrac{\sin\theta}{\cos\theta}$	$\cot\theta = \dfrac{\cos\theta}{\sin\theta}$	

IDENTITY	GENERAL FORM		
Pythagorean	$\sin^2\theta + \cos^2\theta = 1$	$1 + \tan^2\theta = \sec^2\theta$	$1 + \cot^2\theta = \csc^2\theta$
Negative-angle	$\sin(-\theta) = -\sin\theta$ $\csc(-\theta) = -\csc\theta$	$\cos(-\theta) = \cos\theta$ $\sec(-\theta) = \sec\theta$	$\tan(-\theta) = -\tan\theta$ $\cot(-\theta) = -\cot\theta$

7.1 Exercises

Reciprocal Identities

Exercises 1–8: If possible, use a reciprocal identity to find the indicated trigonometric function of θ.

1. $\cot\theta$ if $\tan\theta = \frac{1}{2}$

2. $\csc\theta$ if $\sin\theta = -\frac{5}{6}$

3. $\sec\theta$ if $\cos\theta = \frac{2}{7}$

4. $\tan\theta$ if $\cot\theta = -\frac{3}{7}$

5. $\cos\theta$ if $\sec\theta = -4$

6. $\sin\theta$ if $\csc\theta = 7$

7. $\tan\theta$ if $\cos\theta = 0$

8. $\csc\theta$ if $\tan\theta = 0$

Exercises 9–14: Use reciprocal identities to rewrite the expression in terms of $\sin\theta$ *and* $\cos\theta$.

9. $\dfrac{\tan\theta}{\cot\theta}$

10. $\dfrac{\sec\theta}{\csc\theta}$

11. $\dfrac{\cot^2\theta}{\csc^2\theta}$

12. $\dfrac{\tan^2\theta}{\sec^2\theta}$

13. $\dfrac{1}{\csc\theta} + \dfrac{1}{\sec\theta}$

14. $\csc\theta \sec\theta \tan\theta$

Fundamental Identities

Exercises 15–22: Find the other trigonometric functions of θ.

15. $\sin\theta = \frac{3}{5}$ and $\cos\theta = -\frac{4}{5}$

16. $\tan\theta = -\frac{12}{5}$ and $\cos\theta = \frac{5}{13}$

17. $\cot\theta = \frac{7}{24}$ and $\sin\theta = -\frac{24}{25}$

18. $\sin\theta = \frac{12}{13}$ and $\cos\theta = \frac{5}{13}$

19. $\sin\theta = -\frac{60}{61}$ and $\cos\theta = -\frac{11}{61}$

20. $\sin\theta = \frac{2}{3}$ and $\cos\theta = -\frac{\sqrt{5}}{3}$

21. $\csc\theta = \sqrt{2}$ and $\sec\theta = -\sqrt{2}$

22. $\csc\theta = -\frac{13}{12}$ and $\sec\theta = -\frac{13}{5}$

Exercises 23–44: Simplify each expression.

23. $\sec\theta \cos\theta$

24. $\tan\theta \cot\theta$

25. $\sin\theta \csc\theta$

26. $\tan\theta \cos\theta$

27. $(\sin^2\theta + \cos^2\theta)^3$

28. $(1 + \tan^2\theta)\cos^2\theta$

29. $1 - \sin^2\theta$

30. $1 - \cos^2(-\theta)$

31. $\sec^2\theta - 1$

32. $1 + \dfrac{\cos^2\theta}{\sin^2\theta}$

33. $\dfrac{\sin(-\theta)}{\cos(-\theta)}$

34. $\sin\theta(\csc\theta + \sec\theta)$

35. $\dfrac{\sin^2\theta + \cos^2\theta}{\cos\theta}$

36. $\dfrac{1 + \tan^2\theta}{\sec^2\theta}$

37. $\dfrac{\sec^2(-\theta)}{\csc^2\theta}$

38. $\dfrac{1 - \cos^2\theta}{\sin^2\theta + \cos^2\theta}$

39. $\dfrac{\cot x}{\csc x}$

40. $\dfrac{\tan x}{\sec x}$

41. $(\sin^2 x)(1 + \cot^2 x)$

42. $\dfrac{\cos x}{\sin x \cot x}$

43. $\sec(-x) + \csc(-x)$

44. $-\cos(-x)\sec(-x)$

Exercises 45–48: Determine if the equation represents an identity. If you have a graphing calculator, support your answer by making a table of the left and right sides of the equation.

45. $\sec\theta \cot\theta = \csc\theta$

46. $(\sin\theta + \cos\theta)^2 = 1$

47. $\cot^2\theta - \csc^2\theta = 1$

48. $1 + \tan^2\theta = \dfrac{1}{\cos^2\theta}$

Exercises 49–54: (Refer to Example 6.) Determine the quadrant that contains θ. *If you have a graphing calculator, support your result either graphically or numerically.*

49. $\sin\theta < 0$ and $\cos\theta > 0$

50. $\tan\theta > 0$ and $\cos\theta < 0$

51. $\sec\theta < 0$ and $\sin\theta < 0$

52. $\csc\theta > 0$ and $\tan\theta > 0$

53. $\cot\theta < 0$ and $\sin\theta > 0$

54. $\cos\theta > 0$ and $\cot\theta < 0$

Exercises 55–66: Find the other trigonometric functions of θ.

55. $\cos\theta = \frac{1}{2}$ and $\sin\theta < 0$

56. $\csc\theta = \sqrt{3}$ and $\cos\theta < 0$

57. $\tan\theta = -\frac{11}{60}$ and $\csc\theta < 0$

58. $\sec\theta = -\frac{5}{4}$ and $\sin\theta > 0$

59. $\sin\theta = \frac{7}{25}$ and $\cos\theta > 0$

60. $\cot\theta = \frac{12}{5}$ and $\sec\theta < 0$

61. $\sin\theta = -\frac{1}{3}$ and $\sec\theta < 0$

62. $\tan\theta = -\frac{1}{2}$ and $\sin\theta > 0$

63. $\sec\theta = \frac{37}{12}$ and θ in quadrant IV

64. $\tan\theta = \frac{3}{4}$ and θ in quadrant I

65. $\csc\theta = \frac{7}{3}$ and θ in quadrant II

66. $\cos\theta = -\frac{3}{5}$ and θ in quadrant III

Writing Trigonometric Expressions

67. Write $\sin x$ and $\tan x$ in terms of $\cos x$, if $\csc x > 0$.

68. Write $\cos x$ and $\sec x$ in terms of $\sin x$, if $\cos x < 0$.

69. Write $\sin x$ and $\sec x$ in terms of $\tan x$, if $\cos x < 0$.

70. Write $\cos x$ and $\csc x$ in terms of $\cot x$, if $\sin x > 0$.

71. Write $\cot x$ and $\cos x$ in terms of $\csc x$, if $\cot x < 0$.

72. Write $\tan x$ and $\sin x$ in terms of $\sec x$, if $\tan x > 0$.

Exercises 73–76: (Refer to Example 10.) Write the trigonometric function in terms of x. Then evaluate this trigonometric function if $x = 0.5126$.

73. $\cos\theta$ if $\sin\theta = x$ and θ is acute

74. $\sec\theta$ if $\cos\theta = x$

75. $\sin\theta$ if $\cot\theta = x$ and θ is in quadrant III

76. $\tan\theta$ if $\cos\theta = x$ and θ is in quadrant IV

77. Write $\tan\theta$ in terms of x if $\sin\theta = x$ and θ is acute.

78. Write $\sin\theta$ in terms of x if $\sec\theta = x$ and θ is acute.

Negative-Angle Identities

Exercises 79–84: Use a negative-angle identity to write an equivalent trigonometric expression involving a positive angle.

79. $\sin(-13°)$

80. $\cos\left(-\frac{\pi}{7}\right)$

81. $\tan\left(-\frac{\pi}{11}\right)$

82. $\cot(-75°)$

83. $\sec\left(-\frac{2\pi}{5}\right)$

84. $\csc(-160°)$

Applications

85. Intensity of a Lamp   According to Lambert's law, the intensity of light from a single source on a flat surface at point P is given by $I = k\cos^2\theta$, where k is a constant. See the figure.   (**Source:** C. Winter, *Solar Power Plants.*)

(a) Let $k = 1$ and use degree mode to graph I in the window $[-90, 90, 45]$ by $[-1, 2, 1]$. For what value of θ is I maximum?

(b) Write I in terms of the sine function.

86. Height of a Building   If the angle of elevation of the sun is θ, then a building 40 feet high will cast a shadow x feet long, where $x = \frac{40}{\tan\theta}$. Use a reciprocal identity to rewrite this formula.

87. Radio Tuners   (Refer to Example 5.) Let the energy stored in the inductor L be given by the formula $L(t) = 3\cos^2(6,000,000t)$ and the energy in the capacitor C be given by $C(t) = 3\sin^2(6,000,000t)$, where t is time in seconds. The total energy E in the circuit is given by $E(t) = L(t) + C(t)$.

(a) Graph L, C, and E in the window $[0, 10^{-6}, 10^{-7}]$ by $[-1, 4, 1]$. Interpret the graph.

(b) Make a table of L, C, and E, starting at $t = 0$ and incrementing by 10^{-7}. Interpret your results.

(c) Use a fundamental identity to derive a simplified expression for $E(t)$.

88. Distance to the Stars   The distance d to a star can be found by using

$$d = \frac{93,000,000}{\sin\theta},$$

where θ is the parallax of the star. Use a reciprocal identity to rewrite this formula.

Exercises 89 and 90: **Temperature**   *(Refer to Example 11.) Suppose that the monthly high temperature at a location is modeled by $f(x)$, where x is the month with $x = -6$ corresponding to January, $x = 0$ to July, and $x = 5$ to December.*

(a) Graph f in $[-6, 6, 1]$ by $[0, 100, 10]$. Interpret any symmetry in the graph.

(b) *Make a table of f and discuss whether f is an even or odd function.*

(c) *Express any symmetry symbolically.*

89. $f(x) = 40 \cos\left(\frac{\pi x}{6}\right) + 50$

90. $f(x) = -15 \cos\left(\frac{\pi x}{6}\right) + 60$

91. Oscillating Spring   The distance or displacement y of a weight attached to an oscillating spring from its natural position is modeled by $y = 4 \cos(2\pi t)$, where t is in seconds. See the figure. Potential energy is the energy of position and is given by $P = ky^2$, where k is a constant. The weight has the greatest potential energy when the spring is stretched or compressed the most.   (*Source:* R. Weidner and R. Sells, *Elementary Classical Physics*, Vol. 1.)

(a) Write an expression for P that involves the cosine function.

(b) Let $k = 2$ and graph P in the viewing rectangle $[0, 2, 0.5]$ by $[-1, 40, 8]$. For $0 \le t \le 2$, at what times is P maximum and at what times is P minimum? Interpret your result.

(c) Use a fundamental identity to write P in terms of the sine function.

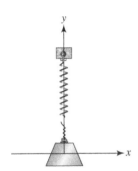

92. Energy in a Spring   (Refer to Exercise 91.) Two types of mechanical energy are kinetic energy and potential energy. Kinetic energy is the energy of motion, and potential energy is the energy of position. A stretched spring has potential energy, which is converted to kinetic energy when it is released. If the potential energy of a weight on a spring is $P(t) = k \cos^2(4\pi t)$, where k is a constant and t is in seconds, then its kinetic energy is given by $K(t) = k \sin^2(4\pi t)$. The total mechanical energy E is $E(t) = P(t) + K(t)$.

(a) If $k = 2$, graph P, K, and E in $[0, 0.5, 0.25]$ by $[-1, 3, 1]$. Interpret the graph.

(b) Make a table of K, P, and E, starting at $t = 0$ and incrementing by 0.05. Interpret the results.

(c) Use a fundamental identity to derive a simplified expression for $E(t)$.

Writing about Mathematics

93. Explain in your own words what a trigonometric identity is. Give two examples.

94. Answer each of the following.
(a) Give two characteristics of an even function. Which of the trigonometric functions are even?

(b) Give two characteristics of an odd function. Which of the trigonometric functions are odd?

95. A student writes "$\cos^2 + \sin^2 = 1$." Comment on the correctness of this expression.

96. Since $\sec^2 \theta = 1 + \tan^2 \theta$ is an identity, does it follow that $\sec \theta = 1 + \tan \theta$? Explain your reasoning.

7.2 Verifying Identities

- **Simplify trigonometric expressions**
- **Learn how to verify identities**

Introduction

In Example 5 of the previous section, we used the identity $\sin^2 \theta + \cos^2 \theta = 1$ to show that the energy stored in a tuner in a radio is constant. Trigonometric identities are used in both applications and calculus. Before we can use an identity, we must verify that it is correct. Although the equality of two trigonometric expressions can be *supported* graphically and numerically, symbolic *verification* is necessary to be certain that an equation is indeed an identity.

Simplifying Trigonometric Expressions

Many of the algebraic skills that you have already learned can be used to simplify trigonometric expressions. For example, suppose we wanted to multiply the following expression.

$$(1 + \cos\theta)(1 - \cos\theta)$$

In algebra we learned that

Product of a sum and a difference

$$(1 + x)(1 - x) = 1 - x + x - x^2$$
$$= 1 - x^2.$$

If we substitute $\cos\theta$ for x, then

Product of a sum and a difference

$$(1 + \cos\theta)(1 - \cos\theta) = 1 - \cos\theta + \cos\theta - \cos^2\theta$$
$$= 1 - \cos^2\theta.$$

In algebra we do not simplify $1 - x^2$ further. However, since $\sin^2\theta + \cos^2\theta = 1$, it follows that $\sin^2\theta = 1 - \cos^2\theta$. As a result,

$$(1 + \cos\theta)(1 - \cos\theta) = \sin^2\theta.$$

NOTE If you use algebraic expressions as an aid in simplifying trigonometric expressions, don't forget to check to see whether the resulting trigonometric expression can be simplified further by using fundamental identities.

MAKING CONNECTIONS

Algebraic and Trigonometric Expressions Many of the techniques used to rewrite algebraic expressions can also be used to rewrite trigonometric expressions. Here are some examples.

1. $\tan^2\theta - 4$
   $= (\tan\theta - 2)(\tan\theta + 2)$ is similar to $x^2 - 4 = (x - 2)(x + 2)$.

2. $\cos\theta\,(\sin\theta + \cos\theta)$
   $= \cos\theta\sin\theta + \cos^2\theta$ is similar to $x(y + x) = xy + x^2$.

3. $\dfrac{\sin\theta}{\cos\theta} + \dfrac{1}{\cos\theta} = \dfrac{\sin\theta + 1}{\cos\theta}$ is similar to $\dfrac{y}{x} + \dfrac{1}{x} = \dfrac{y + 1}{x}$.

The next example illustrates that the addition of two trigonometric expressions is often accomplished in a manner that is similar to that used to add two algebraic expressions.

EXAMPLE 1 Adding two trigonometric expressions

Write $\tan t + \cot t$ as a product of two trigonometric functions.

SOLUTION
Getting Started We begin by writing $\tan t$ and $\cot t$ as ratios involving $\sin t$ and $\cos t$.

$$\tan t + \cot t = \frac{\sin t}{\cos t} + \frac{\cos t}{\sin t}$$

Algebra Review
To review addition of rational expressions, see Chapter R (page R-32).

In algebra we combine $\frac{y}{x} + \frac{x}{y}$ by using the common denominator xy as follows.

$$\frac{y}{x} + \frac{x}{y} = \frac{y}{x}\cdot\frac{y}{y} + \frac{x}{y}\cdot\frac{x}{x} \qquad \text{Multiply each ratio by 1.}$$

Common denominator

$$= \frac{y^2}{xy} + \frac{x^2}{xy} \qquad \text{Simplify.}$$

$$= \frac{y^2 + x^2}{xy} \qquad \text{Add.}$$

Now substitute $\cos t$ for x and $\sin t$ for y. ▶

$$\tan t + \cot t = \frac{\sin t}{\cos t} + \frac{\cos t}{\sin t} \qquad \text{Quotient identities}$$

$$= \frac{\sin t}{\cos t} \cdot \frac{\sin t}{\sin t} + \frac{\cos t}{\sin t} \cdot \frac{\cos t}{\cos t} \qquad \text{Multiply each ratio by 1.}$$

$$= \frac{\sin^2 t}{\cos t \sin t} + \frac{\cos^2 t}{\cos t \sin t} \qquad \text{Simplify.}$$

Common denominator

$$= \frac{\sin^2 t + \cos^2 t}{\cos t \sin t} \qquad \text{Add.}$$

$$= \frac{1}{\cos t \sin t} \qquad \sin^2 t + \cos^2 t = 1$$

$$= \sec t \csc t \qquad \sec t = \frac{1}{\cos t}; \csc t = \frac{1}{\sin t}$$

Thus $\tan t + \cot t$ is equivalent to $\sec t \csc t$.

Now Try Exercise 15

NOTE To simplify a trigonometric expression, it is *not* necessary to first write a similar algebraic expression using x and y, as was done in Example 1. However, sometimes you may find this technique helpful.

EXAMPLE 2 Factoring a trigonometric expression

Factor each expression.
(a) $\sec^2 \theta - 1$ **(b)** $2 \sin^2 t + \sin t - 1$

SOLUTION
(a) In algebra we factor $x^2 - 1$ as $(x - 1)(x + 1)$. This technique can be applied to the given expression.

Difference of squares ——— $\sec^2 \theta - 1 = (\sec \theta - 1)(\sec \theta + 1)$

(b) Since $2y^2 + y - 1$ can be factored as $(2y - 1)(y + 1)$, it follows that

$$2 \sin^2 t + \sin t - 1 = (2 \sin t - 1)(\sin t + 1).$$

Now Try Exercises 29 and 31

An Application from Electricity   Trigonometric expressions are used in applications involving electricity, as illustrated in the next example.

EXAMPLE 3 Analyzing electromagnets

Electromagnets are used in a variety of situations, such as lifting scrap metal, ringing door bells, and opening door locks in apartments. Let the wattage W consumed by an electromagnet at t seconds be

$$W(t) = 100 \sin^2 (120\pi t) \qquad \text{Wattage}$$

and the voltage V in the circuit be

$$V(t) = 160 \cos (120\pi t). \qquad \text{Voltage}$$

(*Source:* A. Howatson, *Electrical Circuits and Systems.*)
(a) Express $W(t)$ in terms of the cosine function. When V is maximum or minimum, what is the value of W? Explain.
(b) Support your answer in part (a) by graphing W and V in the viewing rectangle $[0, 1/30, 1/60]$ by $[-180, 180, 20]$.

[0, 1/30, 1/60] by [−180, 180, 20]

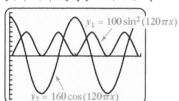

Figure 7.20 Radian Mode

SOLUTION

(a) Let $\theta = 120\pi t$ in the identity $\sin^2\theta = 1 - \cos^2\theta$ to write W as

$$W(t) = 100(1 - \cos^2(120\pi t)). \qquad \sin^2\theta = 1 - \cos^2\theta$$

Since $V(t) = 160\cos(120\pi t)$, the voltage is maximum (160) or minimum (−160) whenever $\cos(120\pi t) = \pm 1$. When $\cos(120\pi t) = \pm 1$, it follows that the value of W is given by $W(t) = 100(1 - (\pm 1)^2) = 0$.

(b) Graph $Y_1 = 100(\sin(120\pi X))^\wedge 2$ and $Y_2 = 160\cos(120\pi X)$, as shown in Figure 7.20. The wattage y_1 is 0 whenever the voltage y_2 is ± 160.

Now Try Exercise 81

Verification of Identities

When verifying that an equation is an identity, we usually begin with one side of the equation and write a sequence of equivalent expressions until it is transformed into the other side. This technique is illustrated in the following examples.

EXAMPLE 4 Verifying an identity

Verify that $(\cos\theta + \sin\theta)^2 = 1 + 2\sin\theta\cos\theta$.

SOLUTION

Getting Started In algebra, the expression $(x + y)^2$ can be expanded as follows.

Square the binomial

$$(x + y)^2 = (x + y)(x + y)$$
$$= x^2 + xy + yx + y^2$$
$$= x^2 + 2xy + y^2$$

We can perform similar steps with the left side of the trigonometric equation. ▶

$$(\cos\theta + \sin\theta)^2 = (\cos\theta + \sin\theta)(\cos\theta + \sin\theta)$$

Square the binomial

$$= \cos^2\theta + \cos\theta\sin\theta + \sin\theta\cos\theta + \sin^2\theta$$
$$= \cos^2\theta + 2\sin\theta\cos\theta + \sin^2\theta$$
$$= 1 + 2\sin\theta\cos\theta$$

The last step is true since $\sin^2\theta + \cos^2\theta = 1$. We have verified the identity since we have shown symbolically that the left side of the given equation is equal to the right side.

Now Try Exercise 37

EXAMPLE 5 Verifying identities

Verify each identity.

(a) $\dfrac{\sin^2\theta}{1 + \cos\theta} = 1 - \cos\theta$ **(b)** $\dfrac{\csc t}{\cot t} - \dfrac{\cot t}{\csc t} = \tan t \sin t$

SOLUTION

(a) Begin by applying a Pythagorean identity.

$$\frac{\sin^2\theta}{1 + \cos\theta} = \frac{1 - \cos^2\theta}{1 + \cos\theta} \qquad \sin^2\theta + \cos^2\theta = 1$$

$$= \frac{(1 - \cos\theta)(1 + \cos\theta)}{1 + \cos\theta} \qquad \text{Factor difference of squares.}$$

$$= 1 - \cos\theta \qquad \text{Simplify.}$$

(b) Begin by finding a common denominator for the expressions on the left side of the equation.

$$\frac{\csc t}{\cot t} - \frac{\cot t}{\csc t} = \frac{\csc t}{\cot t} \cdot \frac{\csc t}{\csc t} - \frac{\cot t}{\csc t} \cdot \frac{\cot t}{\cot t} \qquad \text{Multiply each ratio by 1.}$$

$$= \frac{\csc^2 t}{\cot t \csc t} - \frac{\cot^2 t}{\csc t \cot t} \qquad \text{Simplify.}$$

$$= \frac{\csc^2 t - \cot^2 t}{\cot t \csc t} \qquad \text{Subtract.}$$

$$= \frac{1 + \cot^2 t - \cot^2 t}{\cot t \csc t} \qquad \csc^2 t = 1 + \cot^2 t$$

$$= \frac{1}{\cot t \csc t} \qquad \text{Simplify.}$$

$$= \frac{1}{\cot t} \cdot \frac{1}{\csc t} \qquad \text{Rewrite the expression.}$$

$$= \tan t \sin t \qquad \text{Reciprocal identities}$$

Now Try Exercises 53 and 63

EXAMPLE 6   Verifying an identity

Verify that $\frac{\sin t}{1 - \cos t} = \frac{1 + \cos t}{\sin t}$ is an identity.

SOLUTION

Getting Started Earlier, we saw that $(1 - \cos\theta)(1 + \cos\theta) = \sin^2\theta$. This result can be used to verify the given identity by multiplying the numerator and denominator by 1 written as $\frac{1 + \cos t}{1 + \cos t}$. This technique is demonstrated below. ▶

$$\frac{\sin t}{1 - \cos t} = \frac{\sin t}{1 - \cos t} \cdot \frac{1 + \cos t}{1 + \cos t} \qquad \text{Multiply the ratio by 1.}$$

$$= \frac{\sin t \, (1 + \cos t)}{1 - \cos^2 t} \qquad \text{Simplify.}$$

$$= \frac{\sin t \, (1 + \cos t)}{\sin^2 t} \qquad \sin^2 t = 1 - \cos^2 t$$

$$= \frac{1 + \cos t}{\sin t} \qquad \text{Simplify.}$$

Now Try Exercise 65

EXAMPLE 7   Verifying an identity

Verify that $\frac{\sec x + \tan x}{\sec x - \tan x} = \frac{1 + \sin x}{1 - \sin x}$.

SOLUTION

Getting Started Because $\sec x = \frac{1}{\cos x}$ and $\tan x = \frac{\sin x}{\cos x}$, we start to simplify the expression by multiplying the numerator and denominator by $\cos x$. ▶

$$\frac{\sec x + \tan x}{\sec x - \tan x} = \frac{\sec x + \tan x}{\sec x - \tan x} \cdot \frac{\cos x}{\cos x} \qquad \text{Multiply the ratio by 1.}$$

$$= \frac{\sec x \cos x + \tan x \cos x}{\sec x \cos x - \tan x \cos x} \qquad \text{Distributive property}$$

$$= \frac{\frac{1}{\cos x} \cdot \cos x + \frac{\sin x}{\cos x} \cdot \cos x}{\frac{1}{\cos x} \cdot \cos x - \frac{\sin x}{\cos x} \cdot \cos x} \qquad \text{Reciprocal and quotient identities}$$

$$= \frac{1 + \sin x}{1 - \sin x} \qquad \text{Simplify.}$$

Now Try Exercise 61

In the next example, we show how to give graphical and numerical support.

EXAMPLE 8   Verifying an identity

Verify that $\frac{\tan\theta}{\sec\theta} = \sin\theta$ symbolically. Give graphical and numerical support.

SOLUTION

Symbolic Verification   **Getting Started** We will start with the more complicated expression $\frac{\tan\theta}{\sec\theta}$ and simplify it to $\sin\theta$. We begin by writing $\tan\theta$ and $\sec\theta$ in terms of $\sin\theta$ and $\cos\theta$. ▶

$$\frac{\tan\theta}{\sec\theta} = \frac{\sin\theta/\cos\theta}{1/\cos\theta} \qquad \textit{Quotient and reciprocal identities}$$

$$= \frac{\sin\theta}{\cos\theta} \cdot \frac{\cos\theta}{1} \qquad \textit{Invert and multiply.}$$

$$= \sin\theta \qquad \textit{Simplify.}$$

These steps verify symbolically that $\frac{\tan\theta}{\sec\theta} = \sin\theta$ is an identity.

Graphical Support   Graph $Y_1 = \tan(X)/(1/\cos(X))$ and $Y_2 = \sin(X)$, as shown below in Figures 7.21 and 7.22. Their graphs appear to be identical. Note that because most calculators do not have a secant button, we use the reciprocal identity $\sec\theta = \frac{1}{\cos\theta}$ to write $y_1 = \frac{\tan\theta}{\sec\theta}$ as $y_1 = \frac{\tan\theta}{1/\cos\theta}$.

Numerical Support   See Figure 7.23. Note that when $\theta = \frac{\pi}{2} \approx 1.5708$, the ratio $\frac{\tan\theta}{\sec\theta}$ is undefined, whereas $\sin\theta = 1$. However, the equation $\frac{\tan\theta}{\sec\theta} = \sin\theta$ is nonetheless an identity because $y_1 = y_2$ whenever both expressions are defined. (The step size for this table is $\frac{\pi}{6}$.)

$[-2\pi, 2\pi, \pi/2]$ by $[-2, 2, 1]$ $[-2\pi, 2\pi, \pi/2]$ by $[-2, 2, 1]$

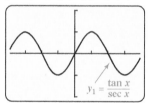

$y_1 = \frac{\tan x}{\sec x}$

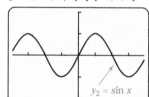

$y_2 = \sin x$

X	Y1	Y2
0	0	0
.5236	.5	.5
1.0472	.86603	.86603
1.5708	ERROR	1
2.0944	.86603	.86603
2.618	.5	.5
3.1416	0	0

X=0

Figure 7.21 Radian Mode   **Figure 7.22** Radian Mode   **Figure 7.23** Radian Mode

Now Try Exercise 73

7.2 Putting It All Together

Becoming proficient at verifying identities requires practice. Many of the skills learned in algebra can be used to help verify identities. The following table lists some suggestions that may be helpful.

SUGGESTIONS FOR VERIFYING IDENTITIES

1. Become familiar with the fundamental identities found in Section 7.1.
2. Use your knowledge of simplifying algebraic expressions as a guide, particularly when factoring or combining ratios.
3. When verifying an identity, start by simplifying the more complicated side of the equation. Otherwise, choose a side of the equation that you can transform into a different expression.
4. If you are simplifying the left side of the equation, work toward making the left side appear more like the right. For example, if the left side contains an addition sign but the right side does not, add the terms on the left side.
5. If you are uncertain how to proceed, one strategy is to write each trigonometric function in terms of sine and cosine and then simplify. Another strategy is to apply fundamental identities, if possible.
6. If a ratio contains $1 + \sin\theta$, it is sometimes helpful to multiply the numerator and denominator by $1 - \sin\theta$. Then

$$(1 + \sin\theta)(1 - \sin\theta) = 1 - \sin^2\theta = \cos^2\theta.$$

Similar statements can be made for $1 - \sin\theta$, $1 + \cos\theta$, and $1 - \cos\theta$. See Example 6.

7.2 Exercises

Simplifying Expressions

Exercises 1–6: Multiply the algebraic expression. Then multiply the corresponding trigonometric expression. If possible, simplify the resulting trigonometric expression.

1. (a) $(1 + x)(1 - x)$ **(b)** $(1 + \sin\theta)(1 - \sin\theta)$

2. (a) $(x - 1)(x + 1)$ **(b)** $(\csc\theta - 1)(\csc\theta + 1)$

3. (a) $x(x - 1)$ **(b)** $\sec\theta(\sec\theta - 1)$

4. (a) $(x + 1)(2x - 1)$ **(b)** $(\tan\theta + 1)(2\tan\theta - 1)$

5. (a) $\dfrac{x}{1} \cdot \dfrac{y}{x}$ **(b)** $\cos\theta \cdot \tan\theta$

6. (a) $\dfrac{1}{x} \cdot \dfrac{x}{y}$ **(b)** $\csc\theta \cdot \tan\theta$

Exercises 7–12: Factor the algebraic expression. Then factor the corresponding trigonometric expression. If possible, simplify the resulting trigonometric expression.

7. (a) $x^2 + 2x + 1$ **(b)** $\cos^2\theta + 2\cos\theta + 1$

8. (a) $2x^2 - 3x + 1$ **(b)** $2\sin^2 t - 3\sin t + 1$

9. (a) $x^2 - 2x$ **(b)** $\sec^2 t - 2\sec t$

10. (a) $3x - 9x^2$ **(b)** $3\tan\theta - 9\tan^2\theta$

11. (a) $x + x^3$ **(b)** $\tan\theta + \tan^3\theta$

12. (a) $x^2 + x^2 y^2$ **(b)** $\sin^2\theta + \sin^2\theta\tan^2\theta$

Exercises 13–20: Simplify the algebraic expression. Then simplify the corresponding trigonometric expression completely.

13. (a) $\dfrac{1}{1 - x} + \dfrac{1}{1 + x}$ **(b)** $\dfrac{1}{1 - \cos\theta} + \dfrac{1}{1 + \cos\theta}$

14. (a) $x + \dfrac{1}{x}$ **(b)** $\tan t + \dfrac{1}{\tan t}$

15. (a) $\dfrac{x}{y} + \dfrac{y}{x}$ **(b)** $\dfrac{\cos t}{\sin t} + \dfrac{\sin t}{\cos t}$

16. (a) $\dfrac{1}{y} - \dfrac{x^2}{y}$ **(b)** $\dfrac{1}{\sin\theta} - \dfrac{\cos^2\theta}{\sin\theta}$

17. (a) $\dfrac{1}{1/y^2} + \dfrac{1}{1/x^2}$ **(b)** $\dfrac{1}{\csc^2 t} + \dfrac{1}{\sec^2 t}$

18. (a) $\left(\dfrac{1}{x} + x\right)^2$ **(b)** $(\cot\theta + \tan\theta)^2$

19. (a) $\dfrac{x/y}{1/y}$ **(b)** $\dfrac{\cot\theta}{\csc\theta}$

20. (a) $\dfrac{1 - x^2}{1 + x}$ **(b)** $\dfrac{1 - \cos^2\theta}{1 + \cos\theta}$

Exercises 21–28: Perform the indicated operations and simplify.

21. $\cos\theta\tan\theta$ **22.** $\sin^2\theta\csc\theta$

23. $\tan\theta(\cos\theta - \csc\theta)$ **24.** $(\sin\theta - \cos\theta)^2$

25. $(1 + \tan t)^2$ **26.** $(\sin t - 1)(\sin t + 1)$

27. $\dfrac{\csc^2\theta - 1}{\csc^2\theta}$ **28.** $\sin^2 t(1 + \cot^2 t)$

Exercises 29–34: Factor the trigonometric expression and simplify, if possible.

29. $1 - \tan^2\theta$ **30.** $\sin^2 t - \cos^2 t$

31. $\sec^2 t - \sec t - 6$ **32.** $\cos\theta\sin^2\theta + \cos^3\theta$

33. $\tan^4\theta + 3\tan^2\theta + 2$ **34.** $\sin^4 t - \cos^4 t$

Verifying Identities

Exercises 35–72: Verify the identity.

35. $\csc^2\theta - \cot^2\theta = 1$ **36.** $\dfrac{\tan^2\theta + 1}{\sec\theta} = \sec\theta$

37. $(1 - \sin t)^2 = 1 - 2\sin t + \sin^2 t$

38. $\dfrac{\sin^2 t}{\cos t} = \sec t - \cos t$ **39.** $\dfrac{\sin t + \cos t}{\sin t} = 1 + \cot t$

40. $\sec^4\theta - \sec^2\theta = \tan^4\theta + \tan^2\theta$

41. $\sec^2\theta - 1 = \tan^2\theta$ **42.** $\dfrac{\csc^2\theta}{\cot\theta} = \csc\theta\sec\theta$

43. $\dfrac{\tan^2 t}{\sec t} = \sec t - \cos t$ **44.** $\dfrac{\sec^2\theta - 1}{\sec^2\theta} = \sin^2\theta$

45. $\cot x + 1 = \csc x(\cos x + \sin x)$

46. $\dfrac{1 + \sin x}{\cos x} = \dfrac{\cos x}{1 - \sin x}$ **47.** $\dfrac{\sec t}{1 + \sec t} = \dfrac{1}{\cos t + 1}$

48. $\sec^2 t + \csc^2 t = \sec^2 t\csc^2 t$

49. $(\sec t - 1)(\sec t + 1) = \tan^2 t$

50. $\csc^4\theta - \cot^4\theta = \csc^2\theta + \cot^2\theta$

51. $\dfrac{1 - \sin^2\theta}{\cos\theta} = \cos\theta$ **52.** $\dfrac{\tan^2 t - 1}{1 + \tan^2 t} = 1 - 2\cos^2 t$

53. $\dfrac{\sec t}{\tan t} - \dfrac{\tan t}{\sec t} = \cos t\cot t$

54. $\dfrac{\sin^4 t - \cos^4 t}{\sin^2 t - \cos^2 t} = 1$ **55.** $\dfrac{\cot^2 t}{\csc t + 1} = \csc t - 1$

56. $\sec\theta - \cos\theta = \tan\theta\sin\theta$

57. $\dfrac{\cot t}{\cot t + 1} = \dfrac{1}{1 + \tan t}$

58. $\cos^4 t - \sin^4 t = 2\cos^2 t - 1$

59. $\dfrac{1}{1 - \sin t} + \dfrac{1}{1 + \sin t} = 2\sec^2 t$

60. $\cot\theta + \tan\theta = \csc\theta\sec\theta$

61. $\dfrac{\csc t + \cot t}{\csc t - \cot t} = (\csc t + \cot t)^2$

62. $\dfrac{\csc t}{1 + \csc t} - \dfrac{\csc t}{1 - \csc t} = 2\sec^2 t$

63. $\dfrac{\cos^2 t}{1 - \sin t} = 1 + \sin t$

64. $\csc t + \dfrac{\sec t}{\tan t} = \dfrac{2}{\sin t}$ **65.** $\dfrac{1}{1 + \sin\theta} = \dfrac{1 - \sin\theta}{\cos^2\theta}$

66. $\dfrac{2\sin^2 t + 3\sin t - 2}{\sin t + 2} = 2\sin t - 1$

67. $\sqrt{1 - \sin^2\theta} = \cos\theta$, where θ is acute

68. $\sqrt{\sec^2\theta - 1} = \tan\theta$, where θ is acute

69. $\dfrac{1 + 2\sin x + \sin^2 x}{\cos^2 x} = \dfrac{1 + \sin x}{1 - \sin x}$

70. $\dfrac{\tan t - \cot t}{\sin t \cos t} = \sec^2 t - \csc^2 t$

71. $(1 - \cos^2 x)(1 + \cos^2 x) = 2\sin^2 x - \sin^4 x$

72. $\sin^4 x - \cos^4 x = 2\sin^2 x - 1$

Exercises 73–80: Verify the identity. If you have a graphing calculator, give graphical or numerical support.

73. $\cot\theta\sin\theta = \cos\theta$ **74.** $\tan\theta\cos\theta = \sin\theta$

75. $(1 - \cos^2\theta)(1 + \tan^2\theta) = \tan^2\theta$

76. $\cos^2\theta\,(1 + \cot^2\theta) = \cot^2\theta$

77. $\cos t\,(\tan t - \sec t) = \sin t - 1$

78. $\dfrac{\cos\theta}{1 - \sin\theta} = \sec\theta + \tan\theta$

79. $\dfrac{\tan(-\theta)}{\sin(-\theta)} = \sec\theta$

80. $\tan^2 t - \sin^2 t = \tan^2 t \sin^2 t$

Applications

81. Electromagnets (Refer to Example 3.) Let the wattage consumed by an electromagnet be given by the formula $W(t) = 5\cos^2(120\pi t)$ and the voltage be given by the formula $V(t) = 25\sin(120\pi t)$, where t is in seconds.
 (a) Express $W(t)$ in terms of the sine function. When V is maximum or minimum, what is the value of W?

 (b) Support your answer in part (a) by graphing W and V in $[0, 1/15, 1/60]$ by $[-30, 30, 10]$.

82. An Oscillating Spring The potential energy P of a weight on a spring is given by $P(t) = 5\cos^2(4\pi t)$, and its kinetic energy K is given by $K(t) = 5\sin^2(4\pi t)$, where t is in seconds.
 (a) Express $P(t)$ in terms of the sine function. When K is maximum or minimum, what is the value of P?

 (b) Support your answer in part (a) by graphing P and K in $[0, 0.5, 0.25]$ by $[-1, 5, 1]$. Interpret the graph.

Writing about Mathematics

83. Create a trigonometric identity of your own. Verify the identity symbolically and then give graphical and numerical support.

84. Explain how to show that an equation is not an identity. Give an example.

CHECKING BASIC CONCEPTS FOR SECTIONS 7.1 AND 7.2

1. Determine the quadrant containing θ if $\cot\theta > 0$ and $\sin\theta < 0$.

2. Determine the other trigonometric functions of θ using the given information.
 (a) $\sin\theta = \frac{5}{13}$ and $\cos\theta = -\frac{12}{13}$

 (b) $\sec\theta = \frac{5}{4}$ and $\sin\theta < 0$

 (c) $\tan\theta = -\frac{1}{2}$ and $\cos\theta = \frac{2}{\sqrt{5}}$

3. Simplify each expression.
 (a) $(1 - \sin\theta)(1 + \sin\theta)$

 (b) $\tan^2 t \csc^2 t - 1$

4. Factor the trigonometric expression.
 (a) $\tan^2 t - 1$ **(b)** $3\sin^2 t + \sin t - 2$

5. Verify each identity.
 (a) $(1 - \sin^2\theta)(1 + \cot^2\theta) = \cot^2\theta$

 (b) $\dfrac{\cot^2 t}{\csc t} = \csc t - \sin t$

7.3 Trigonometric Equations

- Find and use reference angles
- Solve trigonometric equations and applications
- Solve inverse trigonometric equations

Introduction

In previous chapters we saw how applications that involve functions result in the need to solve equations. In a similar manner, applications that involve trigonometric functions result in the need to solve trigonometric equations. For example, the number of daylight hours near 30°N latitude can be modeled by

$$f(x) = 1.95 \cos\left(\frac{\pi}{6}(x - 6.6)\right) + 12.15,$$

where $x = 1$ corresponds to January 1, $x = 2$ to February 1, and so on. To estimate when there are 11 hours of daylight, we can solve the *trigonometric equation* $f(x) = 11$.

Trigonometric Equation

$$1.95 \cos\left(\frac{\pi}{6}(x - 6.6)\right) + 12.15 = 11$$

Like other types of equations, trigonometric equations can be solved graphically, numerically, and symbolically. We begin by discussing reference angles, which are used when solving trigonometric equations symbolically.

Reference Angles

A **reference angle** for an angle θ, written θ_R, is the acute angle made by the terminal side of θ and the x-axis. It is assumed that θ is in standard position and its terminal side does not lie on either the x- or the y-axis. Examples of reference angles in the four quadrants are shown in Figures 7.24–7.27.

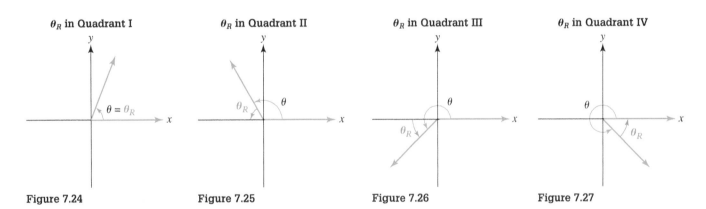

Figure 7.24   Figure 7.25   Figure 7.26   Figure 7.27

EXAMPLE 1 Finding reference angles

Find the reference angle for θ.

(a) $\theta = 43°$ **(b)** $\theta = \dfrac{2\pi}{3}$ **(c)** $\theta = -55°$ **(d)** $\theta = -\dfrac{3\pi}{4}$

SOLUTION
(a) Since θ is in quadrant I, θ and θ_R are equal. Thus $\theta_R = 43°$.
(b) The terminal side of $\theta = \frac{2\pi}{3}$ lies in quadrant II, as in Figure 7.25. In this case, the acute angle θ_R between the terminal side of θ and the x-axis is given by

$$\theta_R = \pi - \theta = \pi - \frac{2\pi}{3} = \frac{\pi}{3}.$$

(c) The terminal side of $\theta = -55°$ lies in quadrant IV, and the acute angle between it and the *x*-axis is $\theta_R = 55°$. See Figure 7.28.

(d) The terminal side of $\theta = -\frac{3\pi}{4}$ (or $-135°$) lies in quadrant III, and the acute angle between it and the *x*-axis is $\theta_R = \frac{\pi}{4}$. See Figure 7.29.

> **CLASS DISCUSSION**
>
> Let $0 < \theta < 2\pi$. Find expressions for θ_R given the quadrant containing θ.

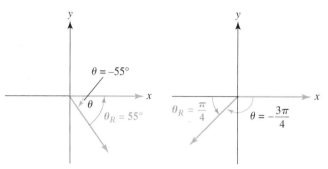

Figure 7.28   **Figure 7.29**

> **Now Try Exercises 3, 5, 7, and 9**

The reference angle is important because it can help determine trigonometric values.

REFERENCE ANGLES AND TRIGONOMETRIC FUNCTIONS

Let θ be an angle in standard position with reference angle θ_R. Then

$$|\sin\theta| = \sin\theta_R \qquad |\cos\theta| = \cos\theta_R \qquad |\tan\theta| = \tan\theta_R$$
$$|\csc\theta| = \csc\theta_R \qquad |\sec\theta| = \sec\theta_R \qquad |\cot\theta| = \cot\theta_R.$$

The signs of the trigonometric functions of θ are determined by the quadrant that contains θ. (See Figure 7.9 in the See the Concept on page 558.)

NOTE The equation $|\sin\theta| = \sin\theta_R$ implies that $\sin\theta = \pm\sin\theta_R$. A similar statement can be made for each of the other trigonometric functions.

The note above suggests that if we know the quadrant containing θ, then the value of a trigonometric function of θ_R can be used to determine the value of the corresponding trigonometric function of θ. Table 7.1 shows how reference angles are used to find the values of different trigonometric functions at specified values of θ.

Using Reference Angles to Find Values of Trigonometric Functions

Desired Function Value	θ	θ_R	Trigonometric Function of θ_R	Quadrant Containing θ	Positive or Negative	Resulting Value
$\cos -\frac{3\pi}{4}$	$-\frac{3\pi}{4}$	$\frac{\pi}{4}$	$\cos\frac{\pi}{4} = \frac{1}{\sqrt{2}}$	III	$\cos\theta < 0$ in quadrant III	$\cos -\frac{3\pi}{4} = -\frac{1}{\sqrt{2}}$
$\csc 150°$	$150°$	$30°$	$\csc 30° = 2$	II	$\csc\theta > 0$ in quadrant II	$\csc 150° = 2$
$\sin\frac{11\pi}{6}$	$\frac{11\pi}{6}$	$\frac{\pi}{6}$	$\sin\frac{\pi}{6} = \frac{1}{2}$	IV	$\sin\theta < 0$ in quadrant IV	$\sin\frac{11\pi}{6} = -\frac{1}{2}$
$\tan -315°$	$-315°$	$45°$	$\tan 45° = 1$	I	$\tan\theta > 0$ in quadrant I	$\tan -315° = 1$

Table 7.1

Basic Trigonometric Equations

In general, trigonometric equations are solved symbolically by using algebraic properties to write the equation as an equivalent *basic trigonometric equation*. For this reason, it is important to be able to solve basic trigonometric equations such as $\cos\theta = -\frac{\sqrt{3}}{2}$, $\sin\theta = -\frac{1}{2}$, and $\tan\theta = 1$. The following See the Concept shows how a reference angle is used as an aid in solving $\cos\theta = -\frac{\sqrt{3}}{2}$ for θ in $[0, 2\pi)$.

See the Concept: Solving a Basic Trigonometric Equation

θ_R in Quadrant II

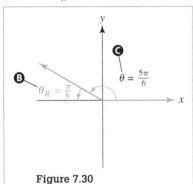

Figure 7.30

θ_R in Quadrant III

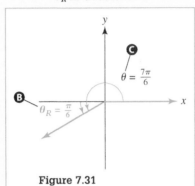

Figure 7.31

Solve $\cos\theta = -\frac{\sqrt{3}}{2}$ for θ in $[0, 2\pi)$.

Ⓐ Begin by finding the reference angle for θ. Since $\cos\theta_R = |\cos\theta|$, we know that $\cos\theta_R = \frac{\sqrt{3}}{2}$. So $\theta_R = \cos^{-1}\frac{\sqrt{3}}{2} = \frac{\pi}{6}$.

Ⓑ Because $\cos\theta < 0$, angle θ is a second or third quadrant angle. Locate θ_R in quadrants II and III as shown in Figures 7.30 and 7.31, respectively.

Ⓒ The angles in $[0, 2\pi)$ with $\cos\theta < 0$ and whose reference angles are $\theta_R = \frac{\pi}{6}$ represent the solutions to the given equation. The solutions are $\frac{5\pi}{6}$ and $\frac{7\pi}{6}$.

EXAMPLE 2 Solving trigonometric equations using reference angles

Solve the following equations.
(a) $\sin\theta = -\frac{1}{2}$ for θ in $[0°, 360°)$ **(b)** $\tan\theta = 1$ for θ in $[0, 2\pi)$

SOLUTION
(a) We start by solving the equation $\sin\theta_R = \frac{1}{2}$. The solution to this equation is $\theta_R = \sin^{-1}\frac{1}{2} = 30°$. The sine function is negative in quadrants III and IV. Therefore the solution to $\sin\theta = -\frac{1}{2}$ is an angle θ, located in either quadrant III or quadrant IV, that has a reference angle of $30°$. There are two such angles: 210° and 330°. See Figures 7.32 and 7.33. Thus 210° and 330° are solutions.
(b) The solution to $\tan\theta_R = 1$ is $\theta_R = \tan^{-1}1 = \frac{\pi}{4}$. The tangent function is positive in quadrants I and III. Thus $\frac{\pi}{4}$ and $\frac{5\pi}{4}$ are solutions. See Figures 7.34 and 7.35.

θ_R in Quadrant III

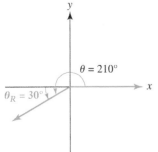

Figure 7.32

θ_R in Quadrant IV

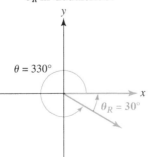

Figure 7.33

θ_R in Quadrant I

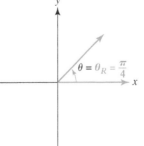

Figure 7.34

θ_R in Quadrant III

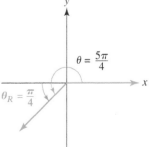

Figure 7.35

Now Try Exercises 13 and 15

Solving Trigonometric Equations

In the previous section we verified trigonometric *identities*. Identities are equations that are true for all meaningful values of the variable. In this section we discuss trigonometric equations that are *conditional*. Conditional equations are satisfied by some but not all values of the variable. For example,

$$\cos \theta = 1$$

is a conditional trigonometric equation since the cosine function equals 1 only for certain values of θ, such as $\theta = 0$ or $\theta = 2\pi$.

EXAMPLE 3   Solving a trigonometric equation

Solve $2 \sin \theta - 1 = 1$ on the interval $[0°, 360°)$ symbolically and graphically.

SOLUTION

Symbolic Solution   **Getting Started** To solve the linear equation $2x - 1 = 1$, we first add 1 to each side and then divide each side by 2 to obtain $x = 1$. This technique can be applied to the equation $2 \sin \theta - 1 = 1$ to obtain $\sin \theta = 1$. ▶

Begin by solving the given equation for $\sin \theta$.

Solving $2 \sin \theta - 1 = 1$
$[0, 360, 90]$ by $[-4, 4, 1]$

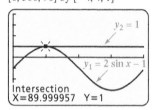

Figure 7.36 Degree Mode

$$2 \sin \theta - 1 = 1 \qquad \text{Given equation}$$
$$2 \sin \theta = 2 \qquad \text{Add 1 to each side.}$$
$$\sin \theta = 1 \qquad \text{Divide each side by 2.}$$

The only solution to $\sin \theta = 1$ on the interval $[0°, 360°)$ is $\theta = \sin^{-1} 1 = 90°$.

Graphical Solution   Graph $y_1 = 2 \sin x - 1$ and $y_2 = 1$, as in Figure 7.36. Their graphs intersect at $x = 90°$.

Now Try Exercise 31

An Application from Astronomy   In the next example, we find all the phase angles associated with a particular phase F of the moon. The fraction of the moon that appears illuminated is called the *phase F*. The *phase angle* θ is shown in Figure 7.37. (**Source:** M. Zeilik et al., *Introductory Astronomy and Astrophysics.*)

A Phase of the Moon with Phase Angle θ

Figure 7.37 (Not to scale)

EXAMPLE 4   Finding phase angles for the moon

The phase F associated with a phase angle θ is given by

$$F = \frac{1}{2}(1 - \cos \theta).$$

Find all phase angles θ in degrees when $F = 0.75$. (Note that $F = 0.5$ corresponds to a first quarter moon or last quarter moon and $F = 1$ corresponds to a full moon.)

SOLUTION Let $F = 0.75$ and solve the given equation.

$$0.75 = \frac{1}{2}(1 - \cos\theta) \qquad \text{Let } F = 0.75.$$

$$1.5 = 1 - \cos\theta \qquad \text{Multiply each side by 2.}$$

$$\cos\theta = -0.5 \qquad \text{Solve for } \cos\theta.$$

Start by solving the equation $\cos\theta_R = 0.5$. The solution is $\theta_R = \cos^{-1} 0.5 = 60°$. The cosine function is negative in quadrants II and III. Angles in these quadrants with a 60° reference angle are 120° and 240°, where $0° \le \theta \le 360°$. Verify this fact. Since the cosine function has period 360°, all solutions can be written in the form

$$\theta = 120° + 360° \cdot n \qquad \text{or} \qquad \theta = 240° + 360° \cdot n,$$

> The cosine function has period 360°.

where n is an integer. For example, 120°, 120° ± 360°, and 120° ± 720° are solutions, as well as 240°, 240° ± 360°, and 240° ± 720°.

> **Now Try Exercise 117**

Finding All Solutions Many of the techniques used to solve polynomial equations can be applied to trigonometric equations, as illustrated in the next example.

EXAMPLE 5 Solving trigonometric equations

Find all solutions to each equation. Express your results in radians.
(a) $2\cot t + 1 = -1$ **(b)** $2\sin^2 t - 5\sin t + 2 = 0$

SOLUTION
(a) In algebra the equation $2x + 1 = -1$ implies $x = -1$. In a similar manner,

$$2\cot t + 1 = -1 \qquad \text{implies} \qquad \cot t = -1.$$
> Subtract 1 and then divide by 2.

If $\cot t = -1$, then $\tan t = \frac{1}{\cot t} = -1$ and t has a reference angle of $\tan^{-1} 1 = \frac{\pi}{4}$. The cotangent is negative in quadrants II and IV, so the solutions to $\cot t = -1$ in $[0, 2\pi)$ are $t = \frac{3\pi}{4}$ and $t = \frac{7\pi}{4}$. Note that these angles both have a reference angle of $\frac{\pi}{4}$. Since cotangent has a period of π, all solutions can be expressed in the form

$$t = \frac{3\pi}{4} + \pi n \qquad \text{or} \qquad t = \frac{7\pi}{4} + \pi n,$$

> The cotangent function has period π.

where n is an integer. These solutions are equivalent to just $t = \frac{3\pi}{4} + \pi n$ because the difference between $\frac{7\pi}{4}$ and $\frac{3\pi}{4}$ is π.

(b) Getting Started In algebra the equation $2x^2 - 5x + 2 = 0$ can be solved by factoring.

$$2x^2 - 5x + 2 = (2x - 1)(x - 2) = 0$$

The solutions are $\frac{1}{2}$ and 2. We can factor a trigonometric expression in the same way. ▶

$$2\sin^2 t - 5\sin t + 2 = (2\sin t - 1)(\sin t - 2) = 0$$
> Factor the quadratic expression as the product of two binomials.

We must solve the equations $\sin t = \frac{1}{2}$ and $\sin t = 2$. If $\sin t = \frac{1}{2}$, the reference angle is $\sin^{-1}\frac{1}{2} = \frac{\pi}{6}$. The sine function is positive in quadrants I and II, so the solutions in $[0, 2\pi)$ are $t = \frac{\pi}{6}$ and $t = \frac{5\pi}{6}$. Since $-1 \le \sin t \le 1$ for all t, the equation $\sin t = 2$

has no solutions. The sine function has period 2π, and all solutions to the given equation can be expressed as

$$t = \frac{\pi}{6} + 2\pi n \quad \text{or} \quad t = \frac{5\pi}{6} + 2\pi n.$$

The sine function has period 2π.

Now Try Exercises 55 and 59

MAKING CONNECTIONS

Polynomial and Trigonometric Equations   A polynomial equation of degree n has at most n solutions. However, a trigonometric equation typically has an infinite number of solutions, as demonstrated in Examples 4 and 5.

Approximating Solutions   Sometimes equations have solutions that are not multiples of common angles such as $\frac{\pi}{6}$ or $\frac{\pi}{4}$. In the next example, we find and then approximate solutions to a trigonometric equation.

EXAMPLE 6   Approximating solutions

Solve $1.7 \csc t + 2.3 = 0$ to the nearest thousandth for t in $[0, 2\pi)$.

SOLUTION   Begin by solving the equation for $\csc t$.

$$1.7 \csc t + 2.3 = 0 \qquad \text{Given equation}$$

$$1.7 \csc t = -2.3 \qquad \text{Subtract 2.3 from each side.}$$

$$\csc t = -\frac{2.3}{1.7} \qquad \text{Divide each side by 1.7.}$$

Because $\csc t = \frac{1}{\sin t}$, it follows that $\sin t = -\frac{1.7}{2.3}$, or $\sin t = -\frac{17}{23}$. The reference number (angle) is $t_R = \sin^{-1}\frac{17}{23} \approx 0.832$ (radian). The sine function is negative in quadrants III and IV. For t in $[0, 2\pi)$, there are two solutions given by

$$\pi + \sin^{-1}\frac{17}{23} \approx 3.973 \quad \text{and} \quad 2\pi - \sin^{-1}\frac{17}{23} \approx 5.451.$$

See Figures 7.38 and 7.39. (Note that 0.832 radian is approximately equivalent to 47.7°.)

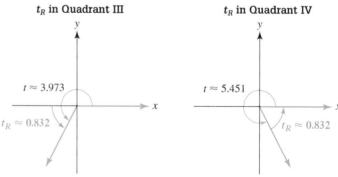

t_R in Quadrant III	t_R in Quadrant IV
$t \approx 3.973$	$t \approx 5.451$
$t_R \approx 0.832$	$t_R \approx 0.832$
Figure 7.38	**Figure 7.39**

Now Try Exercise 93

An Application   Solar power companies are interested in the number of daylight hours during different times of the year and at different latitudes. In the next example, we solve the trigonometric equation

$$1.95 \cos\left(\frac{\pi}{6}(x - 6.6)\right) + 12.15 = 11$$

presented in the introduction to this section. The solution to this equation tells us when there are 11 hours of daylight at 30°N latitude.

EXAMPLE 7   Analyzing daylight hours

The number of daylight hours at 30°N latitude can be modeled by

$$f(x) = 1.95 \cos\left(\frac{\pi}{6}(x - 6.6)\right) + 12.15,$$

where $x = 1$ corresponds to January 1, $x = 2$ to February 1, and so on. Estimate graphically and numerically when there are 11 hours of daylight.

SOLUTION

Graphical Solution   Graph $Y_1 = 1.95 \cos(\pi/6(X - 6.6)) + 12.15$ and $Y_2 = 11$ in radian mode. Their graphs intersect near $x = 2.4$ and $x = 10.8$. See Figures 7.40 and 7.41. These values correspond to about February 11 and October 25. (Note that four-tenths of February is $0.4 \times 28 \approx 11$ days and eight-tenths of October is $0.8 \times 31 \approx 25$ days.)

Numerical Solution   Make a table of Y_1, starting at $x = 2$ and incrementing by 0.1. The table in Figure 7.42 shows that $Y_1 \approx 11$ when $x = 2.4$. Scrolling down the table would also show that $Y_1 \approx 11$ when $x = 10.8$.

[0, 13, 1] by [8, 16, 1]   [0, 13, 1] by [8, 16, 1]

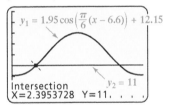

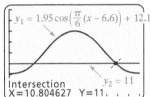

X	Y1	Y2
2	10.701	11
2.1	10.771	11
2.2	10.845	11
2.3	10.923	11
2.4	11.004	11 ←
2.5	11.088	11
2.6	11.175	11
X=2.4		

Figure 7.40 Radian Mode   **Figure 7.41** Radian Mode   **Figure 7.42** Radian Mode

Now Try Exercise 121

More Trigonometric Equations   Some equations contain trigonometric functions such as $\cos 2t$ or $\tan 3\theta$, where the argument is a multiple of t or θ. An additional step is required when solving this type of equation. In the next example, we solve a trigonometric equation for all real numbers t, where the argument of the trigonometric function is $4t$.

EXAMPLE 8   Solving a trigonometric equation

Solve $-0.6 \sin 4t = 0.3$, where t is any real number.

SOLUTION   First we let $\theta = 4t$. Then the given equation becomes

$$-0.6 \sin\theta = 0.3.$$

Next we solve this modified equation for all real numbers θ.

$$-0.6 \sin\theta = 0.3 \qquad \text{Let } \theta = 4t.$$

$$\sin\theta = -\frac{1}{2} \qquad \text{Divide each side by } -0.6.$$

From Example 2(a), the solutions to $\sin\theta = -\frac{1}{2}$ on the interval $[0°, 360°)$ are $210°$ and $330°$. In radian measure these solutions are $\theta = \frac{7\pi}{6}$ and $\frac{11\pi}{6}$. Thus all real number solutions to the equation $-0.6\sin\theta = 0.3$ are

$$\theta = \frac{7\pi}{6} + 2\pi n \qquad \text{or} \qquad \theta = \frac{11\pi}{6} + 2\pi n,$$

where n is an integer. Because $\theta = 4t$, we can determine t by substituting $4t$ for θ.

$$4t = \frac{7\pi}{6} + 2\pi n \qquad \text{or} \qquad 4t = \frac{11\pi}{6} + 2\pi n$$

Finally we divide each equation by 4 to obtain

$$t = \frac{7\pi}{24} + \frac{\pi n}{2} \qquad \text{or} \qquad t = \frac{11\pi}{24} + \frac{\pi n}{2}.$$

Now Try Exercise 75

Some equations contain more than one type of trigonometric function. In these situations it is sometimes helpful to use trigonometric identities to rewrite the equation in terms of one trigonometric function. This is illustrated in the next example.

EXAMPLE 9 Solving a trigonometric equation

Solve $2\tan\theta = \sec^2\theta$ symbolically on the interval $[0, 2\pi)$.

SOLUTION This equation contains two different trigonometric functions. We begin by applying the identity $1 + \tan^2\theta = \sec^2\theta$ to rewrite the equation only in terms of $\tan\theta$.

$$2\tan\theta = \sec^2\theta \qquad \text{Given equation}$$
$$2\tan\theta = 1 + \tan^2\theta \qquad \sec^2\theta = 1 + \tan^2\theta$$
$$\tan^2\theta - 2\tan\theta + 1 = 0 \qquad \text{Rewrite the equation.}$$
$$(\tan\theta - 1)(\tan\theta - 1) = 0 \qquad \text{Factor.}$$
$$\tan\theta = 1 \qquad \text{Solve for } \tan\theta.$$

The solutions are $\frac{\pi}{4}$ and $\frac{5\pi}{4}$. See Example 2(b).

Now Try Exercise 45

In the next example, we solve a trigonometric equation by squaring each side. When squaring each side of an equation, it is important to *check the answers*.

EXAMPLE 10 Solving a trigonometric equation by squaring

Solve $\sec t = 1 + \tan t$ for $0 \le t < 2\pi$.

SOLUTION Begin by squaring each side of the equation.

$$\sec t = 1 + \tan t \qquad \text{Given equation}$$
$$\sec^2 t = (1 + \tan t)^2 \qquad \text{Square each side}$$
$$\sec^2 t = 1 + 2\tan t + \tan^2 t \qquad \text{Square the expression.}$$
$$\sec^2 t = \sec^2 t + 2\tan t \qquad 1 + \tan^2 t = \sec^2 t$$
$$0 = 2\tan t \qquad \text{Subtract } \sec^2 t \text{ from each side.}$$
$$\tan t = 0 \qquad \text{Divide each side by 2 and rewrite.}$$
$$t = 0 \qquad \text{or} \qquad t = \pi \qquad \text{Solve for } t \text{ when } 0 \le t < 2\pi.$$

Algebra Review

To review squaring a binomial, see Chapter R (page R-17).

Since we squared each side of the equation, we check $t = 0$ and $t = \pi$ in the given equation.

Solution checks —— $\sec 0 \overset{?}{=} 1 + \tan 0$ $\qquad$ $\sec \pi \overset{?}{=} 1 + \tan \pi$ —— Solution does not check

$\qquad\qquad\qquad\quad 1 = 1 + 0$ $\qquad\qquad\quad -1 \neq 1 + 0$

The only solution is 0. The value of π is an *extraneous solution.*

Now Try Exercise 73

More Applications

Highway Curves Highway curves are sometimes banked so that the outside of the curve is slightly elevated or inclined, as shown in Figure 7.43. This inclination is called the *superelevation*. The relationship among a car's velocity v in feet per second, the safe radius r of the curve in feet, and the superelevation θ in degrees is given by

$$r = \frac{v^2}{4.5 + 32.2 \tan \theta}.$$

(*Source:* F. Mannering and W. Kilareski, *Principles of Highway Engineering and Traffic Analysis.*)

Figure 7.43

EXAMPLE 11 Determining superelevation for a highway curve

A highway curve with a radius of 700 feet and a speed limit of 88 feet per second (60 mi/hr) is being designed. Find the appropriate superelevation for the curve.

SOLUTION Let $r = 700$ and $v = 88$ and then solve the equation for θ.

$$700 = \frac{88^2}{4.5 + 32.2 \tan \theta} \qquad \text{Let } r = 700 \text{ and } v = 88.$$

$$4.5 + 32.2 \tan \theta = \frac{88^2}{700} \qquad \text{Properties of ratios}$$

$$32.2 \tan \theta = \frac{88^2}{700} - 4.5 \qquad \text{Subtract 4.5 from each side.}$$

$$\tan \theta = \frac{88^2/700 - 4.5}{32.2} \qquad \text{Divide each side by 32.2.}$$

$$\tan \theta \approx 0.2038 \qquad \text{Approximate.}$$

$$\theta \approx \tan^{-1} 0.2038 \approx 11.5° \qquad \text{Apply the inverse tangent.}$$

The superelevation should be about $11.5°$.

Now Try Exercise 119

Locating the Position of a Planet One step in the process used by astronomers to calculate the position of a planet as it orbits the sun involves finding the solution of Kepler's equation. Kepler's equation is a trigonometric equation that *cannot* be solved symbolically. It must be solved either graphically or numerically. In real applications, it is quite common to encounter equations that cannot be solved symbolically.

Solving Kepler's equation graphically

[0, 0.2, 0.05] by [−0.2, 0.2, 0.1]

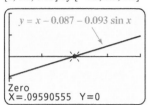

Figure 7.44 Radian Mode

One example of Kepler's equation is given by $\theta = 0.087 + 0.093 \sin\theta$. Solve this equation graphically.   (***Source:*** J. Meeus, *Astronomical Algorithms*.)

SOLUTION The given equation is equivalent to $\theta - 0.087 - 0.093 \sin\theta = 0$. To solve this equation graphically, let $Y_1 = X - 0.087 - 0.093 \sin X$ and graph. (Be sure to use radian mode.) The x-intercept near 0.096 represents the solution. See Figure 7.44.

Solving Inverse Trigonometric Equations

Some types of equations contain inverse trigonometric functions. To solve these equations we often make use of the following inverse properties.

Inverse Trigonometric Properties

$$\sin(\sin^{-1}x) = x \qquad \text{for} \qquad -1 \le x \le 1$$
$$\cos(\cos^{-1}x) = x \qquad \text{for} \qquad -1 \le x \le 1$$
$$\tan(\tan^{-1}x) = x \qquad \text{for} \qquad -\infty < x < \infty$$

These types of equations are solved in the next example.

Solving inverse trigonometric equations

Solve each equation symbolically.

(a) $\cos^{-1}x = \pi$

(b) $\dfrac{\pi}{2} - \tan^{-1}x = \dfrac{\pi}{4}$

(c) $\sin^{-1}2x = \dfrac{\pi}{3}$

SOLUTION

(a) Begin by taking the cosine of each side of the given equation $\cos^{-1}x = \pi$.

$$\cos(\cos^{-1}x) = \cos\pi \qquad \textit{Take the cosine of each side.}$$
$$x = -1 \qquad \textit{Simplify.}$$

(b) Begin by solving the given equation $\frac{\pi}{2} - \tan^{-1}x = \frac{\pi}{4}$ for $\tan^{-1}x$.

$$\frac{\pi}{4} = \tan^{-1}x \qquad \textit{Subtract $\frac{\pi}{2}$; add $\tan^{-1}$x.}$$

$$\tan\frac{\pi}{4} = \tan(\tan^{-1}x) \qquad \textit{Take the tangent of each side.}$$

$$1 = x \qquad \textit{Simplify.}$$

(c) Take the sine of each side of the given equation $\sin^{-1}2x = \frac{\pi}{3}$.

$$\sin(\sin^{-1}2x) = \sin\frac{\pi}{3} \qquad \textit{Take the sine of each side.}$$

$$2x = \frac{\sqrt{3}}{2} \qquad \textit{Simplify.}$$

$$x = \frac{\sqrt{3}}{4} \qquad \textit{Divide each side by 2.}$$

7.3 Putting It All Together

Algebraic skills such as factoring and solving equations can also be used to solve trigonometric equations. Trigonometric equations frequently have infinitely many solutions.

CONCEPT	COMMENTS	EXAMPLES
Reference angles	If an angle θ is in standard position, then its reference angle is the acute angle made by the terminal side of θ and the x-axis.	If $\theta = \frac{11\pi}{6}$, then $\theta_R = \frac{\pi}{6}$.
Trigonometric equations	First, use techniques from algebra to isolate any trigonometric functions. Then solve these simpler equations for the given variable.	$\sqrt{3}\tan\theta = -1$ $\tan\theta = -\frac{1}{\sqrt{3}}$ The reference angle is $\theta_R = \tan^{-1}\frac{1}{\sqrt{3}} = 30°$. Since $\tan\theta$ is negative in quadrants II and IV, the solutions in $[0°, 360°)$ are $150°$ and $330°$.
Inverse trigonometric equations	Equations that involve inverse trigonometric functions can sometimes be solved by using the following properties. $\sin(\sin^{-1}x) = x, -1 \le x \le 1$ $\cos(\cos^{-1}x) = x, -1 \le x \le 1$ $\tan(\tan^{-1}x) = x, -\infty < x < \infty$	$\tan^{-1}x = \frac{\pi}{3}$ $\tan(\tan^{-1}x) = \tan\frac{\pi}{3}$ $x = \sqrt{3}$

7.3 Exercises

Reference Angles

Exercises 1–12: Find the reference angle for θ.

1. $\theta = 120°$

2. $\theta = 230°$

3. $\theta = 85°$

4. $\theta = -130°$

5. $\theta = -65°$

6. $\theta = 340°$

7. $\theta = \frac{5\pi}{6}$

8. $\theta = \frac{7\pi}{4}$

9. $\theta = -\frac{2\pi}{3}$

10. $\theta = -\frac{4\pi}{3}$

11. $\theta = \frac{5\pi}{4}$

12. $\theta = \frac{7\pi}{6}$

Basic Trigonometric Equations

Exercises 13–20: Solve for θ in $[0°, 360°)$ and in $[0, 2\pi)$.

13. **(a)** $\sin\theta = 1$ **(b)** $\sin\theta = -1$

14. **(a)** $\cos\theta = \frac{1}{2}$ **(b)** $\cos\theta = -\frac{1}{2}$

15. **(a)** $\tan\theta = \sqrt{3}$ **(b)** $\tan\theta = -\sqrt{3}$

16. **(a)** $\cot\theta = 1$ **(b)** $\cot\theta = -1$

17. **(a)** $\sec\theta = 2$ **(b)** $\sec\theta = -2$

18. **(a)** $\csc\theta = \sqrt{2}$ **(b)** $\csc\theta = -\sqrt{2}$

19. **(a)** $\sin\theta = 3$ **(b)** $\sin\theta = -3$

20. **(a)** $\cos\theta = \frac{\sqrt{3}}{2}$ **(b)** $\cos\theta = -\frac{\sqrt{3}}{2}$

Exercises 21–26: Find all solutions. Express your answer in radians.

21. **(a)** $\sin t = \frac{1}{2}$ **(b)** $\sin t = -\frac{1}{2}$

22. **(a)** $\cos t = 1$ **(b)** $\cos t = -1$

23. **(a)** $\tan t = 1$ **(b)** $\tan t = -1$

24. **(a)** $\csc t = \frac{1}{4}$ **(b)** $\csc t = -\frac{1}{4}$

25. **(a)** $\sec t = 2$ **(b)** $\sec t = -2$

26. **(a)** $\cot t = \sqrt{3}$ **(b)** $\cot t = -\sqrt{3}$

Solving Trigonometric Equations

Exercises 27–30: Use the graph to estimate any solutions to the given equation for $0 \le t < 2\pi$. Then solve the equation symbolically.

27. $\sin t = \cos t$ **28.** $\csc t = \sec t$

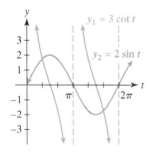 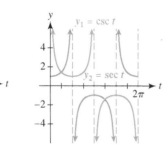

29. $3\cot t = 2\sin t$ **30.** $2\cos^2 t = 1 - \cos t$

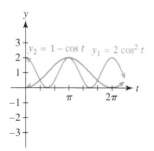

Exercises 31–34: Solve the algebraic equation for x. Then solve the trigonometric equation for $0° \le \theta < 360°$.

31. **(a)** $2x - 1 = 0$ **(b)** $2\sin\theta - 1 = 0$

32. **(a)** $x - 1 = 0$ **(b)** $\cot\theta - 1 = 0$

33. **(a)** $x^2 = x$ **(b)** $\sin^2\theta = \sin\theta$

34. **(a)** $x^2 - x = 0$ **(b)** $\cos^2\theta - \cos\theta = 0$

Exercises 35–38: Solve the algebraic equation for x. Then solve the trigonometric equation for $0 \le t < 2\pi$.

35. **(a)** $x^2 + 1 = 2$ **(b)** $\tan^2 t + 1 = 2$

36. **(a)** $(x - 1)(x + 1) = 0$

   (b) $(\sin t - 1)(\sin t + 1) = 0$

37. **(a)** $x^2 + x = 2$ **(b)** $\cos^2 t + \cos t = 2$

38. **(a)** $2x^2 + 3x = -1$ **(b)** $2\sin^2 t + 3\sin t = -1$

Exercises 39–54: Solve the equation for t in $[0, 2\pi)$.

39. $\tan^2 t - 3 = 0$ **40.** $2\sin t = \sqrt{3}$

41. $3\cos t + 4 = 0$ **42.** $\cos^2 t + \cos t - 6 = 0$

43. $\sin t \cos t = \cos t$ **44.** $\cos^2 t - \sin^2 t = 0$

45. $\csc^2 t = 2\cot t$ **46.** $2\sin^2 t - 3\cos t = 3$

47. $\sin^2 t = \frac{1}{4}$ **48.** $\cos^2 t = -\frac{1}{2}$

49. $\sin t \cos t = 0$ **50.** $\tan t - \cot t = 0$

51. $2\sec t = \tan^2 t + 1$ **52.** $\cos^2 t = 3\sin^2 t$

53. $\tan t + \sec t = 1$ **54.** $\cos t - \sin t = 1$

Exercises 55–74: Find all solutions to the equation. Express your results in radians.

55. $2\tan t - 1 = 1$ **56.** $\sqrt{3}\cot t - 1 = 0$

57. $2\sin t + 2 = 3$ **58.** $2\cos t - 1 = 0$

59. $2\sin^2 t - 3\sin t = -1$ **60.** $2\cos^2 t + 3\cos t + 1 = 0$

61. $\sec^2 t + 3\sec t + 2 = 0$ **62.** $\csc^2 t - 3 = -1$

63. $\tan^2 t - 1 = 0$ **64.** $2\cos t = -1$

65. $\sin^2 t + \sin t - 20 = 0$ **66.** $3\cos t - 5 = 0$

67. $\cos t \sin t = \sin t$ **68.** $2\cos^2 t - 1 = 0$

69. $\sec^2 t = 2\tan t$ **70.** $\cos^2 t - 2\sin t - 1 = 0$

71. $\sin^2 t \cos^2 t = 0$ **72.** $2\cot^2 t \sin t - \cot^2 t = 0$

73. $\sin t + \cos t = 1$ **74.** $\sin t - \cos t = 1$

Exercises 75–92: (Refer to Example 8.) Solve the equation, where t is any real number. Approximate t to three decimal places when appropriate.

75. $\sin 3t = \frac{1}{2}$

76. $\cos 2t = -\frac{1}{2}$

77. $\cos 4t = -\frac{\sqrt{3}}{2}$

78. $\sin 4t = \frac{1}{\sqrt{2}}$

79. $\tan 5t = 1$

80. $\cot 3t = -\sqrt{3}$

81. $2\sin 4t = -1$

82. $5\cos 6t = 2.5$

83. $-\sec 4t = \sqrt{2}$

84. $\sqrt{3}\csc 3t = -2$

85. $2\sin 8t - 3 = -1$

86. $3\cos 8t - 4 = -4$

87. $\cot 4t + 5 = 6$

88. $\sqrt{3}\tan 2t + 2 = 3$

89. $5\cos 3t = 1$

90. $7\cos 5t = -2$

91. $\sin 2t = \frac{1}{3}$

92. $\frac{1}{7}\sin 7t = \frac{1}{20}$

Approximate Solutions

Exercises 93–98: Solve the equation to the nearest thousandth for t in $[0, 2\pi)$.

93. $2.1\sec t - 4.5 = 0$

94. $2\csc t + 2 = 8.3$

95. $5.8\sin t - 3.7 = 0.2$

96. $6\cos t + 2 = 0$

97. $5\tan^2 t - 3 = 0$

98. $7\cot^2 t + 1.2 = 6$

Exercises 99–104: The following equations cannot be solved symbolically. Approximate to two decimal places any solutions on $[0, 2\pi)$ graphically or numerically.

99. $\tan x = x$

100. $x - \cos x = 0$

101. $\sin x = (x - 1)^2$

102. $\sin^2 x - \ln x = 0$

103. $2x\cos(x + 1) = \sin(\cos x)$

104. $e^{-0.1x}\cos x = x\sin x$

Numerical Solutions

Exercises 105 and 106: Use the table to find the solutions to the given equation on $[0°, 360°)$. Then write all solutions to the equation.

105. $\tan\theta - \frac{1}{\sqrt{3}} = 0$

106. $\tan\theta - \sin\theta = 0$

X	Y1
30	0
90	ERROR
150	⁻1.155
210	0
270	ERROR
330	⁻1.155
390	0

Y1▤tan(X)−1/√(3)

X	Y1
0	0
60	.86603
120	⁻2.598
180	0
240	2.5981
300	⁻.866
360	0

Y1▤tan(X)−sin(X)

Solving Inverse Trigonometric Equations

Exercises 107–116: Solve the equation.

107. $\sin^{-1} x = \frac{\pi}{2}$

108. $\sin^{-1} 2x = -\frac{\pi}{4}$

109. $2\cos^{-1} x = \frac{5\pi}{3}$

110. $\cos^{-1} x = 0$

111. $\pi + \tan^{-1} x = \frac{3\pi}{4}$

112. $\tan^{-1} x = -\frac{\pi}{3}$

113. $\tan^{-1}(3x + 1) = \frac{\pi}{4}$

114. $\frac{\pi}{4} + \sin^{-1}(x + 1) = \frac{\pi}{2}$

115. $\cos^{-1} x + 3\cos^{-1} x = \pi$

116. $\frac{\pi}{6} + \sin^{-1} 4x = \frac{\pi}{3}$

Applications

117. First and Third Quarter (Refer to Example 4.) Let $F = 0.25$ and solve the equation $F = \frac{1}{2}(1 - \cos\theta)$ for all θ to determine the phase angles for when 25% of the moon is illuminated.

118. Full Moon (Refer to Example 4.) Let $F = 1$ and solve the equation $F = \frac{1}{2}(1 - \cos\theta)$ for all θ to determine the phase angles for a full moon.

119. Designing Highway Curves (Refer to Example 11.) A highway curve with a radius of $r = 200$ feet and a speed limit of $v = 44$ feet per second (30 mi/hr) is being designed. Use the formula

$$r = \frac{v^2}{4.5 + 32.2\tan\theta}$$

to find an appropriate superelevation θ for the given curve.

120. Designing Highway Curves (Refer to Example 11.) A highway curve with a radius of $r = 800$ feet and a speed limit of $v = 66$ feet per second (45 mi/hr) is being designed. Find the appropriate superelevation for the curve.

121. Daylight Hours (Refer to Example 7.) The number of daylight hours y at 60°N latitude can be modeled by

$$y = 6.5\sin\left(\frac{\pi}{6}(x - 3.65)\right) + 12.4,$$

where $x = 1$ corresponds to January 1, $x = 2$ to February 1, and so on. Estimate graphically or numerically when there are 9 hours of daylight. (*Source:* J. Williams.)

122. Average Temperatures The monthly average high temperature y in degrees Fahrenheit at Phoenix, Arizona, can be modeled by

$$y = 20.3\sin(0.53x - 2.18) + 83.8,$$

where $x = 1$ corresponds to January, $x = 2$ to February, and so on. Estimate graphically or numerically when the monthly average high temperature is 93°F. (*Source:* J. Williams.)

123. Daylight Hours Solve Exercise 121 symbolically.

124. Monthly Average Temperatures Solve Exercise 122 symbolically.

125. Maximum Monthly Sunshine The maximum number of hours of sunshine each month is listed in the table for 50°N latitude.

Month	1	2	3	4	5	6
Hours of Sunshine	261	279	363	407	471	482
Month	7	8	9	10	11	12
Hours of Sunshine	486	442	374	329	267	246

Source: C. Winter, *Solar Power Plants.*

(a) Find a function f that models the data.

(b) Estimate graphically any solutions to the inequality $f(x) \geq 350$ on the interval $[1, 12]$. Interpret the result.

126. Music and Pure Tones A pure tone can be described by a sinusoidal graph. The graph of the function $P = 0.004 \sin(100\pi t)$ shown in the figure represents the pressure of a pure tone on an eardrum in pounds per square foot at time t in seconds. (*Source:* J. Roederer, *Introduction to the Physics and Psychophysics of Music.*)

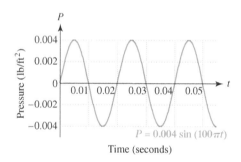

$P = 0.004 \sin(100\pi t)$

Time (seconds)

(a) Estimate all solutions to the equation $P = 0.004$ on the interval $[0, 0.05]$.

(b) Interpret these solutions.

Exercises 127 and 128: **Kepler's Equation** (*Refer to Example 12.*) Solve Kepler's equation to within two decimal places graphically or numerically.

127. $\theta = 0.26 + 0.017 \sin \theta$

128. $\theta = 0.18 + 0.249 \sin \theta$

129. Sums of Pure Tones If two loudspeakers located at different positions produce the same pure tone, the human ear may hear one sound that is equal to the sum of the individual tones. Since the sources are at different locations, their sinusoidal waves will have different phase angles. (*Source:* N. Fletcher and T. Rossing, *The Physics of Musical Instruments.*)

(a) Let two musical tones be given by

$$P_1 = 0.003 \sin(880\pi t - 0.7) \quad \text{and}$$
$$P_2 = 0.002 \sin(880\pi t + 0.6).$$

Graph P_1, P_2, and their sum $P = P_1 + P_2$ separately in the viewing rectangle $[0, 0.01, 0.005]$ by $[-0.005, 0.005, 0.001]$.

(b) Determine the maximum pressure for P.

(c) Is the maximum pressure for P equal to the sum of the maximums of P_1 and P_2? Explain.

130. Sound (Refer to Exercise 129.) Suppose that two loudspeakers located at different positions produce pure tones given by

$$P_1 = A_1 \sin(2\pi Ft + \alpha) \quad \text{and}$$
$$P_2 = A_2 \sin(2\pi Ft + \beta),$$

where F is their common frequency. Then the resulting tone heard by a listener may be written as $P = A \sin(2\pi Ft + \theta)$, where

$$A = \sqrt{(A_1 \cos \alpha + A_2 \cos \beta)^2 + (A_1 \sin \alpha + A_2 \sin \beta)^2}$$

and

$$\theta = \arctan \left[\frac{A_1 \sin \alpha + A_2 \sin \beta}{A_1 \cos \alpha + A_2 \cos \beta} \right].$$

(*Source:* N. Fletcher.)

(a) Find A and θ for P if $F = 440$, $A_1 = 0.003$, $\alpha = -0.7$, $A_2 = 0.002$, and $\beta = 0.6$.

(b) Graph $P = A \sin(2\pi Ft + \theta)$ and $y = P_1 + P_2$ in $[0, 0.01, 0.005]$ by $[-0.005, 0.005, 0.001]$. Do the graphs appear to be identical?

Writing about Mathematics

131. Explain the difference between a conditional equation and an identity. Give one example of each.

132. Explain why knowledge of algebra is important when solving trigonometric equations. Give one example of how knowledge of algebra can be applied to solving a trigonometric equation.

7.4 Sum and Difference Identities

- Apply the sum and difference identities for cosine
- Apply sum and difference identities for sine and tangent

Introduction

Music is made up of vibrations that create pressure on our eardrums. Musical tones can sometimes be modeled with sinusoidal graphs. When more than one tone is played, the resulting pressure is equal to the sum of the individual pressures. Sum and difference identities are sometimes helpful in the analysis of music. This section introduces several trigonometric identities and some of their applications.

Sum and Difference Identities for Cosine

The graph of $y = \cos\left(t - \frac{\pi}{2}\right)$ is translated to the right $\frac{\pi}{2}$ units compared to the graph of $y = \cos t$, as shown in Figure 7.45. If the graph of $y = \cos t$ is translated right $\frac{\pi}{2}$ units, it coincides with the graph of $y = \sin t$, which is shown in Figure 7.46. This discussion suggests that the equation

$$\cos\left(t - \frac{\pi}{2}\right) = \sin t$$

is true for all real numbers t.

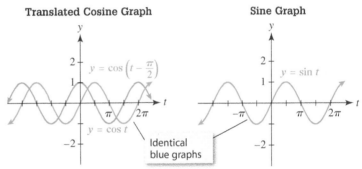

Figure 7.45   Figure 7.46

NOTE It is important to understand that

$$\cos\left(t - \frac{\pi}{2}\right) \neq \cos t - \cos\frac{\pi}{2} = \cos t - 0 = \cos t.$$

To verify this result symbolically, a new identity is needed. Suppose that α and β represent any two angles or real numbers. Then the following identity can be used to calculate the cosine of their difference. (Its proof is given at the end of this section.)

$$\cos(\alpha - \beta) = \cos\alpha \cos\beta + \sin\alpha \sin\beta$$

The next example demonstrates how to apply this identity.

EXAMPLE 1 Using the cosine difference identity

Verify the identity

$$\cos\left(t - \frac{\pi}{2}\right) = \sin t.$$

SOLUTION

Getting Started Start by letting $\alpha = t$ and $\beta = \frac{\pi}{2}$ in the cosine difference identity

$$\cos(\alpha - \beta) = \cos\alpha \cos\beta + \sin\alpha \sin\beta. \blacktriangleright$$

This substitution gives the following result.

$$\cos\left(t - \frac{\pi}{2}\right) = \cos t \cos\frac{\pi}{2} + \sin t \sin\frac{\pi}{2}$$

$$= \cos t (0) + \sin t (1)$$

$$= \sin t$$

Now Try Exercise 29

In the next example, we use the difference identity

$$\cos(\alpha - \beta) = \cos\alpha \cos\beta + \sin\alpha \sin\beta$$

to find the exact value of cos 15°.

EXAMPLE 2 Applying the cosine difference identity

Find the exact value of cos 15°. Use a calculator to support your result.

SOLUTION Since 45° − 30° = 15° and the exact trigonometric values for 45° and 30° are known, we proceed as follows.

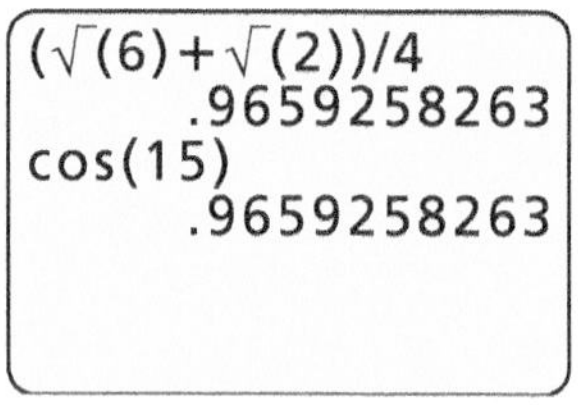

$$\cos 15° = \cos(45° - 30°) \qquad 15° = 45° - 30°$$

$$= \cos 45° \cos 30° + \sin 45° \sin 30° \qquad \text{Difference identity for cosine}$$

$$= \frac{\sqrt{2}}{2} \cdot \frac{\sqrt{3}}{2} + \frac{\sqrt{2}}{2} \cdot \frac{1}{2} \qquad \text{Evaluate each function.}$$

$$= \frac{\sqrt{6} + \sqrt{2}}{4} \qquad \text{Simplify the exact value.}$$

```
(√(6)+√(2))/4
        .9659258263
cos(15)
        .9659258263
```

Figure 7.47 Degree Mode

We see in Figure 7.47 that the value of cos 15° agrees with the symbolic result.

Now Try Exercise 5

With the aid of the difference identity for cosine, we can derive a sum identity.

$$\cos(\alpha + \beta) = \cos(\alpha - (-\beta)) \qquad \alpha + \beta = \alpha - (-\beta)$$

$$= \cos\alpha \cos(-\beta) + \sin\alpha \sin(-\beta) \qquad \text{Difference identity for cosine}$$

$$= \cos\alpha \cos\beta - \sin\alpha \sin\beta \qquad \cos(-\beta) = \cos\beta;$$
$$\qquad\qquad\qquad\qquad\qquad\qquad\qquad \sin(-\beta) = -\sin\beta$$

Sum and difference identities for cosine are as follows.

COSINE OF A SUM OR DIFFERENCE

$$\cos(\alpha + \beta) = \cos\alpha \cos\beta - \sin\alpha \sin\beta$$

$$\cos(\alpha - \beta) = \cos\alpha \cos\beta + \sin\alpha \sin\beta$$

NOTE $\cos(\alpha + \beta) \neq \cos\alpha + \cos\beta$ and $\cos(\alpha - \beta) \neq \cos\alpha - \cos\beta$

Cofunction Identities Section 6.2 introduced the cofunction identities for an acute angle θ. These identities are true for any real number t. We verify one of these identities in the next example.

EXAMPLE 3   Verifying a cofunction identity

Verify that $\cos\left(\frac{\pi}{2} - t\right) = \sin t$.

SOLUTION Let $\alpha = \frac{\pi}{2}$ and $\beta = t$ in the cosine difference identity.

$$\cos\left(\frac{\pi}{2} - t\right) = \cos\frac{\pi}{2}\cos t + \sin\frac{\pi}{2}\sin t$$

$$= (0)\cos t + (1)\sin t$$

$$= \sin t$$

Now Try Exercise 19

The following cofunction identities are valid for *any* real number t.

COFUNCTION IDENTITIES FOR ANY REAL NUMBER t

$$\cos\left(\frac{\pi}{2} - t\right) = \sin t \qquad \sin\left(\frac{\pi}{2} - t\right) = \cos t$$

$$\cot\left(\frac{\pi}{2} - t\right) = \tan t \qquad \tan\left(\frac{\pi}{2} - t\right) = \cot t$$

$$\csc\left(\frac{\pi}{2} - t\right) = \sec t \qquad \sec\left(\frac{\pi}{2} - t\right) = \csc t$$

Sum and Difference Identities for Sine

There are also sum and difference identities for sine.

$$\sin(\alpha + \beta) = \cos\left(\frac{\pi}{2} - (\alpha + \beta)\right) \qquad \text{Cofunction identity}$$

$$= \cos\left(\left(\frac{\pi}{2} - \alpha\right) - \beta\right) \qquad \text{Associative property}$$

$$= \cos\left(\frac{\pi}{2} - \alpha\right)\cos\beta + \sin\left(\frac{\pi}{2} - \alpha\right)\sin\beta \qquad \text{Difference identity for cosine}$$

$$= \sin\alpha\cos\beta + \cos\alpha\sin\beta \qquad \text{Cofunction identities}$$

The difference identity for sine can be derived in a similar manner.

The following box gives the sum and difference identities for sine.

SINE OF A SUM OR DIFFERENCE

$$\sin(\alpha + \beta) = \sin\alpha\cos\beta + \cos\alpha\sin\beta$$

$$\sin(\alpha - \beta) = \sin\alpha\cos\beta - \cos\alpha\sin\beta$$

NOTE $\sin(\alpha + \beta) \neq \sin\alpha + \sin\beta$ and $\sin(\alpha - \beta) \neq \sin\alpha - \sin\beta$

EXAMPLE 4   Analyzing an identity graphically and symbolically

Give graphical support for $\sin(\theta + \pi) = -\sin\theta$. Then verify the identity symbolically.

SOLUTION
Graphical Support   Graph $y = \sin(\theta + \pi)$ and $y = -\sin\theta$, as shown in Figures 7.48 and 7.49 on the next page. Their graphs appear to be identical.

Identical Graphs

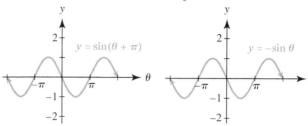

Figure 7.48   Figure 7.49

Symbolic Verification   Let $\alpha = \theta$ and $\beta = \pi$ in the sum identity for sine.

$$\sin(\theta + \pi) = \sin\theta \cos\pi + \cos\theta \sin\pi$$
$$= \sin\theta(-1) + \cos\theta(0)$$
$$= -\sin\theta$$

Thus $\sin(\theta + \pi) = -\sin\theta$.

Now Try Exercise 11

EXAMPLE 5 **Applying sum identities for sine and cosine**

Let $\sin\alpha = \frac{4}{5}$ and $\cos\beta = \frac{3}{5}$. If α is in quadrant II and β is in quadrant IV, find each of the following.

(a) $\sin(\alpha + \beta)$ **(b)** $\cos(\alpha + \beta)$ **(c)** $\tan(\alpha + \beta)$
(d) The quadrant containing $\alpha + \beta$

SOLUTION

Getting Started First sketch possible angles for α and for β, as shown in Figures 7.50 and 7.51. We can see that

$$\sin\alpha = \frac{4}{5}, \quad \cos\alpha = -\frac{3}{5}, \quad \sin\beta = -\frac{4}{5}, \quad \text{and} \quad \cos\beta = \frac{3}{5}. \blacktriangleright$$

α in Quadrant II

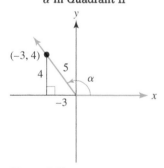

Figure 7.50

β in Quadrant IV

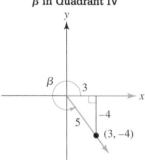

Figure 7.51

(a) To find $\sin(\alpha + \beta)$, apply the sum identity for sine.

$$\sin(\alpha + \beta) = \sin\alpha \cos\beta + \cos\alpha \sin\beta$$
$$= \left(\frac{4}{5}\right)\left(\frac{3}{5}\right) + \left(-\frac{3}{5}\right)\left(-\frac{4}{5}\right)$$
$$= \frac{24}{25}$$

(b) To find $\cos(\alpha + \beta)$, apply the sum identity for cosine.

$$\cos(\alpha + \beta) = \cos\alpha \cos\beta - \sin\alpha \sin\beta$$
$$= \left(-\frac{3}{5}\right)\left(\frac{3}{5}\right) - \left(\frac{4}{5}\right)\left(-\frac{4}{5}\right)$$
$$= \frac{7}{25}$$

(c) $\tan(\alpha + \beta) = \dfrac{\sin(\alpha + \beta)}{\cos(\alpha + \beta)} = \dfrac{24/25}{7/25} = \dfrac{24}{7}$

(d) Since both $\sin(\alpha + \beta)$ and $\cos(\alpha + \beta)$ are positive, $\alpha + \beta$ is in quadrant I.

Now Try Exercise 21

EXAMPLE 6   Verifying an identity

Verify the identity $\dfrac{\sin(\alpha - \beta)}{\sin\alpha \sin\beta} = \cot\beta - \cot\alpha$.

SOLUTION   Begin by expanding the expression $\sin(\alpha - \beta)$.

$$\frac{\sin(\alpha - \beta)}{\sin\alpha \sin\beta} = \frac{\sin\alpha \cos\beta - \cos\alpha \sin\beta}{\sin\alpha \sin\beta} \qquad \text{Difference identity}$$

$$= \frac{\sin\alpha \cos\beta}{\sin\alpha \sin\beta} - \frac{\cos\alpha \sin\beta}{\sin\alpha \sin\beta} \qquad \frac{a-b}{c} = \frac{a}{c} - \frac{b}{c}$$

$$= \frac{\cos\beta}{\sin\beta} - \frac{\cos\alpha}{\sin\alpha} \qquad \text{Simplify each ratio.}$$

$$= \cot\beta - \cot\alpha \qquad \text{Quotient identity}$$

Now Try Exercise 45

Applications

Back Stress   Because human joints both bend and rotate, trigonometry frequently is applied to human physiology. The next example shows how to calculate the force exerted by a person's back muscles and gives a rather amazing result.

EXAMPLE 7   Analyzing stress on a person's back

If a person with weight W bends at the waist with a straight back, then the force F exerted by the lower back muscles may be approximated using $F = 2.89W \sin\left(\theta + \frac{\pi}{2}\right)$, where θ is the angle between a person's torso and the horizontal. See Figure 7.52.   (*Source:* H. Metcalf, *Topics in Classical Biophysics.*)

(a) Let $W = 155$ pounds. The graph of $F = 2.89W \sin\left(\theta + \frac{\pi}{2}\right)$ with $W = 155$ is shown in Figure 7.53. Interpret the graph.

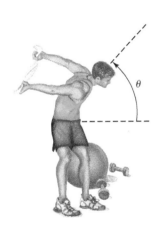

Figure 7.52

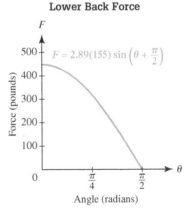

Lower Back Force

$F = 2.89(155) \sin\left(\theta + \frac{\pi}{2}\right)$

Force (pounds)

Angle (radians)

Figure 7.53

(b) Show that $F = 2.89W \cos\theta$.

(c) When $W = 155$ pounds, for what value of θ does F equal 400 pounds?

SOLUTION

(a) When $\theta = 0$, the person's back is parallel to the ground and force F exerted by the back muscles has a maximum of about 450 pounds. This is nearly *three times* the person's weight! As the person straightens up, θ increases, while F decreases. When $\theta = \frac{\pi}{2}$, the person is standing straight up and $F = 0$.

(b) Given $F = 2.89W \sin \left(\theta + \frac{\pi}{2}\right)$, we can show $F = 2.89W \cos\theta$, by applying a sum identity for sine.

$$F = 2.89W \sin\left(\theta + \frac{\pi}{2}\right)$$

$$= 2.89W \left(\sin\theta \cos\frac{\pi}{2} + \cos\theta \sin\frac{\pi}{2}\right)$$

$$= 2.89W \left(\sin\theta\,(0) + \cos\theta\,(1)\right)$$

$$= 2.89W \cos\theta$$

(c) To determine θ when the force is 400 pounds for a person weighing 155 pounds, let $F = 400$ and $W = 155$ in $F = 2.89W \cos\theta$, and then solve for θ.

$$400 = 2.89\,(155) \cos\theta \qquad \textit{F = 400; W = 155}$$

$$\cos\theta = \frac{400}{2.89\,(155)} \qquad \textit{Solve for cos } \theta.$$

$$\theta = \cos^{-1}\left(\frac{400}{2.89\,(155)}\right) \qquad \textit{Solve for } \theta.$$

$$\theta \approx 0.467, \text{ or } 26.8° \qquad \textit{Approximate } \theta.$$

Now Try Exercise 53

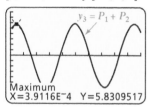

Music and Mathematics   Music is composed of tones with various frequencies. Pressure exerted on the eardrum by a pure tone may be modeled by either $P(t) = a \cos bt$ or $P(t) = a \sin bt$, where a and b are constants and t represents time. When two tuning forks produce the same pure tone, the human ear hears only one sound that is equal to the sum of the individual tones. Trigonometry can be used to model this situation.   (***Source:*** N. Fletcher and T. Rossing, *The Physics of Musical Instruments.*)

EXAMPLE 8   Modeling musical tones

Let the pressure P in grams per square meter exerted on the eardrum by two sources be modeled by

$$P_1(t) = 5 \cos(440\pi t) \qquad \text{and} \qquad P_2(t) = 3 \sin(440\pi t),$$

where t is time in seconds.

(a) Graph the total pressure, $P = P_1 + P_2$, on the eardrum in the viewing rectangle $[0, 0.01, 0.001]$ by $[-8, 8, 1]$.

(b) Use the graph to estimate values for a and k such that $P = a \sin(440\pi t + k)$.

(c) Use a sum or difference identity for sine to verify that $P \approx P_1 + P_2$.

SOLUTION

(a) Let $Y_1 = 5 \cos(440\pi X)$, $Y_2 = 3 \sin(440\pi X)$, and $Y_3 = Y_1 + Y_2$. The graph of $y_3 = P_1 + P_2$ is shown in Figure 7.54.

(b) A maximum y-value occurs near $(0.00039116, 5.831)$. (Note that the x- and y-values shown in Figure 7.54 may vary slightly.) Thus let $a = 5.831$. Since $\sin\theta$ is maximum when $\theta = \frac{\pi}{2}$, we let $t = 0.00039116$ and solve the following equation for k.

$$440\pi\,(0.00039116) + k = \frac{\pi}{2} \qquad \textit{440}\pi\textit{t + k = }\frac{\pi}{2}$$

$$k = \frac{\pi}{2} - 440\pi\,(0.00039116)$$

$$\approx 1.0301$$

Thus let $P \approx 5.831 \sin(440\pi t + 1.0301)$. (Other values for k are possible.)

[0, 0.01, 0.001] by [−8, 8, 1]

$y_3 = P_1 + P_2$

Maximum
X=3.9116E⁻4 Y=5.8309517

Figure 7.54 Radian Mode

Calculator Help
To find a maximum point on a graph, see Appendix A (page AP-8).

(c) Apply the sum identity for sine.

$$P \approx 5.831 \sin(440\pi t + 1.0301)$$
$$= 5.831 \left(\sin(440\pi t) \cos(1.0301) + \cos(440\pi t) \sin(1.0301) \right)$$
$$\approx 5.831 \left(\sin(440\pi t)(0.5147) + \cos(440\pi t)(0.8574) \right)$$
$$\approx 3.00 \sin(440\pi t) + 5.00 \cos(440\pi t)$$
$$= P_1 + P_2$$

Now Try Exercise 55

Sum and Difference Identities for Tangent

Sum and difference identities can also be found for the tangent function.

TANGENT OF A SUM OR DIFFERENCE

$$\tan(\alpha + \beta) = \frac{\tan\alpha + \tan\beta}{1 - \tan\alpha \tan\beta}$$

$$\tan(\alpha - \beta) = \frac{\tan\alpha - \tan\beta}{1 + \tan\alpha \tan\beta}$$

NOTE $\tan(\alpha + \beta) \neq \tan\alpha + \tan\beta$ and $\tan(\alpha - \beta) \neq \tan\alpha - \tan\beta$

These identities are a result of the sum and difference identities for sine and cosine. For example, the difference identity for tangent can be verified as follows.

$$\tan(\alpha - \beta) = \frac{\sin(\alpha - \beta)}{\cos(\alpha - \beta)} \qquad \text{Use } \tan\theta = \frac{\sin\theta}{\cos\theta} \text{ with } \theta = \alpha - \beta.$$

$$= \frac{\sin\alpha \cos\beta - \cos\alpha \sin\beta}{\cos\alpha \cos\beta + \sin\alpha \sin\beta} \qquad \text{Apply difference identities.}$$

$$= \frac{\dfrac{\sin\alpha \cos\beta}{\cos\alpha \cos\beta} - \dfrac{\cos\alpha \sin\beta}{\cos\alpha \cos\beta}}{\dfrac{\cos\alpha \cos\beta}{\cos\alpha \cos\beta} + \dfrac{\sin\alpha \sin\beta}{\cos\alpha \cos\beta}} \qquad \text{Divide each term by } \cos\alpha \cos\beta.$$

$$= \frac{\tan\alpha - \tan\beta}{1 + \tan\alpha \tan\beta} \qquad \text{Simplify.}$$

EXAMPLE 9 Using the tangent difference identity

Use Figure 7.55 to find $\tan\gamma$ if $\tan\alpha = \frac{4}{3}$ and $\tan\beta = \frac{3}{4}$.

SOLUTION From Figure 7.55, α and $\beta + \gamma$ are both supplements of angle BAC. Thus $\alpha = \beta + \gamma$ or $\gamma = \alpha - \beta$.

$$\tan\gamma = \tan(\alpha - \beta) \qquad \gamma = \alpha - \beta$$

$$= \frac{\tan\alpha - \tan\beta}{1 + \tan\alpha \tan\beta} \qquad \text{Tangent difference identity}$$

$$= \frac{\frac{4}{3} - \frac{3}{4}}{1 + \frac{4}{3} \cdot \frac{3}{4}} \qquad \tan\alpha = \frac{4}{3}; \tan\beta = \frac{3}{4}$$

$$= \frac{7}{24} \qquad \text{Simplify.}$$

Now Try Exercise 47

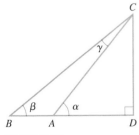

Figure 7.55

Derivation of an Identity

We conclude this section by deriving the difference identity for cosine. Begin by considering the angles α and β in standard position and the unit circle, as shown in Figure 7.56. The terminal side of α intersects the unit circle at $(\cos\alpha, \sin\alpha)$, and the terminal side of β intersects the unit circle at $(\cos\beta, \sin\beta)$. The angle formed between the terminal sides of α and β equals $\alpha - \beta$. Now consider angle $\alpha - \beta$ in standard position. Its terminal side intersects the unit circle at the point $(\cos(\alpha - \beta), \sin(\alpha - \beta))$. This is shown in Figure 7.57.

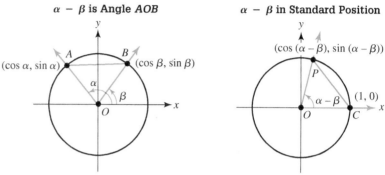

Figure 7.56 Unit Circle   **Figure 7.57** Unit Circle

Since triangles ABO and PCO are congruent, the distance from A to B in Figure 7.56 equals the distance from P to C in Figure 7.57.

$$\underbrace{\sqrt{(\cos\alpha - \cos\beta)^2 + (\sin\alpha - \sin\beta)^2}}_{\text{Distance from } A \text{ to } B} = \underbrace{\sqrt{(\cos(\alpha - \beta) - 1)^2 + (\sin(\alpha - \beta) - 0)^2}}_{\text{Distance from } P \text{ to } C}$$

Squaring each side and clearing parentheses produces

$$\cos^2\alpha - 2\cos\alpha\cos\beta + \cos^2\beta + \sin^2\alpha - 2\sin\alpha\sin\beta + \sin^2\beta =$$
$$\cos^2(\alpha - \beta) - 2\cos(\alpha - \beta) + 1 + \sin^2(\alpha - \beta).$$

Since $\sin^2\theta + \cos^2\theta = 1$ for any θ, the above equation simplifies to

$$2 - 2\cos\alpha\cos\beta - 2\sin\alpha\sin\beta = 2 - 2\cos(\alpha - \beta).$$

Solving this equation for $\cos(\alpha - \beta)$ gives the cosine difference identity

$$\cos(\alpha - \beta) = \cos\alpha\cos\beta + \sin\alpha\sin\beta.$$

7.4 Putting It All Together

The following table lists the important identities in this section.

IDENTITIES	GENERAL FORM
Cosine sum and difference	$\cos(\alpha + \beta) = \cos\alpha\cos\beta - \sin\alpha\sin\beta$ $\cos(\alpha - \beta) = \cos\alpha\cos\beta + \sin\alpha\sin\beta$
Sine sum and difference	$\sin(\alpha + \beta) = \sin\alpha\cos\beta + \cos\alpha\sin\beta$ $\sin(\alpha - \beta) = \sin\alpha\cos\beta - \cos\alpha\sin\beta$

IDENTITIES	GENERAL FORM
Tangent sum and difference	$\tan(\alpha + \beta) = \dfrac{\tan\alpha + \tan\beta}{1 - \tan\alpha\,\tan\beta}$ $\tan(\alpha - \beta) = \dfrac{\tan\alpha - \tan\beta}{1 + \tan\alpha\,\tan\beta}$
Cofunction	$\cos\left(\dfrac{\pi}{2} - t\right) = \sin t \qquad \sin\left(\dfrac{\pi}{2} - t\right) = \cos t$ $\cot\left(\dfrac{\pi}{2} - t\right) = \tan t \qquad \tan\left(\dfrac{\pi}{2} - t\right) = \cot t$ $\csc\left(\dfrac{\pi}{2} - t\right) = \sec t \qquad \sec\left(\dfrac{\pi}{2} - t\right) = \csc t$

7.4 Exercises

Sum and Difference Identities

Exercises 1–10: Find the exact value for each expression. Use a calculator to support your result numerically.

1. $\sin 15°$
2. $\sin 105°$
3. $\tan 15°$
4. $\sin 75°$
5. $\cos 75°$
6. $\cos 105°$
7. $\sin\dfrac{\pi}{12}$ $\left(Hint: \dfrac{\pi}{3} - \dfrac{\pi}{4} = \dfrac{\pi}{12}\right)$
8. $\cos\dfrac{5\pi}{12}$
9. $\sin\dfrac{5\pi}{12}$
10. $\tan\dfrac{\pi}{12}$

Exercises 11–16: Complete the following for the identity.

(a) Give graphical support for the identity.
(b) Verify the identity symbolically.

11. $\sin\left(t + \dfrac{\pi}{2}\right) = \cos t$
12. $\sin\left(t + \dfrac{3\pi}{2}\right) = -\cos t$
13. $\cos(t + \pi) = -\cos t$
14. $\cos\left(t + \dfrac{3\pi}{2}\right) = \sin t$
15. $\sec\left(t - \dfrac{\pi}{2}\right) = \csc t$
16. $\tan\left(t + \dfrac{\pi}{2}\right) = -\cot t$

Exercises 17–20: Use a difference identity to verify the cofunction identity.

17. $\sin\left(\dfrac{\pi}{2} - t\right) = \cos t$
18. $\tan\left(\dfrac{\pi}{2} - t\right) = \cot t$
19. $\sec\left(\dfrac{\pi}{2} - t\right) = \csc t$
20. $\csc\left(\dfrac{\pi}{2} - t\right) = \sec t$

Exercises 21–28: (Refer to Example 5.) Find the following.

(a) $\sin(\alpha + \beta)$ (b) $\cos(\alpha + \beta)$
(c) $\tan(\alpha + \beta)$ (d) The quadrant containing $\alpha + \beta$

21. $\sin\alpha = \dfrac{3}{5}$ and $\sin\beta = \dfrac{5}{13}$, α and β in quadrant I

22. $\cos\alpha = -\dfrac{12}{13}$ and $\cos\beta = -\dfrac{5}{13}$, α and β in quadrant II

23. $\sin\alpha = -\dfrac{8}{17}$ and $\cos\beta = \dfrac{11}{61}$, α in quadrant III and β in quadrant I

24. $\cos\alpha = -\dfrac{24}{25}$ and $\sin\beta = \dfrac{4}{5}$, α in quadrant II and β in quadrant I

25. $\cos\alpha = -\dfrac{3}{5}$ and $\cos\beta = \dfrac{12}{13}$, α in quadrant III and β in quadrant IV

26. $\tan\alpha = \dfrac{3}{4}$ and $\cos\beta = -\dfrac{4}{5}$, α in quadrant I and β in quadrant III

27. $\tan\alpha = -\dfrac{5}{12}$ and $\sec\beta = -\dfrac{61}{11}$, α and β in quadrant II

28. $\cot\alpha = \dfrac{3}{4}$ and $\csc\beta = \dfrac{25}{24}$, α and β in quadrant I

Exercises 29–46: Verify the identity.

29. $\cos\left(t - \dfrac{\pi}{4}\right) = \dfrac{\sqrt{2}}{2}(\cos t + \sin t)$

30. $\sin\left(t + \dfrac{\pi}{4}\right) = \dfrac{\sqrt{2}}{2}(\cos t + \sin t)$

31. $\tan\left(t + \dfrac{\pi}{4}\right) = \dfrac{1 + \tan t}{1 - \tan t}$

32. $\tan(45° - \theta) = \dfrac{1 - \tan\theta}{1 + \tan\theta}$

33. $\dfrac{\cos(x - y)}{\cos(x + y)} = \dfrac{1 + \tan x\,\tan y}{1 - \tan x\,\tan y}$

34. $\dfrac{\sin(x - y)}{\sin(x + y)} = \dfrac{\tan x - \tan y}{\tan x + \tan y}$

35. $\dfrac{\cos(\alpha - \beta)}{\cos\alpha \sin\beta} = \tan\alpha + \cot\beta$

36. $\cos(\theta + \theta) = 1 - 2\sin^2\theta$

37. $\sin 2t = 2\sin t \cos t$

38. $\cos 2t = \cos^2 t - \sin^2 t$

39. $\sin(\alpha + \beta) + \sin(\alpha - \beta) = 2\sin\alpha\cos\beta$

40. $\cos(\alpha + \beta) + \cos(\alpha - \beta) = 2\cos\alpha\cos\beta$

41. $\tan(\pi - \theta) = -\tan\theta$ **42.** $\tan(\theta + \pi) = \tan\theta$

43. $\tan(x - y) - \tan(y - x) = \dfrac{2(\tan x - \tan y)}{1 + \tan x \tan y}$

44. $\dfrac{\sin(x - y)}{\sin y} + \dfrac{\cos(x - y)}{\cos y} = \dfrac{\sin x}{\sin y \cos y}$

45. $\dfrac{\sin(x + y)}{\cos x \cos y} = \tan x + \tan y$

46. $\dfrac{\tan(x + y) - \tan y}{1 + \tan(x + y)\tan y} = \tan x$

Exercises 47 and 48: Solve Example 9 by using the given information.

47. $\tan\alpha = \frac{6}{7}$ and $\tan\beta = \frac{5}{7}$

48. $\cot\alpha = \frac{8}{13}$ and $\cot\beta = \frac{11}{13}$

Lines and Slopes

Exercises 49–52: Suppose two lines, l_1 and l_2, intersect the x-axis making angles α and β, as shown in the figure. Then the slopes of l_1 and l_2 satisfy $m_1 = \tan\alpha$ and $m_2 = \tan\beta$, respectively. If l_1 and l_2 intersect with angle θ as shown, then it follows that $\beta = \alpha + \theta$, or equivalently, $\theta = \beta - \alpha$.

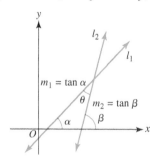

49. Use a difference identity for tangent to show that

$$\tan\theta = \dfrac{m_2 - m_1}{1 + m_1 m_2}.$$

50. Is the formula in Exercise 49 valid if β is an obtuse angle? Explain.

51. Find θ for two intersecting lines given by $y = 2x - 3$ and $y = \frac{3}{5}x + 1$.

52. Find θ for two intersecting lines given by $y = \frac{1}{2}x + 1$ and $y = 3 - x$.

Applications

53. Back Stress   (Refer to Example 7.) Answer the following if $F = 2.89W\cos\theta$.
 (a) Suppose a 200-pound person bends at the waist so that $\theta = \frac{\pi}{4}$. Estimate the force F exerted by the person's back muscles.

 (b) For a 200-pound person, approximate the value of θ that results in the back muscles exerting a force F of 400 pounds.

54. Sound Waves   Sound is a result of waves applying pressure to a person's eardrum. For a particular sound wave radiating outward, the trigonometric function $P(r) = \frac{a}{r}\cos(\pi r - 1000t)$ can be used to express the pressure at a radius of r feet from the source after t seconds. In this formula, a is the maximum sound pressure at the source, measured in pounds per square foot. (*Source:* L. Beranek, *Noise and Vibration Control.*)
 (a) Let $a = 0.4$, $t = 1$, and graph the sound pressure for $0 \le r \le 20$. What happens to the pressure P as the radius r increases?

 (b) Use a difference identity to simplify the expression for $P(r)$ when r is an even integer.

55. Modeling Musical Tones   (Refer to Example 8.) Let the pressure exerted by two sound waves in grams per square meter be given by $P_1(t) = 4\cos(220\pi t)$ and $P_2(t) = 3\sin(220\pi t)$, where t is in seconds.
 (a) Graph the total pressure $P = P_1 + P_2$ in the window $[0, 0.02, 0.001]$ by $[-6, 6, 1]$.

 (b) Use the graph to estimate values for a and k such that $P = a\sin(220\pi t + k)$.

 (c) Use a sum or difference identity for sine to verify that
$$a\sin(220\pi t + k) \approx 4\cos(220\pi t) + 3\sin(220\pi t).$$

56. Electricity   When voltages $V_1 = 50\sin(120\pi t)$ and $V_2 = 120\cos(120\pi t)$ are applied to the same circuit, the resulting voltage V is equal to their sum. (*Source:* D. Bell, *Fundamentals of Electric Circuits.*)
 (a) Graph $V = V_1 + V_2$ in the viewing rectangle $[0, 0.05, 0.01]$ by $[-160, 160, 40]$.

 (b) Use the graph to estimate values for a and k so that $V = a\sin(120\pi t + k)$.

 (c) Use a sum or difference identity for sine to verify part (b).

Writing about Mathematics

57. Are $\sin(45° + 30°)$ and $\sin 45° + \sin 30°$ equivalent expressions? Explain your answer.

58. Are the expressions $\cos(\alpha - \beta)$ and $\cos\alpha - \cos\beta$ equal? Give an example to justify your answer.

Extended and Discovery Exercises

Modeling Musical Beats   Musicians sometimes tune instruments by playing the same tone on two instruments and listening for a phenomenon known as *beats*. The human ear hears beats because the sound pressure slowly rises and falls when two tones vary slightly. When the two instruments are in tune, the beats will disappear. The pressure P on an eardrum can be modeled by $P = a\sin(2\pi Ft)$, where F is the frequency of the tone, t is time in seconds, and P is in pounds per square foot.   (**Source:** J. Pierce, *The Science of Musical Sound.*)

1. Consider two tones with similar frequencies of 440 and 443 cycles per second and pressures

$$P_1 = 0.006\sin(880\pi t) \text{ and } P_2 = 0.004\sin(886\pi t),$$

respectively.

(a) Graph the sum $P = P_1 + P_2$ in [0.15, 1.15, 0.05] by [−0.01, 0.01, 0.001], where P is the total pressure exerted by the tones on an eardrum. How many beats are there in this 1-second interval?

(b) Repeat part (a) with frequencies of 220 and 224.

(c) Determine a way to find the number of beats per second if the frequencies of the tones are F_1 and F_2.

Exercises 2 and 3: **Music and Beats**   *(Refer to Exercise 1.) Given two musical tones P_1 and P_2, graph their sum in* [0.2, 1.2, 0.05] *by* [−0.01, 0.01, 0.001.] *Count the number of beats in 1 second.*

2. $P_1 = 0.007\sin(450\pi t)$, $P_2 = 0.005\sin(454\pi t)$

3. $P_1 = 0.004\cos(830\pi t)$, $P_2 = 0.005\sin(836\pi t)$

CHECKING BASIC CONCEPTS FOR SECTIONS 7.3 AND 7.4

1. Find the reference angle of each angle.
   (a) 225°   **(b)** $\frac{5\pi}{6}$

2. Solve each equation for θ in [0°, 360°).
   (a) $\cos\theta = \frac{1}{2}$ **(b)** $\sin\theta = -\frac{\sqrt{3}}{2}$

3. Find all solutions where t is a real number.
   (a) $\sin t = -\cos t$ **(b)** $2\sin^2 t = 1 - \cos t$

4. Use a sum or difference identity to find $\cos\frac{\pi}{12}$.

5. Verify the identity $\sin(t - \pi) = -\sin t$ symbolically. If you have a graphing calculator, give graphical or numerical support.

7.5 Multiple-Angle Identities

- Learn and use the double-angle identities
- Learn and use power-reducing identities
- Learn and use the half-angle formulas
- Solve equations
- Learn and use product-to-sum and sum-to-product identities

Introduction

In 1831, Michael Faraday discovered that when a wire is passed near a magnet, a small electric current is produced in the wire. By rotating thousands of wires near large electromagnets, massive amounts of electricity can be produced. In 1 year, utilities in the United States generate enough electricity to power a 100-watt light bulb for over 3 billion years!

Voltage, amperage, and wattage are quantities that can be modeled by sinusoidal graphs and functions. To model electricity and other phenomena, trigonometric functions and identities are used. This section introduces several important multiple-angle identities. (**Sources:** R. Weidner and R. Sells, *Elementary Classical Physics*, Vol. 2; J. Wright, *The Universal Almanac.*)

Double-Angle Identities

The double-angle identities for sine, cosine, and tangent can be derived using the sum identities with $\alpha = \theta$ and $\beta = \theta$.

Sine Double-Angle Identity

$$\begin{aligned}
\sin 2\theta &= \sin(\theta + \theta) && 2\theta = \theta + \theta \\
&= \sin\theta\cos\theta + \cos\theta\sin\theta && \sin(\alpha + \beta) = \sin\alpha\cos\beta + \cos\alpha\sin\beta \\
&= 2\sin\theta\cos\theta && \text{Simplify.}
\end{aligned}$$

Cosine Double-Angle Identities

$$\cos 2\theta = \cos(\theta + \theta) \qquad \qquad 2\theta = \theta + \theta$$

$$= \cos\theta\cos\theta - \sin\theta\sin\theta \qquad \cos(\alpha + \beta) = \cos\alpha\cos\beta - \sin\alpha\sin\beta$$

$$= \cos^2\theta - \sin^2\theta \qquad \qquad \text{Simplify.}$$

Applying the Pythagorean identity $\sin^2\theta + \cos^2\theta = 1$, we can write the expression $\cos^2\theta - \sin^2\theta$ as

$$\cos^2\theta - \sin^2\theta = \cos^2\theta - (1 - \cos^2\theta)$$

$$= 2\cos^2\theta - 1$$

or as

$$\cos^2\theta - \sin^2\theta = (1 - \sin^2\theta) - \sin^2\theta$$

$$= 1 - 2\sin^2\theta.$$

Tangent Double-Angle Identity

$$\tan 2\theta = \tan(\theta + \theta) \qquad \qquad 2\theta = \theta + \theta$$

$$= \frac{\tan\theta + \tan\theta}{1 - \tan\theta\tan\theta} \qquad \tan(\alpha + \beta) = \frac{\tan\alpha + \tan\beta}{1 - \tan\alpha\tan\beta}$$

$$= \frac{2\tan\theta}{1 - \tan^2\theta} \qquad \qquad \text{Simplify.}$$

A summary of these double-angle identities is given below.

DOUBLE-ANGLE IDENTITIES

$$\sin 2\theta = 2\sin\theta\cos\theta \qquad \cos 2\theta = \cos^2\theta - \sin^2\theta \qquad \tan 2\theta = \frac{2\tan\theta}{1 - \tan^2\theta}$$

$$\text{or}$$

$$\cos 2\theta = 2\cos^2\theta - 1$$

$$\text{or}$$

$$\cos 2\theta = 1 - 2\sin^2\theta$$

The next example illustrates that $\sin 2\theta \neq 2\sin\theta$.

EXAMPLE 1 Using double-angle identities

Verify symbolically and graphically that $\sin 2\theta$ and $2\sin\theta$ are *not* equivalent expressions.

SOLUTION

Symbolic Verification   The expressions $\sin 2\theta$ and $2\sin\theta$ are not equivalent; rather,

$$\sin 2\theta = 2\sin\theta\cos\theta \neq 2\sin\theta.$$

Graphical Verification   Graph $y = \sin 2\theta$ and $y = 2\sin\theta$, as shown in Figures 7.58 and 7.59. Notice that the graphs are different.

Graphs Showing that $\sin 2\theta \neq 2\sin\theta$

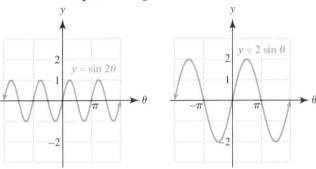

Figure 7.58   Figure 7.59

Now Try Exercise 15

EXAMPLE 2   Using double-angle identities

Given $\cos\theta = -\frac{12}{13}$ and $\sin\theta > 0$, find $\sin 2\theta$, $\cos 2\theta$, and $\tan 2\theta$. Use a calculator to support your result.

SOLUTION

Symbolic Solution   Since $\cos\theta = -\frac{12}{13} < 0$ and $\sin\theta > 0, \theta$ is contained in quadrant II. One possibility for θ is shown in Figure 7.60. We see that $\sin\theta = \frac{5}{13}$. Using double-angle identities, we obtain the following results.

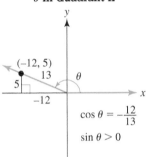

θ in Quadrant II

$(-12, 5)$
13
5
θ
-12

$\cos\theta = -\dfrac{12}{13}$

$\sin\theta > 0$

Figure 7.60

$$\sin 2\theta = 2\sin\theta\cos\theta = 2 \cdot \frac{5}{13} \cdot \left(-\frac{12}{13}\right) = -\frac{120}{169}$$

$$\cos 2\theta = \cos^2\theta - \sin^2\theta = \left(-\frac{12}{13}\right)^2 - \left(\frac{5}{13}\right)^2 = \frac{119}{169}$$

$$\tan 2\theta = \frac{\sin 2\theta}{\cos 2\theta} = \frac{-120/169}{119/169} = -\frac{120}{119}$$

Using $\tan\theta = -\frac{5}{12}$ and the double-angle identity for $\tan 2\theta$ gives the same result.

Calculator Support   Since θ is contained in quadrant II, we can support these results by letting $\theta = \cos^{-1}\left(-\frac{12}{13}\right) \approx 157.38°$ and performing the calculations shown in Figure 7.61 and in Figure 7.62.

Let $\theta = \cos^{-1}(-12/13)$

```
sin(2cos⁻¹(⁻12/13
))▶Frac
              ⁻120/169
cos(2cos⁻¹(⁻12/13
))▶Frac
               119/169
```

```
tan(2cos⁻¹(⁻12/13
))▶Frac
              ⁻120/119
```

Figure 7.61   Figure 7.62

Now Try Exercise 19

EXAMPLE 3   Evaluating expressions with double-angle identities

Use a double-angle identity to evaluate each expression.

(a) $\cos\left(2\sin^{-1}\frac{1}{3}\right)$ **(b)** $\sin\left(2\cos^{-1}\left(-\frac{3}{5}\right)\right)$ **(c)** $\sin(2\tan^{-1}x), x > 0$

SOLUTION

(a) If we let $\theta = \sin^{-1}\frac{1}{3}$, then it follows that $\sin\theta = \frac{1}{3}$. The expression $\cos\left(2\sin^{-1}\frac{1}{3}\right)$ can be evaluated as follows.

$$\cos\left(2\sin^{-1}\frac{1}{3}\right) = \cos(2\theta) \qquad \theta = \sin^{-1}\frac{1}{3}$$

$$= 1 - 2\sin^2\theta \qquad \text{Double-angle identity}$$

$$= 1 - 2\left(\frac{1}{3}\right)^2 \qquad \sin\theta = \frac{1}{3}$$

$$= \frac{7}{9} \qquad \text{Simplify.}$$

θ in Quadrant II

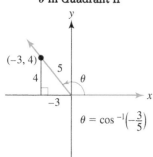

Figure 7.63

(b) Begin by letting $\theta = \cos^{-1}\left(-\frac{3}{5}\right)$ and sketching angle θ in standard position, as shown in Figure 7.63. Notice that $\cos\theta = -\frac{3}{5}$ and that θ is a second quadrant angle. From Figure 7.63 it follows that $\sin\theta = \frac{4}{5}$. The expression $\sin\left(2\cos^{-1}\left(-\frac{3}{5}\right)\right)$ can be evaluated as follows.

$$\sin\left(2\cos^{-1}\left(-\frac{3}{5}\right)\right) = \sin(2\theta) \qquad \theta = \cos^{-1}\left(-\frac{3}{5}\right)$$

$$= 2\sin\theta\cos\theta \qquad \text{Double-angle identity}$$

$$= 2\left(\frac{4}{5}\right)\left(-\frac{3}{5}\right) \qquad \sin\theta = \frac{4}{5}, \cos\theta = -\frac{3}{5}$$

$$= -\frac{24}{25} \qquad \text{Simplify.}$$

θ in Quadrant I

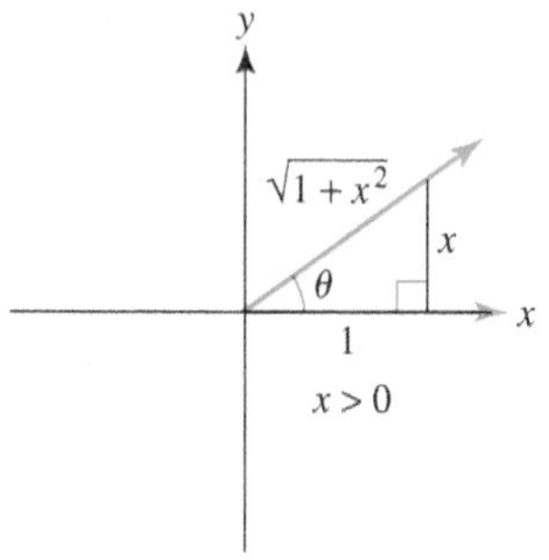

Figure 7.64

(c) Begin by letting $\theta = \tan^{-1}x$ and sketching angle θ in standard position, as shown in Figure 7.64. Since $x > 0$, we have drawn a first quadrant angle θ whose tangent function equals $\frac{x}{1}$. That is, $\tan\theta = x$. From Figure 7.64 it can be concluded that $\sin\theta = \frac{x}{\sqrt{1 + x^2}}$ and $\cos\theta = \frac{1}{\sqrt{1 + x^2}}$. The trigonometric expression $\sin(2\tan^{-1}x)$ can be evaluated as follows.

$$\sin(2\tan^{-1}x) = \sin(2\theta) \qquad \theta = \tan^{-1}x$$

$$= 2\sin\theta\cos\theta \qquad \text{Double-angle identity}$$

$$= 2\left(\frac{x}{\sqrt{1 + x^2}}\right)\left(\frac{1}{\sqrt{1 + x^2}}\right) \qquad \text{Substitute.}$$

$$= \frac{2x}{1 + x^2} \qquad \text{Simplify.}$$

Now Try Exercises 25, 27, and 31

In the next example, we verify an identity by using a double-angle identity.

EXAMPLE 4 Verifying an identity

Verify the identity $\dfrac{\sec^2\theta}{1 - \tan^2\theta} = \sec 2\theta$.

SOLUTION Begin by applying a reciprocal identity.

$$\frac{\sec^2 \theta}{1 - \tan^2 \theta} = \frac{1}{\cos^2 \theta \, (1 - \tan^2 \theta)} \qquad \text{Reciprocal identity}$$

$$= \frac{1}{\cos^2 \theta \left(1 - \dfrac{\sin^2 \theta}{\cos^2 \theta} \right)} \qquad \text{Quotient identity}$$

$$= \frac{1}{\cos^2 \theta - \sin^2 \theta} \qquad \text{Distributive property}$$

$$= \frac{1}{\cos 2\theta} \qquad \text{Double-angle identity}$$

$$= \sec 2\theta \qquad \text{Reciprocal identity}$$

Now Try Exercise 67

EXAMPLE 5   Deriving a triple-angle identity

Write $\cos 3\theta$ in terms of $\cos \theta$.

SOLUTION

$$\cos 3\theta = \cos(2\theta + \theta) \qquad 3\theta = 2\theta + \theta$$

$$= \cos 2\theta \cos \theta - \sin 2\theta \sin \theta \qquad \text{Sum identity for cosine}$$

$$= (2 \cos^2 \theta - 1) \cos \theta - (2 \sin \theta \cos \theta) \sin \theta \qquad \text{Double-angle identities}$$

$$= 2 \cos^3 \theta - \cos \theta - 2 \sin^2 \theta \cos \theta \qquad \text{Multiply.}$$

$$= 2 \cos^3 \theta - \cos \theta - 2 (1 - \cos^2 \theta) \cos \theta \qquad \text{Apply } \sin^2 \theta + \cos^2 \theta = 1.$$

$$= 2 \cos^3 \theta - \cos \theta - 2 \cos \theta + 2 \cos^3 \theta \qquad \text{Distributive property}$$

$$= 4 \cos^3 \theta - 3 \cos \theta \qquad \text{Combine like terms.}$$

Now Try Exercise 71

Power-Reducing Identities

Power-reducing identities for sine, cosine, and tangent can be derived using the double-angle identities.

Sine Power-Reducing Identity   We can solve $\cos 2\theta = 1 - 2 \sin^2 \theta$ for $\sin^2 \theta$ to obtain

$$\sin^2 \theta = \frac{1 - \cos 2\theta}{2}.$$

Cosine Power-Reducing Identity   Solving $\cos 2\theta = 2 \cos^2 \theta - 1$ for $\cos^2 \theta$ gives

$$\cos^2 \theta = \frac{1 + \cos 2\theta}{2}.$$

Tangent Power-Reducing Identity   We can use the power-reducing identities

$$\sin^2 \theta = \frac{1 - \cos 2\theta}{2} \qquad \text{and} \qquad \cos^2 \theta = \frac{1 + \cos 2\theta}{2}$$

to derive

$$\tan^2 \theta = \frac{\sin^2 \theta}{\cos^2 \theta} = \frac{(1 - \cos 2\theta)/2}{(1 + \cos 2\theta)/2} = \frac{1 - \cos 2\theta}{1 + \cos 2\theta}.$$

A summary of these identities is given in the box below.

POWER-REDUCING IDENTITIES

$$\sin^2 \theta = \frac{1 - \cos 2\theta}{2} \qquad \cos^2 \theta = \frac{1 + \cos 2\theta}{2} \qquad \tan^2 \theta = \frac{1 - \cos 2\theta}{1 + \cos 2\theta}$$

In the next example, we write known identities in terms of inputs other than θ.

EXAMPLE 6 Writing identities

Complete each statement.

(a) $\sin^2 \theta = \frac{1 - \cos 2\theta}{2}$, so $\sin^2 4t = $ _____.

(b) $\tan^2 \theta = \frac{1 - \cos 2\theta}{1 + \cos 2\theta}$, so $\tan^2\left(\frac{1}{2}x\right) = $ _____.

(c) $\sin 2\theta = 2 \sin \theta \cos \theta$, so $\sin 8t = $ _____.

SOLUTION

(a) Substitute $4t$ for θ on each side of the given equation.

$$\sin^2 4t = \frac{1 - \cos(2 \cdot 4t)}{2} \qquad \sin^2 \theta = \frac{1 - \cos 2\theta}{2}$$

Let $\theta = 4t$

$$= \frac{1 - \cos 8t}{2}$$

(b) Substitute $\frac{1}{2}x$ for θ on each side of the given equation.

$$\tan^2\left(\frac{1}{2}x\right) = \frac{1 - \cos\left(2 \cdot \frac{1}{2}x\right)}{1 + \cos\left(2 \cdot \frac{1}{2}x\right)} \qquad \tan^2 \theta = \frac{1 - \cos 2\theta}{1 + \cos 2\theta}$$

Let $\theta = \frac{1}{2}x$

$$= \frac{1 - \cos x}{1 + \cos x}$$

(c) Let $2\theta = 8t$, so $\theta = 4t$. Thus $\sin 2\theta = 2 \sin \theta \cos \theta$ implies

Let $\theta = 4t$ ———— $\sin 8t = 2 \sin 4t \cos 4t$.

Now Try Exercises 1, 3, and 5

EXAMPLE 7 Using a power-reducing identity

Find the exact value of $\sin^2 22.5°$. Use a calculator to support your results.

SOLUTION Let $\theta = 22.5°$ and $2\theta = 45°$ and apply the sine power-reducing identity.

$$\sin^2 22.5° = \frac{1 - \cos 45°}{2} \qquad \sin^2 \theta = \frac{1 - \cos 2\theta}{2}$$

$$= \frac{1 - \sqrt{2}/2}{2} \qquad \cos 45° = \frac{\sqrt{2}}{2}$$

$$= \frac{2 - \sqrt{2}}{4} \qquad \text{Multiply by } \frac{2}{2}.$$

Support for this result is shown in Figure 7.65.

Now Try Exercise 45

Degree Mode

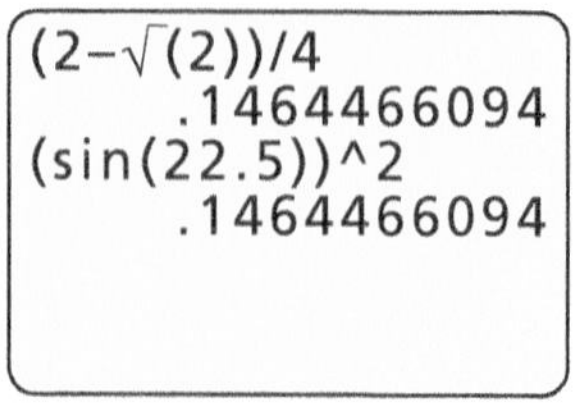

```
(2−√(2))/4
        .1464466094
(sin(22.5))^2
        .1464466094
```

Figure 7.65

An Application Next we apply a power-reducing identity to electrical circuits.

EXAMPLE 8   Using a power-reducing identity to analyze wattage

Amperage I is a measure of the amount of electricity passing through a wire, and voltage V is a measure of the force "pushing" the electricity. The wattage W consumed by an electrical device can be calculated using the equation $W = VI$.   (*Source:* G. Wilcox and C. Hesselberth, *Electricity for Engineering Technology*.)

(a) Voltage in a household circuit is given by $V = 160 \sin(120\pi t)$, where t is in seconds. Suppose that the amperage flowing through a toaster is given by $I = 12 \sin(120\pi t)$. Graph the wattage W consumed by the toaster in $[0, 0.04, 0.01]$ by $[-200, 3000, 200]$.

(b) Write the wattage as $W = a \cos(k\pi t) + d$, where a, k, and d are constants.

(c) Compare the periods of the voltage, amperage, and wattage.

(d) The wattage of this toaster equals half the maximum of W. Find the wattage.

SOLUTION

(a) Since $W = VI$, graph the equation $Y_3 = Y_1 * Y_2$, where $Y_1 = 160 \sin(120\pi X)$ and $Y_2 = 12 \sin(120\pi X)$, as shown in Figure 7.66, where *radian* mode is used.

(b)
$$
\begin{aligned}
W &= VI \\
&= 160 \sin(120\pi t) \cdot 12 \sin(120\pi t) \qquad \text{Substitute for V and I.} \\
&= 1920 \sin^2(120\pi t) \qquad \text{Multiply.} \\
&= 1920 \cdot \frac{1 - \cos(240\pi t)}{2} \qquad \text{Power-reducing identity} \\
&= 960 - 960 \cos(240\pi t) \qquad \text{Simplify.}
\end{aligned}
$$

Thus let $a = -960$, $k = 240$, and $d = 960$. Then the wattage can be written as
$$W = -960 \cos(240\pi t) + 960.$$

(c) The period for both V and I is $\frac{2\pi}{120\pi} = \frac{1}{60}$ second, and the period for W is $\frac{2\pi}{240\pi} = \frac{1}{120}$ second. This result is supported in Figure 7.67, where the graph of V requires twice as much time as W to complete one oscillation.

(d) The maximum wattage is 1920 watts whenever $\cos(240\pi t) = -1$. Half this amount is 960 watts, which is the wattage rating for the toaster.

Now Try Exercise 119

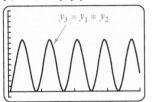

Wattage W

$[0, 0.04, 0.01]$ by $[-200, 3000, 200]$

$y_3 = y_1 * y_2$

Figure 7.66 Radian Mode

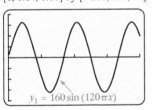

Voltage V

$[0, 0.04, 0.01]$ by $[-200, 200, 50]$

$y_1 = 160 \sin(120\pi x)$

Figure 7.67 Radian Mode

Half-Angle Formulas

We obtain half-angle formulas by using the power-reducing identities. For example,

$$\sin^2 x = \frac{1 - \cos 2x}{2} \qquad \text{Power-reducing identity}$$

$$\sin x = \pm\sqrt{\frac{1 - \cos 2x}{2}} \qquad \text{Square root property}$$

$$\sin \frac{\theta}{2} = \pm\sqrt{\frac{1 - \cos \theta}{2}}. \qquad \text{Let } x = \frac{\theta}{2} \text{ and } 2x = \theta.$$

The following box gives some half-angle formulas. (The second and third half-angle formulas for tangent are verified in Exercises 83 and 84.)

HALF-ANGLE FORMULAS

$$\sin \frac{\theta}{2} = \pm\sqrt{\frac{1 - \cos \theta}{2}} \qquad \cos \frac{\theta}{2} = \pm\sqrt{\frac{1 + \cos \theta}{2}}$$

$$\tan \frac{\theta}{2} = \pm\sqrt{\frac{1 - \cos \theta}{1 + \cos \theta}} \qquad \tan \frac{\theta}{2} = \frac{1 - \cos \theta}{\sin \theta} \qquad \tan \frac{\theta}{2} = \frac{\sin \theta}{1 + \cos \theta}$$

To decide whether a positive or negative sign should be used in a half-angle formula, we must determine the quadrant containing $\frac{\theta}{2}$. This is illustrated in the next example.

EXAMPLE 9 Using a half-angle formula to find an exact value

Find the exact value of $\sin(-15°)$.

SOLUTION We use the fact that $\cos(-30°) = \frac{\sqrt{3}}{2}$ to find $\sin(-15°)$. Note if $\theta = -30°$, then $\frac{\theta}{2}$ is in quadrant IV.

$$\sin(-15°) = \sin\left(\frac{-30°}{2}\right) \qquad \text{Let } \frac{\theta}{2} = -15° \text{ and } \theta = -30°.$$

Sine is negative in quadrant IV.

$$= -\sqrt{\frac{1 - \cos(-30°)}{2}} \qquad \sin\frac{\theta}{2} = \pm\sqrt{\frac{1 - \cos\theta}{2}}$$

$$= -\sqrt{\frac{1 - \sqrt{3}/2}{2}} \qquad \cos(-30°) = \frac{\sqrt{3}}{2}$$

$$= -\sqrt{\frac{2 - \sqrt{3}}{4}} \qquad \begin{array}{l}\text{Multiply numerator}\\\text{and denominator by 2.}\end{array}$$

$$= -\frac{\sqrt{2 - \sqrt{3}}}{2} \qquad \sqrt{4} = 2$$

Now Try Exercise 49

EXAMPLE 10 Using half-angle formulas to find exact values

If $\cos\theta = -\frac{3}{5}$ and $90° \le \theta \le 180°$, find $\sin\frac{\theta}{2}$, $\cos\frac{\theta}{2}$, and $\tan\frac{\theta}{2}$.

SOLUTION Since $90° \le \theta \le 180°$, it follows that $45° \le \frac{\theta}{2} \le 90°$. That is, $\frac{\theta}{2}$ is in quadrant I.

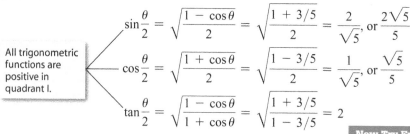

All trigonometric functions are positive in quadrant I.

$$\sin\frac{\theta}{2} = \sqrt{\frac{1 - \cos\theta}{2}} = \sqrt{\frac{1 + 3/5}{2}} = \frac{2}{\sqrt{5}}, \text{ or } \frac{2\sqrt{5}}{5}$$

$$\cos\frac{\theta}{2} = \sqrt{\frac{1 + \cos\theta}{2}} = \sqrt{\frac{1 - 3/5}{2}} = \frac{1}{\sqrt{5}}, \text{ or } \frac{\sqrt{5}}{5}$$

$$\tan\frac{\theta}{2} = \sqrt{\frac{1 - \cos\theta}{1 + \cos\theta}} = \sqrt{\frac{1 + 3/5}{1 - 3/5}} = 2$$

Now Try Exercise 59

Solving Equations

When trigonometric functions are used in modeling to make predictions, there is often a need to solve trigonometric equations.

EXAMPLE 11 Solving a trigonometric equation

Solve the trigonometric equation $\cos\theta - \sin 2\theta = 0$ symbolically, graphically, and numerically for $0° \le \theta < 360°$.

SOLUTION

Symbolic Solution We begin by applying the identity $\sin 2\theta = 2\sin\theta\cos\theta$.

$$\cos\theta - \sin 2\theta = 0 \qquad \text{Given equation}$$

$$\cos\theta - 2\sin\theta\cos\theta = 0 \qquad \text{Double-angle identity}$$

$$\cos\theta(1 - 2\sin\theta) = 0 \qquad \text{Factor out } \cos\theta.$$

$$\cos\theta = 0 \quad \text{or} \quad 1 - 2\sin\theta = 0 \qquad \text{Zero-product property}$$

$$\cos\theta = 0 \quad \text{or} \quad \sin\theta = \frac{1}{2} \qquad \text{Solve for } \sin\theta.$$

$$\theta = 90°, 270° \quad \text{or} \quad \theta = 30°, 150° \qquad \text{Solve for } \theta.$$

On the interval $[0°, 360°)$, the solutions are $30°$, $90°$, $150°$, and $270°$.

Graphical Solution   Graphical support is given in Figure 7.68, where the graph of $Y_1 = \cos(X) - \sin(2X)$ is shown. Note that the four *x*-intercepts 30°, 90°, 150°, and 270° correspond to the four symbolic solutions.

Numerical Solution   Numerical support is shown in Figure 7.69.

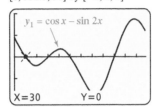

Degree Mode	Degree Mode
[0, 352.5, 30] by [−2, 2, 1]	

Figure 7.68   **Figure 7.69**

Now Try Exercise 95

EXAMPLE 12   Solving a trigonometric equation

Solve the equation $4\cos\frac{\theta}{2} - 2 = 0$ for $0 \le \theta < 2\pi$.

SOLUTION   Begin by solving $4\cos\frac{\theta}{2} - 2 = 0$ for $\cos\frac{\theta}{2}$.

$$4\cos\frac{\theta}{2} - 2 = 0 \qquad \text{\textcolor{gray}{Given equation}}$$

$$\cos\frac{\theta}{2} = \frac{1}{2} \qquad \text{\textcolor{gray}{Solve for $\cos\frac{\theta}{2}$.}}$$

$$\frac{\theta}{2} = \frac{\pi}{3} \quad \text{or} \quad \frac{\theta}{2} = \frac{5\pi}{3} \qquad \text{\textcolor{gray}{Solve for $\frac{\theta}{2}$.}}$$

$$\theta = \frac{2\pi}{3} \quad \text{or} \quad \theta = \frac{10\pi}{3} \qquad \text{\textcolor{gray}{Multiply by 2.}}$$

The only solution on $[0, 2\pi)$ is $\frac{2\pi}{3}$.

Now Try Exercise 99

EXAMPLE 13   Solving trigonometric equations

Find all solutions, expressed in radians.
(a) $\cos 2t + 2\cos^2 t = 0$ **(b)** $2\sin 2t = \sqrt{3}$

SOLUTION
(a) Begin by applying the double-angle identity $\cos 2t = 2\cos^2 t - 1$.

$$\cos 2t + 2\cos^2 t = 0 \qquad \text{\textcolor{gray}{Given equation}}$$

$$2\cos^2 t - 1 + 2\cos^2 t = 0 \qquad \text{\textcolor{gray}{Double-angle identity}}$$

$$4\cos^2 t - 1 = 0 \qquad \text{\textcolor{gray}{Combine terms.}}$$

$$\cos^2 t = \frac{1}{4} \qquad \text{\textcolor{gray}{Solve for $\cos^2 t$.}}$$

$$\cos t = \pm\frac{1}{2} \qquad \text{\textcolor{gray}{Square root property}}$$

On the interval $[0, 2\pi)$, there are four angles whose cosines equal either $\frac{1}{2}$ or $-\frac{1}{2}$. They are $\frac{\pi}{3}, \frac{2\pi}{3}, \frac{4\pi}{3}$, and $\frac{5\pi}{3}$. Since $\cos t$ has period 2π, all solutions can be written as

All Solutions Written as Four Expressions

$$\frac{\pi}{3} + 2\pi n, \qquad \frac{2\pi}{3} + 2\pi n, \qquad \frac{4\pi}{3} + 2\pi n, \qquad \text{or} \qquad \frac{5\pi}{3} + 2\pi n,$$

where n is an integer. Note that since $\frac{4\pi}{3} - \frac{\pi}{3} = \pi$, the two solutions $\frac{\pi}{3} + 2\pi n$ and $\frac{4\pi}{3} + 2\pi n$ can be combined and written as $\frac{\pi}{3} + \pi n$. Similarly, the two solutions $\frac{2\pi}{3} + 2\pi n$ and $\frac{5\pi}{3} + 2\pi n$ can be written as $\frac{2\pi}{3} + \pi n$. As a result, all solutions can also be written as

All Solutions Written as Two Expressions

$$\frac{\pi}{3} + \pi n \quad \text{or} \quad \frac{2\pi}{3} + \pi n.$$

(b) Begin by dividing each side by 2.

$$2 \sin 2t = \sqrt{3} \qquad \textit{Given equation}$$

$$\sin 2t = \frac{\sqrt{3}}{2} \qquad \textit{Divide each side by 2.}$$

Let $\theta = 2t$ and find all values of θ on the interval $[0, 2\pi)$, where $\sin \theta = \frac{\sqrt{3}}{2}$. Because the reference angle for θ is $\theta_R = \sin^{-1}\frac{\sqrt{3}}{2} = \frac{\pi}{3}$ and the sine function is positive in quadrants I and II, it follows that $\theta = \frac{\pi}{3}$ or $\theta = \frac{2\pi}{3}$. Thus all possible solutions in terms of θ can be written as

$$\theta = \frac{\pi}{3} + 2\pi n \quad \text{or} \quad \theta = \frac{2\pi}{3} + 2\pi n.$$

Since $\theta = 2t$, we can write the solutions to the given equation in terms of t.

$$2t = \frac{\pi}{3} + 2\pi n \quad \text{or} \quad 2t = \frac{2\pi}{3} + 2\pi n \qquad \textit{Let } \theta = 2t.$$

To solve for t, divide each term by 2.

$$t = \frac{\pi}{6} + \pi n \quad \text{or} \quad t = \frac{\pi}{3} + \pi n \qquad \textit{Divide by 2.}$$

Now Try Exercises 101 and 107

Product-to-Sum and Sum-to-Product Identities

The sum and difference identities for sine and cosine can be used to derive several identities that make it possible to rewrite a product as a sum. For example, adding the identities for $\cos(\alpha + \beta)$ and $\cos(\alpha - \beta)$ results in the following.

$$\cos(\alpha + \beta) = \cos\alpha \cos\beta - \sin\alpha \sin\beta$$
$$\underline{\cos(\alpha - \beta) = \cos\alpha \cos\beta + \sin\alpha \sin\beta}$$
$$\cos(\alpha + \beta) + \cos(\alpha - \beta) = 2\cos\alpha \cos\beta$$

Rewriting gives $\cos\alpha \cos\beta = \frac{1}{2}(\cos(\alpha + \beta) + \cos(\alpha - \beta))$. Four product-to-sum identities are given below. The other three identities are derived in a similar manner.

PRODUCT-TO-SUM IDENTITIES

$$\cos\alpha \cos\beta = \frac{1}{2}(\cos(\alpha + \beta) + \cos(\alpha - \beta))$$

$$\sin\alpha \sin\beta = \frac{1}{2}(\cos(\alpha - \beta) - \cos(\alpha + \beta))$$

$$\sin\alpha \cos\beta = \frac{1}{2}(\sin(\alpha + \beta) + \sin(\alpha - \beta))$$

$$\cos\alpha \sin\beta = \frac{1}{2}(\sin(\alpha + \beta) - \sin(\alpha - \beta))$$

EXAMPLE 14   Using a product-to-sum identity

Write the product $\cos 5\theta \cos 3\theta$ as a sum.

SOLUTION   We begin by applying the first product-to-sum identity with the substitution $\alpha = 5\theta$ and $\beta = 3\theta$.

$$\cos 5\theta \cos 3\theta = \frac{1}{2}(\cos(5\theta + 3\theta) + \cos(5\theta - 3\theta)) \qquad \alpha = 5\theta, \beta = 3\theta$$

$$= \frac{1}{2}(\cos 8\theta + \cos 2\theta) \qquad \text{Add; subtract.}$$

Now Try Exercise 85

By rewriting the four product-to-sum identities, we can derive four sum-to-product identities. If we let $a = \alpha + \beta$ and $b = \alpha - \beta$, it follows that

$$\frac{a + b}{2} = \frac{\alpha + \beta + \alpha - \beta}{2} = \alpha \quad \text{and} \quad \frac{a - b}{2} = \frac{(\alpha + \beta) - (\alpha - \beta)}{2} = \beta.$$

Now, multiplying both sides of the identity

$$\cos \alpha \cos \beta = \frac{1}{2}(\cos(\alpha + \beta) + \cos(\alpha - \beta))$$

by 2 and substituting yields

$$2 \cos \frac{a + b}{2} \cos \frac{a - b}{2} = \cos a + \cos b.$$

The other three sum-to-product identities can be derived in a similar manner.

SUM-TO-PRODUCT IDENTITIES

$$\cos a + \cos b = 2 \cos \frac{a + b}{2} \cos \frac{a - b}{2}$$

$$\cos a - \cos b = -2 \sin \frac{a + b}{2} \sin \frac{a - b}{2}$$

$$\sin a + \sin b = 2 \sin \frac{a + b}{2} \cos \frac{a - b}{2}$$

$$\sin a - \sin b = 2 \cos \frac{a + b}{2} \sin \frac{a - b}{2}$$

For example, we can write the sum $\cos 70° + \cos 40°$ as follows.

$$\cos 70° + \cos 40° = 2 \cos \frac{70° + 40°}{2} \cos \frac{70° - 40°}{2} = 2 \cos 55° \cos 15°$$

An Application from Telephone Technology   Each number on a touch-tone phone produces a unique pair of frequencies. For example, when 1 is pressed, frequencies of 697 hertz and 1209 hertz are simultaneously transmitted. A *hertz* (Hz) is equal to one cycle per second. When 2 is pressed, the pair of frequencies transmitted is 697 hertz and 1336 hertz. As a result, 2 has a different tone from 1. Table 7.2 shows the frequency pairs for the numbers 0 through 9.

Frequencies Used in Touch-Tone Phones

Number	0	1	2	3	4	5	6	7	8	9
Frequency 1 (Hz)	941	697	697	697	770	770	770	852	852	852
Frequency 2 (Hz)	1336	1209	1336	1477	1209	1336	1477	1209	1336	1477

Table 7.2

A tone with frequencies F_1 and F_2 can be modeled by

$$a_1 \cos(2\pi F_1 t) + a_2 \cos(2\pi F_2 t).$$

If both tones have the same intensity, then we can let $a_1 = a_2 = 1$.

EXAMPLE 15 Analyzing touch-tone phones

For a touch-tone phone, assume that $a_1 = a_2 = 1$.
(a) Write an expression that models the sound of a 5 on a touch-tone phone.
(b) Rewrite the expression in part (a) as a product of trigonometric expressions.

SOLUTION
(a) From Table 7.2 we can see that for number 5, $F_1 = 770$ and $F_2 = 1336$. Thus

$$y = \cos(1540\pi t) + \cos(2672\pi t).$$

(b) Let $a = 1540\pi t$ and $b = 2672\pi t$ in the appropriate sum-to-product identity.

$$\cos 1540\pi t + \cos 2672\pi t$$

$$= 2 \cos \frac{1540\pi t + 2672\pi t}{2} \cos \frac{1540\pi t - 2672\pi t}{2}$$

$$= 2 \cos(2106\pi t) \cos(-566\pi t)$$

$$= 2 \cos(2106\pi t) \cos(566\pi t) \quad\quad \boxed{\cos(-\theta) = \cos\theta}$$

Now Try Exercise 125

7.5 Putting It All Together

The multiple-angle identities or formulas presented in this section are summarized in the following table.

IDENTITY OR FORMULA	GENERAL FORM
Double-angle	$\sin 2\theta = 2 \sin\theta \cos\theta$ $\cos 2\theta = \cos^2\theta - \sin^2\theta = 2\cos^2\theta - 1 = 1 - 2\sin^2\theta$ $\tan 2\theta = \dfrac{2\tan\theta}{1 - \tan^2\theta}$
Power-reducing	$\sin^2\theta = \dfrac{1 - \cos 2\theta}{2} \qquad \cos^2\theta = \dfrac{1 + \cos 2\theta}{2} \qquad \tan^2\theta = \dfrac{1 - \cos 2\theta}{1 + \cos 2\theta}$

IDENTITY OR FORMULA	GENERAL FORM
Half-angle	$\sin\dfrac{\theta}{2} = \pm\sqrt{\dfrac{1 - \cos\theta}{2}}$ $\cos\dfrac{\theta}{2} = \pm\sqrt{\dfrac{1 + \cos\theta}{2}}$ $\tan\dfrac{\theta}{2} = \pm\sqrt{\dfrac{1 - \cos\theta}{1 + \cos\theta}}$ $\tan\dfrac{\theta}{2} = \dfrac{1 - \cos\theta}{\sin\theta}$ $\tan\dfrac{\theta}{2} = \dfrac{\sin\theta}{1 + \cos\theta}$
Product-to-sum	$\cos\alpha\cos\beta = \dfrac{1}{2}(\cos(\alpha + \beta) + \cos(\alpha - \beta))$ $\sin\alpha\sin\beta = \dfrac{1}{2}(\cos(\alpha - \beta) - \cos(\alpha + \beta))$ $\sin\alpha\cos\beta = \dfrac{1}{2}(\sin(\alpha + \beta) + \sin(\alpha - \beta))$ $\cos\alpha\sin\beta = \dfrac{1}{2}(\sin(\alpha + \beta) - \sin(\alpha - \beta))$
Sum-to-product	$\cos a + \cos b = 2\cos\dfrac{a + b}{2}\cos\dfrac{a - b}{2}$ $\cos a - \cos b = -2\sin\dfrac{a + b}{2}\sin\dfrac{a - b}{2}$ $\sin a + \sin b = 2\sin\dfrac{a + b}{2}\cos\dfrac{a - b}{2}$ $\sin a - \sin b = 2\cos\dfrac{a + b}{2}\sin\dfrac{a - b}{2}$

7.5 Exercises

Writing Identities

Exercises 1–8: Complete each statement.

1. $\sin^2\theta = \frac{1 - \cos 2\theta}{2}$, so $\sin^2 10t = $ _____.

2. $\cos^2\theta = \frac{1 + \cos 2\theta}{2}$, so $\cos^2 8x = $ _____.

3. $\tan^2\theta = \frac{1 - \cos 2\theta}{1 + \cos 2\theta}$, so $\tan^2 5t = $ _____.

4. $\tan 2\theta = \frac{2\tan\theta}{1 - \tan^2\theta}$, so $\tan t = $ _____.

5. $\sin 2\theta = 2\sin\theta\cos\theta$, so $\sin 20x = $ _____.

6. $\cos 2\theta = \cos^2\theta - \sin^2\theta$, so $\cos 16t = $ _____.

7. $\tan\frac{\theta}{2} = \frac{1 - \cos\theta}{\sin\theta}$, so $\tan 5x = $ _____.

8. $\tan\frac{\theta}{2} = \frac{\sin\theta}{1 + \cos\theta}$, so $\tan 4t = $ _____.

Double-Angle Identities

Exercises 9–14: If possible, evaluate expressions (a) and (b) and compare their values.

9. **(a)** $\sin 30° + \sin 30°$ **(b)** $\sin 60°$

10. **(a)** $\sin 45° + \sin 45°$ **(b)** $\sin 90°$

11. **(a)** $\cos 60° + \cos 60°$ **(b)** $\cos 120°$

12. **(a)** $\cos 90° + \cos 90°$ **(b)** $\cos 180°$

13. **(a)** $\tan 45° + \tan 45°$ **(b)** $\tan 90°$

14. **(a)** $\tan 30° + \tan 30°$ **(b)** $\tan 60°$

Exercises 15 and 16: (Refer to Example 1.) Verify graphically and symbolically that the two expressions are not equivalent.

15. $\tan 2\theta$, $2 \tan \theta$ **16.** $\cos 3\theta$, $3 \cos \theta$

Exercises 17–24: (Refer to Example 2.) Do the following.

(a) Find $\sin 2\theta$, $\cos 2\theta$, and $\tan 2\theta$.

(b) Use a calculator to support your results.

17. $\cos \theta = \frac{4}{5}$ and $\sin \theta = \frac{3}{5}$

18. $\sin \theta = \frac{12}{13}$ and $\cos \theta = \frac{5}{13}$

19. $\sin \theta = -\frac{24}{25}$ and $\cos \theta > 0$

20. $\cos \theta = -\frac{7}{25}$ and $\tan \theta > 0$

21. $\sin \theta = -\frac{11}{61}$ and $\sec \theta > 0$

22. $\csc \theta = -2$ and $\sec \theta > 0$

23. $\tan \theta = \frac{7}{24}$ and $\cos \theta < 0$

24. $\cot \theta = \frac{5}{12}$ and $\sin \theta > 0$

Exercises 25–34: (Refer to Example 3.) Use an identity to evaluate the expression.

25. $\sin\left(2 \cos^{-1} 1\right)$ **26.** $\cos\left(2 \sin^{-1} \frac{1}{2}\right)$

27. $\cos\left(2 \sin^{-1} \frac{7}{25}\right)$ **28.** $\sin\left(2 \tan^{-1} \frac{3}{4}\right)$

29. $\cos\left(3 \sin^{-1} \frac{5}{13}\right)$ **30.** $\tan\left(2 \tan^{-1} \frac{1}{2}\right)$

31. $\sin(2 \tan^{-1} x), x < 0$

32. $\cos(2 \sin^{-1} x), x > 0$

33. $\cos\left(\sin^{-1} \frac{3}{5} - \sin^{-1} \frac{4}{5}\right)$ *(Hint: Let $\alpha = \sin^{-1} \frac{3}{5}$,*
$\beta = \sin^{-1} \frac{4}{5}$, *and apply a difference identity.)*

34. $\sin\left(\tan^{-1} \frac{12}{5} + \cos^{-1} \frac{12}{13}\right)$

Exercises 35–40: Rewrite using a double-angle identity.

35. $2 \cos \theta \sin \theta$ **36.** $2 \sin 2\theta \cos 2\theta$

37. $\sin \theta \cos \theta$

38. $(\sin \theta - \cos \theta)(\sin \theta + \cos \theta)$

39. $2 \cos^2 2\theta - 1$ **40.** $1 - 2 \sin^2 3\theta$

Exercises 41–44: Write the expression as one term.

41. $\sin^2 3\theta + \cos^2 3\theta$ **42.** $1 + \tan^2 2\theta$

43. $\csc^2 5x - 1$ **44.** $\sin^2 8x + \cos^2 8x$

Power-Reducing Identities and Half-Angle Formulas

Exercises 45–48: Find the exact value of the expression. Use a calculator to support your result.

45. $\cos^2 22.5°$ **46.** $\sin^2 15°$

47. $\tan^2 75°$ **48.** $\csc^2 105°$

Exercises 49–52: Use a half-angle formula to find the exact value of the expression. Use a calculator to support your result.

49. (a) $\cos 15°$ **(b)** $\tan(-15°)$

50. (a) $\sin 67.5°$ **(b)** $\cos(-67.5°)$

51. (a) $\tan \frac{\pi}{8}$ **(b)** $\sin\left(-\frac{\pi}{8}\right)$

52. (a) $\cos \frac{5\pi}{12}$ **(b)** $\cos\left(-\frac{5\pi}{12}\right)$

Exercises 53–58: Use a half-angle formula to simplify the expression. Use a calculator to support your result.

53. $\sqrt{\dfrac{1 - \cos 60°}{2}}$ **54.** $\sqrt{\dfrac{1 + \cos 60°}{2}}$

55. $\sqrt{\dfrac{1 + \cos 50°}{2}}$ **56.** $\sqrt{\dfrac{1 - \cos 50°}{2}}$

57. $\sqrt{\dfrac{1 - \cos 40°}{1 + \cos 40°}}$ **58.** $\sqrt{\dfrac{1 + \cos 26°}{1 - \cos 26°}}$

Exercises 59–64: (Refer to Example 10.) Find $\sin \frac{\theta}{2}$, $\cos \frac{\theta}{2}$, and $\tan \frac{\theta}{2}$.

59. $\cos \theta = \frac{4}{5}$ and $0° < \theta < 90°$

60. $\cos \theta = \frac{1}{3}$ and $0° < \theta < 90°$

61. $\tan \theta = -\frac{5}{12}$ and $-90° < \theta < 0°$

62. $\sec \theta = -2$ and $90° < \theta < 180°$

63. $\csc \theta = \frac{25}{24}$ and $90° < \theta < 180°$

64. $\sin \theta = \frac{4}{5}$ and $0° < \theta < 90°$

Verifying Identities

Exercises 65–74: Verify the identity. Give graphical or numerical support.

65. $4 \sin 2x = 8 \sin x \cos x$

66. $\cos 4\theta = 1 - 2 \sin^2 2\theta$

67. $\dfrac{2 - \sec^2 x}{\sec^2 x} = \cos 2x$

68. $(\sin x + \cos x)^2 = \sin 2x + 1$

69. $\sec 2x = \dfrac{1}{1 - 2 \sin^2 x}$

70. $2 \csc 2t = \csc t \sec t$

71. $\sin 3\theta = 3 \sin \theta - 4 \sin^3 \theta$

72. $\dfrac{2 \tan x}{1 + \tan^2 x} = \sin 2x$

73. $\sin 4\theta = 4 \sin \theta \cos \theta \cos 2\theta$

74. $\cos 4t = 8 \cos^4 t - 8 \cos^2 t + 1$

Exercises 75–84: Verify the identity.

75. $\dfrac{\sin 2\theta}{\sin \theta} = 2 \cos \theta$ **76.** $2 \sin^2 4\theta = 1 - \cos 8\theta$

77. $2 \cos^2 \dfrac{\theta}{2} = 1 + \cos \theta$

78. $\dfrac{\sin^2 2\theta}{1 + \cos 2\theta} = 2 \sin^2 \theta$ **79.** $\cos^4 \theta - \sin^4 \theta = \cos 2\theta$

80. $\dfrac{1 - \tan^2 x}{1 + \tan^2 x} = \cos 2x$ **81.** $\csc 2t = \dfrac{\csc t}{2 \cos t}$

82. $\tan \theta + \cot \theta = \dfrac{2}{\sin 2\theta}$

83. $\tan \dfrac{x}{2} = \dfrac{\sin x}{1 + \cos x}$ $\left(\textit{Hint: Let } \tan \dfrac{x}{2} = \dfrac{\sin \frac{x}{2}}{\cos \frac{x}{2}}.\right)$

84. $\tan \dfrac{x}{2} = \dfrac{1 - \cos x}{\sin x}$ *(Hint: Use the identity in Exercise 83.)*

Product-to-Sum and Sum-to-Product Identities

Exercises 85–88: Write each expression as a sum or difference of trigonometric functions.

85. (a) $\cos 50° \sin 20°$ **(b)** $\cos 2x \cos x$

86. (a) $2 \sin 74° \sin 24°$ **(b)** $8 \sin 18x \cos 13x$

87. (a) $\sin 7\theta \cos 3\theta$ **(b)** $\sin 8x \sin 4x$

88. (a) $2 \cos 5x \cos 7x$ **(b)** $4 \cos 9\theta \sin 2\theta$

Exercises 89–92: Write each expression as a product of trigonometric functions.

89. (a) $\sin 40° + \sin 30°$ **(b)** $\cos 45° + \cos 35°$

90. (a) $\cos 104° - \cos 24°$ **(b)** $\sin 32° - \sin 64°$

91. (a) $\cos 6\theta + \cos 4\theta$ **(b)** $\sin 7x + \sin 4x$

92. (a) $\sin 3x - \sin 5x$ **(b)** $\cos 3\theta - \cos \theta$

Solving Equations

Exercises 93–96: Find the solutions to the equation in the interval $[0°, 360°)$

(a) symbolically, (b) graphically, and (c) numerically.

93. $\cos 2\theta = 1$ **94.** $\sin 2\theta = \dfrac{1}{2}$

95. $\sin 2\theta + \cos \theta = 0$ **96.** $\cos \dfrac{\theta}{2} = -\dfrac{\sqrt{3}}{2}$

Exercises 97–100: Find the solutions to the equation in the interval $[0, 2\pi)$.

97. $\sin \dfrac{\theta}{2} = 1$ **98.** $\cos 2\theta + \cos \theta = 0$

99. $\sqrt{2} \sin \dfrac{\theta}{2} - 1 = 0$

100. $2 \cos \dfrac{\theta}{2} + 1 = 0$

Exercises 101–116: Find all solutions, expressed in radians.

101. $2 \cos 2t = \sqrt{3}$ **102.** $2 \sin 2t = -1$

103. $\sin 2t + \sin t = 0$ **104.** $\sin t - \cos 2t = 0$

105. $2 \sin \dfrac{t}{2} - 1 = 0$ **106.** $\sin 2t = 2 \cos^2 t$

107. $\cos 2t = \sin t$ **108.** $\cos 2t - \cos t = 0$

109. $\tan 2t = 1$ **110.** $\cot 2t = \sqrt{3}$

111. $2 \cos \dfrac{t}{2} = 1$ **112.** $\tan \dfrac{t}{2} = 1$

113. $\cos 2t = 2 \sin t \cos t$

114. $2 \cos^2 2t = 1 - \cos 2t$

115. $2 \sin^2 2t + \sin 2t - 1 = 0$

116. $2 \cos \dfrac{t}{2} + 1 = 0$

Exercises 117 and 118: Approximate to the nearest thousandth all solutions on $[0, 2\pi)$.

117. $\sin t + \sin 2t = \cos t$

118. $\sin 3t + \sin 2t = 2 \cos t$

Applications

119. Electricity (Refer to Example 8.) Suppose that the voltage in a 220-volt electrical circuit is modeled by $V(t) = 310 \sin(120\pi t)$ and that the amperage flowing through a heater is $I = 7 \sin(120\pi t)$. (*Source:* G. Wilcox and C. Hesselberth, *Electricity for Engineering Technology.*)

    (a) Graph the wattage $W = VI$ consumed by the heater in $[0, 0.04, 0.01]$ by $[-500, 2500, 500]$.

    (b) Find values for the constants a, k, and d so that $W = a \cos(k\pi t) + d$.

120. Electricity If a toaster is plugged into a common household outlet, the wattage W used varies according to the equation $W = \dfrac{V^2}{R}$, where V is the voltage and R is a constant that measures the resistance of the toaster in ohms. (*Source:* D. Bell, *Fundamentals of Electric Circuits.*)

    (a) Graph W if $R = 15$ and $V = 163 \sin(120\pi t)$ in $[0, 0.05, 0.01]$ by $[-500, 2000, 500]$.

    (b) Approximate the maximum wattage consumed by the toaster.

    (c) Use a power-reducing identity to express the wattage as $W = a \cos(240\pi t) + d$, where a and d are constants.

Exercises 121 and 122: **Electricity** *Let the voltage in an electrical outlet be given by* $V(t) = 320 \sin(120\pi t)$ *at time t in seconds. Find the times when V equals the following values.*

121. 160 volts

122. $160\sqrt{3}$ volts

123. **Highway Curves** When an automobile travels along a circular curve, objects like trees and buildings situated on the inside of the curve can obstruct the driver's vision. If the cars in the figure are a safe stopping distance apart, then the distance d that should be cleared on the inside of the curve is $d = r\left(1 - \cos\frac{\beta}{2}\right)$, where r is the radius of the curve and β is the central angle between the cars. (*Source:* F. Mannering and W. Kilareski, *Principles of Highway Engineering and Traffic Analysis.*)

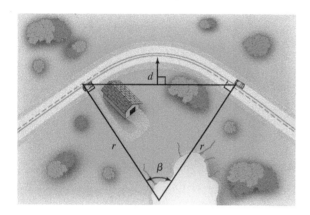

(a) Find d if $\beta = 80°$ and $r = 600$ feet.
(b) Use the figure to justify this formula.

(c) Is the given formula equivalent to the formula $d = r\left(1 - \frac{1}{2}\cos\beta\right)$? Explain.

124. **Highway Curves** The figure at the top of the next column represents a circular curve with radius r and central angle θ. The tangent length T is an important distance used by surveyors. (*Source:* F. Mannering.)

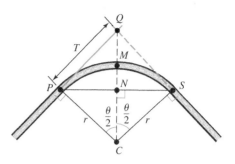

(a) Show that $T = r\tan\frac{\theta}{2}$.

(b) Find T for a curve with a 1500-foot radius and $\theta = 80°$.

125. **Touch-Tone Phones** (Refer to Example 15.) For the numbers 3 and 4 on a touch-tone phone, complete the following.
(a) Write formulas, f for 3 and g for 4, that are the *sum* of two cosine functions and that model the tone generated by each number.

(b) Write the formulas for each tone from part (a) as a *product* of two trigonometric functions.

126. **Musical Tones and Beats** If two musical tones with nearly the same frequency are played simultaneously, a phenomenon called *beats* occurs. Let $P_1 = 0.04\cos(110\pi t)$ and $P_2 = 0.04\cos(116\pi t)$ represent these tones.

(a) Graph $P = P_1 + P_2$ in the viewing rectangle $[0.2, 1.2, 0.2]$ by $[-0.08, 0.08, 0.01]$. How many beats are there?

(b) Use a sum-to-product identity to write $P_1 + P_2$ as a product of trigonometric expressions.

Writing about Mathematics

127. Suppose a student believes that an equation is an identity but cannot verify it symbolically. Discuss techniques that the student could use to support this belief.

128. Does the equation $\sin^2 3\theta + \cos^2 2\theta = 1$ represent an identity? Explain your reasoning.

CHECKING BASIC CONCEPTS FOR SECTION 7.5

1. Find values for $\sin 2\theta$ and $\cos 2\theta$ if $\cos\theta = -\frac{7}{25}$ and $\sin\theta = \frac{24}{25}$.

2. Use a half-angle formula to find the exact value of $\sin 22.5°$.

3. Find $\sin\frac{\theta}{2}$ and $\cos\frac{\theta}{2}$ if $\sin\theta = \frac{4}{5}$ and θ is acute.

4. Verify that $\dfrac{\cos 2\theta}{\cos^2\theta} = 2 - \sec^2\theta$.

5. Solve $\sin 2\theta = 2\cos\theta$ for $0 \le \theta < 2\pi$.

7 | Summary

CONCEPT	EXPLANATION AND EXAMPLES

Section 7.1 Fundamental Identities

Reciprocal Identities

$$\sin\theta = \frac{1}{\csc\theta} \qquad \cos\theta = \frac{1}{\sec\theta} \qquad \tan\theta = \frac{1}{\cot\theta}$$

$$\csc\theta = \frac{1}{\sin\theta} \qquad \sec\theta = \frac{1}{\cos\theta} \qquad \cot\theta = \frac{1}{\tan\theta}$$

Example: If $\sin\theta = \frac{3}{5}$, then $\csc\theta = \frac{5}{3}$.

Quotient Identities

$$\tan\theta = \frac{\sin\theta}{\cos\theta} \qquad \cot\theta = \frac{\cos\theta}{\sin\theta}$$

Example: If $\sin\theta = -\frac{3}{5}$ and $\cos\theta = \frac{4}{5}$, then $\tan\theta = \frac{-3/5}{4/5} = -\frac{3}{4}$.

Pythagorean Identities

$$\sin^2\theta + \cos^2\theta = 1 \qquad 1 + \tan^2\theta = \sec^2\theta \qquad 1 + \cot^2\theta = \csc^2\theta$$

Examples: $\sin^2 30° + \cos^2 30° = 1$
$$1 + \tan^2\frac{\pi}{4} = \sec^2\frac{\pi}{4}$$

Negative-Angle Identities

$$\sin(-\theta) = -\sin\theta \qquad \cos(-\theta) = \cos\theta \qquad \tan(-\theta) = -\tan\theta$$
$$\csc(-\theta) = -\csc\theta \qquad \sec(-\theta) = \sec\theta \qquad \cot(-\theta) = -\cot\theta$$

Note: Cosine and secant are even functions, having graphs that are symmetric with respect to the *y*-axis. Sine, cosecant, tangent, and cotangent are odd functions, having graphs that are symmetric with respect to the origin.

Examples: $\cos(-45°) = \cos 45°$, $\sin(-60°) = -\sin 60°$

Section 7.2 Verifying Identities

Verifying Identities

To verify an identity, simplify one side of the equation until it equals the other side of the equation. Make use of the fundamental identities from Section 7.1.

Example: Verify that $\dfrac{1 - \sin^2\theta}{\cos\theta} = \cos\theta$.

$$\frac{1 - \sin^2\theta}{\cos\theta} = \frac{\cos^2\theta}{\cos\theta} \qquad \textit{sin}^2\theta + \textit{cos}^2\theta = 1$$

$$= \cos\theta \qquad \textit{Simplify.}$$

Section 7.3 Trigonometric Equations

Reference Angle

The reference angle θ_R for an angle θ in standard position is the acute angle between the terminal side of θ and the *x*-axis.

Example: The reference angle for $\theta = 120°$ is $\theta_R = 60°$.

CONCEPT	EXPLANATION AND EXAMPLES

Section 7.3 Trigonometric Equations (CONTINUED)

Trigonometry Equations	Unlike polynomial equations, which have a finite number of solutions, trigonometric equations can have infinitely many solutions.

$$\textbf{Example:}\quad \text{Find all solutions to } 2\sin\theta - 1 = 0.$$

$$2\sin\theta - 1 = 0$$

$$2\sin\theta = 1$$

$$\sin\theta = \frac{1}{2}$$

Since $\theta_R = \sin^{-1}\frac{1}{2} = 30°$ and the sine function is positive in quadrants I and II, the solutions to $\sin\theta = \frac{1}{2}$ for $0° \le \theta < 360°$ are 30° and 150°.

Since $\sin\theta$ has period 360°, all solutions to the equation can be written as
$\theta = 30° + 360° \cdot n$ or $\theta = 150° + 360° \cdot n,$ where n is an integer.

Section 7.4 Sum and Difference Identities

Cosine Sum and Difference	$\cos(\alpha + \beta) = \cos\alpha\cos\beta - \sin\alpha\sin\beta$ $\cos(\alpha - \beta) = \cos\alpha\cos\beta + \sin\alpha\sin\beta$ **Example:** $\cos(60° - 45°) = \cos 60° \cos 45° + \sin 60° \sin 45°$
Sine Sum and Difference	$\sin(\alpha + \beta) = \sin\alpha\cos\beta + \cos\alpha\sin\beta$ $\sin(\alpha - \beta) = \sin\alpha\cos\beta - \cos\alpha\sin\beta$ **Example:** $\sin(60° - 45°) = \sin 60° \cos 45° - \cos 60° \sin 45°$
Tangent Sum and Difference	$\tan(\alpha + \beta) = \dfrac{\tan\alpha + \tan\beta}{1 - \tan\alpha\tan\beta},\qquad \tan(\alpha - \beta) = \dfrac{\tan\alpha - \tan\beta}{1 + \tan\alpha\tan\beta}$ **Example:** $\tan(60° - 45°) = \dfrac{\tan 60° - \tan 45°}{1 + \tan 60° \tan 45°}$
Cofunction Identities	$\cos\left(\dfrac{\pi}{2} - t\right) = \sin t \qquad \sin\left(\dfrac{\pi}{2} - t\right) = \cos t$ $\cot\left(\dfrac{\pi}{2} - t\right) = \tan t \qquad \tan\left(\dfrac{\pi}{2} - t\right) = \cot t$ $\csc\left(\dfrac{\pi}{2} - t\right) = \sec t \qquad \sec\left(\dfrac{\pi}{2} - t\right) = \csc t$ **Example:** $\tan\dfrac{\pi}{3} = \tan\left(\dfrac{\pi}{2} - \dfrac{\pi}{6}\right) = \cot\dfrac{\pi}{6}$

CONCEPT	EXPLANATION AND EXAMPLES

Section 7.5 Multiple-Angle Identities

Double-Angle Identities

$$\sin 2\theta = 2\sin\theta\cos\theta \qquad \cos 2\theta = \cos^2\theta - \sin^2\theta \qquad \tan 2\theta = \frac{2\tan\theta}{1 - \tan^2\theta}$$

or

$$\cos 2\theta = 2\cos^2\theta - 1$$

or

$$\cos 2\theta = 1 - 2\sin^2\theta$$

Example: $\sin 120° = \sin(2 \cdot 60°) = 2\sin 60° \cos 60°$

Power-Reducing Identities

$$\sin^2\theta = \frac{1 - \cos 2\theta}{2} \qquad \cos^2\theta = \frac{1 + \cos 2\theta}{2} \qquad \tan^2\theta = \frac{1 - \cos 2\theta}{1 + \cos 2\theta}$$

Example: $\sin^2 30° = \frac{1 - \cos 60°}{2}$

Half-Angle Formulas

$$\sin\frac{\theta}{2} = \pm\sqrt{\frac{1 - \cos\theta}{2}} \qquad \cos\frac{\theta}{2} = \pm\sqrt{\frac{1 + \cos\theta}{2}}$$

$$\tan\frac{\theta}{2} = \pm\sqrt{\frac{1 - \cos\theta}{1 + \cos\theta}} \qquad \tan\frac{\theta}{2} = \frac{1 - \cos\theta}{\sin\theta} \qquad \tan\frac{\theta}{2} = \frac{\sin\theta}{1 + \cos\theta}$$

Example: $\cos 15° = \cos\frac{30°}{2} = \sqrt{\frac{1 + \cos 30°}{2}}$

Product-to-Sum Identities

$$\cos\alpha\cos\beta = \frac{1}{2}(\cos(\alpha + \beta) + \cos(\alpha - \beta))$$

$$\sin\alpha\sin\beta = \frac{1}{2}(\cos(\alpha - \beta) - \cos(\alpha + \beta))$$

$$\sin\alpha\cos\beta = \frac{1}{2}(\sin(\alpha + \beta) + \sin(\alpha - \beta))$$

$$\cos\alpha\sin\beta = \frac{1}{2}(\sin(\alpha + \beta) - \sin(\alpha - \beta))$$

Example: $\cos 45° \cos 60° = \frac{1}{2}(\cos(45° + 60°) + \cos(45° - 60°))$

Sum-to-Product Identities

$$\cos a + \cos b = 2\cos\frac{a + b}{2}\cos\frac{a - b}{2}$$

$$\cos a - \cos b = -2\sin\frac{a + b}{2}\sin\frac{a - b}{2}$$

$$\sin a + \sin b = 2\sin\frac{a + b}{2}\cos\frac{a - b}{2}$$

$$\sin a - \sin b = 2\cos\frac{a + b}{2}\sin\frac{a - b}{2}$$

Example: $\cos 60° + \cos 30° = 2\cos\frac{60° + 30°}{2}\cos\frac{60° - 30°}{2}$

7 Review Exercises

Exercises 1 and 2: Determine the quadrant that contains θ.

1. $\sec\theta < 0$ and $\sin\theta > 0$

2. $\cot\theta > 0$ and $\cos\theta < 0$

Exercises 3–6: Use the given information to find the other trigonometric functions of θ.

3. $\sin\theta = \frac{3}{5}$ and $\cos\theta = -\frac{4}{5}$

4. $\sec\theta = -\frac{13}{12}$ and $\csc\theta = -\frac{13}{5}$

5. $\tan\theta = -\frac{7}{24}$ and $\cos\theta = \frac{24}{25}$

6. $\cot\theta = -\frac{1}{2}$ and $\sin\theta > 0$

Exercises 7–10: Use a negative-angle identity to write an equivalent trigonometric expression involving a positive angle.

7. $\sin(-13°)$

8. $\cos(-106°)$

9. $\sec\left(-\frac{3\pi}{7}\right)$

10. $\tan\left(-\frac{5\pi}{11}\right)$

Exercises 11–16: Simplify each expression.

11. $\sec\theta \cot\theta \sin\theta$

12. $\sin\theta \csc\theta$

13. $(\sec^2 t - 1)(\csc^2 t - 1)$

14. $\dfrac{\sec\theta}{\csc\theta} + \dfrac{\sin\theta}{\cos\theta}$

15. $\dfrac{\csc\theta \sin\theta}{\sec\theta}$

16. $\dfrac{\cos^2\theta}{1 - \sin\theta}$

Exercises 17–20: Use a calculator to approximate the other trigonometric functions of θ to four decimal places.

17. $\tan\theta = 1.2367$ and θ is acute

18. $\sin\theta = -0.3434$ and θ is in quadrant IV

19. $\cos\theta = -0.4544$ and θ is in quadrant II

20. $\tan\theta = -0.8595$ and θ is in quadrant IV

Exercises 21–24: Factor the trigonometric expression.

21. $\sin^2\theta + 2\sin\theta + 1$

22. $2\cos^2 t - 3\cos t + 1$

23. $\tan^2\theta - 9$

24. $2\sec^2\theta - 3\sec\theta - 5$

Exercises 25–38: Verify the identity.

25. $(\sec\theta - 1)(\sec\theta + 1) = \tan^2\theta$

26. $(\cos\theta + \sin\theta)^2 + (\cos\theta - \sin\theta)^2 = 2$

27. $(1 + \tan t)^2 = \sec^2 t + 2\tan t$

28. $(1 - \cos^2 t)(1 + \tan^2 t) = \tan^2 t$

29. $\sin(x - \pi) = -\sin x$

30. $\cos(\pi + x) = -\cos x$

31. $\sin 8x = 2\sin 4x \cos 4x$

32. $\cos^4 x - \sin^4 x = \cos 2x$

33. $\sec 2x = \dfrac{1}{2\cos^2 x - 1}$

34. $\dfrac{1 + \tan^2 x}{\sin^2 x + \cos^2 x} = \sec^2 x$

35. $\cos^4 x \sin^3 x = (\cos^4 x - \cos^6 x)\sin x$

36. $\sin^4 x = \frac{3}{8} - \frac{1}{2}\cos 2x + \frac{1}{8}\cos 4x$

37. $\sec^4\theta - \tan^4\theta = 1 + 2\tan^2\theta$

38. $\dfrac{1 + \cos\theta}{\sin\theta} + \dfrac{\sin\theta}{1 + \cos\theta} = 2\csc\theta$

Exercises 39–42: Find the reference angle for θ.

39. $\theta = 240°$

40. $\theta = 320°$

41. $\theta = \frac{9\pi}{7}$

42. $\theta = -\frac{7\pi}{6}$

Exercises 43 and 44: Use the graph to estimate any solutions to the trigonometric equation for $[0, 2\pi)$. Then solve the equation symbolically.

43. $\cos^2\theta - 2\cos\theta = 0$ **44.** $2\sin t \cos t - \cos t = 0$

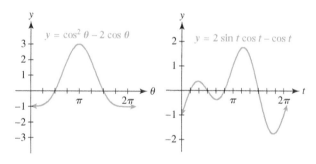

Exercises 45 and 46: Solve the given trigonometric equation for $0° \le \theta < 360°$.

45. (a) $\tan\theta = \sqrt{3}$ **(b)** $\cot\theta = -\sqrt{3}$

46. (a) $\sin\theta = 1$ **(b)** $\cos\theta = -1$

Exercises 47–52: Solve the equation for $0 \le t < 2\pi$.

47. $2\cos t - 1 = 0$ **48.** $\cot^2 t = 1$

49. $2 \sin^2 t + \sin t - 3 = 0$

50. $\sin^2 t + 2 \cos t = 1$

51. $\tan^2 t - 2 \tan t + 1 = 0$

52. $2 \sin t = \sqrt{3}$

Exercises 53–56: Find all solutions to the equation. Express your results in both degrees and radians.

53. $3 \tan^2 t - 1 = 0$ **54.** $2 \sin^2 t - \sin t - 1 = 0$

55. $\sin 2t + 3 \cos t = 0$ **56.** $\cos 2t = 1$

Exercises 57 and 58: Use a half-angle formula to find the exact value for the expression. Use a calculator to support your result.

57. $\cos 105°$ **58.** $\sin \frac{\pi}{12}$

Exercises 59 and 60: Estimate any solutions in the interval $[-2\pi, 2\pi]$ graphically to two decimal places.

59. $\tan x = x + 1$ **60.** $\sin(\cos x) = \tan x$

Exercises 61 and 62: Find the following.

(a) $\sin(\alpha + \beta)$ *(b)* $\cos(\alpha + \beta)$
(c) $\tan(\alpha + \beta)$ *(d) The quadrant containing $\alpha + \beta$*

61. $\cos \alpha = \frac{3}{5}$ and $\cos \beta = \frac{12}{13}$, where α and β are both in quadrant I.

62. $\sin \alpha = -\frac{12}{13}$ and $\tan \beta = -\frac{4}{3}$, where α and β are both in quadrant IV.

Exercises 63 and 64: Complete the following.

(a) Find $\sin 2\theta$, $\cos 2\theta$, and $\tan 2\theta$.
(b) Use a calculator to support your results.

63. $\sin \theta = \frac{4}{5}$ and $\tan \theta = -\frac{4}{3}$

64. $\sin \theta = -\frac{12}{13}$ and $\cos \theta = -\frac{5}{13}$

Exercises 65 and 66: Complete the following.

(a) Find $\sin \frac{\theta}{2}$, $\cos \frac{\theta}{2}$, and $\tan \frac{\theta}{2}$.
(b) Use a calculator to support your results.

65. $\cos \theta = \frac{1}{4}$ and $0° < \theta < 90°$

66. $\tan \theta = -\frac{8}{15}$ and $-90° < \theta < 0°$

Exercises 67 and 68: Evaluate the expression.

67. $\cos\left(2 \tan^{-1} \frac{11}{60}\right)$ **68.** $\sin(2 \sin^{-1} x)$, $x > 0$

Applications

69. Daylight Hours The number of daylight hours y at 20° S latitude can be modeled by

$$y = 1.2 \cos\left(\frac{\pi}{6}(x - 0.7)\right) + 12.1,$$

where $x = 1$ corresponds to January 1, $x = 2$ to February 1, and so on. Estimate when the number of daylight hours equals 11.5 hours. (*Source:* J. Williams.)

70. Music and Pure Tones A pure tone is modeled by the graph of $P(t) = 0.006 \cos(50\pi t)$, where P represents the pressure on an eardrum in pounds per square foot at time t in seconds. (*Source:* J. Roederer, *Introduction to the Physics and Psychophysics of Music.*)

(a) Graph P in $[0, 0.1, 0.01]$ by $[-0.008, 0.008, 0.001]$.

(b) Estimate all solutions to the equation $P = 0$ on the interval $0 \le t \le 0.1$.

71. Modeling Musical Tones Let the pressure exerted on the eardrum by two sound waves in pounds per square foot be given by

$$P_1(t) = 0.006 \cos(100\pi t) \quad \text{and}$$

$$P_2(t) = 0.008 \sin(100\pi t).$$

(a) Graph the pressure on the eardrum $P = P_1 + P_2$ in $[0, 0.06, 0.01]$ by $[-0.012, 0.012, 0.002]$.

(b) Use the graph to find values for a and k such that $P = a \sin(100\pi t + k)$.

(c) Use a sum or difference identity for sine to verify your result in part (b).

72. Electricity Suppose the voltage in an electrical heater is given by $V(t) = 17 \sin(120\pi t)$ and the amperage flowing through the heater is $I(t) = 2 \sin(120\pi t)$, where t is in seconds. (*Source:* G. Wilcox and C. Hesselberth, *Electricity for Engineering Technology.*)

(a) Graph the wattage $W = VI$ consumed by the heater in $[0, 0.04, 0.01]$ by $[-40, 40, 10]$.

(b) Use a power-reducing identity to express the wattage in the form $W = a \cos(k\pi t) + d$, where a, k, and d are constants.

73. Electromagnets Let the wattage consumed by an electromagnet be given by $W(t) = 7 \cos^2(240\pi t)$ and the voltage be given by $V(t) = 50 \sin(240\pi t)$, where t is in seconds. Express $W(t)$ in terms of the sine function. When V is maximum or minimum, what is the value of W? Explain.

74. Average Temperatures Let the monthly average high temperature y in degrees Fahrenheit at a location be given by $y = 15 \sin\left(\frac{\pi}{6}(x - 4)\right) + 60$, where x is the month and $x = 1$ corresponds to January. Estimate when the monthly average high temperature is 60° F.

75. Back Stress The force exerted by the back muscles of a 100-pound person can be estimated by $F = 289 \cos\theta$. Find θ in degrees and radians when $F = 250$ pounds.

76. Electricity Let $V(t) = 80 \sin(120\pi t)$ denote the voltage in an electrical outlet at time t in seconds, where t is a real number. Find all times when the voltage is 40 volts.

Extended and Discovery Exercises

1. Piano Strings If a piano key with a frequency of f_1 is played, then the corresponding string will not only vibrate at f_1 but also vibrate at the higher frequencies of $2f_1$, $3f_1$, $4f_1$, and so on. The *fundamental frequency* of the string is f_1, and the higher frequencies are called the *upper harmonics*. The human ear will hear the sum of these frequencies as one complex tone. (*Source:* J. Roederer, *Introduction to the Physics and Psychophysics of Music.*)

(a) If the A note above middle C is played, its fundamental frequency is $f_1 = 440$ hertz. (One hertz equals one cycle per second.) The piano string also vibrates at frequencies of $f_2 = 2(440) = 880$, $f_3 = 3(440) = 1320$, $f_4 = 4(440) = 1760$, and so on. The pressure for each frequency in pounds per square foot is modeled by

$$P_1 = 0.002 \sin(2\pi(440)t),$$

$$P_2 = \frac{0.002}{2} \sin(2\pi(880)t),$$

$$P_3 = \frac{0.002}{3} \sin(2\pi(1320)t),$$

$$P_4 = \frac{0.002}{4} \sin(2\pi(1760)t), \quad \text{and}$$

$$P_5 = \frac{0.002}{5} \sin(2\pi(2200)t),$$

where t is in seconds. Graph each of the following expressions for P in the viewing rectangle given by $[0, 0.01, 0.002]$ by $[-0.005, 0.005, 0.001]$.

   i. $P = P_1$

   ii. $P = P_1 + P_2$

   iii. $P = P_1 + P_2 + P_3$

   iv. $P = P_1 + P_2 + P_3 + P_4$

   v. $P = P_1 + P_2 + P_3 + P_4 + P_5$

(b) The final graph of P models what the human ear hears. Describe this graph.

(c) Estimate the maximum pressure of

$$P = P_1 + P_2 + P_3 + P_4 + P_5.$$

(d) A pure tone with a frequency of 440 hertz is modeled by $P = P_1$, whereas a piano generates the graph of $P = P_1 + P_2 + P_3 + P_4 + P_5$. Compare and contrast these two graphs.

2. Low Tones and Small Speakers Small speakers often cannot vibrate at frequencies less than 200 hertz. Nonetheless, these tones can still be heard on such speakers. When a piano string creates a tone of 110 hertz, it also creates tones at 220, 330, 440, 550, and 660 hertz. A small speaker cannot reproduce the 110 hertz vibration, but it can reproduce the higher frequencies. The low tones can still be heard because the speaker produces *difference tones* of these *upper harmonics*. The difference between consecutive frequencies is 110 hertz, and this difference tone will be heard on a small speaker even though the speaker cannot vibrate at 110 hertz. This phenomenon can be visualized with a graphing calculator. (*Source:* A. Benade.)

(a) Graph the upper harmonics represented by the pressure wave

$$P = \frac{1}{2} \sin(2\pi(220)t) + \frac{1}{3} \sin(2\pi(330)t)$$
$$+ \frac{1}{4} \sin(2\pi(440)t)$$

in $[0, 0.03, 0.01]$ by $[-1.2, 1.2, 0.5]$.

(b) Estimate the t-values on the interval $0 \le t \le 0.03$ where P is maximum.

(c) Approximate the frequency of these maximum values. What does a person hear in addition to the frequencies of 220, 330, and 440 hertz?

(d) Discuss the advantage of having large speakers instead of smaller ones. (*Hint:* Try graphing the pressure produced by a speaker that can vibrate both at 110 hertz and at the upper harmonics.)

3. Piano Strings When a string is set into vibration by striking it, the amplitude A of the vibrations decreases over time, while the frequency of the vibration remains constant. This phenomenon is called *exponential decay* and can be modeled by $A = A_0 e^{-kt} \sin(2\pi Ft)$, where F is the frequency, t is time in seconds, and k and A_0 are positive constants. (*Source:* J. Roederer.)

(a) Graph A when $A_0 = 0.1$, $F = 15$, and $k = 1.2$ in the window $[0, 1, 0.1]$ by $[-0.15, 0.15, 0.05]$.

(b) Now graph the equations $y_1 = -0.1e^{-1.2t}$ and $y_2 = 0.1e^{-1.2t}$ with A. Describe how the graphs of y_1 and y_2 relate to the graph of A.

(c) The *decay half-time* is the time it takes for the maximum amplitude of A_0 to decrease to $\frac{1}{2}A_0$. Estimate this time graphically. (The decay half-time for a typical piano string is about 0.4 second.)

8

Further Topics in Trigonometry

> There is no branch of mathematics, however abstract, which may not some day be applied to the real world.
>
> —Nikolai Lobachevsky

Many unusual scientific concepts defy intuition, and mathematics is necessary for their understanding. For example, world technology took a giant step forward when the Large Hadron Collider (LHC) was put into operation in September 2008. The LHC, a 17-mile-long nuclear particle accelerator located 100 meters beneath the border between France and Switzerland, now propels particles near light speed. With the LHC, scientists now believe that they have found a new particle, called the Higgs (or god) particle, which was first predicted by five equations in 1964. Scientists also hope to create tiny black holes that will fortunately disappear rapidly, according to mathematical predictions made by Stephen Hawking. The LHC may even reveal the existence of higher dimensions. Even though there is *no experimental evidence* for many of these phenomena, *mathematical equations predict them*, so scientists are looking. The LHC is one of the most expensive scientific instruments ever built, yet the confidence in its success relies heavily on mathematics.

Angles, triangles, vectors, and complex numbers help make new technologies such as the LHC, the Global Positioning System, aerial photography, and navigation possible. In this chapter, we use these mathematical concepts to solve a variety of applications.

8.1 Law of Sines

- Learn about oblique triangles
- Derive the law of sines
- Solve triangles
- Solve the ambiguous case

Introduction

In Chapter 6, we solved right triangles. Solving a triangle involves finding the length of each side and the measure of each angle in the triangle. In many areas of study, triangles without right angles often occur. For example, the height of the Gateway to the West Arch in St. Louis can be found from the ground by using triangles without right angles. (See Exercise 63.) To solve these *oblique triangles*, we will use the law of sines and the law of cosines. In this section, the law of sines is derived and used to solve several problems.

Oblique Triangles

If a triangle is not a right triangle, then it is called an **oblique triangle**. There are four different situations, or cases, that can occur when attempting to solve an oblique triangle.

1. SSS: All three sides are given. This situation determines a unique triangle and is referred to as SSS. See Figure 8.1. Note that the length of any one side must be less than the sum of the lengths of the other two sides.
2. SAS: Two sides and the angle included (between them) are given. This situation determines a unique triangle and is referred to as SAS. See Figure 8.2.
3. AAS or ASA: One side and two angles are given. This situation determines a unique triangle and is referred to as AAS or ASA. See Figure 8.3. Note that whenever two angles of a triangle are known, the third angle can be found by using the fact that the sum of the measures of the angles equals 180°.
4. SSA: Two sides and an angle opposite one of the sides are given. This situation does *not always* determine a unique triangle and is referred to as SSA. There may be zero, one, or two triangles that can satisfy SSA. As a result, we call SSA the **ambiguous case**. See Figures 8.4–8.6.

Cases 1–3: One Triangle Possible
(Unique)

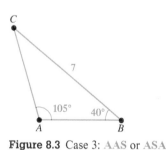

Figure 8.1 Case 1: SSS   **Figure 8.2** Case 2: SAS   **Figure 8.3** Case 3: AAS or ASA

Case 4: Zero, One, or Two Triangles Possible
(Ambiguous Case)

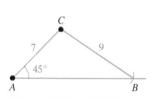

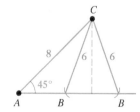

Figure 8.4 Case 4: SSA (No Triangles)   **Figure 8.5** Case 4: SSA (One Triangle)   **Figure 8.6** Case 4: SSA (Two Triangles)

Cases 1 and 2 are solved in Section 8.2 using the *law of cosines*, and Cases 3 and 4 are solved in this section using the *law of sines*.

Standard Labeling

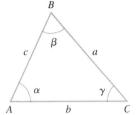

Figure 8.7

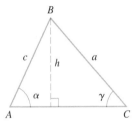

Figure 8.8

Solving Triangles with the Law of Sines

We will label triangles as shown in Figure 8.7 and refer to this labeling as the **standard labeling**. For example, angle α is located at vertex A and side a is opposite angle α. Note that angle γ need *not* be a right angle.

Derivation of Law of Sines   The law of sines can be derived using the oblique triangle shown in Figure 8.8.

$$\sin \alpha = \frac{h}{c}, \quad \text{or} \quad h = c \sin \alpha$$

$$\sin \gamma = \frac{h}{a}, \quad \text{or} \quad h = a \sin \gamma$$

Since $h = c \sin \alpha$ and $h = a \sin \gamma$, it follows that

$$c \sin \alpha = a \sin \gamma,$$

or, if we divide each side by ac,

$$\frac{\sin \alpha}{a} = \frac{\sin \gamma}{c}.$$

In a similar manner it can be shown that

$$\frac{\sin \alpha}{a} = \frac{\sin \beta}{b}.$$

This discussion supports the following result.

LAW OF SINES

Any triangle with standard labeling satisfies

$$\frac{\sin \alpha}{a} = \frac{\sin \beta}{b} = \frac{\sin \gamma}{c}, \quad \text{or equivalently,} \quad \frac{a}{\sin \alpha} = \frac{b}{\sin \beta} = \frac{c}{\sin \gamma}.$$

We usually use these equations to find angles $\alpha, \beta,$ or γ.

We usually use these equations to find sides $a, b,$ or c.

In the next example we solve a triangle by using the law of sines.

EXAMPLE 1   Solving a triangle (ASA)

Solve the triangle shown in Figure 8.9

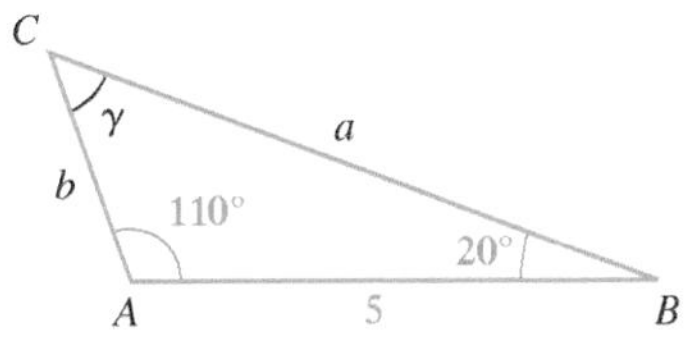

SOLUTION In Figure 8.9, $\alpha = 110°, \beta = 20°,$ and $c = 5$. To solve this triangle we need to find $a, b,$ and angle γ located at vertex C. Because we are given ASA, we can apply the law of sines.

Figure 8.9

Find γ   The sum of the measures of the angles in a triangle equal $180°$, so it follows that $\alpha + \beta + \gamma = 180°$.

$$\gamma = 180° - \alpha - \beta \qquad \text{Solve for } \gamma.$$

$$= 180° - 110° - 20° \qquad \text{Substitute.}$$

$$= 50° \qquad \text{Simplify.}$$

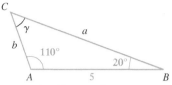

Figure 8.9 (Repeated)

Find a and b We can find a and b by writing the law of sines so that a is the only unknown in one equation and b is the only unknown in the other equation.

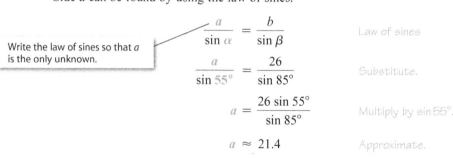

Find Side a		Find Side b	
$\dfrac{a}{\sin \alpha} = \dfrac{c}{\sin \gamma}$		$\dfrac{b}{\sin \beta} = \dfrac{c}{\sin \gamma}$	Law of sines
$\dfrac{a}{\sin 110°} = \dfrac{5}{\sin 50°}$		$\dfrac{b}{\sin 20°} = \dfrac{5}{\sin 50°}$	Substitute.
$a = \dfrac{5 \sin 110°}{\sin 50°}$		$b = \dfrac{5 \sin 20°}{\sin 50°}$	Solve for the variable.
$a \approx 6.13$		$b \approx 2.23$	Approximate.

Now Try Exercise 3

EXAMPLE 2 Solving a triangle (AAS)

If $\beta = 85°$, $\gamma = 40°$, and $b = 26$, solve triangle ABC.

SOLUTION Sketch triangle ABC as shown in Figure 8.10.

$$\alpha = 180° - \beta - \gamma = 180° - 85° - 40° = 55°$$

Side a can be found by using the law of sines.

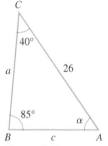

Figure 8.10

Write the law of sines so that a is the only unknown.

$$\frac{a}{\sin \alpha} = \frac{b}{\sin \beta} \qquad \text{Law of sines}$$

$$\frac{a}{\sin 55°} = \frac{26}{\sin 85°} \qquad \text{Substitute.}$$

$$a = \frac{26 \sin 55°}{\sin 85°} \qquad \text{Multiply by } \sin 55°.$$

$$a \approx 21.4 \qquad \text{Approximate.}$$

Side c can be found in a similar manner.

Write the law of sines so that c is the only unknown.

$$\frac{c}{\sin \gamma} = \frac{b}{\sin \beta} \qquad \text{Law of sines}$$

$$\frac{c}{\sin 40°} = \frac{26}{\sin 85°} \qquad \text{Substitute.}$$

$$c = \frac{26 \sin 40°}{\sin 85°} \qquad \text{Multiply by } \sin 40°.$$

$$c \approx 16.8 \qquad \text{Approximate.}$$

Now Try Exercise 27

Applications The next two examples illustrate how the law of sines is used in applications.

EXAMPLE 3 Using aerial photography to find distances (ASA)

Figure 8.11 depicts a situation in which a camera lens has an angular coverage of 75°. As a picture is taken over level ground, the airplane's distance is 4800 feet from a house located on the edge of the photograph and the angle of elevation of the airplane from the house is 48°. Find the ground distance a shown in the photograph. (***Source:*** F. Moffitt, *Photogrammetry.*)

Aerial Photography

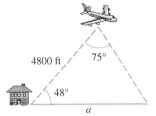

Figure 8.11

SOLUTION In this example we are given two angles and the side included (ASA), so let $\alpha = 75°$, $\beta = 48°$, and $c = 4800$, as shown in Figure 8.12. To find the third angle γ we can use the fact that the angles sum to 180°.

$$\gamma = 180° - \alpha - \beta$$
$$= 180° - 75° - 48°$$
$$= 57°$$

Side a corresponds to the ground distance shown in the photograph and can be found by using the law of sines.

$$\frac{a}{\sin \alpha} = \frac{c}{\sin \gamma} \qquad \text{Law of sines}$$

$$\frac{a}{\sin 75°} = \frac{4800}{\sin 57°} \qquad \text{Substitute.}$$

$$a = \frac{4800 \sin 75°}{\sin 57°} \qquad \text{Multiply by } \sin 75°.$$

$$a \approx 5528 \qquad \text{Approximate.}$$

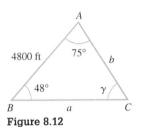

Figure 8.12

The photograph will show about 5528 feet of ground distance from one edge of the photograph to the other.

Now Try Exercise 45

EXAMPLE 4 Estimating the distance to the moon (ASA)

Since the moon is a relatively close celestial object, its distance can be approximated using trigonometry. To find this distance, two photographs of the moon were taken at precisely the same time from two locations. On April 29, 1976, at 11:35 A.M., the lunar angles of elevation during a partial solar eclipse at Bochum in upper Germany and at Donaueschingen in lower Germany were measured as $\alpha = 52.6997°$ and $\theta = 52.7430°$, respectively. See Figure 8.13. If the two cities are 398.02 kilometers apart, approximate the distance to the moon. Disregard the curvature of Earth in this calculation. (*Source:* W. Schlosser, *Challenges of Astronomy.*)

Finding the Distance to the Moon

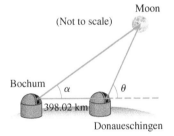

Figure 8.13

SOLUTION

Getting Started Consider triangle ABC shown in Figure 8.14, where $\alpha = 52.6997°$, $\theta = 52.7430°$, and $c = 398.02$. Because $\alpha + \gamma$ and θ are both supplements of angle β, it follows that $\alpha + \gamma = \theta$ and so

$$\gamma = \theta - \alpha = 52.7430° - 52.6997° = 0.0433°.$$

The distance to the moon can be approximated by finding either a or b. Why? ▶
  We find a by applying the law of sines.

$$\frac{a}{\sin \alpha} = \frac{c}{\sin \gamma} \qquad \text{Law of sines}$$

$$\frac{a}{\sin 52.6997°} = \frac{398.02}{\sin 0.0433°} \qquad \text{Substitute.}$$

$$a = \frac{398.02 \sin 52.6997°}{\sin 0.0433°} \qquad \text{Multiply by } \sin 52.6997°.$$

$$a \approx 419{,}000 \text{ km} \qquad \text{Approximate.}$$

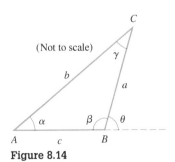

Figure 8.14

The distance to the moon on that day was about 419,000 kilometers.

Now Try Exercise 47

Bearings Bearings are used in both surveying and aerial navigation to determine directions. If a single angle is used for a **bearing**, then it is understood that the bearing is measured *clockwise* from due north. See Figure 8.15.

Examples of Bearings

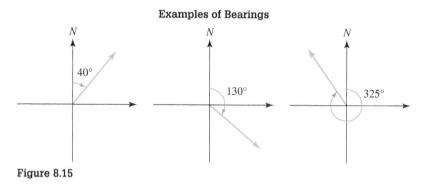

Figure 8.15

In the next example, we locate a fire by using bearings. (**Source:** I. Mueller and K. Ramsayer, *Introduction to Surveying.*)

EXAMPLE 5 Determining the location of a forest fire

A fire is spotted from two ranger stations that are 4 miles apart, as illustrated in Figure 8.16. From station *A* the bearing of the fire is 35°, and from station *B* the bearing of the fire is 335°. Find the distance to the nearest hundredth of a mile between the fire and each ranger station if station *A* lies directly west of station *B*.

Finding the Distance to a Fire

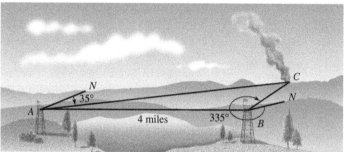

Figure 8.16

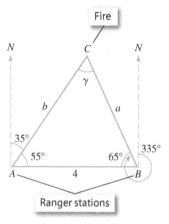

Figure 8.17

SOLUTION See triangle *ABC* in Figure 8.17, where $\alpha = 55°$, $\beta = 335° - 270° = 65°$, and $c = 4$. Thus

$$\gamma = 180° - 55° - 65° = 60°.$$

Using the law of sines, we can find *a*.

$$\frac{a}{\sin \alpha} = \frac{c}{\sin \gamma} \qquad \text{Law of sines}$$

$$\frac{a}{\sin 55°} = \frac{4}{\sin 60°} \qquad \text{Substitute.}$$

$$a = \frac{4 \sin 55°}{\sin 60°} \qquad \text{Multiply by } \sin 55°.$$

$$a \approx 3.78 \text{ mi} \qquad \text{Approximate.}$$

In a similar manner, we can find b.

$$\frac{b}{\sin\beta} = \frac{c}{\sin\gamma} \qquad \text{Law of sines}$$

$$\frac{b}{\sin 65°} = \frac{4}{\sin 60°} \qquad \text{Substitute.}$$

$$b = \frac{4\sin 65°}{\sin 60°} \qquad \text{Multiply by } \sin 65°.$$

$$b \approx 4.19 \text{ mi} \qquad \text{Approximate.}$$

The fire is 4.19 miles from station A and 3.78 miles from station B.

Now Try Exercise 49

The Ambiguous Case (SSA)

If we are given two sides and an angle opposite one of the sides (SSA), there may be zero, one, or two triangles that satisfy these conditions. For this reason SSA is called the *ambiguous case*.

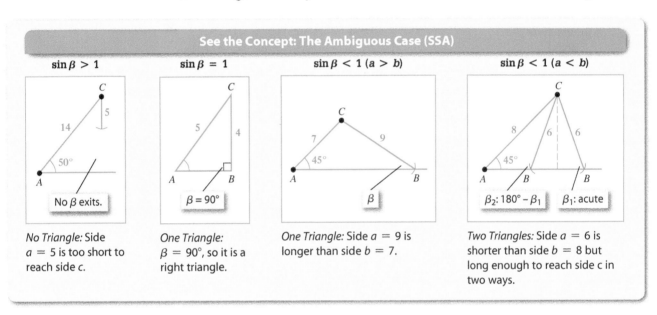

See the Concept: The Ambiguous Case (SSA)

$\sin\beta > 1$	$\sin\beta = 1$	$\sin\beta < 1 \ (a > b)$	$\sin\beta < 1 \ (a < b)$

No Triangle: Side $a = 5$ is too short to reach side c.

One Triangle: $\beta = 90°$, so it is a right triangle.

One Triangle: Side $a = 9$ is longer than side $b = 7$.

Two Triangles: Side $a = 6$ is shorter than side $b = 8$ but long enough to reach side c in two ways.

The following box summarizes the steps needed to recognize and solve each situation of the ambiguous case, where we are given two sides and an angle opposite one side.

SOLVING THE AMBIGUOUS CASE (SSA)

Given SSA, the following steps can be used to determine whether there are zero, one, or two triangles that satisfy the conditions. For simplicity, assume that a, b, and α are given.

STEP 1: Use the law of sines to find $\sin\beta$, where β is the unknown angle opposite b.

> **No Solutions:** If $\sin\beta > 1$, there are no possible triangles.
>
> **One Solution:** If $\sin\beta = 1$, then $\beta = 90°$. Find γ and c.

STEP 2: If $\sin\beta = k$, where $k < 1$, calculate $\beta_1 = \sin^{-1} k$ and $\beta_2 = 180° - \beta_1$. Note that β_1 and β_2 are the two *possible* solutions to $\sin\beta = k$.

> **One Solution:** If $\alpha + \beta_2 \geq 180°$ (or $a > b$), there is one triangle determined by β_1. Find γ and c.
>
> **Two Solutions:** If $\alpha + \beta_2 < 180°$ (or $a < b$), there are two triangles. Let $\gamma_1 = 180° - \alpha - \beta_1$ and $\gamma_2 = 180° - \alpha - \beta_2$. Find c_1 and c_2.

EXAMPLE 6 Solving the ambiguous case (no solutions)

Let $\alpha = 62°$, $a = 6$, and $b = 10$. If possible, solve the triangle.

SOLUTION

STEP 1: We begin by using the law of sines to find $\sin \beta$.

No Triangle Exists

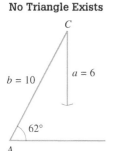

Figure 8.18

> Write the law of sines so that $\sin \beta$ is the only unknown.

$$\frac{\sin \beta}{b} = \frac{\sin \alpha}{a} \qquad \textit{Law of sines}$$

$$\frac{\sin \beta}{10} = \frac{\sin 62°}{6} \qquad \textit{Substitute.}$$

$$\sin \beta = \frac{10 \sin 62°}{6} \qquad \textit{Multiply by 10.}$$

$$\sin \beta \approx 1.47 > 1 \qquad \textit{Approximate } \sin \beta.$$

Since the sine function is never greater than 1, there are no solutions for β. No such triangle exists. See Figure 8.18.

Now Try Exercise 37

A Bridge Truss

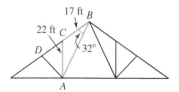

Figure 8.19

An Application from Construction Trusses are used in construction to support roofs, radio towers, bridges, and aircraft frames. Many times the smaller shapes within a truss are triangles. See Figure 8.19. In the next example, we determine that a particular truss design results in a unique truss. (***Source:*** W. Riley, *Statics and Mechanics of Materials.*)

EXAMPLE 7 Solving the ambiguous case (one solution)

Suppose that an engineer has designed the truss in Figure 8.19 and specified that in triangle *ABC*, *BC* = 17 feet, *AC* = 22 feet, and angle *ABC* = 32°. Determine the length of *AB* to the nearest tenth of a foot. Is this value for *AB* unique?

SOLUTION

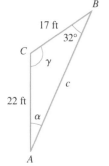

Figure 8.20

STEP 1: Triangle *ABC* from the truss in Figure 8.19 is shown in Figure 8.20. Using standard labeling, let $a = 17$, $b = 22$, and $\beta = 32°$. Start by finding $\sin \alpha$.

$$\frac{\sin \alpha}{a} = \frac{\sin \beta}{b} \qquad \textit{Law of sines}$$

$$\frac{\sin \alpha}{17} = \frac{\sin 32°}{22} \qquad \textit{Substitute.}$$

$$\sin \alpha = \frac{17 \sin 32°}{22} \qquad \textit{Multiply by 17.}$$

$$\sin \alpha \approx 0.4095 \qquad \textit{Approximate } \sin \alpha.$$

STEP 2: There are two values possible for angle α if $\sin \alpha \approx 0.4095$. Angle α lies in quadrant I or II with reference angle $\alpha_R \approx \sin^{-1}(0.4095) \approx 24.2°$. Thus

$$\alpha_1 \approx 24.2° \qquad \text{and} \qquad \alpha_2 \approx 180° - 24.2° = 155.8°.$$

However, if $\alpha_2 \approx 155.8°$, then $\alpha_2 + \beta \approx 155.8° + 32° \geq 180°$, which is not possible in a triangle. Therefore $\alpha_1 \approx 24.2°$ is the only possibility and

$$\gamma \approx 180° - 24.2° - 32° = 123.8°.$$

There is only one triangle possible.

The law of sines allows us to find AB, or side c.

$$\frac{c}{\sin \gamma} = \frac{b}{\sin \beta} \qquad \text{Law of sines}$$

$$\frac{c}{\sin 123.8°} \approx \frac{22}{\sin 32°} \qquad \text{Substitute.}$$

$$c \approx \frac{22 \sin 123.8°}{\sin 32°} \qquad \text{Multiply by } \sin 123.8°.$$

$$c \approx 34.5 \text{ ft} \qquad \text{Approximate } c.$$

Thus AB is about 34.5 feet long, and this value is unique.

Now Try Exercise 33

EXAMPLE 8 Solving the ambiguous case (two solutions)

Let $\alpha = 55°$, $b = 8.5$, and $a = 7.3$. Solve the triangle. Round to the nearest tenth.

SOLUTION

STEP 1: Begin by finding $\sin \beta$.

$$\frac{\sin \beta}{b} = \frac{\sin \alpha}{a} \qquad \text{Law of sines}$$

$$\frac{\sin \beta}{8.5} = \frac{\sin 55°}{7.3} \qquad \text{Substitute.}$$

$$\sin \beta = \frac{8.5 \sin 55°}{7.3} \qquad \text{Multiply by 8.5.}$$

$$\sin \beta \approx 0.9538 \qquad \text{Approximate } \sin \beta.$$

First Triangle

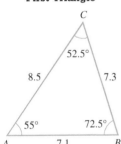

Figure 8.21 Solution 1

STEP 2: Two angles that satisfy $\sin \beta \approx 0.9538$ in quadrants I or II are

$$\beta_1 \approx \sin^{-1}(0.9538) \approx 72.5° \quad \text{and} \quad \beta_2 \approx 180° - 72.5° = 107.5°.$$

Both of these values for β are valid, since they do not result in the sum of the angles exceeding 180°. There are *two* solutions. (Note that $a < b$.)

Solution 1 Let $\beta_1 \approx 72.5°$. Then $\gamma_1 \approx 180° - 72.5° - 55° = 52.5°$. Side c_1 can then be found.

$$\frac{c_1}{\sin \gamma_1} = \frac{a}{\sin \alpha} \qquad \text{Law of sines}$$

$$c_1 \approx \frac{7.3 \sin 52.5°}{\sin 55°} \qquad \text{Substitute and solve for } c_1.$$

$$c_1 \approx 7.1 \qquad \text{Approximate } c_1.$$

A sketch of first triangle ABC is shown in Figure 8.21.

Second Triangle

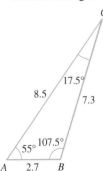

Figure 8.22 Solution 2

Solution 2 Let $\beta_2 \approx 107.5°$. Then $\gamma_2 \approx 180° - 107.5° - 55° = 17.5°$. Then side c_2 can be found.

$$\frac{c_2}{\sin \gamma_2} = \frac{a}{\sin \alpha} \qquad \text{Law of sines}$$

$$c_2 \approx \frac{7.3 \sin 17.5°}{\sin 55°} \qquad \text{Substitute and solve for } c_2.$$

$$c_2 \approx 2.7 \qquad \text{Approximate } c_2.$$

A sketch of second triangle ABC is shown in Figure 8.22.

Now Try Exercise 29

8.1 Putting It All Together

The law of sines can be expressed as either

$$\frac{\sin \alpha}{a} = \frac{\sin \beta}{b} = \frac{\sin \gamma}{c} \quad \text{or} \quad \frac{a}{\sin \alpha} = \frac{b}{\sin \beta} = \frac{c}{\sin \gamma}.$$

When using the law of sines, a good strategy is to select an equation with the unknown variable in the numerator. We can use the law of sines to solve triangles when we are given ASA, AAS, or SSA. The cases ASA and AAS occur when two angles are given. In these cases a unique triangle is determined. The case where we are given SSA is called the ambiguous case, since there may be zero, one, or two triangles that satisfy the conditions. The ambiguous case is shown in the accompanying table.

THE AMBIGUOUS CASE	EXAMPLES
No solutions for triangle ABC	$\sin \beta > 1$ (α acute) $\sin \beta > 1$ (α obtuse)
One solution for triangle ABC	$\sin \beta = 1$ (α acute) $\sin \beta < 1$ and $a > b$ (α acute) $\sin \beta < 1$ and $a > b$ (α obtuse)
Two solutions for triangle ABC	$\sin \beta < 1$ and $a < b$ (α acute)

8.1 Exercises

Solving for Unique Triangles

Exercises 1–4: Solve the triangle. Approximate values to the nearest tenth.

1.
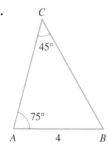

2.
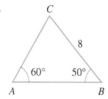

3.
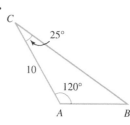

4.
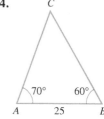

Exercises 5–12: Solve the triangle. Approximate values to the nearest tenth.

5. $\alpha = 40°$, $\beta = 60°$, $c = 10$

6. $\alpha = 35°$, $\beta = 75°$, $c = 8.1$

7. $\alpha = 25°$, $\gamma = 40°$, $a = 9.7$

8. $\beta = 36°$, $\gamma = 72°$, $b = 6$

9. $\beta = 40.2°$, $\gamma = 60.7°$, $a = 5.5$

10. $\alpha = 15.7°$, $\gamma = 23°$, $c = 7.2$

11. $\alpha = 27°$, $\gamma = 49°$, $b = 67$

12. $\beta = 39°$, $\gamma = 67°$, $a = 79$

Recognizing the Ambiguous Case (SSA)

Exercises 13–20: Let triangle ABC have standard labeling. Given the following angles and sides, decide if solving the triangle results in the ambiguous case.

13. α, β, and a

14. α, γ, and c

15. a, b, and c

16. α, a, and b

17. β, b, and c

18. α, b, and c

19. γ, a, and c

20. β, b, and α

Solving the Ambiguous Case

Exercises 21–26: Solve the triangle, if possible. Approximate values to the nearest tenth.

21.

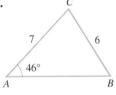

22.

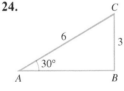

23.

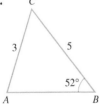

24.

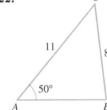

25.

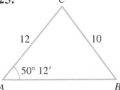

26.

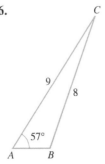

Solving Triangles

Exercises 27–44: Solve the triangle, if possible. Approximate values to the nearest tenth when appropriate.

27. $\alpha = 32°$, $\beta = 55°$, $b = 12$

28. $\beta = 20°$, $\gamma = 67°$, $c = 9$

29. $\alpha = 20°$, $b = 9$, $a = 7$

30. $\alpha = 20°$, $b = 7$, $a = 9$

31. $b = 10$, $\beta = 30°$, $c = 20$

32. $a = 13.5$, $\alpha = 46°$, $c = 27.8$

33. $\gamma = 102°$, $c = 51.6$, $a = 42.1$

34. $\beta = 43°$, $b = 22.1$, $c = 30.7$

35. $\alpha = 55.2°$, $\gamma = 114.8°$, $b = 19.5$

36. $c = 225$, $\alpha = 103.2°$, $\beta = 62.5°$

37. $b = 6.2$, $c = 7.4$, $\beta = 73°$

38. $\alpha = 45°$, $a = 5$, $b = 5\sqrt{2}$

39. $\alpha = 35°15'$, $a = 5$, $b = 12$

40. $\gamma = 71°35'$, $c = 6$, $b = 9$

41. $\beta = 46°45'$, $a = 6$, $b = 5$

42. $\alpha = 54°12'$, $c = 12$, $a = 10$

43. $\alpha = 56°30'$, $\beta = 23°45'$, $c = 100$

44. $\beta = 56°48'$, $\gamma = 10°12'$, $a = 55$

Applications

45. Aerial Photography   (Refer to Example 3.) The plane shown in the figure is taking an aerial photograph with a camera lens that has an angular coverage of 70°. The ground below is inclined at 7°. If the angle of elevation of the plane at B is 52° and distance BC is 3500 feet, estimate the ground distance AB (to the nearest foot) that will appear in the picture.   (*Source:* F. Moffit, *Photogrammetry.*)

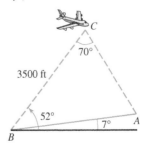

46. Aerial Photography As a picture is taken over level ground, the airplane's distance from a building located at the edge of the photograph is 7500 feet and the angle of depression to the building is 56°. See the figure. Find the ground distance *b* shown in the photograph to the nearest hundred feet.

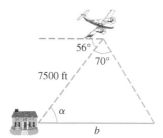

47. Distance to the Moon (Refer to Example 4 and Figure 8.13.) Suppose that the lunar angle at Bochum in upper Germany had been measured as $\alpha = 52.6901°$ instead of 52.6997°. Determine the effect that this would have on the estimation of the distance to the moon. Interpret the result.

48. Distance to the Moon (Refer to Example 4 and Figure 8.13.) Suppose that the distance between two locations is 452.45 kilometers and that their angles of elevation to the moon are $\alpha = 47.8981°$ and $\theta = 47.9443°$. Estimate the distance to the moon (to the nearest thousand kilometers).

49. Locating a Ship The figure shows the bearings of a ship from two observation points located on a straight shoreline. The bearing from the first observation point is 54.3°, and the bearing from the second observation point is 325.2°. If the distance between these points is 15 miles, how far is it from the ship to shore? Assume that the first observation point is directly west of the second observation point.

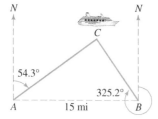

50. Distance A ship is traveling west on Lake Superior at 18 miles per hour. The bearing of Split Rock Lighthouse is 285°. After 1 hour, the bearing of the lighthouse is 340°. Find the distance between the ship and the lighthouse when the second bearing was determined.

51. Truss Construction For the truss shown at the top of the next column, *AB* is 24.2 feet, angle *ABD* is 118°, and angle *BDF* is 28°. Find the length of *BD*.

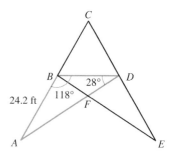

52. Truss Construction Use the results of Example 7 to solve triangle *ACD* in Figure 8.19 if angle *BAD* is 90°.

53. Distance Across a River To find the distance *AB* across a river, a distance *BC* = 354 meters is measured off on one side of the river. See the figure. It is found that angle *ABC* = 112°10′ and that angle *BCA* = 15°20′. Find the distance *AB*.

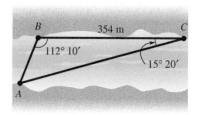

54. Distance Across a Canyon To find the distance *RS* across a canyon, a distance *TR* = 582 yards is measured off on one side of the canyon. See the figure. It is found that angle *TRS* = 102°20′ and that angle *RTS* = 32°50′. Find the distance *RS*.

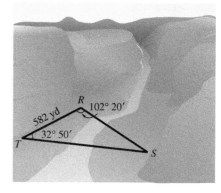

55. Height of a Helicopter A helicopter is sighted at the same time by two ground observers who are 3 miles apart on the same side of the helicopter. See the figure. They report angles of elevation of 20.5° and 27.8°. How high is the helicopter?

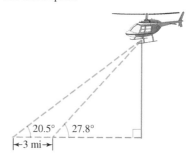

56. Height of a Hot-Air Balloon   Two observation points A and B are 1500 feet apart. From these points the angles of elevation of a hot-air balloon are 43° and 47°, as illustrated in the figure. Find the height of the balloon to the nearest foot.

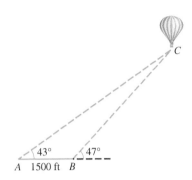

57. Height of a Balloon   A balloonist is directly above a straight road 1.5 miles long that joins two towns, as illustrated in the figure. She finds that the town closer to her is at an angle of depression of 35° and the farther town is at an angle of depression of 31°. How high above the ground is the balloon?

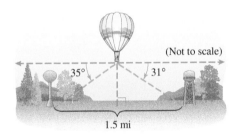

58. Highway Construction   In a *reverse curve*, or S-curve, two circular curves are used to connect two straight portions of highway that are offset, as illustrated in the figure. Angles α and β will not be equal if the two straight portions of highway have different directions. Typically the same radius r is used for both portions of the reverse curve. If r = 480 feet, α = 38°, β = 15°, and θ = 75°, find the distance between A and B to the nearest foot. (*Source:* P. Kissam, *Surveying Practice.*)

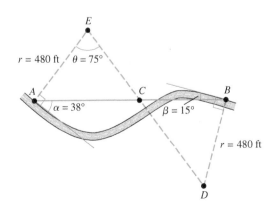

59. Surveying   To find the distance between two points A and B on opposite sides of a small pond, a surveyor determines that AC is 97.3 feet, angle ACB is 55.1°, and angle CAB is 75.7°, as illustrated in the figure. Find the distance between A and B.

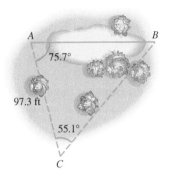

60. Trigonometric Leveling   In surveying it is often necessary to determine the height of an inaccessible point P, as illustrated in the figure. Points A, B, and C lie on level ground.   (*Source:* P. Kissam, *Surveying Practice.*)

(a) If angle ABP is 50°, angle PAB is 53.3°, and AB is 102 feet, find PB.

(b) If angle PBC is 47° and C is directly below P, find PC.

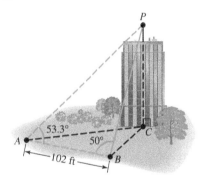

61. Locating a Ship   From two observation points A and B, a sinking ship is spotted at point C. Angle CAB and angle ABC are measured as 28° and 60°, and the distance AB is about 4.12 miles, as illustrated in the figure.

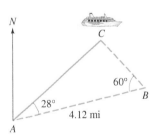

(a) How far is the ship from point A, to the nearest hundredth of a mile?

(b) If the coordinates of A are (0, 0) and the coordinates of B are (4, 1), find the bearing of the ship from point A to the nearest degree.

62. Airplane Navigation An airplane takes off with a bearing of 55° and flies 480 miles, after which it changes its course to a bearing of 285°. Finally the airplane flies back to its starting point with a bearing of 180°. Find the total mileage flown by the airplane.

63. Height of the Gateway Arch The tallest monument in the world is the Gateway to the West Arch in St. Louis. From point *A*, the top of the arch has an angle of elevation of 64.91°, and from point *B* the angle of elevation is 60.81°. See the figure. If distance *AB* is 57 feet, find the height of this monument to the nearest foot. (***Source:*** *The Guinness Book of Records.*)

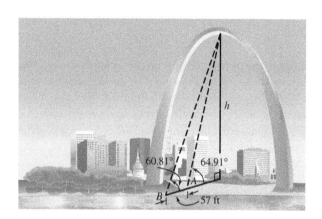

64. Height of a Tower A vertical tower supporting a cable for chairlifts to transport skiers up a mountain is located on a ski slope inclined at 28°, as illustrated in the figure. If the length of the tower's shadow is 21 feet along the mountain side when the angle of the sun is 57° with respect to the ski slope, calculate the height of the tower.

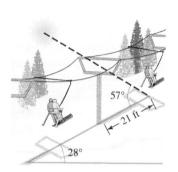

Writing about Mathematics

65. In your own words, describe two situations where the law of sines can be applied. Give an example of each situation.

66. Suppose that you are given α, a, and b for triangle *ABC*. If α is obtuse, what is the maximum number of triangles that could satisfy these conditions? What is the maximum number if α is acute? Explain your reasoning and give examples.

8.2 Law of Cosines

- Derive the law of cosines
- Solve triangles
- Find areas of triangles

Introduction

Surveying has been used for centuries in construction and in the determination of boundaries. Today the Global Positioning System (GPS) is being used to determine distances on Earth. The signal from a GPS satellite contains the information necessary for hand-held receivers to calculate both the position of a GPS satellite and its distance from the receiver. This information can be used to accurately calculate distances and angles between points on the ground. The law of cosines, which is a generalization of the Pythagorean theorem, is used in GPS calculations. In this section, the law of cosines is introduced and used to solve several applications. (***Source:*** J. Van Sickle, *GPS for Land Surveyors.*)

Derivation of the Law of Cosines

The law of cosines can be used to solve a triangle given either all three sides (SSS) or two sides and the angle included (SAS). In both cases a unique triangle is formed, as illustrated in Figures 8.23 and 8.24 at the top of the next page.

Next consider triangle *ABC* shown in Figure 8.25 on the next page, with point *B* having coordinates (x, y). Using definitions of sine and cosine, we find

$$\cos \gamma = \frac{x}{a} \quad \text{and} \quad \sin \gamma = \frac{y}{a},$$

or equivalently,

$$x = a \cos \gamma \quad \text{and} \quad y = a \sin \gamma.$$

Law of Cosines Solves SSS **and** SAS

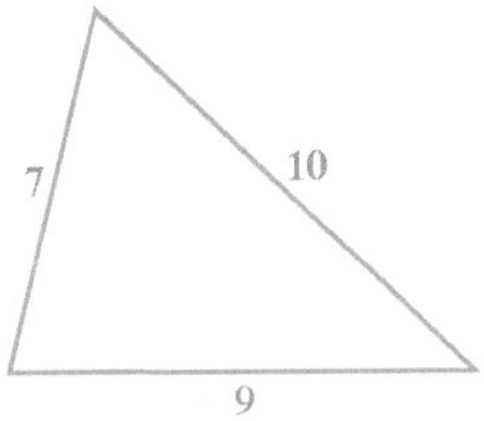

Figure 8.23 Given SSS 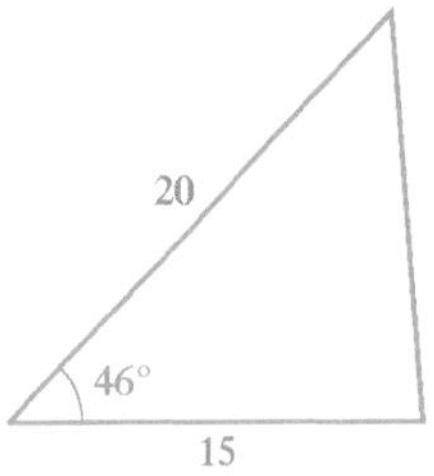   Figure 8.24 Given SAS

General Triangle

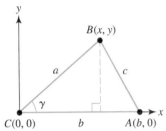

Figure 8.25

As a result, the coordinates of B are $(a \cos \gamma, a \sin \gamma)$. Since the coordinates of point A are $(b, 0)$, the distance c between points A and B can be found.

$$c = \sqrt{(a \cos \gamma - b)^2 + (a \sin \gamma - 0)^2}$$ Distance formula

$$c^2 = (a \cos \gamma - b)^2 + (a \sin \gamma - 0)^2$$ Square each side.

$$c^2 = a^2 \cos^2 \gamma - 2ab \cos \gamma + b^2 + a^2 \sin^2 \gamma$$ Expand each expression.

$$c^2 = a^2 (\cos^2 \gamma + \sin^2 \gamma) - 2ab \cos \gamma + b^2$$ Distributive property

$$c^2 = a^2 + b^2 - 2ab \cos \gamma$$ $\cos^2 \gamma + \sin^2 \gamma = 1$

This result is valid for any triangle ABC and is known as the *law of cosines*. Since the vertices in Figure 8.25 could be rearranged, three possible equations are associated with the law of cosines.

CLASS DISCUSSION

Let $\gamma = 90°$ in the formula

$$c^2 = a^2 + b^2 - 2ab \cos \gamma$$

and simplify. Discuss the relationship between the law of cosines and the Pythagorean theorem.

LAW OF COSINES

Any triangle with standard labeling satisfies

$$a^2 = b^2 + c^2 - 2bc \cos \alpha$$

$$b^2 = a^2 + c^2 - 2ac \cos \beta$$

$$c^2 = a^2 + b^2 - 2ab \cos \gamma.$$

Solving Triangles

In the first example we use the law of cosines to find the missing side, given SAS.

EXAMPLE 1   Applying the law of cosines (SAS)

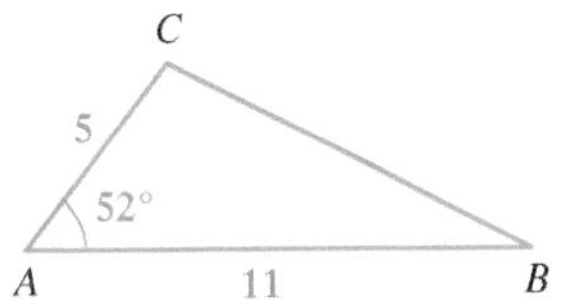

Find the missing side in the triangle shown in Figure 8.26.

SOLUTION   We are given SAS, so let $\alpha = 52°$, $b = 5$, and $c = 11$. The unknown side is side a. We will use the first equation for the law of cosines.

$$a^2 = b^2 + c^2 - 2bc \cos \alpha$$ Law of cosines

$$= 5^2 + 11^2 - 2(5)(11) \cos 52°$$ Substitute.

$$\approx 78.277$$ Approximate.

Thus $a \approx \sqrt{78.277} \approx 8.85$.

Figure 8.26

Now Try Exercise 9

Surveying   A common problem in surveying is to find the distance between two points A and B situated on opposite sides of a building, as illustrated in Figure 8.27 on the next page. This distance can be found by applying the law of cosines.

EXAMPLE 2 Finding the distance between two points (SAS)

Finding Distance *AB*

Figure 8.27

The surveyor in Figure 8.27 determines that CA is 75 feet, CB is 58 feet, and angle ACB is 83°. Find distance AB to the nearest foot.

SOLUTION Note that $CA = b$, $CB = a$, and angle $ACB = \gamma$. So let $b = 75$, $a = 58$, and $\gamma = 83°$. To find c, apply the law of cosines.

$$
\begin{aligned}
c^2 &= a^2 + b^2 - 2ab \cos \gamma && \text{Law of cosines}\\
&= (58)^2 + (75)^2 - 2(58)(75) \cos 83° && \text{Substitute.}\\
&\approx 7929 && \text{Approximate.}\\
c &\approx 89.04 && \text{Take the square root.}
\end{aligned}
$$

The points A and B are about 89 feet apart.

Now Try Exercise 53

Global Positioning System In the next example, the distance between two GPS receivers is found. Finding the distance between two points might be important to surveyors or to search parties looking for lost hikers. The distance between two GPS receivers is sometimes called the *baseline*.

EXAMPLE 3 Using GPS to find a baseline distance (SAS)

A search party and an injured hiker both have hand-held GPS receivers, as illustrated in Figure 8.28. The distance from the satellite to the search party is $b = 20{,}231.15$ kilometers, and the distance from the satellite to the hiker is $c = 20{,}231.57$ kilometers. If it is determined that $\alpha = 0.01456°$, estimate the baseline a between the search party and the hiker to the nearest hundredth of a kilometer.

Locating an Injured Hiker

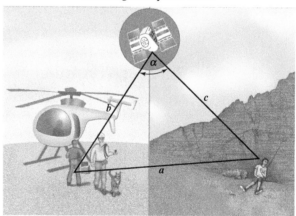

Figure 8.28 (Not to scale)

SOLUTION We can use the law of cosines to find a.

$$
\begin{aligned}
a^2 &= b^2 + c^2 - 2bc \cos \alpha\\
&= (20{,}231.15)^2 + (20{,}231.57)^2 - 2(20{,}231.15)(20{,}231.57) \cos 0.01456°\\
&\approx 26.61\\
a &\approx 5.16
\end{aligned}
$$

The distance between the search party and the hiker is about 5.16 kilometers.

Now Try Exercise 55

In the next example we use the law of cosines to find a missing angle, given SSS.

EXAMPLE 4 Applying the law of cosines (SSS)

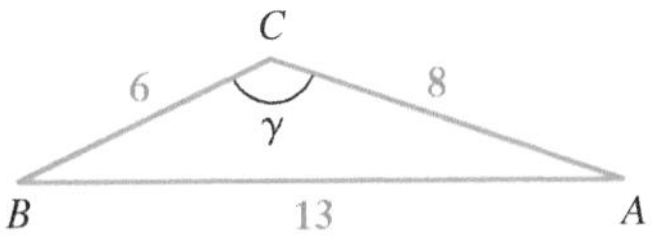

Find angle γ in the triangle shown in Figure 8.29.

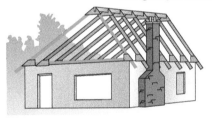

Figure 8.29

SOLUTION We are given SSS, so let $a = 6$, $b = 8$, and and $c = 13$. Angle γ is opposite side c. We use the third equation for law of cosines that contains $\cos \gamma$ and solve for $\cos \gamma$.

$$c^2 = a^2 + b^2 - 2ab \cos \gamma \qquad \text{Law of cosines}$$

$$2ab \cos \gamma = a^2 + b^2 - c^2 \qquad \text{Rewrite the equation.}$$

$$\cos \gamma = \frac{a^2 + b^2 - c^2}{2ab} \qquad \text{Divide by 2ab.}$$

$$\cos \gamma = \frac{6^2 + 8^2 - 13^2}{2(6)(8)} \qquad \text{Substitute.}$$

$$\cos \gamma = -0.71875 \qquad \text{Simplify.}$$

Thus $\gamma = \cos^{-1}(-0.71875) \approx 136.0°$.

Now Try Exercise 11

An Application from Construction Trusses are frequently used to support roofs on buildings, as illustrated in Figure 8.30. The simplest type of roof truss is a triangle, as shown in Figure 8.31. One basic task when constructing a roof truss is to cut the ends of the rafters so that the roof has the correct slope. (*Source:* W. Riley, *Statics and Mechanics of Materials.*)

Designing a Triangular Roof Truss

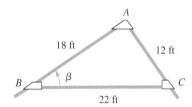

Figure 8.30

Figure 8.31

EXAMPLE 5 Designing a roof truss (SSS)

Find β to the nearest degree for the truss shown in Figure 8.31.

SOLUTION Begin by letting $a = 22$, $b = 12$, and $c = 18$, and then use the law of cosines to find β.

$$b^2 = a^2 + c^2 - 2ac \cos \beta \qquad \text{Law of cosines}$$

$$2ac \cos \beta = a^2 + c^2 - b^2 \qquad \text{Rewrite the equation.}$$

$$\cos \beta = \frac{a^2 + c^2 - b^2}{2ac} \qquad \text{Divide by 2ac.}$$

$$\cos \beta = \frac{22^2 + 18^2 - 12^2}{2(22)(18)} \qquad \text{Substitute.}$$

$$\cos \beta \approx 0.8384 \qquad \text{Approximate.}$$

Thus $\beta \approx \cos^{-1}(0.8384) \approx 33°$.

Now Try Exercise 63

EXAMPLE 6   Solving a triangle (SSS)

Find α, β, and γ in triangle ABC to the nearest tenth of a degree if $a = 5$, $b = 6$, and $c = 9$.

SOLUTION

Getting Started When solving SSS, always start by finding the largest angle. The largest angle, γ, is opposite the largest side, c. We start by finding γ. ▶

$$c^2 = a^2 + b^2 - 2ab \cos \gamma \qquad \text{Law of cosines}$$

$$2ab \cos \gamma = a^2 + b^2 - c^2 \qquad \text{Transpose terms.}$$

$$\cos \gamma = \frac{a^2 + b^2 - c^2}{2ab} \qquad \text{Divide by 2ab.}$$

$$\cos \gamma = \frac{5^2 + 6^2 - 9^2}{2(5)(6)} \qquad \text{Let } a = 5, b = 6, \text{ and } c = 9.$$

$$\cos \gamma = -\frac{1}{3} \qquad \text{Simplify.}$$

Thus $\gamma \approx \cos^{-1}\left(-\frac{1}{3}\right) \approx 109.5°$. The law of cosines could be used again to find either α or β. However, we use the law of sines to find α.

$$\frac{\sin \alpha}{a} = \frac{\sin \gamma}{c} \qquad \text{Law of sines}$$

$$\sin \alpha = \frac{a \sin \gamma}{c} \qquad \text{Multiply by a.}$$

$$\sin \alpha \approx \frac{5 \sin 109.5°}{9} \qquad \text{Let } a = 5, c = 9, \text{ and } \gamma \approx 109.5°.$$

$$\sin \alpha \approx 0.5237 \qquad \text{Simplify.}$$

Because γ is the largest angle, it follows that α must be an acute angle and that $\alpha \approx \sin^{-1}(0.5237) \approx 31.6°$. To find β we use the fact that the measures of the angles sum to 180° in a triangle.

$$\beta \approx 180° - 109.5° - 31.6° = 38.9°$$

Now Try Exercise 21

NOTE   In solving the case SSS, first find the largest angle, which is opposite the longest side. There can be at most one obtuse angle in a triangle, and the law of cosines finds an obtuse angle, if it exists, because the cosine of an obtuse angle is negative, as was the case in Example 6.

See the Concept: Applying the Law of Cosines

SAS   ### SSS

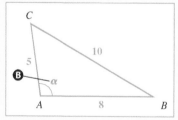

A Find a:

$a^2 = 5^2 + 8^2 - 2(5)(8) \cos 60°$,

so $a = \sqrt{49} = 7$.

B Find α:

$\cos \alpha = \dfrac{5^2 + 8^2 - 10^2}{2(5)(8)}$,

so $\alpha = \cos^{-1}(-0.1375) \approx 97.9°$.

A SAS Given two sides and the angle between, find the side opposite the given angle.

$$a^2 = b^2 + c^2 - 2bc \cos \alpha$$

B SSS Given three sides, first find the angle opposite the *longest* side.

$$\cos \alpha = \frac{b^2 + c^2 - a^2}{2bc}$$

Area Formulas

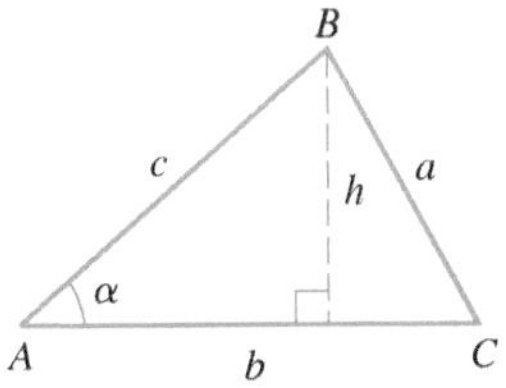

One task that is frequently performed by surveyors is to find the acreage of a lot using a technique called triangulation. *Triangulation* divides a parcel of land into triangles. The area of the lot equals the sum of the areas of the triangles. We begin our discussion by developing some area formulas for triangles.

The area K of any triangle is given by $K = \frac{1}{2}bh$, where b is its base and h is its height. Using trigonometry, we can find a formula for the area of the triangle shown in Figure 8.32.

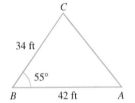
Figure 8.32

$$\sin \alpha = \frac{h}{c}, \quad \text{or} \quad h = c \sin \alpha$$

Thus the area equals

$$K = \frac{1}{2}bh = \frac{1}{2}bc \sin \alpha.$$

Since the labels for the vertices in triangle ABC could be rearranged, three area formulas can be written as follows. Notice that these formulas can be applied when we are given SAS. (We use K for area rather than A so as not to cause confusion with vertex A.)

> **AREA OF A TRIANGLE**
>
> For any triangle with standard labeling, the area K is given by
>
> $$K = \frac{1}{2}ab \sin \gamma, \qquad K = \frac{1}{2}ac \sin \beta, \qquad \text{or} \qquad K = \frac{1}{2}bc \sin \alpha.$$

EXAMPLE 7   Finding the area of a triangle (SAS)

Find the area of triangle ABC in Figure 8.33 to the nearest square foot.

SOLUTION We are given $\beta = 55°$, $a = 34$ feet, and $c = 42$ feet. Thus the area K is given by the following.

$$K = \frac{1}{2}ac \sin \beta = \frac{1}{2}(34)(42) \sin 55° \approx 585 \text{ square feet}$$

Now Try Exercise 37

Figure 8.33

Heron's Formula   The next formula can be used to find the area of a triangle when the lengths of three sides are known. It is named after the Greek mathematician Heron.

> **HERON'S FORMULA**
>
> If a triangle has sides with lengths a, b, and c, then its area K is given by
>
> $$K = \sqrt{s(s - a)(s - b)(s - c)},$$
>
> where $s = \frac{1}{2}(a + b + c)$ and s is called the **semiperimeter**.

EXAMPLE 8   Finding the area of a triangle (SSS)

Approximate the area of triangle ABC with sides $a = 4$, $b = 5$, and $c = 7$.

SOLUTION

Getting Started Begin by calculating $s = \frac{1}{2}(4 + 5 + 7) = 8$. ▶

Then the area is

$$K = \sqrt{8(8 - 4)(8 - 5)(8 - 7)} = \sqrt{96} \approx 9.8.$$

Now Try Exercise 39

An Application from Surveying One method for finding the area of a lot is called the *distance method*. This method can be used to find the area of an irregular lot, as illustrated in the next example. The distance method does not measure angles—it measures only distances between points. Triangulation and Heron's formula can be used to find the area of the lot. (***Source:*** I. Mueller and K. Ramsayer, *Introduction to Surveying.*)

EXAMPLE 9 Applying the distance method to find the area of a lot

Find the area of the parcel of land determined by *ABCDE* in Figure 8.34.

Finding Area of a Lot

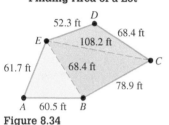

Figure 8.34

SOLUTION For triangle *ABE*, $s = \frac{1}{2}(60.5 + 68.4 + 61.7) = 95.3$, and its area is

$$K_1 = \sqrt{95.3(95.3 - 60.5)(95.3 - 68.4)(95.3 - 61.7)} \approx 1731.$$

For triangle *BCE*, $s = \frac{1}{2}(78.9 + 108.2 + 68.4) = 127.75$, and its area is

$$K_2 = \sqrt{127.75(127.75 - 78.9)(127.75 - 108.2)(127.75 - 68.4)} \approx 2691.$$

For triangle *CDE*, $s = \frac{1}{2}(68.4 + 52.3 + 108.2) = 114.45$, and its area is

$$K_3 = \sqrt{114.45(114.45 - 68.4)(114.45 - 52.3)(114.45 - 108.2)} \approx 1431.$$

The area of the lot is

$$K_1 + K_2 + K_3 \approx 1731 + 2691 + 1431 = 5853 \text{ square feet.}$$

Now Try Exercise 77

8.2 Putting It All Together

The law of cosines can be used to solve triangles when either three sides (SSS) or two sides and the angle included (SAS) are given. Heron's formula can be used to find the area of a triangle given SSS.

CONCEPT	EXPLANATION	EXAMPLES
Law of cosines	$a^2 = b^2 + c^2 - 2bc \cos \alpha$ $b^2 = a^2 + c^2 - 2ac \cos \beta$ $c^2 = a^2 + b^2 - 2ab \cos \gamma$ Can be used to solve a triangle given either SSS or SAS	If $b = 3$, $c = 4$, and $\alpha = 60°$, then $a^2 = 3^2 + 4^2 - 2(3)(4) \cos 60° = 13$ and $a = \sqrt{13}$.
Area formulas (SAS)	$K = \frac{1}{2}ab \sin \gamma$ $K = \frac{1}{2}ac \sin \beta$ $K = \frac{1}{2}bc \sin \alpha$ Can be used to find the area of a triangle given SAS	If $a = 2$ feet, $b = 3$ feet, and $\gamma = 30°$, then the area of the triangle is $K = \frac{1}{2}(2)(3) \sin 30° = 1.5 \text{ ft}^2$.

CONCEPT	EXPLANATION	EXAMPLES
Heron's formula (SSS)	$K = \sqrt{s(s-a)(s-b)(s-c)}$, where $s = \frac{1}{2}(a+b+c)$ Can be used to find the area of a triangle given SSS	If $a = 3$ feet, $b = 5$ feet, and $c = 4$ feet, then $$s = \tfrac{1}{2}(3+5+4) = 6,$$ and the area of the triangle is $$K = \sqrt{6(6-3)(6-5)(6-4)} = 6 \text{ ft}^2.$$ 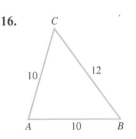

8.2 Exercises

Determining a Method to Solve a Triangle

Exercises 1–8: Assume triangle ABC has standard labeling and complete the following.

(a) Determine if AAS, ASA, SSA, SAS, or SSS is given.
(b) Decide if the law of sines or the law of cosines should be used first to solve the triangle.

1. a, b, and γ

2. α, γ, and c

3. a, b, and α

4. a, b, and c

5. α, β, and c

6. a, c, and α

7. β, a, and γ

8. b, c, and α

Solving Triangles

Exercises 9 and 10: Find the length of the remaining side of each triangle. Approximate to the nearest tenth when appropriate.

9.
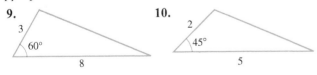

10.

Exercises 11 and 12: Find the value of θ in each triangle. Approximate to the nearest tenth when appropriate.

11.
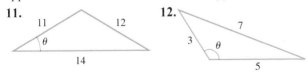

12.

Exercises 13–18: Solve the triangle. Approximate values to the nearest tenth.

13.
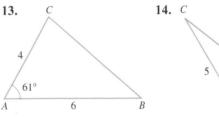

14.

15.
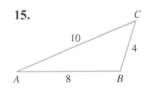

16.
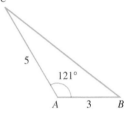

17.
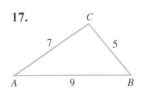

18.
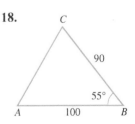

Exercises 19–30: Solve the triangle. Round values to the nearest tenth when appropriate.

19. $a = 45$, $\gamma = 35°$, $b = 24$

20. $c = 7.9$, $\beta = 52°$, $a = 9.6$

21. $a = 2.4, b = 1.7, c = 1.4$

22. $a = 43, b = 41, c = 34$

23. $\alpha = 10°30', b = 24.1, c = 15.8$

24. $a = 12.8, b = 15.8, \gamma = 36°$

25. $a = 10.6, b = 25.8, c = 20.6$

26. $a = 104, b = 121, c = 111$

27. $\beta = 122°10', a = 20, c = 15$

28. $b = 9.1, \alpha = 43°30', c = 12.5$

29. $a = 5.3, b = 6.7, c = 7.1$

30. $a = 4.2, b = 5.1, c = 3.7$

Does This Triangle Exist?

Exercises 31–36: Decide if a triangle exists that satisfies the conditions. Justify your answer.

31. $a = 10, b = 12, c = 25$

32. $a = 10, \beta = 51°, c = 5$

33. $\alpha = 89°, b = 63, \gamma = 112°$

34. $a = 2, b = 10, \alpha = 50°$

35. $\gamma = 54°, b = 63, \alpha = 63°$

36. $a = 5, b = 6, c = 8$

Area of Triangles

Exercises 37–40: Approximate the area of the triangle to the nearest tenth.

37.

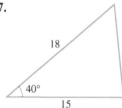

38.

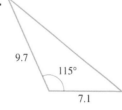

39.

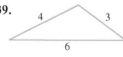

40.

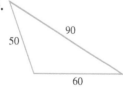

Exercises 41–52: Approximate the area of the triangle to the nearest tenth.

41. $a = 10, b = 12, \gamma = 58°$

42. $\alpha = 40°, b = 5.8, c = 8.8$

43. $\beta = 78°, a = 5.5, c = 6.8$

44. $\alpha = 23°, \gamma = 47°, b = 53$

45. $\beta = 31°, \alpha = 54°, a = 2.6$

46. $a = 7, b = 8, c = 9$

47. $a = 5.5, b = 6.7, c = 9.2$

48. $a = 104, b = 98, c = 112$

49. $a = 11, b = 13, c = 20$

50. $a = 13, b = 14, c = 15$

51. $a = 21, \alpha = 42°, c = 16$

52. $b = 35, c = 38, \gamma = 50°48'$

Applications

53. Obstructed View (Refer to Example 2.) In the figure, a surveyor is attempting to find the distance between points A and B. A grove of trees is obstructing the view, so the surveyor determines that AC is 143 feet, BC is 123 feet, and angle ACB is $78°35'$. Find the distance between A and B to the nearest foot.

54. Distance Across a Lake Points A and B are on opposite sides of a lake. From a third point, C, the angle between the lines of sight to A and B is $46.3°$. If AC is 350 meters and BC is 286 meters, find AB.

55. Ship Navigation Two ships set sail with bearings of $52°$ and $121°$, traveling at 20 miles per hour and 14 miles per hour, respectively. See the figure. Find the approximate distance between the ships after 1.5 hours.

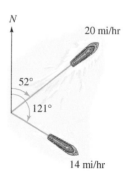

56. Distance Between Two Boats Two boats leave a dock together. Each travels in a straight line. The angle between their courses measures 54°10′. One boat travels 36.2 kilometers per hour and the other 45.6 kilometers per hour. How far apart will they be after 3 hours?

57. Diagonals of a Parallelogram One side of a parallelogram is 3.5 feet and another side is 5.2 feet. The angle between these two sides is 56°. Find the lengths of the diagonals to the nearest tenth of a foot.

58. Diagonals of a Parallelogram The sides of a parallelogram are 4.0 centimeters and 6.0 centimeters. One angle is 58° while another is 122°. Find the lengths of the diagonals.

59. Air Navigation An airplane flies in the triangular course shown in the figure. To the nearest degree, find the bearings of the plane while traveling from A to B and from B to C.

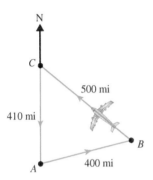

60. Flight Distance Airports A and B are 450 kilometers apart, on an east-west line. A pilot flies in a northeast direction from A to airport C. From C, the pilot flies 359 kilometers on a bearing of 128°40′ to B. How far is C from A?

61. Area of a Lot A surveyor measures the sides of a triangular lot to be $a = 145.2$, $b = 136.8$, and $c = 95.3$, where measurements are in feet.
(a) Approximate angles α, β, and γ.

(b) What is the area of the lot to the nearest square foot?

62. Angle in a Parallelogram One side of a parallelogram is 6.4 yards and another side is 5.3 yards. The shorter diagonal is 3.5 yards. Find the angle opposite the shorter diagonal to the nearest tenth of a degree.

63. Truss Construction (Refer to Example 5.) Find angle θ for the triangular truss shown in the figure.

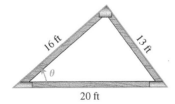

64. Robotics The figure illustrates the MIT Scheinman robotic arm. Suppose the length of the upper arm is 20 centimeters and the combined length of the forearm and hand is 30 centimeters. If the arm is positioned so that $\theta = 126°$, find the distance between the hand at point A and the shoulder joint at point B. (*Source:* G. Beni and S. Hackwood, *Recent Advances in Robotics.*)

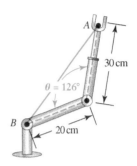

65. Distance Between Airports Airports A and B are 515 miles apart, and airport A is directly west of airport B. Airport C is located in a northeasterly direction from airport A and is 357 miles from airport B. See the figure. If the bearing from airport C to airport B is 125°, find the distance between airports A and C to the nearest mile.

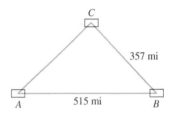

66. Navigation A ship is sailing east. At one moment, the bearing of a submerged rock is 38°45′. After the ship sails 20.4 miles, the bearing of the rock is 291°15′. Find the distance between the ship and the rock (to the nearest tenth of a mile) when the second bearing is taken.

67. Distance Between a Ship and a Submarine From an airplane flying over the ocean, the angle of depression to a submarine lying just under the surface is 24°10′. At the same moment, the angle of depression from the airplane to a battleship is 17°30′. See the figure. The distance from the airplane to the battleship is 5120 feet. Find the distance between the battleship and the submarine. (Assume the airplane, submarine, and battleship are in a vertical plane.)

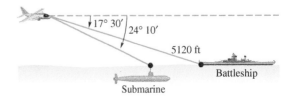

68. Distance Between a Ship and a Rock A ship is sailing east. At one point, the bearing of a submerged rock is 45°20′. After the ship has sailed 15.2 miles, the bearing of the rock has become 308°40′. Find the distance of the ship from the rock at the latter point.

69. Distance Between Two Ships Two ships leave a harbor together, traveling on courses that have an angle of 135°40′ between them. If they each travel 402 miles, how far apart are they?

70. Highway Curve The most common highway curve consists of a circular arc connecting two sections of straight road, as illustrated in the figure. Find the straight-line distance between *PC* (point of curve) and *PT* (point of tangency). (***Source:*** P. Kissam, *Surveying Practice*.)

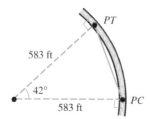

71. Painting A painter needs to cover a triangular region with sides of 25 feet and 15 feet. The angle between these two sides is 128°. Find the area of the region to the nearest tenth of a square foot.

72. Painting A painter needs to cover a triangular region with sides of 30 feet, 40 feet, and 38 feet. If each can of paint covers 125 square feet, how many cans of paint are needed?

73. Area of Regular Polygons If a regular polygon has *n* sides of equal length *L*, then its area *A* is computed by

$$A = \frac{nL^2}{4} \cot \frac{\pi}{n}.$$

(***Source:*** M. Mortenson, *Computer Graphics*.)
(a) Using this formula, find the area of an equilateral triangle with sides of 6 inches.

(b) Using Heron's formula, find the area of this triangle. Compare answers.

74. Area of Regular Polygons (Refer to Exercise 73.) The measure of an interior angle in a regular polygon with *n* sides is given by $180°\left(1 - \frac{2}{n}\right)$. For example, a square is a regular polygon with $n = 4$ and each interior angle equals $180°\left(1 - \frac{2}{4}\right) = 90°$.
(a) Find the area of a regular pentagon with sides of length 8 inches, using the formula given in Exercise 73. See the figure at the top of the next column.

(b) Using triangulation and Heron's formula, find the area of this regular pentagon.

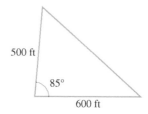

75. Area of a Lot Find the area of the lot in the figure to the nearest square foot.

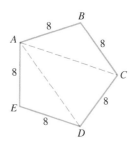

76. Area of a Lot Find the area of the quadrangular lot shown in the figure to the nearest square foot.

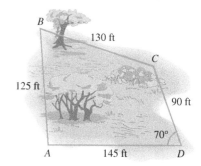

77. Area of a Lot Apply the distance method discussed in Example 9 to find the area of the lot in the figure to the nearest square foot.

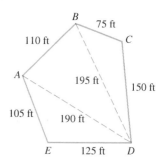

78. Area of the Bermuda Triangle Find the area of the Bermuda Triangle (to the nearest thousand square miles) if the sides of the triangle have approximate lengths of 850 miles, 925 miles, and 1300 miles.

Writing about Mathematics

79. Describe two different situations where the law of cosines can be applied. Give an example of each situation.

80. Describe two methods to find the area of a triangle. What information do you need to apply each method? Give an example of each situation.

Extended and Discovery Exercise

1. **Distance Between a Satellite and a Tracking Station**
   A satellite traveling in a circular orbit 1600 kilometers above Earth is due to pass directly over a tracking station at noon. See the figure. Assume that the satellite takes 2 hours to make an orbit and that the radius of Earth is 6400 kilometers. Find the distance between the satellite and the tracking station at 12:03 P.M. (*Source:* NASA.)

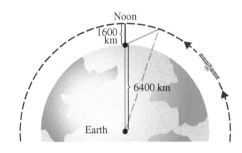

CHECKING BASIC CONCEPTS FOR SECTIONS 8.1 AND 8.2

1. Solve triangle ABC if $\alpha = 44°$, $\gamma = 62°$, and $a = 12$.

2. Solve triangle ABC if $\alpha = 32°$, $a = 6$, and $b = 8$. How many solutions are there?

3. Use the law of cosines to solve the triangles.

   (a)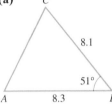

   (b)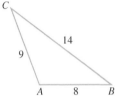

4. Find the area of triangle ABC to the nearest hundredth.

   (a) $a = 4.5, b = 5.2, \gamma = 55°$

   (b) $a = 6, b = 7, c = 9$

8.3 Vectors

- **Learn basic concepts about vectors**
- **Learn representations of vectors**
- **Find the magnitude, direction angle, and components of a vector**
- **Perform operations on vectors**
- **Learn to apply the dot product**
- **Use vectors to calculate work**

Introduction

The beginnings of vectors go back centuries to the notion of a directed line segment, but the formal development of vectors occurred during the 19th and 20th centuries, after the invention of complex numbers. It was not until Einstein used vectors in his theory of relativity that their importance became readily accepted.

Vectors are a profound invention. In science and technology they provide a simple model for visualizing difficult concepts such as force, velocity, and electric fields. Vectors are essential to creating today's amazing computer graphics. This section discusses some of the important properties and applications of vectors. (*Sources:* Historical Topics for the Mathematical Classroom, Thirty-first Yearbook, NCTM; M. Mortenson, Computer Graphics.)

Basic Concepts

Many quantities in mathematics can be described using real numbers, or **scalars**. Examples include a person's weight, the cost of a DVD player, and the gas mileage of a car. Other quantities must be represented using vector quantities. A **vector quantity** involves both *magnitude* and *direction*. Magnitude can be interpreted as size or length. For example, if a car is traveling north at 50 miles per hour, then the direction *north* coupled with a *speed* of 50 miles per hour represents a vector quantity called *velocity*. In science a distinction is made between speed and velocity—speed is the magnitude of velocity.

A vector quantity can be represented by a directed line segment called a **vector**. A vector **v** representing the velocity of a car traveling 50 miles per hour north is shown in Figure 8.35; the vector **u** represents a velocity of 25 miles per hour east. Notice that the length of **u** is half the length of **v**. Vectors do *not* have position—rather, they have magnitude and direction. A vector can be translated, provided its direction and magnitude (length) do not change. Two vectors are **equal** if they have the same magnitude and direction. In Figure 8.36 each directed line segment represents the same vector **v**.

Vectors: Magnitude and Direction

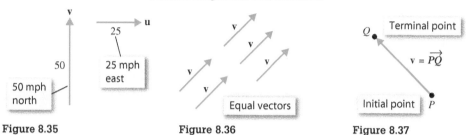

Figure 8.35   Figure 8.36   Figure 8.37

A vector is usually represented symbolically by a letter printed in boldface type, such as **a**, **b**, **v**, or **F**. A second way to denote a vector is to use two points. If the **initial point** of a vector **v** is P and its **terminal point** is Q, then $\mathbf{v} = \overrightarrow{PQ}$, as illustrated in Figure 8.37.

Representations of Vectors

If we place the initial point of vector **v** at the origin, as in Figure 8.38, then its terminal point (a_1, a_2) can be used to determine **v**. To distinguish the *point* (a_1, a_2) from the *vector* **v**, we use the notation $\mathbf{v} = \langle a_1, a_2 \rangle$. The **horizontal component** of **v** is a_1 and the **vertical component** of **v** is a_2. See Figure 8.39.

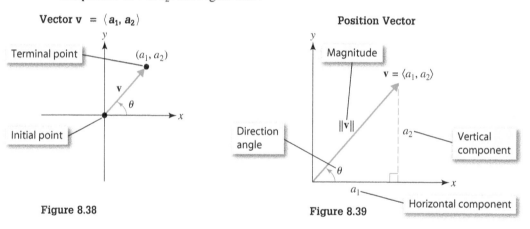

Figure 8.38   Figure 8.39

A vector with its initial point at the origin in the rectangular coordinate system is called a **position vector**. Figure 8.39 shows the position vector **v**. The *positive* angle θ ($0° \leq \theta < 360°$) between the x-axis and the position vector is called the **direction angle** for the vector. In Figure 8.39, θ is the direction angle for vector **v**. If $\mathbf{v} = \langle a_1, a_2 \rangle$, then its direction angle θ satisfies

$$\tan \theta = \frac{a_2}{a_1}, \quad \text{where} \quad a_1 \neq 0.$$

The length of a vector equals its magnitude. If $\mathbf{v} = \langle a_1, a_2 \rangle$, then the *magnitude* of **v** is denoted $\|\mathbf{v}\|$. Applying the Pythagorean theorem to Figure 8.39 gives $\|\mathbf{v}\| = \sqrt{a_1^2 + a_2^2}$.

MAGNITUDE OF A VECTOR

If $\mathbf{v} = \langle a_1, a_2 \rangle$, then the **magnitude** (or length) of **v** is given by

$$\|\mathbf{v}\| = \sqrt{a_1^2 + a_2^2}.$$

If $\|\mathbf{v}\| = 1$, then **v** is a **unit vector**.

EXAMPLE 1 Finding magnitude and direction angle

Find the magnitude and direction angle of $\mathbf{u} = \langle 3, -2 \rangle$.

SOLUTION Figure 8.40 shows the position vector for $\mathbf{u} = \langle 3, -2 \rangle$. The magnitude of vector $\mathbf{u}$ is

$$\|\mathbf{u}\| = \sqrt{3^2 + (-2)^2} = \sqrt{13}.$$

To find the direction angle θ, start with $\tan\theta = \frac{a_2}{a_1} = \frac{-2}{3} = -\frac{2}{3}$. A calculator reveals that $\tan^{-1}\left(-\frac{2}{3}\right) \approx -33.7°$. Adding $360°$ yields the positive direction angle $\theta \approx 326.3°$. See Figure 8.40.

Now Try Exercise 27

Finding $\|\mathbf{u}\|$ and θ

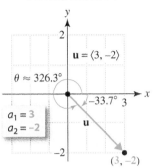

Figure 8.40

If the magnitude and the direction angle of a vector $\mathbf{v}$ are known, then horizontal and vertical components of $\mathbf{v}$ can be found by using the following equations. (Explain why.)

HORIZONTAL AND VERTICAL COMPONENTS

The horizontal and vertical components for a vector $\mathbf{v} = \langle a_1, a_2 \rangle$ having direction angle θ are given by

$$a_1 = \|\mathbf{v}\| \cos\theta \qquad \text{and} \qquad a_2 = \|\mathbf{v}\| \sin\theta.$$

That is, $\mathbf{v} = \langle \|\mathbf{v}\| \cos\theta, \|\mathbf{v}\| \sin\theta \rangle$.

EXAMPLE 2 Finding horizontal and vertical components

Vector $\mathbf{w}$ in Figure 8.41 has magnitude 25.0 and direction angle 41.7°. Find the horizontal and vertical components. Round to the nearest tenth.

SOLUTION Let $\|\mathbf{w}\| = 25.0$ and $\theta = 41.7°$.

$a_1 = \|\mathbf{w}\| \cos\theta$	$a_2 = \|\mathbf{w}\| \sin\theta$
$a_1 = 25.0 \cos 41.7°$	$a_2 = 25.0 \sin 41.7°$
$a_1 \approx 18.7$	$a_2 \approx 16.6$

Therefore $\mathbf{w} \approx \langle 18.7, 16.6 \rangle$. The horizontal component is 18.7, and the vertical component is 16.6 (rounded to the nearest tenth).

Now Try Exercise 35

Finding a_1 and a_2

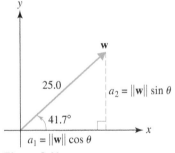

Figure 8.41

EXAMPLE 3 Writing vectors in the form $\langle a_1, a_2 \rangle$

Write each vector in Figure 8.42 in the form $\langle a_1, a_2 \rangle$.

SOLUTION

$$\mathbf{u} = \langle 5 \cos 60°, 5 \sin 60° \rangle = \langle 5 \cdot \tfrac{1}{2}, 5 \cdot \tfrac{\sqrt{3}}{2} \rangle = \langle \tfrac{5}{2}, \tfrac{5\sqrt{3}}{2} \rangle$$
$$\mathbf{v} = \langle 2 \cos 180°, 2 \sin 180° \rangle = \langle 2(-1), 2(0) \rangle = \langle -2, 0 \rangle$$
$$\mathbf{w} = \langle 6 \cos 280°, 6 \sin 280° \rangle \approx \langle 1.04, -5.91 \rangle$$

Now Try Exercises 39 and 43

Finding $\langle a_1, a_2 \rangle$

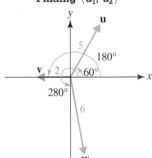

Figure 8.42

Using Two Points to Determine a Vector If a vector has initial point P with coordinates (a_1, b_1) and terminal point Q with coordinates (a_2, b_2), then vector $\overrightarrow{PQ}$ is given by $\overrightarrow{PQ} = \langle a_2 - a_1, b_2 - b_1 \rangle$. See the next example. Note that $\overrightarrow{QP} = \langle a_1 - a_2, b_1 - b_2 \rangle$.

EXAMPLE 4 Finding a vector graphically and symbolically

Let P have coordinates $(-1, 2)$ and Q have coordinates $(3, 4)$. Find vector $\overrightarrow{PQ}$ graphically and symbolically. Calculate the magnitude of $\overrightarrow{PQ}$

Determing $\overrightarrow{PQ}$ from 2 Points

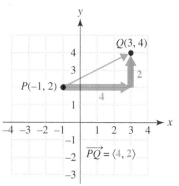

Figure 8.43

SOLUTION To graph $\overrightarrow{PQ}$ plot the points P and Q. Then sketch a directed line segment from P to Q, as shown in Figure 8.43. We can see that the horizontal component is 4 and the vertical component is 2. A symbolic representation of $\overrightarrow{PQ}$ is given by

$$\overrightarrow{PQ} = \langle 3 - (-1), 4 - 2 \rangle = \langle 4, 2 \rangle.$$

The magnitude, or length, of $\overrightarrow{PQ}$ is

$$\|\overrightarrow{PQ}\| = \sqrt{4^2 + 2^2} = \sqrt{20} \approx 4.47.$$

Now Try Exercise 49

Operations on Vectors

Vector Addition   Suppose that a swimmer heads directly across a river at 3 miles per hour. If the current is 4 miles per hour, then the person will be carried a distance downstream before reaching the other side, as illustrated in Figure 8.44. We can use vectors to visually find the direction and speed that the swimmer will travel across the river.

A Swimmer in a Current

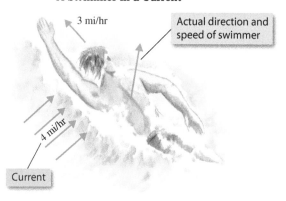

Figure 8.44

Let vector **a** represent the speed and direction of the swimmer with no current, vector **b** represent the direction and speed of the current, and vector **c** represent the final direction and speed of the swimmer. We can find the length and direction of **c** by applying the **parallelogram rule**, as shown in Figure 8.45. The speed and direction of the swimmer are represented by the diagonal **c** of the parallelogram (rectangle), which is determined by **a** and **b**. Vector **c** is called the **sum** or **resultant** of vectors **a** and **b**.

We can represent the velocity of the swimmer with no current by $\mathbf{a} = \langle 0, 3 \rangle$, the velocity of the current by $\mathbf{b} = \langle 4, 0 \rangle$, and the velocity of the swimmer in the current by $\mathbf{c} = \langle 4, 3 \rangle$. Vector **c** is the sum of vectors **a** and **b** and can be found as follows.

Vector Addition: c = a + b

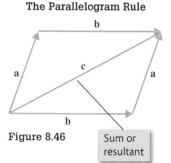

Figure 8.45

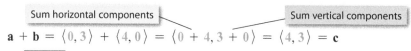

Sum horizontal components   Sum vertical components

$$\mathbf{a} + \mathbf{b} = \langle 0, 3 \rangle + \langle 4, 0 \rangle = \langle 0 + 4, 3 + 0 \rangle = \langle 4, 3 \rangle = \mathbf{c}$$

Since $\|\mathbf{c}\| = \sqrt{4^2 + 3^2} = 5$, the swimmer moves 5 miles per hour in the direction of **c**.

Figure 8.46 illustrates graphically how to find $\mathbf{c} = \mathbf{a} + \mathbf{b}$ in general by using the parallelogram rule. The following box defines vector addition symbolically.

The Parallelogram Rule

Figure 8.46   Sum or resultant

VECTOR ADDITION

If $\mathbf{a} = \langle a_1, a_2 \rangle$ and $\mathbf{b} = \langle b_1, b_2 \rangle$, then the **sum** of **a** and **b** is given by

$$\mathbf{a} + \mathbf{b} = \langle a_1, a_2 \rangle + \langle b_1, b_2 \rangle = \langle a_1 + b_1, a_2 + b_2 \rangle.$$

Suppose that vector **a** represents a force of 80 pounds pulling on a water-ski towrope and **b** represents a force of 60 pounds pulling on a second towrope with an angle of 25° between them. See Figure 8.47. The resultant force **c** = **a** + **b** is given by the diagonal of the parallelogram shown in Figure 8.48. Vector **c** represents the net force exerted by the two water skiers.

Force on a Boat

Figure 8.47

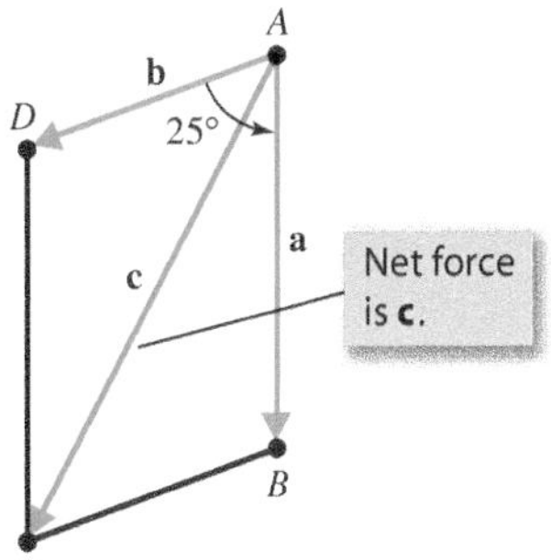

Figure 8.48

EXAMPLE 5   Applying the parallelogram rule

Find the magnitude of the resultant force on the ski boat in the preceding discussion.

SOLUTION The magnitude of the force equals the length of the diagonal *AC* in Figure 8.48. Angle *BAD* equals 25°. Since angle *ABC* is 180° − 25° = 155°, we find *AC* by applying the law of cosines.

$$AC^2 = 60^2 + 80^2 - 2(60)(80)\cos 155° \approx 18{,}701$$

$$AC \approx 137 \text{ pounds}$$

> Now Try Exercise 53

Vector Notation Using i and j   A second type of vector notation involves the vectors **i** = $\langle 1, 0 \rangle$ and **j** = $\langle 0, 1 \rangle$. A vector **a** = $\langle a_1, a_2 \rangle$ can be expressed as

$$\mathbf{a} = a_1\mathbf{i} + a_2\mathbf{j}.$$

For example, $\langle 3, -4 \rangle$ and $3\mathbf{i} - 4\mathbf{j}$ represent the same vector.

> **MAKING CONNECTIONS**
>
> **Imaginary unit *i* and unit vector i**   Section 3.3 discussed the *imaginary unit i*, where $i = \sqrt{-1}$ and $i^2 = -1$. The *vector* **i** = $\langle 1, 0 \rangle$ represents a different concept.

EXAMPLE 6   Finding resultant forces

Forces $\mathbf{F}_1 = 5\mathbf{i} + 12\mathbf{j}$ and $\mathbf{F}_2 = 4\mathbf{i} - 3\mathbf{j}$ act at the same point. Find the resultant force **F** and its magnitude.

SOLUTION The position vectors for $\mathbf{F}_1$ and $\mathbf{F}_2$ and the resultant force **F** are shown in Figure 8.49. The resultant force **F** equals $\mathbf{F}_1 + \mathbf{F}_2$.

$$\mathbf{F} = \mathbf{F}_1 + \mathbf{F}_2$$
$$= (5\mathbf{i} + 12\mathbf{j}) + (4\mathbf{i} - 3\mathbf{j}) \qquad \text{Add } \mathbf{j} \text{ components}$$
$$= (5 + 4)\mathbf{i} + (12 + (-3))\mathbf{j}$$
$$= 9\mathbf{i} + 9\mathbf{j} \qquad \text{Add } \mathbf{i} \text{ components}$$

It follows that $\|\mathbf{F}\| = \sqrt{9^2 + 9^2} = \sqrt{162} \approx 12.7$.

> Now Try Exercise 57

Resultant Force

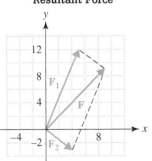

Figure 8.49

Scalar Multiplication   Scalar multiplication occurs when a vector **v** is multiplied by a real number, or *scalar, k* to form *k***v**. Vectors **v** and *k***v** are parallel if $k \neq 0$. Vector *k***v** points in the *same* direction as **v** if $k > 0$, and *k***v** points in the *opposite* direction of **v** if $k < 0$. The magnitude of *k***v** is $|k|$ times the magnitude of **v**. These ideas are illustrated by Figures 8.50 and 8.51 in the following See the Concept, where vector **v** represents the wind.

See the Concept: Scalar Multiplication

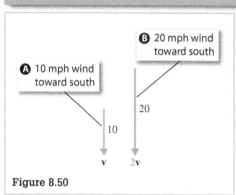

Figure 8.50

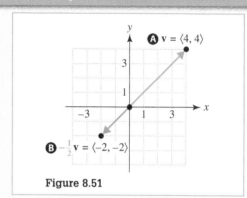

Figure 8.51

Ⓐ Represent the wind by $\mathbf{v} = \langle 0, -10 \rangle$.

Ⓑ If the wind doubles in speed but does not change direction, then the *scalar multiple* 2**v** models this situation.

$$2\mathbf{v} = 2\langle 0, -10 \rangle = \langle 2 \cdot 0, \, 2 \cdot (-10) \rangle = \langle 0, -20 \rangle$$

Ⓐ A wind toward the northeast is modeled by $\mathbf{v} = \langle 4, 4 \rangle$.

Ⓑ Then a wind in the opposite direction of **v** with half the speed is modeled by

$$-\frac{1}{2}\mathbf{v} = -\frac{1}{2}\langle 4, 4 \rangle = \left\langle -\frac{1}{2} \cdot 4, \, -\frac{1}{2} \cdot 4 \right\rangle = \langle -2, -2 \rangle.$$

The following is a definition of scalar multiplication.

SCALAR MULTIPLICATION

If $\mathbf{v} = \langle v_1, v_2 \rangle$ and k is a real number, then the **scalar multiple** $k\mathbf{v}$ is given by

$$k\mathbf{v} = k\langle v_1, v_2 \rangle = \langle kv_1, kv_2 \rangle.$$

Sums and scalar multiples can be calculated graphically and symbolically, as illustrated in the next example.

EXAMPLE 7   Performing operations on vectors

Find each of the following expressions graphically and symbolically if $\mathbf{a} = \langle -3, 4 \rangle$ and $\mathbf{b} = \langle -1, -2 \rangle$.

(a) $\|\mathbf{a}\|$ (b) $-2\mathbf{b}$ (c) $\mathbf{a} + 2\mathbf{b}$

SOLUTION

(a) Graph $\mathbf{a} = \langle -3, 4 \rangle$, as shown in Figure 8.52. The length of **a** appears to be about 5. This can be verified symbolically.

$$\|\mathbf{a}\| = \sqrt{(-3)^2 + (4)^2} = 5$$

(b) Graph $\mathbf{b} = \langle -1, -2 \rangle$. The scalar multiple $-2\mathbf{b}$ points in the opposite direction of **b** with twice the length. See Figure 8.53, where $-2\mathbf{b} = \langle 2, 4 \rangle$. Symbolically this is given by

$$-2\mathbf{b} = -2\langle -1, -2 \rangle = \langle -2 \cdot (-1), \, -2 \cdot (-2) \rangle = \langle 2, 4 \rangle.$$

(c) Graph $\mathbf{a} = \langle -3, 4 \rangle$ and $2\mathbf{b} = \langle -2, -4 \rangle$. See Figure 8.54. By the parallelogram rule, the diagonal represents $\mathbf{a} + 2\mathbf{b} = \langle -5, 0 \rangle$. This can be verified symbolically.

$$\mathbf{a} + 2\mathbf{b} = \langle -3, 4 \rangle + 2\langle -1, -2 \rangle = \langle -3, 4 \rangle + \langle -2, -4 \rangle = \langle -5, 0 \rangle$$

Finding ‖a‖

Finding −2b

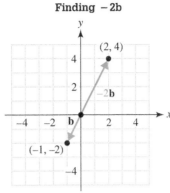

Finding a + 2b

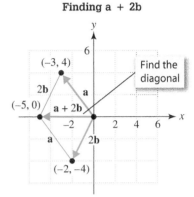

Figure 8.52   Figure 8.53   Figure 8.54

Now Try Exercise 79

Vector Subtraction   Subtraction can be defined both symbolically and graphically. The difference $\mathbf{a} - \mathbf{b}$ can be thought of as the sum $\mathbf{a} + (-\mathbf{b})$. Then,

$$\begin{aligned}
\mathbf{a} - \mathbf{b} &= \mathbf{a} + (-\mathbf{b}) \\
&= \langle a_1, a_2 \rangle + \langle -b_1, -b_2 \rangle \\
&= \langle a_1 + (-b_1), a_2 + (-b_2) \rangle \\
&= \langle a_1 - b_1, a_2 - b_2 \rangle.
\end{aligned}$$

Vector subtraction is defined symbolically as follows.

VECTOR SUBTRACTION

If $\mathbf{a} = \langle a_1, a_2 \rangle$ and $\mathbf{b} = \langle b_1, b_2 \rangle$, then the **difference** of $\mathbf{a}$ and $\mathbf{b}$ is given by
$$\mathbf{a} - \mathbf{b} = \langle a_1, a_2 \rangle - \langle b_1, b_2 \rangle = \langle a_1 - b_1, a_2 - b_2 \rangle.$$

The difference $\mathbf{a} - \mathbf{b}$ is shown graphically in Figure 8.55 in the following See the Concept.

See the Concept: Vector Subtraction (Graphical)

To find $\mathbf{a} - \mathbf{b}$:

Ⓐ Find $-\mathbf{b}$.

Ⓑ Add $\mathbf{a} + (-\mathbf{b})$ using the parallelogram rule.

Ⓒ The resultant is $\mathbf{a} - \mathbf{b}$. Notice that by the parallelogram rule $\mathbf{b} + (\mathbf{a} - \mathbf{b}) = \mathbf{a}$.

Figure 8.55

EXAMPLE 8   Adding and subtracting vectors

Let $\mathbf{a} = \langle -3, 4 \rangle$ and $\mathbf{b} = \langle 5, -6 \rangle$. Find $\mathbf{a} + \mathbf{b}$, $\mathbf{a} - \mathbf{b}$, and $2\mathbf{a} - 3\mathbf{b}$.

SOLUTION   To add two vectors, we add corresponding components.

$$\mathbf{a} + \mathbf{b} = \langle -3, 4 \rangle + \langle 5, -6 \rangle = \langle -3 + 5, 4 + (-6) \rangle = \langle 2, -2 \rangle$$

To subtract two vectors, we subtract corresponding components.

$$\mathbf{a} - \mathbf{b} = \langle -3, 4 \rangle - \langle 5, -6 \rangle = \langle -3 - 5, 4 - (-6) \rangle = \langle -8, 10 \rangle$$

| Subtract horizontal components | Subtract vertical components |

To subtract scalar multiples of two vectors, we do the following.

$$2\mathbf{a} - 3\mathbf{b} = 2\langle -3, 4 \rangle - 3\langle 5, -6 \rangle = \langle -6, 8 \rangle - \langle 15, -18 \rangle$$
$$= \langle -6 - 15, 8 - (-18) \rangle = \langle -21, 26 \rangle$$

Now Try Exercises 63 and 83

Operations on Vectors

```
{-3,4}+{5,-6}
              {2  -2}
{-3,4}-{5,-6}
              {-8  10}
2{-3,4}-3{5,-6}
              {-21  26}
```

Figure 8.56

Graphing Calculators (optional)   On some graphing calculators the list feature can be used to perform operations on vectors. In Figure 8.56 a calculator has been used to evaluate the expressions in Example 8. On other calculators vectors can be represented by ordered pairs with parentheses.

EXAMPLE 9   Performing operations on vectors

Find $-3\mathbf{a} + 5\mathbf{b}$ if $\mathbf{a} = 2\mathbf{i} + 3\mathbf{j}$ and $\mathbf{b} = 6\mathbf{i} - 7\mathbf{j}$.

SOLUTION

$$-3\mathbf{a} + 5\mathbf{b} = -3(2\mathbf{i} + 3\mathbf{j}) + 5(6\mathbf{i} - 7\mathbf{j})$$
$$= (-6\mathbf{i} - 9\mathbf{j}) + (30\mathbf{i} - 35\mathbf{j})$$
$$= (-6 + 30)\mathbf{i} + (-9 - 35)\mathbf{j}$$
$$= 24\mathbf{i} - 44\mathbf{j}$$

Now Try Exercise 81

Robotic Arm

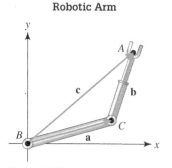

Figure 8.57

An Application from Robotics   Robotic arms are sometimes modeled using vectors. Consider the *planar two-arm manipulator* in Figure 8.57. If $\overrightarrow{BC} = \mathbf{a}$ and $\overrightarrow{CA} = \mathbf{b}$, then the position of the hand is given by $\overrightarrow{BA} = \mathbf{c}$. Since $\mathbf{c} = \mathbf{a} + \mathbf{b}$, we can easily locate the position of the hand if $\mathbf{a}$ and $\mathbf{b}$ are known.   (***Source:*** J. Craig, *Introduction to Robotics.*)

EXAMPLE 10   Using vectors to locate a robotic hand

Let $\mathbf{a} = \langle 3.1, 1.5 \rangle$ and $\mathbf{b} = \langle 1.4, 2.4 \rangle$ in Figure 8.57.
(a) Find the position of the robotic hand.
(b) Suppose the upper arm represented by $\mathbf{a}$ doubles its length and the forearm represented by $\mathbf{b}$ reduces its length by half. Find the new position of the hand.

SOLUTION
(a) To find the position of the hand, evaluate $\mathbf{a} + \mathbf{b}$.

$$\mathbf{a} + \mathbf{b} = \langle 3.1, 1.5 \rangle + \langle 1.4, 2.4 \rangle = \langle 4.5, 3.9 \rangle$$

The hand is located at the point (4.5, 3.9).
(b) The new position is represented by

$$2\mathbf{a} + \frac{1}{2}\mathbf{b} = 2\langle 3.1, 1.5 \rangle + \frac{1}{2}\langle 1.4, 2.4 \rangle$$
$$= \langle 6.2, 3.0 \rangle + \langle 0.7, 1.2 \rangle$$
$$= \langle 6.9, 4.2 \rangle.$$

The new coordinates of the robotic hand are (6.9, 4.2).

Now Try Exercise 117

An Application from Navigation   Vectors are frequently used to describe air and fluid flow. The next example uses vectors to describe the motion of an airplane.

EXAMPLE 11   Using vectors in navigation

An airplane is flying with an airspeed of 300 miles per hour and a bearing of 40° in a 30-mile-per-hour west wind.
(a) Find vectors **v** and **u** that model the velocity of the airplane and the velocity of the wind, respectively.
(b) Use vectors to determine the groundspeed of the plane.
(c) Find the final bearing of the plane in the wind.

SOLUTION

(a) Consider Figure 8.58, which shows vectors **v** and **u** graphically. Since **u** models a west wind, it points to the right with length 30 and can be represented symbolically by $\mathbf{u} = \langle 30, 0 \rangle$. Let a_1 be the horizontal component and a_2 be the vertical component of **v**. Since $\|\mathbf{v}\| = 300$, it follows that $a_1 = 300 \cos 50°$ and $a_2 = 300 \sin 50°$. Thus

$$\mathbf{v} = \langle 300 \cos 50°, 300 \sin 50° \rangle \approx \langle 192.8, 229.8 \rangle.$$

(b) The true course of the plane is given by $\mathbf{c} = \mathbf{v} + \mathbf{u}$.

$$\mathbf{c} = \mathbf{v} + \mathbf{u}$$
$$= \langle 300 \cos 50°, 300 \sin 50° \rangle + \langle 30, 0 \rangle$$
$$= \langle 300 \cos 50° + 30, 300 \sin 50° \rangle$$

The groundspeed of the plane equals $\|\mathbf{c}\|$.

$$\|\mathbf{c}\| = \sqrt{(300 \cos 50° + 30)^2 + (300 \sin 50°)^2} \approx 320.1$$

The groundspeed of the airplane is approximately 320 miles per hour.

(c) Since $\mathbf{c} = \langle 300 \cos 50° + 30, 300 \sin 50° \rangle$, the direction angle θ is determined by the vector **c** and the positive x-axis (East). Thus $\tan \theta = \frac{300 \sin 50°}{300 \cos 50° + 30} \approx 1.0313$ and $\theta \approx \tan^{-1} 1.0313 \approx 45.9°$. The final bearing of the plane in the wind equals $90° - 45.9° = 44.1°$.

Now Try Exercise 109

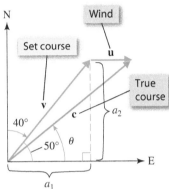

Bearing of an Airplane

Figure 8.58

The Dot Product

Thus far we have discussed addition, subtraction, and scalar multiplication of vectors. Another operation on vectors, called the *dot product*, is important because it can be used to find angles between vectors. The dot product has applications in computer graphics, solar energy, and physics. We begin by defining the dot product.

DOT PRODUCT

Let $\mathbf{a} = \langle a_1, a_2 \rangle$ and $\mathbf{b} = \langle b_1, b_2 \rangle$. The **dot product** of **a** and **b**, denoted $\mathbf{a} \cdot \mathbf{b}$, is a *real number* given by

$$\mathbf{a} \cdot \mathbf{b} = a_1 b_1 + a_2 b_2.$$

In the next example, we calculate dot products. Notice that the dot product of two vectors is a real number, rather than a vector.

EXAMPLE 12   Calculating dot products

Calculate $\mathbf{a} \cdot \mathbf{b}$.
(a) $\mathbf{a} = \langle 4, -3 \rangle$, $\mathbf{b} = \langle -1, 2 \rangle$
(b) $\mathbf{a} = 2\mathbf{i} + 5\mathbf{j}$, $\mathbf{b} = -3\mathbf{i} + 2\mathbf{j}$

SOLUTION

(a) $\mathbf{a} \cdot \mathbf{b} = \langle 4, -3 \rangle \cdot \langle -1, 2 \rangle = (4)(-1) + (-3)(2) = -10$

(b) $\mathbf{a} \cdot \mathbf{b} = (2\mathbf{i} + 5\mathbf{j}) \cdot (-3\mathbf{i} + 2\mathbf{j}) = (2)(-3) + (5)(2) = 4$

Now Try Exercises 87(a) and 91(a)

Angle Between Vectors

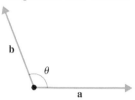

Figure 8.59

In Figure 8.59 the *angle between vectors* **a** *and* **b** is θ, where $0° \le \theta \le 180°$. If $\theta = 90°$ the vectors are **perpendicular**, and if $\theta = 0°$ or $180°$ the vectors are **parallel**. If $\theta = 0°$ the vectors point in the *same* direction, and if $\theta = 180°$ they point in *opposite* directions.

It is shown in Exercise 5 of the Extended Exercises at the end of the chapter that for any two nonzero vectors **a** and **b**,

$$\mathbf{a} \cdot \mathbf{b} = \|\mathbf{a}\| \, \|\mathbf{b}\| \cos\theta.$$

This result can be used to find the angle θ between **a** and **b**.

> ### ANGLE BETWEEN TWO VECTORS
>
> If **a** and **b** are nonzero vectors, then the **angle θ between a and b** is given by
>
> $$\theta = \cos^{-1} \frac{\mathbf{a} \cdot \mathbf{b}}{\|\mathbf{a}\| \, \|\mathbf{b}\|}.$$
>
> Vectors **a** and **b** are perpendicular if and only if $\mathbf{a} \cdot \mathbf{b} = 0$.

EXAMPLE 13 Finding the angle between two vectors

Sketch the vectors **a** and **b**. Then find the angle θ between **a** and **b**.

(a) $\mathbf{a} = 2\mathbf{i} - 3\mathbf{j}, \mathbf{b} = 3\mathbf{i} + 2\mathbf{j}$ (b) $\mathbf{a} = \langle -4, 3 \rangle, \mathbf{b} = \langle 1, -2 \rangle$

Perpendicular Vectors

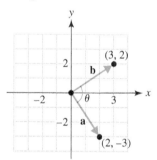

Figure 8.60

SOLUTION

(a) Vectors **a** and **b** appear to be perpendicular in Figure 8.60. Since

$$\mathbf{a} \cdot \mathbf{b} = (2)(3) + (-3)(2) = 0,$$

the vectors are perpendicular and $\theta = 90°$.

(b) A sketch of the vectors is shown in Figure 8.61. They are neither perpendicular nor parallel. Since $\mathbf{a} \cdot \mathbf{b} = (-4)(1) + (3)(-2) = -10$,

$$\|\mathbf{a}\| = \sqrt{(-4)^2 + (3)^2} = 5, \quad \text{and} \quad \|\mathbf{b}\| = \sqrt{(1)^2 + (-2)^2} = \sqrt{5},$$

it follows that

$$\theta = \cos^{-1} \frac{-10}{5\sqrt{5}} \approx 153.4°.$$

Now Try Exercise 87(b) and (c)

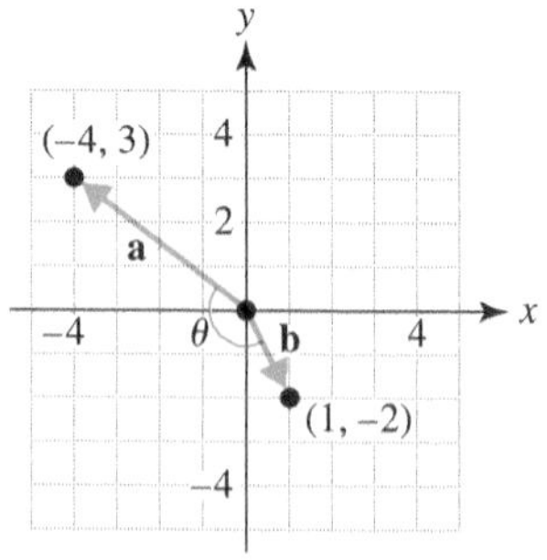

Figure 8.61

Work

In science a force does work only when an object moves. For example, a person pushing against a brick wall does no work, whereas a person lifting a 20-pound weight does work. Work equals force times distance, *provided the force is in the same direction as the movement of the object.* If a 150-pound person climbs up a 20-foot rope, then the work W done is

$$W = 150 \times 20 = 3000 \text{ foot-pounds.}$$

A **foot-pound** equals the work required to lift 1 pound a vertical distance of 1 foot. If the force is not in the same direction as the movement, then we must use trigonometry to determine work.

Consider a person pulling a wagon, as shown in Figure 8.62, where **F** represents the force on the handle and **D** represents the distance and direction that the wagon is pulled. The force **F** can be expressed as the sum of a horizontal vector in the direction of **D** and a vertical vector perpendicular to **D**, as illustrated in Figure 8.63. Using the right triangle in Figure 8.64, we see that the horizontal component of **F** is given by $\|\mathbf{F}\| \cos \theta$ and the vertical component of **F** is given by $\|\mathbf{F}\| \sin \theta$.

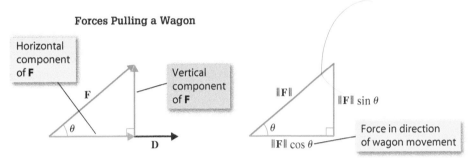

Forces Pulling a Wagon

Figure 8.62

Figure 8.63

Figure 8.64

CLASS DISCUSSION

Suppose a force vector **F** is perpendicular to **D**. How much work is done? Interpret your answer.

The work W done pulling the wagon is equal to the horizontal component $\|\mathbf{F}\| \cos \theta$ times the distance the wagon moves, which is given by $\|\mathbf{D}\|$. That is,

$$W = \|\mathbf{F}\| \|\mathbf{D}\| \cos \theta = \mathbf{F} \cdot \mathbf{D}.$$

Work equals the dot product of the force vector **F** and the displacement vector **D**.

> **WORK**
>
> If a constant force **F** is applied to an object that moves along a vector **D**, then the work W done is
>
> $$W = \mathbf{F} \cdot \mathbf{D}.$$

EXAMPLE 14 Calculating work

Find the work done when a force $\mathbf{F} = \langle 3, -2 \rangle$ moves an object from point $P = (-2, 1)$ to point $Q = (3, -1)$, where force is measured in pounds and distance in feet.

SOLUTION First we must find the displacement vector $\mathbf{D} = \overrightarrow{PQ}$, where

$$\overrightarrow{PQ} = \langle 3 - (-2), -1 - 1 \rangle = \langle 5, -2 \rangle.$$

The work W done can be calculated as follows.

$$W = \mathbf{F} \cdot \mathbf{D} = \langle 3, -2 \rangle \cdot \langle 5, -2 \rangle = 15 + 4 = 19 \text{ foot-pounds}$$

Now Try Exercise 103

EXAMPLE 15 Calculating work

A 150-pound person walks 500 feet up a hiking trail that is inclined at 20°. Use vectors to compute the work done by the person, as illustrated in Figure 8.65.

SOLUTION Vector **D** is 500 feet long and is given by $\mathbf{D} = \langle 500 \cos 20°, 500 \sin 20° \rangle$. Since gravity pulls downward, the force exerted by the 150-pound person against gravity is given by $\mathbf{F} = \langle 0, 150 \rangle$. The work done is

$$W = \mathbf{F} \cdot \mathbf{D} = (0)(500 \cos 20°) + (150)(500 \sin 20°) \approx 25,650 \text{ foot-pounds}.$$

Now Try Exercise 121

Figure 8.65

8.3 Putting It All Together

Vectors are an important invention of the 19th and 20th centuries that have enabled science and technology to model a wide variety of phenomena. The following table summarizes some basic concepts regarding vectors.

CONCEPT	EXPLANATION	EXAMPLES
Vectors	Vector quantities denote both magnitude and direction. A vector $\mathbf{a}$ can be expressed as either $\mathbf{a} = \langle a_1, a_2 \rangle$ or $\mathbf{a} = a_1\mathbf{i} + a_2\mathbf{j}$. Its magnitude is given by $\|\mathbf{a}\| = \sqrt{a_1^2 + a_2^2}$. The numbers a_1 and a_2 are called the horizontal and vertical components of $\mathbf{a}$, respectively. A vector with its initial point at the origin is called a position vector. The positive angle between the x-axis and the position vector is called the direction angle θ, where $0° \le \theta < 360°$. If vector $\mathbf{a}$ has direction angle θ, then $$\mathbf{a} = \langle \|\mathbf{a}\| \cos\theta, \|\mathbf{a}\| \sin\theta \rangle.$$	$\mathbf{a} = \langle 1, 2 \rangle$ and $\mathbf{a} = \mathbf{i} + 2\mathbf{j}$ represent the same vector. The magnitude of $\mathbf{a}$ is given by $\|\mathbf{a}\| = \sqrt{1^2 + 2^2} = \sqrt{5}$. The horizontal component is 1, and the vertical component is 2.
Operations on vectors	Let $\mathbf{a} = \langle a_1, a_2 \rangle$, $\mathbf{b} = \langle b_1, b_2 \rangle$, and k be a real number. $$\begin{aligned} \mathbf{a} + \mathbf{b} &= \langle a_1, a_2 \rangle + \langle b_1, b_2 \rangle \\ &= \langle a_1 + b_1, a_2 + b_2 \rangle \quad \text{Sum} \\ \mathbf{a} - \mathbf{b} &= \langle a_1, a_2 \rangle - \langle b_1, b_2 \rangle \\ &= \langle a_1 - b_1, a_2 - b_2 \rangle \quad \text{Difference} \\ k\mathbf{a} &= k\langle a_1, a_2 \rangle = \langle ka_1, ka_2 \rangle \quad \text{Scalar multiple} \end{aligned}$$	Let $\mathbf{a} = \langle 4, 1 \rangle$, $\mathbf{b} = \langle 3, 2 \rangle$. $$\begin{aligned} \mathbf{a} + \mathbf{b} &= \langle 4, 1 \rangle + \langle 3, 2 \rangle \\ &= \langle 7, 3 \rangle \\ \mathbf{a} - \mathbf{b} &= \langle 4, 1 \rangle - \langle 3, 2 \rangle \\ &= \langle 1, -1 \rangle \\ 3\mathbf{a} &= 3\langle 4, 1 \rangle = \langle 12, 3 \rangle \end{aligned}$$
Dot product	If $\mathbf{a} = \langle a_1, a_2 \rangle$ and $\mathbf{b} = \langle b_1, b_2 \rangle$, then $\mathbf{a} \cdot \mathbf{b} = a_1 b_1 + a_2 b_2$.	Let $\mathbf{a} = \langle 2, -2 \rangle$, $\mathbf{b} = \langle 3, 1 \rangle$. $\mathbf{a} \cdot \mathbf{b} = (2)(3) + (-2)(1) = 4$
Angle θ between two vectors	If $\mathbf{a} = \langle a_1, a_2 \rangle$ and $\mathbf{b} = \langle b_1, b_2 \rangle$, then $$\theta = \cos^{-1}\frac{\mathbf{a} \cdot \mathbf{b}}{\|\mathbf{a}\|\,\|\mathbf{b}\|}.$$ Vectors $\mathbf{a}$ and $\mathbf{b}$ are perpendicular ($\theta = 90°$) if and only if $\mathbf{a} \cdot \mathbf{b} = 0$.	If $\mathbf{a} = \langle 1, 0 \rangle$ and $\mathbf{b} = \langle 3, 4 \rangle$, then $$\begin{aligned} \theta &= \cos^{-1}\frac{\langle 1, 0 \rangle \cdot \langle 3, 4 \rangle}{\|\langle 1, 0 \rangle\|\,\|\langle 3, 4 \rangle\|} \\ &= \cos^{-1}\frac{3}{(1)(5)} \approx 53.1°. \end{aligned}$$ If $\mathbf{a} = \langle 4, -3 \rangle$ and $\mathbf{b} = \langle 3, 4 \rangle$, then $\mathbf{a} \cdot \mathbf{b} = (4)(3) + (-3)(4) = 0$. Thus $\mathbf{a}$ and $\mathbf{b}$ are perpendicular.
Work	If a constant force $\mathbf{F}$ is applied to an object that moves along a vector $\mathbf{D}$, then the work done is $W = \mathbf{F} \cdot \mathbf{D}$.	If $\mathbf{F} = 3\mathbf{i} - 4\mathbf{j}$ and $\mathbf{D} = 10\mathbf{i} - 20\mathbf{j}$, then $$\begin{aligned} W &= \mathbf{F} \cdot \mathbf{D} \\ &= (3)(10) + (-4)(-20) \\ &= 110 \text{ foot-pounds}, \end{aligned}$$ where units are in feet and pounds.

8.3 | Exercises

Representing Vectors and Their Magnitudes

Exercises 1–4: Use the graphical representation of **v** *to complete the following.*

(a) *Estimate integer values for components* a_1 *and* a_2 *so that* **v** $= \langle a_1, a_2 \rangle$.

(b) *Calculate* $\|\mathbf{v}\|$.

1. 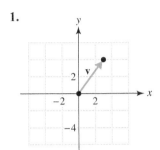   **2.**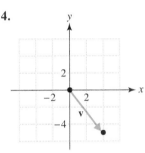

3.   **4.**

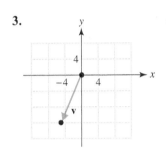

Exercises 5–10: Complete the following.

(a) *Sketch a vector* **v** *that models the situation.*

(b) *Express* **v** *as* $\langle a_1, a_2 \rangle$.

(c) *Find* $2\mathbf{v}$ *and* $-\frac{1}{2}\mathbf{v}$. *Interpret each result.*

5. A 20-mile-per-hour wind from the north

6. A 10-mile-per-hour wind from the west

7. A 5-mile-per-hour wind from the northeast

8. A 7-mile-per-hour wind from the southeast

9. A 30-pound force upward

10. A 15-pound force pulling at a 45° angle in standard position

Exercises 11–18: Complete the following for vector **v**.

(a) *Find the horizontal and vertical components.*

(b) *Calculate* $\|\mathbf{v}\|$ *and decide if* **v** *is a unit vector.*

(c) *Graph* **v** *and interpret* $\|\mathbf{v}\|$.

11. $\mathbf{v} = \langle 1, 1 \rangle$ **12.** $\mathbf{v} = \langle -1, 0 \rangle$

13. $\mathbf{v} = \langle 3, -4 \rangle$ **14.** $\mathbf{v} = \langle -2, -2 \rangle$

15. $\mathbf{v} = \mathbf{i}$ **16.** $\mathbf{v} = -3\mathbf{j}$

17. $\mathbf{v} = 5\mathbf{i} + 12\mathbf{j}$ **18.** $\mathbf{v} = -\frac{3}{5}\mathbf{i} - \frac{4}{5}\mathbf{j}$

Direction Angles and Components

Exercises 19–30: Find the magnitude and the direction angle θ *for the given vector. Let* $0° \leq \theta < 360°$ *and round* θ *to the nearest tenth when appropriate.*

19. $\langle 3, 0 \rangle$ **20.** $\langle 0, -2 \rangle$

21. $\langle -1, 1 \rangle$ **22.** $\langle 2, 2 \rangle$

23. $\langle \sqrt{3}, -1 \rangle$ **24.** $\langle -1, \sqrt{3} \rangle$

25. $\langle -5, -12 \rangle$ **26.** $\langle 7, -24 \rangle$

27. $\langle 13, -84 \rangle$ **28.** $\langle -11, -60 \rangle$

29. $\langle -20, 21 \rangle$ **30.** $\langle 16, -63 \rangle$

Exercises 31–38: Find the horizontal and vertical components for **v**, *given magnitude* $\|\mathbf{v}\|$ *and direction angle* θ. *Round values to the nearest tenth.*

31. $\|\mathbf{v}\| = 4, \theta = 180°$ **32.** $\|\mathbf{v}\| = 1, \theta = 270°$

33. $\|\mathbf{v}\| = \sqrt{2}, \theta = 135°$ **34.** $\|\mathbf{v}\| = \sqrt{2}, \theta = 225°$

35. $\|\mathbf{v}\| = 23, \theta = 54°$ **36.** $\|\mathbf{v}\| = 71, \theta = 163°$

37. $\|\mathbf{v}\| = 34, \theta = 312°$ **38.** $\|\mathbf{v}\| = 25, \theta = 73°$

Exercises 39–42: Write the vector in the form $\langle a_1, a_2 \rangle$.

39.   **40.**

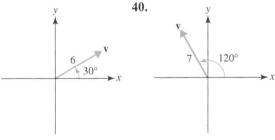

41.   **42.**

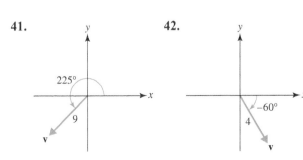

Exercises 43–46: Write the vector in the form $\langle a_1, a_2 \rangle$. *Round values to the nearest hundredth.*

43.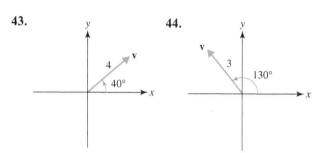

44.

45.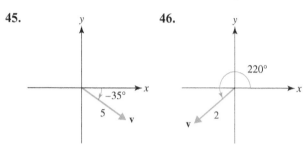

46.

Exercises 47–52: A vector **v** *has initial point P and terminal point Q.*

(a) *Graph* $\overrightarrow{PQ}$.

(b) *Write* $\overrightarrow{PQ}$ *as* $\mathbf{v} = \langle a_1, a_2 \rangle$.

(c) *Find the magnitude of* $\overrightarrow{PQ}$.

47. $P = (0, 0)$, $Q = (-1, 2)$

48. $P = (0, 0)$, $Q = (4, -6)$

49. $P = (1, 2)$, $Q = (3, 6)$

50. $P = (-1, -2)$, $Q = (4, 4)$

51. $P = (-2, 4)$, $Q = (3, -2)$

52. $P = (0, -4)$, $Q = (1, 3)$

Resultant Forces

Exercises 53–56: Use the parallelogram rule to find the magnitude of the resultant force for the two forces shown in the figure (to the nearest tenth of a pound).

53.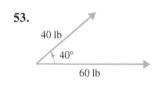

54.

55.

56.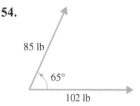

Exercises 57–62: Forces $\mathbf{F}_1$ *and* $\mathbf{F}_2$ *act at the same point. Find the resultant force* $\mathbf{F}$ *and its magnitude.*

57. $\mathbf{F}_1 = 3\mathbf{i} - 4\mathbf{j}$, $\mathbf{F}_2 = -8\mathbf{i} + 16\mathbf{j}$

58. $\mathbf{F}_1 = -7\mathbf{i} + 3\mathbf{j}$, $\mathbf{F}_2 = -\mathbf{i} + 12\mathbf{j}$

59. $\mathbf{F}_1 = \langle 8, 9 \rangle$, $\mathbf{F}_2 = \langle 1, -31 \rangle$

60. $\mathbf{F}_1 = \langle 48, 0 \rangle$, $\mathbf{F}_2 = \langle 0, -55 \rangle$

61. $\mathbf{F}_1 = 0.5\mathbf{i} + 0.7\mathbf{j}$, $\mathbf{F}_2 = -1.5\mathbf{i} - 5.7\mathbf{j}$

62. $\mathbf{F}_1 = \frac{1}{4}\mathbf{i} + \frac{1}{2}\mathbf{j}$, $\mathbf{F}_2 = -\frac{1}{2}\mathbf{i} + \frac{3}{4}\mathbf{j}$

Operations on Vectors

Exercises 63–70: Evaluate each of the following.

(a) $\mathbf{a} + \mathbf{b}$ (b) $\mathbf{a} - \mathbf{b}$

63. $\mathbf{a} = \langle 0, 2 \rangle$, $\mathbf{b} = \langle 3, 0 \rangle$

64. $\mathbf{a} = \langle 1, 1 \rangle$, $\mathbf{b} = \langle -2, 3 \rangle$

65. $\mathbf{a} = 2\mathbf{i} + \mathbf{j}$, $\mathbf{b} = \mathbf{i} - 2\mathbf{j}$

66. $\mathbf{a} = \mathbf{i} + 2\mathbf{j}$, $\mathbf{b} = -2\mathbf{i} + 3\mathbf{j}$

67. $\mathbf{a} = \langle -\sqrt{2}, \frac{1}{2} \rangle$, $\mathbf{b} = \langle \sqrt{2}, -\frac{3}{4} \rangle$

68. $\mathbf{a} = \langle \frac{4}{5}, -\frac{5}{6} \rangle$, $\mathbf{b} = \langle \frac{3}{10}, \frac{2}{3} \rangle$

69. $\mathbf{a} = \left(\cos \frac{\pi}{4} \right)\mathbf{i} + \left(\sin \frac{\pi}{4} \right)\mathbf{j}$,
    $\mathbf{b} = \left(\cos \frac{\pi}{2} \right)\mathbf{i} + \left(\sin \frac{\pi}{2} \right)\mathbf{j}$

70. $\mathbf{a} = \left(\cos \frac{3\pi}{2} \right)\mathbf{i} + \left(\sin \frac{3\pi}{2} \right)\mathbf{j}$,
    $\mathbf{b} = (\cos \pi)\mathbf{i} + (\sin \pi)\mathbf{j}$

Exercises 71–76: Use the figure to evaluate each of the following.

(a) $\mathbf{a} + \mathbf{b}$ (b) $\mathbf{a} - \mathbf{b}$ (c) $-\mathbf{a}$

71.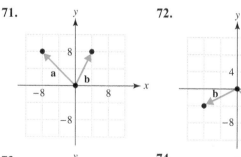

72.

73.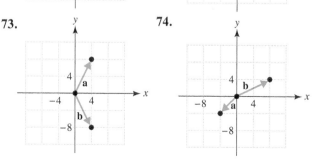

74.

75. 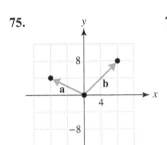   **76.**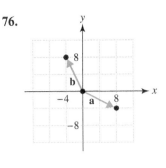

92. **a** = −2**i** + 6**j**,   **b** = 3**i** + **j**

93. **a** = **i** + 3**j**,   **b** = 0.5**i** − 1.5**j**

94. **a** = −12**i** + 16**j**,   **b** = −3**i** + 4**j**

Exercises 95–98: Find the work done in each situation.

95. Lifting a 30-pound weight 5 feet into the air

96. Lifting a 15-pound bucket 8 feet into the air

97. Pushing a stalled car on level ground with a force of 100 pounds for 1000 feet

98. A 150-pound person running up 5 flights of steps with 10 feet between floors

Exercises 99–102: Find the work done when a constant force **F** *is applied to an object that moves along the vector* **D**, *where units are in pounds and feet. Find the magnitude of* **F**.

99. **F** = ⟨10, 20⟩,   **D** = ⟨15, 22⟩

100. **F** = ⟨64, 36⟩,   **D** = ⟨22, −33⟩

101. **F** = 5**i** − 3**j**,   **D** = 3**i** − 4**j**

102. **F** = 7**i** − 24**j**,   **D** = −2**i** − 5**j**

Exercises 103–106: Calculate the work done when the force **F** = 5**i** + 3**j** *moves an object from P to Q.*

103. P = (−2, 3),   Q = (1, 6)

104. P = (−2, −1),   Q = (1, 3)

105. P = (2, −3),   Q = (4, −5)

106. P = (1, 1),   Q = (−1, 6)

Exercises 77–80: Evaluate each of the following graphically and symbolically.

(a) ‖**a**‖   *(b)* 2**a**   *(c)* 2**a** + 3**b**

77. **a** = 2**i**,   **b** = **i** + **j**

78. **a** = −**i** + **j**,   **b** = **i** − **j**

79. **a** = ⟨−1, 2⟩,   **b** = ⟨3, 0⟩

80. **a** = ⟨−2, −1⟩,   **b** = ⟨−3, 2⟩

Exercises 81–86: Given vectors **a** *and* **b**, *evaluate each of the following.*

(a) −**a** + 4**b**   *(b)* 2**a** − 3**b**

81. **a** = **i** − 2**j**,   **b** = −5**i** + 2**j**

82. **a** = −6**i** + **j**,   **b** = 7**i** − 3**j**

83. **a** = ⟨1, −4⟩,   **b** = ⟨−3, 5⟩

84. **a** = ⟨−5, 13⟩,   **b** = ⟨0, −1⟩

85. **a** = ⟨−7, −2⟩,   **b** = ⟨9, −1⟩

86. **a** = ⟨5, 1⟩,   **b** = ⟨−2, −4⟩

Dot Product and Work

Exercises 87–94: Complete the following for vectors **a** *and* **b**.

(a) Find **a** · **b**.

(b) Approximate the angle θ between **a** *and* **b** *to the nearest tenth of a degree.*

(c) State if vectors **a** *and* **b** *are perpendicular, parallel, or neither. If* **a** *and* **b** *are parallel, state whether they point in the same direction or in opposite directions.*

87. **a** = ⟨1, −2⟩,   **b** = ⟨3, 1⟩

88. **a** = ⟨4, −5⟩,   **b** = ⟨2, −2⟩

89. **a** = ⟨6, 8⟩,   **b** = ⟨−4, 3⟩

90. **a** = ⟨1, −2⟩,   **b** = ⟨−2, 4⟩

91. **a** = 5**i** + 6**j**,   **b** = 10**i** + 12**j**

Applications

107. **Swimming in a Current** A swimmer heads directly north across a river at 3 miles per hour, in a current that flows west to east at 2 miles per hour, as illustrated in the figure. Find a vector that models the resulting direction and speed of the swimmer. With what speed is the swimmer moving in the river?

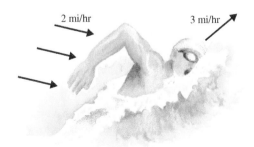

108. Wind and Vectors A wind can be described by **v** = 6**i** + 8**j**, where vector **j** points north and represents a south wind of 1 mile per hour.

(a) What is the speed of the wind?

(b) Find 3**v**. Interpret the result.

(c) Interpret the wind if it switches to **u** = −8**i** + 8**j**.

109. Air Navigation (Refer to Example 11.) An airplane heads west at 400 miles per hour in a 50-mile-per-hour northwest wind. Find a vector that models the resulting direction and speed of the airplane. Find the groundspeed and bearing of the airplane in the wind.

110. Air Navigation A plane with an airspeed of 240 miles per hour is headed on a bearing of 110°. A wind is blowing from the north at 18 miles per hour. Find the groundspeed and the final bearing of the plane in the wind.

111. Course and Groundspeed A plane flies 450 miles per hour on a bearing of 160°. A 20-mile-per-hour wind is blowing from the south. Find the groundspeed and the final bearing of the plane in the wind.

112. Course and Groundspeed A plane flies on a bearing of 230° at 350 miles per hour. A wind is blowing from the west at 30 miles per hour. Find the groundspeed and the final bearing of the plane in the wind.

113. Airspeed and Groundspeed A pilot wants to fly on a course of 75°. By flying due east, the pilot finds that a 40-mile-per-hour wind, blowing from the south, puts the plane on course. Find the airspeed and the groundspeed.

114. Force and Water-Ski Towropes (Refer to Example 5.) Forces of 65 pounds and 110 pounds are exerted by two water-ski towropes. If the angle between the towropes is 19°, find the magnitude of the resultant force.

115. Measuring Rainfall Suppose that vector **R** models the amount of rainfall in inches and the direction it falls, and vector **A** models the area in square inches and orientation of the opening of a rain gauge, as illustrated in the figure at the top of next column. The total volume *V* of water collected in the rain gauge is given by $V = |\mathbf{R} \cdot \mathbf{A}|$. This formula calculates the volume of water collected even if the wind is blowing the rain in a slanted direction or the rain gauge is not exactly vertical. Let **R** = **i** − 2**j** and **A** = 0.5**i** + **j**.
(a) Find ‖**R**‖ and ‖**A**‖. Interpret your results.

(b) Calculate *V* and interpret this result.

(c) For the rain gauge to collect the maximum amount of water, what must be true about vectors **R** and **A**?

116. Solar Panels Suppose that the sun's intensity (in watts per square centimeter) and direction are given by vector **I**, and a solar panel's area (in square centimeters) and orientation are given by vector **A**, as illustrated in the figure. Then the total number of watts *W* that are collected by the solar panel is given by $W = |\mathbf{I} \cdot \mathbf{A}|$. Let **I** = 0.01**i** − 0.02**j** and **A** = 400**i** + 300**j**.

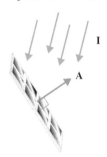

(a) Find ‖**I**‖ and ‖**A**‖. Interpret your results.

(b) Calculate *W* and interpret this result.

(c) For the solar panel to absorb maximum wattage, what must be true about vectors **I** and **A**?

117. Robotics (Refer to Example 10.) Consider the planar two-arm manipulator shown in the figure. Let the upper arm be modeled by **a** = ⟨3, 2⟩ and the forearm be modeled by **b** = ⟨−2, 2⟩, where units are in feet. (*Source:* J. Craig, *Introduction to Robotics.*)

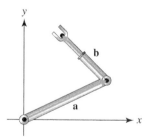

(a) Find a vector **c** that represents the position of the hand.

(b) How far is the hand from the origin?

(c) Find the position of the hand if the length of the upper arm triples and the length of the forearm is reduced by half.

118. Robotics A planar three-arm manipulator is shown in the figure, with joint angles measured relative to a positive horizontal axis.

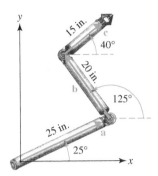

(a) Find vectors **a**, **b**, and **c** that represent each part of the robotic arm.

(b) Find a vector **d** that represents the position of the hand. How far is the hand from the origin?

119. Translations in Computer Graphics Vectors are used in computer graphics to compute translations of points. For example, suppose we would like to translate the point $(-1, 2)$ by $\mathbf{v} = \langle 2, 1 \rangle$, as illustrated in the figure, where the *point* $(-1, 2)$ has been represented by the *vector* $\mathbf{a} = \langle -1, 2 \rangle$. The new location of $(-1, 2)$ is modeled by

$$\mathbf{b} = \mathbf{a} + \mathbf{v} = \langle -1, 2 \rangle + \langle 2, 1 \rangle = \langle 1, 3 \rangle.$$

Thus $(-1, 2)$ has been translated by **v** to $(1, 3)$. (*Source:* J. Foley, *Introduction to Computer Graphics.*)

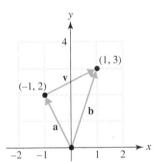

(a) Find the new coordinates of $(-2, 4)$ if it is translated by $\mathbf{v} = \langle 4, -2 \rangle$.

(b) Represent this situation graphically.

120. Translations in Computer Graphics (Refer to Exercise 119.) Let triangle ABC have vertices $(1, 1)$, $(3, 0)$, and $(4, 3)$.

(a) Find the new vertices D, E, and F if the triangle ABC is translated by $\mathbf{v} = \langle -2, 1 \rangle$.

(b) Describe the change in triangle ABC if it were translated by $-2\mathbf{v}$.

121. Work (Refer to Example 15.) A 145-pound person walks 1.5 miles up a hiking trail inclined at 15°. Use

a dot product to calculate the work W done (in foot-pounds).

122. Work A wagon is pulled 500 feet using a force of 10 pounds applied to the handle, which makes a 40° angle with the horizontal. See Figure 8.62. Use a dot product to calculate the work W done.

123. Air Navigation A pilot would like to fly to a city that is 200 miles away and has a bearing of 135°. The wind is blowing from the north at 30 miles per hour, and the trip is to take 1 hour. Find the direction and speed that the pilot should adopt to accomplish this.

124. Work Calculate the work required to push an 1800-pound car up a 7° incline for 0.1 mile.

Writing about Mathematics

125. State the basic properties of a vector. Does a vector have position? Explain. Give two examples of how to write a vector.

126. State one application of vectors. Give a specific example of a vector for this application and explain how the vector models that application.

Extended and Discovery Exercises

1. Computer Graphics Vectors frequently are used to determine the color of pixels on computer screens. For example, suppose that we would like to color the right side of the screen blue and the left side yellow, where the boundary is positioned along vector $\overrightarrow{PQ}$, as illustrated in the figure below.

First find $\overrightarrow{PR}$ perpendicular to $\overrightarrow{PQ}$. Then to determine if a pixel at point S should be blue or yellow, consider the angle θ between vectors $\overrightarrow{PS}$ and $\overrightarrow{PR}$. If θ is acute, then S must be on the same side of $\overrightarrow{PQ}$ as R and is colored blue, as illustrated in the left figure below. If angle θ is obtuse, then S is on the opposite side of $\overrightarrow{PQ}$ from R and is colored yellow, as shown in the right figure below.

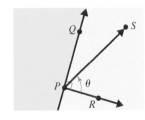
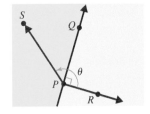

We can determine whether θ is acute or obtuse by calculating the dot product $\overrightarrow{PS} \cdot \overrightarrow{PR}$. If the dot product is positive, then

$$\theta = \cos^{-1}\left(\frac{\overrightarrow{PS} \cdot \overrightarrow{PR}}{\|\overrightarrow{PS}\| \, \|\overrightarrow{PR}\|} \right)$$

is acute and S should be blue. If the dot product is negative, then θ is obtuse and S should be yellow.

Let P be $(-1, 2)$, S be $(-2, -5)$, $\overrightarrow{PQ} = \mathbf{i} + 5\mathbf{j}$, and $\overrightarrow{PR} = 5\mathbf{i} - \mathbf{j}$. Determine the appropriate color at point S. See the figure below.

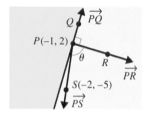

2. Dot Products in Computer Graphics A computer screen is gray to the left of vector $\overrightarrow{PQ} = 2\mathbf{i} - 3\mathbf{j}$ and blue to the right, where vector $\overrightarrow{PR} = 3\mathbf{i} + 2\mathbf{j}$ is perpendicular to $\overrightarrow{PQ}$. Let point P be $(2, 1)$. Determine the color of a pixel located at S.
(a) $S = (3, -2)$ **(b)** $S = (2, 2)$

3. Dot Products in Computer Graphics A computer screen is to be blue above vector $\overrightarrow{PQ} = 5\mathbf{i} - \mathbf{j}$ and white below, where point P is $(2, 1)$. Determine the color of a pixel located at S.
(a) $S = (100, -10)$ **(b)** $S = (-500, 50)$

8.4 Parametric Equations

- Learn basic concepts about parametric equations
- Graph parametric equations
- Use parametric equations to solve applications

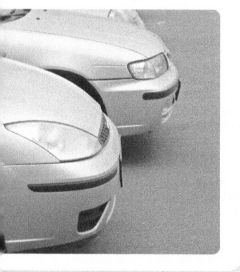

Introduction

Sometimes a curve cannot be modeled by a function. For example, a circle cannot be described by a single function because a circle fails the vertical line test. *Parametric equations* represent a different approach to describing curves in the xy-plane. They are used in industry to draw complicated curves and surfaces, such as the hood of an automobile. Parametric equations are also used in computer graphics, engineering, and physics.   (***Source:*** F. Hill, *Computer Graphics.*)

Basic Concepts

Some curves cannot be represented by $y = f(x)$, but they can be represented by parametric equations. See Figures 8.66–8.68.

Curves That Are Not Functions

$[-6, 6, 1]$ by $[-4, 4, 1]$ $[-6, 6, 1]$ by $[-4, 4, 1]$ $[-6, 6, 1]$ by $[-4, 4, 1]$

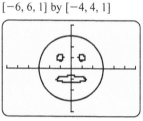

Figure 8.66

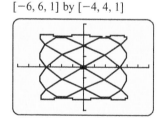

Figure 8.67

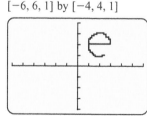

Figure 8.68

We now define parametric equations of a plane curve.

> **PARAMETRIC EQUATIONS OF A PLANE CURVE**
>
> A **plane curve** is a set of points (x, y) such that $x = f(t)$ and $y = g(t)$, where f and g are continuous functions on an interval $a \leq t \leq b$. The equations $x = f(t)$ and $y = g(t)$ are **parametric equations** with **parameter** t.

Parametric equations can be represented symbolically, numerically, graphically, and verbally. This is illustrated in the next example.

EXAMPLE 1 Representing parametric equations

Let $x = t + 3$ and $y = t^2$ for $-3 \le t \le 3$.
(a) Make a table of values for x and y with $t = -3, -2, -1, \ldots, 3$.
(b) Plot the points in the table and graph the curve. Add arrows to show how the curve is traced out.
(c) Describe the curve.

SOLUTION
(a) *Numerical Representation* A numerical representation of the parametric equations is shown in Table 8.1. For example, if $t = 2$, then $x = 2 + 3 = 5$ and $y = 2^2 = 4$.

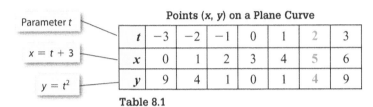

Points (*x*, *y*) on a Plane Curve

t	-3	-2	-1	0	1	2	3
x	0	1	2	3	4	5	6
y	9	4	1	0	1	4	9

Table 8.1

(b) *Graphical Representation* Each ordered pair (x, y) in Table 8.1 is plotted in Figure 8.69, and then the points are connected to obtain the curve.

Curve Defined Parametrically

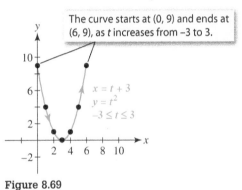

The curve starts at (0, 9) and ends at (6, 9), as *t* increases from –3 to 3.

Figure 8.69

(c) *Verbal Representation* The curve in Figure 8.69 appears to be the lower portion of a parabola with vertex $(3, 0)$. See Example 2.

Now Try Exercise 1

Graphing Calculators (Optional) Graphing calculators are capable of using parametric equations to make tables and graphs. In addition to setting values for the viewing rectangle, we must specify the interval for t. A window setting, table, and graph for the parametric equations in Example 1 are shown in Figures 8.70–8.72. The variable Tstep represents the increment in the parameter t and has a value of 0.1 in this case.

Calculator Help
To create the graph shown in Figure 8.72 with parametric equations, see Appendix A (page AP-18).

Setting a Window

```
WINDOW
 Tmin=‾3
 Tmax=3
 Tstep=.1
 Xmin=‾2
 Xmax=10
 Xscl=1
↓Ymin=‾2
```

Figure 8.70

Table of Points

T	X1T	Y1T
‾3	0	9
‾2	1	4
‾1	2	1
0	3	0
1	4	1
2	5	4
3	6	9
T=‾3		

Figure 8.71

Plane Curve
$[-2, 10, 1]$ by $[-2, 10, 1]$

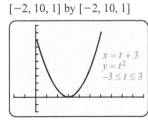

$x = t + 3$
$y = t^2$
$-3 \le t \le 3$

Figure 8.72

Converting and Graphing Equations

We can verify symbolically that the curve in Figure 8.69 in Example 1 is indeed a portion of a parabola, as demonstrated in the next example.

EXAMPLE 2 Finding an equivalent rectangular equation

Find an equivalent rectangular equation for $x = t + 3$ and $y = t^2$, where $-3 \leq t \leq 3$. Note that these parametric equations were discussed in Example 1.

SOLUTION Begin by solving $x = t + 3$ for t to obtain $t = x - 3$. Substituting for t in $y = t^2$ results in

$$y = (x - 3)^2,$$

which represents a parabola with vertex $(3, 0)$. When $t = -3$ then $x = 0$, and when $t = 3$ then $x = 6$. Thus the domain is restricted to $0 \leq x \leq 6$. See Figure 8.69.

Now Try Exercise 15

EXAMPLE 3 Finding equivalent rectangular equations

Find an equivalent rectangular equation for each pair of parametric equations. Use the rectangular equation to help graph the parametric equation. Add arrows to show how the curve is traced out.
(a) $x = 4t$, $y = t - 3$; $-\infty < t < \infty$
(b) $x = \sqrt{4 - t^2}$, $y = t$; $-2 \leq t \leq 2$

A Line

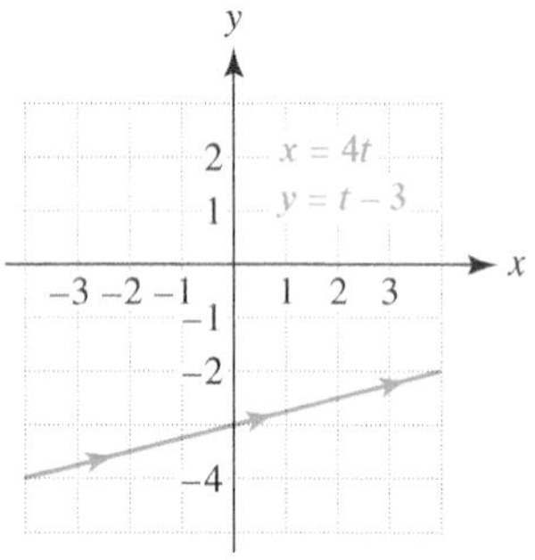

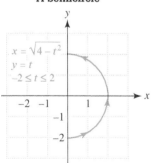

Figure 8.73

SOLUTION
(a) Start by solving $x = 4t$ for t to obtain $t = \frac{1}{4}x$. Substitute for t in the given parametric equation for y.

$$y = t - 3 \qquad \text{Given parametric equation}$$
$$y = \frac{1}{4}x - 3 \qquad \text{Let } t = \frac{1}{4}x.$$

Because $y = \frac{1}{4}x - 3$, these parametric equations trace out a line with slope $\frac{1}{4}$ and y-intercept -3. As t increases, x also increases, so this line is traced out from left to right, as illustrated in Figure 8.73. Note that t can be any real number.
(b) Because $y = t$, it follows that a rectangular equation is $x = \sqrt{4 - y^2}$. To determine the graph of this equation, square each side.

$$x = \sqrt{4 - y^2} \qquad \text{Rectangular equation}$$
$$x^2 = 4 - y^2 \qquad \text{Square each side.}$$
$$x^2 + y^2 = 4 \qquad \text{Add } y^2 \text{ to each side.}$$

The equation $x^2 + y^2 = 4$ is a circle with center $(0, 0)$ and radius 2. Because $\sqrt{4 - y^2}$ is never negative, it follows that $x \geq 0$. Thus the parametric equation traces out only the right half of this circle. See Figure 8.74. Because $y = t$, this semicircle is traced from bottom to top as y increases from -2 to 2.

Now Try Exercises 9 and 13

A Semicircle

Figure 8.74

Parametric equations can model a circle, as shown in the next example.

EXAMPLE 4 Graphing a circle with parametric equations

Graph $x = 2 \cos t$ and $y = 2 \sin t$ for $0 \leq t \leq 2\pi$. Find an equivalent equation by using rectangular coordinates.

SOLUTION Enter and graph these parametric equations, as shown in Figures 8.75 and 8.76. Be sure to have the mode of the calculator set for parametric equations. (Note that Tstep = 0.1.)

Enter Parametric Equations

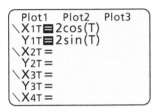

Plot1   Plot2   Plot3
\X1T■2cos(T)
 Y1T■2sin(T)
\X2T=
 Y2T=
\X3T=
 Y3T=
\X4T=

Figure 8.75

Graph Equations to Form a Circle (r = 2)
$[-3, 3, 1]$ by $[-2, 2, 1]$

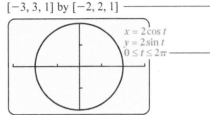

$x = 2\cos t$
$y = 2\sin t$
$0 \le t \le 2\pi$

Figure 8.76

The window must be square for a circle to appear circular, rather than elliptical.

t must increase from 0 to 2π for entire circle to appear.

To verify that this is a circle, consider the following.

$$x^2 + y^2 = (2\cos t)^2 + (2\sin t)^2 \qquad x = 2\cos t, y = 2\sin t$$
$$= 4\cos^2 t + 4\sin^2 t \qquad \text{Properties of exponents}$$
$$= 4(\cos^2 t + \sin^2 t) \qquad \text{Distributive property}$$
$$= 4 \qquad \cos^2 t + \sin^2 t = 1$$

The parametric equations are equivalent to $x^2 + y^2 = 4$, which is a circle with its center at $(0, 0)$ and having radius 2.

> **Now Try Exercise 19**

In the next two examples, an equation written in terms of x and y is converted to parametric equations.

> **EXAMPLE 5** Converting to parametric equations

Convert $x = y^2 - 4y + 4$ to parametric equations.

SOLUTION There is more than one way to convert this equation to parametric equations. One simple way is to let $y = t$ and then write the parametric equations as

$$x = t^2 - 4t + 4, \quad y = t,$$

where t is any real number. To write a different pair of parametric equations, note that

$$x = y^2 - 4y + 4 = (y - 2)^2.$$

Let $t = y - 2$, or $y = t + 2$, and then another pair of parametric equations is

$$x = t^2, y = t + 2.$$

> **Now Try Exercise 53**

> **EXAMPLE 6** Converting to parametric equations

Given the equation $x^2 + y^2 = 1$, complete the following.
(a) Find parametric equations for this equation.
(b) What portion of the graph appears for $0 \le t \le \pi$?

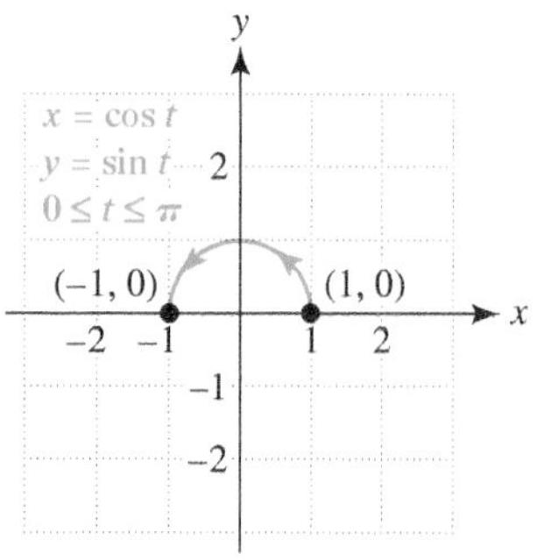

$x = \cos t$
$y = \sin t$
$0 \le t \le \pi$

Figure 8.77

SOLUTION

(a) The graph of $x^2 + y^2 = 1$ is the unit circle. From trigonometry we know that on the unit circle $x = \cos t$ and $y = \sin t$. Since $\cos^2 t + \sin^2 t = 1$ for all t, we have the following result.

$$x^2 + y^2 = \cos^2 t + \sin^2 t = 1$$

Thus parametric equations for the unit circle are

$$x = \cos t, \quad y = \sin t; \quad 0 \le t \le 2\pi.$$

(b) When t increases from 0 to π, the upper half of the circle is graphed, moving from the point $(1, 0)$ to the point $(-1, 0)$. See Figure 8.77.

Now Try Exercise 49

NOTE The equations $x = a \cos t, y = a \sin t$ for $0 \le t \le 2\pi$ trace out a circle with radius $r = a$. If t is limited to an interval that is less than 2π in length, then only a portion of a circle will appear.

Applications of Parametric Equations

Parametric equations are used to simulate motion. If a ball or shot is thrown with a velocity of v feet per second at an angle θ with the horizontal, its flight can be modeled by the parametric equations

$$x = (v \cos \theta) t \quad \text{and} \quad y = (v \sin \theta) t - 16t^2 + h,$$

where t is in seconds and h is the initial height above the ground. The term $-16t^2$ occurs because gravity is pulling downward. See Figure 8.78. (These equations ignore air resistance.)

Modeling the Path of a Shot

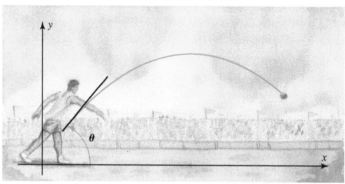

Figure 8.78

EXAMPLE 7 Simulating motion with parametric equations

Three golf balls are hit simultaneously into the air at 132 feet per second (90 miles per hour), making angles of 30°, 50°, and 70° with the horizontal.
(a) Assuming the ground is level, determine graphically which ball travels the farthest horizontally. Estimate this distance.
(b) Which ball reaches the greatest height? Estimate this height.

Golf Ball Hit at Three Angles
[0, 600, 50] by [0, 400, 50]

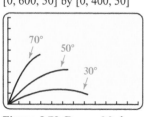

Figure 8.79 Degree Mode

SOLUTION

(a) The three sets of parametric equations determined by the three golf balls are as follows. Since $h = 0$, the only difference between the three balls is the angle of elevation.

$X_1 = 132 \cos (30)T, \quad Y_1 = 132 \sin (30)T - 16T^2$ — Hit at 30°

$X_2 = 132 \cos (50)T, \quad Y_2 = 132 \sin (50)T - 16T^2$ — Hit at 50°

$X_3 = 132 \cos (70)T, \quad Y_3 = 132 \sin (70)T - 16T^2$ — Hit at 70°

Angles Affect the Distance
[0, 600, 50] by [0, 400, 50]

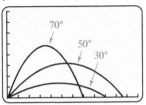

Figure 8.80 Degree Mode

The graphs of the three sets of parametric equations are shown in Figures 8.79 and 8.80, where $0 \le t \le 9$. A graphing calculator in *simultaneous mode* has been used so that we can view all three balls in flight at the same time. From the second graph we can see that the ball hit at 50° travels the farthest distance. Using the trace feature, we estimate this horizontal distance to be about 540 feet.

(b) Using the trace feature, the ball hit at 70° reaches the greatest height of about 240 feet.

Now Try Exercise 71

CLASS DISCUSSION

If a golf ball is hit at 88 feet per second (60 mi/hr), use trial and error to find the angle θ that results in a maximum distance for the ball.

EXAMPLE 8 Modeling the flight of a baseball

A baseball is hit from a height of 4 feet at a 30° angle above the horizontal. Its initial velocity is 128 feet per second. See Figure 8.81.
(a) Write parametric equations that model the flight of the baseball.
(b) Determine the horizontal distance that the ball travels in the air, assuming that the ground is level.
(c) What is the maximum height of the baseball?
(d) Would the ball clear a 4-foot-high fence that is 400 feet from the batter?

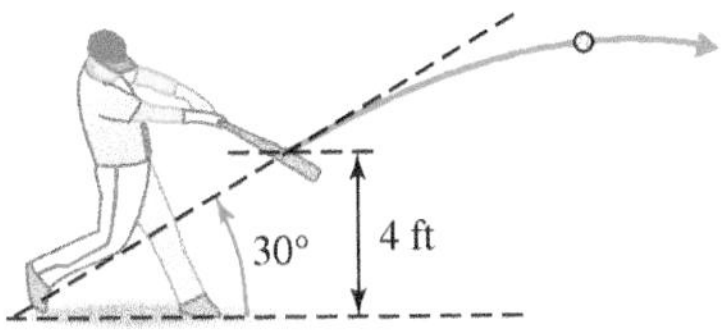

Figure 8.81

SOLUTION
(a) Let $v = 128$, $\theta = 30°$, and $h = 4$. Then the parametric equations become

$$x = (128 \cos 30°)t \quad \text{and} \quad y = (128 \sin 30°)t - 16t^2 + 4.$$

Since $\cos 30° = \frac{\sqrt{3}}{2}$ and $\sin 30° = \frac{1}{2}$, these equations can be rewritten as

$$x = (64\sqrt{3})t \quad \text{and} \quad y = 64t - 16t^2 + 4.$$

(b) To find how far the ball travels, we first determine the length of time that the ball is in flight. The ball hits the ground when $y = 0$.

$$64t - 16t^2 + 4 = 0 \qquad \text{Substitute for } y.$$
$$16t^2 - 64t - 4 = 0 \qquad \text{Rewrite quadratic equation.}$$
$$t = \frac{64 \pm \sqrt{(-64)^2 - 4(16)(-4)}}{2(16)} \qquad \text{Quadratic formula}$$
$$t \approx 4.0616 \quad \text{or} \quad t \approx -0.0616 \qquad \text{Approximate.}$$

After 4.0616 seconds, the ball traveled *horizontally* $x = 64\sqrt{3}(4.0616) \approx 450.2$ feet.

(c) The graph of $y = 64t - 16t^2 + 4$ is a parabola that opens downward. Using the *vertex formula*, we find that the maximum height of the ball occurs after

$$t = -\frac{b}{2a} = -\frac{64}{2(-16)} = 2 \text{ seconds.}$$

The maximum height is $y = 64(2) - 16(2)^2 + 4 = 68$ feet.

(d) Because $x = (64\sqrt{3})t$, we can determine how long it takes the ball to reach the fence by solving the equation $(64\sqrt{3})t = 400$.

$$(64\sqrt{3})t = 400, \quad \text{or} \quad t = \frac{400}{64\sqrt{3}} \approx 3.61 \text{ seconds}$$

After 3.61 seconds, the ball has traveled horizontally 400 feet and is

$$y = 64(3.61) - 16(3.61)^2 + 4 \approx 27 \text{ feet}$$

high. The baseball easily clears the 4-foot fence.

Now Try Exercise 75

An Application from Computer Graphics Parametric equations are used frequently in computer graphics to design a variety of figures and letters. Computer fonts are sometimes designed using parametric equations. In the next example, we use parametric equations to design a "smiley" face consisting of a head, two eyes, and a mouth. (**Source:** F. Hill, *Computer Graphics.*)

EXAMPLE 9 Creating drawings with parametric equations

Graph a "smiley" face using parametric equations. Answers may vary.

SOLUTION

Head We can use a circle centered at the origin for the head. If the radius is 2, then let $x = 2 \cos t$ and $y = 2 \sin t$ for $0 \le t \le 2\pi$. These equations are graphed in Figure 8.82.

Eyes For the eyes we can use two small circles. The eye in the first quadrant can be modeled by $x = 1 + 0.3 \cos t$ and $y = 1 + 0.3 \sin t$ for $0 \le t \le 2\pi$. This represents a circle centered at $(1, 1)$ with radius 0.3. The eye in the second quadrant can be modeled by $x = -1 + 0.3 \cos t$ and $y = 1 + 0.3 \sin t$ for $0 \le t \le 2\pi$, which is a circle centered at $(-1, 1)$ with radius 0.3. These equations are graphed in Figure 8.83.

Start with the Head	Add Eyes	Add Mouth and Pupils
$[-3, 3, 1]$ by $[-2, 2, 1]$	$[-3, 3, 1]$ by $[-2, 2, 1]$	$[-3, 3, 1]$ by $[-2, 2, 1]$

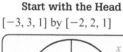

Figure 8.82 **Figure 8.83** **Figure 8.84**

CLASS DISCUSSION

Modify the face in Example 9 so that it is frowning. Try to find a way to make the right eye shut rather than open.

Mouth For the smile we can use the lower half of a circle. Using trial and error, we might arrive at $x = 0.5 \cos \frac{1}{2}t$ and $y = -0.5 - 0.5 \sin \frac{1}{2}t$. This is a semicircle centered at $(0, -0.5)$ with radius 0.5. Since we are letting $0 \le t \le 2\pi$, the term $\frac{1}{2}t$ ensures that only half a circle (a semicircle) is drawn. The minus sign before $0.5 \sin \frac{1}{2}t$ in the y-equation causes the lower half of the semicircle to be drawn rather than the upper half. The final result is shown in Figure 8.84. The pupils have been added by plotting the points $(1, 1)$ and $(-1, 1)$, and the coordinate axes have been turned off.

Now Try Exercise 69

8.4 Putting It All Together

Parametric equations can be used to model a wide variety of curves in the xy-plane that cannot be represented by a single function.

CONCEPT	EXPLANATION	EXAMPLES
Plane curve and parametric equations	A plane curve is a set of points (x, y) such that $x = f(t)$ and $y = g(t)$, where f and g are continuous on an interval $a \le t \le b$. The equations $x = f(t)$ and $y = g(t)$ are parametric equations with parameter t.	If $x = 2t$ and $y = t^2$ for $-1 \le t \le 2$, then the resulting graph is a portion of a parabola. 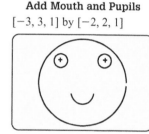

CONCEPT	EXPLANATION	EXAMPLES
Writing parametric equations in terms of x and y	Solve one of the parametric equations for t and substitute into the second equation.	If $x = t^3$ and $y = t^2 - 2$, solve $x = t^3$ for t to obtain $t = x^{1/3}$. Substituting gives $y = x^{2/3} - 2$.
Converting to parametric equations	If possible, solve the equation for one of the variables. Let the other variable equal t. Now write the first variable in terms of t. Answers may vary.	If $4x = y^2$, solve the equation for x to obtain $x = \frac{1}{4}y^2$. Let $y = t$. Then $$x = \frac{1}{4}t^2 \quad \text{and} \quad y = t.$$ Another possibility is $$x = t^2 \quad \text{and} \quad y = 2t.$$

8.4 Exercises

Graphs of Parametric Equations

Exercises 1–8: Use the parametric equations to complete the following.

(a) *Make a table of values for $t = 0, 1, 2, 3$.*
(b) *Plot the points from the table and graph the curve for $0 \le t \le 3$. Add arrows to show how the curve is traced out.*
(c) *Describe the curve.*

1. $x = t - 1,$ $\qquad y = 2t$

2. $x = t + 1,$ $\qquad y = t - 2$

3. $x = t + 2,$ $\qquad y = (t - 2)^2$

4. $x = \frac{1}{3}t^2,$ $\qquad y = t - 1$

5. $x = \sqrt{9 - t^2},$ $\qquad y = t$

6. $x = t^2,$ $\qquad y = 2t + 1$

7. $x = t,$ $\qquad y = \sqrt{9 - t^2}$

8. $x = 3t,$ $\qquad y = t^2 + 2$

Exercises 9–24: Find a rectangular equation for each curve and describe the curve. Support your result by graphing the parametric equations.

9. $x = 3t,$ $\qquad y = t - 1;$ $\qquad -\infty < t < \infty$

10. $x = t + 3,$ $\qquad y = 2t;$ $\qquad -\infty < t < \infty$

11. $x = 3t^2,$ $\qquad y = t + 1;$ $\qquad -\infty < t < \infty$

12. $x = t^2 - 2t + 1,$ $\qquad y = t - 1;$ $\qquad -\infty < t < \infty$

13. $x = \sqrt{1 - t^2},$ $\qquad y = t;$ $\qquad -1 \le t \le 1$

14. $x = t,$ $\qquad y = \sqrt{9 - t^2};$ $\qquad -3 \le t \le 3$

15. $x = t,$ $\qquad y = \frac{1}{2}t^2;$ $\qquad -2 \le t \le 2$

16. $x = \sqrt[3]{t},$ $\qquad y = t;$ $\qquad -2 \le t \le 2$

17. $x = t - 2,$ $\qquad y = t^2 + 1;$ $\qquad -1 \le t \le 2$

18. $x = 2t,$ $\qquad y = t^2 + 1;$ $\qquad -1 \le t \le 2$

19. $x = 3 \sin t,$ $\qquad y = 3 \cos t;$ $\qquad -\pi \le t \le \pi$

20. $x = 4 \cos t,$ $\qquad y = 4 \sin t;$ $\qquad 0 \le t \le 2\pi$

21. $x = 2 \sin t,$ $\qquad y = -2 \cos t;$ $\qquad 0 \le t \le 2\pi$

22. $x = \cos 2t,$ $\qquad y = \sin 2t;$ $\qquad 0 \le t \le \pi$

23. $x = 3 \cos 2t,$ $\qquad y = 3 \sin 2t;$ $\qquad 0 \le t \le \pi$

24. $x = 2 \cos^2 t,$ $\qquad y = 2 \sin^2 t;$ $\qquad 0 \le t \le \frac{\pi}{2}$

Exercises 25–42: Graph the parametric equations.

25. $x = \frac{1}{3}t,$ $\qquad y = \frac{2}{3}t + 1;$ $\qquad -\infty < t < \infty$

26. $x = t + 3,$ $\qquad y = 2t - 1;$ $\qquad -\infty < t < \infty$

27. $x = t^2,$ $\qquad y = 2t;$ $\qquad -\infty < t < \infty$

28. $x = \frac{1}{2}(t + 2)^2,$ $\qquad y = t + 2;$ $\qquad -\infty < t < \infty$

29. $x = \cos t,$ $\qquad y = \sin t;$ $\qquad 0 \le t \le \pi$

30. $x = 2 \sin t,$ $\qquad y = 2 \cos t;$ $\qquad -\pi \le t \le 0$

31. $x = t^3,$ $\qquad$ $y = t^2;$ $\qquad$ $-2 \le t \le 2$

32. $x = e^t,$ $\qquad$ $y = t - 1;$ $\qquad$ $-2 \le t \le 2$

33. $x = t^2,$ $\qquad$ $y = \ln t;$ $\qquad$ $0 < t \le 2$

34. $x = t^3 - t,$ $\qquad$ $y = e^t;$ $\qquad$ $-1.5 \le t \le 1.5$

35. $x = t - \sin t,$ $\qquad$ $y = 1 - \cos t;$ $\qquad$ $0 \le t \le 6\pi$

36. $x = t^3 + 3t,$ $\qquad$ $y = 2\cos t;$ $\qquad$ $-1 \le t \le 1$

37. $x = 2 + \cos t,$ $\qquad$ $y = \sin t - 1;$ $\qquad$ $0 \le t \le 2\pi$

38. $x = -2 + \cos t,$ $\qquad$ $y = \sin t + 1;$ $\qquad$ $0 \le t \le 2\pi$

39. $x = \cos^3 t,$ $\qquad$ $y = \sin^3 t;$ $\qquad$ $0 \le t \le 2\pi$

40. $x = \cos^5 t,$ $\qquad$ $y = \sin^5 t;$ $\qquad$ $0 \le t \le 2\pi$

41. $x = |3 \sin t|,$ $\qquad$ $y = |3 \cos t|;$ $\qquad$ $0 \le t \le \pi$

42. $x = 3 \sin 2t,$ $\qquad$ $y = 3 \cos t;$ $\qquad$ $0 \le t \le 2\pi$

Exercises 43–54: Convert the given equation to parametric equations. Answers may vary.

43. $2x + y = 4$ $\qquad\qquad$ **44.** $5x - 4y = 20$

45. $y = 4 - x^2$ $\qquad\qquad$ **46.** $x = y^2 - 2$

47. $x = y^2 + y - 3$ $\qquad$ **48.** $5x = y^3 + 1$

49. $x^2 + y^2 = 4$ $\qquad\qquad$ **50.** $x^2 + y^2 = 9$

51. $\ln y = 0.1x^2$ $\qquad\qquad$ **52.** $e^x = |1 - y|$

53. $x = y^2 - 2y + 1$ $\qquad$ **54.** $x = 4y^2 + 4y + 1$

Exercises 55–60: Graph each pair of parametric equations for $0 \le t \le 2\pi$. Describe any differences in the two graphs.

55. (a) $x = 3 \cos t,$ $\qquad$ $y = 3 \sin t$
$\quad$ (b) $x = 3 \cos 2t,$ $\qquad$ $y = 3 \sin 2t$

56. (a) $x = 2 \cos t,$ $\qquad$ $y = 2 \sin t$
$\quad$ (b) $x = 2 \cos t,$ $\qquad$ $y = -2 \sin t$

57. (a) $x = 3 \cos t,$ $\qquad$ $y = 3 \sin t$
$\quad$ (b) $x = 3 \sin t,$ $\qquad$ $y = 3 \cos t$

58. (a) $x = t,$ $\qquad\qquad$ $y = t^2$
$\quad$ (b) $x = t^2,$ $\qquad\qquad$ $y = t$

59. (a) $x = -1 + \cos t,$ $\qquad$ $y = 2 + \sin t$
$\quad$ (b) $x = 1 + \cos t,$ $\qquad$ $y = 2 + \sin t$

60. (a) $x = 2 \cos \frac{1}{2}t,$ $\qquad$ $y = 2 \sin \frac{1}{2}t$
$\quad$ (b) $x = 2 \cos t,$ $\qquad$ $y = 2 \sin t$

Designing Shapes and Figures

Exercises 61–64: Graph the following set of parametric equations for $0 \le t \le 2\pi$ in the viewing rectangle $[0, 6, 1]$ by $[0, 4, 1]$. Identify the letter of the alphabet that is graphed.

61. $x_1 = 1,$ $\qquad\qquad$ $y_1 = 1 + t/\pi$
$\quad x_2 = 1 + t/(3\pi),$ $\qquad$ $y_2 = 2$
$\quad x_3 = 1 + t/(2\pi),$ $\qquad$ $y_3 = 3$

62. $x_1 = 1,$ $\qquad\qquad$ $y_1 = 1 + t/\pi$
$\quad x_2 = 1 + t/(3\pi),$ $\qquad$ $y_2 = 2$
$\quad x_3 = 1 + t/(2\pi),$ $\qquad$ $y_3 = 3$
$\quad x_4 = 1 + t/(2\pi),$ $\qquad$ $y_4 = 1$

63. $x_1 = 1,$ $\qquad\qquad\qquad$ $y_1 = 1 + t/\pi$
$\quad x_2 = 1 + 1.3 \sin(0.5t),$ $\qquad$ $y_2 = 2 + \cos(0.5t)$

64. $x_1 = 2 + 0.8 \cos(0.85t),$ $\qquad$ $y_1 = 2 + \sin(0.85t)$
$\quad x_2 = 1.2 + t/(1.3\pi),$ $\qquad\quad$ $y_2 = 2$

Exercises 65–68: **Designing Letters** *Find a set of parametric equations that results in a letter similar to the one shown in the figure. Use the viewing rectangle given by $[-4.7, 4.7, 1]$ by $[-3.1, 3.1, 1]$ and turn off the coordinate axes. Answers may vary.*

65.

66.

67.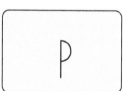

68.

69. Designing a Face (Refer to Example 9.) Use parametric equations to create your own "smiley" face. This face should have a head, a mouth, and eyes.

70. Designing a Face Add a nose to the face that you designed in Exercise 69.

Applications

71. Flight of a Golf Ball (Refer to Example 7.) Two golf balls are hit into the air at 66 feet per second (45 mi/hr), making angles of 35° and 50° with the horizontal. If the ground is level, estimate the horizontal distance traveled by each golf ball.

72. Flight of a Golf Ball Solve Exercise 71 if, instead of the ground being level, the ground is inclined with a slope of $m = 0.1$.

73. Flight of a Golf Ball If a golf ball is hit at 88 feet per second (60 mi/hr), making an angle of 45° with the horizontal, will it go over a fence 10 feet high that is 200 feet away on level ground?

74. Simulating Gravity on the Moon   (Refer to Example 7.) If an object is thrown on the moon, the parametric equations of flight are

$$x = (v \cos \theta)t \quad \text{and} \quad y = (v \sin \theta)t - 2.66t^2 + h.$$

Estimate the horizontal distance that a golf ball hit 88 feet per second (60 mi/hr) at an angle of 45° with the horizontal travels on the moon if the moon's surface is level.

75. Flight of a Baseball   (Refer to Example 8.) A baseball is hit with an angle of elevation of 45°, from the top of a ridge that is 50 feet above an area of level ground. The initial velocity of the ball is 88 feet per second, or 60 miles per hour. Find the horizontal distance traveled by the ball in the air.

76. Flight of a Baseball   A baseball is hit from a height of 3 feet at a 60° angle above the horizontal. Its initial velocity is 64 feet per second.
  (a) Write parametric equations that model the flight of the baseball.

  (b) Determine the horizontal distance traveled by the ball in the air. Assume that the ground is level.

  (c) What is the maximum height of the baseball? At that time, how far has the ball traveled horizontally?

  (d) Would the ball clear a 5-foot high fence that is 100 feet from the batter?

Exercises 77–80: **Lissajous Figures**   *Lissajous figures occur in electronics and may be used to find the frequency of an unknown voltage. (See Extended and Discovery Exercises 1–4.) Graph the Lissajous figure for $0 \le t \le 6.5$ in the viewing rectangle $[-6, 6, 1]$ by $[-4, 4, 1]$.*

77. $x = 2 \cos t,$ $y = 3 \sin 2t$

78. $x = 3 \cos 2t,$ $y = 3 \sin 3t$

79. $x = 3 \sin 4t,$ $y = 3 \cos 3t$

80. $x = 4 \sin 4t,$ $y = 3 \sin 5t$

Writing about Mathematics

81. Describe the basic form of parametric equations. Give an example. Explain how graphs of parametric equations can differ from graphs of functions.

82. Suppose that a function is defined by $y = f(x)$, where the domain of f is $a \le x \le b$. Explain how we could represent f with parametric equations. Apply your method to $f(x) = x^2 + 1$, where $-2 \le x \le 2$.

Extended and Discovery Exercises

Exercises 1–4: **Electronic Technology**   *Parametric equations have applications in electricity. If two sinusoidal voltages, denoted by $x = V_1(t)$ and $y = V_2(t)$, are applied to an oscilloscope, a stationary pattern called a Lissajous figure may appear, as shown in the figure below. If the frequency F_1 of V_1 is known and the frequency F_2 of V_2 is unknown, then a Lissajous figure may be used to find F_2. The ratio $\frac{F_1}{F_2}$ is equal to the ratio of the corresponding number of tangents to the enclosing rectangle. The number of tangents along a vertical side of the rectangle corresponds to F_1, and the number of tangents along a horizontal side corresponds to F_2. In this figure $\frac{F_1}{F_2} = \frac{3}{2}$. Therefore $F_2 = \frac{2}{3}F_1$. Determine F_2 given the Lissajous figure and the frequency F_1 in cycles per second.   (**Source:** R. Smith and R. Dorf, Circuits, Devices, and Systems.)*

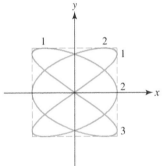

1. $F_1 = 150$

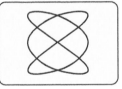

2. $F_1 = 60$

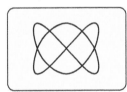

3. $F_1 = 400$

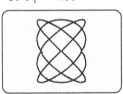

4. $F_1 = 1200$

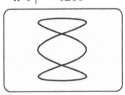

CHECKING BASIC CONCEPTS FOR SECTIONS 8.3 AND 8.4

1. Let the point P be $(-1, 3)$ and the point Q be $(3, 7)$. Find the following.
  (a) $\mathbf{v} = \overrightarrow{PQ}$ (b) $\|\mathbf{v}\|$ (c) $\overrightarrow{PQ} + \overrightarrow{QP}$

2. Let $\mathbf{v} = 2\mathbf{i} - \mathbf{j}$ and $\mathbf{u} = -3\mathbf{i} + 2\mathbf{j}$. Find the following graphically and symbolically.
  (a) $2\mathbf{v} + \mathbf{u}$ (b) $2\mathbf{v}$ (c) $\mathbf{v} - 3\mathbf{u}$

3. Let $\mathbf{a} = \langle 3, -2 \rangle$ and $\mathbf{b} = \langle -1, 3 \rangle$. Find the following.
  (a) $\mathbf{a} \cdot \mathbf{b}$

  (b) The angle θ between $\mathbf{a}$ and $\mathbf{b}$ rounded to the nearest tenth of a degree

4. Graph the parametric equations given by $x = t + 1$ and $y = (t - 1)^2$ for $-1 \le t \le 5$. Write these parametric equations in terms of x and y.

8.5 Polar Equations

- Learn the polar coordinate system
- Graph polar equations
- Graph polar equations with graphing calculators (optional)
- Solve polar equations

Introduction

Many times a change in a frame of reference can have a profound effect on the solution of a problem. Thus far we have graphed functions only in the xy-plane. Many interesting curves, such as a spiral, cannot be represented by a function since these curves fail the vertical line test. Creating a new coordinate system makes some types of equations simpler. For example, the equation $x^2 + y^2 = 1$ describes the unit circle in the rectangular coordinate system. Every point lying on the unit circle is 1 unit from the origin. If we specify a new variable r that represents the radius of the circle, then $r = 1$ also describes the unit circle in the *polar coordinate system*. A change of variable has resulted in a simpler equation.

The Polar Coordinate System

In the xy-plane we are accustomed to identifying points using (x, y), where x and y are real numbers. However, using the xy-plane is not the only way to locate a point in a plane. The **polar coordinate system** uses r and θ instead of x and y to locate a point P, as shown in Figures 8.85 and 8.86 in the following See the Concept.

See the Concept: Polar Coordinates

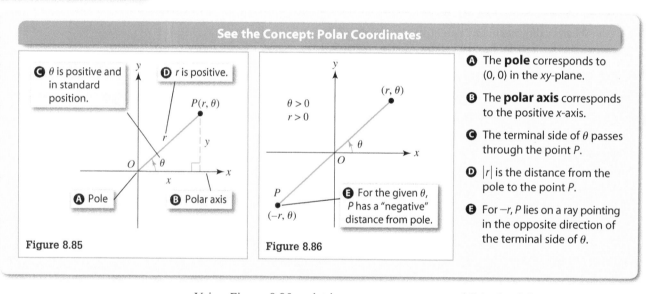

Figure 8.85

Figure 8.86

Ⓐ The **pole** corresponds to (0, 0) in the xy-plane.

Ⓑ The **polar axis** corresponds to the positive x-axis.

Ⓒ The terminal side of θ passes through the point P.

Ⓓ $|r|$ is the distance from the pole to the point P.

Ⓔ For $-r$, P lies on a ray pointing in the opposite direction of the terminal side of θ.

Using Figure 8.85 and trigonometry, we can establish the following relationships between rectangular and polar coordinates.

RECTANGULAR AND POLAR COORDINATES

If a point has rectangular coordinates (x, y) and polar coordinates (r, θ), then these coordinates are related as follows. (Both r and θ can be negative.)

$$x = r\cos\theta, \qquad y = r\sin\theta$$

$$r^2 = x^2 + y^2, \qquad \tan\theta = \frac{y}{x} \ (x \neq 0)$$

EXAMPLE 1 Plotting points in polar coordinates

Plot the points (r, θ) on a polar grid.

(a) $(2, 45°)$ **(b)** $(-3, 150°)$ **(c)** $\left(3.5, -\frac{\pi}{3}\right)$

SOLUTION

(a) Let $r = 2$ and $\theta = 45°$. Plot a point 2 units from the pole on the terminal side of $\theta = 45°$, as shown in Figure 8.87. Note that θ is in standard position.

(b) Since $r = -3 < 0$ and $\theta = 150°$, begin by locating the terminal side of θ in the second quadrant. Next plot a point 3 units from the pole in the *opposite* direction of the terminal side of θ, as shown in Figure 8.88.

(c) Since $r = 3.5$ and $\theta = -\frac{\pi}{3}$ (radians), the point is in the fourth quadrant with a distance of 3.5 from the pole. See Figure 8.89.

$r > 0$ and $\theta > 0$	$r < 0$ and $\theta > 0$	$r > 0$ and $\theta < 0$

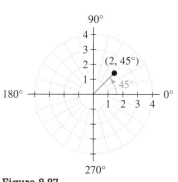

Figure 8.87

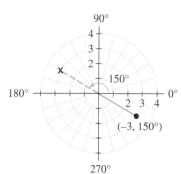

Figure 8.88

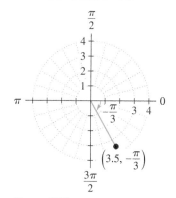

Figure 8.89

Now Try Exercises 1 and 3

MAKING CONNECTIONS

Vectors and Polar Coordinates If a vector $\mathbf{v} = \langle a, b \rangle$ has magnitude $\|\mathbf{v}\|$ and direction angle θ, then

$$a = \|\mathbf{v}\| \cos\theta \quad \text{and} \quad b = \|\mathbf{v}\| \sin\theta,$$

where $\|\mathbf{v}\| = \sqrt{a^2 + b^2}$ and $\tan\theta = \frac{b}{a}, a \neq 0$. See Figure 8.90. Similarly, if a point has rectangular coordinates (a, b) and polar coordinates (r, θ) with $r > 0$, then

$$a = r \cos\theta \quad \text{and} \quad b = r \sin\theta,$$

where $r = \sqrt{a^2 + b^2}$ and $\tan\theta = \frac{b}{a}, a \neq 0$. See Figure 8.91.

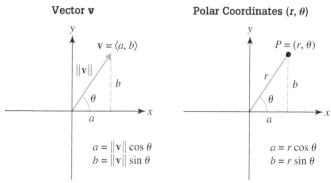

Figure 8.90   Figure 8.91

CLASS DISCUSSION

What can be said about a point (r, θ) if $r = 0$?

NOTE Unlike xy-coordinates, polar coordinates are *not* unique. For example, the $r\theta$-coordinates of $(2, 0°)$, $(2, 360°)$, $(2, -360°)$, and $(-2, 180°)$ all represent the same point.

In the next example, we convert polar coordinates to rectangular coordinates.

EXAMPLE 2 Converting to rectangular coordinates

Convert each point from polar coordinates to rectangular coordinates.

(a) $(5, 180°)$ **(b)** $\left(3, -\dfrac{\pi}{3}\right)$

SOLUTION

(a) To convert $(5, 180°)$ to rectangular coordinates, use the equations $x = r\cos\theta$ and $y = r\sin\theta$ with $r = 5$ and $\theta = 180°$.

$$x = 5\cos(180°) = -5$$
$$y = 5\sin(180°) = 0$$

The corresponding rectangular coordinates are $(-5, 0)$.

(b) To convert $\left(3, -\dfrac{\pi}{3}\right)$ to rectangular coordinates, let $r = 3$ and $\theta = -\dfrac{\pi}{3}$, where θ is in radians.

$$x = 3\cos\left(-\dfrac{\pi}{3}\right) = \dfrac{3}{2}, \qquad y = 3\sin\left(-\dfrac{\pi}{3}\right) = -\dfrac{3\sqrt{3}}{2} \approx -2.6$$

The rectangular coordinates are $\left(\dfrac{3}{2}, -\dfrac{3\sqrt{3}}{2}\right)$.

Now Try Exercises 11 and 15

In the next example, points expressed in rectangular coordinates are converted to polar coordinates. However, this conversion is *not* unique because, unlike rectangular coordinates, polar coordinates are not unique.

EXAMPLE 3 Expressing a point in polar coordinates

Given the point $\left(1, \sqrt{3}\right)$ in rectangular coordinates, find polar coordinates (r, θ) that satisfy each condition.

(a) $r > 0$, $0° \le \theta < 360°$
(b) $r > 0$, $-360° \le \theta < 0°$
(c) $r < 0$, $0° \le \theta < 360°$

SOLUTION

(a) $r > 0, \ 0° \le \theta < 360°$ Because $r^2 = x^2 + y^2$, let $r = \sqrt{1 + 3} = 2$. The point $\left(1, \sqrt{3}\right)$ is located in the first quadrant of the xy-plane. Therefore $\tan\theta = \dfrac{y}{x} = \dfrac{\sqrt{3}}{1}$ and $\theta = \tan^{-1}\sqrt{3} = 60°$. Let $(r, \theta) = (2, 60°)$. See Figure 8.92.

Polar Coordinates Are Not Unique

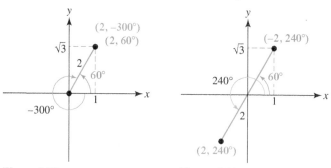

Figure 8.92   Figure 8.93

(b) $r > 0, \ -360° \le \theta < 0°$ Rather than let $\theta = 60°$, we can use $\theta = -300°$, so $(r, \theta) = (2, -300°)$. See Figure 8.92. Notice that $60°$ and $-300°$ are coterminal angles.

(c) $r < 0, \ 0° \le \theta < 360°$ We can let $r = -2$, but then we need to let angle $\theta = 60° + 180° = 240°$. Thus $(r, \theta) = (-2, 240°)$, as illustrated in Figure 8.93.

Now Try Exercise 23

Graphs of Polar Equations

When we graph $y = f(x)$ in the xy-coordinate system, we are graphing a function. A vertical line can intersect the graph of a function at most once. As a result, many shapes such as circles, hearts, and leaves cannot be represented by a function. Like parametric equations, polar equations can be valuable for representing a variety of curves.

EXAMPLE 4   Representing polar equations

Make a table of values and graph each curve. Then describe the curve.

(a) $\theta = \dfrac{\pi}{4}$ (b) $r = 3$ (c) $r = 2 + 2\cos\theta$

SOLUTION

(a) *Numerical Representation* Since $\theta = \frac{\pi}{4}$, every point lying on this graph is of the form $\left(r, \frac{\pi}{4}\right)$, where r can be any real number. Five of these points are listed in Table 8.2.

$$\theta = \frac{\pi}{4}$$

θ	$\frac{\pi}{4}$	$\frac{\pi}{4}$	$\frac{\pi}{4}$	$\frac{\pi}{4}$	$\frac{\pi}{4}$
r	-2	-1	0	1	2

Table 8.2

Graphical Representation A graph of $\theta = \frac{\pi}{4}$ and the points in Table 8.2 are shown in Figure 8.94.

Verbal Representation The graph is a line with slope 1 passing through the pole.

(b) *Numerical Representation* A table of values is shown in Table 8.3.

$$r = 3$$

θ	0°	60°	120°	180°	240°	300°
r	3	3	3	3	3	3

Table 8.3

Graphical Representation A graph, with these points, is shown in Figure 8.95.

Verbal Representation The polar equation represents a circle with radius 3.

(c) *Numerical Representation* A table of values for $r = 2 + 2\cos\theta$ is shown in Table 8.4. For example, when $\theta = 60°$, then

$$r = 2 + 2\cos 60° = 2 + 2(0.5) = 3.$$

$$r = 2 + 2\cos\theta$$

θ	0°	60°	120°	180°	240°	300°	360°
r	4	3	1	0	1	3	4

Table 8.4

Graphical Representation To help graph the equation we can plot the points in Table 8.4. See Figure 8.96. Notice that since the cosine function has period 360°, the graph repeats after 360°.

Verbal Representation The polar equation represents a heart-shaped graph called a **cardioid**.

Now Try Exercises 31, 33, and 37

Line

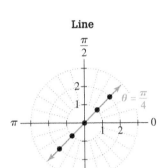

Figure 8.94

Circle

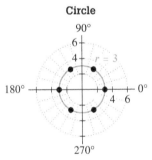

Figure 8.95

Cardioid

Figure 8.96

EXAMPLE 5 Graphing in polar coordinates

Graph each polar equation.
(a) $r = 2 \sin\theta$ **(b)** $r = 2 + \cos\theta$

Circle

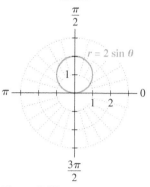

Figure 8.97

SOLUTION

(a) The polar equation $r = 2 \sin\theta$ can be converted to rectangular coordinates by first multiplying each side of the equation by r.

$$r = 2 \sin\theta \quad \text{Given polar equation}$$
$$r^2 = 2r \sin\theta \quad \text{Multiply by } r.$$
$$x^2 + y^2 = 2y \quad \text{Convert to xy-coordinates.}$$
$$x^2 + y^2 - 2y = 0 \quad \text{Subtract } 2y.$$
$$x^2 + y^2 - 2y + 1 = 1 \quad \text{Complete the square by adding 1.}$$
$$x^2 + (y - 1)^2 = 1 \quad \text{Perfect square trinomial}$$

This final equation represents a circle with center $(0, 1)$ and radius 1. The graph of $r = 2 \sin\theta$ is shown in Figure 8.97.

(b) To graph this polar equation, start by making a table of values as shown in Table 8.5, where values are rounded to the nearest tenth. (Degree measure could also be used.)

Limaçon

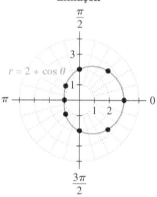

Figure 8.98

θ	0	$\frac{\pi}{4}$	$\frac{\pi}{2}$	$\frac{3\pi}{4}$	π	$\frac{5\pi}{4}$	$\frac{3\pi}{2}$	$\frac{7\pi}{4}$
$r = 2 + \cos\theta$	3	2.7	2	1.3	1	1.3	2	2.7

Table 8.5

The points in Table 8.5 and the equation $r = 2 + \cos\theta$ are graphed in Figure 8.98. The graph is called a **limaçon** *without an inner loop.*

Now Try Exercises 47 and 51

Rose Curves Polar equations in the form $r = a \sin n\theta$ or $r = a \cos n\theta$ result in graphs of rose curves. It can be shown that when n is odd there are n leaves and when n is even there are $2n$ leaves. In the next example, we graph this type of equation.

EXAMPLE 6 Graphing a four-leaved rose

Four-Leaved Rose

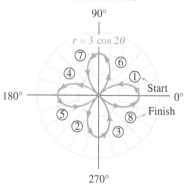

Figure 8.99

Graph $r = 3 \cos 2\theta$.

SOLUTION

To graph this polar equation by hand, start by making a table of values like the one shown in Table 8.6. Degree measure has been used, and values for r have been rounded to the nearest tenth. Notice that the values repeat themselves starting at 180°.

θ	0°	15°	30°	45°	60°	75°	90°
$r = 3 \cos 2\theta$	3	2.6	1.5	0	-1.5	-2.6	-3

θ	105°	120°	135°	150°	165°	180°
$r = 3 \cos 2\theta$	-2.6	-1.5	0	1.5	2.6	3

Table 8.6

Plotting these points in order gives the graph, called a **four-leaved rose**. Note in Figure 8.99 that the graph is developed with a continuous curve, beginning with the upper half of the right horizontal leaf and ending with the lower half of that leaf. As the graph is traced, the curve passes through the pole four times. Each leaf has length 3.

Now Try Exercise 55

EXAMPLE 7 Writing polar equations in rectangular form

Write the polar equation in terms of x and y. Describe its graph.

(a) $r = 3 \csc \theta$ **(b)** $r = \dfrac{2}{4 \cos \theta - 3 \sin \theta}$

SOLUTION

(a) Begin by applying a reciprocal identity.

$$r = 3 \csc \theta \qquad \text{Given equation}$$

$$r = \frac{3}{\sin \theta} \qquad \text{Reciprocal identity: } \csc \theta = \frac{1}{\sin \theta}$$

$$r \sin \theta = 3 \qquad \text{Multiply by } \sin \theta.$$

$$y = 3 \qquad y = r \sin \theta$$

Its graph is a horizontal line.

(b) Start by cross multiplying.

$$r = \frac{2}{4 \cos \theta - 3 \sin \theta} \qquad \text{Given equation}$$

$$4r \cos \theta - 3r \sin \theta = 2 \qquad \text{Cross multiply.}$$

$$4x - 3y = 2 \qquad \text{Substitute.}$$

$$y = \frac{4}{3}x - \frac{2}{3} \qquad \text{Solve for y.}$$

Its graph is a line with slope $\frac{4}{3}$ and y-intercept $-\frac{2}{3}$.

Now Try Exercises 69 and 71

Logarithmic Spiral

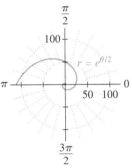

Figure 8.100

Logarithmic Spiral In 1638, René Descartes described a *logarithmic spiral* using the complicated equation $y = x \tan (\ln (x^2 + y^2))$. This curve, shown in Figure 8.100, cannot be represented by a function. With polar coordinates, this rectangular equation reduces to the much simpler equation $r = e^{\theta/2}$. Johann Bernoulli was so entranced by this remarkable curve that he ordered it carved on his tombstone. (***Source:*** H. Resnikoff and R. Wells, *Mathematics in Civilization.*)

Graphing Calculators and Polar Equations (Optional)

Technology can be used to make tables and graphs in polar coordinates. The table and graph in Example 4(c) are shown in Figures 8.101 and 8.102.

Cardioid

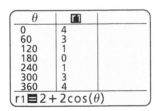

Figure 8.101 Degree Mode

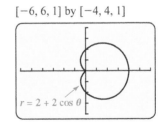

Figure 8.102

As is the case with rectangular and parametric equations, a viewing rectangle must be selected before graphing a polar equation. First choose whether the graph should be plotted in radian or degree mode. Next determine an interval for θ. Many times the interval $0° \le \theta \le 360°$ is sufficient to have the entire graph generated. Then select a square viewing rectangle, if possible.

EXAMPLE 8 Representing polar equations

Graph each curve. Then describe the curve.
(a) $r = 3 \cos 2\theta$ **(b)** $r = 1 - 2 \sin \theta$

SOLUTION

(a) This equation was graphed by hand in Example 6. In Figure 8.103 a graphing calculator has been used to create a graph of $r = 3 \cos 2\theta$. Turn on the polar grid and try tracing the graph to see how each leaf of the rose is generated by the polar equation. Notice, for example, the location of the point $(-1.5, 60°)$ in Figure 8.103.

Four-Leaved Rose

$[-6, 6, 1]$ by $[-4, 4, 1]$

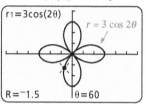

Figure 8.103

Limaçon with Inner Loop

$[-6, 6, 1]$ by $[-4, 4, 1]$

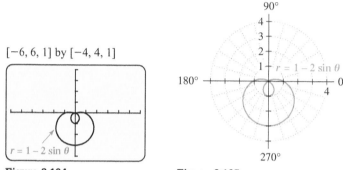

Figure 8.104   **Figure 8.105**

(b) A graph of $r = 1 - 2 \sin \theta$ is shown in Figure 8.104. The graph is called a limaçon *with an inner loop*. A graph with better resolution is shown in Figure 8.105. Notice that the inner loop occurs when $30° \le \theta \le 150°$ and $r \le 0$.

Now Try Exercises 79 and 83

Distances and Eccentricities

Planet	a	e
Jupiter	5.20	0.048
Saturn	9.54	0.056
Uranus	19.2	0.047
Neptune	30.1	0.009
Pluto	39.4	0.249

Table 8.7

Polar Equations of Conics   The polar equation

$$r = \frac{a(1 - e^2)}{1 + e \cos\theta}$$

can be used to model the orbits of planets and comets, where a is the average distance of the celestial body from the sun in astronomical units and e is a constant called the *eccentricity*. (Smaller values of e indicate that an orbit is more circular, whereas larger values indicate a more elliptical orbit. Note that values for e vary between 0 and 1. One astronomical unit equals 93 million miles.) The sun is located at the pole. Table 8.7 lists a and e for the outer planets and Pluto.   (*Source:* H. Karttunen et al., *Fundamental Astronomy.*)

EXAMPLE 9 Determining orbits

Use graphing to determine if Pluto is always farther from the sun than Neptune is.

SOLUTION   The orbital equations, given below, are graphed in Figure 8.106.

$$\text{Neptune: } r_1 = \frac{30.1(1 - 0.009^2)}{1 + 0.009 \cos\theta} \qquad a = 30.1, e = 0.009$$

$$\text{Pluto: } r_2 = \frac{39.4(1 - 0.249^2)}{1 + 0.249 \cos\theta} \qquad a = 39.4, e = 0.249$$

The graph shows that their orbits pass near each other. By zooming in we can determine that the orbit of Pluto actually passes inside the orbit of Neptune. See Figure 8.107.

Therefore there are times when Neptune—not Pluto—is farther from the sun. However, Pluto's average distance from the sun is considerably greater than Neptune's average distance. Neptune was farther from the sun than Pluto was for a 20-year period that ended in 1999.

Orbits of Neptune and Pluto

$[-60, 60, 10]$ by $[-40, 40, 10]$

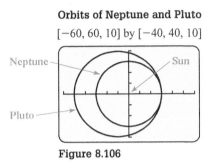

Figure 8.106

A Magnified View

$[27, 33, 1]$ by $[-2, 2, 1]$

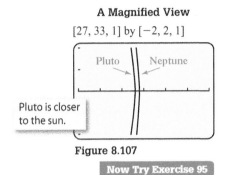

Figure 8.107

Now Try Exercise 95

Solving Polar Equations

We can solve polar equations symbolically, graphically, and numerically.

EXAMPLE 10 Solving a polar equation

Find values for θ where the circle $r = 3$ intersects the cardioid $r = 2 + 2\cos\theta$. Assume that $0° \leq \theta \leq 360°$.

SOLUTION

Symbolic Solution Begin by setting the two equations equal.

$$3 = 2 + 2\cos\theta \quad \text{Set equations equal.}$$

$$\cos\theta = \frac{1}{2} \quad \text{Solve for } \cos\theta.$$

$$\theta = 60° \text{ or } 300° \quad \text{The angle in quadrant IV with a reference angle of } 60° \text{ is } 300°.$$

$\theta = \cos^{-1}\frac{1}{2} = 60°$

(Be sure to check symbolic solutions.)

Graphical Solution Using the intersection-of-graphs method, let $r_1 = 3$ and let $r_2 = 2 + 2\cos(\theta)$. Their graphs intersect when $\theta = 60°$ and $300°$, as shown in Figures 8.108 and 8.109.

Solving $2 + 2\cos\theta = 3$ Graphically and Numerically

$[-6, 6, 1]$ by $[-4, 4, 1]$

Figure 8.108 Degree Mode

$[-6, 6, 1]$ by $[-4, 4, 1]$

Figure 8.109 Degree Mode

θ	r1	r2	
0	3	4	
60	3	3	← $r_1 = r_2$
120	3	1	
180	3	0	
240	3	1	
300	3	3	← $r_1 = r_2$
360	3	4	

r2 = 2+2cos(θ)

Figure 8.110 Degree Mode

Numerical Solution Numerical support is shown in Figure 8.110, where $r_1 = r_2 = 3$ when $\theta = 60°$ and $300°$.

Now Try Exercise 91

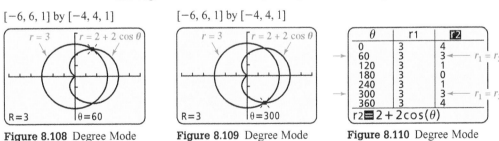

8.5 Putting It All Together

$\mathbf{P}$olar equations and graphs can be used to describe curves that are not easily represented by equations involving x and y. Polar coordinates are not unique for a given point, whereas rectangular coordinates are unique for a given point.

CONCEPT	EXAMPLES AND EXPLANATIONS
Polar coordinates	A point is determined by r and θ. To convert between rectangular and polar coordinates, use $x = r\cos\theta$, $y = r\sin\theta$, $\tan\theta = \frac{y}{x}$, and $r^2 = x^2 + y^2$.
Graphs in polar coordinates	**Circle** $r = a$ **Cardioid** $r = a \pm a\sin\theta$ or $r = a \pm a\cos\theta$ **Rose Curve** $r = a\sin n\theta$ or $r = a\cos n\theta$ The number of leaves equals n when n is odd and is twice n when n is even. **Limaçon** ($b \neq a$) $r = a \pm b\sin\theta$ or $r = a \pm b\cos\theta$ $a > b$; no inner loop $a < b$; one inner loop

8.5 Exercises

Polar Coordinates

Exercises 1–4: Plot the points (r, θ).

1. (a) $(2, 0°)$ (b) $(3, 120°)$ (c) $(-1, 135°)$

2. (a) $(-2, 60°)$ (b) $(1, 120°)$ (c) $(2, 270°)$

3. (a) $\left(2, \frac{\pi}{3}\right)$ (b) $\left(-3, -\frac{\pi}{6}\right)$ (c) $\left(0, \frac{3\pi}{4}\right)$

4. (a) $(4, \pi)$ (b) $\left(1, \frac{\pi}{4}\right)$ (c) $\left(-3, -\frac{3\pi}{2}\right)$

Exercises 5–10: Determine if the pair of polar coordinates represents the same point.

5. $(2, 180°), (2, -180°)$ 6. $(1, 90°), (-1, -90°)$

7. $(3, 45°), (3, -45°)$ 8. $(-2, 135°), (2, -135°)$

9. $(0, 40°), (0, 50°)$ 10. $(-3, 30°), (3, 210°)$

Exercises 11–20: Change the polar coordinates (r, θ) to rectangular coordinates (x, y).

11. $(3, 45°)$ 12. $(-4, 225°)$

13. $(10, 90°)$ 14. $\left(-1, \frac{\pi}{3}\right)$

15. $(5, 2\pi)$ 16. $\left(-3, -\frac{\pi}{2}\right)$

17. $(-3, 60°)$ 18. $(4, \pi)$

19. $\left(-2, -\frac{3\pi}{2}\right)$ 20. $\left(10, \frac{2\pi}{3}\right)$

Exercises 21–26: For the point given in rectangular coordinates, find equivalent polar coordinates (r, θ) that satisfy the conditions.

(a) $r > 0$, $0° \leq \theta < 360°$
(b) $r < 0$, $-180° < \theta \leq 180°$

21. $(0, 3)$ 22. $(-3, 0)$

23. $(-1, -\sqrt{3})$ 24. $(\sqrt{3}, -1)$

25. $(3, -3)$ 26. $(2, 2)$

Exercises 27–30: For the point given in rectangular coordinates, find equivalent polar coordinates (r, θ) that satisfy $r > 0$ and $0 \leq \theta < 2\pi$. Approximate θ to the nearest hundredth of a radian.

27. $(7, 24)$ 28. $(3, -4)$

29. $(-5, 12)$ 30. $(11, -60)$

Graphs of Polar Equations

Exercises 31 and 32: Graph the equation.

31. $\theta = 60°$ 32. $\theta = -135°$

Exercises 33–40: Complete the following.
(a) Make a table of values with $\theta = 0°, 90°, 180°, 270°$.

(b) Plot the points from the table and graph the curve for $0° \leq \theta \leq 360°$.

33. $r = 2$ 34. $r = 1$

35. $r = 3 \sin \theta$ 36. $r = 2 - 2 \sin \theta$

37. $r = 2 + 2 \sin \theta$ 38. $r = 3 - 2 \cos \theta$

39. $r = 2 - \cos \theta$ 40. $r = 2 + \sin \theta$

Exercises 41–58: Graph the polar equation by hand.

41. $\theta = 60°$ 42. $\theta = -\frac{\pi}{4}$

43. $r = 3$ 44. $r = \cos \theta$

45. $r \sin \theta = 3$ 46. $r \cos \theta = -2$

47. $r = 2 \cos \theta$ 48. $r = -2 \sin \theta$

49. $r = \sin 2\theta$ 50. $r = \cos 2\theta$

51. $r = 3 + \cos \theta$ 52. $r = 3 - \sin \theta$

53. $r = 1 - 2 \sin \theta$ 54. $r = 1 + 2 \cos \theta$

55. $r = 3 \sin 2\theta$ 56. $r = 2 \cos 2\theta$

57. $r = 2 \cos 3\theta$ 58. $r = 4 \sin 3\theta$

Exercises 59–66: Write the equation in polar form.

59. $y = 3$ 60. $x = -5$

61. $y = x$ 62. $y = -\sqrt{3}$

63. $x^2 + y^2 = 9$ 64. $x^2 + y^2 = 36$

65. $x^2 + y^2 = 2x$ 66. $x^2 + y^2 = -4y$

Exercises 67–74: (Refer to Example 7.) Write the polar equation in terms of x and y.

67. $r = 3$ 68. $r = 5$

69. $r = 2 \sec \theta$ 70. $r = 2 \csc \theta$

71. $r = \dfrac{3}{2 \cos \theta + 4 \sin \theta}$ 72. $r = \dfrac{2}{5 \cos \theta - \sin \theta}$

73. $r = \cos \theta$ 74. $r = 2 \sin \theta$

Exercises 75–88: Graph the curve.

75. $r = 3 + 3 \cos \theta$ (cardioid)

76. $r = 2 - 2 \sin \theta$ (cardioid)

77. $r = 3 - 2 \sin \theta$ (limaçon)

78. $r = 4 + \cos \theta$ (limaçon)

79. $r = 2 - 4\cos\theta$ (limaçon with a loop)

80. $r = 1 + 2\sin\theta$ (limaçon with a loop)

81. $r = 4\sin\theta$ (circle)

82. $r = 2\cos 3\theta$ (three-leaved rose)

83. $r = 2\cos 5\theta$ (five-leaved rose)

84. $r = 3\sin 4\theta$ (eight-leaved rose)

85. $r = \frac{\theta}{2}$ (spiral)

86. $r = e^{\theta/4}$ (logarithmic spiral)

87. $r^2 = 2\sin 2\theta$ (lemniscate)

88. $r^2 = 4\cos 2\theta$ (lemniscate)

Solving Equations in Polar Coordinates

Exercises 89 and 90: Find values for θ that satisfy the equation $r_1 = r_2$, where $0° \le \theta \le 360°$. Check any solutions.

89. $r_1 = 3, r_2 = 2 + 2\sin\theta$

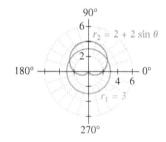

90. $r_1 = 1, r_2 = 2\cos\theta$

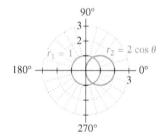

Exercises 91–94: Solve the polar equation $r_1 = r_2$, where $0° \le \theta \le 360°$,

(a) symbolically,   (b) graphically, and   (c) numerically.

91. $r_1 = 3, r_2 = 2 - 2\sin\theta$

92. $r_1 = 3, r_2 = 2 - \sin\theta$ **93.** $r_1 = 1, r_2 = 2\sin\theta$

94. $r_1 = 2 - \sin\theta, r_2 = 2 + \cos\theta$

Applications

*Exercises 95 and 96: **Planetary Orbits** (Refer to Example 9 and Table 8.7.) Graph the planetary orbits in a square viewing rectangle using polar coordinates.*

95. Saturn and Uranus   **96.** Jupiter and Neptune

*Exercises 97 and 98: **Planetary Orbits** (Refer to Example 9.)*

Planet	*a*	*e*
Mercury	0.39	0.206
Venus	0.78	0.007
Earth	1.00	0.017
Mars	1.52	0.093

Source: H. Karttunen et al., *Fundamental Astronomy.*

97. Graph the orbits of the four inner planets in the same square viewing rectangle.

98. NASA is planning future missions to Mars. Estimate graphically the closest distance possible between Earth and Mars.

*Exercises 99 and 100: **Broadcasting Patterns** Many times radio stations do not broadcast in all directions with the same intensity. To avoid interference with an existing station to the north, a new station may be licensed to broadcast only east and west. To create an east–west signal, two radio towers are sometimes used, as illustrated in the figure. Locations where the radio signal is received correspond to the interior of the curve defined by $r^2 = 40{,}000\cos 2\theta$, where the polar axis (or positive x-axis) points east.   (**Source:** R. Weidner and R. Sells, Elementary Classical Physics, Vol. 2.)*

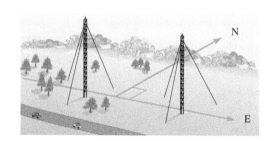

99. Graph $r^2 = 40{,}000\cos 2\theta$ for $0° \le \theta \le 360°$, where units are in miles. Assuming the radio towers are located near the pole, use the graph to describe the regions where the signal can be received and where the signal cannot be received.

100. (Refer to Exercise 99.) Suppose a radio signal pattern is given by $r^2 = 22{,}500\sin 2\theta$. Graph this pattern and interpret the results.

Writing about Mathematics

101. Explain why (r, θ) and $(-r, \theta + 180°)$ represent the same points in polar coordinates. Give two examples.

102. Give an example of a curve other than a circle that is more convenient to express in polar coordinates than in rectangular coordinates. Give an example of a curve that is more convenient to express using rectangular coordinates. Explain your reasoning.

Extended and Discovery Exercises

1. **Logarithmic Spiral**   Figure 8.100 shows a logarithmic spiral that can be described in rectangular coordinates by $y = x \tan (\ln (x^2 + y^2))$ and can be described in polar coordinates by the simpler equation $r = e^{\theta/2}$. Show that the first equation reduces to the second equation by assuming that $-\frac{\pi}{2} < \theta < \frac{\pi}{2}$. (*Hint*: Let $\tan \theta = \frac{y}{x}$ and $r^2 = x^2 + y^2$.)

2. **Polar Graphs**   Consider the graphs of $r = a \cos n\theta$ and $r = a \sin n\theta$, where n is a positive integer and θ is given by $0° \leq \theta < 360°$.

   (a) How many times are these graphs traced over when n is even?

   (b) How many times are these graphs traced over when n is odd?

8.6 Trigonometric Form and Roots of Complex Numbers

- Learn trigonometric form
- Find products and quotients of complex numbers
- Apply De Moivre's theorem
- Find roots of complex numbers

Introduction

One of the earliest encounters with the square root of a negative number was in A.D. 50, when Heron of Alexandria derived the expression $\sqrt{81 - 144}$. Square roots of negative numbers resulted in the invention (or discovery) of complex numbers. As late as the 16th and 17th centuries, mathematicians felt uneasy about negative numbers and square roots of negative numbers. The famous mathematician René Descartes rejected complex numbers and coined the term "imaginary" numbers.

In the historical development of our present-day number system, the introduction of new numbers was often met with resistance. Today, complex numbers are readily accepted and play an important role in the design of airplanes, ships, fractals, and electrical circuits. See Exercises 67 and 68.   (***Sources:*** M. Kline, *Mathematics: The Loss of Certainty; Historical Topics for the Mathematics Classroom, Thirty-first Yearbook*, NCTM.)

Trigonometric Form

Complex numbers were introduced in Section 3.3. Any complex number can be expressed in *standard form* as $a + bi$, where a and b are real numbers. The *real part* is a and the *imaginary part* is b.

Real numbers can be plotted on a number line. Since complex numbers are determined by both the real part a and the imaginary part b, we use the **complex plane** to plot complex numbers. The horizontal axis is the **real axis** and the vertical axis is the **imaginary axis**. For example, $2 + 3i$ can be plotted in the complex plane as the point $(2, 3)$, and $3 - 4i$ can be plotted as the point $(3, -4)$. See Figure 8.111.

The Complex Plane

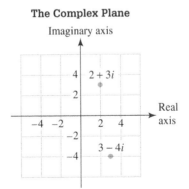

Figure 8.111

Finding Trigonometric Form

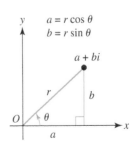

Figure 8.112

A second form for complex numbers is called *trigonometric form*, which uses the variables r and θ to locate a complex number. In Figure 8.112 we see that

$$\cos \theta = \frac{a}{r} \quad \text{and} \quad \sin \theta = \frac{b}{r}.$$

Finding Trigonometric Form

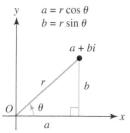

Figure 8.112 (Repeated)

Solving $\cos\theta = \frac{a}{r}$ and $\sin\theta = \frac{b}{r}$ for a and b gives

$$a = r\cos\theta \quad \text{and} \quad b = r\sin\theta. \quad \text{\small{Solve for a and b.}}$$

As a result, we can write the complex number $a + bi$ as follows.

$$a + bi = r\cos\theta + (r\sin\theta)i \quad \text{\small{Substitute.}}$$

Trigonometric form $$= r(\cos\theta + i\sin\theta) \quad \text{\small{Factor out r.}}$$

By the Pythagorean theorem, $r = \sqrt{a^2 + b^2}$. It also follows that

$$\tan\theta = \frac{b}{a} \quad (a \neq 0).$$

TRIGONOMETRIC FORM OF A COMPLEX NUMBER

The expression

$$r(\cos\theta + i\sin\theta)$$

is called a **trigonometric form** of the complex number $a + bi$, where $a = r\cos\theta$ and $b = r\sin\theta$. The number $r = \sqrt{a^2 + b^2}$ is the **modulus** of $a + bi$, and θ is the **argument** of $a + bi$.

NOTE The expression $\cos\theta + i\sin\theta$ can be written as cis θ. The expression $|a + bi|$ is sometimes used to denote the *modulus* of the complex number $a + bi$. The modulus equals the distance in the complex plane between the point $a + bi$ and the origin.

EXAMPLE 1 Converting standard form to trigonometric form

Find the trigonometric form for each complex number, where $0° \leq \theta < 360°$.
(a) $1 + i$
(b) $-1 - i\sqrt{3}$

SOLUTION
(a) Plot $1 + i$ in the complex plane, as shown in Figure 8.113. The modulus r is

$$r = \sqrt{1^2 + 1^2} = \sqrt{2}.$$

We can see that $\tan\theta = \frac{b}{a} = \frac{1}{1}$. Therefore $\theta = \tan^{-1} 1 = 45°$. The trigonometric form is

$$\sqrt{2}(\cos 45° + i\sin 45°).$$

Converting to Trigonometric Form

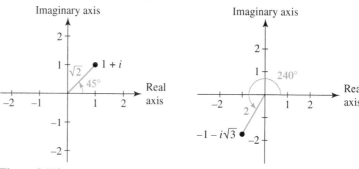

Figure 8.113   **Figure 8.114**

(b) Plot $-1 - i\sqrt{3}$, as shown in Figure 8.114. The modulus r is

$$r = \sqrt{(-1)^2 + (-\sqrt{3})^2} = 2.$$

The argument θ is in quadrant III and satisfies $\tan \theta = \frac{-\sqrt{3}}{-1} = \sqrt{3}$. The reference angle for θ is $\theta_R = \tan^{-1}(\sqrt{3}) = 60°$. Thus $\theta = 60° + 180° = 240°$ and the trigonometric form is $2(\cos 240° + i \sin 240°)$.

> **Now Try Exercises 13 and 19**

Graphing Calculators (Optional) Some calculators have the capability to convert the complex number $a + bi$ to trigonometric or **polar form**. This is illustrated in Figures 8.115 and 8.116, where the first computation gives the modulus and the second gives the argument. See Example 1. Notice that angles of 240° and −120° are coterminal angles. The value of θ is *not unique* in a trigonometric form. If θ_1 and θ_2 are *coterminal angles*, then

$$r(\cos \theta_1 + i \sin \theta_1) \qquad \text{and} \qquad r(\cos \theta_2 + i \sin \theta_2)$$

represent equivalent trigonometric forms.

Converting to Trigonometric Form

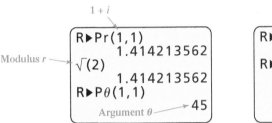

Figure 8.115 Degree Mode

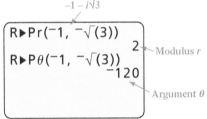

Figure 8.116 Degree Mode

MAKING CONNECTIONS

Vectors, Polar Coordinates, and Trigonometric Forms The following are equivalent concepts.

1. Finding the magnitude $\|\mathbf{v}\|$ and direction angle θ for $\mathbf{v} = \langle a, b \rangle$
2. Finding polar coordinates (r, θ), where $r > 0$, for the point (a, b)
3. Finding the trigonometric form $r(\cos \theta + i \sin \theta)$ for $a + bi$

For example:

1. Given $\mathbf{v} = \langle 3, 4 \rangle$, then $\|\mathbf{v}\| = \sqrt{3^2 + 4^2} = 5$ and $\theta = \tan^{-1}\frac{4}{3} \approx 53.1°$. It follows that $\mathbf{v} \approx \langle 5 \cos 53.1°, 5 \sin 53.1° \rangle$. See Figure 8.117.
2. Given the point $(3, 4)$, then $r = \sqrt{3^2 + 4^2} = 5$ and $\theta = \tan^{-1}\frac{4}{3} \approx 53.1°$. It follows that $P \approx (5, 53.1°)$ in polar coordinates. See Figure 8.118.
3. Given $3 + 4i$, then $r = \sqrt{3^2 + 4^2} = 5$ and $\theta = \tan^{-1}\frac{4}{3} \approx 53.1°$. It follows that $3 + 4i \approx 5(\cos 53.1° + i \sin 53.1°)$ in trigonometric form. See Figure 8.119.

See also Extended and Discovery Exercises 1–4 at the end of this section.

Vector

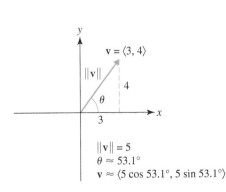

Figure 8.117

Polar Coordinates

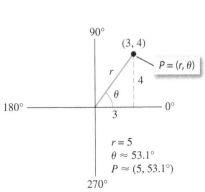

Figure 8.118

Trigonometric Form

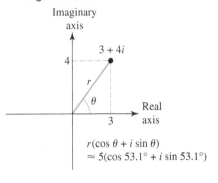

Figure 8.119

EXAMPLE 2 Converting trigonometric form to standard form

Write the complex number as $a + bi$, where a and b are real numbers.

(a) $4\left(\cos\frac{\pi}{2} + i\sin\frac{\pi}{2}\right)$

(b) $\sqrt{3}(\cos 150° + i\sin 150°)$

SOLUTION

(a) $4\left(\cos\frac{\pi}{2} + i\sin\frac{\pi}{2}\right) = 4(0 + i(1)) = 4i$

(b) $\sqrt{3}(\cos 150° + i\sin 150°) = \sqrt{3}\left(-\frac{\sqrt{3}}{2} + \frac{1}{2}i\right) = -\frac{3}{2} + \frac{\sqrt{3}}{2}i$

Now Try Exercises 27 and 31

Products and Quotients of Complex Numbers

If two complex numbers, z_1 and z_2, are expressed in trigonometric form, it is straightforward to find either their product or their quotient. To see this, let

$$z_1 = r_1(\cos\theta_1 + i\sin\theta_1) \quad \text{and} \quad z_2 = r_2(\cos\theta_2 + i\sin\theta_2).$$

Then

$$z_1 z_2 = r_1(\cos\theta_1 + i\sin\theta_1) \cdot r_2(\cos\theta_2 + i\sin\theta_2)$$
$$= r_1 r_2(\cos\theta_1\cos\theta_2 + i\cos\theta_1\sin\theta_2 + i\sin\theta_1\cos\theta_2 + i^2\sin\theta_1\sin\theta_2)$$
$$= r_1 r_2((\cos\theta_1\cos\theta_2 - \sin\theta_1\sin\theta_2) + i(\cos\theta_1\sin\theta_2 + \sin\theta_1\cos\theta_2)).$$

Using the sum identities for cosine and sine, we can simplify the last expression to

$$z_1 z_2 = r_1 r_2(\cos(\theta_1 + \theta_2) + i\sin(\theta_1 + \theta_2)).$$

Using similar reasoning, it can be shown that

$$\frac{z_1}{z_2} = \frac{r_1}{r_2}(\cos(\theta_1 - \theta_2) + i\sin(\theta_1 - \theta_2)).$$

These results are summarized in the following box.

PRODUCTS AND QUOTIENTS OF COMPLEX NUMBERS

Let $z_1 = r_1(\cos\theta_1 + i\sin\theta_1)$ and $z_2 = r_2(\cos\theta_2 + i\sin\theta_2)$. Then

$$z_1 z_2 = r_1 r_2(\cos(\theta_1 + \theta_2) + i\sin(\theta_1 + \theta_2))$$

$$\frac{z_1}{z_2} = \frac{r_1}{r_2}(\cos(\theta_1 - \theta_2) + i\sin(\theta_1 - \theta_2)), \quad r_2 \neq 0.$$

EXAMPLE 3 Finding products and quotients

Find the product and quotient of

$$z_1 = 4(\cos 45° + i\sin 45°) \quad \text{and} \quad z_2 = 2(\cos 135° + i\sin 135°).$$

Express the answer in standard form.

SOLUTION

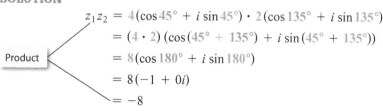

$$z_1 z_2 = 4(\cos 45° + i\sin 45°) \cdot 2(\cos 135° + i\sin 135°)$$
$$= (4 \cdot 2)(\cos(45° + 135°) + i\sin(45° + 135°))$$
Product
$$= 8(\cos 180° + i\sin 180°)$$
$$= 8(-1 + 0i)$$
$$= -8$$

$$\frac{z_1}{z_2} = \frac{4(\cos 45° + i \sin 45°)}{2(\cos 135° + i \sin 135°)}$$

$$= \frac{4}{2}(\cos(45° - 135°) + i \sin(45° - 135°))$$

Quotient

$$= 2(\cos(-90°) + i \sin(-90°))$$

$$= 2(0 + -1i)$$

$$= -2i$$

Now Try Exercise 35

Fractals and Complex Numbers   During the past 30 years, computer graphics and complex numbers have made it possible to produce many beautiful fractals. In 1977, Benoit B. Mandelbrot first used the term *fractal*. Largely because of his efforts, fractal geometry has become a new field of study. A fractal is an enchanting geometric figure with an endless self-similarity property, repeating itself infinitely with ever decreasing dimensions. If you look at smaller and smaller portions of the figure, you will continue to see the whole—much like when you look into two parallel mirrors that are facing each other. Not only do fractals have aesthetic appeal, they also have applications in science. An example of a fractal is the *Mandelbrot set* shown in Figure 8.120.   (***Source:*** B. Mandelbrot, *The Fractal Geometry of Nature.*)

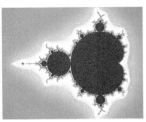

Figure 8.120

EXAMPLE 4   Analyzing the Mandelbrot set

The fractal called the Mandelbrot set is shown in Figure 8.120. To determine if a complex number $z = a + bi$ is in the Mandelbrot set, we can perform the following sequence of calculations. Let

$$z_0 = z$$
$$z_1 = z_0^2 + z_0$$
$$z_2 = z_1^2 + z_0$$
$$z_3 = z_2^2 + z_0$$

and so on. If the modulus of any z_k ever exceeds 2, then z is not in the Mandelbrot set; otherwise, z is in the Mandelbrot set. Determine if the complex number belongs to the Mandelbrot set.   (***Source:*** F. Hill, *Computer Graphics.*)
(a) $z = 1 + i$ **(b)** $z = 0.5i$

SOLUTION
(a) Let $z_0 = 1 + i$. Then

$$z_1 = (1 + i)^2 + (1 + i) = 1 + 3i. \qquad z_1 = z_0^2 + z_0$$

Since the modulus of z_1 is

$$|1 + 3i| = \sqrt{1^2 + 3^2} = \sqrt{10} > 2,$$

the complex number $1 + i$ is not in the Mandelbrot set.
(b) Let $z_0 = 0.5i$. Then

$$z_1 = (0.5i)^2 + 0.5i = -0.25 + 0.5i$$
$$z_2 = (-0.25 + 0.5i)^2 + 0.5i = -0.1875 + 0.25i$$
$$z_3 = (-0.1875 + 0.25i)^2 + 0.5i \approx -0.0273 + 0.406i.$$

The modulus of each consecutive z_k never exceeds 2. Thus $0.5i$ is in the Mandelbrot set. You may find it helpful to use a calculator to perform these calculations. See Figure 8.121.

Now Try Exercises 63 and 65

$z_0^2 + z_0$

```
(.5i)^2+(.5i)
            -.25+.5i
Ans^2+(.5i)
            -.1875+.25i
-.02734375+.406...
```

Figure 8.121

De Moivre's Theorem

If a complex number z is expressed in trigonometric form, then z^n for any positive integer n can be computed easily. Let $z = r(\cos\theta + i\sin\theta)$ and consider the following.

$$z^2 = r(\cos\theta + i\sin\theta) \cdot r(\cos\theta + i\sin\theta)$$
$$= r^2(\cos(\theta + \theta) + i\sin(\theta + \theta))$$
$$= r^2(\cos 2\theta + i\sin 2\theta)$$
$$z^3 = zz^2$$
$$= r(\cos\theta + i\sin\theta) \cdot r^2(\cos 2\theta + i\sin 2\theta)$$
$$= r^3(\cos 3\theta + i\sin 3\theta)$$

In general it can be shown that

$$z^n = r^n(\cos n\theta + i\sin n\theta).$$

This result is summarized in the following theorem, which is due to Abraham De Moivre (1667–1754), a French Huguenot who was a close friend of Isaac Newton. This theorem has become a keystone of analytic trigonometry. (***Source:*** H. Eves, *An Introduction to the History of Mathematics.*)

DE MOIVRE'S THEOREM

Let $z = r(\cos\theta + i\sin\theta)$ and n be a positive integer. Then

$$z^n = r^n(\cos n\theta + i\sin n\theta).$$

EXAMPLE 5 Finding a power of a complex number

Use De Moivre's theorem to evaluate $(1 + i)^8$ and express the result in standard form.

SOLUTION From Example 1(a), the trigonometric form of $z = 1 + i$ is

$$z = \sqrt{2}(\cos 45° + i\sin 45°).$$

By De Moivre's theorem,

$$z^8 = (\sqrt{2})^8(\cos(8 \cdot 45°) + i\sin(8 \cdot 45°))$$
$$= 16(\cos 360° + i\sin 360°)$$
$$= 16(1 + 0i)$$
$$= 16.$$

Now Try Exercise 47

Roots of Complex Numbers

A number w is the ***nth root*** of a number z if $w^n = z$. De Moivre's theorem can be used to find roots of complex numbers. To see this, let the trigonometric forms of w and z be

$$w = s(\cos\alpha + i\sin\alpha) \qquad \text{and} \qquad z = r(\cos\theta + i\sin\theta).$$

Then, by De Moivre's theorem, $w^n = z$ implies that

$$s^n(\cos n\alpha + i\sin n\alpha) = r(\cos\theta + i\sin\theta).$$

Thus $s^n = r$, or $s = \sqrt[n]{r}$. Furthermore, the following two equations must be satisfied.

$$\cos n\alpha = \cos\theta \qquad \text{and} \qquad \sin n\alpha = \sin\theta$$

Since the cosine and sine functions have period $360°$, $n\alpha = \theta + 360° \cdot k$ for some integer k, or

$$\alpha = \frac{\theta + 360° \cdot k}{n}.$$

Substituting these results in the trigonometric form for w gives

$$w_k = \sqrt[n]{r}\left(\cos\frac{\theta + 360° \cdot k}{n} + i\sin\frac{\theta + 360° \cdot k}{n}\right).$$

We obtain a unique value of w_k for $k = 0, 1, 2, \ldots, n - 1$. This discussion is summarized in the following box.

ROOTS OF A COMPLEX NUMBER

Let $z = r(\cos\theta + i\sin\theta)$ be a nonzero complex number and n be any positive integer. Then z has exactly n distinct nth roots given by

$$w_k = \sqrt[n]{r}\left(\cos\frac{\theta + 360° \cdot k}{n} + i\sin\frac{\theta + 360° \cdot k}{n}\right),$$

where $k = 0, 1, 2, \ldots, n - 1$. If radian measure is used, then let

$$w_k = \sqrt[n]{r}\left(\cos\frac{\theta + 2\pi k}{n} + i\sin\frac{\theta + 2\pi k}{n}\right).$$

EXAMPLE 6   Finding cube roots of a complex number

Find the three cube roots of $8i$. Check your results with a calculator.

SOLUTION

Getting Started   First write the complex number $8i$ in trigonometric form.

$$8i = 8(\cos 90° + i\sin 90°)$$

The three cube roots of $8i$ can be found by letting $n = 3, r = 8, \theta = 90°$, and $k = 0, 1, 2.$ ▶

$k=0$
$$w_0 = \sqrt[3]{8}\left(\cos\frac{90° + 360° \cdot 0}{3} + i\sin\frac{90° + 360° \cdot 0}{3}\right)$$
$$= 2(\cos 30° + i\sin 30°)$$
$$= 2\left(\frac{\sqrt{3}}{2} + \frac{1}{2}i\right)$$
$$= \sqrt{3} + i$$

$k=1$
$$w_1 = \sqrt[3]{8}\left(\cos\frac{90° + 360° \cdot 1}{3} + i\sin\frac{90° + 360° \cdot 1}{3}\right)$$
$$= 2(\cos 150° + i\sin 150°)$$
$$= 2\left(-\frac{\sqrt{3}}{2} + \frac{1}{2}i\right)$$
$$= -\sqrt{3} + i$$

$k=2$
$$w_2 = \sqrt[3]{8}\left(\cos\frac{90° + 360° \cdot 2}{3} + i\sin\frac{90° + 360° \cdot 2}{3}\right)$$
$$= 2(\cos 270° + i\sin 270°)$$
$$= 2(0 - i)$$
$$= -2i$$

```
(√(3)+i)^3
                8i
(⁻√(3)+i)^3
                8i
(⁻2i)^3
                8i
```

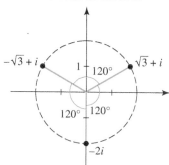

Figure 8.122

CLASS DISCUSSION

One cube root of the complex number $z = -1$ is $w = -1$. Find the other two cube roots of z graphically.

The three cube roots of $8i$ are $\sqrt{3} + i$, $-\sqrt{3} + i$, and $-2i$. These can be checked using a calculator, as shown in Figure 8.122.

Now Try Exercise 59

Graphical Interpretation If the three cube roots of $8i$ are plotted in the complex plane, they lie on a circle of radius 2, equally spaced 120° apart, as shown in Figure 8.123. In general, the nth roots of a complex number $z = r(\cos\theta + i\sin\theta)$ will lie equally spaced on a circle of radius $\sqrt[n]{r}$.

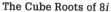

The Cube Roots of 8i

Figure 8.123

EXAMPLE 7 Finding square roots of a complex number

Find the two square roots of $1 + i\sqrt{3}$.

SOLUTION First write the complex number $1 + i\sqrt{3}$ in trigonometric form.

$$1 + i\sqrt{3} = 2\left(\cos\frac{\pi}{3} + i\sin\frac{\pi}{3}\right)$$

The two square roots of $1 + i\sqrt{3}$ can be found by letting $n = 2, r = 2, \theta = \frac{\pi}{3}$, and $k = 0, 1$.

$k=0$

$$\begin{aligned} w_0 &= \sqrt{2}\left(\cos\frac{\frac{\pi}{3} + 2\pi\cdot 0}{2} + i\sin\frac{\frac{\pi}{3} + 2\pi\cdot 0}{2}\right) \\ &= \sqrt{2}\left(\cos\frac{\pi}{6} + i\sin\frac{\pi}{6}\right) \\ &= \sqrt{2}\left(\frac{\sqrt{3}}{2} + \frac{1}{2}i\right) \\ &= \frac{\sqrt{6}}{2} + \frac{\sqrt{2}}{2}i \end{aligned}$$

$k=1$

$$\begin{aligned} w_1 &= \sqrt{2}\left(\cos\frac{\frac{\pi}{3} + 2\pi\cdot 1}{2} + i\sin\frac{\frac{\pi}{3} + 2\pi\cdot 1}{2}\right) \\ &= \sqrt{2}\left(\cos\frac{7\pi}{6} + i\sin\frac{7\pi}{6}\right) \\ &= \sqrt{2}\left(-\frac{\sqrt{3}}{2} - \frac{1}{2}i\right) \\ &= -\frac{\sqrt{6}}{2} - \frac{\sqrt{2}}{2}i \end{aligned}$$

Thus the two square roots of $1 + i\sqrt{3}$ are $\frac{\sqrt{6}}{2} + \frac{\sqrt{2}}{2}i$ and $-\frac{\sqrt{6}}{2} - \frac{\sqrt{2}}{2}i$.

Now Try Exercise 55

8.6 Putting It All Together

The following table summarizes some of the important topics in this section.

CONCEPT	EXPLANATION	EXAMPLES
Trigonometric form	If $z = a + bi$, then its trigonometric form is $z = r(\cos\theta + i\sin\theta)$, where $r = \sqrt{a^2 + b^2}$ and $\tan\theta = \dfrac{b}{a}$ $(a \neq 0)$. The modulus is r and the argument is θ.	If $z = 1 + i\sqrt{3}$, then $$r = \sqrt{1^2 + (\sqrt{3})^2} = 2$$ and $\theta = \tan^{-1}\dfrac{\sqrt{3}}{1} = 60°$. Thus $z = 2(\cos 60° + i\sin 60°)$.
Products and quotients	Let $z_1 = r_1(\cos\theta_1 + i\sin\theta_1)$ and $z_2 = r_2(\cos\theta_2 + i\sin\theta_2)$. Then $$z_1 z_2 = r_1 r_2(\cos(\theta_1 + \theta_2) + i\sin(\theta_1 + \theta_2))$$ and for $r_2 \neq 0$, $$\frac{z_1}{z_2} = \frac{r_1}{r_2}(\cos(\theta_1 - \theta_2) + i\sin(\theta_1 - \theta_2)).$$	If $z_1 = 3(\cos 66° + i\sin 66°)$ and $z_2 = 2(\cos 22° + i\sin 22°)$, then $$z_1 z_2 = 6(\cos 88° + i\sin 88°)$$ and $$\frac{z_1}{z_2} = \frac{3}{2}(\cos 44° + i\sin 44°).$$
De Moivre's theorem	Let $z = r(\cos\theta + i\sin\theta)$. Then $$z^n = r^n(\cos n\theta + i\sin n\theta).$$	If $z = 2(\cos 7° + i\sin 7°)$, then $$z^3 = 8(\cos 21° + i\sin 21°).$$
Roots of complex numbers	Let $z = r(\cos\theta + i\sin\theta)$ and n be any positive integer. Then the nth roots of z are given by $$w_k = \sqrt[n]{r}\left(\cos\frac{\theta + 360° \cdot k}{n} + i\sin\frac{\theta + 360° \cdot k}{n}\right),$$ where $k = 0, 1, 2, \ldots, n-1$.	The three cube roots of $8 = 8(\cos 0° + i\sin 0°)$ are as follows. $$w_0 = \sqrt[3]{8}\left(\cos\frac{0° + 360° \cdot 0}{3} + i\sin\frac{0° + 360° \cdot 0}{3}\right)$$ $$= 2$$ $$w_1 = \sqrt[3]{8}\left(\cos\frac{0° + 360° \cdot 1}{3} + i\sin\frac{0° + 360° \cdot 1}{3}\right)$$ $$= 2(\cos 120° + i\sin 120°) = -1 + i\sqrt{3}$$ $$w_2 = \sqrt[3]{8}\left(\cos\frac{0° + 360° \cdot 2}{3} + i\sin\frac{0° + 360° \cdot 2}{3}\right)$$ $$= 2(\cos 240° + i\sin 240°) = -1 - i\sqrt{3}$$

8.6 Exercises

The Complex Plane

Exercises 1–4: Plot the numbers in the complex plane.

1. (a) $3 + 2i$ (b) $-1 + i$ (c) $3i$

2. (a) $-2i$ (b) $2 + 2i$ (c) $2 - 2i$

3. (a) -3 (b) $4 - 2i$ (c) $-1 - 3i$

4. (a) $-1 - i$ (b) $4 + 3i$ (c) 4

Trigonometric Form

Exercises 5–12: Find the modulus of the number.

5. $1 + i$ 6. $3 - 4i$

7. $12 - 5i$ 8. $-24 + 7i$

9. -6 10. $15i$

11. $2 - 3i$ 12. $11 - 60i$

Exercises 13–22: Write the number in trigonometric form. Let $0° \le \theta < 360°$.

13. $-1 + i$

14. $1 - i$

15. 5

16. -3

17. $4i$

18. $-i$

19. $-1 + i\sqrt{3}$

20. $-\sqrt{2} - i\sqrt{2}$

21. $\sqrt{3} + i$

22. $-\frac{\sqrt{3}}{2} + \frac{1}{2}i$

Exercises 23–26: Write the number in trigonometric form. Let $0 \le \theta < 2\pi$.

23. -2

24. $4i$

25. $-2 + 2i$

26. $1 + i\sqrt{3}$

Exercises 27–34: Write the number in standard form.

27. $5(\cos 180° + i \sin 180°)$

28. $3(\cos 90° + i \sin 90°)$ **29.** $2(\cos 45° + i \sin 45°)$

30. $\cos 150° + i \sin 150°$ **31.** $2\left(\cos \frac{\pi}{6} + i \sin \frac{\pi}{6}\right)$

32. $4\left(\cos \frac{3\pi}{2} + i \sin \frac{3\pi}{2}\right)$ **33.** $3(\cos 2\pi + i \sin 2\pi)$

34. $5\left(\cos \frac{3\pi}{4} + i \sin \frac{3\pi}{4}\right)$

Exercises 35–40: Find $z_1 z_2$ and $\frac{z_1}{z_2}$. Express your answer in standard form.

35. $z_1 = 9(\cos 45° + i \sin 45°)$,
$z_2 = 3(\cos 15° + i \sin 15°)$

36. $z_1 = 5(\cos 90° + i \sin 90°)$,
$z_2 = 2(\cos 30° + i \sin 30°)$

37. $z_1 = 6\left(\cos \frac{3\pi}{4} + i \sin \frac{3\pi}{4}\right)$,
$z_2 = \cos \frac{\pi}{4} + i \sin \frac{\pi}{4}$

38. $z_1 = 4(\cos 300° + i \sin 300°)$,
$z_2 = 2(\cos 60° + i \sin 60°)$

39. $z_1 = \cos 15° + i \sin 15°$,
$z_2 = \cos\left(-\frac{\pi}{4}\right) + i \sin\left(-\frac{\pi}{4}\right)$

40. $z_1 = 11\left(\cos \frac{2\pi}{3} + i \sin \frac{2\pi}{3}\right)$,
$z_2 = 22(\cos 30° + i \sin 30°)$

Powers of Complex Numbers

Exercises 41–46: Use De Moivre's theorem to evaluate the expression. Write the result in standard form.

41. $(2(\cos 30° + i \sin 30°))^3$

42. $(3(\cos 45° + i \sin 45°))^4$

43. $(\cos 10° + i \sin 10°)^{36}$

44. $(\cos 1° + i \sin 1°)^{90}$

45. $(5(\cos 60° + i \sin 60°))^2$

46. $(2(\cos 90° + i \sin 90°))^5$

Exercises 47–50: Use De Moivre's theorem to evaluate the expression. Write the result in standard form and check it using a calculator.

47. $(1 + i)^3$ **48.** $(3i)^4$

49. $(\sqrt{3} + i)^5$ **50.** $(2 - 2i)^6$

Roots of Complex Numbers

Exercises 51–62: Find the following roots and express them in standard form. Check your results with a calculator.

51. The square roots of $4(\cos 120° + i \sin 120°)$

52. The cube roots of $27(\cos 180° + i \sin 180°)$

53. The cube roots of $\cos 180° + i \sin 180°$

54. The fourth roots of $16(\cos 240° + i \sin 240°)$

55. The square roots of i

56. The cube roots of 1

57. The cube roots of -8

58. The square roots of $-4i$

59. The cube roots of $64i$

60. The fourth roots of -1

61. The fourth roots of 81

62. The square roots of $-1 + i\sqrt{3}$

Fractals

Exercises 63–66: **Mandelbrot Set** *(Refer to Example 4.) Determine if the complex number belongs to the Mandelbrot set.*

63. $-0.4i$ **64.** $0.5 + i$

65. $1 + i$ **66.** $-0.2 + 0.2i$

Applications

67. Electrical Circuits *Impedance* is a measure of the opposition to the flow of current in an electrical circuit. It consists of two parts called the *resistance* and the *reactance*. Light bulbs add resistance to an electrical circuit, and reactance occurs when electricity passes through coils of wire like those found in electric motors. Impedance Z in ohms (Ω) may be expressed as a complex number, where the real part represents the resistance and the imaginary part represents the reactance. For example, if the resistive part is 3 ohms and the reactive part is 4 ohms, then the impedance could be described by the complex number $Z = 3 + 4i$. The modulus of Z gives the total impedance in ohms. In a series circuit like the one shown in the figure, the total impedance is the sum of the individual impedances. (*Source:* R. Smith and R. Dorf, *Circuits, Devices and Systems.*)

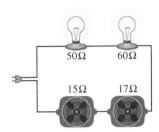

(a) The circuit contains two light bulbs and two electric motors. If it is assumed that the light bulbs represent resistance and the motors represent reactance, express impedance as $Z = a + bi$.

(b) Find total impedance in ohms by calculating the modulus of Z.

68. Electrical Circuits   (Continuation of Exercise 67.) In the parallel electrical circuit shown in the figure, impedance Z is given by

$$Z = \frac{1}{\frac{1}{Z_1} + \frac{1}{Z_2}},$$

where Z_1 and Z_2 represent the impedances for the two branches of the circuit.   (*Source:* G. Wilcox and C. Hesselberth, *Electricity for Engineering Technology.*)

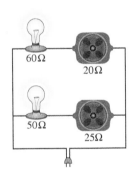

(a) Find Z.

(b) Find total impedance to the nearest tenth of an ohm by calculating the modulus of Z.

Writing about Mathematics

69. Explain how to find a trigonometric form of a complex number $a + bi$. Give an example. Is trigonometric form unique for a given complex number z? Explain.

70. Suppose that one fourth root w of a complex number z is known. Explain how to find the other fourth roots of z graphically.

Extended and Discovery Exercises

Exercises 1–4: **Making Connections**   *Complete the following. Choose angles in* $[0°, 360°)$ *and round to the nearest tenth.*

(a) Write the vector in terms of its magnitude and direction angle.
(b) Write the point (a, b) in polar coordinates.
(c) Write the complex number $a + bi$ in trigonometric form.

1. $\langle \sqrt{3}, 1 \rangle, (\sqrt{3}, 1), \sqrt{3} + i$

2. $\langle 5, 12 \rangle, (5, 12), 5 + 12i$

3. $\langle 4, -3 \rangle, (4, -3), 4 - 3i$

4. $\langle -7, 24 \rangle, (-7, 24), -7 + 24i$

---

1. Plot the following points (r, θ) on a polar grid.
   (a) $(2, 30°)$ (b) $(3, -60°)$ (c) $(-4, 120°)$

2. Graph the equation.
   (a) $r = 2$ (b) $\theta = -\frac{\pi}{4}$
   (c) $r = 3 + 3\cos\theta$ (d) $r = 3\cos 2\theta$

3. Plot the numbers in the complex plane.
   (a) $-3 + 2i$ (b) $-4 - 3i$

4. Find the trigonometric form of $1 + i\sqrt{3}$.

5. Find the three cube roots of i.

8 Summary

CONCEPT	EXPLANATION AND EXAMPLES

Section 8.1 Law of Sines

Law of Sines

$$\frac{\sin\alpha}{a} = \frac{\sin\beta}{b} = \frac{\sin\gamma}{c}, \quad \text{or} \quad \frac{a}{\sin\alpha} = \frac{b}{\sin\beta} = \frac{c}{\sin\gamma}$$

The law of sines can be used to solve triangles given ASA, AAS, or SSA. SSA is called the ambiguous case and can have zero, one, or two solutions.

Example: Given $\beta = 32°$, $\gamma = 46°$, and $c = 10$, find b.
We are given AAS, as illustrated in the figure.

$$\frac{b}{\sin\beta} = \frac{c}{\sin\gamma} \quad \text{implies that} \quad b = \frac{10\sin 32°}{\sin 46°} \approx 7.37.$$

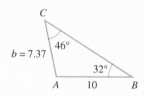

Section 8.2 Law of Cosines

Law of Cosines

$$a^2 = b^2 + c^2 - 2bc\cos\alpha$$
$$b^2 = a^2 + c^2 - 2ac\cos\beta$$
$$c^2 = a^2 + b^2 - 2ab\cos\gamma$$

The law of cosines can be used to solve triangles given SAS or SSS. Each situation results in a unique solution.

Example: Given $a = 5$, $b = 6$, and $c = 7$, find α.
We are given SSS, as illustrated in the figure.
$a^2 = b^2 + c^2 - 2bc\cos\alpha$ implies that

$$\cos\alpha = \frac{b^2 + c^2 - a^2}{2bc} = \frac{6^2 + 7^2 - 5^2}{2(6)(7)} \approx 0.714.$$

Thus $\alpha \approx \cos^{-1}(0.714) \approx 44.4°$.

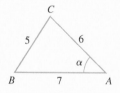

Section 8.3 Vectors

Vectors

A vector is a directed line segment that has both magnitude (length) and direction. Three different representations for a vector are

$$\mathbf{v} = \langle a_1, a_2 \rangle, \quad \mathbf{v} = a_1\mathbf{i} + a_2\mathbf{j}, \quad \text{and} \quad \mathbf{v} = \overrightarrow{PQ}.$$

Horizontal component $= a_1$; *vertical component* $= a_2$

Magnitude: $\|\mathbf{v}\| = \sqrt{a_1{}^2 + a_2{}^2}$

Direction angle: The positive angle θ $(0° \le \theta < 360°)$ between the x-axis and the position vector $\mathbf{v}$, where

$$\mathbf{v} = \langle \|\mathbf{v}\|\cos\theta, \|\mathbf{v}\|\sin\theta \rangle.$$

The horizontal component is $\|\mathbf{v}\|\cos\theta$ and the vertical component is $\|\mathbf{v}\|\sin\theta$.

CONCEPT	EXPLANATION AND EXAMPLES

Section 8.3 Vectors (CONTINUED)

Calculations Involving Vectors

Let $\mathbf{a} = \langle a_1, a_2 \rangle$ and $\mathbf{b} = \langle b_1, b_2 \rangle$.

Sum: $\mathbf{a} + \mathbf{b} = \langle a_1 + b_1, a_2 + b_2 \rangle$
Difference: $\mathbf{a} - \mathbf{b} = \langle a_1 - b_1, a_2 - b_2 \rangle$
Scalar Multiple: $k\mathbf{a} = \langle ka_1, ka_2 \rangle$
Dot Product: $\mathbf{a} \cdot \mathbf{b} = a_1 b_1 + a_2 b_2$

Angle θ between $\mathbf{a}$ and $\mathbf{b}$: $\theta = \cos^{-1}\left(\dfrac{\mathbf{a} \cdot \mathbf{b}}{\|\mathbf{a}\| \, \|\mathbf{b}\|} \right)$

Work

If a constant force $\mathbf{F}$ is applied to an object that moves along a vector $\mathbf{D}$, then the work done is $W = \mathbf{F} \cdot \mathbf{D}$.

Section 8.4 Parametric Equations

Plane Curve and Parametric Equations

A plane curve can be defined by the parametric equations $x = f(t)$ and $y = g(t)$, where f and g are continuous and t is the parameter.

Example: $x = \cos t, y = \sin t; 0 \leq t \leq 2\pi$
Since $x^2 + y^2 = \cos^2 t + \sin^2 t = 1$,
this curve describes the unit circle.
See the figure.

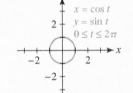

Section 8.5 Polar Equations

Polar Coordinates and Equations

Points are identified using r and θ instead of x and y. Polar equations are plotted in the polar plane, where the pole corresponds to the origin and the polar axis corresponds to the positive x-axis. Polar coordinates are not unique.

Example: $r = \cos 5\theta$ (rose curve with 5 leaves)

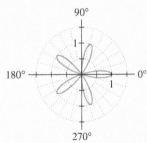

Section 8.6 Trigonometric Form and Roots of Complex Numbers

Trigonometric Form and Complex Numbers

The expression $r(\cos \theta + i \sin \theta)$ is the trigonometric form of $a + bi$, where $a = r \cos \theta$ and $b = r \sin \theta$.

Modulus: $|z| = r = \sqrt{a^2 + b^2}$; *argument*: θ

Example: $z = 2(\cos 30° + i \sin 30°) = \sqrt{3} + i$
Modulus: $r = 2$; argument: $\theta = 30°$

CONCEPT	EXPLANATION AND EXAMPLES

Section 8.6 Trigonometric Form and Roots of Complex Numbers (CONTINUED)

Operations on Complex Numbers and Trigonometric Form

Let $z_1 = r_1(\cos\theta_1 + i\sin\theta_1)$ and $z_2 = r_2(\cos\theta_2 + i\sin\theta_2)$.

$$z_1 z_2 = r_1 r_2 (\cos(\theta_1 + \theta_2) + i\sin(\theta_1 + \theta_2))$$

$$\frac{z_1}{z_2} = \frac{r_1}{r_2}(\cos(\theta_1 - \theta_2) + i\sin(\theta_1 - \theta_2))$$

$$z_1{}^n = r_1{}^n(\cos(n\theta_1) + i\sin(n\theta_1)) \qquad \text{De Moivre's theorem}$$

Example: Let $z_1 = 6(\cos 120 + i\sin 120°)$ and $z_2 = 2(\cos 80° + i\sin 80°)$.

$$z_1 z_2 = 12(\cos 200° + i\sin 200°)$$

$$\frac{z_1}{z_2} = 3(\cos 40° + i\sin 40°)$$

$$z_1{}^4 = 6^4(\cos(4 \cdot 120°) + i\sin(4 \cdot 120°))$$

Roots of Complex Numbers

If $z = r(\cos\theta + i\sin\theta)$, then the *n*th roots of *z* are given by

$$w_k = \sqrt[n]{r}\left(\cos\frac{\theta + 360° \cdot k}{n} + i\sin\frac{\theta + 360° \cdot k}{n}\right),$$

where $k = 0, 1, 2, \ldots, n - 1$.

Example: Let $z = 4i = 4(\cos 90° + i\sin 90°)$.
The square roots of *z* are as follows.

$$w_k = \sqrt{4}\left(\cos\frac{90° + 360° \cdot k}{2} + i\sin\frac{90° + 360° \cdot k}{2}\right) \quad \text{for } k = 0 \text{ and } 1$$

Simplifying gives

$$w_0 = 2(\cos 45° + i\sin 45°) = \sqrt{2} + i\sqrt{2} \quad \text{and}$$
$$w_1 = 2(\cos 225° + i\sin 225°) = -\sqrt{2} - i\sqrt{2}.$$

8 Review Exercises

Exercises 1–4: Solve the triangle. Approximate values to the nearest tenth.

1.

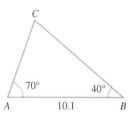

2.

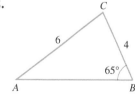

3.

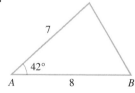

4.

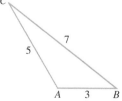

Exercises 5–10: Solve the triangle. Approximate values to the nearest tenth.

5. $\alpha = 19°, \beta = 46°, b = 13$

6. $\alpha = 30°, b = 10, a = 8$

7. $\gamma = 20°, b = 8, c = 11$

8. $\alpha = 70°, b = 17, a = 5$

9. $b = 23, \gamma = 35°, a = 18$

10. $a = 65, b = 45, c = 32$

Exercises 11–14: Approximate the area of the triangle to the nearest tenth.

11. $a = 12.3, b = 13.7, \gamma = 39°$

12. $\alpha = 40°, \beta = 55°, c = 67$

13. $a = 34, b = 67, c = 53$

14. $a = 2.1, b = 1.7, c = 2.2$

Exercises 15 and 16: Complete the following for vector **v**.

(a) Give the horizontal and vertical components.
(b) Find $\|\mathbf{v}\|$.
(c) Graph **v** *and interpret* $\|\mathbf{v}\|$.

15. $\mathbf{v} = \langle 3, 4 \rangle$ **16.** $\mathbf{v} = -5\mathbf{i} + 12\mathbf{j}$

Exercises 17 and 18: A vector **v** *has initial point P and terminal point Q.*

(a) Graph $\overrightarrow{PQ}$.
(b) Write $\overrightarrow{PQ}$ *as* $\mathbf{v} = a_1\mathbf{i} + a_2\mathbf{j}$.
(c) Find $\|\overrightarrow{PQ}\|$.

17. $P = (0, 0), Q = (-2, -4)$

18. $P = (3, 2), Q = (-3, -1)$

Exercises 19–22: Find each of the following.

(a) $2\mathbf{a}$ *(b)* $\mathbf{a} - 3\mathbf{b}$ *(c)* $\mathbf{a} \cdot \mathbf{b}$
(d) The angle θ *between* **a** *and* **b** *rounded to a tenth of a degree*

19. $\mathbf{a} = \langle 3, -2 \rangle, \mathbf{b} = \langle 1, 1 \rangle$

20. $\mathbf{a} = \langle 3, 2 \rangle, \mathbf{b} = \langle -2, -3 \rangle$

21. $\mathbf{a} = 2\mathbf{i} + 2\mathbf{j}, \mathbf{b} = \mathbf{i} + \mathbf{j}$

22. $\mathbf{a} = \mathbf{i} - 2\mathbf{j}, \mathbf{b} = 2\mathbf{i} + \mathbf{j}$

23. Resultant Force   Use the parallelogram rule to find the magnitude of the resultant force of the two forces shown in the figure.

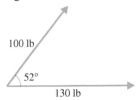

100 lb

52°

130 lb

24. Work   Find the work done when $\mathbf{F} = 300\mathbf{i} + 400\mathbf{j}$ is applied to an object that moves along the vector $\mathbf{D} = 10\mathbf{i} - 2\mathbf{j}$, where units are in pounds and feet. Find the magnitude of $\mathbf{F}$ and interpret the result.

Exercises 25–27: Graph the parametric equations.

25. $x = t + 2,$ $y = t^2 - 3;$ $-2 \le t \le 2$

26. $x = t^3 - 4,$ $y = t - 1;$ $0 \le t \le 2$

27. $x = 2\cos t,$ $y = -2\sin t;$ $0 \le t \le 2\pi$

28. Change the polar coordinates (r, θ) to rectangular coordinates (x, y).

(a) $(2, 135°)$ (b) $(-1, 60°)$

Exercises 29–34: Graph the polar equation.

29. $r = 1 + \cos\theta$ **30.** $r = \sin\theta$

31. $r = 3\sin 3\theta$ **32.** $r = 2 - \cos\theta$

33. $r = 3 + 3\sin\theta$ **34.** $r = 1 - 2\sin\theta$

35. Plot each number in the complex plane.
   (a) $4 - i$ (b) $-2 + 2i$

   (c) $-2i$ (d) -4

36. Write each complex number in trigonometric form. Let θ satisfy $0° \le \theta < 360°$.
   (a) $-2 + 2i$ (b) $\sqrt{3} + i$

   (c) $5i$ (d) -6

37. Find $z_1 z_2$ and $\dfrac{z_1}{z_2}$ in standard form, if
$$z_1 = 4(\cos 150° + i\sin 150°) \text{ and}$$
$$z_2 = 2(\cos 30° + i\sin 30°).$$

38. Use De Moivre's theorem to evaluate z^4 if the trigonometric form of z is $z = 2(\cos 45° + i\sin 45°)$. Write the result in standard form.

Exercises 39 and 40: Find the following roots.

39. The square roots of $4(\cos 60° + i\sin 60°)$

40. The cube roots of $27i$

Applications

41. Airplane Navigation   An airplane takes off with a bearing of 130° and flies 350 miles. Then it changes its course to a bearing of 60° and flies for 500 miles. Determine how far the plane is from its takeoff point.

42. Obstructed View   To find the distance between two points A and B on opposite sides of a small building, a surveyor measures AC as 63.15 feet, angle ACB as 43.56°, and CB as 103.53 feet. Find the distance between A and B to the nearest tenth of a foot.

43. Height of an Airplane   Two observation points A and B are 950 feet apart. From these points the angles of elevation of an airplane are 52° and 57°, as illustrated in the figure. Find the height of the airplane to the nearest foot.

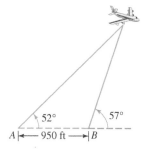

44. Area of a Lot   A surveyor measures two sides and the included angle of a triangular lot as $a = 93.6$ feet, $b = 110.6$ feet, and $\gamma = 51.8°$. Find the area of the lot.

45. Area of a Lot   Find the area of the quadrangular lot shown in the figure to the nearest square foot.

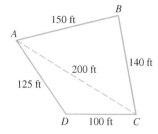

46. Interpreting a Vector   A boat is heading west at 20 miles per hour in a current that is flowing south at 6 miles per hour. Find a vector $\mathbf{v}$ that models the direction and speed of the boat. What does $\|\mathbf{v}\|$ represent?

47. Robotics   Consider the planar two-arm manipulator shown in the figure, where units are in centimeters. Let the upper arm be modeled by the vector $\mathbf{a} = 40\mathbf{i} - 20\mathbf{j}$ and the forearm be modeled by the vector $\mathbf{b} = 20\mathbf{i} + 30\mathbf{j}$. (*Source:* J. Craig, *Introduction to Robotics.*)

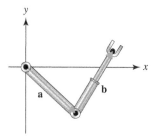

(a) Find a vector $\mathbf{c}$ that gives the position of the hand.

(b) How far is the hand from the origin?

(c) Find the position of the hand if the length of the forearm doubles.

48. Work   A 200-pound person walks 0.75 mile up a hiking trail inclined at 15°. Use a dot product to compute the work done in foot-pounds.

49. Flight of a Golf Ball   A golf ball is hit at 50 feet per second, making an angle of 45° with the horizontal as it leaves the club. If the ground is level, estimate the horizontal distance traveled by the golf ball in the air.

50. Aerial Photography   A camera lens has an angular coverage of 86°. Suppose an aerial photograph is taken vertically with no tilt at an altitude of 3500 feet over ground with an increasing slope of 5°, as shown in the figure. Calculate the ground distance CB that would appear in the resulting photograph (to the nearest foot). (*Source:* F. Moffitt, *Photogrammetry.*)

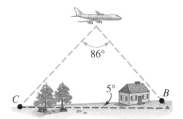

Extended and Discovery Exercises

1. Velocity of a Star   The velocity vector $\mathbf{v}$ of a star relative to the sun can be expressed as the resultant vector of two perpendicular vectors—the radial velocity $\mathbf{v}_r$ and the tangential velocity $\mathbf{v}_t$, where $\mathbf{v} = \mathbf{v}_r + \mathbf{v}_t$, as illustrated in the figure. If a star is located near the sun and its velocity is large, then its motion across the sky will also be large. Barnard's Star is relatively close to the sun with a distance of 35 trillion miles. Relative to the sun, it moves across the sky through an angle of $10.34''$ per year, which is the largest of any known star. Its radial velocity is $\mathbf{v}_r = 67$ miles per second toward the sun. (*Sources:* A. Acker and C. Jaschek, *Astronomical Methods and Calculations;* M. Zeilik, *Introductory Astronomy and Astrophysics.*)

(a) Approximate $\|\mathbf{v}_t\|$ for Barnard's Star in miles per second. (*Hint:* Use $s = r\theta$.)

(b) Compute $\|\mathbf{v}\|$.

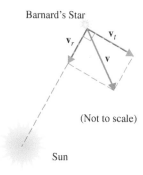

2. Fractals   The fractal called the *Julia set* is shown in the figure. To determine if a complex number $z = a + bi$ belongs to this set, repeatedly compute the sequence of values

$$z_1 = z^2 - 1, \quad z_2 = z_1^2 - 1, \quad z_3 = z_2^2 - 1,$$

and so on. If the modulus of any of the resulting complex numbers exceeds 2, then the complex number z is not in the Julia set. Otherwise z is in this set. Determine if the complex numbers belong to the Julia set.

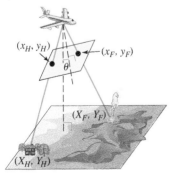

(a) $z = 0 + 0i$ **(b)** $z = 1 + i$

(c) $z = -0.2i$

3. Aerial Photography   Aerial photography from satellites and planes has become important to many applications such as map-making, national security, and surveying. If a photograph is taken from a plane with the camera tilted at an angle θ, then trigonometry can be used to find the ground coordinates of the object, as illustrated in the figure. If an object's photographic coordinates in inches are (x, y), then its ground coordinates (X, Y) in feet can be computed using the formulas

$$X = \frac{ax}{f \sec \theta - y \sin \theta},$$

$$Y = \frac{ay \cos \theta}{f \sec \theta - y \sin \theta},$$

where f is the focal length of the camera in inches and a is the altitude of the airplane in feet. Suppose the photographic coordinates of a house and nearby forest fire are $(x_H, y_H) = (0.9, 3.5)$ and $(x_F, y_F) = (2.1, -2.4)$, respectively.   (***Source:*** F. Moffitt, *Photogrammetry.*)

(a) Find the distance between the house and the fire on the photograph to the nearest hundredth of an inch.

(b) If the photograph was taken at 7400 feet by a camera with a focal length of 6 inches and a tilt of $\theta = 4.1°$, find the ground distance in feet between the house and the fire.

4. Shadows in Computer Graphics   Vectors are used frequently in computer graphics to simulate realistic shadows. For example, suppose an airplane is taking off from a runway, as illustrated in the figure. Let the length and direction of the airplane at takeoff be given by vector $\mathbf{L}$. If the sunlight is assumed to be perpendicular to the runway, then the length of the airplane's shadow cast on the runway equals $\|\mathbf{L}\| \cos \theta$. From previous work, we know that if vector $\mathbf{R}$ points in the direction of the runway, then

$$\mathbf{L} \cdot \mathbf{R} = \|\mathbf{L}\| \|\mathbf{R}\| \cos \theta.$$

Solving for $\|\mathbf{L}\| \cos \theta$ results in

$$\|\mathbf{L}\| \cos \theta = \frac{\mathbf{L} \cdot \mathbf{R}}{\|\mathbf{R}\|}.$$

The expression $\frac{\mathbf{L} \cdot \mathbf{R}}{\|\mathbf{R}\|}$ represents the **component of L in the direction of R**. Find the length of the shadow on the runway for each $\mathbf{L}$ and $\mathbf{R}$. Assume units are in feet.   (***Source:*** C. Pokorny and C. Gerald, *Computer Graphics.*)

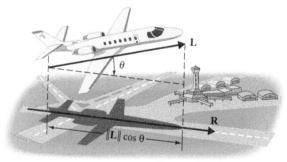

(a) $\mathbf{L} = 40\mathbf{i} + 10\mathbf{j}$, $\mathbf{R} = \mathbf{i}$

(b) $\mathbf{L} = 35\mathbf{i} + 5\mathbf{j}$, $\mathbf{R} = 10\mathbf{i} + \mathbf{j}$

(c) $\mathbf{L} = 100\mathbf{i} + 8\mathbf{j}$, $\mathbf{R} = 30\mathbf{i} + 2\mathbf{j}$

5. The Dot Product   In the figure,

$$\mathbf{a} = \langle a_1, a_2 \rangle, \quad \mathbf{b} = \langle b_1, b_2 \rangle, \quad \text{and}$$

$$\mathbf{a} - \mathbf{b} = \langle a_1 - b_1, a_2 - b_2 \rangle.$$

Apply the law of cosines to the triangle and derive the equation $\mathbf{a} \cdot \mathbf{b} = \|\mathbf{a}\| \|\mathbf{b}\| \cos \theta$.

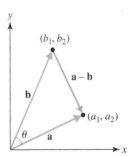

1-8 Cumulative Review Exercises

1. Find the exact distance between $(3, -2)$ and $(7, -9)$.

2. Graph $y = g(x)$ by hand.
   (a) $g(x) = \frac{1}{2}x - 1$
   (b) $g(x) = |x + 2|$
   (c) $g(x) = \sqrt{x + 1}$
   (d) $g(x) = \frac{1}{x + 1}$
   (e) $g(x) = -3\cos\left(2\left(x - \frac{\pi}{2}\right)\right)$

3. Find the domain of $f(x) = \sqrt{4 - x}$ and evaluate $f(-5)$.

4. Find the average rate of change of $f(x) = 3x^2 - 2x$ from $x = 1$ to $x = 3$.

5. Find the difference quotient for $f(x) = 4x^2$.

6. Write the slope-intercept form for a line that passes through $(-1, 4)$ and $(1, -3)$.

7. Determine the x- and y-intercepts on the graph of $4x + 3y = -12$. Graph the equation.

8. If $G(t) = 300 - 10t$ calculates the gallons of water in a tank after t seconds, interpret the numbers 300 and -10 in the formula for $G(t)$.

9. Solve each equation.
   (a) $|2x - 5| = 6$
   (b) $6x^2 + 22x = 8$
   (c) $x^3 = x$
   (d) $x^4 - 2x^2 - 3 = 0$
   (e) $2e^{3x} - 1 = 50$
   (f) $3x^{2/3} = 12$
   (g) $\sin t = \frac{1}{2}, 0 \le t < 2\pi$
   (h) $\tan 2t = -\sqrt{3}$
   (i) $2\cos^2 t + \cos t = 1$

10. Evaluate $f(-1)$ and graph $y = f(x)$. Is f continuous on its domain?
$$f(x) = \begin{cases} x + 2 & \text{if } -3 \le x \le -1 \\ -2x - 1 & \text{if } -1 < x < 1 \\ x^2 - 4 & \text{if } 1 \le x \le 3 \end{cases}$$

11. Solve each inequality. Use interval notation.
    (a) $4(x - 3) > 1 - x$
    (b) $|2x - 1| \le 3$
    (c) $x^2 - 2x - 3 > 0$
    (d) $x^3 - 4x > 0$
    (e) $\frac{x}{x - 1} \le 0$
    (f) $-4 \le 4 - 3x \le 12$

12. Find the vertex on the graph of $f(x) = 2x^2 - 4x + 1$.

13. Divide each expression.
    (a) $\dfrac{3x^3 - x + 2}{x + 2}$
    (b) $\dfrac{2x^3 - 3x^2 + x - 1}{2x - 1}$

14. A cubic function f has zeros -2, 3, and 5 and leading coefficient 4. Write the complete factored form of $f(x)$.

15. State the domain of $f(x) = \frac{3x + 4}{2 - 3x}$. Find any vertical or horizontal asymptotes on the graph of $y = f(x)$.

16. Let $f(x) = \frac{1}{x^2 - 3}$ and $g(x) = 2x + 1$. Find each of the following.
    (a) $(f + g)(2)$
    (b) $(g \circ f)(2)$
    (c) $(g/f)(x)$
    (d) $(f \circ g)(x)$

17. Find $f^{-1}(x)$ if $f(x) = 3x - 2$.

18. Find an exponential function given by $f(x) = Ca^x$ that models the data in the table.

x	0	1	2	3
$f(x)$	2	6	18	54

19. There are initially 5000 bacteria, and this number doubles in size every 1.5 hours. Find C and a so that $f(t) = Ca^t$ models the number of bacteria after t hours.

20. One thousand dollars is deposited in an account that pays 7% annual interest compounded quarterly. Find the amount in the account after 8 years.

21. Simplify each logarithm by hand.
    (a) $\log_3 \frac{1}{27}$
    (b) $\ln \frac{1}{e^3}$
    (c) $\log \sqrt[3]{10}$
    (d) $\log_4 32 - \log_4 \frac{1}{2}$

22. Expand the expression $\ln \sqrt[3]{\frac{x^3 y}{z^2}}$.

23. Convert $225°$ to radians.

24. Convert $\frac{11\pi}{6}$ radians to degrees.

25. Find the six trigonometric functions of θ.

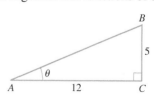

26. Find exact values of the six trigonometric functions of $\theta = \frac{2\pi}{3}$.

27. Find the values of the six trigonometric functions of θ if $\sin \theta = -\frac{7}{25}$ and $\sec \theta < 0$.

28. Evaluate $\tan^{-1} \sqrt{3}$.

29. Solve the right triangle shown in Exercise 25.

30. Simplify $(1 - \cos t)(1 + \cos t)$.

31. Factor $\cot^2 \theta - 2 \cot \theta + 1$.

32. Verify each identity.
   (a) $(1 - \cos^2 \theta)(1 + \tan^2 \theta) = \tan^2 \theta$
   (b) $\dfrac{\sin(\alpha + \beta)}{\cos \alpha \cos \beta} = \tan \alpha + \tan \beta$
   (c) $\dfrac{\csc^2 \theta}{1 - \cot^2 \theta} = -\sec 2\theta$

33. Solve triangle ABC. Approximate to the nearest tenth.
   (a) $\alpha = 31°, \gamma = 53°, b = 15$

   (b) $\alpha = 31°, a = 6, b = 5$

   (c) $\beta = 56°, a = 6, c = 8$

   (d) $a = 6, b = 7, c = 8$

34. Find the area of a triangle with sides of length 7, 10, and 15 feet.

35. Let $\mathbf{a} = \langle -5, 12 \rangle$ and $\mathbf{b} = \langle 7, -24 \rangle$. Find the following.
   (a) $\|\mathbf{b}\|$ **(b)** $2\mathbf{a} - 3\mathbf{b}$ **(c)** $\mathbf{a} \cdot \mathbf{b}$

   (d) The angle between $\mathbf{a}$ and $\mathbf{b}$

36. Graph the parametric equations $x = \frac{1}{2}t$, $y = (t - 1)^2$ for any real number t.

37. Graph the polar equation $r = 3 - 2 \sin \theta$ for θ satisfying $0° \le \theta < 360°$.

38. Find the three cube roots of $27i$.

Applications

39. Construction   A box is being constructed by cutting 3-inch squares from the corners of a rectangular sheet of metal that is 4 inches longer than it is wide. If the box is to have a volume of 351 cubic inches, find the dimensions of the metal sheet.

40. Modeling Data   Find a quadratic function in the form $f(x) = a(x - h)^2 + k$ that models the data in the table at the top of the next column *exactly*.

x	-1	0	1	2	3	4
y	-26	-11	-2	1	-2	-11

41. Designing a Box   A box with rectangular sides and a top is being designed to hold 288 cubic inches and to have a surface area of 288 square inches. If the width is half the length, find possible dimensions for the box.

42. Inverse Variation   The force of gravity F varies inversely with the square of the distance r from the *center* of the moon. If a rock weighs 50 pounds on the surface of the moon ($r = 1750$ kilometers), how much would this rock weigh at a distance of 7000 kilometers from the center of the moon?

43. Length of a Shadow   The angle of elevation of the sun is 63°. Find the length of the shadow cast by a person who is 5 feet tall. Round to the nearest tenth of a foot.

44. Modeling Temperature   The monthly average high temperatures for a location are shown in the table. Model these data using $f(x) = a \sin(b(x - c)) + d$.

Month	1	2	3	4	5	6
Temperature (°F)	25	28	37	50	63	72

Month	7	8	9	10	11	12
Temperature (°F)	75	72	62	50	38	28

45. Angle of Elevation   An 85-foot tree casts a 57-foot shadow. Estimate the angle of elevation of the sun to the nearest tenth of a degree.

46. Distance   An ore ship is traveling east at 20 miles per hour. The bearing of a submerged rock is 75°. After 2 hours, the bearing of the rock is 305°. Find the distance between the ship and the rock when the second bearing is determined.

47. Surveyor   A surveyor measures two sides of a triangular lot to be $a = 242$ feet and $b = 165$ feet. The angle between these sides is $\gamma = 72°$.
   (a) Find the length of the third side c.

   (b) Estimate the area of the lot.

48. Flight of a Golf Ball   A golf ball is hit into the air at 96 feet per second, making an angle of 60° with the horizontal. Use parametric equations to estimate the horizontal distance traveled by the golf ball before it strikes the ground.

9 Systems of Equations and Inequalities

In 2000, less than 6% of the world's population had Internet access. Today, the majority of people on Earth are able to get online. It would be impossible for billions of people to download, post, tweet, and stream data, without the mathematics used to create and manage Internet networks. Systems of equations and matrices are vitally important to the success of social networks such as Facebook, Twitter, Spotify, and Pinterest.

Special types of graphs can be used to represent simple networks, and matrices can be used to summarize these graphs. With matrices it is possible to identify the connections between friends in a social network or to analyze web page links. (See Examples 2 and 9 in Section 9.5.)

In this chapter, we will see that mathematics can be used to solve systems of equations, compute movement in computer graphics, analyze web page links, and even represent social networks. Throughout history, many important discoveries have been based on the insights of a few people. The mathematicians who first worked with matrices and systems of equations could not have imagined the profound impact their work would have in the 21st century.

> Go deep enough into anything and you will find mathematics.
> —Dean Schlicter

Source: Internet World Stats; R. Hanneman and M. Riddle, *Introduction to Social Network Methods.*

9.1 Functions and Systems of Equations in Two Variables

- ▪ **Evaluate functions of two variables**
- ▪ **Understand basic concepts about systems of equations**
- ▪ **Recognize types of linear systems**
- ▪ **Apply the method of substitution**
- ▪ **Apply the elimination method**
- ▪ **Apply graphical and numerical methods**
- ▪ **Solve problems involving joint variation**

Introduction

Many quantities in everyday life depend on more than one variable.

- Finding the area of a rectangular room requires both its *length* and *width*.
- The heat index is a function of *temperature* and *humidity*.
- Grade point average is computed using *grades* and *credit hours*.

Quantities determined by more than one variable often are computed by a *function* of more than one variable. The mathematical concepts that we have already studied concerning functions of one input also apply to functions of more than one input. One unifying concept about every function is that it produces *at most one output* each time it is evaluated.

Functions of Two Variables

In order to perform addition, two numbers must be provided. The addition of x and y results in one output, z. The addition function f can be represented symbolically by

$$f(x, y) = x + y, \text{ where } z = f(x, y).$$

For example, the addition of 3 and 4 can be written as

$$z = f(3, 4) = 3 + 4 = 7.$$

In this case, $f(x, y)$ is a **function of two inputs** or a **function of two variables**. The **independent variables** are x and y, and z is the **dependent variable**. The output z depends on the inputs x and y. Other arithmetic operations can be defined similarly. For example, a division function can be defined by $g(x, y) = \frac{x}{y}$, where $z = g(x, y)$.

EXAMPLE 1 Evaluating functions of more than one input

For each function, evaluate the expression and interpret the result.
(a) $f(3, -4)$, where $f(x, y) = xy$ represents the multiplication function
(b) $M(120, 5)$, where $M(m, g) = \frac{m}{g}$ computes the gas mileage when traveling m miles on g gallons of gasoline
(c) $V(0.5, 2)$, where $V(r, h) = \pi r^2 h$ calculates the volume of a cylindrical barrel with radius r feet and height h feet. (See Figure 9.1.)

Figure 9.1

SOLUTION
(a) $f(3, -4) = (3)(-4) = -12$. The product of 3 and -4 is -12.
(b) $M(120, 5) = \frac{120}{5} = 24$. If a car travels 120 miles on 5 gallons of gasoline, its gas mileage is 24 miles per gallon.
(c) $V(0.5, 2) = \pi(0.5)^2(2) = 0.5\pi \approx 1.57$. If a barrel has a radius of 0.5 foot and a height of 2 feet, it holds about 1.57 cubic feet of liquid.

Now Try Exercises 1, 3, and 5

Systems of Equations in Two Variables

A **linear equation in two variables** can be written in the form

$$ax + by = k,$$

where a, b, and k are constants and a and b are not equal to 0. Examples of linear equations in two variables include

$$2x - 3y = 4, \qquad -x - 5y = 0, \qquad \text{and} \qquad 5x - y = 10.$$

Many situations involving two variables result in the need to determine values for x and y that satisfy *two* equations. For example, suppose that we would like to find a pair of numbers whose average is 10 and whose difference is 2. The function $f(x, y) = \frac{x + y}{2}$ calculates the average of two numbers, and $g(x, y) = x - y$ computes their difference. The solution can be found by solving two linear equations $f(x, y) = 10$ and $g(x, y) = 2$.

$$\frac{x + y}{2} = 10$$
$$x - y = 2$$

System of linear equations

This pair of equations is called a **system of linear equations** because we are solving more than one linear equation at once. A **solution** to a system of equations in two variables consists of an x-value *and* a y-value that satisfy *both* equations simultaneously. The set of all solutions is called the **solution set**. Using trial and error, we see that $x = 11$ and $y = 9$ satisfy both equations. This is the only solution and it can be expressed as the *ordered pair* $(11, 9)$.

Systems of equations that have at least one nonlinear equation are called **nonlinear systems of equations**.

Nonlinear Systems of Equations

One nonlinear equation
$$x^2 - 5y = 8$$
$$2x + 3y = 3$$

and

$$x^2 + y^2 = 5$$
$$\sqrt{x} - y = -2$$
Two nonlinear equations

Types of Linear Systems in Two Variables

CLASS DISCUSSION

Explain why a system of linear equations in two variables cannot have two or three solutions.

Any system of linear equations in two variables can be written in the form

$$a_1 x + b_1 y = c_1$$
$$a_2 x + b_2 y = c_2,$$

where a_1, b_1, c_1, a_2, b_2, and c_2 are constants. The graph of this system consists of *two* lines in the xy-plane. The following See the Concept summarizes the three possible types of linear systems. Note that **coincident lines** are identical lines and indicate that the two equations are equivalent and have the same graph. (See **B** below.)

See the Concept: Three Types of Linear Systems

One Solution

A Intersecting lines

Consistent System
Independent Equations

A The solution is given by the coordinates of the point of intersection.

Infinitely Many Solutions

B Coincident lines

Consistent System
Dependent Equations

B Every point on the coincident lines represents a solution.

No Solutions

C Parallel lines

Inconsistent System

C The distinct parallel lines have no points in common.

A **consistent system** of linear equations has either one solution, meaning the equations are **independent**, or infinitely many solutions, meaning the equations are **dependent.** An **inconsistent system** has no solutions.

EXAMPLE 2 Recognizing types of linear systems

Graph each system of equations and find any solutions. Identify the system as consistent or inconsistent. If the system is consistent, state whether the equations are dependent or independent.

(a) $\quad x - y = 2$
$\quad\quad -x + y = 1$

(b) $4x - y = 2$
$\quad\quad x - 2y = -3$

(c) $\quad 2x - y = 1$
$\quad\quad -4x + 2y = -2$

SOLUTION

Getting Started Start by solving each equation for y. Use the resulting slope-intercept form to graph each line. Determine any points of intersection. ▶

(a) Graph $y = x - 2$ and $y = x + 1$, as shown in Figure 9.2. Their graphs (parallel lines) do not intersect, so there are no solutions. The system is inconsistent.

(b) Graph $y = 4x - 2$ and $y = \frac{1}{2}x + \frac{3}{2}$, as shown in Figure 9.3. Their graphs intersect at $(1, 2)$. There is one solution, so the system is consistent and the equations are independent. Because graphical solutions can be approximate, we check this solution by substituting 1 for x and 2 for y in the given system.

$$4(1) - \ \ 2 \ = \ \ 2 \ \checkmark \quad \text{True}$$
$$(1) - 2(2) = -3 \ \checkmark \quad \text{True}$$

Because $(1, 2)$ satisfies *both* equations, it is the solution.

(c) Solving the equations $2x - y = 1$ and $-4x + 2y = -2$ for y results in the same equation: $y = 2x - 1$. Therefore their graphs coincide, as shown in Figure 9.4. (Note that the second equation results when the first equation is multiplied by -2, so the equations are equivalent.) Any point on this line is a solution to both equations. Thus the system has infinitely many solutions of the form $\{(x, y) \mid 2x - y = 1\}$ and is consistent. The equations are dependent.

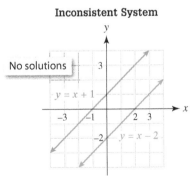

Inconsistent System

Figure 9.2

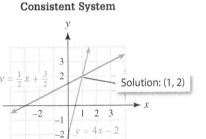

Consistent System

Figure 9.3

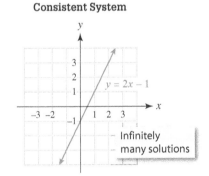

Consistent System

Figure 9.4

Now Try Exercises 31, 33, and 37

The Method of Substitution

The **method of substitution** is often used to solve systems of equations symbolically. It is summarized by the following steps.

> ### THE METHOD OF SUBSTITUTION
>
> To use the method of substitution to solve a system of two equations in two variables, perform the following steps.
>
> **STEP 1:** Choose a variable in one of the two equations. Solve the equation for that variable.
>
> **STEP 2:** Substitute the result from Step 1 into the other equation and solve for the remaining variable.
>
> **STEP 3:** Use the value of the variable from Step 2 to determine the value of the other variable. To do this, you may want to use the equation you found in Step 1.
>
> To check your answer, substitute the value of each variable into the *given* equations. These values should satisfy *both* equations.

An Application In the next example, we use the method of substitution to solve an example involving real data.

EXAMPLE 3 Applying the method of substitution

In the first quarter of 2011, Apple Corporation sold a combined total of 35.7 million iPods and iPhones. There were 3.3 million more iPods sold than iPhones. (*Source:* Apple Corporation.)
(a) Write a system of equations whose solution gives the individual sales of iPods and of iPhones.
(b) Solve the system of equations. Interpret the results.
(c) Is your system consistent or inconsistent? If it is consistent, state whether the equations are dependent or independent.

SOLUTION

Getting Started When setting up a system of equations, it is important to identify what each variable represents. Then express the situation with equations. Finally, apply the method of substitution. ▶

(a) Let x be the number of iPods sold in millions and y be the number of iPhones sold in millions. The combined total is 35.7 million, so let $x + y = 35.7$. Because iPod sales exceeded iPhone sales by 3.3 million, let $x - y = 3.3$. Thus the system of equations is as follows.

$$x + y = 35.7 \qquad \text{Total sales are 35.7 million.}$$
$$x - y = 3.3 \qquad \text{iPod sales exceeded iPhone sales by 3.3 million.}$$

(b) **STEP 1:** With this system, we can solve for either variable in either equation. If we solve for x in the second equation, we obtain the equation $x = y + 3.3$.

STEP 2: Substitute $(y + 3.3)$ for x in the first equation, $x + y = 35.7$, and solve.

$$(y + 3.3) + y = 35.7 \qquad \text{Substitute } (y + 3.3) \text{ for } x.$$
$$2y = 32.4 \qquad \text{Subtract 3.3; combine terms.}$$
$$y = 16.2 \qquad \text{Divide each side by 2.}$$

STEP 3: To find x, substitute 16.2 for y in the equation $x = y + 3.3$ from Step 1 to obtain $x = 16.2 + 3.3 = 19.5$. The solution is $(19.5, 16.2)$.

Thus, there were 19.5 million iPods and 16.2 million iPhones sold.

(c) There is one solution, so the system is consistent and the equations are independent.

Now Try Exercise 113

In the next example, we solve a system and check our result.

EXAMPLE 4 Using the method of substitution

Solve the system symbolically. Check your answer.

$$5x - 2y = -16$$
$$x + 4y = -1$$

SOLUTION

STEP 1: Begin by solving one of the equations for one of the variables. One possibility is to solve the second equation for x.

$$x + 4y = -1 \qquad \textit{Second equation}$$
$$x = -4y - 1 \qquad \textit{Subtract 4y from each side.}$$

STEP 2: Next, substitute $(-4y - 1)$ for x in the first equation and solve the resulting equation for y.

$$5x - 2y = -16 \qquad \textit{First equation}$$
$$5(-4y - 1) - 2y = -16 \qquad \textit{Let } x = -4y - 1.$$
$$-20y - 5 - 2y = -16 \qquad \textit{Distributive property}$$
$$-5 - 22y = -16 \qquad \textit{Combine like terms.}$$
$$-22y = -11 \qquad \textit{Add 5 to each side.}$$
$$y = \frac{1}{2} \qquad \textit{Divide each side by } -22; \textit{ Simplify.}$$

STEP 3: Now find the value of x by using the equation $x = -4y - 1$ from Step 1. Since $y = \frac{1}{2}$, it follows that $x = -4\left(\frac{1}{2}\right) - 1 = -3$. The solution can be written as an ordered pair: $\left(-3, \frac{1}{2}\right)$.

Check: Substitute $x = -3$ and $y = \frac{1}{2}$ in both given equations.

$$5(-3) - 2\left(\frac{1}{2}\right) \stackrel{?}{=} -16 \ \checkmark \qquad \textit{True}$$

$$-3 + 4\left(\frac{1}{2}\right) \stackrel{?}{=} -1 \ \checkmark \qquad \textit{True}$$

Both equations are satisfied, so the solution is $\left(-3, \frac{1}{2}\right)$.

Now Try Exercise 39

Nonlinear Systems of Equations The method of substitution can also be used to solve nonlinear systems of equations. In the next example, we solve a nonlinear system of equations having two solutions. In general, a nonlinear system of equations can have *any number of solutions*.

EXAMPLE 5 Solving a nonlinear system of equations

Solve the system symbolically.

$$6x + 2y = 10$$
$$2x^2 - 3y = 11$$

SOLUTION

STEP 1: Begin by solving one of the equations for one of the variables. One possibility is to solve the first equation for y.

$$6x + 2y = 10 \qquad \textit{First equation}$$
$$2y = 10 - 6x \qquad \textit{Subtract 6x from each side.}$$
$$y = 5 - 3x \qquad \textit{Divide each side by 2.}$$

STEP 2: Next, substitute $(5 - 3x)$ for y in the second equation and solve the resulting quadratic equation for x.

Algebra Review
To review factoring, see Chapter R (pages R-22–R-23).

$$2x^2 - 3y = 11 \qquad \text{Second equation}$$
$$2x^2 - 3(5 - 3x) = 11 \qquad \text{Let } y = 5 - 3x.$$
$$2x^2 - 15 + 9x = 11 \qquad \text{Distributive property}$$
$$2x^2 + 9x - 26 = 0 \qquad \text{Subtract 11 from each side; rewrite.}$$
$$(2x + 13)(x - 2) = 0 \qquad \text{Factor.}$$
$$x = -\frac{13}{2} \quad \text{or} \quad x = 2 \qquad \text{Zero-product property}$$

STEP 3: Now find the corresponding y-values for each x-value. From Step 1 we know that $y = 5 - 3x$, so it follows that $y = 5 - 3\left(-\frac{13}{2}\right) = \frac{49}{2}$ or $y = 5 - 3(2) = -1$. Thus the solutions are $\left(-\frac{13}{2}, \frac{49}{2}\right)$ and $(2, -1)$.

Now Try Exercise 51

EXAMPLE 6 Solving a nonlinear system of equations

Use the method of substitution to determine the points where the line $y = 2x$ intersects the circle $x^2 + y^2 = 5$. Sketch a graph that illustrates the solutions.

SOLUTION Substitute $(2x)$ for y in the equation $x^2 + y^2 = 5$.

$$x^2 + y^2 = 5 \qquad \text{Second equation}$$
$$x^2 + (2x)^2 = 5 \qquad y = 2x$$
$$x^2 + 4x^2 = 5 \qquad \text{Square the expression.}$$
$$5x^2 = 5 \qquad \text{Add like terms.}$$
$$x^2 = 1 \qquad \text{Divide each side by 5.}$$
$$x = \pm 1 \qquad \text{Square root property}$$

Two Solutions

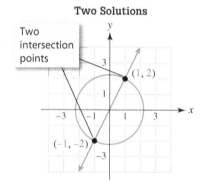

Figure 9.5

Since $y = 2x$ we see that when $x = 1$, $y = 2$ and when $x = -1$, $y = -2$. The graphs of $x^2 + y^2 = 5$ and $y = 2x$ intersect at the points $(1, 2)$ and $(-1, -2)$. This nonlinear system has two solutions, which are shown in Figure 9.5.

Now Try Exercise 99

EXAMPLE 7 Identifying a system with zero or infinitely many solutions

If possible, solve each system of equations.
(a) $x^2 + y = 1$ **(b)** $2x - 4y = 5$
$\ x^2 - y = -2$ $\ -x + 2y = -\frac{5}{2}$

SOLUTION
(a) STEP 1: Solve the second equation for y, which gives $y = x^2 + 2$.

STEP 2: Substitute $(x^2 + 2)$ for y in the first equation and then solve for x, if possible.

$$x^2 + y = 1 \qquad \text{First equation}$$
$$x^2 + (x^2 + 2) = 1 \qquad \text{Let } y = x^2 + 2.$$
$$2x^2 + 2 = 1 \qquad \text{Combine like terms.}$$
$$2x^2 = -1 \qquad \text{Subtract 2 from each side.}$$

Because $2x^2 \geq 0$, it follows that there are no real solutions and the system is inconsistent.

No Solutions

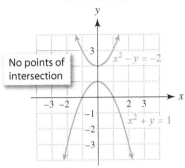

Figure 9.6

Infinitely Many Solutions

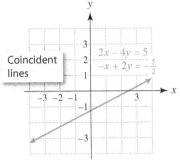

Figure 9.7

STEP 3: This step is not necessary because there are no real solutions for x. Figure 9.6 shows that the graphs, which are parabolas, do not intersect.

(b) STEP 1: First solve the second equation for x to obtain $x = 2y + \frac{5}{2}$.

STEP 2: Substitute $\left(2y + \frac{5}{2} \right)$ for x in the first equation and then solve for y.

$$2x - 4y = 5 \qquad \text{First equation}$$

$$2\left(2y + \frac{5}{2} \right) - 4y = 5 \qquad \text{Let } x = 2y + \frac{5}{2}.$$

$$4y + 5 - 4y = 5 \qquad \text{Distributive property}$$

$$5 = 5 \qquad \text{Combine like terms.}$$

The equation $5 = 5$ is an identity and indicates that there are infinitely many solutions. The system is consistent and the equations are dependent. Note that we can multiply each side of the second equation by -2 to obtain the first equation.

$$-2(-x + 2y) = -2\left(-\frac{5}{2} \right) \qquad \text{Multiply second equation by } -2.$$

$$2x - 4y = 5 \qquad \text{Distributive property}$$

STEP 3: In Figure 9.7 the graphs of the equations are identical lines. The solution set is $\{(x, y) \mid 2x - 4y = 5\}$ and includes all points on this line; $\left(0, -\frac{5}{4} \right)$ and $\left(2, -\frac{1}{4} \right)$ are examples of solutions to this system.

Now Try Exercises 45 and 57

The Elimination Method

The **elimination method** is another way to solve systems of equations symbolically. This method is based on the property that *equals added to equals are equal*. That is, if

$$a = b \quad \text{and} \quad c = d, \quad \text{then} \quad a + c = b + d.$$

The goal of this method is to obtain an equation where one of the two variables has been eliminated. This task is sometimes accomplished by adding two equations. The elimination method is demonstrated in the next example for three types of linear systems.

EXAMPLE 8 Using elimination to solve a system

Use elimination to solve each system of equations, if possible. Identify the system as consistent or inconsistent. If the system is consistent, state whether the equations are dependent or independent. Support your results graphically.

(a) $2x - y = -4$ **(b)** $4x - y = 10$ **(c)** $x - y = 6$
    $3x + y = -1$ $-4x + y = -10$ $x - y = 3$

SOLUTION

(a) *Symbolic Solution*   We can eliminate the y-variable by adding the equations.

$$2x - y = -4 \qquad \text{First equation}$$

$$\underline{3x + y = -1} \qquad \text{Second equation}$$

$$5x \qquad = -5 \quad \text{or} \quad x = -1 \qquad \text{Add equations.}$$

Now the y-variable can be determined by substituting $x = -1$ in either equation.

$$2x - y = -4 \qquad \text{First equation}$$

$$2(-1) - y = -4 \qquad \text{Let } x = -1.$$

$$-y = -2 \qquad \text{Add 2.}$$

$$y = 2 \qquad \text{Multiply by } -1.$$

One Solution

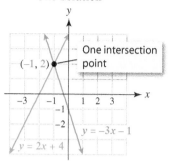

Figure 9.8

Infinitely Many Solutions

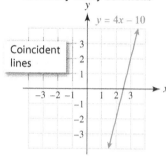

Figure 9.9

No Solutions

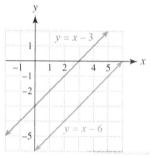

Figure 9.10

No points of intersection

The solution is $(-1, 2)$. There is a unique solution so the system is consistent and the equations are independent.

Graphical Solution   Start by solving each given equation for y.

$$2x - y = -4 \quad \text{is equivalent to} \quad y = 2x + 4.$$
$$3x + y = -1 \quad \text{is equivalent to} \quad y = -3x - 1.$$

The graphs of $y = 2x + 4$ and $y = -3x - 1$ intersect at the point $(-1, 2)$, as shown in Figure 9.8.

(b) *Symbolic Solution*   If we add the equations, we obtain the following result.

$$
\begin{array}{ll}
4x - y = 10 & \text{First equation} \\
\underline{-4x + y = -10} & \text{Second equation} \\
0 = 0 & \text{Add equations.}
\end{array}
$$

The equation $0 = 0$ is an identity. The two given equations are equivalent: if we multiply the first equation by -1, we obtain the second equation. Thus there are infinitely many solutions, and we can write the solution set in set-builder notation.

$$\{(x, y) \mid 4x - y = 10\}$$

Some examples of solutions are $(3, 2)$, $(4, 6)$, and $(1, -6)$. The system is consistent and the equations are dependent.

Graphical Solution   For a graphical solution, start by solving each equation for y. Both equations are equivalent to $y = 4x - 10$. Their graphs are identical and coincide. The graph of $y = 4x - 10$ is shown in Figure 9.9. Any point on the line represents a solution to the system. For example, $(3, 2)$ is a solution.

(c) *Symbolic Solution*   If we subtract the second equation from the first, we obtain the following result. (Note that subtracting the second equation from the first is equivalent to multiplying the second equation by -1 and then adding it to the first.)

$$
\begin{array}{ll}
x - y = 6 & \\
\underline{x - y = 3} & \\
0 = 3 & \text{Subtract.}
\end{array}
$$

The equation $0 = 3$ is a contradiction. Therefore there are no solutions, and the system is inconsistent.

Graphical Solution   For a graphical solution, start by solving each equation for y to obtain $y = x - 6$ and $y = x - 3$. The graphs of $y = x - 6$ and $y = x - 3$, shown in Figure 9.10, are parallel lines that never intersect, so there are no solutions.

Now Try Exercises **71, 75, and 77**

Sometimes multiplication is performed before elimination is used, as illustrated in the next example.

EXAMPLE 9   Multiplying before using elimination

Solve each system of equations by using elimination.
(a) $2x - 3y = 18$ **(b)** $5x + 10y = 10$
$\ \ 5x + 2y = 7$ $\ \ \ x + 2y = 2$

SOLUTION
(a)   If we multiply the first equation by 2 and the second equation by 3, then the y-coefficients become -6 and 6. Addition eliminates the y-variable.

$$
\begin{array}{ll}
4x - 6y = 36 & \text{Multiply first equation by 2.} \\
\underline{15x + 6y = 21} & \text{Multiply second equation by 3.} \\
19x \quad\ = 57, \quad \text{or} \quad x = 3 & \text{Add equations.}
\end{array}
$$

Substituting $x = 3$ in $2x - 3y = 18$ (first equation) results in

$$2(3) - 3y = 18, \text{ or } y = -4.$$

The solution is $(3, -4)$.

(b) If the second equation is multiplied by -5, addition eliminates both variables.

$$5x + 10y = 10 \qquad \text{First equation}$$
$$-5x - 10y = -10 \qquad \text{Multiply second equation by } -5.$$
$$0 = 0 \qquad \text{Add equations.}$$

The statement $0 = 0$ is an identity. The equations are dependent and there are infinitely many solutions. The solution set is $\{(x, y) \mid x + 2y = 2\}$.

> **Now Try Exercises 81 and 83**

Elimination and Nonlinear Systems   Elimination can also be used to solve some nonlinear systems of equations, as illustrated in the next example.

EXAMPLE 10   Using elimination to solve a nonlinear system

Solve the system of equations.

$$x^2 + y^2 = 4$$
$$2x^2 - y = 7$$

SOLUTION   If we multiply each side of the first equation by 2, multiply each side of the second equation by -1, and then add the equations, the x variable is eliminated.

$$2x^2 + 2y^2 = 8 \qquad \text{Multiply first equation by 2.}$$
$$\underline{-2x^2 + y = -7} \qquad \text{Multiply second equation by } -1.$$
$$2y^2 + y = 1 \qquad \text{Add equations.}$$

Next we solve $2y^2 + y - 1 = 0$ for y.

$$(2y - 1)(y + 1) = 0 \qquad \text{Factor.}$$

$$y = \frac{1}{2} \quad \text{or} \quad y = -1 \qquad \text{Solve.}$$

Solving $x^2 + y^2 = 4$ for x results in $x = \pm\sqrt{4 - y^2}$. If $y = \frac{1}{2}$, then $x = \pm\sqrt{\frac{15}{4}}$, which can be written as $\pm\frac{\sqrt{15}}{2}$. If $y = -1$, then $x = \pm\sqrt{3}$. Thus there are four solutions: $\left(\pm\frac{\sqrt{15}}{2}, \frac{1}{2}\right)$ and $(\pm\sqrt{3}, -1)$.

A graph of the system of equations is shown in Figure 9.11. The four points of intersection correspond to the four solutions. In Figure 9.12 the four points of intersection are labeled.

Four Solutions to a Nonliner System

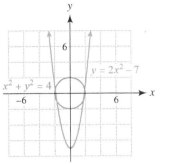

Figure 9.11

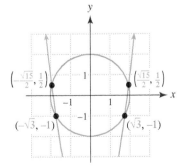

Figure 9.12

> **Now Try Exercise 93**

Graphical and Numerical Methods

An Application The next example illustrates how a system with two variables can be solved symbolically, graphically, and numerically.

EXAMPLE 11 Modeling roof trusses

Linear systems occur in the design of roof trusses for homes and buildings. See Figure 9.13. One of the simplest types of roof trusses is an equilateral triangle. If a 200-pound force is applied to the peak of a truss, as shown in Figure 9.14, then the weights W_1 and W_2 exerted on each rafter of the truss are determined by the following system of linear equations. (*Source:* R. Hibbeler, *Structural Analysis.*)

$$W_1 - W_2 = 0$$
$$\frac{\sqrt{3}}{2}(W_1 + W_2) = 200$$

Estimate the solution symbolically, graphically, and numerically.

Equilateral Triangle Roof Trusses

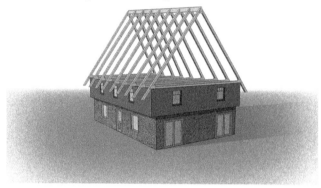

Figure 9.13

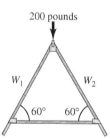

Figure 9.14

SOLUTION

Symbolic Solution The system of equations can be written as follows.

$$W_1 - W_2 = 0 \qquad \text{First equation}$$
$$\frac{\sqrt{3}}{2}W_1 + \frac{\sqrt{3}}{2}W_2 = 200 \qquad \text{Distributive property}$$

We can apply elimination by multiplying the first equation by $\frac{\sqrt{3}}{2}$ and then adding.

$$\frac{\sqrt{3}}{2}W_1 - \frac{\sqrt{3}}{2}W_2 = 0 \qquad \text{Multiply by } \frac{\sqrt{3}}{2}.$$
$$\frac{\sqrt{3}}{2}W_1 + \frac{\sqrt{3}}{2}W_2 = 200$$
$$\overline{\rule{4cm}{0.4pt}}$$
$$\sqrt{3}\,W_1 = 200 \qquad \text{Add equations.}$$

Dividing by $\sqrt{3}$ gives $W_1 = \frac{200}{\sqrt{3}} \approx 115.47$ pounds. From the first equation, it follows that $W_1 = W_2$, and so $W_2 \approx 115.47$ pounds.

Graphical Solution Begin by solving each equation for the variable W_2.

$$W_2 = W_1$$
$$W_2 = \frac{400}{\sqrt{3}} - W_1$$

Solve each equation for W_2.

Graph the equations $y_1 = x$ and $y_2 = \dfrac{400}{\sqrt{3}} - x$. Their graphs intersect near the point (115.47, 115.47), as shown in Figure 9.15. This means that each rafter supports a weight of approximately 115 pounds.

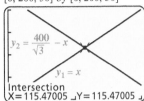

Graphical Solution

[0, 200, 50] by [0, 200, 50]

$y_2 = \dfrac{400}{\sqrt{3}} - x$

$y_1 = x$

Intersection
X=115.47005 Y=115.47005

Figure 9.15

Numerical Solution

X	Y1	Y2
112	112	118.94
113	113	117.94
114	114	116.94
115	115	115.94 ←
116	116	114.94
117	117	113.94
118	118	112.94

X=115

Figure 9.16

Numerical Solution   In Figure 9.16, $y_1 \approx y_2$ for $x = 115$.

Now Try Exercise 115

EXAMPLE 12   Determining the dimensions of a cylinder

The volume V of a cylindrical container with a radius r and height h is computed by $V(r, h) = \pi r^2 h$. See Figure 9.17. The lateral surface area S of the container, *excluding* the circular top and bottom, is computed by $S(r, h) = 2\pi rh$.

Volume and Lateral Surface Area of a Cylinder

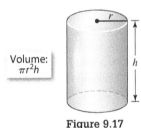

Geometry Review

To review formulas related to cylinders, see Chapter R (page R-4).

Volume: $\pi r^2 h$

$2\pi r$

Lateral surface area: $2\pi rh$

Figure 9.17

(a) Write a system of equations whose solution is the dimensions for a cylinder with a volume of 38 cubic inches and a lateral surface area of 63 square inches.

(b) Solve the system of equations graphically and symbolically.

SOLUTION

(a) The equations $V(r, h) = 38$ and $S(r, h) = 63$ must be satisfied. This results in the following system of nonlinear equations.

$$\pi r^2 h = 38 \qquad \text{Volume}$$

$$2\pi rh = 63 \qquad \text{Lateral surface area}$$

(b) *Graphical Solution*   To find the solution graphically, we can solve each equation for h and then apply the intersection-of-graphs method.

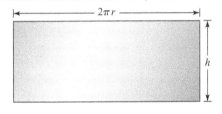

$$h = \frac{38}{\pi r^2}$$

$$h = \frac{63}{2\pi r}$$

Solve each equation for h.

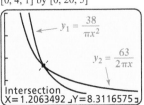

Graphical Solution

[0, 4, 1] by [0, 20, 5]

$y_1 = \dfrac{38}{\pi x^2}$

$y_2 = \dfrac{63}{2\pi x}$

Intersection
X=1.2063492 Y=8.3116575

Figure 9.18

Let r correspond to x and h to y. Graph $y_1 = \dfrac{38}{\pi x^2}$ and $y_2 = \dfrac{63}{2\pi x}$. Their graphs intersect near the point (1.206, 8.312), as shown in Figure 9.18. Therefore a cylinder with a radius of $r \approx 1.206$ inches and height of $h \approx 8.312$ inches has a volume of 38 cubic inches and lateral surface area of 63 square inches.

Symbolic Solution Because $h = \frac{38}{\pi r^2}$ and $h = \frac{63}{2\pi r}$, we can determine r by solving the following equation.

$$\frac{38}{\pi r^2} = \frac{63}{2\pi r} \qquad \text{Equation to be solved}$$

$$2\pi r^2\left(\frac{38}{\pi r^2}\right) = 2\pi r^2\left(\frac{63}{2\pi r}\right) \qquad \text{Multiply each side by the LCD, } 2\pi r^2.$$

$$76 = 63r \qquad \text{Simplify.}$$

$$\frac{76}{63} = r \qquad \text{Divide each side by 63.}$$

Because $r = \frac{76}{63} \approx 1.206$, $h = \frac{63}{2\pi r} = \frac{63}{2\pi(76/63)} \approx 8.312$; the symbolic result verifies our graphical result.

Now Try Exercise 117

An Example That Requires a Graphical Solution Sometimes it is either difficult or impossible to solve a nonlinear system of equations symbolically. However, it might be possible to solve such a system graphically.

EXAMPLE 13 Solving a nonlinear system of equations graphically

Solve the system graphically to the nearest thousandth.

$$2x^3 - y = 2$$
$$\ln x^2 - 3y = -1$$

SOLUTION Begin by solving both equations for y. The first equation becomes $y = 2x^3 - 2$. Solving the second equation for y gives the following results.

$$\ln x^2 - 3y = -1 \qquad \text{Second equation}$$

$$\ln x^2 + 1 = 3y \qquad \text{Add } 3y \text{ and 1 to each side.}$$

$$\frac{\ln x^2 + 1}{3} = y \qquad \text{Divide each side by 3.}$$

The graphs of $y_1 = 2x^3 - 2$ and $y_2 = \frac{\ln x^2 + 1}{3}$ in Figure 9.19 intersect at one point. To the nearest thousandth, the solution is $(1.058, 0.371)$.

Now Try Exercise 107

Graphical Solution

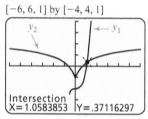

$[-6, 6, 1]$ by $[-4, 4, 1]$

Intersection
X=1.0583853 Y=.37116297

Figure 9.19

Joint Variation

A quantity may depend on more than one variable. For example, the volume V of a cylinder is given by $V = \pi r^2 h$. We say that V *varies jointly* with h and the square of r. The *constant of variation* is π.

JOINT VARIATION

Let m and n be real numbers. Then z **varies jointly** with the mth power of x and the nth power of y if a nonzero real number k exists such that

$$z = kx^m y^n.$$

In the following example we use joint variation to determine the amount of timber in a tree with a specified diameter and height.

EXAMPLE 14   Modeling the amount of wood in a tree

To estimate the volume of timber in a given area of forest, formulas have been developed to find the amount of wood contained in a tree with height h in feet and diameter d in inches. See Figure 9.20. One study concluded that the volume V of wood in a tree varies jointly with the 1.12 power of h and the 1.98 power of d. (The diameter is measured 4.5 feet above the ground.)   (***Source:*** B. Ryan, B. Joiner, and T. Ryan, *Minitab Handbook.*)

(a) Write an equation that relates V, h, and d.

(b) A tree with a 13.8-inch diameter and a 64-foot height has a volume of 25.14 cubic feet. Estimate the constant of variation k.

(c) Estimate the volume of wood in a tree with $d = 11$ inches and $h = 47$ feet.

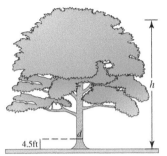

Figure 9.20

SOLUTION

(a) $V = kh^{1.12}d^{1.98}$, where k is the constant of variation.

(b) Substitute $d = 13.8$, $h = 64$, and $V = 25.14$ into the equation and solve for k.

$$25.14 = k(64)^{1.12}(13.8)^{1.98}$$

$$k = \frac{25.14}{(64)^{1.12}(13.8)^{1.98}} \approx 0.00132$$

Thus let $V = 0.00132\,h^{1.12}d^{1.98}$.

(c) $V = 0.00132(47)^{1.12}(11)^{1.98} \approx 11.4$ cubic feet

Now Try Exercise 143

9.1 Putting It All Together

The following table summarizes some mathematical concepts involved with functions and equations in two variables.

CONCEPT	COMMENTS	EXAMPLE
Function of two inputs or variables	$z = f(x, y)$ where x and y are inputs and z is the output.	$f(x, y) = x^2 + 5y$ $f(2, 3) = 2^2 + 5(3) = 19$
System of two linear equations	The equations can be written as $ax + by = k$. A solution is an ordered pair (x, y) that satisfies both equations.	$2x - 3y = 6$ $5x + 4y = -8$ Solution: $(0, -2)$
Nonlinear system of two equations	A system of equations that has at least one nonlinear equation is a nonlinear system. A solution is an ordered pair (x, y) that satisfies both equations. A nonlinear system of equations can have any number of solutions.	$5x^2 - 4xy = -3$ $\dfrac{5}{x} - 2y = 1$ Solutions: $(1, 2), \left(-\frac{7}{5}, -\frac{16}{7}\right)$
Consistent system of linear equations in two variables	A consistent linear system has either one or infinitely many solutions. Its graph is either distinct, intersecting lines or identical lines.	$x + y = 10$ $\underline{x - y = 4}$ $2x = 14$ Solution is given by $x = 7$ and $y = 3$. The equations are independent.
System of dependent linear equations in two variables	A system of dependent linear equations has infinitely many solutions. The graph consists of two identical lines.	$2x + 2y = 2$ and $x + y = 1$ are equivalent (dependent) equations. The solution set is $\{(x, y) \mid x + y = 1\}$.

continued on next page

CONCEPT	COMMENTS	EXAMPLE
Inconsistent system of linear equations in two variables	An inconsistent linear system has no solutions. The graph is two parallel lines.	$x + y =\ \ 1$ $x + y =\ \ 2$ Subtract. $\overline{\qquad 0 = -1}$ Always false
Method of substitution	Solve one equation for a variable. Then substitute the result in the second equation and solve.	$x - y = 1$ $x + y = 5$ If $x - y = 1$, then $x = 1 + y$. Substitute in the second equation: $(1 + y) + y = 5$. This results in $y = 2$ and $x = 3$. The solution is $(3, 2)$.
Elimination method	By performing arithmetic operations on a system, a variable is eliminated.	$2x + y = 5$ $\underline{\ \ x - y = 1}$ Add. $3x\qquad = 6$ so $x = 2$ and $y = 1$.
Graphical method for two equations	Solve both equations for the same variable. Then apply the intersection-of-graphs method.	If $x + y = 3$, then $y = 3 - x$. If $4x - y = 2$, then $y = 4x - 2$. Graph and locate the point of intersection at $(1, 2)$.

9.1 Exercises

Functions of More Than One Input

Exercises 1 and 2: Evaluate the function for the indicated inputs and interpret the result.

1. $A(5, 8)$, where $A(b, h) = \frac{1}{2}bh$ (A computes the area of a triangle with base b and height h.)

2. $A(20, 35)$, where $A(w, l) = wl$ (A computes the area of a rectangle with width w and length l.)

Exercises 3–8: Evaluate the expression for the given $f(x, y)$.

3. $f(2, -3)$ if $f(x, y) = x^2 + y^2$

4. $f(-1, 3)$ if $f(x, y) = 2x^2 - y^2$

5. $f(-2, 3)$ if $f(x, y) = 3x - 4y$

6. $f(5, -2)$ if $f(x, y) = 6y - \frac{1}{2}x$

7. $f\left(\frac{1}{2}, -\frac{7}{4}\right)$ if $f(x, y) = \frac{2x}{y + 3}$

8. $f(0.2, 0.5)$ if $f(x, y) = \frac{5x}{2y + 1}$

Exercises 9–12: Write a symbolic representation for $f(x, y)$ if the function f computes the following quantity.

9. The sum of y and twice x

10. The product of x^2 and y^2

11. The product of x and y divided by $1 + x$

12. The square root of the sum of x and y

Exercises 13–18: Solve the equation for x and then solve it for y.

13. $3x - 4y = 7$

14. $-x - 5y = 4$

15. $x - y^2 = 5$

16. $2x^2 + y = 4$

17. $\dfrac{2x - y}{3y} = 1$

18. $\dfrac{x + y}{x - y} = 2$

Solutions to Systems of Equations

Exercises 19–22: Determine which ordered pairs are solutions to the given system of equations. State whether the system is linear or nonlinear.

19. $(2, 1), (-2, 1), (1, 0)$
$$2x + y = 5$$
$$x + y = 3$$

20. $(3, 2), (3, -4), (5, 0)$
$$x - y = 5$$
$$2x + y = 10$$

21. $(4, -3), (0, 5), (4, 3)$
$$x^2 + y^2 = 25$$
$$2x + 3y = -1$$

22. $(4, 8), (8, 4), (-4, -8)$
$$xy = 32$$
$$x + y = 12$$

Exercises 23–26: The figure shows the graph of a system of two linear equations. Use the graph to estimate the solution to this system of equations. Then solve the system symbolically.

23.

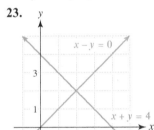

24.

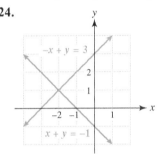

25.

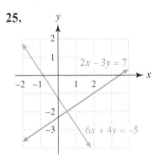

26.

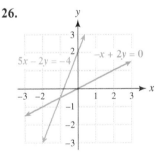

Consistent and Inconsistent Linear Systems

Exercises 27–30: The figure represents a system of linear equations. Classify the system as consistent or inconsistent. Solve the system graphically and symbolically, if possible.

27.

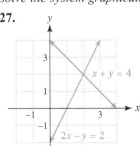

28.

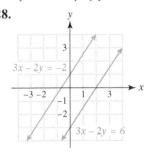

29.

30.

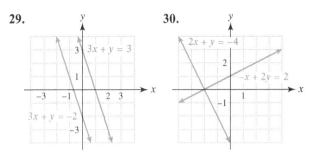

Exercises 31–38: Graph each system of equations and find any solutions. Check your answers. Identify the system as consistent or inconsistent. If the system is consistent, state whether the equations are dependent or independent.

31.
$$2x + y = 3$$
$$-2x - y = 4$$

32.
$$x - 4y = 4$$
$$2x - 8y = 4$$

33.
$$3x - y = 7$$
$$-2x + y = -5$$

34.
$$-x + 2y = 3$$
$$3x - y = 1$$

35.
$$x - 2y = -6$$
$$-2x + y = 6$$

36.
$$2x - 3y = 1$$
$$x + y = -2$$

37.
$$2x - y = -4$$
$$-4x + 2y = 8$$

38.
$$3x - y = -2$$
$$-3x + y = 2$$

The Method of Substitution

Exercises 39–50: If possible, solve the system of linear equations and check your answer.

39.
$$x + 2y = 0$$
$$3x + 7y = 1$$

40.
$$-2x - y = -2$$
$$3x + 4y = -7$$

41.
$$2x - 9y = -17$$
$$8x + 5y = 14$$

42.
$$3x + 6y = 0$$
$$4x - 2y = -5$$

43.
$$\tfrac{1}{2}x - y = -5$$
$$x + \tfrac{1}{2}y = 10$$

44.
$$-x - \tfrac{1}{3}y = -4$$
$$\tfrac{1}{3}x + 2y = 7$$

45.
$$3x - 2y = 5$$
$$-6x + 4y = -10$$

46.
$$\tfrac{1}{2}x - \tfrac{3}{4}y = \tfrac{1}{2}$$
$$\tfrac{1}{5}x - \tfrac{3}{10}y = \tfrac{1}{5}$$

47.
$$2x - 7y = 8$$
$$-3x + \tfrac{21}{2}y = 5$$

48.
$$0.6x - 0.2y = 2$$
$$-1.2x + 0.4y = 3$$

49.
$$0.2x - 0.1y = 0.5$$
$$0.4x + 0.3y = 2.5$$

50.
$$100x + 200y = 300$$
$$200x + 100y = 0$$

Exercises 51–64: If possible, solve the nonlinear system of equations.

51.
$$x^2 - y = 0$$
$$2x + y = 0$$

52.
$$x^2 - y = 3$$
$$x + y = 3$$

53.
$$xy = 8$$
$$x + y = 6$$

54.
$$2x - y = 0$$
$$2xy = 4$$

55.
$$x^2 + y^2 = 20$$
$$y = 2x$$

56.
$$x^2 + y^2 = 9$$
$$x + y = 3$$

57. $\sqrt{x} - 2y = 0$
$x - y = -2$

58. $x^2 + y^2 = 4$
$2x^2 + y = -3$

59. $2x^2 - y = 5$
$-4x^2 + 2y = -10$

60. $-6\sqrt{x} + 2y = -3$
$2\sqrt{x} - \frac{2}{3}y = 1$

61. $x^2 - y = 4$
$x^2 + y = 4$

62. $x^2 + x = y$
$2x^2 - y = 2$

63. $x^3 - x = 3y$
$x - y = 0$

64. $x^4 + y = 4$
$3x^2 - y = 0$

Exercises 65–68: Write a system of linear equations with two variables whose solution satisfies the problem. State what each variable represents. Then solve the system.

65. Screen Dimensions The screen of a rectangular television set is 2 inches wider than it is high. If the perimeter of the screen is 38 inches, find its dimensions.

66. Numbers The sum of two numbers is 300 and their difference is 8. Find the two numbers.

67. Tickets Admission prices to a movie are $4 for children and $7 for adults. If 75 tickets were sold for $456, how many of each type of ticket were sold?

68. Coins A sample of 16 dimes and quarters has a value of $2.65. How many of each type of coin are there?

Exercises 69 and 70: **Area and Perimeter** *The area of a rectangle with length l and width w is computed by $A(l, w) = lw$, and its perimeter is calculated by $P(l, w) = 2l + 2w$. Assume that $l > w$ and use the method of substitution to solve the system of equations for l and w.*

69. $A(l, w) = 35$
$P(l, w) = 24$

70. $A(l, w) = 300$
$P(l, w) = 70$

The Elimination Method

Exercises 71–80: Use elimination to solve the system of equations, if possible. Identify the system as consistent or inconsistent. If the system is consistent, state whether the equations are dependent or independent. Support your results graphically or numerically.

71. $x + y = 20$
$x - y = 8$

72. $2x + y = 15$
$x - y = 0$

73. $x + 3y = 10$
$x - 2y = -5$

74. $4x + 2y = 10$
$-2x - y = 10$

75. $x + y = 500$
$-x - y = -500$

76. $2x + 3y = 5$
$5x - 2y = 3$

77. $2x + 4y = 7$
$-x - 2y = 5$

78. $4x - 3y = 5$
$3x + 4y = 2$

79. $2x + 3y = 2$
$x - 2y = -5$

80. $x - 3y = 1$
$2x - 6y = 2$

Exercises 81–92: Solve the system, if possible.

81. $\frac{1}{2}x - y = 5$
$x - \frac{1}{2}y = 4$

82. $\frac{1}{2}x - \frac{1}{3}y = 1$
$\frac{1}{3}x - \frac{1}{2}y = 1$

83. $7x - 3y = -17$
$-21x + 9y = 51$

84. $-\frac{1}{3}x + \frac{1}{6}y = -1$
$2x - y = 6$

85. $\frac{2}{3}x + \frac{4}{3}y = \frac{1}{3}$
$-2x - 4y = 5$

86. $5x - 2y = 7$
$10x - 4y = 6$

87. $0.2x + 0.3y = 8$
$-0.4x + 0.2y = 0$

88. $2x - 3y = 1$
$3x - 2y = 2$

89. $2x + 3y = 7$
$-3x + 2y = -4$

90. $5x + 4y = -3$
$3x - 6y = -6$

91. $7x - 5y = -15$
$-2x + 3y = -2$

92. $-5x + 3y = -36$
$4x - 5y = 34$

Exercises 93–98: Use elimination to solve the nonlinear system of equations.

93. $x^2 + y = 12$
$x^2 - y = 6$

94. $x^2 + 2y = 15$
$2x^2 - y = 10$

95. $x^2 + y^2 = 25$
$x^2 + 7y = 37$

96. $x^2 + y^2 = 36$
$x^2 - 6y = 36$

97. $x^2 + y^2 = 4$
$2x^2 + y^2 = 8$

98. $x^2 + y^2 = 4$
$x^2 - y^2 = 4$

Using More Than One Method

Exercises 99–102: Solve the nonlinear system of equations (a) *symbolically and* (b) *graphically.*

99. $x^2 + y^2 = 16$
$x - y = 0$

100. $x^2 - y = 1$
$3x + y = -1$

101. $xy = 12$
$x - y = 4$

102. $x^2 + y^2 = 2$
$x^2 - y = 0$

Exercises 103–106: Solve the system of linear equations (a) *graphically,* (b) *numerically, and* (c) *symbolically.*

103. $2x + y = 1$
$x - 2y = 3$

104. $3x + 2y = -2$
$2x - y = -6$

105. $-2x + y = 0$
$7x - 2y = 3$

106. $x - 4y = 15$
$3x - 2y = 15$

Finding Approximate Solutions

Exercises 107–112: Approximate, to the nearest thousandth, any solutions to the nonlinear system of equations graphically.

107. $x^3 - 3x + y = 1$
$x^2 + 2y = 3$

108. $x^2 + y = 5$
$x + y^2 = 6$

109. $2x^3 - x^2 = 5y$
$2^{-x} - y = 0$

110. $x^4 - 3x^3 = y$
$\log x^2 - y = 0$

111. $e^{2x} + y = 4$
$\ln x - 2y = 0$

112. $3x^2 + y = 3$
$(0.3)^x + 4y = 1$

Applications

113. Population In 2010, the combined population of Minneapolis/St. Paul, Minnesota, was 670,000. The population of Minneapolis was 98,000 greater than the population of St. Paul. (*Source:* Census Bureau.)

(a) Write a system of equations whose solution gives the population of each city in thousands.

(b) Solve the system of equations.

(c) Is your system consistent or inconsistent? If it is consistent, state whether the equations are dependent or independent.

114. U.S. Energy Consumption In 2010, the United States consumed 94.58 quadrillion (10^{15}) Btu of energy from renewable and nonrenewable sources. It used 79.44 quadrillion Btu more from nonrenewable sources than from renewable sources. (*Source:* Department of Energy.)

(a) Write a system of equations whose solution gives the consumption of energy from renewable and nonrenewable sources (in quadrillion Btu).

(b) Solve the system of equations.

(c) Is your system consistent or inconsistent? If it is consistent, state whether the equations are dependent or independent.

115. Roof Truss (Refer to Example 11.) The weights W_1 and W_2 exerted on each rafter for the roof truss shown in the figure are determined by the system of linear equations. Solve the system.

$$W_1 + \sqrt{2}W_2 = 300$$
$$\sqrt{3}W_1 - \sqrt{2}W_2 = 0$$

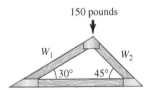

150 pounds

W_1 W_2

30°   45°

116. Time on the Internet From 2001 to 2010 the average number of hours that a user spent on the Internet each week increased by 180%. This percent increase amounted to 8 hours. Find the average number of hours that a user spent on the Internet each week in 2001 and 2010. (*Source:* eMarketer.)

117. Geometry (Refer to Example 12.) Find the radius and height of a cylindrical container with a volume of 50 cubic inches and a lateral surface area of 65 square inches.

118. Geometry (Refer to Example 12.) Determine if it is possible to construct a cylindrical container, *including* the top and bottom, with a volume of 38 cubic inches and a surface area of 38 square inches.

119. Dimensions of a Box A box has an *open* top, rectangular sides, and a square base. Its volume is 576 cubic inches, and its outside surface area is 336 square inches. Find the dimensions of the box.

120. Dimensions of a Box A box has rectangular sides, and its rectangular top and base are twice as long as they are wide. Its volume is 588 cubic inches, and its outside surface area is 448 square inches. Find its dimensions.

121. Bank Theft The total incidences of bank theft in 2009 and 2010 was 11,693. There were 437 fewer incidences in 2009 than in 2010. (*Source:* FBI.)

(a) Write a system of equations whose solution represents the incidences of bank theft in each of these years.

(b) Solve the system symbolically.

(c) Solve the system graphically.

122. e-Waste The United States and China together produce 5.9 million tons of e-waste each year. About 0.7 million more tons are produced in the United States than in China.

(a) Write a system of equations whose solution represents the amount of e-waste produced in each country.

(b) Solve the system symbolically.

(c) Solve the system graphically.

123. Student Loans A student takes out two loans totaling $3000 to help pay for college expenses. One loan is at 8% interest, and the other is at 10%. Interest for both loans is compounded annually.

(a) If the first-year interest is $264, write a system of equations whose solution is the amount of each loan.

(b) Find the amount of each loan.

124. Student Loans (Refer to Exercise 123.) Suppose that both loans have an interest rate of 10% and the total first-year interest is $300. If possible, determine the amount of each loan. Interpret your results.

125. Student Loans (Refer to Exercises 123 and 124.) Suppose that both loans are at 10% and the total annual interest is $264. If possible, determine the amount of each loan. Interpret your results.

126. Investments A student invests $5000 at two annual interest rates, 5% and 7%. After 1 year the student receives a total of $325 in interest. How much did the student invest at each interest rate?

127. Air Speed A jet airliner travels 1680 miles in 3 hours with a tail wind. The return trip, into the wind, takes 3.5 hours. Find both the speed of the jet with no wind and the wind speed. (*Hint:* First find the ground speed of the airplane in each direction.)

128. River Current A tugboat can pull a barge 60 miles upstream in 15 hours. The same tugboat and barge can make the return trip downstream in 6 hours. Determine the speed of the current in the river.

129. Maximizing Area Suppose a rectangular pen for a pet is to be made using 40 feet of fence. Let l represent its length and w its width, with $l \geq w$.
(a) Find l and w if the area is 91 square feet.

(b) Write a formula for the area A in terms of w.

(c) What is the maximum area possible for the pen? Interpret this result.

130. The Toll of War American battlefield deaths in World Wars I and II totaled about 345,000. There were about 5.5 times as many deaths in World War II as World War I. Find the number of American battlefield deaths in each war. Round your answers to the nearest whole number. (*Source:* Defense Department.)

131. Height and Weight The relationship between a professional basketball player's height h in inches and weight w in pounds was modeled using two samples of players. The resulting modeling equations for the two samples were $w = 7.46h - 374$ and $w = 7.93h - 405$. Assume that $65 \leq h \leq 85$.
(a) Use each equation to predict the weight of a professional basketball player who is 6′11″.

(b) Determine graphically the height where the two models give the same weight.

(c) For each model, what change in weight is associated with a 1-inch increase in height?

132. Heart Rate In one study a group of athletes were exercised to exhaustion. Let x and y represent an athlete's heart rate 5 seconds and 10 seconds after stopping exercise, respectively. It was found that the maximum heart rate H for these athletes satisfied the following two equations.

$$H = \quad 0.491x + 0.468y + 11.2$$
$$H = -0.981x + 1.872y + 26.4$$

If an athlete had a maximum heart rate of $H = 180$, determine x and y graphically. Interpret your answer. (*Source:* V. Thomas, *Science and Sport*.)

133. Surface Area and the Human Body The surface area of the skin covering the human body is a function of more than one variable. A taller person tends to have a larger surface area, as does a heavier person. Both height and weight influence the surface area of a person's body. A formula used to determine the surface area of a person's body in square meters is given by

$$S(w, h) = 0.007184w^{0.425}h^{0.725},$$

where w is weight in kilograms and h is height in centimeters. Use S to estimate the surface area of a person who is 65 inches (165.1 centimeters) tall and weighs 154 pounds (70 kilograms). (*Source:* H. Lancaster, *Quantitative Methods in Biological and Medical Sciences*.)

Exercises 134–136: **Skin and the Human Body** (*Refer to Exercise 133.*) *Estimate, to the nearest tenth, the surface area of a person with weight w and height h.*

134. $w = 86$ kilograms, $h = 185$ centimeters

135. $w = 132$ pounds, $h = 62$ inches

136. $w = 220$ pounds, $h = 75$ inches

Joint Variation

Exercises 137 and 138: Approximate the constant of variation to the nearest hundredth.

137. The variable z varies jointly with the second power of x and the third power of y. When $x = 2$ and $y = 2.5$, $z = 31.9$.

138. The variable z varies jointly with the 1.5 power of x and the 2.1 power of y. When $x = 4$ and $y = 3.5$, $z = 397$.

139. The variable z varies jointly with the square root of x and the cube root of y. If $z = 10.8$ when $x = 4$ and $y = 8$, find z when $x = 16$ and $y = 27$.

140. The variable z varies jointly with the third powers of x and y. If $z = 2160$ when $x = 3$ and $y = 4$, find z when $x = 2$ and $y = 5$.

141. **Wind Power** The electrical power generated by a windmill varies jointly with the square of the diameter of the area swept out by the blades and the cube of the wind velocity. If a windmill with an 8-foot diameter and a 10-mile-per-hour wind generates 2405 watts, how much power would be generated if the blades swept out an area 6 feet in diameter and the wind was 20 miles per hour?

142. **Strength of a Beam** The strength of a rectangular beam varies jointly with its width and the square of its thickness. If a beam 5.5 inches wide and 2.5 inches thick supports 600 pounds, how much can a similar beam that is 4 inches wide and 1.5 inches thick support?

143. **Volume of Wood** (Refer to Example 14.) One cord of wood contains 128 cubic feet. Estimate the number of cords in a tree that is 105 feet tall and has a diameter of 38 inches.

144. **Carpeting** The cost of carpet for a rectangular room varies jointly with its width and length. If a room 10 feet wide and 12 feet long costs $1560 to carpet, find the cost to carpet a room that is 11 feet by 23 feet. Interpret the constant of variation.

145. **Surface Area** Use the results of Exercise 133 to find a formula for $S(w, h)$ that calculates the surface area of a person if w is given in *pounds* and h is given in *inches*.

146. **Surface Area** Use the results of Exercise 145 to solve Exercises 135 and 136.

Writing about Mathematics

147. Give an example of a quantity occurring in everyday life that can be computed by a function of more than one input. Identify the inputs and the output.

148. Give an example of a system of linear equations with two variables. Explain how to solve the system graphically and symbolically

9.2 Systems of Inequalities in Two Variables

- Solve inequalities in two variables graphically
- Solve systems of inequalities in two variables
- Learn basic properties of linear programming in two variables

Introduction

For people who regularly consume caffeinated beverages, too much caffeine may cause "caffeine jitters," while too little caffeine may bring on a caffeine withdrawal headache. These caffeine amounts vary depending on an individual's weight. Figure 9.21 shows one possible relationship between a person's weight and the effects of caffeine, while Table 9.1 gives the caffeine content of selected beverages. To describe the middle shaded region in the figure, we need a *system of linear inequalities*. See Exercises 37–40. (*Source:* Mayo Clinic)

Effects of Caffeine

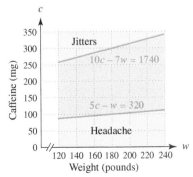

Figure 9.21

Beverage Caffeine Content

Beverage	Caffeine
7-Up: 12 oz	0 mg
Mt Dew: 12 oz	54 mg
Red Bull: 8.4 oz	80 mg
Brewed Coffee: 8 oz	108 mg
Monster: 16 oz	160 mg
Starbucks Tall Coffee: 12 oz	260 mg
All City NRG: 16 oz	300 mg

Source: Energy Fiend

Table 9.1

Systems of Linear and Nonlinear Inequalities

A linear inequality in two variables can be written as

$$ax + by \leq c,$$

where a, b, and c are constants with a and b not equal to zero. (The symbol $\leq$ can be replaced by $\geq$, $<$, or $>$.) If an ordered pair (x, y) makes the inequality a true statement, then (x, y) is a solution. The set of all solutions is called the *solution set*. The graph of an inequality includes all points (x, y) in the solution set.

The graph of a linear inequality is a (shaded) **half-plane,** which may include the boundary. To determine which half-plane to shade, select a **test point** that is not on the boundary. If the test point satisfies the given inequality, then shade the half-plane containing the test point. Otherwise, shade the other half-plane. For example, the following See the Concept demonstrates how to graph the solution to the inequality $3x - 2y \leq 6$.

See the Concept: Graphing a Linear Inequality

To graph $3x - 2y \leq 6$:

Ⓐ Solve the inequality for y.

$$3x - 2y \leq 6$$
$$-2y \leq -3x + 6$$
$$y \geq \tfrac{3}{2}x - 3$$

Ⓑ Graph the *equation* $y = \tfrac{3}{2}x - 3$.

Ⓒ Choose a test point that is not on the line.

Ⓓ Substitute the test point $(0, 0)$ in the given inequality. Since $3(0) - 2(0) \leq 6$ is true, shade the half-plane containing the test point.

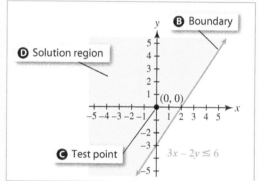

EXAMPLE 1 Graphing inequalities

Graph the solution set to each inequality.
(a) $2x - 3y \leq -6$ (b) $x^2 + y^2 < 9$

SOLUTION

(a) For $2x - 3y \leq -6$ start by graphing the line $2x - 3y = -6$, as in Figure 9.22. Note that this line is solid because equality is included. We can determine which side of the line to shade by using test points. For example, the test point $(-2, 2)$ lies above the line and the test point $(0, 0)$ lies below the line.

The Boundary

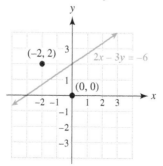

Figure 9.22

Checking Test Points

Test Point	$2x - 3y \leq -6$	True or False?
$(-2, 2)$	$2(-2) - 3(2) \overset{?}{\leq} -6$	True
$(0, 0)$	$2(0) - 3(0) \overset{?}{\leq} -6$	False

Table 9.2

In Table 9.2, the test point $(-2, 2)$ satisfies the given inequality, so shade the region above the line that contains the point $(-2, 2)$. See Figure 9.23.

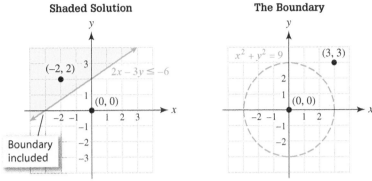

Shaded Solution

The Boundary

Figure 9.23   Figure 9.24

(b) For $x^2 + y^2 < 9$ start by graphing the circle $x^2 + y^2 = 9$, as shown in Figure 9.24. Note that this circle is dashed because equality is *not* included. The test point $(3, 3)$ lies outside the circle and the test point $(0, 0)$ lies inside the circle.

Checking Test Points

Test Point	$x^2 + y^2 < 9$	True or False?
$(3, 3)$	$3^2 + 3^2 \overset{?}{<} 9$	False
$(0, 0)$	$0^2 + 0^2 \overset{?}{<} 9$	True

Table 9.3

In Table 9.3, the test point $(0, 0)$ satisfies the given inequality, so shade the region inside the circle. The actual circle is not part of the solution set. See Figure 9.25.

> **Now Try Exercises 7 and 9**

Shaded Solution

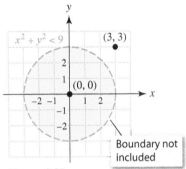

Figure 9.25

In Section 9.1, we saw that systems of equations could be linear or nonlinear. Similarly, systems of inequalities can be linear or nonlinear. The next example illustrates a system of each type. Both are solved graphically.

EXAMPLE 2   Solving systems of inequalities graphically

Solve each system of inequalities by shading the solution set. Identify one solution.

(a) $\quad y > x^2$ **(b)** $x + 3y \leq 9$
$\quad\quad x + y < 4$ $\quad\quad 2x - y \leq -1$

SOLUTION

(a) This is a nonlinear system. Graph the parabola $y = x^2$ and the line $y = 4 - x$. Since $y > x^2$ and $y < 4 - x$, the region satisfying the system lies above the parabola and below the line. It does not include the boundaries, which are shown using a dashed line and curve. See Figure 9.26.

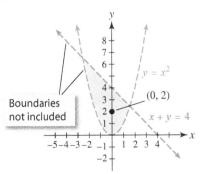

Figure 9.26

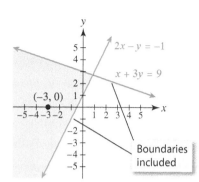

Figure 9.27

Any point in the shaded region represents a solution. For example, $(0, 2)$ lies in the shaded region and is a solution, since $x = 0$ and $y = 2$ satisfy *both* inequalities.

(b) Begin by solving each linear inequality for y.

$$y \leq -\frac{1}{3}x + 3$$

$$y \geq 2x + 1$$

Graph $y = -\frac{1}{3}x + 3$ and $y = 2x + 1$. The region satisfying the system is below the first (red) line and above the second (blue) line. Because equality is included, the boundaries, which are shown as solid lines in Figure 9.27, are part of the region. The point $(-3, 0)$ is a solution, since it satisfies both inequalities.

> **Now Try Exercises 17 and 19**

Calculator Help

To shade a graph, see Appendix A (pages AP-10 and AP-12).

Graphing Calculators (Optional) Graphing calculators can be used to shade regions in the xy-plane. See Figure 9.28. The solution set shown in Figure 9.26 is also shown in Figure 9.29, where a graphing calculator has been used. However, the boundary is not dashed.

Figures 9.30 and 9.31 show a different method of shading a solution set; we have shaded the area below $y_1 = -\frac{1}{3}x + 3$ and above $y_2 = 2x + 1$. The solution set is the region shaded with both vertical *and* horizontal lines and corresponds to the shaded region in Figure 9.27.

Shading using the "Shade" Function

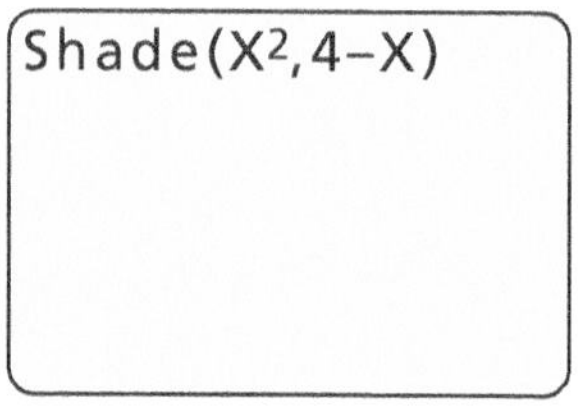

Figure 9.28

Figure 9.29

Shading using the Y= Menu

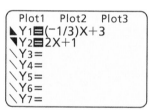

Figure 9.30

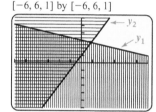

Figure 9.31

An Application of Inequalities The next example discusses how a system of inequalities can be used to determine where forests, grasslands, and deserts will occur.

EXAMPLE 3 Modeling plant growth

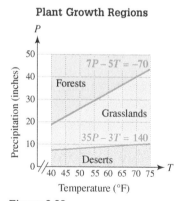

Figure 9.32

If a region has too little precipitation, it will be a desert. Forests tend to exist in regions where temperatures are relatively low and there is sufficient rainfall. At other levels of precipitation and temperature, grasslands may prevail. Figure 9.32 illustrates the relationship among forests, grasslands, and deserts, as suggested by annual average temperature T in degrees Fahrenheit and precipitation P in inches. (*Source:* A. Miller and J. Thompson, *Elements of Meteorology.*)

(a) Determine a system of linear inequalities that describes where grasslands occur.

(b) Bismarck, North Dakota, has an annual average temperature of 40°F and precipitation of 15 inches. According to the graph, what type of plant growth would you expect near Bismarck? Do these values satisfy the system of inequalities from part (a)?

SOLUTION

(a) Grasslands occur for ordered pairs (T, P) lying between the two lines in Figure 9.32. The boundary between deserts and grasslands is determined by $35P - 3T = 140$. Solving for P (the variable on the vertical axis) results in

$$P = \frac{3}{35}T + \frac{140}{35}.$$

Grasslands grow where values of P are above the line. This region is described by $P > \frac{3}{35}T + \frac{140}{35}$, or equivalently, $35P - 3T > 140$. In a similar manner, the region below the boundary between grasslands and forests is represented by the inequality $7P - 5T < -70$. Thus grasslands satisfy the following system of inequalities.

$$35P - 3T > 140$$
$$7P - 5T < -70$$

Grasslands satisfy both inequalities.

(b) For Bismarck, $T = 40$ and $P = 15$. Figure 9.32 shows that the point $(40, 15)$ lies between the two lines, so the graph predicts that grasslands will exist around Bismarck. Substituting these values for T and P into the system of inequalities results in the following true statements.

$$35(15) - 3(40) = 405 > 140 \checkmark \quad \text{True}$$
$$7(15) - 5(40) = -95 < -70 \checkmark \quad \text{True}$$

The temperature and precipitation values for Bismarck satisfy the system of inequalities for grasslands.

Now Try Exercises 43 and 45

Linear Programming

Linear programming is a procedure used to optimize quantities such as cost and profit. It was developed during World War II as a method of efficiently allocating supplies. Linear programming applications frequently contain thousands of variables and are solved by computers. However, here we focus on problems involving two variables.

A linear programming problem consists of a linear **objective function** and a system of linear inequalities called **constraints**. The solution set for the system of linear inequalities is called the set of **feasible solutions**. The objective function describes a quantity that is to be optimized. For example, linear programming is often used to maximize profit or minimize cost. The following example illustrates these concepts.

EXAMPLE 4 Finding maximum profit

Suppose a small company manufactures two products—car radios and stereos. Each radio results in a profit of $15, and each stereo provides a profit of $35. Due to demand, the company must produce at least 5 and not more than 25 radios per day. The number of radios cannot exceed the number of stereos, and the number of stereos cannot exceed 30. How many of each should the company manufacture to obtain maximum profit?

SOLUTION Let x be the number of car radios produced daily and y be the number of stereos produced daily. Since the profit from x radios is $15x$ dollars and the profit from y stereos is $35y$ dollars, the total daily profit P is given by

$$P = 15x + 35y.$$

The company produces from 5 to 25 radios per day, so the inequalities

$$x \geq 5 \quad \text{and} \quad x \leq 25$$

must be satisfied. The requirements that the number of radios cannot exceed the number of stereos and the number of stereos cannot exceed 30 indicate that

$$x \leq y \quad \text{and} \quad y \leq 30.$$

Since the numbers of radios and stereos cannot be negative, we have

$$x \geq 0 \quad \text{and} \quad y \geq 0.$$

Listing all the constraints on production gives

$$x \geq 5, \qquad x \leq 25, \qquad y \leq 30, \qquad x \leq y, \qquad x \geq 0, \quad \text{and} \quad y \geq 0.$$

Graphing these constraints results in the shaded region shown in Figure 9.33. This shaded region is the set of feasible solutions. The vertices (or corners) of this region are (5, 5), (25, 25), (25, 30), and (5, 30).

It can be shown that maximum profit occurs at a vertex of the region of feasible solutions. Thus we evaluate P at each vertex, as shown in Table 9.4.

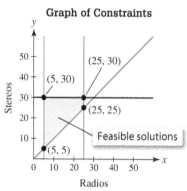

Graph of Constraints

Figure 9.33

Checking Vertices in the Profit Equation

Vertex	$P = 15x + 35y$
(5, 5)	$15(5) + 35(5) = 250$
(25, 25)	$15(25) + 35(25) = 1250$
(25, 30)	$15(25) + 35(30) = 1425$ — Maximum profit
(5, 30)	$15(5) + 35(30) = 1125$

Table 9.4

The maximum value of P is 1425 at vertex (25, 30). Thus the maximum profit is $1425, and it occurs when 25 car radios and 30 stereos are manufactured.

Now Try Exercise 63

The following theorem holds for linear programming problems.

FUNDAMENTAL THEOREM OF LINEAR PROGRAMMING

If the optimal value for a linear programming problem exists, then it occurs at a vertex of the region of feasible solutions.

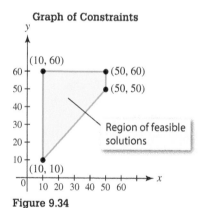

Graph of Constraints

Figure 9.34

Justification of the Fundamental Theorem To better understand the fundamental theorem of linear programming, consider the following example. Suppose that we want to maximize $P = 30x + 70y$ subject to the following four constraints:

$$x \geq 10, \qquad x \leq 50, \qquad y \geq x, \quad \text{and} \quad y \leq 60.$$

The corresponding region of feasible solutions is shown in Figure 9.34.

Each value of P determines a unique line. For example, if $P = 7000$, then the equation for P becomes $30x + 70y = 7000$. The resulting line, shown in Figure 9.35, does not intersect the region of feasible solutions. Thus there are no values for x and y that lie in this region and result in a profit of 7000. Figure 9.35 also shows the lines that result from letting $P = 0, 1000,$ and 3000. If $P = 1000$, then the line intersects the region of feasible solutions only at the vertex (10, 10). This means that if $x = 10$ and $y = 10$, then $P = 30(10) + 70(10) = 1000$. If $P = 3000$, then the line $30x + 70y = 3000$ intersects the region of feasible solutions infinitely many times. However, it appears that values greater than 3000 are possible for P.

In Figure 9.36 lines are drawn for $P = 5700, 6300,$ and 7000. Notice that there are no points of intersection for $P = 6300$ or $P = 7000$, but there is one vertex in the region of feasible solutions at (50, 60) that gives $P = 5700$. Thus the maximum value of P is 5700 and this maximum occurs at a vertex of the region of feasible solutions. The fundamental theorem of linear programming generalizes this result.

How the Objective Function Intersects the Region of Feasible Solutions

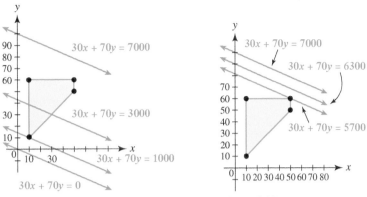

Figure 9.35   Figure 9.36

EXAMPLE 5   Finding the minimum of an objective function

Find the minimum value of $C = 2x + 3y$ subject to the following constraints.

$$x + y \geq 4$$
$$2x + y \leq 8$$
$$x \geq 0, \quad y \geq 0$$

SOLUTION   Sketch the region determined by the constraints and find all vertices, as shown in Figure 9.37.

Evaluate the objective function C at each vertex, as shown in Table 9.5.

Graph of Constraints

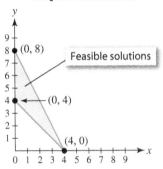

Figure 9.37

Checking Vertices in the Objective Function

Vertex	$C = 2x + 3y$	
(4, 0)	$2(4) + 3(0) = 8$	Minimum value
(0, 8)	$2(0) + 3(8) = 24$	
(0, 4)	$2(0) + 3(4) = 12$	

Table 9.5

The minimum value for C is 8 and it occurs at vertex (4, 0), or when $x = 4$ and $y = 0$.

Now Try Exercise 59

The following procedure describes how to solve a linear programming problem.

SOLVING A LINEAR PROGRAMMING PROBLEM

STEP 1: Read the problem carefully. Consider making a table to display the given information.

STEP 2: Use the table to write the objective function and all the constraints.

STEP 3: Sketch a graph of the region of feasible solutions. Identify all vertices, or corner points.

STEP 4: Evaluate the objective function at each vertex. A maximum (or a minimum) occurs at a vertex. If the region is unbounded, a maximum (or minimum) may not exist.

EXAMPLE 6   Minimizing cost

A breeder is buying two brands of food, A and B, for her animals. Each serving is a mixture of the two foods and should contain at least 40 grams of protein and at least 30 grams of fat. Brand A costs 90 cents per unit, and Brand B costs 60 cents per unit. Each unit of Brand A contains 20 grams of protein and 10 grams of fat, whereas each unit of Brand B contains 10 grams of protein and 10 grams of fat. Determine how much of each brand should be bought to obtain a minimum cost per serving.

SOLUTION

STEP 1: After reading the problem carefully, begin by listing the information, as illustrated in Table 9.6. (Your table may be different.)

Protein and Fat Content by Brand, with Cost

Brand	Units	Protein/Unit	Total Protein	Fat/Unit	Total Fat	Cost
A	x	20	$20x$	10	$10x$	$90x$
B	y	10	$10y$	10	$10y$	$60y$

Minimum Total Protein ———— 40   30 —— Minimum Total Fat

Table 9.6

STEP 2: If x units of Brand A are purchased at 90¢ per unit and y units of Brand B are purchased at 60¢ per unit, then the cost C is given by $C = 90x + 60y$. Each serving requires at least 40 grams of protein. If x units of Brand A are bought (each containing 20 grams of protein), y units of Brand B are bought (each containing 10 grams of protein), and each serving requires at least 40 grams of protein, then we can write $20x + 10y \geq 40$. Similarly, since each serving requires at least 30 grams of fat, we can write $10x + 10y \geq 30$. The linear programming problem can be written as follows.

Minimize: $C = 90x + 60y$ Cost

Subject to: $20x + 10y \geq 40$ Protein

$10x + 10y \geq 30$ Fat

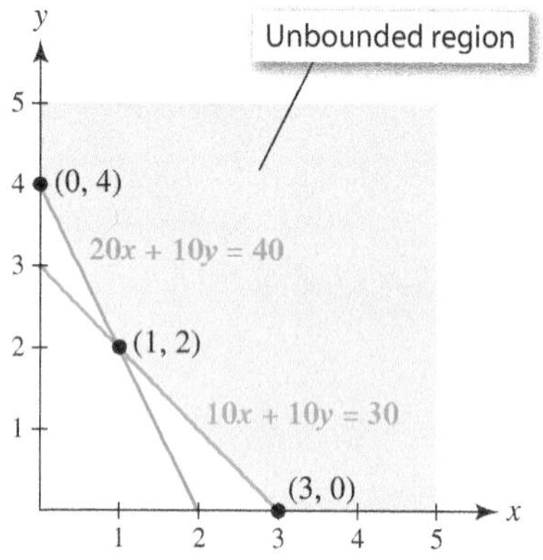

$x \geq 0, \quad y \geq 0$

Graph of Constraints

Unbounded region

$20x + 10y = 40$

$(0, 4)$

$(1, 2)$

$10x + 10y = 30$

$(3, 0)$

Figure 9.38

STEP 3: The region of feasible solutions is unbounded and shown in Figure 9.38. The vertices for this region are $(0, 4)$, $(1, 2)$, and $(3, 0)$.

STEP 4: Evaluate the objective function C at each vertex, as shown in Table 9.7.

Checking Vertices in
the Cost Equation

Vertex	$C = 90x + 60y$
$(0, 4)$	240
$(1, 2)$	210 —— Minimum cost
$(3, 0)$	270

Table 9.7

The minimum cost occurs when 1 unit of Brand A and 2 units of Brand B are mixed, at a cost of $2.10 per serving.

Now Try Exercise 65

9.2 Putting It All Together

The following table summarizes some important mathematical concepts from this section.

CONCEPT	COMMENTS	EXAMPLE
Linear inequality in two variables	$ax + by \leq c$ ($\leq$ may be replaced by $<$, $>$, or $\geq$) The solution set is typically a shaded region in the xy-plane.	$2x - 3y \leq 12$ $-2x + y \leq 4$
Linear programming	In a linear programming problem, the maximum or minimum of an objective function is found, subject to constraints. If a solution exists, it occurs at a vertex of the region of feasible solutions.	Maximize the objective function $$P = 2x + 3y$$ subject to the following constraints. $$2x + y \leq 6$$ $$x + 2y \leq 6$$ $$x \geq 0, \ y \geq 0$$ The maximum of $P = 10$ occurs at vertex (2, 2).

9.2 Exercises

Inequalities

Exercises 1–12: Graph the solution set to the inequality.

1. $x \geq y$

2. $y > -3$

3. $x < 1$

4. $y > 2x$

5. $x + y \leq 2$

6. $x + y > -3$

7. $2x + y > 4$

8. $2x + 3y \leq 6$

9. $x^2 + y^2 > 4$

10. $x^2 + y^2 \leq 1$

11. $x^2 + y \leq 2$

12. $2x^2 - y < 1$

Exercises 13–16: Match the system of inequalities with the appropriate graph (a–d). Use the graph to identify one solution.

13. $x + y \geq 2$
$x - y \leq 1$

14. $2x - y > 0$
$x - 2y \leq 1$

15. $\frac{1}{2}x^3 - y > 0$
$2x - y \leq 1$

16. $x^2 + y \leq 4$
$x^2 - y \leq 2$

a.

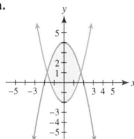

b.

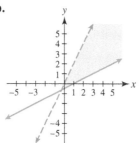

c.

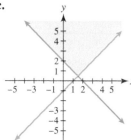

d.

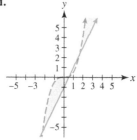

Exercises 17–24: Graph the solution set to the system of inequalities. Use the graph to identify one solution.

17. $y \geq x^2$
$x + y \leq 6$

18. $y \leq \sqrt{x}$
$y \geq 1$

19. $x + 2y > -2$
$x + 2y < 5$

20. $x - y \leq 3$
$x + y \leq 3$

21. $x^2 + y^2 \leq 16$
$x + y < 2$

22. $x^2 + y \leq 4$
$x^2 - y \leq 3$

23. $x^2 + y > 2$
$x^2 + y^2 \leq 9$

24. $x^2 + y^2 > 4$
$x^2 + y^2 < 16$

Exercises 25–36: Graph the solution set to the system of inequalities.

25. $x + 2y \leq 4$
$2x - y \geq 6$

26. $3x - y \leq 3$
$x + 2y \leq 2$

27. $3x + 2y < 6$
$x + 3y \leq 6$

28. $4x + 3y \geq 12$
$2x + 6y \geq 4$

29. $x - 2y \geq 0$
$x - 3y \leq 3$

30. $2x - 4y \geq 4$
$x + y \leq 0$

31. $x^2 + y^2 \leq 4$
$y \geq 1$

32. $x^2 - y \leq 0$
$x^2 + y^2 \leq 6$

33. $2x^2 + y \leq 0$
$x^2 - y \leq 3$

34. $x^2 + 2y \leq 4$
$x^2 - y \leq 0$

35. $x^2 + y^2 \leq 4$
$x^2 + 2y \leq 2$

36. $2x + 3y \leq 6$
$\frac{1}{2}x^2 - y \leq 2$

Applications

Exercises 37–40: **Caffeine Consumption** *(Refer to the introduction to this section.) The following graph shows one possible relationship between a person's weight and the effects of caffeine.* (**Source:** Mayo Clinic)

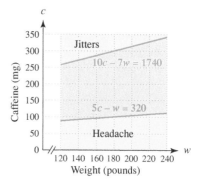
Weight (pounds)

37. What does the graph indicate about the effects of caffeine on 140-pound person who has consumed 335 mg of caffeine?

38. Suppose a 180-pound person wishes to avoid both a headache and the jitters. What range of caffeine consumption is suggested?

39. (Refer to Table 9.1.) For what weights could a person drink a 16-ounce can of All City NRG without experiencing the jitters?

40. (Refer to Table 9.1.) According to this graph, does a single 12-ounce can of Mountain Dew contain enough caffeine for most people to avoid a headache?

41. **Traffic Control** The figure shows two intersections, labeled A and B, that involve one-way streets. The numbers and variables represent the average traffic flow rates measured in vehicles per hour. For example, an average of 500 vehicles per hour enter intersection A from the west, whereas 150 vehicles per hour enter this intersection from the north. A stoplight will control the unknown traffic flow denoted by the variables x and y. Use the fact that the number of vehicles entering an intersection must equal the number leaving to determine x and y.

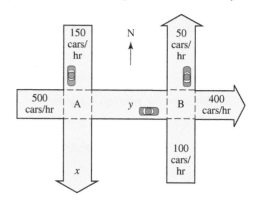

42. Traffic Control (Refer to Exercise 41.) Suppose that the number of vehicles entering intersection A from the west varies between 400 and 600. If all other traffic flows remain the same as in the figure, what effect does this have on the ranges of the values for x and y?

Exercises 43–46: **Weight and Height** *The following graph shows a weight and height chart. The weight w is listed in pounds and the height h in inches. The shaded area is a recommended region. (**Source:** Department of Agriculture.)*

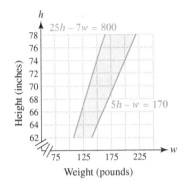

43. What does this chart indicate about an individual who weighs 125 pounds and is 70 inches tall?

44. Use the graph to estimate the recommended weight range for a person 74 inches tall.

45. Use the graph to find a system of linear inequalities that describes the recommended region.

46. Explain why inequalities are more appropriate than equalities for describing recommended weight and height combinations.

Linear Programming

Exercises 47–50: Shade the region of feasible solutions for the following constraints.

47. $x + y \leq 4$
$\quad x + y \geq 1$
$\quad x \geq 0, y \geq 0$

48. $x + 2y \leq 8$
$\quad 2x + y \geq 2$
$\quad x \geq 0, y \geq 0$

49. $3x + 2y \leq 12$
$\quad 2x + 3y \leq 12$
$\quad x \geq 0, y \geq 0$

50. $x + y \leq 4$
$\quad x + 4y \geq 4$
$\quad x \geq 0, y \geq 0$

Exercises 51 and 52: The graph shows a region of feasible solutions for P. Find the maximum and minimum values of P.

51. $P = 3x + 5y$

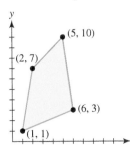

52. $P = 6x + y$

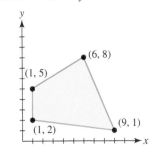

Exercises 53–56: The graph shows a region of feasible solutions for C. Find the maximum and minimum values of C.

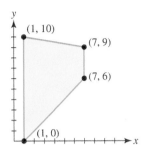

53. $C = 3x + 5y$

54. $C = 5x + 5y$

55. $C = 10y$

56. $C = 3x - y$

Exercises 57 and 58: Write a system of linear inequalities that describes the shaded region.

57.

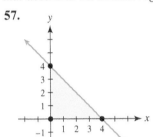

58.

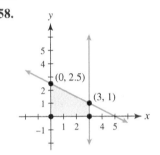

59. Find the minimum value of $C = 4x + 2y$ subject to the following constraints.

$$x + y \geq 3$$
$$2x + 3y \leq 12$$
$$x \geq 0, y \geq 0$$

60. Find the maximum value of $P = 3x + 5y$ subject to the following constraints.

$$3x + y \leq 8$$
$$x + 3y \leq 8$$
$$x \geq 0, y \geq 0$$

Exercises 61 and 62: If possible, maximize and minimize z subject to the given constraints.

61. $z = 7x + 6y$

$$x + y \leq 8$$
$$x + y \geq 4$$
$$x \geq 0, y \geq 0$$

62. $z = 8x + 3y$

$$4x + y \geq 12$$
$$x + 2y \geq 6$$
$$x \geq 0, y \geq 0$$

63. Maximizing Profit Rework Example 4 if the profit from each radio is $20 and the profit from each CD player is $15.

64. Maximizing Revenue A refinery produces both gasoline and fuel oil, and sells gasoline for $4.00 per gallon and fuel oil for $3.60 per gallon. The refinery can produce at most 600,000 gallons a day but must produce at least 2 gallons of fuel oil for every gallon of gasoline. At least 150,000 gallons of fuel oil must be made each day for the coming winter. Determine how much of each type of fuel should be produced to maximize revenue.

65. Minimizing Cost (Refer to Example 6.) A breeder is mixing Brand A and Brand B. Each serving should contain at least 60 grams of protein and 30 grams of fat. Brand A costs 80 cents per unit, and Brand B costs 50 cents per unit. Each unit of Brand A contains 15 grams of protein and 10 grams of fat, whereas each unit of Brand B contains 20 grams of protein and 5 grams of fat. Determine how much of each food should be bought to achieve a minimum cost per serving.

66. Pet Food Cost A pet owner is buying two brands of food, X and Y, for his animals. Each serving of the mixture of the two foods should contain at least 60 grams of protein and 40 grams of fat. Brand X costs 75 cents per unit, and Brand Y costs 50 cents per unit. Each unit of Brand X contains 20 grams of protein and 10 grams of fat, whereas each unit of Brand Y contains 10 grams of protein and 10 grams of fat. How much of each brand should be bought to obtain a minimum cost per serving?

67. Raising Animals A breeder can raise no more than 50 hamsters and mice and no more than 20 hamsters. If she sells the hamsters for $15 each and the mice for $10 each, find the maximum revenue produced.

68. Maximizing Storage A manager wants to buy filing cabinets. Cabinet X costs $100, requires 6 square feet of floor space, and holds 8 cubic feet. Cabinet Y costs $200, requires 8 square feet of floor space, and holds 12 cubic feet. No more than $1400 can be spent, and the office has room for no more than 72 square feet of cabinets. The manager wants the maximum storage capacity within the limits imposed by funds and space. How many of each type of cabinet should be bought?

69. Maximizing Profit A business manufactures two parts, X and Y. Machines A and B are needed to make each part. To make part X, machine A is needed for 4 hours and machine B is needed for 2 hours. To make part Y, machine A is needed for 1 hour and machine B is needed for 3 hours. Machine A is available for 40 hours each week and machine B is available for 30 hours. The profit from part X is $500 and the profit from part Y is $600. How many parts of each type should be made to maximize weekly profit?

70. Minimizing Cost Two substances, X and Y, are found in pet food. Each substance contains the ingredients A and B. Substance X is 20% ingredient A and 50% ingredient B. Substance Y is 50% ingredient A and 30% ingredient B. The cost of substance X is $2 per pound, and the cost of substance Y is $3 per pound. The pet store needs at least 251 pounds of ingredient A and at least 200 pounds of ingredient B. If cost is to be minimal, how many pounds of each substance should be ordered? Find the minimum cost.

Writing about Mathematics

71. Give the general form of a system of linear inequalities in two variables. Discuss what distinguishes a system of linear inequalities from a nonlinear system of inequalities.

72. Discuss how to use test points to solve a linear inequality. Give an example.

CHECKING BASIC CONCEPTS FOR SECTIONS 9.1 AND 9.2

1. Evaluate $d(13, 18)$ if

$$d(x, y) = \sqrt{(x - 1)^2 + (y - 2)^2}.$$

2. Solve the nonlinear system of equations using the method of substitution.

$$2x^2 - y = 0$$
$$3x + 2y = 7$$

3. Solve $z = x^2 + y^2$ for y.

4. Solve the system of linear equations by using elimination.

$$3x - 2y = 4$$
$$-x + 6y = 8$$

5. Graph the solution set to $3x - 2y \leq 6$.

6. Graph the solution set to the system of inequalities. Use the graph to identify one solution.

$$x^2 - y < 3$$
$$x - y \geq 1$$

7. HDTV Sales In 2010 there were 220 million HDTVs sold worldwide. For every 2 HDTVs sold with plasma screens, 9 HDTVs were sold with LCD screens. (**Source:** Home Theater Review.)

(a) Write a linear system whose solution gives the number of HDTVs sold (in millions) with plasma screens and the number of HDTVs sold (in millions) with LCD screens.

(b) Solve the system and interpret the result.

9.3 Systems of Linear Equations in Three Variables

- Learn basic concepts about systems in three variables
- Solve systems using elimination and substitution
- Identify systems with no solutions
- Solve systems with infinitely many solutions

Introduction

In Section 9.1 we discussed how to solve systems of linear equations in two variables. Systems of linear equations can have any number of variables. For example, Internet search sites such as Google, Yahoo!, and Bing use algorithms that involve linear systems with millions of variables. Computers are necessary to solve these systems efficiently. However, in this section we discuss solving systems of linear equations containing three variables by hand.

Basic Concepts

When writing systems of linear equations in three variables it is common, but not necessary, to use the variables x, y, and z. For example,

$$\left.\begin{array}{r} 2x - 3y + 4z = 4 \\ -y + 2z = 0 \\ x + 5y - 6z = 7 \end{array}\right\}$$ Linear System with three variables

represents a system of linear equations in three variables. The solution to this system is given by $x = 3$, $y = 2$, and $z = 1$ because each equation is satisfied when these values are substituted for the variables in the system of linear equations.

$$2(3) - 3(2) + 4(1) \stackrel{?}{=} 4 \ \checkmark \quad \text{True}$$
$$-(2) + 2(1) \stackrel{?}{=} 0 \ \checkmark \quad \text{True}$$
$$(3) + 5(2) - 6(1) \stackrel{?}{=} 7 \ \checkmark \quad \text{True}$$

The solution to this system can be written as the **ordered triple** $(3, 2, 1)$. This system of linear equations has exactly one solution. In general, systems of linear equations can have zero, one, or infinitely many solutions.

EXAMPLE 1   Checking for solutions

Determine whether $(-1, -3, 2)$ or $(1, -10, -13)$ is a solution to the system of equations.

$$\begin{array}{r} x - 4y + 2z = 15 \\ 4x - y + z = 1 \\ 6x - 2y - 3z = -6 \end{array}$$

SOLUTION   First substitute $x = -1$, $y = -3$, and $z = 2$ in the system of linear equations, and then substitute $x = 1$, $y = -10$, and $z = -13$.

$(-1) - 4(-3) + 2(2) \stackrel{?}{=} 15$ True	$(1) - 4(-10) + 2(-13) \stackrel{?}{=} 15$ True
$4(-1) - (-3) + (2) \stackrel{?}{=} 1$ True	$4(1) - (-10) + (-13) \stackrel{?}{=} 1$ True
$6(-1) - 2(-3) - 3(2) \stackrel{?}{=} -6$ True	$6(1) - 2(-10) - 3(-13) \stackrel{?}{=} -6$ False

The ordered triple $(-1, -3, 2)$ satisfies all three equations, so it is a solution to the system of equations. The ordered triple $(1, -10, -13)$ is not a solution to the system of equations because it satisfies only two of the three equations.

Now Try Exercise 7

Solving with Elimination and Substitution

We can solve systems of linear equations in three variables by hand. The following procedure uses substitution and elimination and assumes that the variables are x, y, and z.

SOLVING A SYSTEM OF LINEAR EQUATIONS IN THREE VARIABLES

STEP 1: Eliminate one variable, such as x, from two of the equations.

STEP 2: Apply the techniques discussed in Section 9.1 to solve the two resulting equations in two variables from Step 1. If x is eliminated, then solve these equations to find y and z.

If there are no solutions for y and z, then the given system also has no solutions. If there are infinitely many solutions for y and z, then write y in terms of z and proceed to Step 3.

STEP 3: Substitute the values for y and z in one of the given equations to find x. The solution is (x, y, z). If possible, check your answer as in Example 1.

EXAMPLE 2 Solving a linear system in three variables

Solve the following system.

$$\begin{aligned} x - y + 2z &= 6 \\ 2x + y - 2z &= -3 \\ -x - 2y + 3z &= 7 \end{aligned}$$

SOLUTION

STEP 1: We begin by eliminating the variable x from the second and third equations. To eliminate x from the second equation, we multiply the first equation by -2 and then add it to the second equation. To eliminate x from the third equation, we add the first and third equations.

$\begin{aligned}-2x + 2y - 4z &= -12 \quad \text{\small First equation times } -2\\ \underline{2x + y - 2z = -3} \quad \text{\small Second equation}\\ 3y - 6z = -15 \quad \text{\small Add.}\end{aligned}$	$\begin{aligned}x - y + 2z &= 6 \quad \text{\small First equation}\\ \underline{-x - 2y + 3z = 7} \quad \text{\small Third equation}\\ -3y + 5z = 13 \quad \text{\small Add.}\end{aligned}$

STEP 2: Take the two resulting equations from Step 1 and eliminate either variable. Here we add the two equations to eliminate y.

$$\begin{aligned} 3y - 6z &= -15 \\ \underline{-3y + 5z} &= \underline{13} \\ -z &= -2 \quad \text{\small Add the equations.}\\ z &= 2 \quad \text{\small Multiply each side by } -1. \end{aligned}$$

Now we can use substitution to find the value of y. We let $z = 2$ in *either* equation used in Step 2 to find y.

$$\begin{aligned} 3y - 6z &= -15 \quad \text{\small Equation from Step 2}\\ 3y - 6(2) &= -15 \quad \text{\small Substitute } z = 2.\\ 3y - 12 &= -15 \quad \text{\small Multiply.}\\ 3y &= -3 \quad \text{\small Add 12 to each side.}\\ y &= -1 \quad \text{\small Divide each side by 3.} \end{aligned}$$

STEP 3: Finally, we substitute $y = -1$ and $z = 2$ in any of the *given* equations to find x.

$$\begin{aligned} x - y + 2z &= 6 \quad \text{\small First given equation}\\ x - (-1) + 2(2) &= 6 \quad \text{\small Let } y = -1 \text{ and } z = 2.\\ x + 1 + 4 &= 6 \quad \text{\small Simplify.}\\ x &= 1 \quad \text{\small Subtract 5 from each side.} \end{aligned}$$

The solution is $(1, -1, 2)$. Check this solution.

Now Try Exercise 11

In the next example, we determine numbers of tickets sold for a play.

EXAMPLE 3 Finding numbers of tickets sold

One thousand tickets were sold for a play, generating $3800 in revenue. The prices of the tickets were $3 for children, $4 for students, and $5 for adults. There were 100 fewer student tickets sold than adult tickets. Find the number of each type of ticket sold.

SOLUTION Let x be the number of tickets sold to children, y be the number of tickets sold to students, and z be the number of tickets sold to adults. The total number of tickets sold was 1000, so

$$x + y + z = 1000.$$

Each child's ticket costs $3, so the revenue generated from selling x tickets is $3x$. Similarly, the revenue generated from students is $4y$, and the revenue from adults is $5z$. Total ticket sales were $3800, so

$$3x + 4y + 5z = 3800.$$

The equation $z - y = 100$, or $y - z = -100$, must also be satisfied, because 100 fewer tickets were sold to students than adults.

To find the price of a ticket, we need to solve the following system of linear equations.

$$
\begin{aligned}
x + y + z &= 1000 \qquad \text{\small Total number of tickets is 1000.} \\
3x + 4y + 5z &= 3800 \qquad \text{\small Total revenue is \$3800.} \\
 y - z &= -100 \qquad \text{\small 100 fewer student tickets than adult tickets}
\end{aligned}
$$

STEP 1: We begin by eliminating the variable x from the first equation. To do this, we multiply the first equation by 3 and subtract the second equation.

$$
\begin{aligned}
3x + 3y + 3z &= 3000 \qquad \text{\small First given equation times 3} \\
3x + 4y + 5z &= 3800 \qquad \text{\small Second equation} \\
\hline
-y - 2z &= -800 \qquad \text{\small Subtract.}
\end{aligned}
$$

STEP 2: We then use the equation that resulted from Step 1 and the third given equation to eliminate y.

$$
\begin{aligned}
-y - 2z &= -800 \qquad \text{\small Equation from Step 1} \\
y - z &= -100 \qquad \text{\small Third given equation} \\
\hline
-3z &= -900 \qquad \text{\small Add the equations.}
\end{aligned}
$$

Thus $z = 300$. To find y, we can substitute $z = 300$ in the third equation.

$$
\begin{aligned}
y - z &= -100 \qquad \text{\small Third given equation} \\
y - 300 &= -100 \qquad \text{\small Let } z = 300. \\
y &= 200 \qquad \text{\small Add 300.}
\end{aligned}
$$

STEP 3: Finally, we substitute $y = 200$ and $z = 300$ in the first equation.

$$
\begin{aligned}
x + y + z &= 1000 \qquad \text{\small First given equation} \\
x + 200 + 300 &= 1000 \qquad \text{\small Let } y = 200 \text{ and } z = 300. \\
x &= 500 \qquad \text{\small Subtract 500.}
\end{aligned}
$$

Thus 500 tickets were sold to children, 200 to students, and 300 to adults. Check this answer.

Now Try Exercise 33

Systems with No Solutions

Regardless of the number of variables, a system of linear equations can have zero, one, or infinitely many solutions. In the next example, a system of linear equations has no solutions.

EXAMPLE 4 Identifying a system with no solutions

Three students buy lunch in the cafeteria. One student buys 2 hamburgers, 1 order of fries, and 1 soda for $9. Another student buys 1 hamburger, 2 orders of fries, and 1 soda for $8. The third student buys 3 hamburgers, 3 orders of fries, and 2 sodas for $18. If possible, find the cost of each item. Interpret the results.

SOLUTION Let x be the cost of a hamburger, y be the cost of an order of fries, and z be the cost of a soda. Then the purchases of the three students can be expressed as a system of linear equations.

$$
\begin{aligned}
2x + y + z &= 9 &&\text{2 burgers, 1 order of fries, and 1 soda for \$9} \\
x + 2y + z &= 8 &&\text{1 burger, 2 orders of fries, and 1 soda for \$8} \\
3x + 3y + 2z &= 18 &&\text{3 burgers, 3 orders of fries, and 2 sodas for \$18}
\end{aligned}
$$

STEP 1: We can eliminate z in the first equation by subtracting the second equation from the first equation. We can eliminate z in the third equation by subtracting twice the second equation from the third equation.

$2x + y + z = 9$	First equation	$3x + 3y + 2z = 18$	Third equation
$x + 2y + z = 8$	Second equation	$2x + 4y + 2z = 16$	Twice second equation
$x - y \quad\;\; = 1$	Subtract.	$x - y \quad\quad = 2$	Subtract.

STEP 2: The equations $x - y = 1$ and $x - y = 2$ are *inconsistent* because the difference between two numbers cannot be both 1 and 2. Step 3 is not necessary—the system of equations has no solutions.

NOTE In this problem the third student bought the same amount of food as the first and second students bought together. Therefore the third student should have paid $9 + $8 = $17 rather than $18. *Inconsistent pricing* led to an *inconsistent system* of linear equations.

Now Try Exercise 35

Systems with Infinitely Many Solutions

Some systems of linear equations have infinitely many solutions. In this case, we say that the system of linear equations is consistent, but the equations are dependent. A system of dependent equations is solved in the next example.

EXAMPLE 5 Solving a system with infinitely many solutions

Solve the following system of linear equations.

$$
\begin{aligned}
x + y - z &= -2 \\
x + 2y - 2z &= -3 \\
y - z &= -1
\end{aligned}
$$

SOLUTION

STEP 1: Because x does not appear in the third equation, begin by eliminating x from the first equation. To do this, subtract the second equation from the first equation.

$x + y - z = -2$	First equation
$x + 2y - 2z = -3$	Second equation
$-y + z = 1$	Subtract.

STEP 2: Adding the resulting equation from Step 1 and the third given equation gives the equation $0 = 0$, which indicates that there are infinitely many solutions.

$$\begin{aligned} -y + z &= 1 \\ y - z &= -1 \\ \hline 0 &= 0 \end{aligned}$$

Dependent equations: Solve either equation for y.

Add.

Three students buy lunch in the cafeteria. One student buys 1 hamburger, 1 order of fries, and 1 soda for $5. Another student buys 2 hamburgers, 2 orders of fries, and 2 sodas for $10. The third student buys 3 hamburgers, 3 orders of fries, and 3 sodas for $15. Can you find the cost of each item? Interpret your answer.

The variable y can be written in terms of z as $y = z - 1$.

STEP 3: To find x, substitute the results from Step 2 in the first given equation.

$$\begin{aligned} x + y - z &= -2 && \text{First given equation} \\ x + (z - 1) - z &= -2 && \text{Let } y = z - 1. \\ x &= -1 && \text{Solve for } x. \end{aligned}$$

Solutions to the given system are of the form $(-1, z - 1, z)$, where z is any real number. For example, if $z = 2$, then $(-1, 1, 2)$ is one possible solution.

Now Try Exercise 17

9.3 Putting It All Together

In this section we discussed how to solve a system of three linear equations in three variables by hand. Systems of linear equations can have no solutions, one solution, or infinitely many solutions. The following table summarizes some of the important concepts presented in this section.

CONCEPT	EXPLANATION
System of linear equations in three variables	The following is a system of three linear equations in three variables. $$\begin{aligned} x - 2y + z &= 0 \\ -x + y + z &= 4 \\ -y + 4z &= 10 \end{aligned}$$
Solution to a linear system in three variables	The solution to a linear system in three variables is an ordered triple, expressed as (x, y, z). The solution to the preceding system is $(1, 2, 3)$ because substituting $x = 1, y = 2$, and $z = 3$ in each equation results in a true statement. $$\begin{aligned} (1) - 2(2) + (3) &= 0 \checkmark && \text{True} \\ -(1) + (2) + (3) &= 4 \checkmark && \text{True} \\ -(2) + 4(3) &= 10 \checkmark && \text{True} \end{aligned}$$
Solving a linear system with substitution and elimination	Refer to Example 2. **STEP 1:** Eliminate one variable, such as x, from two of the equations. **STEP 2:** Apply the techniques discussed in Section 9.1 to solve the two resulting equations in two variables from Step 1. If x is eliminated, then solve these equations to find y and z. If there are no solutions for y and z, then the given system also has no solutions. If there are infinitely many solutions for y and z, then write y in terms of z and proceed to Step 3. **STEP 3:** Substitute the values for y and z in one of the given equations to find x. The solution is (x, y, z). If possible, check your answer.

9.3 Exercises

1. Can a system of linear equations have exactly three solutions?

2. Does the ordered triple $(1, 2, 3)$ satisfy the equation $3x + 2y + z = 10$?

3. To solve a system of linear equations in two variables, how many equations do you usually need?

4. To solve a system of linear equations in three variables, how many equations do you usually need?

5. If a system of linear equations has infinitely many solutions, are the equations dependent or independent?

6. If a system of linear equations is inconsistent, how many solutions does it have?

Exercises 7–10: Determine whether each ordered triple is a solution to the system of linear equations.

7. $(0, 2, -2), (-1, 3, -2)$

$$x + y - z = 4$$
$$-x + y + z = 2$$
$$x + y + z = 0$$

8. $(5, 2, 2), (2, -1, 1)$

$$2x - 3y + 3z = 10$$
$$x - 2y - 3z = 1$$
$$4x - y + z = 10$$

9. $\left(-\frac{5}{11}, \frac{20}{11}, -2\right), (1, 2, -1)$

$$x + 3y - 2z = 9$$
$$-3x + 2y + 4z = -3$$
$$-2x + 5y + 2z = 6$$

10. $(1, 2, 3), (11, 16, -3)$

$$4x - 2y + 2z = 6$$
$$2x - 4y - 6z = -24$$
$$-3x + 3y + 2z = 9$$

Exercises 11–32: If possible, solve the system.

11.
$$x + y + z = 6$$
$$-x + 2y + z = 6$$
$$y + z = 5$$

12.
$$x - y + z = -2$$
$$x - 2y + z = 0$$
$$y - z = 1$$

13.
$$x + 2y + 3z = 4$$
$$2x + y + 3z = 5$$
$$x - y + z = 2$$

14.
$$x - y + z = 2$$
$$3x - 2y + z = -1$$
$$x + y = -3$$

15.
$$3x + y + z = 0$$
$$4x + 2y + z = 1$$
$$2x - 2y - z = 2$$

16.
$$-x - 5y + 2z = 2$$
$$x + y + 2z = 2$$
$$3x + y - 4z = -10$$

17.
$$x + 3y + z = 6$$
$$3x + y - z = 6$$
$$x - y - z = 0$$

18.
$$2x - y + 2z = 6$$
$$-x + y + z = 0$$
$$-x - 3z = -6$$

19.
$$x - 4y + 2z = -2$$
$$x + 2y - 2z = -3$$
$$x - y = 4$$

20.
$$2x + y + 3z = 4$$
$$-3x - y - 4z = 5$$
$$x + y + 2z = 0$$

21.
$$4a - b + 2c = 0$$
$$2a + b - c = -11$$
$$2a - 2b + c = 3$$

22.
$$a - 4b + 3c = 2$$
$$-a - 2b + 5c = 9$$
$$a + 2b + c = 6$$

23.
$$a + b + c = 0$$
$$a - b - c = 3$$
$$a + 3b + 3c = 5$$

24.
$$a - 2b + c = -1$$
$$a + 5b = -3$$
$$2a + 3b + c = -2$$

25.
$$3x + 2y + z = -1$$
$$3x + 4y - z = 1$$
$$x + 2y + z = 0$$

26.
$$x - 2y + z = 1$$
$$x + y + 2z = 2$$
$$2x + 3y + z = 6$$

27.
$$-x + 3y + z = 3$$
$$2x + 7y + 4z = 13$$
$$4x + y + 2z = 7$$

28.
$$x + 2y + z = 0$$
$$3x + 2y - z = 4$$
$$-x + 2y + 3z = -4$$

29.
$$-x + 2z = -9$$
$$y + 4z = -13$$
$$3x + y = 13$$

30.
$$x + y + z = -1$$
$$2x + z = -6$$
$$2y + 3z = 0$$

31.
$$\frac{1}{2}x - y + \frac{1}{2}z = -4$$
$$x + 2y - 3z = 20$$
$$-\frac{1}{2}x + 3y + 2z = 0$$

32.
$$\frac{3}{4}x + y + \frac{1}{2}z = -3$$
$$x + y - z = -8$$
$$\frac{1}{4}x - 2y + z = -4$$

Applications

33. **Tickets Sold** Five hundred tickets were sold for a play, generating $3560. The prices of the tickets were $5 for children, $7 for students, and $10 for adults. There were 180 more student tickets sold than adult tickets. Find the number of each type of ticket sold.

34. **Tickets Sold** One thousand tickets were sold for a baseball game. There were one hundred more adult tickets sold than student tickets, and there were four times as many tickets sold to students as to children. How many of each type of ticket were sold?

35. **Buying Lunch** Three students buy lunch in the cafeteria. One student buys 2 hamburgers, 2 orders of fries, and 1 soda for $9. Another student buys 1 hamburger, 1 order of fries, and 1 soda for $5. The third student buys 1 hamburger and 1 order of fries for $5. If possible, find the cost of each item. Interpret the results.

36. Cost of DVDs The table shows the total cost of purchasing various combinations of differently priced DVDs. The types of DVDs are labeled A, B, and C.

A	B	C	Total Cost
2	1	1	$48
3	2	1	$71
1	1	2	$53

(a) Let a be the cost of a DVD of type A, b be the cost of a DVD of type B, and c be the cost of a DVD of type C. Write a system of three linear equations whose solution gives the cost of each type of DVD.

(b) Solve the system of equations and check your answer.

37. Geometry The largest angle in a triangle is 25° more than the smallest angle. The sum of the measures of the two smaller angles is 30° more than the measure of the largest angle.

(a) Let x, y, and z be the measures of the three angles from largest to smallest. Write a system of three linear equations whose solution gives the measure of each angle.

(b) Solve the system of equations and check your answer.

38. Geometry The perimeter of a triangle is 105 inches. The longest side is 22 inches longer than the shortest side. The sum of the lengths of the two shorter sides is 15 inches more than the length of the longest side. Find the lengths of the sides of the triangle.

39. Investment Mixture A sum of $20,000 is invested in three mutual funds. In one year the first fund grew by 5%, the second by 7%, and the third by 10%. Total earnings for the year were $1650. The amount invested in the third fund was four times the amount invested in the first fund. Find the amount invested in each fund.

40. Home Prices Prices of homes can depend on several factors such as size and age. The table shows the selling prices for three homes. In this table, price P is given in thousands of dollars, age A in years, and home size S in thousands of square feet. These data may be modeled by $P = a + bA + cS$.

Price (P)	Age (A)	Size (S)
190	20	2
320	5	3
50	40	1

(a) Write a system of linear equations whose solution gives a, b, and c.

(b) Solve this system of linear equations.

(c) Predict the price of a home that is 10 years old and has 2500 square feet.

41. Mixture Problem One type of lawn fertilizer consists of a mixture of nitrogen, N; phosphorus, P; and potassium, K. An 80-pound sample contains 8 more pounds of nitrogen and phosphorus than of potassium. There is nine times as much potassium as phosphorus.

(a) Write a system of three equations whose solution gives the amount of nitrogen, phosphorus, and potassium in this sample.

(b) Solve the system of equations.

42. Business Production A business has three machines that manufacture containers. Together they can make 100 containers per day, whereas the two fastest machines can make 80 containers per day. The fastest machine makes 34 more containers per day than the slowest machine.

(a) Let x, y, and z be the numbers of containers that the machines make from fastest to slowest. Write a system of three equations whose solution gives the number of containers each machine can make.

(b) Solve the system of equations.

Writing about Mathematics

43. When using elimination and substitution, explain how to recognize a system of linear equations that has no solutions.

44. When using elimination and substitution, explain how to recognize a system of linear equations that has infinitely many solutions.

9.4 Solutions to Linear Systems Using Matrices

- Represent systems of linear equations with matrices
- Learn row-echelon form
- Perform Gaussian elimination
- Learn reduced row-echelon form
- Perform Gauss-Jordan elimination
- Solve systems of linear equations with technology (optional)

Introduction

After its release in 2010, the iPad recorded remarkable quarterly sales growth. The three points plotted in Figure 9.39 give the *cumulative* sales y in millions of units, sold x quarters after the iPad's release. For example, the point (5, 29) indicates that Apple sold 29 million iPads by the end of the 5th quarter after its release. Because three distinct points (that are not collinear) determine the graph of a quadratic function, we can model these data by finding a unique parabola that passes though the given points, as illustrated in Figure 9.39. (*Source:* Apple Corporation.)

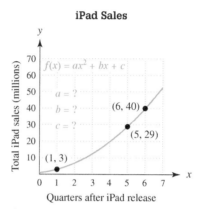

iPad Sales

Figure 9.39

One way to accomplish this task is to set up a linear system of equations in three variables and solve it by using a matrix. This section discusses matrices and how they can be used to solve systems of linear equations. (See Example 11 and Exercise 87.)

Representing Systems of Linear Equations with Matrices

Arrays of numbers occur frequently in many different situations. Spreadsheets often make use of arrays, where data are displayed in a tabular format. A **matrix** is a rectangular array of elements. The following are examples of matrices whose elements are real numbers.

Examples of Matrices

$$
\begin{bmatrix} 4 & -7 \\ -2 & 9 \end{bmatrix}
\begin{bmatrix} -1 & -5 & 3 \\ 1.2 & 0 & -1.3 \\ 4.1 & 5 & 7 \end{bmatrix}
\begin{bmatrix} -3 & -6 & 9 & 5 \\ \sqrt{2} & -8 & -8 & 0 \\ 3 & 0 & 19 & -7 \\ -11 & -3 & 7 & 8 \end{bmatrix}
\begin{bmatrix} 5 & -2 \\ -2 & \pi \\ 1 & -1 \end{bmatrix}
\begin{bmatrix} 1 & -0.5 & 9 \\ 5 & 0.4 & -3 \end{bmatrix}
$$

$2 \times 2 \qquad\qquad 3 \times 3 \qquad\qquad\qquad 4 \times 4 \qquad\qquad 3 \times 2 \qquad 2 \times 3$

The dimension of a matrix is given much like the dimensions of a rectangular room. We might say a room is m feet long and n feet wide. The **dimension** of a matrix is $m \times n$ (m by n) if it has m rows and n columns. For example, the last matrix has a dimension of 2×3 because it has 2 rows and 3 columns. If the numbers of rows and columns are equal, the matrix is a **square matrix.** The first three matrices are square matrices.

Give a general form of a system of linear equations with four equations and four variables. Write its augmented matrix.

Matrices are frequently used to represent systems of linear equations.

See the Concept: Representing a Linear System with a Matrix

A | **B** | **C**
System of Three Equations | **Coefficient Matrix** | **Augmented Matrix**

$$a_1x + b_1y + c_1z = d_1$$
$$a_2x + b_2y + c_2z = d_2$$
$$a_3x + b_3y + c_3z = d_3$$

$$\begin{bmatrix} a_1 & b_1 & c_1 \\ a_2 & b_2 & c_2 \\ a_3 & b_3 & c_3 \end{bmatrix}$$

$$\begin{bmatrix} a_1 & b_1 & c_1 & | & d_1 \\ a_2 & b_2 & c_2 & | & d_2 \\ a_3 & b_3 & c_3 & | & d_3 \end{bmatrix}$$

A The a_k, b_k, c_k, and d_k are constants and x, y, and z are variables.

B The coefficients of the variables are represented in a square matrix called the **coefficient matrix** of the linear system.

C The matrix is enlarged to include the constants d_k. The vertical line in this matrix corresponds to where the equals sign occurs in each equation. This matrix is commonly called an **augmented matrix**.

EXAMPLE 1 Representing a linear system with an augmented matrix

Express each linear system with an augmented matrix. State the dimension of the matrix.
(a) $3x - 4y = 6$
        $-5x + y = -5$
(b) $2x - 5y + 6z = -3$
        $3x + 7y - 3z = 8$
        $x + 7y = 5$

SOLUTION
(a) This system has two equations with two variables. It can be represented by an augmented matrix having dimension 2×3.

$$\begin{bmatrix} 3 & -4 & | & 6 \\ -5 & 1 & | & -5 \end{bmatrix} \quad \begin{matrix} 3x - 4y = 6 \\ -5x + y = -5 \end{matrix}$$

(b) This system has three equations with three variables. Note that variable z does not appear in the third equation. A value of 0 is inserted for its coefficient.

$$\begin{bmatrix} 2 & -5 & 6 & | & -3 \\ 3 & 7 & -3 & | & 8 \\ 1 & 7 & 0 & | & 5 \end{bmatrix} \quad \begin{matrix} 2x - 5y + 6z = -3 \\ 3x + 7y - 3z = 8 \\ x + 7y = 5 \end{matrix}$$

This matrix has dimension 3×4.

Now Try Exercises 7 and 9

EXAMPLE 2 Converting an augmented matrix into a linear system

Write the linear system represented by the augmented matrix. Let the variables be x, y, and z.

(a) $\begin{bmatrix} 1 & 0 & 2 & | & -3 \\ 2 & 2 & 10 & | & 3 \\ -1 & 2 & 3 & | & 5 \end{bmatrix}$ **(b)** $\begin{bmatrix} 1 & 2 & 3 & | & -4 \\ 0 & 1 & -6 & | & 7 \\ 0 & 0 & 1 & | & 8 \end{bmatrix}$

SOLUTION
Getting Started The first column corresponds to x, the second to y, and the third to z. When a 0 appears, the variable for that column does not appear in the equation. The vertical line gives the location of the equals sign. The last column represents the constant terms. ▶

$$\begin{bmatrix} 1 & 0 & 2 & -3 \\ 2 & 2 & 10 & 3 \\ -1 & 2 & 3 & 5 \end{bmatrix}$$

$$\begin{bmatrix} 1 & 2 & 3 & -4 \\ 0 & 1 & -6 & 7 \\ 0 & 0 & 1 & 8 \end{bmatrix}$$

(a) The augmented matrix (repeated in the margin) represents the following linear system.

$$\begin{array}{rl} x \quad\quad + 2z = -3 & \text{First row in the matrix} \\ 2x + 2y + 10z = 3 & \text{Second row in the matrix} \\ -x + 2y + 3z = 5 & \text{Third row in the matrix} \end{array}$$

(b) The augmented matrix (repeated in the margin) represents the following linear system.

$$\begin{array}{rl} x + 2y + 3z = -4 & \text{First row in the matrix} \\ y - 6z = 7 & \text{Second row in the matrix} \\ z = 8 & \text{Third row in the matrix} \end{array}$$

> **Now Try Exercises 11 and 13**

Row-Echelon Form

To solve a linear system with an augmented matrix, it is convenient to get the matrix in **row-echelon form.** The following matrices are in row-echelon form.

$$\begin{bmatrix} 1 & 3 & 0 & -1 \\ 0 & 1 & -6 & 1 \\ 0 & 0 & 1 & -2 \end{bmatrix} \begin{bmatrix} 1 & 2 & 0 \\ 0 & 1 & 4 \end{bmatrix} \begin{bmatrix} 1 & 3 & -1 & 5 \\ 0 & 1 & -1 & 3 \\ 0 & 0 & 1 & 0 \end{bmatrix} \begin{bmatrix} 1 & 3 & -1 & 5 \\ 0 & 0 & 1 & 3 \\ 0 & 0 & 0 & 0 \end{bmatrix} \begin{bmatrix} 1 & 3 & 5 \\ 0 & 0 & 1 \end{bmatrix}$$

The elements of the **main diagonal** are blue in each matrix. Scanning down the main diagonal of a matrix in row-echelon form, we see that this diagonal first contains only 1's, and then possibly 0's. The first nonzero element in any row is 1. Rows containing only 0's occur at the bottom of the matrix. All elements below the main diagonal are 0.

The next example demonstrates a technique called **backward substitution.** It can be used to solve linear systems represented by an augmented matrix in row-echelon form.

EXAMPLE 3 Solving a linear system with backward substitution

Solve the system of linear equations represented by the augmented matrix.

(a) $\begin{bmatrix} 1 & 1 & 3 & 12 \\ 0 & 1 & -2 & -4 \\ 0 & 0 & 1 & 3 \end{bmatrix}$ **(b)** $\begin{bmatrix} 1 & -1 & 5 & 5 \\ 0 & 1 & 3 & 3 \\ 0 & 0 & 0 & 0 \end{bmatrix}$

SOLUTION
(a) The matrix represents the following linear system.

$$\begin{array}{rl} x + y + 3z = 12 & \text{First row in the matrix} \\ y - 2z = -4 & \text{Second row in the matrix} \\ z = 3 & \text{Third row in the matrix} \end{array}$$

Since $z = 3$, substitute this value in the second equation to find y.

> Second equation with $z = 3$ ——— $y - 2(3) = -4,$ or $y = 2$

Then $y = 2$ and $z = 3$ can be substituted in the first equation to determine x.

> First equation with $y = 2$ and $z = 3$ ——— $x + 2 + 3(3) = 12,$ or $x = 1$

The solution is given by $x = 1, y = 2$, and $z = 3$ and can be expressed as the *ordered triple* $(1, 2, 3)$.

(b) The matrix represents the following linear system.

$$\begin{array}{rl} x - y + 5z = 5 & \text{First row in the matrix} \\ y + 3z = 3 & \text{Second row in the matrix} \\ 0 = 0 & \text{Third row in the matrix} \end{array}$$

The last equation, $0 = 0$, is an identity. Its presence usually indicates infinitely many solutions. Use the second equation to write y in terms of z.

Solve second equation for y. $\longrightarrow y = 3 - 3z$

Next, substitute $(3 - 3z)$ for y in the first equation and write x in terms of z.

$$x - (3 - 3z) + 5z = 5 \qquad \text{Substitute (3 – 3z) for y}$$
$$x - 3 + 3z + 5z = 5 \qquad \text{Distributive property}$$
$$x = 8 - 8z \qquad \text{Solve for x.}$$

All solutions can be written as the ordered triple $(8 - 8z, 3 - 3z, z)$, where z is any real number. There are infinitely many solutions. Sometimes we say that all solutions can be written in terms of the **parameter** z, where z is any real number. For example, if we let $z = 1$, then $y = 3 - 3(1) = 0$ and $x = 8 - 8(1) = 0$. Thus one solution to the system is $(0, 0, 1)$.

> **Now Try Exercises 21 and 23**

Gaussian Elimination

The methods of elimination and substitution from Section 9.1 can be combined to create a state-of-the-art numerical method capable of solving systems of linear equations that contain thousands of variables. Even though this method, called *Gaussian elimination with backward substitution*, dates back to Carl Friedrich Gauss (1777–1855), it continues to be one of the most efficient methods for solving systems of linear equations.

If an augmented matrix is not in row-echelon form, it can be transformed into row-echelon form using *Gaussian elimination*. This method uses the following three basic matrix row transformations.

MATRIX ROW TRANSFORMATIONS

For any augmented matrix representing a system of linear equations, the following row transformations result in an equivalent system of linear equations.
1. Any two rows may be interchanged.
2. The elements of any row may be multiplied by a nonzero constant.
3. Any row may be changed by adding to (or subtracting from) its elements a multiple of the corresponding elements of another row.

When we transform a matrix into row-echelon form, we also are transforming a system of linear equations. The next two examples illustrate how Gaussian elimination with backward substitution is performed.

EXAMPLE 4   Transforming a matrix into row-echelon form

Use Gaussian elimination with backward substitution to solve the linear system of equations.

$$\begin{aligned} x + y + \ z &= 1 \\ -x + y + \ z &= 5 \\ y + 2z &= 5 \end{aligned}$$

SOLUTION

Getting Started The goal is to apply matrix row transformations that transform the given matrix into row-echelon form. Then we can perform backward substitution to determine the solution. ▶

The linear system is written to the right to illustrate how each row transformation affects the corresponding system of linear equations. Note that it is *not* necessary to write the system of equations to the right of the augmented matrix.

Augmented Matrix   **Linear System**

$$\begin{bmatrix} 1 & 1 & 1 & | & 1 \\ -1 & 1 & 1 & | & 5 \\ 0 & 1 & 2 & | & 5 \end{bmatrix}$$

$$\begin{aligned} x + y + z &= 1 \\ -x + y + z &= 5 \\ y + 2z &= 5 \end{aligned}$$

We can add the first equation to the second equation to obtain a 0 where the coefficient of x in the second row is highlighted. This row operation is denoted $R_2 + R_1$, and the result becomes the new row 2.

The row that is changing is written first. $\longrightarrow R_2 + R_1 \rightarrow$

$$\begin{bmatrix} 1 & 1 & 1 & | & 1 \\ 0 & 2 & 2 & | & 6 \\ 0 & 1 & 2 & | & 5 \end{bmatrix}$$

$$\begin{aligned} x + y + z &= 1 \\ 2y + 2z &= 6 \\ y + 2z &= 5 \end{aligned}$$

To have the matrix in row-echelon form, we need the highlighted 2 in the second row to be a 1. Multiply each element in row 2 by $\frac{1}{2}$ and denote the operation $\frac{1}{2}R_2$.

Row 2 is changing. $\longrightarrow \frac{1}{2}R_2 \rightarrow$

$$\begin{bmatrix} 1 & 1 & 1 & | & 1 \\ 0 & 1 & 1 & | & 3 \\ 0 & 1 & 2 & | & 5 \end{bmatrix}$$

$$\begin{aligned} x + y + z &= 1 \\ y + z &= 3 \\ y + 2z &= 5 \end{aligned}$$

Next, we need a 0 where the 1 is highlighted in row 3. Subtract row 2 from row 3 and denote the operation $R_3 - R_2$.

Row 3 is changing. $\searrow R_3 - R_2 \rightarrow$

$$\begin{bmatrix} 1 & 1 & 1 & | & 1 \\ 0 & 1 & 1 & | & 3 \\ 0 & 0 & 1 & | & 2 \end{bmatrix}$$

$$\begin{aligned} x + y + z &= 1 \\ y + z &= 3 \\ z &= 2 \end{aligned}$$

Because we have a 1 in the highlighted box, the matrix is now in row-echelon form, and we see that $z = 2$. Backward substitution may be applied now to find the solution. Substituting $z = 2$ in the second equation gives

$$y + 2 = 3, \quad \text{or} \quad y = 1.$$

Finally, let $y = 1$ and $z = 2$ in the first equation to determine x.

$$x + 1 + 2 = 1, \quad \text{or} \quad x = -2$$

The solution to the system is given by $x = -2, y = 1$, and $z = 2$, or $(-2, 1, 2)$.

Now Try Exercise 33

EXAMPLE 5 Transforming a matrix into row-echelon form

Use Gaussian elimination with backward substitution to solve the linear system of equations.

$$\begin{aligned} 2x + 4y + 4z &= 4 \\ x + 3y + z &= 4 \\ -x + 3y + 2z &= -1 \end{aligned}$$

SOLUTION   The initial linear system and augmented matrix are written first.

Augmented Matrix   **Linear System**

$$\begin{bmatrix} 2 & 4 & 4 & | & 4 \\ 1 & 3 & 1 & | & 4 \\ -1 & 3 & 2 & | & -1 \end{bmatrix}$$

$$\begin{aligned} 2x + 4y + 4z &= 4 \\ x + 3y + z &= 4 \\ -x + 3y + 2z &= -1 \end{aligned}$$

First we obtain a 1 where the x-coefficient of 2 in the first row is highlighted. This can be accomplished by either multiplying the first equation by $\frac{1}{2}$ or interchanging rows 1 and 2. We multiply row 1 by $\frac{1}{2}$. This operation is denoted $\frac{1}{2}R_1$.

$$\frac{1}{2}R_1 \rightarrow \begin{bmatrix} 1 & 2 & 2 & | & 2 \\ 1 & 3 & 1 & | & 4 \\ -1 & 3 & 2 & | & -1 \end{bmatrix} \qquad \begin{aligned} x + 2y + 2z &= 2 \\ x + 3y + z &= 4 \\ -x + 3y + 2z &= -1 \end{aligned}$$

The next step is to eliminate the x-variable in rows 2 and 3 by obtaining zeros in the highlighted positions. To do this, subtract row 1 from row 2, and add row 1 to row 3.

$$\begin{aligned} R_2 - R_1 &\rightarrow \\ R_3 + R_1 &\rightarrow \end{aligned} \begin{bmatrix} 1 & 2 & 2 & | & 2 \\ 0 & 1 & -1 & | & 2 \\ 0 & 5 & 4 & | & 1 \end{bmatrix} \qquad \begin{aligned} x + 2y + 2z &= 2 \\ y - z &= 2 \\ 5y + 4z &= 1 \end{aligned}$$

Since we have a 1 for the y-coefficient in the second row, the next step is to eliminate the y-variable in row 3 and obtain a zero where the y-coefficient of 5 is highlighted. Multiply row 2 by 5, and subtract the result from row 3.

$$R_3 - 5R_2 \rightarrow \begin{bmatrix} 1 & 2 & 2 & | & 2 \\ 0 & 1 & -1 & | & 2 \\ 0 & 0 & 9 & | & -9 \end{bmatrix} \qquad \begin{aligned} x + 2y + 2z &= 2 \\ y - z &= 2 \\ 9z &= -9 \end{aligned}$$

Finally, make the z-coefficient of 9 in the third row equal 1 by multiplying row 3 by $\frac{1}{9}$.

$$\frac{1}{9}R_3 \rightarrow \begin{bmatrix} 1 & 2 & 2 & | & 2 \\ 0 & 1 & -1 & | & 2 \\ 0 & 0 & 1 & | & -1 \end{bmatrix} \qquad \begin{aligned} x + 2y + 2z &= 2 \\ y - z &= 2 \\ z &= -1 \end{aligned}$$

The final matrix is in row-echelon form. Backward substitution may be applied to find the solution. Substituting $z = -1$ in the second equation gives

$$y - (-1) = 2, \qquad \text{or} \qquad y = 1.$$

Next, substitute $y = 1$ and $z = -1$ in the first equation to determine x.

$$x + 2(1) + 2(-1) = 2, \qquad \text{or} \qquad x = 2$$

The solution to the system is $(2, 1, -1)$.

Now Try Exercise 37

EXAMPLE 6   Transforming a system that has no solutions

Solve the system of linear equations, if possible.

$$\begin{aligned} x - 2y + 3z &= 2 \\ 2x + 3y + 2z &= 7 \\ 4x - y + 8z &= 8 \end{aligned}$$

SOLUTION   Because it is not necessary to write the linear system next to the matrix, we write the matrices in a horizontal format in this example.

$$\begin{bmatrix} 1 & -2 & 3 & | & 2 \\ 2 & 3 & 2 & | & 7 \\ 4 & -1 & 8 & | & 8 \end{bmatrix} \begin{aligned} R_2 - 2R_1 &\rightarrow \\ R_3 - 4R_1 &\rightarrow \end{aligned} \begin{bmatrix} 1 & -2 & 3 & | & 2 \\ 0 & 7 & -4 & | & 3 \\ 0 & 7 & -4 & | & 0 \end{bmatrix} R_3 - R_2 \rightarrow \begin{bmatrix} 1 & -2 & 3 & | & 2 \\ 0 & 7 & -4 & | & 3 \\ 0 & 0 & 0 & | & -3 \end{bmatrix}$$

The last row of the last matrix represents $0x + 0y + 0z = -3$, which has no solutions because $0 \neq -3$. There are no solutions.

Now Try Exercise 69

A Geometric Interpretation   The graph of a single linear equation in three variables is a plane in three-dimensional space. For a system of three equations in three variables, the possible intersections of the planes are illustrated in Figure 9.40. The solution set of such a system may be either a single ordered triple (x, y, z), an infinite set of ordered triples (dependent equations), or the empty set (an inconsistent system).

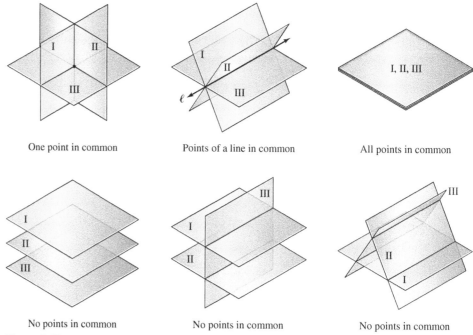

One point in common   Points of a line in common   All points in common

No points in common   No points in common   No points in common

Figure 9.40

Reduced Row-Echelon Form   Sometimes it is convenient to express a matrix in *reduced* row-echelon form. A matrix in row-echelon form is in **reduced row-echelon form** if every element above and below a 1 on the main diagonal is 0. The following matrices are examples of reduced row-echelon form.

$$\begin{bmatrix} 1 & 0 \\ 0 & 1 \end{bmatrix} \quad \begin{bmatrix} 1 & 0 \\ 0 & 0 \end{bmatrix} \quad \begin{bmatrix} 1 & 0 & 0 \\ 0 & 1 & 0 \\ 0 & 0 & 1 \end{bmatrix} \quad \begin{bmatrix} 1 & 0 & 3 \\ 0 & 1 & -2 \end{bmatrix} \quad \begin{bmatrix} 1 & 0 & 0 & 3 \\ 0 & 1 & 0 & 1 \\ 0 & 0 & 1 & -1 \end{bmatrix} \quad \begin{bmatrix} 1 & 0 & 4 & 8 \\ 0 & 1 & -1 & 2 \\ 0 & 0 & 0 & 0 \end{bmatrix}$$

If an augmented matrix is in reduced row-echelon form, solving the system of linear equations is often straightforward.

EXAMPLE 7   Determining a solution from a matrix in reduced row-echelon form

Each matrix represents a system of linear equations. Find the solution.

(a) $\begin{bmatrix} 1 & 0 & | & 6 \\ 0 & 1 & | & -5 \end{bmatrix}$

(b) $\begin{bmatrix} 1 & 0 & 0 & | & 3 \\ 0 & 1 & 0 & | & -1 \\ 0 & 0 & 1 & | & 2 \end{bmatrix}$

(c) $\begin{bmatrix} 1 & 0 & 0 & | & 4 \\ 0 & 1 & 0 & | & 3 \\ 0 & 0 & 0 & | & 2 \end{bmatrix}$

(d) $\begin{bmatrix} 1 & 0 & -2 & | & -3 \\ 0 & 1 & 2 & | & 1 \\ 0 & 0 & 0 & | & 0 \end{bmatrix}$

SOLUTION

(a) To see how the matrix in reduced row-echelon form provides immediate access to the solution to the related system of linear equations, we write the corresponding system of equations next to the given matrix.

Given Matrix   *Linear System*

$\begin{bmatrix} 1 & 0 & | & 6 \\ 0 & 1 & | & -5 \end{bmatrix}$

$\begin{array}{l} 1x + 0y = 6 \quad \text{or} \quad x = 6 \\ 0x + 1y = -5 \quad \text{or} \quad y = -5 \end{array}$

The solution is $(6, -5)$.

(b) The top row represents $1x + 0y + 0z = 3$, or $x = 3$. Using similar reasoning for the second and third rows yields $y = -1$ and $z = 2$. The solution is $(3, -1, 2)$.

(c) The last row represents $0x + 0y + 0z = 2$, which has no solutions because $0 \neq 2$. Therefore there are no solutions to the system of equations.

(d) The last row simplifies to $0 = 0$, which is an identity and is always true. The second row gives $y + 2z = 1$, or $y = -2z + 1$. The first row represents $x - 2z = -3$, or $x = 2z - 3$. Thus this system of linear equations has infinitely many solutions. Every solution can be written as an ordered triple in the form $(2z - 3, -2z + 1, z)$, where z can be any real number.

> **Now Try Exercises 55, 57, 59, and 61**

Gauss-Jordan Elimination   Matrix row transformations can be used to transform an augmented matrix into reduced row-echelon form. This approach requires more effort than transforming a matrix into row-echelon form, but often eliminates the need for backward substitution. The technique is sometimes called **Gauss-Jordan elimination.**

EXAMPLE 8   Transforming a matrix into reduced row-echelon form

Use Gauss-Jordan elimination to solve the linear system.

$$
\begin{aligned}
2x + y + 2z &= 10 \\
x + 2z &= 5 \\
x - 2y + 2z &= 1
\end{aligned}
$$

SOLUTION   The linear system has been written to the right for illustrative purposes.

Augmented Matrix   **Linear System**

$$
\begin{bmatrix}
2 & 1 & 2 & | & 10 \\
1 & 0 & 2 & | & 5 \\
1 & -2 & 2 & | & 1
\end{bmatrix}
\qquad
\begin{aligned}
2x + y + 2z &= 10 \\
x + 2z &= 5 \\
x - 2y + 2z &= 1
\end{aligned}
$$

Obtain a 1 in the highlighted position in row 1 by interchanging rows 1 and 2.

$$
\begin{matrix}
R_2 \rightarrow \\
R_1 \rightarrow \\

\end{matrix}
\begin{bmatrix}
1 & 0 & 2 & | & 5 \\
2 & 1 & 2 & | & 10 \\
1 & -2 & 2 & | & 1
\end{bmatrix}
\qquad
\begin{aligned}
x + 2z &= 5 \\
2x + y + 2z &= 10 \\
x - 2y + 2z &= 1
\end{aligned}
$$

Next subtract 2 times row 1 from row 2. Then subtract row 1 from row 3. This eliminates the x-variable from the second and third equations.

$$
\begin{matrix}
 \\
R_2 - 2R_1 \rightarrow \\
R_3 - R_1 \rightarrow
\end{matrix}
\begin{bmatrix}
1 & 0 & 2 & | & 5 \\
0 & 1 & -2 & | & 0 \\
0 & -2 & 0 & | & -4
\end{bmatrix}
\qquad
\begin{aligned}
x + 2z &= 5 \\
y - 2z &= 0 \\
-2y &= -4
\end{aligned}
$$

To eliminate the y-variable in row 3, add 2 times row 2 to row 3.

$$
\begin{matrix}
 \\
 \\
R_3 + 2R_2 \rightarrow
\end{matrix}
\begin{bmatrix}
1 & 0 & 2 & | & 5 \\
0 & 1 & -2 & | & 0 \\
0 & 0 & -4 & | & -4
\end{bmatrix}
\qquad
\begin{aligned}
x + 2z &= 5 \\
y - 2z &= 0 \\
-4z &= -4
\end{aligned}
$$

To obtain a 1 in the highlighted position in row 3, multiply row 3 by $-\frac{1}{4}$.

$$
\begin{matrix}
\phantom{-\frac{1}{4}R_3} \\
\phantom{-\frac{1}{4}R_3} \\
-\frac{1}{4}R_3 \rightarrow
\end{matrix}
\begin{bmatrix}
1 & 0 & 2 & | & 5 \\
0 & 1 & -2 & | & 0 \\
0 & 0 & 1 & | & 1
\end{bmatrix}
\qquad
\begin{aligned}
x + 2z &= 5 \\
y - 2z &= 0 \\
z &= 1
\end{aligned}
$$

Finally, the matrix can be transformed into reduced row-echelon form by subtracting 2 times row 3 from row 1, and adding 2 times row 3 to row 2.

$$\begin{matrix} R_1 - 2R_3 \rightarrow \\ R_2 + 2R_3 \rightarrow \\ {} \end{matrix} \left[\begin{array}{ccc|c} 1 & 0 & 0 & 3 \\ 0 & 1 & 0 & 2 \\ 0 & 0 & 1 & 1 \end{array} \right] \qquad \begin{matrix} x = 3 \\ y = 2 \\ z = 1 \end{matrix}$$

This final matrix is in reduced row-echelon form. The solution is (3, 2, 1).

Now Try Exercise 65

Solving Systems of Linear Equations with Technology (Optional)

If the arithmetic at each step of Gaussian elimination is done exactly, then it may be thought of as an exact symbolic procedure. However, when calculators and computers are used to solve systems of equations, their solutions often are approximate. The next three examples use a graphing calculator to solve systems of linear equations.

EXAMPLE 9   Solving a system of equations using technology

Use a graphing calculator to solve the system of linear equations in Example 8.

SOLUTION   To solve this system, enter the augmented matrix

$$A = \left[\begin{array}{ccc|c} 2 & 1 & 2 & 10 \\ 1 & 0 & 2 & 5 \\ 1 & -2 & 2 & 1 \end{array} \right],$$

as shown in Figures 9.41–9.43.

Calculator Help

To enter the elements of a matrix, see Appendix A (page AP-12).

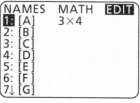

Figure 9.41

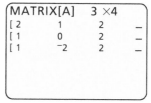

Figure 9.42

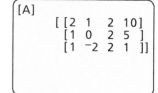

Figure 9.43

A graphing calculator can transform matrix *A* into reduced row-echelon form, as illustrated in Figures 9.44 and 9.45. Notice that the reduced row-echelon form obtained from the graphing calculator agrees with our results from Example 8. The solution is (3, 2, 1).

Calculator Help

To transform a matrix into reduced row-echelon form, see Appendix A (page AP-13).

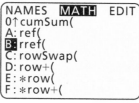

Figure 9.44

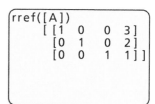

Figure 9.45

Now Try Exercise 71

| EXAMPLE 10 | Transforming a matrix into reduced row-echelon form |

For three food shelters operated by a charitable organization, three different quantities are computed: monthly food costs F in dollars, number of people served per month N, and monthly charitable receipts R in dollars. The data are shown in Table 9.8.

Food Shelter Operations

Food Costs (F)	Number Served (N)	Charitable Receipts (R)
3000	2400	8000
4000	2600	10,000
8000	5900	14,000

Table 9.8

(a) Model these data by using $F = aN + bR + c$, where a, b, and c are constants.
(b) Predict the food costs for a shelter that serves 4000 people and receives charitable receipts of $12,000. Round your answer to the nearest hundred dollars.

SOLUTION
(a) Getting Started Table 9.8 provides several values for F, N, and R in the equation $F = aN + bR + c$. The goal is to write a system of linear equations whose solution gives the values of a, b, and c. ▶
Since $F = aN + bR + c$, the constants a, b, and c satisfy the following equations.

$$3000 = a(2400) + b(8000) \ \ + c$$
$$4000 = a(2600) + b(10{,}000) + c$$
$$8000 = a(5900) + b(14{,}000) + c$$

This system can be rewritten as

$$2400a + \ \ 8000b + c = 3000$$
$$2600a + 10{,}000b + c = 4000$$
$$5900a + 14{,}000b + c = 8000.$$

The associated augmented matrix is

$$A = \begin{bmatrix} 2400 & 8000 & 1 & \big| & 3000 \\ 2600 & 10{,}000 & 1 & \big| & 4000 \\ 5900 & 14{,}000 & 1 & \big| & 8000 \end{bmatrix}.$$

Figure 9.46 shows the matrix A. The fourth column of A may be viewed by using the arrow keys. In Figure 9.47, A has been transformed into reduced row-echelon form where $a \approx 0.6897$, $b \approx 0.4310$, and $c \approx -2103$. Thus let $F = 0.6897N + 0.431R - 2103$.

```
[A]
[ [2400   8000    1 ...
  [2600   10000   1 ...
  [5900   14000   1 ...
```

```
rref([A])
[ [1  0  0   .689655...
  [0  1  0   .431034...
  [0  0  1  -2103.4...
```

Figure 9.46   Figure 9.47

(b) To predict the food costs for a shelter that serves 4000 people and receives charitable receipts of $12,000, let $N = 4000$ and $R = 12,000$ and evaluate F.

$$F = 0.6897(4000) + 0.431(12,000) - 2103 = 5827.8.$$

This model predicts monthly food costs of about $5800.

Now Try Exercise 79

Determining a Quadratic Function   The introduction to this section discussed how three points can be used to determine a quadratic function whose graph passes through these points. The next example illustrates this method.

EXAMPLE 11   Determining a quadratic function

More than half of private-sector employees cannot carry vacation days into a new year. The average number y of paid days off for full-time workers at medium to large companies after x years of employment is listed in Table 9.9.

Paid Days Off

x (years)	1	15	30
y (days)	9.4	18.8	21.9

Source: Bureau of Labor Statistics.
Table 9.9

(a) Determine the coefficients for $f(x) = ax^2 + bx + c$ so that f models these data.
(b) Graph f with the data in $[-4, 32, 5]$ by $[8, 23, 2]$.
(c) Estimate the number of paid days off after 3 years of employment. Compare it to the actual value of 11.2 days.

Calculator Help
To plot data and to graph an equation, see Appendix A (page AP-6).

SOLUTION
(a) For f to model the data, the equations $f(1) = 9.4$, $f(15) = 18.8$, and $f(30) = 21.9$ must be satisfied. See Table 9.9.

$$f(1) = a(1)^2 + b(1) + c = 9.4$$
$$f(15) = a(15)^2 + b(15) + c = 18.8$$
$$f(30) = a(30)^2 + b(30) + c = 21.9$$

The associated augmented matrix is

$$\begin{bmatrix} 1^2 & 1 & 1 & 9.4 \\ 15^2 & 15 & 1 & 18.8 \\ 30^2 & 30 & 1 & 21.9 \end{bmatrix}.$$

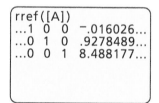

```
rref([A])
...1 0 0  -.016026...
...0 1 0  .9278489...
...0 0 1  8.488177...
```

Figure 9.48

Figure 9.48 shows a portion of the matrix represented in reduced row-echelon form. The solution is $a \approx -0.016026$, $b \approx 0.92785$, and $c \approx 8.4882$.

(b) Graph $y_1 = -0.016026x^2 + 0.92785x + 8.4882$ together with the points $(1, 9.4)$, $(15, 18.8)$, and $(30, 21.9)$. The graph of f passes through the points. See Figure 9.49.
(c) To estimate the number of paid days off after 3 years of employment, evaluate $f(3)$.

$$f(3) = -0.016026(3)^2 + 0.92785(3) + 8.4882 \approx 11.1$$

This is quite close to the actual value of 11.2 days.

Now Try Exercise 87

$[-4, 32, 5]$ by $[8, 23, 2]$

Figure 9.49

9.4 Putting It All Together

$\mathbf{T}$hrough a sequence of matrix row operations known as Gaussian elimination, an augmented matrix can be transformed into row-echelon form or reduced row-echelon form. Backward substitution is frequently used to find the solution when a matrix is in row-echelon form.

AUGMENTED MATRIX

A linear system can be represented by an augmented matrix.

$$\left[\begin{array}{ccc|c} 2 & 0 & -3 & 2 \\ -1 & 2 & -2 & -5 \\ 1 & -2 & -1 & 7 \end{array}\right] \qquad \begin{array}{rcr} 2x & -3z = & 2 \\ -x + 2y & -2z = & -5 \\ x - 2y & -z = & 7 \end{array}$$

ROW-ECHELON FORM

The following matrices are in row-echelon form. They represent three possible situations: no solutions, one solution, and infinitely many solutions.

$$\left[\begin{array}{ccc|c} 1 & -2 & 1 & 0 \\ 0 & 1 & 2 & 3 \\ 0 & 0 & 0 & 1 \end{array}\right] \qquad \left[\begin{array}{ccc|c} 1 & -2 & 1 & 0 \\ 0 & 1 & 2 & 3 \\ 0 & 0 & 1 & 1 \end{array}\right] \qquad \left[\begin{array}{ccc|c} 1 & -2 & 1 & 0 \\ 0 & 1 & 2 & 3 \\ 0 & 0 & 0 & 0 \end{array}\right]$$

No solutions   *One solution*   *Infinitely many solutions*
                      (1, 1, 1)   *(6 − 5z, 3 − 2z, z)*

BACKWARD SUBSTITUTION

Backward substitution can be used to solve a system of linear equations represented by an augmented matrix in row-echelon form.

Augmented Matrix

$$\left[\begin{array}{ccc|c} 1 & -2 & 1 & 3 \\ 0 & 1 & -2 & -3 \\ 0 & 0 & 1 & 2 \end{array}\right]$$

From the last row, $z = 2$.
Substitute $z = 2$ in the second row: $y - 2(2) = -3$, or $y = 1$.
Let $z = 2$ and $y = 1$ in the first row: $x - 2(1) + 2 = 3$, or $x = 3$.
The solution is $(3, 1, 2)$.

REDUCED ROW-ECHELON FORM

The Gauss-Jordan elimination method can be used to transform an augmented matrix into reduced row-echelon form, which often eliminates the need for backward substitution. The following matrices are in reduced row-echelon form. The solution is given below the matrix.

$$\left[\begin{array}{ccc|c} 1 & 0 & 0 & 4 \\ 0 & 1 & 0 & 5 \\ 0 & 0 & 0 & 2 \end{array}\right] \qquad \left[\begin{array}{ccc|c} 1 & 0 & 0 & 1 \\ 0 & 1 & 0 & 2 \\ 0 & 0 & 1 & 3 \end{array}\right] \qquad \left[\begin{array}{ccc|c} 1 & 0 & 3 & 2 \\ 0 & 1 & 2 & 3 \\ 0 & 0 & 0 & 0 \end{array}\right]$$

No solutions   *One solution*   *Infinitely many solutions*
                      (1, 2, 3)   *(2 − 3z, 3 − 2z, z)*

9.4 Exercises

Dimensions of Matrices and Augmented Matrices

Exercises 1–6: State the dimension of each matrix.

1. $\begin{bmatrix} 1 \\ 2 \\ 3 \end{bmatrix}$

2. $\begin{bmatrix} a & b & c \\ d & e & b \end{bmatrix}$

3. $\begin{bmatrix} 3 & 0 \\ 1 & -4 \end{bmatrix}$

4. $[-1 \quad 1]$

5. $\begin{bmatrix} 1 & -1 \\ 7 & 5 \\ -4 & 0 \end{bmatrix}$

6. $\begin{bmatrix} 1 & 3 & 8 & -3 \\ 1 & -1 & 1 & -2 \\ 4 & 5 & 0 & -1 \end{bmatrix}$

Exercises 7–10: Represent the linear system by an augmented matrix, and state the dimension of the matrix.

7. $\begin{aligned} 5x - 2y &= 3 \\ -x + 3y &= -1 \end{aligned}$

8. $\begin{aligned} 3x + y &= 4 \\ -x + 4y &= 5 \end{aligned}$

9. $\begin{aligned} -3x + 2y + z &= -4 \\ 5x \quad\quad - z &= 9 \\ x - 3y - 6z &= -9 \end{aligned}$

10. $\begin{aligned} x + 2y - z &= 2 \\ -2x + y - 2z &= -3 \\ 7x + y - z &= 7 \end{aligned}$

Exercises 11–14: Write the system of linear equations that the augmented matrix represents.

11. $\left[\begin{array}{cc|c} 3 & 2 & 4 \\ 0 & 1 & 5 \end{array}\right]$

12. $\left[\begin{array}{cc|c} -2 & 1 & 5 \\ 7 & 9 & 2 \end{array}\right]$

13. $\left[\begin{array}{ccc|c} 3 & 1 & 4 & 0 \\ 0 & 5 & 8 & -1 \\ 0 & 0 & -7 & 1 \end{array}\right]$

14. $\left[\begin{array}{ccc|c} 1 & -1 & 3 & 2 \\ -2 & 1 & 1 & -2 \\ -1 & 0 & -2 & 1 \end{array}\right]$

Row-Echelon Form

Exercises 15 and 16: Is the matrix in row-echelon form?

15. (a) $\left[\begin{array}{cc|c} 1 & 3 & 2 \\ 0 & 1 & -1 \end{array}\right]$
(b) $\left[\begin{array}{ccc|c} 1 & 4 & -1 & 0 \\ 0 & -1 & 1 & 3 \\ 0 & 2 & 1 & 7 \end{array}\right]$

(c) $\left[\begin{array}{ccc|c} 1 & 6 & -8 & 5 \\ 0 & 1 & 7 & 9 \\ 0 & 0 & 1 & 11 \end{array}\right]$

16. (a) $\left[\begin{array}{cc|c} 1 & 3 & 2 \\ 0 & -1 & -1 \end{array}\right]$
(b) $\left[\begin{array}{ccc|c} 1 & 3 & -1 & 8 \\ 0 & 1 & 5 & 3 \\ 0 & 0 & 0 & 0 \end{array}\right]$

(c) $\left[\begin{array}{ccc|c} 0 & 0 & 1 & 1 \\ 0 & 1 & 7 & 9 \\ 1 & 2 & -1 & 11 \end{array}\right]$

Exercises 17–26: The augmented matrix is in row-echelon form and represents a linear system. Solve the system by using backward substitution, if possible. Write the solution as either an ordered pair or an ordered triple.

17. $\left[\begin{array}{cc|c} 1 & 2 & 3 \\ 0 & 1 & -1 \end{array}\right]$

18. $\left[\begin{array}{cc|c} 1 & -5 & 6 \\ 0 & 0 & 1 \end{array}\right]$

19. $\left[\begin{array}{cc|c} 1 & -1 & 2 \\ 0 & 1 & 0 \end{array}\right]$

20. $\left[\begin{array}{cc|c} 1 & 4 & -2 \\ 0 & 1 & 3 \end{array}\right]$

21. $\left[\begin{array}{ccc|c} 1 & 1 & -1 & 4 \\ 0 & 1 & -1 & 2 \\ 0 & 0 & 1 & 1 \end{array}\right]$

22. $\left[\begin{array}{ccc|c} 1 & -2 & -1 & 0 \\ 0 & 1 & -3 & 1 \\ 0 & 0 & 1 & 2 \end{array}\right]$

23. $\left[\begin{array}{ccc|c} 1 & 2 & -1 & 5 \\ 0 & 1 & -2 & 1 \\ 0 & 0 & 0 & 0 \end{array}\right]$

24. $\left[\begin{array}{ccc|c} 1 & -1 & 2 & 8 \\ 0 & 1 & -4 & 2 \\ 0 & 0 & 0 & 0 \end{array}\right]$

25. $\left[\begin{array}{ccc|c} 1 & 2 & 1 & -3 \\ 0 & 1 & -3 & \frac{1}{2} \\ 0 & 0 & 0 & 4 \end{array}\right]$

26. $\left[\begin{array}{ccc|c} 1 & 0 & -4 & \frac{3}{4} \\ 0 & 1 & 2 & 1 \\ 0 & 0 & 0 & -3 \end{array}\right]$

Solving Systems with Gaussian Elimination

Exercises 27–30: Perform each row operation on the given matrix by completing the matrix at the right.

27. $\left[\begin{array}{ccc|c} 2 & -4 & 6 & 10 \\ -3 & 5 & 3 & 2 \\ 4 & 8 & 4 & -8 \end{array}\right]\begin{array}{l} \frac{1}{2}R_1 \to \\ \\ \frac{1}{4}R_3 \to \end{array} \left[\begin{array}{ccc|c} 1 & & & \\ -3 & 5 & 3 & 2 \\ & & 1 & \end{array}\right]$

28. $\left[\begin{array}{ccc|c} 1 & -2 & 1 & 3 \\ 1 & 4 & 0 & -1 \\ 2 & 0 & 1 & 5 \end{array}\right]\begin{array}{l} \\ R_2 - R_1 \to \\ R_3 - 2R_1 \to \end{array} \left[\begin{array}{ccc|c} 1 & -2 & 1 & 3 \\ & 6 & & \\ & & & -1 \end{array}\right]$

29. $\left[\begin{array}{ccc|c} 1 & -1 & 1 & 2 \\ -1 & 2 & -2 & 0 \\ 1 & 7 & 0 & 5 \end{array}\right]\begin{array}{l} \\ R_2 + R_1 \to \\ R_3 - R_1 \to \end{array} \left[\begin{array}{ccc|c} 1 & -1 & 1 & 2 \\ & & & \\ & & & \end{array}\right]$

30. $\left[\begin{array}{ccc|c} 1 & -2 & 3 & 6 \\ 2 & 1 & 4 & 5 \\ -3 & 5 & 3 & 2 \end{array}\right]\begin{array}{l} \\ R_2 - 2R_1 \to \\ R_3 + 3R_1 \to \end{array} \left[\begin{array}{ccc|c} 1 & -2 & 3 & 6 \\ & & & \\ & & & \end{array}\right]$

Exercises 31–42: Use Gaussian elimination with backward substitution to solve the system of linear equations. Write the solution as an ordered pair or an ordered triple whenever possible.

31. $\begin{aligned} x + 2y &= 3 \\ -x - y &= 7 \end{aligned}$

32. $\begin{aligned} 2x + 4y &= 10 \\ x - 2y &= -3 \end{aligned}$

33. $\begin{aligned} x + 2y + z &= 3 \\ x + y - z &= 3 \\ -x - 2y + z &= -5 \end{aligned}$ **34.** $\begin{aligned} x + y + z &= 6 \\ 2x + 3y - z &= 3 \\ x + y + 2z &= 10 \end{aligned}$

35. $\begin{aligned} x + 2y - z &= -1 \\ 2x - y + z &= 0 \\ -x - y + 2z &= 7 \end{aligned}$ **36.** $\begin{aligned} x + 3y - 2z &= -4 \\ 2x + 6y + z &= -3 \\ x + y - 4z &= -2 \end{aligned}$

37. $\begin{aligned} 3x + y + 3z &= 14 \\ x + y + z &= 6 \\ -2x - 2y + 3z &= -7 \end{aligned}$ **38.** $\begin{aligned} x + 3y - 2z &= 3 \\ -x - 2y + z &= -2 \\ 2x - 7y + z &= 1 \end{aligned}$

39. $\begin{aligned} 2x + 5y + z &= 8 \\ x + 2y - z &= 2 \\ 3x + 7y &= 5 \end{aligned}$ **40.** $\begin{aligned} x + y + z &= 3 \\ x + y + 2z &= 4 \\ 2x + 2y + 3z &= 7 \end{aligned}$

41. $\begin{aligned} -x + 2y + 4z &= 10 \\ 3x - 2y - 2z &= -12 \\ x + 2y + 6z &= 8 \end{aligned}$ **42.** $\begin{aligned} 4x - 2y + 4z &= 8 \\ 3x - 7y + 6z &= 4 \\ -x - 5y + 2z &= 7 \end{aligned}$

Exercises 43–54: Solve the system, if possible.

43. $\begin{aligned} x - y + z &= 1 \\ x + 2y - z &= 2 \\ y - z &= 0 \end{aligned}$ **44.** $\begin{aligned} x - y - 2z &= -11 \\ x - 2y - z &= -11 \\ -x + y + 3z &= 14 \end{aligned}$

45. $\begin{aligned} 2x - 4y + 2z &= 11 \\ x + 3y - 2z &= -9 \\ 4x - 2y + z &= 7 \end{aligned}$ **46.** $\begin{aligned} x - 4y + z &= 9 \\ 3y - 2z &= -7 \\ -x + z &= 0 \end{aligned}$

47. $\begin{aligned} 3x - 2y + 2z &= -18 \\ -x + 2y - 4z &= 16 \\ 4x - 3y - 2z &= -21 \end{aligned}$ **48.** $\begin{aligned} 2x - y - z &= 0 \\ x - y - z &= -2 \\ 3x - 2y - 2z &= -2 \end{aligned}$

49. $\begin{aligned} x - 4y + 3z &= 26 \\ -x + 3y - 2z &= -19 \\ -y + z &= 10 \end{aligned}$ **50.** $\begin{aligned} 4x - y - z &= 0 \\ 4x - 2y &= 0 \\ 2x + z &= 1 \end{aligned}$

51. $\begin{aligned} 5x + 4z &= 7 \\ 2x - 4y &= 6 \\ 3y + 3z &= 3 \end{aligned}$ **52.** $\begin{aligned} y + 2z &= -5 \\ 3x - 2z &= -6 \\ -x - 4y &= 11 \end{aligned}$

53. $\begin{aligned} 5x - 2y + z &= 5 \\ x + y - 2z &= -2 \\ 4x - 3y + 3z &= 7 \end{aligned}$ **54.** $\begin{aligned} 2x - 4y - z &= 2 \\ x + y - 3z &= 10 \\ -x - 7y + 8z &= 2 \end{aligned}$

Exercises 55–62: (Refer to Example 7.) The augmented matrix is in reduced row-echelon form and represents a system of linear equations. If possible, solve the system.

55. $\begin{bmatrix} 1 & 0 & | & 12 \\ 0 & 1 & | & 3 \end{bmatrix}$ **56.** $\begin{bmatrix} 1 & -1 & | & 1 \\ 0 & 0 & | & 0 \end{bmatrix}$

57. $\begin{bmatrix} 1 & 0 & 0 & | & -2 \\ 0 & 1 & 0 & | & 4 \\ 0 & 0 & 1 & | & \frac{1}{2} \end{bmatrix}$ **58.** $\begin{bmatrix} 1 & 0 & 0 & | & 7 \\ 0 & 1 & 0 & | & -9 \\ 0 & 0 & 1 & | & 3 \end{bmatrix}$

59. $\begin{bmatrix} 1 & 0 & 2 & | & 4 \\ 0 & 1 & -1 & | & -3 \\ 0 & 0 & 0 & | & 0 \end{bmatrix}$ **60.** $\begin{bmatrix} 1 & 0 & 1 & | & -2 \\ 0 & 1 & 3 & | & 5 \\ 0 & 0 & 0 & | & 0 \end{bmatrix}$

61. $\begin{bmatrix} 1 & 0 & 0 & | & \frac{3}{4} \\ 0 & 1 & 0 & | & -1 \\ 0 & 0 & 0 & | & \frac{2}{3} \end{bmatrix}$ **62.** $\begin{bmatrix} 1 & 0 & 0 & | & 10 \\ 0 & 1 & 0 & | & 21 \\ 0 & 0 & 0 & | & -2 \end{bmatrix}$

Exercises 63–70: **Reduced Row-Echelon Form** *Use Gauss-Jordan elimination to solve the system of equations.*

63. $\begin{aligned} x - y &= 1 \\ x + y &= 5 \end{aligned}$ **64.** $\begin{aligned} 2x + 3y &= 1 \\ x - 2y &= -3 \end{aligned}$

65. $\begin{aligned} x + 2y + z &= 3 \\ y - z &= -2 \\ -x - 2y + 2z &= 6 \end{aligned}$ **66.** $\begin{aligned} x + z &= 2 \\ x - y - z &= 0 \\ -2x + y &= -2 \end{aligned}$

67. $\begin{aligned} x - y + 2z &= 7 \\ 2x + y - 4z &= -27 \\ -x + y - z &= 0 \end{aligned}$ **68.** $\begin{aligned} 2x - 4y - 6z &= 2 \\ x - 3y + z &= 12 \\ 2x + y + 3z &= 5 \end{aligned}$

69. $\begin{aligned} 2x + y - z &= 2 \\ x - 2y + z &= 0 \\ x + 3y - 2z &= 4 \end{aligned}$ **70.** $\begin{aligned} -2x - y + z &= 3 \\ x + y - 3z &= 1 \\ x - 2y - 4z &= 2 \end{aligned}$

Exercises 71–76: **Technology** *Use technology to find the solution. Approximate values to the nearest thousandth.*

71. $\begin{aligned} 5x - 7y + 9z &= 40 \\ -7x + 3y - 7z &= 20 \\ 5x - 8y - 5z &= 15 \end{aligned}$

72. $\begin{aligned} 12x - 4y - 7z &= 8 \\ -8x - 6y + 9z &= 7 \\ 34x + 6y - 2z &= 5 \end{aligned}$

73. $\begin{aligned} 2.1x + 0.5y + 1.7z &= 4.9 \\ -2x + 1.5y - 1.7z &= 3.1 \\ 5.8x - 4.6y + 0.8z &= 9.3 \end{aligned}$

74. $\begin{aligned} 53x + 95y + 12z &= 108 \\ 81x - 57y - 24z &= -92 \\ -9x + 11y - 78z &= 21 \end{aligned}$

75. $\begin{aligned} 0.1x + 0.3y + 1.7z &= 0.6 \\ 0.6x + 0.1y - 3.1z &= 6.2 \\ 2.4y + 0.9z &= 3.5 \end{aligned}$

76. $\begin{aligned} 103x - 886y + 431z &= 1200 \\ -55x + 981y &= 1108 \\ -327x + 421y + 337z &= 99 \end{aligned}$

Applications

77. Pumping Water Three pumps are being used to empty a small swimming pool. The first pump is twice as fast as the second pump. The first two pumps can empty the pool in 8 hours, while all three pumps can empty it in 6 hours. How long would it take each pump to empty the pool individually? (*Hint:* Let x represent the fraction of the pool that the first pump can empty in 1 hour. Let y and z represent this fraction for the second and third pumps, respectively.)

78. Pumping Water Suppose in Exercise 77 that the first pump is three times as fast as the third pump, the first and second pumps can empty the pool in 6 hours, and all three pumps can empty the pool in 8 hours.

(a) Are these data realistic? Explain your reasoning.

(b) Make a conjecture about a solution to these data.

(c) Test your conjecture by solving the problem.

79. Food Shelters (Refer to Example 10.) For three food shelters, monthly food costs F in dollars, number of people served per month N, and monthly charitable receipts R in dollars are as shown in the table.

Food Costs (F)	Number Served (N)	Charitable Receipts (R)
1300	1800	5000
5300	3200	12,000
6500	4500	13,000

(a) Model these data using $F = aN + bR + c$, where a, b, and c are constants.

(b) Predict the food costs for a shelter that serves 3500 people and receives charitable receipts of $12,500. Round your answer to the nearest hundred dollars.

80. Estimating the Weight of a Bear The following table shows the weight W, neck size N, and chest size C for a representative sample of black bears.

W (pounds)	N (inches)	C (inches)
100	17	27
272	25	36
381	30	43

Source: M. Triola, *Elementary Statistics.*

(a) Find values for a, b, and c so that the equation $W = a + bN + cC$ models these data.

(b) Estimate the weight of a bear with a 20-inch neck and a 31-inch chest size.

(c) Explain why it is reasonable for the coefficients b and c to be positive.

81. Electricity In the study of electrical circuits, the application of Kirchoff's rules frequently results in systems of linear equations. To determine the current I (in amperes) in each branch of the circuit shown in the figure, solve the system of linear equations. Round values to the nearest hundredth.

$$I_1 = I_2 + I_3$$
$$15 + 4I_3 = 14I_2$$
$$10 + 4I_3 = 5I_1$$

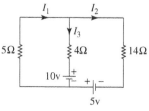

82. Electricity (Refer to Exercise 81.) Find the current (in amperes) in each branch of the circuit shown in the figure by solving the system of linear equations. Round values to the nearest hundredth.

$$I_1 = I_2 + I_3$$
$$20 = 4I_1 + 7I_3$$
$$10 + 7I_3 = 6I_2$$

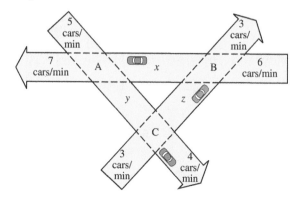

83. Investment A sum of $5000 is invested in three mutual funds that pay 8%, 11%, and 14% annual interest rates. The amount of money invested in the fund paying 14% equals the total amount of money invested in the other two funds, and the total annual interest from all three funds is $595.

(a) Write a system of equations whose solution gives the amount invested in each mutual fund. Be sure to state what each variable represents.

(b) Solve the system of equations.

84. Investment A sum of $10,000 is invested in three accounts that pay 3%, 4%, and 5% interest. Twice as much money is invested in the account paying 5% as in the account paying 3%, and the total annual interest from all three accounts is $421.

(a) Write a system of equations whose solution gives the amount invested in each account. Be sure to state what each variable represents.

(b) Solve the system of equations.

Exercises 85 and 86: **Traffic Flow** *The figure shows three one-way streets with intersections* A, B, *and* C. *Numbers indicate the average traffic flow in vehicles per minute. The variables* x, y, *and* z *denote unknown traffic flows that need to be determined for timing of stoplights.*

(a) *If the number of vehicles per minute entering an intersection must equal the number exiting an intersection, verify that the accompanying system of linear equations describes the traffic flow.*

(b) *Rewrite the system and solve.*

(c) *Interpret your solution.*

85. A: $x + 5 = y + 7$
B: $z + 6 = x + 3$
C: $y + 3 = z + 4$

86. A: $x + 7 = y + 4$
B: $4 + 5 = x + z$
C: $y + 8 = 9 + 4$

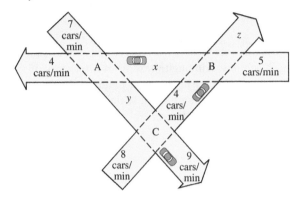

Exercises 87–90: Each set of data can be modeled by the quadratic function $f(x) = ax^2 + bx + c$.

(a) *Write a linear system whose solution represents values of a, b, and c.*

(b) *Use technology to find the solution.*

(c) *Graph f and the data in the same viewing rectangle.*

(d) *Make your own prediction using f.*

87. Estimating iPad Sales (Refer to the introduction to this section.) The table lists total iPad sales y in millions x quarters after its release.

x	1	5	6
y	3	29	40

Source: Apple Corporation.

88. Head Start Enrollment The table lists annual enrollment in thousands for the Head Start program x years after 1980.

x	0	10	26
y	376	541	909

Source: Dept. of Health and Human Services.

89. Chronic Health Care A large percentage of the U.S. population will require chronic health care in the coming decades. The average age of caregivers is 50–64, while the typical person needing chronic care is 85 or older. The ratio y of potential caregivers to those needing chronic health care will shrink in the coming years x, as shown in the table.

x	1990	2010	2030
y	11	10	6

Source: Robert Wood Johnson Foundation, *Chronic Care in America: A 21st Century Challenge.*

90. Carbon Dioxide Levels Carbon dioxide (CO_2) is a greenhouse gas. The table lists its concentration y in parts per million (ppm) measured at Mauna Loa, Hawaii, for three selected years x.

x	1958	1973	2003
y	315	325	376

Source: A. Nilsson, *Greenhouse Earth.*

Writing about Mathematics

91. A linear equation in three variables can be represented by a flat plane. Describe geometrically situations that can occur when a system of three linear equations has either no solution or an infinite number of solutions.

92. Give an example of an augmented matrix in row-echelon form that represents a system of linear equations that has no solution. Explain your reasoning.

Extended and Discovery Exercises

Exercises 1 and 2: Solve the system of four equations with four variables.

1.
$$\begin{aligned} w + x + 2y - z &= 4 \\ 2w + x + 2y + z &= 5 \\ -w + 3x + y - 2z &= -2 \\ 3w + 2x + y + 3z &= 3 \end{aligned}$$

2.
$$\begin{aligned} 2w - 5x + 3y - 2z &= -13 \\ 3w + 2x + 4y - 9z &= -28 \\ 4w + 3x - 2y - 4z &= -13 \\ 5w - 4x - 3y + 3z &= 0 \end{aligned}$$

CHECKING BASIC CONCEPTS FOR SECTIONS 9.3 AND 9.4

1. If possible, solve the system of linear equations.

(a)
$$\begin{aligned} x - 2y + z &= -2 \\ x + y + 2z &= 3 \\ 2x - y - z &= 5 \end{aligned}$$

(b)
$$\begin{aligned} x - 2y + z &= -2 \\ x + y + 2z &= 3 \\ 2x - y + 3z &= 1 \end{aligned}$$

(c)
$$\begin{aligned} x - 2y + z &= -2 \\ x + y + 2z &= 3 \\ 2x - y + 3z &= 5 \end{aligned}$$

2. Tickets Sold Two thousand tickets were sold for a play, generating $19,700. The prices of the tickets were $5 for children, $10 for students, and $12 for adults. There were 100 more adult tickets sold than student tickets. Find the number of each type of ticket sold.

3. Solve the system of linear equations using Gaussian elimination and backward substitution.

$$\begin{aligned} x \quad\;\; + z &= 2 \\ x + y - z &= 1 \\ -x - 2y - z &= 0 \end{aligned}$$

4. Use technology to solve the system of linear equations in Exercise 3.

9.5 Properties and Applications of Matrices

- Learn matrix notation
- Learn how matrices are used in social networks
- Find sums, differences, and scalar multiples of matrices
- Find matrix products
- Use technology (optional)

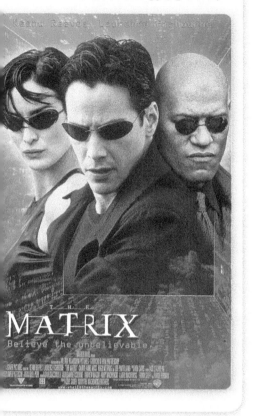

Introduction

In the movie trilogy *The Matrix,* the reality that most humans perceive is nothing more than a simulated reality constructed by machines. Although these films are works of fiction, matrices make it possible for programmers to create popular, multiplayer virtual reality games for the Internet. Matrices are also vitally important in social networks and Internet browsing. In this section we discuss properties of matrices and some of their applications.

Matrix Notation

The following notation is used to denote elements in a matrix A.

$$\begin{bmatrix} a_{11} & a_{12} \\ a_{21} & a_{22} \end{bmatrix} \quad \begin{bmatrix} a_{11} & a_{12} & a_{13} \\ a_{21} & a_{22} & a_{23} \\ a_{31} & a_{32} & a_{33} \end{bmatrix} \quad \begin{bmatrix} a_{11} & a_{12} & a_{13} & a_{14} \\ a_{21} & a_{22} & a_{23} & a_{24} \\ a_{31} & a_{32} & a_{33} & a_{34} \\ a_{41} & a_{42} & a_{43} & a_{44} \end{bmatrix} \quad \begin{bmatrix} a_{11} & a_{12} \\ a_{21} & a_{22} \\ a_{31} & a_{32} \end{bmatrix} \quad \begin{bmatrix} a_{11} & a_{12} & a_{13} \\ a_{21} & a_{22} & a_{23} \end{bmatrix}$$

A general element is denoted by a_{ij}. This refers to the element in the ith row, jth column. For example, a_{23} would be the element of A located in the second row, third column. Two m by n matrices A and B are **equal** if corresponding elements are equal. If A and B have different dimensions, they cannot be equal. For example,

$$\begin{bmatrix} 3 & -3 & 7 \\ 2 & 6 & -2 \\ 4 & 2 & 5 \end{bmatrix} = \begin{bmatrix} 3 & -3 & 7 \\ 2 & 6 & -2 \\ 4 & 2 & 5 \end{bmatrix} \qquad \text{Equal matrices}$$

because *all* corresponding elements are equal. However,

$$\begin{bmatrix} 1 & 4 \\ -3 & 2 \\ 4 & -7 \end{bmatrix} \neq \begin{bmatrix} 1 & 4 \\ -3 & 2 \\ 5 & -7 \end{bmatrix} \qquad \begin{array}{l}\text{Unequal matrices:} \\ a_{31} \neq b_{31}\end{array}$$

because $4 \neq 5$ in row 3 and column 1, and

$$\begin{bmatrix} 1 & 2 & 3 \\ 4 & 5 & 6 \end{bmatrix} \neq \begin{bmatrix} 1 & 2 \\ 4 & 5 \end{bmatrix} \qquad \begin{array}{l}\text{Unequal matrices:} \\ \text{different dimensions}\end{array}$$

$$\quad\; 2 \times 3 \qquad\quad 2 \times 2$$

because the matrices have different dimensions.

EXAMPLE 1 Determining matrix elements

Let a_{ij} denote a general element in A and b_{ij} a general element in B, where

$$A = \begin{bmatrix} 3 & -3 & 7 \\ 1 & 6 & -2 \\ 4 & 2 & 5 \end{bmatrix} \quad \text{and} \quad B = \begin{bmatrix} 3 & x & 7 \\ 1 & 6 & -2 \\ 4 & 5 & 2 \end{bmatrix}.$$

(a) Identify a_{12}, b_{32}, and a_{13}.
(b) Compute $a_{31} b_{13} + a_{32} b_{23} + a_{33} b_{33}$.
(c) Is there a value for x that will make the statement $A = B$ true?

SOLUTION

(a) The element a_{12} is located in the first row, second column of A. Thus, $a_{12} = -3$. In a similar manner, we find that $b_{32} = 5$ and $a_{13} = 7$.

(b) $a_{31}b_{13} + a_{32}b_{23} + a_{33}b_{33} = (4)(7) + (2)(-2) + (5)(2) = 34$

(c) No, since $a_{32} = 2 \neq 5 = b_{32}$ and $a_{33} = 5 \neq 2 = b_{33}$. Even if we let $x = -3$, other corresponding elements in A and B are not equal.

Now Try Exercise 1

Matrices and Social Networks

People with Internet access often choose to participate in at least one social network such as Facebook, Pinterest, or Twitter. Mathematics is essential to the success of these social networks, and matrices play an important role in processing social network data. Consider the diagram in Figure 9.50, which represents a simple social network of four people.

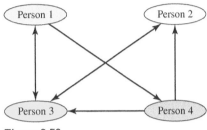

Figure 9.50

The arrows in Figure 9.50 show the social relationships among these people. For example, an arrow from Person 1 to Person 4 indicates that Person 1 likes Person 4. But Person 4 does not like Person 1 because there is no arrow pointing in the opposite direction. On the other hand Person 2 and Person 3 like each other, which is indicated by a double arrow between them. In the next example we see how a matrix can represent this social network.

EXAMPLE 2 Representing a social network with a matrix

Use a matrix to represent the social network shown in Figure 9.50.

SOLUTION A social network with four people can be represented by a 4×4 square matrix. Because Person 1 likes Person 4, we put a 1 in row 1 column 4. Similarly, Person 4 likes Person 2, so we put a 1 in row 4 column 2. When no arrow exists to indicate that one person likes another, we place a 0 in the appropriate row and column of the matrix. Using this process results in the following matrix.

$$\begin{bmatrix} 0 & 0 & 1 & 1 \\ 0 & 0 & 1 & 0 \\ 1 & 1 & 0 & 0 \\ 0 & 1 & 1 & 0 \end{bmatrix}$$

Now Try Exercise 53

Sums, Differences, and Scalar Multiples of Matrices

An Application As a result of an FCC mandate, all television stations are now required to broadcast digital signals. HDTVs can display digital images with a resolution up to 1920×1080 pixels. Matrices play an important role in processing digital images.

Matrix Addition and Subtraction To simplify the concept of a digital image, we reduce the resolution to 3×3 pixels and have just four gray levels, rather than colors.

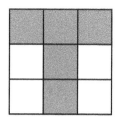

Figure 9.51

Figure 9.52 Gray Levels

Figure 9.53

We will let 0 represent white, 1 light gray, 2 dark gray, and 3 black. Suppose that we would like to digitize the letter T shown in Figure 9.51, using the gray levels shown in Figure 9.52. Since the T is dark gray and the background is white, Figure 9.51 can be represented by

$$A = \begin{bmatrix} 2 & 2 & 2 \\ 0 & 2 & 0 \\ 0 & 2 & 0 \end{bmatrix}.$$

Suppose that we want to make the entire picture darker. If we changed every element in A to 3, the entire picture would be black. A more acceptable solution would be to darken each pixel by one gray level. This corresponds to adding 1 to each element in the matrix A and can be accomplished efficiently using matrix notation.

Matrix Addition: Add Corresponding Elements

$$\begin{bmatrix} 2 & 2 & 2 \\ 0 & 2 & 0 \\ 0 & 2 & 0 \end{bmatrix} + \begin{bmatrix} 1 & 1 & 1 \\ 1 & 1 & 1 \\ 1 & 1 & 1 \end{bmatrix} = \begin{bmatrix} 2+1 & 2+1 & 2+1 \\ 0+1 & 2+1 & 0+1 \\ 0+1 & 2+1 & 0+1 \end{bmatrix} = \begin{bmatrix} 3 & 3 & 3 \\ 1 & 3 & 1 \\ 1 & 3 & 1 \end{bmatrix}$$

To add two matrices of equal dimension, add corresponding elements. The result is shown in picture form in Figure 9.53. Notice that the background is now light gray and the T is black. The entire picture is darker.

To lighten the picture in Figure 9.53, subtract 1 from each element. *To subtract two matrices of equal dimension, subtract corresponding elements.*

Matrix Subtraction: Subtract Corresponding Elements

$$\begin{bmatrix} 3 & 3 & 3 \\ 1 & 3 & 1 \\ 1 & 3 & 1 \end{bmatrix} - \begin{bmatrix} 1 & 1 & 1 \\ 1 & 1 & 1 \\ 1 & 1 & 1 \end{bmatrix} = \begin{bmatrix} 3-1 & 3-1 & 3-1 \\ 1-1 & 3-1 & 1-1 \\ 1-1 & 3-1 & 1-1 \end{bmatrix} = \begin{bmatrix} 2 & 2 & 2 \\ 0 & 2 & 0 \\ 0 & 2 & 0 \end{bmatrix}$$

EXAMPLE 3 Adding and subtracting matrices

If $A = \begin{bmatrix} 7 & 8 & -1 \\ 0 & -1 & 6 \end{bmatrix}$ and $B = \begin{bmatrix} 5 & -2 & 10 \\ -3 & 2 & 4 \end{bmatrix}$, find the following.

(a) $A + B$ **(b)** $B + A$ **(c)** $A - B$

SOLUTION

(a) $A + B = \begin{bmatrix} 7 & 8 & -1 \\ 0 & -1 & 6 \end{bmatrix} + \begin{bmatrix} 5 & -2 & 10 \\ -3 & 2 & 4 \end{bmatrix}$

$= \begin{bmatrix} 7+5 & 8+(-2) & -1+10 \\ 0+(-3) & -1+2 & 6+4 \end{bmatrix}$

$= \begin{bmatrix} 12 & 6 & 9 \\ -3 & 1 & 10 \end{bmatrix}$

(b) $B + A = \begin{bmatrix} 5 & -2 & 10 \\ -3 & 2 & 4 \end{bmatrix} + \begin{bmatrix} 7 & 8 & -1 \\ 0 & -1 & 6 \end{bmatrix}$

$= \begin{bmatrix} 5+7 & -2+8 & 10+(-1) \\ -3+0 & 2+(-1) & 4+6 \end{bmatrix}$

$= \begin{bmatrix} 12 & 6 & 9 \\ -3 & 1 & 10 \end{bmatrix}$

Notice that $A + B = B + A$. The commutative property for matrix addition holds in general, provided that A and B have the same dimension.

CLASS DISCUSSION

If matrices A and B have the same dimension, does $A - B = B - A$?

(c) $A - B = \begin{bmatrix} 7 & 8 & -1 \\ 0 & -1 & 6 \end{bmatrix} - \begin{bmatrix} 5 & -2 & 10 \\ -3 & 2 & 4 \end{bmatrix}$

$= \begin{bmatrix} 7 - 5 & 8 - (-2) & -1 - 10 \\ 0 - (-3) & -1 - 2 & 6 - 4 \end{bmatrix}$

$= \begin{bmatrix} 2 & 10 & -11 \\ 3 & -3 & 2 \end{bmatrix}$

Now Try Exercise 9

An Application   Increasing the contrast in a digital image causes light areas to become lighter and dark areas to become darker. As a result, there are fewer pixels with intermediate gray levels. Changing contrast is different from making the entire picture lighter or darker.

EXAMPLE 4   Applying matrix addition to a digital image

Increase the contrast of the + sign in Figure 9.54 by changing light gray to white and dark gray to black. Use matrices to represent this computation.

Less Contrast

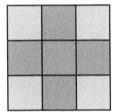

Figure 9.54

SOLUTION   Figure 9.54 can be represented by the matrix A.

$$A = \begin{bmatrix} 1 & 2 & 1 \\ 2 & 2 & 2 \\ 1 & 2 & 1 \end{bmatrix}$$

To change the contrast, we reduce each 1 in matrix A to 0 and increase each 2 to 3. The addition of matrix B can accomplish this task.

Matrix Addition for Changing Contrast

$$A + B = \begin{bmatrix} 1 & 2 & 1 \\ 2 & 2 & 2 \\ 1 & 2 & 1 \end{bmatrix} + \begin{bmatrix} -1 & 1 & -1 \\ 1 & 1 & 1 \\ -1 & 1 & -1 \end{bmatrix} = \begin{bmatrix} 0 & 3 & 0 \\ 3 & 3 & 3 \\ 0 & 3 & 0 \end{bmatrix}$$

The picture corresponding to $A + B$ is shown in Figure 9.55.

More Contrast

Figure 9.55

Now Try Exercises 23 and 25

Multiplication of a Matrix by a Scalar   The matrix

$$B = \begin{bmatrix} 1 & 1 & 1 \\ 1 & 1 & 1 \\ 1 & 1 & 1 \end{bmatrix}$$

can be used to darken a digital picture. Suppose that a photograph is represented by a matrix A with gray levels 0 through 11. Every time matrix B is added to A, the picture becomes slightly darker. For example, if

$$A = \begin{bmatrix} 0 & 5 & 0 \\ 5 & 5 & 5 \\ 0 & 5 & 0 \end{bmatrix}$$

then the addition of $A + B + B$ would darken the picture by two gray levels and could be computed by

$$A + B + B = \begin{bmatrix} 0 & 5 & 0 \\ 5 & 5 & 5 \\ 0 & 5 & 0 \end{bmatrix} + \begin{bmatrix} 1 & 1 & 1 \\ 1 & 1 & 1 \\ 1 & 1 & 1 \end{bmatrix} + \begin{bmatrix} 1 & 1 & 1 \\ 1 & 1 & 1 \\ 1 & 1 & 1 \end{bmatrix} = \begin{bmatrix} 2 & 7 & 2 \\ 7 & 7 & 7 \\ 2 & 7 & 2 \end{bmatrix}.$$

A simpler way to write the expression $A + B + B$ is $A + 2B$. Multiplying B by 2 to obtain $2B$ is called **scalar multiplication.**

Scalar Multiplication: Multiply Each Element by the Scalar

Scalar

$$2B = 2\begin{bmatrix} 1 & 1 & 1 \\ 1 & 1 & 1 \\ 1 & 1 & 1 \end{bmatrix} = \begin{bmatrix} 2(1) & 2(1) & 2(1) \\ 2(1) & 2(1) & 2(1) \\ 2(1) & 2(1) & 2(1) \end{bmatrix} = \begin{bmatrix} 2 & 2 & 2 \\ 2 & 2 & 2 \\ 2 & 2 & 2 \end{bmatrix}$$

Every element of B is multiplied by the real number (scalar) 2.

Sometimes a matrix B is denoted $B = [b_{ij}]$, where b_{ij} represents the element in the ith row, jth column. In this way, we could write $2B$ as $2[b_{ij}] = [2b_{ij}]$. This indicates that to calculate $2B$, multiply each b_{ij} by 2. In a similar manner, a matrix A is sometimes denoted by $[a_{ij}]$.

Some operations on matrices are now summarized.

OPERATIONS ON MATRICES

Matrix Addition

The sum of two $m \times n$ matrices A and B is the $m \times n$ matrix $A + B$, in which each element is the sum of the corresponding elements of A and B. This is written as $A + B = [a_{ij}] + [b_{ij}] = [a_{ij} + b_{ij}]$. If A and B have different dimensions, then $A + B$ is undefined.

Matrix Subtraction

The difference of two $m \times n$ matrices A and B is the $m \times n$ matrix $A - B$, in which each element is the difference of the corresponding elements of A and B. This is written as $A - B = [a_{ij}] - [b_{ij}] = [a_{ij} - b_{ij}]$. If A and B have different dimensions, then $A - B$ is undefined.

Multiplication of a Matrix by a Scalar

The product of a scalar (real number) k and an $m \times n$ matrix A is the $m \times n$ matrix kA, in which each element is k times the corresponding element of A. This is written as $kA = k[a_{ij}] = [ka_{ij}]$.

EXAMPLE 5 Performing scalar multiplication

If $A = \begin{bmatrix} 2 & 7 & 11 \\ -1 & 3 & -5 \\ 0 & 9 & -12 \end{bmatrix}$, find $-4A$.

SOLUTION

$$-4A = -4\begin{bmatrix} 2 & 7 & 11 \\ -1 & 3 & -5 \\ 0 & 9 & -12 \end{bmatrix} = \begin{bmatrix} -4(2) & -4(7) & -4(11) \\ -4(-1) & -4(3) & -4(-5) \\ -4(0) & -4(9) & -4(-12) \end{bmatrix} = \begin{bmatrix} -8 & -28 & -44 \\ 4 & -12 & 20 \\ 0 & -36 & 48 \end{bmatrix}$$

Now Try Exercise 11(*b*)

EXAMPLE 6 Performing operations on matrices

If possible, perform the indicated operations using

$$A = \begin{bmatrix} 4 & -2 \\ 3 & 5 \end{bmatrix}, B = \begin{bmatrix} 0 & 1 \\ -2 & 3 \end{bmatrix}, C = \begin{bmatrix} 1 & -1 \\ 0 & 7 \\ -4 & 2 \end{bmatrix}, \text{ and } D = \begin{bmatrix} -1 & -3 \\ 9 & -7 \\ 1 & 8 \end{bmatrix}.$$

(a) $A + 3B$ **(b)** $A - C$ **(c)** $-2C - 3D$

SOLUTION

(a) $A + 3B = \begin{bmatrix} 4 & -2 \\ 3 & 5 \end{bmatrix} + 3\begin{bmatrix} 0 & 1 \\ -2 & 3 \end{bmatrix}$

$$= \begin{bmatrix} 4 & -2 \\ 3 & 5 \end{bmatrix} + \begin{bmatrix} 0 & 3 \\ -6 & 9 \end{bmatrix} = \begin{bmatrix} 4 & 1 \\ -3 & 14 \end{bmatrix}$$

(b) $A - C$ is undefined because the dimension of A is 2×2 and unequal to the dimension of C, which is 3×2.

(c) $-2C - 3D = -2\begin{bmatrix} 1 & -1 \\ 0 & 7 \\ -4 & 2 \end{bmatrix} - 3\begin{bmatrix} -1 & -3 \\ 9 & -7 \\ 1 & 8 \end{bmatrix}$

$$= \begin{bmatrix} -2 & 2 \\ 0 & -14 \\ 8 & -4 \end{bmatrix} - \begin{bmatrix} -3 & -9 \\ 27 & -21 \\ 3 & 24 \end{bmatrix} = \begin{bmatrix} 1 & 11 \\ -27 & 7 \\ 5 & -28 \end{bmatrix}$$

Now Try Exercises 13 and 15

Matrix Products

Addition, subtraction, and multiplication can be performed on numbers, variables, and functions. The same operations apply to matrices. Matrix multiplication is different from scalar multiplication.

An Application Suppose two students are taking day classes at one college and night classes at another, in order to graduate on time. Tables 9.10 and 9.11 list the number of credits taken by the students and the cost per credit at each college.

The cost of tuition is computed by multiplying the number of credits and the cost of each credit. Student 1 is taking 10 credits at $60 each and 7 credits at $80 each. The total tuition for Student 1 is $10(\$60) + 7(\$80) = \$1160$. In a similar manner, the tuition for Student 2 is given by $11(\$60) + 4(\$80) = \$980$. The information in these tables can be represented by matrices. Let A represent Table 9.10 and B represent Table 9.11. B is called a **column matrix** because it has exactly one column.

Credits Taken

	College A	College B
Student 1	10	7
Student 2	11	4

Table 9.10

Credit Cost

	Cost per Credit
College A	$60
College B	$80

Table 9.11

$$A = \begin{bmatrix} 10 & 7 \\ 11 & 4 \end{bmatrix} \quad \text{and} \quad B = \begin{bmatrix} 60 \\ 80 \end{bmatrix} \text{ —— Column matrix}$$

The matrix product AB calculates total tuition for each student.

Matrix Multiplication

$$AB = \begin{bmatrix} 10 & 7 \\ 11 & 4 \end{bmatrix}\begin{bmatrix} 60 \\ 80 \end{bmatrix} = \begin{bmatrix} 10(60) + 7(80) \\ 11(60) + 4(80) \end{bmatrix} = \begin{bmatrix} 1160 \\ 980 \end{bmatrix}$$

Generalizing from this example provides the following definition of matrix multiplication.

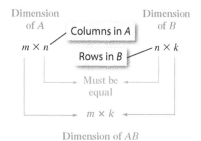

Figure 9.56

MATRIX MULTIPLICATION

The **product** of an $m \times n$ matrix A and an $n \times k$ matrix B is the $m \times k$ matrix AB, which is computed as follows. To find the element of AB in the ith row and jth column, multiply each element in the ith row of A by the corresponding element in the jth column of B. The sum of these products will give the element in row i, column j of AB.

NOTE In order to compute the product of two matrices, the number of columns in the first matrix must equal the number of rows in the second matrix, as illustrated in Figure 9.56.

EXAMPLE 7 Multiplying matrices

If possible, compute each product using

$$A = \begin{bmatrix} 1 & -1 \\ 0 & 3 \\ 4 & -2 \end{bmatrix}, B = \begin{bmatrix} -1 \\ -2 \end{bmatrix}, C = \begin{bmatrix} 1 & 2 & 3 \\ 4 & 5 & 6 \end{bmatrix}, \text{ and } D = \begin{bmatrix} 1 & -1 & 2 \\ 0 & 3 & -2 \\ -3 & 4 & 5 \end{bmatrix}.$$

(a) AB **(b)** CA **(c)** DC **(d)** CD

SOLUTION

(a) The dimension of A is 3×2 and the dimension of B is 2×1. The dimension of AB is 3×1, as shown in Figure 9.57. The product AB is found as follows.

$$AB = \begin{bmatrix} 1 & -1 \\ 0 & 3 \\ 4 & -2 \end{bmatrix} \begin{bmatrix} -1 \\ -2 \end{bmatrix} = \begin{bmatrix} (1)(-1) + (-1)(-2) \\ (0)(-1) + (3)(-2) \\ (4)(-1) + (-2)(-2) \end{bmatrix} = \begin{bmatrix} 1 \\ -6 \\ 0 \end{bmatrix}$$

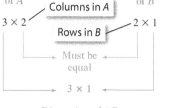

Figure 9.57

(b) The dimension of C is 2×3 and the dimension of A is 3×2. Thus CA is 2×2.

$$CA = \begin{bmatrix} 1 & 2 & 3 \\ 4 & 5 & 6 \end{bmatrix} \begin{bmatrix} 1 & -1 \\ 0 & 3 \\ 4 & -2 \end{bmatrix}$$

$$= \begin{bmatrix} 1(1) + 2(0) + 3(4) & 1(-1) + 2(3) + 3(-2) \\ 4(1) + 5(0) + 6(4) & 4(-1) + 5(3) + 6(-2) \end{bmatrix}$$

$$= \begin{bmatrix} 13 & -1 \\ 28 & -1 \end{bmatrix}$$

(c) The dimension of D is 3×3 and the dimension of C is 2×3. Therefore DC is undefined. Note that D has 3 columns and C has only 2 rows.

(d) The dimension of C is 2×3 and the dimension of D is 3×3. Thus CD is 2×3.

$$CD = \begin{bmatrix} 1 & 2 & 3 \\ 4 & 5 & 6 \end{bmatrix} \begin{bmatrix} 1 & -1 & 2 \\ 0 & 3 & -2 \\ -3 & 4 & 5 \end{bmatrix}$$

$$= \begin{bmatrix} 1(1) + 2(0) + 3(-3) & 1(-1) + 2(3) + 3(4) & 1(2) + 2(-2) + 3(5) \\ 4(1) + 5(0) + 6(-3) & 4(-1) + 5(3) + 6(4) & 4(2) + 5(-2) + 6(5) \end{bmatrix}$$

$$= \begin{bmatrix} -8 & 17 & 13 \\ -14 & 35 & 28 \end{bmatrix}$$

Now Try Exercises 27, 31, 33, and 43

MAKING CONNECTIONS

The Commutative Property and Matrix Multiplication   Example 7 shows that $CD \neq DC$. Unlike multiplication of numbers, variables, and functions, matrix multiplication is *not* commutative. Instead, matrix multiplication is similar to function composition, where for a general pair of functions $f \circ g \neq g \circ f$.

Square matrices have the same number of rows as columns and have dimension $n \times n$ for some natural number n. When we multiply two square matrices, both having dimension $n \times n$, the resulting matrix also has dimension $n \times n$.

EXAMPLE 8   Multiplying square matrices

If $A = \begin{bmatrix} 1 & 0 & 7 \\ 3 & 2 & -1 \\ -5 & -2 & 5 \end{bmatrix}$ and $B = \begin{bmatrix} 4 & -6 & 7 \\ 8 & 9 & 10 \\ 0 & 1 & -3 \end{bmatrix}$, find AB.

SOLUTION

$$AB = \begin{bmatrix} 1 & 0 & 7 \\ 3 & 2 & -1 \\ -5 & -2 & 5 \end{bmatrix}\begin{bmatrix} 4 & -6 & 7 \\ 8 & 9 & 10 \\ 0 & 1 & -3 \end{bmatrix}$$

$$= \begin{bmatrix} 1(4) + 0(8) + 7(0) & 1(-6) + 0(9) + 7(1) & 1(7) + 0(10) + 7(-3) \\ 3(4) + 2(8) - 1(0) & 3(-6) + 2(9) - 1(1) & 3(7) + 2(10) - 1(-3) \\ -5(4) - 2(8) + 5(0) & -5(-6) - 2(9) + 5(1) & -5(7) - 2(10) + 5(-3) \end{bmatrix}$$

$$= \begin{bmatrix} 4 & 1 & -14 \\ 28 & -1 & 44 \\ -36 & 17 & -70 \end{bmatrix}$$

Now Try Exercise 37

An Application   People can navigate from one web page to another by clicking a link. Figure 9.58 shows the links connecting four web pages. An arrow from one web page to another indicates a link. For example, it is possible to navigate from Page 1 to Page 3 in a single click, but it is not possible to navigate from Page 2 to Page 4 in a single click.

Web Page Links

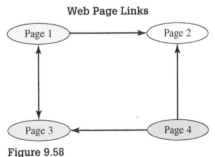

Figure 9.58

These web page links can be represented by a 4×4 square matrix. Because there is a link from Page 1 to Page 2, we put a 1 in row 1 column 2. Similarly, a link exists from Page 4 to Page 3, so we put a 1 in row 4 column 3. When no link exists from one web page to another, we place a 0 in the appropriate row and column of the matrix. Using this process results in the following matrix.

$$A = \begin{bmatrix} 0 & 1 & 1 & 0 \\ 0 & 0 & 0 & 0 \\ 1 & 0 & 0 & 0 \\ 0 & 1 & 1 & 0 \end{bmatrix}$$

In the next example we use matrix multiplication to find all of the 2-click paths between web pages.

EXAMPLE 9   Finding 2-click paths between web pages

Use matrix multiplication to find all 2-click paths among the web pages in Figure 9.58 on the previous page.

SOLUTION
The computation A^2 can be used to determine if it is possible to get from web page i to web page j in 2 clicks (links).

$$A^2 = \begin{bmatrix} 0 & 1 & 1 & 0 \\ 0 & 0 & 0 & 0 \\ 1 & 0 & 0 & 0 \\ 0 & 1 & 1 & 0 \end{bmatrix} \cdot \begin{bmatrix} 0 & 1 & 1 & 0 \\ 0 & 0 & 0 & 0 \\ 1 & 0 & 0 & 0 \\ 0 & 1 & 1 & 0 \end{bmatrix} = \begin{bmatrix} 1 & 0 & 0 & 0 \\ 0 & 0 & 0 & 0 \\ 0 & 1 & 1 & 0 \\ 1 & 0 & 0 & 0 \end{bmatrix}$$

The 1 in row 3 column 2 of A^2 indicates that there is a 2-click path from Page 3 to Page 2 (Page 3 to Page 1 to Page 2.) The other 1's in A^2 can be interpreted similarly.

Now Try Exercises 77, 79

NOTE   In Example 9, computing A^3 would give all 3-click paths between the web pages. Similar statements can be made for A^n, where n is a positive integer.

Real numbers satisfy the commutative, associative, and distributive properties for various arithmetic operations. Matrices also satisfy some of these properties, provided that their dimensions are valid so the resulting expressions are defined.

PROPERTIES OF MATRICES

Let A, B, and C be matrices. Assume that each matrix operation is defined.

1. $A + B = B + A$ Commutative property for matrix addition (No commutative property for matrix multiplication)

2. $(A + B) + C = A + (B + C)$ Associative property for matrix addition
3. $(AB)C = A(BC)$ Associative property for matrix multiplication
4. $A(B + C) = AB + AC$ Distributive property

Technology and Matrices (Optional)

Computing arithmetic operations on large matrices by hand can be a difficult task. Many graphing calculators have the capability to perform addition, subtraction, multiplication, and scalar multiplication with matrices, as the next two examples demonstrate.

EXAMPLE 10   Multiplying matrices with technology

Use a graphing calculator to find the product AB from Example 8.

SOLUTION   First enter the matrices A and B into your calculator, as illustrated in Figures 9.59 and 9.60. Then find their product on the home screen, as shown in Figure 9.61. Notice that the answer agrees with our results from Example 8.

Calculator Help
To enter the elements of a matrix, see Appendix A (page AP-12). To multiply two matrices, see Appendix A (page AP-13).

```
MATRIX[A]   3 ×3
[ 1      0       7     ]
[ 3      2      ⁻1     ]
[⁻5     ⁻2       5     ]
```

Figure 9.59

```
MATRIX[B]   3 ×3
[ 4     ⁻6       7     ]
[ 8      9      10     ]
[ 0      1      ⁻3     ]
```

Figure 9.60

```
[A]*[B]
[ [ 4     1     ⁻14]
  [28    ⁻1     44 ]
  [⁻36   17    ⁻70]]
```

Figure 9.61

Now Try Exercise 45

EXAMPLE 11 Using technology to evaluate a matrix expression

Evaluate the expression $2A + 3B^3$, where

$$A = \begin{bmatrix} 3 & -1 & 2 \\ -1 & 6 & -1 \\ 2 & -1 & 9 \end{bmatrix} \quad \text{and} \quad B = \begin{bmatrix} 1 & -2 & 5 \\ 3 & 1 & -1 \\ 5 & 2 & 1 \end{bmatrix}.$$

```
2[A]+3[B]^3
  [[300   -32   322]
   [133    63    73 ]
   [358    28   348]]
```

Figure 9.62

SOLUTION In the expression $2A + 3B^3$, B^3 is equal to BBB. Enter each matrix into a calculator and evaluate the expression. Figure 9.62 shows the result of this computation.

Now Try Exercise 47

9.5 Putting It All Together

Addition, subtraction, and multiplication can be performed on numbers, variables, and functions. In this section we looked at how these operations also apply to matrices. The following table provides examples of these operations.

MATRIX ADDITION
$$\begin{bmatrix} 1 & 2 & 3 \\ 5 & 6 & 7 \end{bmatrix} + \begin{bmatrix} -1 & 0 & 8 \\ 9 & -2 & 10 \end{bmatrix} = \begin{bmatrix} 1 + (-1) & 2 + 0 & 3 + 8 \\ 5 + 9 & 6 + (-2) & 7 + 10 \end{bmatrix} = \begin{bmatrix} 0 & 2 & 11 \\ 14 & 4 & 17 \end{bmatrix}$$
The matrices must have the same dimension for their sum to be defined.
MATRIX SUBTRACTION
$$\begin{bmatrix} 1 & -4 \\ -3 & 4 \\ 2 & 7 \end{bmatrix} - \begin{bmatrix} 5 & 1 \\ 3 & 6 \\ 8 & -9 \end{bmatrix} = \begin{bmatrix} 1 - 5 & -4 - 1 \\ -3 - 3 & 4 - 6 \\ 2 - 8 & 7 - (-9) \end{bmatrix} = \begin{bmatrix} -4 & -5 \\ -6 & -2 \\ -6 & 16 \end{bmatrix}$$
The matrices must have the same dimension for their difference to be defined.
SCALAR MULTIPLICATION
$$3\begin{bmatrix} 3 & -2 \\ 0 & 1 \end{bmatrix} = \begin{bmatrix} 3(3) & 3(-2) \\ 3(0) & 3(1) \end{bmatrix} = \begin{bmatrix} 9 & -6 \\ 0 & 3 \end{bmatrix}$$
MATRIX MULTIPLICATION
$$\begin{bmatrix} 0 & 1 \\ 2 & -3 \end{bmatrix}\begin{bmatrix} 3 & -5 \\ 4 & 6 \end{bmatrix} = \begin{bmatrix} 0(3) + 1(4) & 0(-5) + 1(6) \\ 2(3) + (-3)(4) & 2(-5) + (-3)(6) \end{bmatrix} = \begin{bmatrix} 4 & 6 \\ -6 & -28 \end{bmatrix}$$
For a matrix product to be defined, the number of columns in the first matrix must equal the number of rows in the second matrix. Matrix multiplication is not commutative. That is, $AB \neq BA$ in general.

9.5 Exercises

Elements of Matrices

Exercises 1 and 2: Let a_{ij} and b_{ij} be general elements for the given matrices A and B.

(a) Identify a_{12}, b_{32}, and b_{22}.
(b) Compute $a_{11}b_{11} + a_{12}b_{21} + a_{13}b_{31}$.
(c) If possible, find a value for x that makes $A = B$.

1. $A = \begin{bmatrix} 1 & 3 & -4 \\ 3 & 0 & 7 \\ x & 1 & -1 \end{bmatrix}$, $B = \begin{bmatrix} 1 & x & -4 \\ 3 & 0 & 7 \\ 3 & 1 & -1 \end{bmatrix}$

2. $A = \begin{bmatrix} 0 & -1 & 6 \\ 2 & x & -1 \\ 9 & -2 & 1 \end{bmatrix}$, $B = \begin{bmatrix} 0 & -1 & x \\ 2 & 6 & -1 \\ 7 & -2 & 1 \end{bmatrix}$

Exercises 3–6: If possible, find values for x and y so that the matrices A and B are equal.

3. $A = \begin{bmatrix} x & 2 \\ -2 & 1 \end{bmatrix}$, $B = \begin{bmatrix} 1 & 2 \\ -2 & y \end{bmatrix}$

4. $A = \begin{bmatrix} 1 & x+y & 3 \\ 4 & -1 & 6 \\ 3 & 7 & -2 \end{bmatrix}$, $B = \begin{bmatrix} 1 & 2 & 3 \\ 4 & -1 & 6 \\ 3 & y & -2 \end{bmatrix}$

5. $A = \begin{bmatrix} x & 3 \\ 6 & -2 \end{bmatrix}$, $B = \begin{bmatrix} 1 & y & 0 \\ 6 & -2 & 0 \\ 0 & 0 & 0 \end{bmatrix}$

6. $A = \begin{bmatrix} 4 & -2 \\ 3 & -4 \\ x & y \end{bmatrix}$, $B = \begin{bmatrix} 4 & -2 & -2 \\ 3 & -4 & -4 \\ 7 & 8 & 8 \end{bmatrix}$

Addition, Subtraction, and Scalar Multiplication

Exercises 7–10: For the given matrices A and B find each of the following.

(a) $A + B$ (b) $B + A$ (c) $A - B$

7. $A = \begin{bmatrix} 4 & -1 \\ -1 & 4 \end{bmatrix}$, $B = \begin{bmatrix} -1 & 4 \\ 4 & -1 \end{bmatrix}$

8. $A = \begin{bmatrix} 2 & -4 \\ -1 & \frac{1}{2} \\ 3 & -2 \end{bmatrix}$, $B = \begin{bmatrix} 5 & 0 \\ 3 & \frac{1}{2} \\ -1 & 1 \end{bmatrix}$

9. $A = \begin{bmatrix} 3 & 4 & -1 \\ 0 & -3 & 2 \\ -2 & 5 & 10 \end{bmatrix}$, $B = \begin{bmatrix} 11 & 5 & -2 \\ 4 & -7 & 12 \\ 6 & 6 & 6 \end{bmatrix}$

10. $A = \begin{bmatrix} 1 & 6 & 1 & -2 \\ 0 & 1 & 3 & 5 \\ 0 & 0 & 1 & -2 \end{bmatrix}$, $B = \begin{bmatrix} 1 & 0 & 0 & 9 \\ 3 & 1 & 0 & 3 \\ -1 & 4 & 1 & -2 \end{bmatrix}$

Exercises 11–16: If possible, find each of the following.
(a) $A + B$ (b) $3A$ (c) $2A - 3B$

11. $A = \begin{bmatrix} 2 & -6 \\ 3 & 1 \end{bmatrix}$, $B = \begin{bmatrix} -1 & 0 \\ -2 & 3 \end{bmatrix}$

12. $A = \begin{bmatrix} 1 & -2 & 5 \\ 3 & -4 & -1 \end{bmatrix}$, $B = \begin{bmatrix} 0 & -1 & -5 \\ -3 & 1 & 2 \end{bmatrix}$

13. $A = \begin{bmatrix} 1 & -1 & 0 \\ 1 & 5 & 9 \\ -4 & 8 & -5 \end{bmatrix}$, $B = \begin{bmatrix} 2 & 8 & -1 \\ 6 & -1 & 3 \end{bmatrix}$

14. $A = \begin{bmatrix} 6 & 2 & 9 \\ 3 & -2 & 0 \\ -1 & 4 & 8 \end{bmatrix}$, $B = \begin{bmatrix} 1 & 0 & -1 \\ 3 & 0 & 7 \\ 0 & -2 & -5 \end{bmatrix}$

15. $A = \begin{bmatrix} -2 & -1 \\ -5 & 1 \\ 2 & -3 \end{bmatrix}$, $B = \begin{bmatrix} 2 & -1 \\ 3 & 1 \\ 7 & -5 \end{bmatrix}$

16. $A = \begin{bmatrix} 0 & 1 \\ 3 & 2 \\ 4 & -9 \end{bmatrix}$, $B = \begin{bmatrix} 5 & 2 & -7 \\ 8 & -2 & 0 \end{bmatrix}$

Exercises 17–22: Evaluate the matrix expression.

17. $2\begin{bmatrix} 2 & -1 \\ 5 & 1 \\ 0 & 3 \end{bmatrix} + \begin{bmatrix} 5 & 0 \\ 7 & -3 \\ 1 & 1 \end{bmatrix} - \begin{bmatrix} 9 & -4 \\ 4 & 4 \\ 1 & 6 \end{bmatrix}$

18. $-3\begin{bmatrix} 3 & 8 \\ -1 & -9 \end{bmatrix} + 5\begin{bmatrix} 4 & -8 \\ 1 & 6 \end{bmatrix}$

19. $\begin{bmatrix} 4 & 6 \\ 3 & -7 \end{bmatrix} - 2\begin{bmatrix} 1 & 0 \\ -4 & 1 \end{bmatrix}$

20. $\begin{bmatrix} 5 & -1 & 6 \\ -2 & 10 & 12 \\ 5 & 2 & 9 \end{bmatrix} - \begin{bmatrix} -1 & 2 & 2 \\ 2 & -1 & 2 \\ 2 & 2 & -1 \end{bmatrix}$

21. $2\begin{bmatrix} 2 & -1 & -1 \\ -1 & 2 & -1 \\ -1 & -1 & 2 \end{bmatrix} + 3\begin{bmatrix} 1 & 2 & 3 \\ 2 & 1 & 3 \\ 2 & 3 & 1 \end{bmatrix}$

22. $3\begin{bmatrix} 1 & 0 & 3 & -1 \\ 0 & 1 & 2 & -1 \\ 1 & 0 & -3 & 1 \end{bmatrix} - 4\begin{bmatrix} -1 & 0 & 0 & 4 \\ 0 & -1 & 3 & 2 \\ 2 & 0 & 1 & -1 \end{bmatrix}$

Matrices and Digital Photography

Exercises 23–26: **Digital Photography**   *(Refer to the discussion of digital images in this section.) Consider the following simplified digital image, which has a 3×3 grid with four gray levels numbered from 0 to 3. It shows the number 1 in dark gray on a light gray background. Let A be the 3×3 matrix that represents this image digitally.*

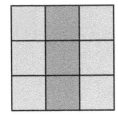

23. Find the matrix A.

24. Find a matrix B such that adding B to A will cause the entire image to become one gray level darker. Evaluate the expression $A + B$.

25. (Refer to Example 4.) Find a matrix B such that adding B to A will enhance the contrast of A by one gray level. Evaluate $A + B$.

26. Find a matrix B such that subtracting B from A will cause the entire image to become lighter by one gray level. Evaluate the expression $A - B$.

Matrix Multiplication

Exercises 27–44: If possible, find AB and BA.

27. $A = \begin{bmatrix} 1 & -1 \\ 2 & 0 \end{bmatrix}$, $B = \begin{bmatrix} -2 & 3 \\ 1 & 2 \end{bmatrix}$

28. $A = \begin{bmatrix} -3 & 5 \\ 2 & 7 \end{bmatrix}$, $B = \begin{bmatrix} -1 & 2 \\ 0 & 7 \end{bmatrix}$

29. $A = \begin{bmatrix} 5 & -7 & 2 \\ 0 & 1 & 5 \end{bmatrix}$, $B = \begin{bmatrix} 9 & 8 & 7 \\ 1 & -1 & -2 \end{bmatrix}$

30. $A = \begin{bmatrix} 2 & 1 & -1 \\ 0 & 2 & 1 \\ 3 & 2 & -1 \end{bmatrix}$, $B = \begin{bmatrix} 1 & 0 \\ 2 & -1 \\ 3 & 1 \end{bmatrix}$

31. $A = \begin{bmatrix} 3 & -1 \\ 1 & 0 \\ -2 & -4 \end{bmatrix}$, $B = \begin{bmatrix} -2 & 5 & -3 \\ 9 & -7 & 0 \end{bmatrix}$

32. $A = \begin{bmatrix} -1 & 0 & -2 \\ 4 & -2 & 1 \end{bmatrix}$, $B = \begin{bmatrix} 2 & -2 \\ 5 & -1 \\ 0 & 1 \end{bmatrix}$

33. $A = \begin{bmatrix} 1 & -1 & 0 \\ 2 & -1 & 5 \\ 6 & 1 & -4 \end{bmatrix}$, $B = \begin{bmatrix} -1 & 3 & -1 \\ 7 & -7 & 1 \end{bmatrix}$

34. $A = \begin{bmatrix} 2 & -1 & -5 \\ 4 & -1 & 6 \\ -2 & 0 & 9 \end{bmatrix}$, $B = \begin{bmatrix} 1 & 2 \\ -1 & -1 \\ 2 & 0 \end{bmatrix}$

35. $A = \begin{bmatrix} 2 & -3 \\ 5 & 3 \end{bmatrix}$, $B = \begin{bmatrix} -3 \\ 4 \\ 1 \end{bmatrix}$

36. $A = \begin{bmatrix} 3 & -1 \\ 2 & -2 \\ 0 & 4 \end{bmatrix}$, $B = \begin{bmatrix} 1 & -4 & 0 \\ -1 & 3 & 2 \end{bmatrix}$

37. $A = \begin{bmatrix} 2 & -1 & 3 \\ 0 & 1 & 0 \\ 2 & -2 & 3 \end{bmatrix}$, $B = \begin{bmatrix} 1 & 5 & -1 \\ 0 & 1 & 3 \\ -1 & 2 & 1 \end{bmatrix}$

38. $A = \begin{bmatrix} 1 & -2 & 5 \\ 1 & 0 & -2 \\ 1 & 3 & 2 \end{bmatrix}$, $B = \begin{bmatrix} -1 & 4 & 2 \\ -3 & 0 & 1 \\ 5 & 1 & 0 \end{bmatrix}$

39. $A = \begin{bmatrix} 2 & -1 \\ 3 & 1 \end{bmatrix}$, $B = \begin{bmatrix} 1 \\ 3 \end{bmatrix}$

40. $A = \begin{bmatrix} 5 & -3 \end{bmatrix}$, $B = \begin{bmatrix} 1 \\ 3 \end{bmatrix}$

41. $A = \begin{bmatrix} -3 & 1 \\ 2 & -4 \end{bmatrix}$, $B = \begin{bmatrix} 1 & 0 & -2 \\ -4 & 8 & 1 \end{bmatrix}$

42. $A = \begin{bmatrix} 6 & 1 & 0 \\ -2 & 5 & 1 \\ 4 & -7 & 10 \end{bmatrix}$, $B = \begin{bmatrix} 10 \\ 20 \\ 30 \end{bmatrix}$

43. $A = \begin{bmatrix} 1 & 0 & -2 \\ 3 & -4 & 1 \\ 2 & 0 & 5 \end{bmatrix}$, $B = \begin{bmatrix} 1 \\ -1 \\ 3 \end{bmatrix}$

44. $A = \begin{bmatrix} 1 & -1 & 3 & -2 \\ 1 & 0 & 3 & 4 \\ 2 & -2 & 0 & 8 \end{bmatrix}$, $B = \begin{bmatrix} 1 & -1 \\ 0 & 5 \\ 2 & 3 \\ -5 & 4 \end{bmatrix}$

Technology and Matrices

Exercises 45–48: Use the given A and B to evaluate each expression.

$$A = \begin{bmatrix} 3 & -2 & 4 \\ 5 & 2 & -3 \\ 7 & 5 & 4 \end{bmatrix}, \quad B = \begin{bmatrix} 1 & 1 & -5 \\ -1 & 0 & -7 \\ -6 & 4 & 3 \end{bmatrix}$$

45. AB

46. BA

47. $3A^2 + 2B$

48. $B^2 - 3A$

Exercises 49–52: **Properties of Matrices** *Use a graphing calculator to evaluate the expression with the given matrices A, B, and C. Compare your answers for parts (a) and (b). Then interpret the results.*

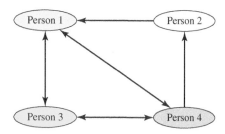

$$A = \begin{bmatrix} 2 & -1 & 3 \\ 1 & 3 & -5 \\ 0 & -2 & 1 \end{bmatrix}, B = \begin{bmatrix} 6 & 2 & 7 \\ 3 & -4 & -5 \\ 7 & 1 & 0 \end{bmatrix},$$

$$C = \begin{bmatrix} 1 & 4 & -3 \\ 8 & 1 & -1 \\ 4 & 6 & -2 \end{bmatrix}$$

49. (a) $A(B + C)$ (b) $AB + AC$

50. (a) $(A - B)C$ (b) $AC - BC$

51. (a) $(A - B)^2$ (b) $A^2 - AB - BA + B^2$

52. (a) $(AB)C$ (b) $A(BC)$

Applications

Exercises 53–56: **Social Networks** *(Refer to Example 2.) The following graph shows a simple social network.*

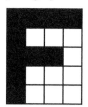

53. Use a matrix to represent this social network.

54. Which person is the most liked person in the network?

55. Which person is the least liked person in the network?

56. Which person likes the most people in the network?

Exercises 57–60: **Social Networks** *(Refer to the previous four exercises.) The following matrix represents a simple social network.*

$$\begin{bmatrix} 0 & 0 & 1 & 0 \\ 0 & 0 & 0 & 0 \\ 1 & 1 & 0 & 0 \\ 1 & 0 & 1 & 0 \end{bmatrix}$$

57. Draw a graph of this network.

58. Row 2 in the matrix contains only 0's. What does this tell us about Person 2?

59. Column 4 in the matrix contains only 0's. What does this tell us about Person 4?

60. If a column of a social network matrix contains only 1's (except on the main diagonal), what can be said about the person represented by that column?

61. **Negative Image** The negative image of a picture interchanges black and white. The number 1 is represented by the matrix A. Determine a matrix B such that $B - A$ represents the negative image of the picture represented by A. Evaluate $B - A$.

$$A = \begin{bmatrix} 0 & 3 & 0 \\ 0 & 3 & 0 \\ 0 & 3 & 0 \end{bmatrix}$$

62. **Negative Image** (Refer to the previous exercise.) Matrix A represents a digital photograph. Find a matrix B that represents the negative image of this picture.

$$A = \begin{bmatrix} 0 & 3 & 0 \\ 1 & 3 & 1 \\ 2 & 3 & 2 \end{bmatrix}$$

Exercises 63 and 64: **Digital Photography** *The digital image represents the letter F using 20 pixels in a 5 × 4 grid. Assume that there are four gray levels from 0 to 3.*

63. Find a matrix A that represents this digital image of the letter F.

64. (Continuation of Exercise 63)
(a) Find a matrix B such that $B - A$ represents the negative image of the picture represented by A.

(b) Find a matrix C such that $A + C$ represents a decrease in the contrast of A by one gray level.

Exercises 65–68: **Digitizing Letters** *(Refer to Exercise 61.) Complete the following.*

(a) *Design a matrix A with dimension 4 × 4 that represents a digital image of the given letter. Assume that there are four gray levels from 0 to 3.*
(b) *Find a matrix B such that B − A represents the negative image of the picture represented by matrix A from part (a).*

65. Z   **66.** N

67. L   **68.** O

Exercises 69–72: **Tuition Costs**   *(Refer to the discussion after Example 6.)*

(a) *Find a matrix A and a column matrix B that describe the following tables.*

(b) *Find the matrix product AB, and interpret the result.*

69.

	College A	College B
Student 1	12	4
Student 2	8	7

	Cost per Credit
College A	$55
College B	$70

70.

	College A	College B
Student 1	15	2
Student 2	12	4

	Cost per Credit
College A	$90
College B	$75

71.

	College A	College B
Student 1	10	5
Student 2	9	8
Student 3	11	3

	Cost per Credit
College A	$60
College B	$70

72.

	College A	College B	College C
Student 1	6	0	3
Student 2	11	3	0
Student 3	0	12	3

	Cost per Credit
College A	$50
College B	$65
College C	$60

73. Auto Parts   A store owner makes two separate orders for three types of auto parts: I, II, and III. The numbers of parts ordered are represented by the matrix A.

$$A = \begin{bmatrix} & \text{I} & \text{II} & \text{III} \\ & 3 & 4 & 8 \\ & 5 & 6 & 2 \end{bmatrix} \begin{matrix} \\ \text{Order 1} \\ \text{Order 2} \end{matrix}$$

For example, Order 1 called for 4 parts of type II. The cost in dollars of each part can be represented by the matrix B.

$$B = \begin{bmatrix} \text{Cost} \\ 10 \\ 20 \\ 30 \end{bmatrix} \begin{matrix} \text{Part I} \\ \text{Part II} \\ \text{Part III} \end{matrix}$$

Find AB and interpret the result.

74. Car Sales   Two car dealers buy four different makes of cars: I, II, III, and IV. The number of each make of automobile bought by each dealer is represented by the matrix A.

$$A = \begin{bmatrix} \text{I} & \text{II} & \text{III} & \text{IV} \\ 1 & 3 & 8 & 4 \\ 3 & 5 & 7 & 0 \end{bmatrix} \begin{matrix} \\ \text{Dealer 1} \\ \text{Dealer 2} \end{matrix}$$

For example, Dealer 2 bought 7 cars of type III. The cost in thousands of dollars of each type of car can be represented by the matrix B.

$$B = \begin{bmatrix} \text{Cost} \\ 15 \\ 21 \\ 28 \\ 38 \end{bmatrix} \begin{matrix} \text{Make I} \\ \text{Make II} \\ \text{Make III} \\ \text{Make IV} \end{matrix}$$

Find AB and interpret the result.

Exercises 75–80: **Web Page Links**   *(Refer to Example 9 and the application preceding it.) The following graph shows web page links.*

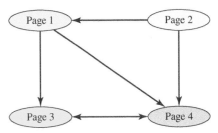

75. Create a matrix A that represents this situation.

76. Which page can be reached in a single click from every other page in the network?

77. Compute A^2.

78. Which two pages cannot be reached using a 2-click path from any other page in the network?

79. There is a 2 in row 2 column 3 of A^2. What does this tell us?

80. There is a 1 in row 4 column 4 of A^2. What does this tell us?

Writing about Mathematics

81. Discuss whether matrix multiplication is more like multiplication of functions or composition of functions. Explain your reasoning.

82. Describe one application of matrices.

Extended and Discovery Exercises

Exercises 1–4: **Representing Colors**   *Colors for computer monitors are often described using ordered triples. One model, called the RGB system, uses red, green, and blue to generate all colors. The figure describes the relationships of these colors in this system. Red is* $(1, 0, 0)$, *green is* $(0, 1, 0)$, *and blue is* $(0, 0, 1)$. *Since equal amounts of red and green combine to form yellow, yellow is represented by* $(1, 1, 0)$. *Similarly, magenta (a deep reddish purple) is a mixture of blue and red and is represented by* $(1, 0, 1)$. *Cyan is* $(0, 1, 1)$, *since it is a mixture of blue and green.*

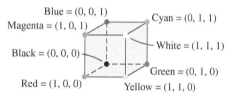

Another color model uses cyan, magenta, and yellow. Referred to as the CMY model, it is used in the four-color printing process for textbooks like this one. In this system, cyan is $(1, 0, 0)$, *magenta is* $(0, 1, 0)$, *and yellow is* $(0, 0, 1)$.

In the CMY model, red is created by mixing magenta and yellow. Thus, red is $(0, 1, 1)$ *in this system. To convert ordered triples in the RGB model to ordered triples in the CMY model, we can use the following matrix equation. In both of these systems, color intensities vary between 0 and 1.* (**Sources:** I. Kerlow, *The Art of 3-D Computer Animation and Imaging*; R. Wolff.)

$$\begin{bmatrix} C \\ M \\ Y \end{bmatrix} = \begin{bmatrix} 1 \\ 1 \\ 1 \end{bmatrix} - \begin{bmatrix} R \\ G \\ B \end{bmatrix}$$

1. In the RGB model, aquamarine is $(0.631, 1, 0.933)$. Use the matrix equation to determine the mixture of cyan, magenta, and yellow that makes aquamarine in the CMY model.

2. In the RGB model, rust is $(0.552, 0.168, 0.066)$. Use the matrix equation to determine the mixture of cyan, magenta, and yellow that makes rust in the CMY model.

3. Use the given matrix equation to find a matrix equation that changes colors represented by ordered triples in the CMY model into ordered triples in the RGB model.

4. In the CMY model, $(0.012, 0, 0.597)$ is a cream color. Use the matrix equation from Exercise 3 to determine the mixture of red, green, and blue that makes a cream color in the RGB model.

9.6 Inverses of Matrices

- Understand matrix inverses and the identity matrices
- Find inverses symbolically
- Represent linear systems with matrix equations
- Solve linear systems with matrix inverses

Introduction

Section 5.2 discussed how the inverse function f^{-1} will undo or cancel the computation performed by the function f. Like functions, some matrices have inverses. The inverse of a matrix A will undo or cancel the computation performed by A. For example, in computer graphics, if a matrix A rotates a figure on the screen 90° clockwise, then the inverse matrix will rotate the figure 90° counterclockwise. Similarly, if a matrix B translates a figure 3 units right, then B^{-1} will restore the figure to its original position by translating it 3 units left. This section discusses matrix inverses and some of their applications.

Understanding Matrix Inverses

An Application   In computer graphics, the matrix

$$A = \begin{bmatrix} 1 & 0 & h \\ 0 & 1 & k \\ 0 & 0 & 1 \end{bmatrix} \quad \text{Matrix for translating a point}$$

is used to translate a point (x, y) horizontally h units and vertically k units. The translation is to the right if $h > 0$ and to the left if $h < 0$. Similarly, the translation is upward if

$k > 0$ and downward if $k < 0$. A point (x, y) is represented by the 3×1 *column matrix*

$$X = \begin{bmatrix} x \\ y \\ 1 \end{bmatrix}. \qquad \text{Column matrix}$$

The third element in X is always equal to 1. For example, the point $(-1, 2)$ could be translated 3 units right and 4 units downward by computing the following matrix product.

Translating ($-1, 2$) Right 3 Units and Downward 4 Units

$$AX = \begin{bmatrix} 1 & 0 & 3 \\ 0 & 1 & -4 \\ 0 & 0 & 1 \end{bmatrix} \begin{bmatrix} -1 \\ 2 \\ 1 \end{bmatrix} = \begin{bmatrix} 2 \\ -2 \\ 1 \end{bmatrix} = Y$$

Its new location is $(2, -2)$. In the matrix $A, h = 3$ and $k = -4$. See Figure 9.63. (*Source:* C. Pokorny and C. Gerald, *Computer Graphics.*)

If A translates a point 3 units right and 4 units downward, then the inverse matrix translates a point 3 units left and 4 units upward. This would return a point to its original position after being translated by A. Therefore the *inverse matrix of A*, denoted A^{-1}, is given by

$$A^{-1} = \begin{bmatrix} 1 & 0 & -3 \\ 0 & 1 & 4 \\ 0 & 0 & 1 \end{bmatrix}. \qquad \text{Inverse matrix}$$

In $A^{-1}, h = -3$ and $k = 4$. The matrix product $A^{-1}Y$ results in

Translating (2, –2) Left 3 Units and Upward 4 Units

$$A^{-1}Y = \begin{bmatrix} 1 & 0 & -3 \\ 0 & 1 & 4 \\ 0 & 0 & 1 \end{bmatrix} \begin{bmatrix} 2 \\ -2 \\ 1 \end{bmatrix} = \begin{bmatrix} -1 \\ 2 \\ 1 \end{bmatrix} = X.$$

The matrix A^{-1} translates $(2, -2)$ to its original coordinates of $(-1, 2)$. The two translations acting on the point $(-1, 2)$ can be represented by the following computation.

$$A^{-1}AX = \begin{bmatrix} 1 & 0 & -3 \\ 0 & 1 & 4 \\ 0 & 0 & 1 \end{bmatrix} \begin{bmatrix} 1 & 0 & 3 \\ 0 & 1 & -4 \\ 0 & 0 & 1 \end{bmatrix} \begin{bmatrix} -1 \\ 2 \\ 1 \end{bmatrix} = \begin{bmatrix} 1 & 0 & 0 \\ 0 & 1 & 0 \\ 0 & 0 & 1 \end{bmatrix} \begin{bmatrix} -1 \\ 2 \\ 1 \end{bmatrix} = \begin{bmatrix} -1 \\ 2 \\ 1 \end{bmatrix} = X$$

That is, the action of A followed by A^{-1} on the point $(-1, 2)$ results in $(-1, 2)$. In a similar manner, if we reverse the order of A^{-1} and A to compute $AA^{-1}X$, the result is again X.

$$AA^{-1}X = \begin{bmatrix} 1 & 0 & 3 \\ 0 & 1 & -4 \\ 0 & 0 & 1 \end{bmatrix} \begin{bmatrix} 1 & 0 & -3 \\ 0 & 1 & 4 \\ 0 & 0 & 1 \end{bmatrix} \begin{bmatrix} -1 \\ 2 \\ 1 \end{bmatrix} = \begin{bmatrix} 1 & 0 & 0 \\ 0 & 1 & 0 \\ 0 & 0 & 1 \end{bmatrix} \begin{bmatrix} -1 \\ 2 \\ 1 \end{bmatrix} = \begin{bmatrix} -1 \\ 2 \\ 1 \end{bmatrix} = X$$

Notice that both matrix products $A^{-1}A$ and AA^{-1} resulted in a matrix with 1's on its main diagonal and 0's elsewhere.

The Identity Matrix

An $n \times n$ matrix with 1's on its main diagonal and 0's elsewhere is called the $n \times n$ *identity matrix*. This matrix is important because its product with any $n \times n$ matrix A always equals A.

Translating a Point

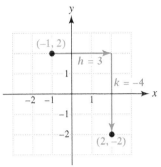

Figure 9.63

> **THE $n \times n$ IDENTITY MATRIX**
>
> The $n \times n$ **identity matrix,** denoted I_n, has only 1's on its main diagonal and 0's elsewhere.

Some examples of identity matrices are shown here.

Identity Matrices

$$I_2 = \begin{bmatrix} 1 & 0 \\ 0 & 1 \end{bmatrix}, \qquad I_3 = \begin{bmatrix} 1 & 0 & 0 \\ 0 & 1 & 0 \\ 0 & 0 & 1 \end{bmatrix}, \qquad \text{and} \qquad I_4 = \begin{bmatrix} 1 & 0 & 0 & 0 \\ 0 & 1 & 0 & 0 \\ 0 & 0 & 1 & 0 \\ 0 & 0 & 0 & 1 \end{bmatrix}$$

If A is any $n \times n$ matrix, then $I_n A = A$ and $A I_n = A$. For instance, if

$$A = \begin{bmatrix} 2 & 3 \\ 4 & 5 \end{bmatrix},$$

then

$$I_2 A = \begin{bmatrix} 1 & 0 \\ 0 & 1 \end{bmatrix}\begin{bmatrix} 2 & 3 \\ 4 & 5 \end{bmatrix} = \begin{bmatrix} 2 & 3 \\ 4 & 5 \end{bmatrix} = A \qquad \text{and}$$

$$A I_2 = \begin{bmatrix} 2 & 3 \\ 4 & 5 \end{bmatrix}\begin{bmatrix} 1 & 0 \\ 0 & 1 \end{bmatrix} = \begin{bmatrix} 2 & 3 \\ 4 & 5 \end{bmatrix} = A.$$

Matrix Inverses

Next we formally define the inverse of an $n \times n$ matrix A, whenever it exists.

> **INVERSE OF A SQUARE MATRIX**
>
> Let A be an $n \times n$ matrix. If there exists an $n \times n$ matrix, denoted A^{-1}, that satisfies
>
> $$A^{-1}A = I_n \qquad \text{and} \qquad AA^{-1} = I_n,$$
>
> then A^{-1} is the **inverse** of A.

If A^{-1} exists, then A is **invertible** or **nonsingular.** On the other hand, if a matrix A is not invertible, then it is **singular.** Not every matrix has an inverse. For example, the **zero matrix** with dimension 3×3 is given by

$$O_3 = \begin{bmatrix} 0 & 0 & 0 \\ 0 & 0 & 0 \\ 0 & 0 & 0 \end{bmatrix}. \qquad \textit{Zero matrix}$$

The matrix O_3 does not have an inverse. The product of O_3 with any 3×3 matrix B would be O_3, rather than the identity matrix I_3.

EXAMPLE 1   Verifying an inverse

Determine if B is the inverse of A, where

$$A = \begin{bmatrix} 5 & 3 \\ -3 & -2 \end{bmatrix} \qquad \text{and} \qquad B = \begin{bmatrix} 2 & 3 \\ -3 & -5 \end{bmatrix}.$$

SOLUTION For B to be the inverse of A, it must satisfy $AB = I_2$ and $BA = I_2$.

$$AB = \begin{bmatrix} 5 & 3 \\ -3 & -2 \end{bmatrix}\begin{bmatrix} 2 & 3 \\ -3 & -5 \end{bmatrix} = \begin{bmatrix} 1 & 0 \\ 0 & 1 \end{bmatrix} = I_2$$

$$BA = \begin{bmatrix} 2 & 3 \\ -3 & -5 \end{bmatrix}\begin{bmatrix} 5 & 3 \\ -3 & -2 \end{bmatrix} = \begin{bmatrix} 1 & 0 \\ 0 & 1 \end{bmatrix} = I_2$$

Thus B is the inverse of A. That is, $B = A^{-1}$.

Now Try Exercise 1

An Application   The next example discusses the significance of an inverse matrix in computer graphics.

EXAMPLE 2   Interpreting an inverse matrix

The matrix A can be used to rotate a point $90°$ clockwise about the origin, where

$$A = \begin{bmatrix} 0 & 1 & 0 \\ -1 & 0 & 0 \\ 0 & 0 & 1 \end{bmatrix} \quad \text{and} \quad A^{-1} = \begin{bmatrix} 0 & -1 & 0 \\ 1 & 0 & 0 \\ 0 & 0 & 1 \end{bmatrix}.$$

(a) Use A to rotate the point $(-2, 0)$ clockwise $90°$ about the origin.
(b) Make a conjecture about the effect of A^{-1} on the resulting point.
(c) Test this conjecture.

SOLUTION

(a) First, let the point $(-2, 0)$ be represented by the column matrix

$$X = \begin{bmatrix} -2 \\ 0 \\ 1 \end{bmatrix}.$$

Rotating a Point About the Origin

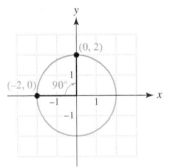

Figure 9.64

Then compute

$$AX = \begin{bmatrix} 0 & 1 & 0 \\ -1 & 0 & 0 \\ 0 & 0 & 1 \end{bmatrix}\begin{bmatrix} -2 \\ 0 \\ 1 \end{bmatrix} = \begin{bmatrix} 0 \\ 2 \\ 1 \end{bmatrix} = Y.$$

If the point $(-2, 0)$ is rotated $90°$ clockwise about the origin, its new location is $(0, 2)$. See Figure 9.64.

(b) Since A^{-1} represents the inverse operation of A, A^{-1} will rotate the point located at $(0, 2)$ counterclockwise $90°$, back to $(-2, 0)$.

(c) This conjecture is correct, since

$$A^{-1}Y = \begin{bmatrix} 0 & -1 & 0 \\ 1 & 0 & 0 \\ 0 & 0 & 1 \end{bmatrix}\begin{bmatrix} 0 \\ 2 \\ 1 \end{bmatrix} = \begin{bmatrix} -2 \\ 0 \\ 1 \end{bmatrix} = X.$$

Now Try Exercise 67

CLASS DISCUSSION

What will the results be of the computations AAX and $A^{-1}A^{-1}X$?

Finding Inverses Symbolically

The inverse matrix of an $n \times n$ matrix A can be found symbolically by first forming the augmented matrix $[A \mid I_n]$ and then performing matrix row operations, until the left side of the augmented matrix becomes the identity matrix. The resulting augmented matrix can be written as $[I_n \mid A^{-1}]$, where the right side of the matrix is A^{-1}.

In the next example, we find A^{-1} from Example 2 by hand.

EXAMPLE 3 Finding an inverse symbolically

Find A^{-1} if

$$A = \begin{bmatrix} 0 & 1 & 0 \\ -1 & 0 & 0 \\ 0 & 0 & 1 \end{bmatrix}.$$

SOLUTION

Getting Started Begin by forming the following 3×6 augmented matrix with the 3×3 identity matrix on the right half.

Augmented Matrix $[A\,|\,I_3]$

$$\left[\begin{array}{ccc|ccc} 0 & 1 & 0 & 1 & 0 & 0 \\ -1 & 0 & 0 & 0 & 1 & 0 \\ 0 & 0 & 1 & 0 & 0 & 1 \end{array}\right]$$

Next use row transformations to obtain the 3×3 identity on the left side. ▶

To obtain a 1 in the first row and first column, we negate the elements in row 2 and then interchange row 1 and row 2. The same row transformations are also applied to the right side of the augmented matrix.

$$\left[\begin{array}{ccc|ccc} 0 & 1 & 0 & 1 & 0 & 0 \\ -1 & 0 & 0 & 0 & 1 & 0 \\ 0 & 0 & 1 & 0 & 0 & 1 \end{array}\right] \begin{array}{c} -R_2 \rightarrow \\ R_1 \rightarrow \\ R_3 \rightarrow \end{array} \left[\begin{array}{ccc|ccc} 1 & 0 & 0 & 0 & -1 & 0 \\ 0 & 1 & 0 & 1 & 0 & 0 \\ 0 & 0 & 1 & 0 & 0 & 1 \end{array}\right]$$

Because the left side of the augmented matrix is now the 3×3 identity, we stop. The right side of the augmented matrix is A^{-1}. Thus

$$A^{-1} = \begin{bmatrix} 0 & -1 & 0 \\ 1 & 0 & 0 \\ 0 & 0 & 1 \end{bmatrix}, \qquad \text{Inverse matrix}$$

and our result agrees with the information in Example 2.

Now Try Exercise 21

Many times finding inverses requires several steps of row transformations. In the next two examples, we find the inverse of a 2×2 matrix and a 3×3 matrix.

EXAMPLE 4 Finding the inverse of a 2×2 matrix symbolically

Find A^{-1} if

$$A = \begin{bmatrix} 1 & 4 \\ 2 & 9 \end{bmatrix}.$$

SOLUTION Begin by forming a 2×4 augmented matrix. Perform matrix row operations to obtain the identity matrix on the left side, and perform the same operation on the right side of this matrix.

$$\left[\begin{array}{cc|cc} 1 & 4 & 1 & 0 \\ 2 & 9 & 0 & 1 \end{array}\right] \begin{array}{c} \\ R_2 - 2R_1 \rightarrow \end{array} \left[\begin{array}{cc|cc} 1 & 4 & 1 & 0 \\ 0 & 1 & -2 & 1 \end{array}\right] \begin{array}{c} R_1 - 4R_2 \rightarrow \\ \\ \end{array} \left[\begin{array}{cc|cc} 1 & 0 & 9 & -4 \\ 0 & 1 & -2 & 1 \end{array}\right]$$

Since the 2×2 identity matrix appears on the left side, it follows that the right side equals A^{-1}. That is,

$$A^{-1} = \begin{bmatrix} 9 & -4 \\ -2 & 1 \end{bmatrix}.$$

Furthermore, it can be verified that $A^{-1}A = I_2 = AA^{-1}$.

Now Try Exercise 15

EXAMPLE 5   Finding the inverse of a 3 × 3 matrix symbolically

Find A^{-1} if

$$A = \begin{bmatrix} 1 & 0 & 1 \\ 2 & 1 & 3 \\ -1 & 1 & 1 \end{bmatrix}.$$

SOLUTION   Begin by forming the following 3 × 6 augmented matrix. Perform matrix row operations to obtain the identity matrix on the left side, and perform the same operation on the right side of this matrix.

$$\begin{bmatrix} 1 & 0 & 1 & | & 1 & 0 & 0 \\ 2 & 1 & 3 & | & 0 & 1 & 0 \\ -1 & 1 & 1 & | & 0 & 0 & 1 \end{bmatrix} \begin{matrix} \\ R_2 - 2R_1 \rightarrow \\ R_3 + R_1 \rightarrow \end{matrix} \begin{bmatrix} 1 & 0 & 1 & | & 1 & 0 & 0 \\ 0 & 1 & 1 & | & -2 & 1 & 0 \\ 0 & 1 & 2 & | & 1 & 0 & 1 \end{bmatrix}$$

$$\begin{matrix} \\ \\ R_3 - R_2 \rightarrow \end{matrix} \begin{bmatrix} 1 & 0 & 1 & | & 1 & 0 & 0 \\ 0 & 1 & 1 & | & -2 & 1 & 0 \\ 0 & 0 & 1 & | & 3 & -1 & 1 \end{bmatrix} \begin{matrix} R_1 - R_3 \rightarrow \\ R_2 - R_3 \rightarrow \\ \\ \end{matrix} \begin{bmatrix} 1 & 0 & 0 & | & -2 & 1 & -1 \\ 0 & 1 & 0 & | & -5 & 2 & -1 \\ 0 & 0 & 1 & | & 3 & -1 & 1 \end{bmatrix}$$

The right side is equal to A^{-1}. That is,

$$A^{-1} = \begin{bmatrix} -2 & 1 & -1 \\ -5 & 2 & -1 \\ 3 & -1 & 1 \end{bmatrix}.$$

It can be verified that $A^{-1}A = I_3 = AA^{-1}$.

Now Try Exercise 25

NOTE   If it is not possible to obtain the identity matrix on the left side of the augmented matrix by using matrix row operations, then A^{-1} does *not* exist.

Representing Linear Systems with Matrix Equations

In Section 9.4 linear systems were solved using Gaussian elimination with backward substitution. This method used an augmented matrix to represent a system of linear equations. A system of linear equations can also be represented by a matrix equation.

$$3x - 2y + 4z = 5$$
$$2x + y + 3z = 9$$
$$-x + 5y - 2z = 5$$

Let A, X, and B be matrices defined as

Coefficient Matrix   **Variable Matrix**   **Constant Matrix**

$$A = \begin{bmatrix} 3 & -2 & 4 \\ 2 & 1 & 3 \\ -1 & 5 & -2 \end{bmatrix}, \quad X = \begin{bmatrix} x \\ y \\ z \end{bmatrix}, \quad \text{and} \quad B = \begin{bmatrix} 5 \\ 9 \\ 5 \end{bmatrix}.$$

The matrix product AX is given by

$$AX = \begin{bmatrix} 3 & -2 & 4 \\ 2 & 1 & 3 \\ -1 & 5 & -2 \end{bmatrix} \begin{bmatrix} x \\ y \\ z \end{bmatrix} = \begin{bmatrix} 3x + (-2)y + 4z \\ 2x + 1y + 3z \\ (-1)x + 5y + (-2)z \end{bmatrix} = \begin{bmatrix} 3x - 2y + 4z \\ 2x + y + 3z \\ -x + 5y - 2z \end{bmatrix}.$$

Thus the matrix equation $AX = B$ simplifies to

$$\begin{bmatrix} 3x - 2y + 4z \\ 2x + y + 3z \\ -x + 5y - 2z \end{bmatrix} = \begin{bmatrix} 5 \\ 9 \\ 5 \end{bmatrix}.$$

This matrix equation $AX = B$ is equivalent to the original system of linear equations. Any system of *linear* equations can be represented by a matrix equation.

EXAMPLE 6 Representing linear systems with matrix equations

Represent each system of linear equations in the form $AX = B$.

(a) $\begin{aligned} 3x - 4y &= 7 \\ -x + 6y &= -3 \end{aligned}$
(b) $\begin{aligned} x - 5y &= 2 \\ -3x + 2y + z &= -7 \\ 4x + 5y + 6z &= 10 \end{aligned}$

SOLUTION

(a) This linear system comprises two equations and two variables. The equivalent matrix equation is

$$AX = \begin{bmatrix} 3 & -4 \\ -1 & 6 \end{bmatrix}\begin{bmatrix} x \\ y \end{bmatrix} = \begin{bmatrix} 7 \\ -3 \end{bmatrix} = B.$$

(b) The equivalent matrix equation is

$$AX = \begin{bmatrix} 1 & -5 & 0 \\ -3 & 2 & 1 \\ 4 & 5 & 6 \end{bmatrix}\begin{bmatrix} x \\ y \\ z \end{bmatrix} = \begin{bmatrix} 2 \\ -7 \\ 10 \end{bmatrix} = B.$$

> **Now Try Exercises 39 and 43**

Solving Linear Systems with Inverses

The matrix equation $AX = B$ can be solved by using A^{-1}, if it exists.

$$AX = B \qquad \text{Linear system}$$
$$A^{-1}AX = A^{-1}B \qquad \text{Multiply each side by } A^{-1}.$$
$$I_nX = A^{-1}B \qquad A^{-1}A = I_n$$
$$X = A^{-1}B \qquad I_nX = X \text{ for any } n \times 1 \text{ matrix } X$$

To solve a linear system, multiply each side of the matrix equation $AX = B$ by A^{-1}, if it exists. The solution to the system is unique and can be written as $X = A^{-1}B$.

> **NOTE** Since matrix multiplication is not commutative, it is essential to multiply each side of the equation on the *left* by A^{-1}. That is, $X = A^{-1}B \ne BA^{-1}$ in general.

EXAMPLE 7 Solving a linear system using the inverse of a 2 × 2 matrix

Write the linear system as the matrix equation $AX = B$. Find A^{-1} and solve for X.

$$x + 4y = 3$$
$$2x + 9y = 5$$

SOLUTION The linear system can be written as

$$AX = \begin{bmatrix} 1 & 4 \\ 2 & 9 \end{bmatrix}\begin{bmatrix} x \\ y \end{bmatrix} = \begin{bmatrix} 3 \\ 5 \end{bmatrix} = B.$$

The matrix A^{-1} was found in Example 4. Thus we can solve for X as follows.

$$X = A^{-1}B = \begin{bmatrix} 9 & -4 \\ -2 & 1 \end{bmatrix}\begin{bmatrix} 3 \\ 5 \end{bmatrix} = \begin{bmatrix} 7 \\ -1 \end{bmatrix}$$

The solution to the system is $(7, -1)$. Check this.

> **Now Try Exercise 47**

Technology and Inverse Matrices (Optional)   In the next two examples, we use technology to solve the system of linear equations. Technology is especially helpful when finding A^{-1}.

EXAMPLE 8   Solving a linear system using the inverse of a 3 × 3 matrix

Write the linear system as the matrix equation $AX = B$. Find A^{-1} and solve for X.

$$\begin{aligned} x + 3y - z &= 6 \\ -2y + z &= -2 \\ -x + y - 3z &= 4 \end{aligned}$$

SOLUTION   The linear system can be written as

$$AX = \begin{bmatrix} 1 & 3 & -1 \\ 0 & -2 & 1 \\ -1 & 1 & -3 \end{bmatrix} \begin{bmatrix} x \\ y \\ z \end{bmatrix} = \begin{bmatrix} 6 \\ -2 \\ 4 \end{bmatrix} = B.$$

The matrix A^{-1} can be found by hand or with a graphing calculator, as shown in Figure 9.65. The solution to the system is given by $x = 4.5$, $y = -0.5$, and $z = -3$. See Figure 9.66.

Calculator Help
To find the inverse of a matrix, see Appendix A (page AP-14). To solve a linear system with a matrix inverse, see Appendix A (page AP-14).

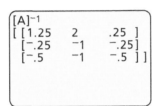

```
[A]⁻¹
[ [1.25    2     .25 ]
  [⁻.25   ⁻1    ⁻.25]
  [⁻.5    ⁻1    ⁻.5 ]]
```

Figure 9.65

```
[A]⁻¹*[B]
          [ [4.5]
            [⁻.5]
            [⁻3 ] ]
```

Figure 9.66

Now Try Exercise 59

EXAMPLE 9   Modeling blood pressure

In one study of adult males, the effect of both age A in years and weight W in pounds on systolic blood pressure P was found to be modeled by $P(A, W) = a + bA + cW$, where a, b, and c are constants. Table 9.12 lists three individuals with representative blood pressures.

(a) Use Table 9.12 to approximate values for the constants a, b, and c.
(b) Estimate a typical systolic blood pressure for an individual who is 55 years old and weighs 175 pounds.

P	A	W
113	39	142
138	53	181
152	65	191

Table 9.12

SOLUTION

(a) Determine the constants a, b, and c in $P(A, W) = a + bA + cW$ by solving the following three equations.

$$P(39, 142) = a + b(39) + c(142) = 113$$
$$P(53, 181) = a + b(53) + c(181) = 138$$
$$P(65, 191) = a + b(65) + c(191) = 152$$

These three equations can be rewritten as follows.

$$a + 39b + 142c = 113$$
$$a + 53b + 181c = 138$$
$$a + 65b + 191c = 152$$

```
[A]⁻¹*[B]
[[32.7804878  ]
 [.9024390244 ]
 [.3170731707 ]]
```

Figure 9.67

This system can be represented by the matrix equation $AX = B$.

$$AX = \begin{bmatrix} 1 & 39 & 142 \\ 1 & 53 & 181 \\ 1 & 65 & 191 \end{bmatrix} \begin{bmatrix} a \\ b \\ c \end{bmatrix} = \begin{bmatrix} 113 \\ 138 \\ 152 \end{bmatrix} = B$$

The solution, $X = A^{-1}B$, is shown in Figure 9.67. The values for the constants are $a \approx 32.78$, $b \approx 0.9024$, and $c \approx 0.3171$. Thus it follows that P is given by the equation $P(A, W) = 32.78 + 0.9024A + 0.3171W$.

(b) Evaluate $P(55, 175) = 32.78 + 0.9024(55) + 0.3171(175) \approx 137.9$. This model predicts that a typical (male) individual 55 years old, weighing 175 pounds, has a systolic blood pressure of approximately 138. Clearly, this could vary greatly among individuals.

Now Try Exercise 73

9.6 Putting It All Together

The following table summarizes some of the mathematical concepts presented in this section.

CONCEPT	COMMENTS	EXAMPLES
Identity matrix	The $n \times n$ identity matrix I_n has only 1's on the main diagonal and 0's elsewhere. When it is multiplied by any $n \times n$ matrix A, the result is A.	$\begin{bmatrix} 1 & 0 \\ 0 & 1 \end{bmatrix} \begin{bmatrix} 2 & 3 \\ 4 & 5 \end{bmatrix} = \begin{bmatrix} 2 & 3 \\ 4 & 5 \end{bmatrix}$ and $\begin{bmatrix} 2 & 3 \\ 4 & 5 \end{bmatrix} \begin{bmatrix} 1 & 0 \\ 0 & 1 \end{bmatrix} = \begin{bmatrix} 2 & 3 \\ 4 & 5 \end{bmatrix}$, where $I_2 = \begin{bmatrix} 1 & 0 \\ 0 & 1 \end{bmatrix}$.
Matrix inverse	If an $n \times n$ matrix A has an inverse, it is unique, is denoted A^{-1}, and satisfies the equations $AA^{-1} = I_n$ and $A^{-1}A = I_n$. Matrix inverses can be found by using technology. They can also be found with pencil and paper by performing matrix row operations on the augmented matrix $[A\,|\,I_n]$ until it is transformed to $[I_n\,|\,A^{-1}]$.	If $A = \begin{bmatrix} 2 & 3 \\ 3 & 5 \end{bmatrix}$, then $A^{-1} = \begin{bmatrix} 5 & -3 \\ -3 & 2 \end{bmatrix}$ because $AA^{-1} = \begin{bmatrix} 2 & 3 \\ 3 & 5 \end{bmatrix} \begin{bmatrix} 5 & -3 \\ -3 & 2 \end{bmatrix} = \begin{bmatrix} 1 & 0 \\ 0 & 1 \end{bmatrix} = I_2$ $A^{-1}A = \begin{bmatrix} 5 & -3 \\ -3 & 2 \end{bmatrix} \begin{bmatrix} 2 & 3 \\ 3 & 5 \end{bmatrix} = \begin{bmatrix} 1 & 0 \\ 0 & 1 \end{bmatrix} = I_2$.
Matrix equations	Systems of linear equations can be written by using the matrix equation $AX = B$. If A is invertible, then there will be a unique solution given by $X = A^{-1}B$. If A is not invertible, then there could be either no solution or infinitely many solutions. In the latter case, Gaussian elimination should be applied.	The linear system $2x - y = 3$ $x + 2y = 4$ can be written as $AX = B$, where $A = \begin{bmatrix} 2 & -1 \\ 1 & 2 \end{bmatrix}$, $X = \begin{bmatrix} x \\ y \end{bmatrix}$, and $B = \begin{bmatrix} 3 \\ 4 \end{bmatrix}$. The solution to the system is given by $X = A^{-1}B = \begin{bmatrix} 0.4 & 0.2 \\ -0.2 & 0.4 \end{bmatrix} \begin{bmatrix} 3 \\ 4 \end{bmatrix} = \begin{bmatrix} 2 \\ 1 \end{bmatrix}$. The solution is $(2, 1)$.

9.6 Exercises

Inverse and Identity Matrices

Exercises 1–6: Determine if B is the inverse matrix of A by calculating AB and BA.

1. $A = \begin{bmatrix} 4 & 3 \\ 5 & 4 \end{bmatrix}$, $B = \begin{bmatrix} 4 & -3 \\ -5 & 4 \end{bmatrix}$

2. $A = \begin{bmatrix} -1 & 2 \\ -3 & 8 \end{bmatrix}$, $B = \begin{bmatrix} -4 & 1 \\ -2 & 0.5 \end{bmatrix}$

3. $A = \begin{bmatrix} 1 & -1 & 2 \\ 0 & 1 & -1 \\ 1 & 0 & 2 \end{bmatrix}$, $B = \begin{bmatrix} 2 & 2 & -1 \\ -1 & 0 & 1 \\ -1 & -1 & 1 \end{bmatrix}$

4. $A = \begin{bmatrix} 2 & 1 & 1 \\ -1 & 0 & -1 \\ 0 & 2 & -1 \end{bmatrix}$, $B = \begin{bmatrix} 2 & 3 & -1 \\ -1 & -2 & 1 \\ -2 & -4 & 1 \end{bmatrix}$

5. $A = \begin{bmatrix} 2 & 1 & -1 \\ 3 & 0 & 2 \\ -1 & 0 & 1 \end{bmatrix}$, $B = \begin{bmatrix} 0 & 1 & -2 \\ 1 & -3 & 7 \\ 0 & -1 & 3 \end{bmatrix}$

6. $A = \begin{bmatrix} 1 & -1 & 1 \\ 0 & 1 & 0 \\ 1 & 1 & 2 \end{bmatrix}$, $B = \begin{bmatrix} 2 & 3 & -1 \\ 0 & 1 & 0 \\ -1 & -2 & 1 \end{bmatrix}$

Exercises 7–10: Find the value of the constant k in A^{-1}.

7. $A = \begin{bmatrix} 1 & 1 \\ 1 & 2 \end{bmatrix}$, $A^{-1} = \begin{bmatrix} 2 & -1 \\ -1 & k \end{bmatrix}$

8. $A = \begin{bmatrix} -2 & 2 \\ 1 & -2 \end{bmatrix}$, $A^{-1} = \begin{bmatrix} -1 & k \\ -0.5 & -1 \end{bmatrix}$

9. $A = \begin{bmatrix} 1 & 3 \\ -1 & -5 \end{bmatrix}$, $A^{-1} = \begin{bmatrix} k & 1.5 \\ -0.5 & -0.5 \end{bmatrix}$

10. $A = \begin{bmatrix} -2 & 5 \\ -3 & 4 \end{bmatrix}$, $A^{-1} = \begin{bmatrix} \frac{4}{7} & -\frac{5}{7} \\ k & -\frac{2}{7} \end{bmatrix}$

Exercises 11–14: Predict the results of I_nA and AI_n. Then verify your prediction.

11. $I_2 = \begin{bmatrix} 1 & 0 \\ 0 & 1 \end{bmatrix}$, $A = \begin{bmatrix} 1 & -2 \\ 4 & 3 \end{bmatrix}$

12. $I_3 = \begin{bmatrix} 1 & 0 & 0 \\ 0 & 1 & 0 \\ 0 & 0 & 1 \end{bmatrix}$, $A = \begin{bmatrix} 1 & -4 & 3 \\ 1 & 9 & 5 \\ 3 & -5 & 0 \end{bmatrix}$

13. $I_3 = \begin{bmatrix} 1 & 0 & 0 \\ 0 & 1 & 0 \\ 0 & 0 & 1 \end{bmatrix}$, $A = \begin{bmatrix} 0 & 0 & 0 \\ 0 & 0 & 0 \\ 0 & 0 & 0 \end{bmatrix}$

14. $I_4 = \begin{bmatrix} 1 & 0 & 0 & 0 \\ 0 & 1 & 0 & 0 \\ 0 & 0 & 1 & 0 \\ 0 & 0 & 0 & 1 \end{bmatrix}$, $A = \begin{bmatrix} 5 & -2 & 6 & -3 \\ 0 & 1 & 4 & -1 \\ -5 & 7 & 9 & 8 \\ 0 & 0 & 3 & 1 \end{bmatrix}$

Calculating Inverses

Exercises 15–28: (Refer to Examples 3–5.) Let A be the given matrix. Find A^{-1} without a calculator.

15. $\begin{bmatrix} 1 & 2 \\ 1 & 3 \end{bmatrix}$ **16.** $\begin{bmatrix} 1 & 0 \\ 1 & -1 \end{bmatrix}$

17. $\begin{bmatrix} -1 & 2 \\ 3 & -5 \end{bmatrix}$ **18.** $\begin{bmatrix} 1 & 3 \\ 2 & 5 \end{bmatrix}$

19. $\begin{bmatrix} 8 & 5 \\ 2 & 1 \end{bmatrix}$ **20.** $\begin{bmatrix} -2 & 4 \\ -5 & 9 \end{bmatrix}$

21. $\begin{bmatrix} 0 & 0 & 1 \\ 1 & 0 & 0 \\ 0 & 1 & 0 \end{bmatrix}$ **22.** $\begin{bmatrix} 1 & 0 & 0 \\ 1 & 1 & 0 \\ 0 & 1 & 1 \end{bmatrix}$

23. $\begin{bmatrix} 1 & 0 & 1 \\ 2 & 1 & 3 \\ -1 & 1 & 1 \end{bmatrix}$ **24.** $\begin{bmatrix} -2 & 1 & 0 \\ 1 & 0 & 1 \\ -1 & 1 & 0 \end{bmatrix}$

25. $\begin{bmatrix} 1 & 2 & -1 \\ 2 & 5 & 0 \\ -1 & -1 & 2 \end{bmatrix}$ **26.** $\begin{bmatrix} 2 & -2 & 1 \\ 1 & 3 & 2 \\ 4 & -2 & 4 \end{bmatrix}$

27. $\begin{bmatrix} -2 & 1 & -3 \\ 0 & 1 & 2 \\ 1 & -2 & 1 \end{bmatrix}$ **28.** $\begin{bmatrix} 1 & -1 & 1 \\ -1 & 2 & 1 \\ 0 & 2 & 1 \end{bmatrix}$

Exercises 29–38: Let A be the given matrix. Find A^{-1}.

29. $\begin{bmatrix} 0.5 & -1.5 \\ 0.2 & -0.5 \end{bmatrix}$ **30.** $\begin{bmatrix} -0.5 & 0.5 \\ 3 & 2 \end{bmatrix}$

31. $\begin{bmatrix} 1 & 2 & 0 \\ -1 & 4 & -1 \\ 2 & -1 & 0 \end{bmatrix}$ **32.** $\begin{bmatrix} -2 & 0 & 1 \\ 5 & -4 & 1 \\ 1 & -2 & 0 \end{bmatrix}$

33. $\begin{bmatrix} 2 & -2 & 1 \\ 0 & 5 & 8 \\ 0 & 0 & -1 \end{bmatrix}$ **34.** $\begin{bmatrix} 2 & 0 & 2 \\ 1 & 5 & 0 \\ -1 & 0 & 2 \end{bmatrix}$

35. $\begin{bmatrix} 3 & -1 & -1 \\ -1 & 3 & -1 \\ -1 & -1 & 3 \end{bmatrix}$ **36.** $\begin{bmatrix} 2 & -3 & 1 \\ 5 & -6 & 3 \\ 3 & 2 & 0 \end{bmatrix}$

37. $\begin{bmatrix} 1 & -1 & 0 & 0 \\ -1 & 5 & -1 & 0 \\ 0 & -1 & 5 & -1 \\ 0 & 0 & -1 & 1 \end{bmatrix}$ **38.** $\begin{bmatrix} 3 & 1 & 0 & 0 \\ 1 & 3 & 1 & 0 \\ 0 & 1 & 3 & 1 \\ 0 & 0 & 1 & 3 \end{bmatrix}$

Matrices and Linear Systems

Exercises 39–46: Represent the system of linear equations in the form AX = B.

39. $2x - 3y = 7$
$-3x - 4y = 9$

40. $-x + 3y = 10$
$2x - 6y = -1$

41. $\frac{1}{2}x - \frac{3}{2}y = \frac{1}{4}$
$-x + 2y = 5$

42. $-1.1x + 3.2y = -2.7$
$5.6x - 3.8y = -3.0$

43. $x - 2y + z = 5$
$3y - z = 6$
$5x - 4y - 7z = 0$

44. $4x - 3y + 2z = 8$
$-x + 4y + 3z = 2$
$-2x - 5z = 2$

45. $4x - y + 3z = -2$
$x + 2y + 5z = 11$
$2x - 3y = -1$

46. $x - 2y + z = 12$
$4y + 3z = 13$
$-2x + 7y = -2$

Solving Linear Systems

Exercises 47–54: Complete the following.

(a) *Write the system in the form AX = B.*
(b) *Solve the system by finding A^{-1} and then using the equation $X = A^{-1}B$. (Hint: Some of your answers from Exercises 15–28 may be helpful.)*

47. $x + 2y = 3$
$x + 3y = 6$

48. $2x + y = 4$
$-x + 2y = -1$

49. $-x + 2y = 5$
$3x - 5y = -2$

50. $x + 3y = -3$
$2x + 5y = -2$

51. $x + z = -7$
$2x + y + 3z = -13$
$-x + y + z = -4$

52. $-2x + y = -5$
$x + z = -5$
$-x + y = -4$

53. $x + 2y - z = 2$
$2x + 5y = -1$
$-x - y + 2z = 0$

54. $2x - 2y + z = 1$
$x + 3y + 2z = 3$
$4x - 2y + 4z = 4$

Exercises 55–62: Complete the following for the given system of linear equations.

(a) *Write the system in the form AX = B.*
(b) *Solve the linear system by computing $X = A^{-1}B$ with a calculator. Approximate the solution to the nearest hundredth when appropriate.*

55. $1.5x + 3.7y = 0.32$
$-0.4x - 2.1y = 0.36$

56. $31x + 18y = 64.1$
$5x - 23y = -59.6$

57. $0.08x - 0.7y = -0.504$
$1.1x - 0.05y = 0.73$

58. $-231x + 178y = -439$
$525x - 329y = 2282$

59. $3.1x + 1.9y - z = 1.99$
$6.3x - 9.9z = -3.78$
$-x + 1.5y + 7z = 5.3$

60. $17x - 22y - 19z = -25.2$
$3x + 13y - 9z = 105.9$
$x - 2y + 6.1z = -23.55$

61. $3x - y + z = 4.9$
$5.8x - 2.1y = -3.8$
$-x + 2.9z = 3.8$

62. $1.2x - 0.3y - 0.7z = -0.5$
$-0.4x + 1.3y + 0.4z = 0.9$
$1.7x + 0.6y + 1.1z = 1.3$

Interpreting Inverses

*Exercises 63 and 64: **Translations** (Refer to the discussion in this section about translating a point.) The matrix product AX performs a translation on the point (x, y), where*

$$A = \begin{bmatrix} 1 & 0 & h \\ 0 & 1 & k \\ 0 & 0 & 1 \end{bmatrix} \quad \text{and} \quad X = \begin{bmatrix} x \\ y \\ 1 \end{bmatrix}.$$

(a) *Predict the new location of the point (x, y) when it is translated by A. Compute $Y = AX$ to verify your prediction.*
(b) *Make a conjecture as to what $A^{-1}Y$ represents. Find A^{-1} and calculate $A^{-1}Y$ to test your conjecture.*
(c) *What will AA^{-1} and $A^{-1}A$ equal?*

63. $A = \begin{bmatrix} 1 & 0 & 2 \\ 0 & 1 & 3 \\ 0 & 0 & 1 \end{bmatrix}$, $(x, y) = (0, 1)$, and $X = \begin{bmatrix} 0 \\ 1 \\ 1 \end{bmatrix}$

64. $A = \begin{bmatrix} 1 & 0 & -4 \\ 0 & 1 & 5 \\ 0 & 0 & 1 \end{bmatrix}$, $(x, y) = (4, 2)$, and $X = \begin{bmatrix} 4 \\ 2 \\ 1 \end{bmatrix}$

*Exercises 65 and 66: **Translations** (Refer to the discussion in this section about translating a point.) Find a 3 × 3 matrix A that performs the following translation of a point (x, y) represented by X. Find A^{-1} and describe what it computes.*

65. 3 units to the left and 5 units downward

66. 6 units to the right and 1 unit upward

67. Rotation (Refer to Example 2.) The matrix B rotates the point (x, y) clockwise about the origin 45°, where

$$B = \begin{bmatrix} \frac{1}{\sqrt{2}} & \frac{1}{\sqrt{2}} & 0 \\ -\frac{1}{\sqrt{2}} & \frac{1}{\sqrt{2}} & 0 \\ 0 & 0 & 1 \end{bmatrix} \quad \text{and} \quad B^{-1} = \begin{bmatrix} \frac{1}{\sqrt{2}} & -\frac{1}{\sqrt{2}} & 0 \\ \frac{1}{\sqrt{2}} & \frac{1}{\sqrt{2}} & 0 \\ 0 & 0 & 1 \end{bmatrix}.$$

(a) Let X represent the point $(-\sqrt{2}, -\sqrt{2})$. Compute $Y = BX$.

(b) Find $B^{-1}Y$. Interpret what B^{-1} computes.

68. Rotation (Refer to Exercise 67.) Predict the result of the computations $BB^{-1}X$ and $B^{-1}BX$ for any point (x, y) represented by X. Explain this result geometrically.

69. Translations The matrix A translates a point to the right 4 units and downward 2 units, and the matrix B translates a point to the left 3 units and upward 3 units, where

$$A = \begin{bmatrix} 1 & 0 & 4 \\ 0 & 1 & -2 \\ 0 & 0 & 1 \end{bmatrix} \quad \text{and} \quad B = \begin{bmatrix} 1 & 0 & -3 \\ 0 & 1 & 3 \\ 0 & 0 & 1 \end{bmatrix}.$$

(a) Let X represent the point $(1, 1)$. Predict the result of $Y = ABX$. Check your prediction.

(b) Find AB mentally, and then compute AB.

(c) Would you expect $AB = BA$? Verify your answer.

(d) Find $(AB)^{-1}$ mentally. Explain your reasoning.

70. Rotation (Refer to Exercises 63 and 67 for A and B.)
(a) Let X represent the point $(0, \sqrt{2})$. If this point is rotated about the origin 45° clockwise and then translated 2 units to the right and 3 units upward, determine its new coordinates geometrically.

(b) Compute $Y = ABX$, and explain the result.

(c) Is ABX equal to BAX? Interpret your answer.

(d) Find a matrix that translates Y back to X.

Applications

71. Cost of CDs A music store marks its compact discs A, B, or C to indicate one of three selling prices. The last column in the table shows the total cost of a purchase. Use this information to determine the cost of one CD of each type by setting up a matrix equation and solving it with an inverse.

A	B	C	Total
2	3	4	$120.91
1	4	0	$62.95
2	1	3	$79.94

72. Traffic Flow (Refer to Exercises 85 and 86 in Section 9.4.) The figure at the top of the next column shows four one-way streets with intersections A, B, C, and D. Numbers indicate the average traffic flow in vehicles per minute. The variables $x_1, x_2, x_3,$ and x_4 denote unknown traffic flows.

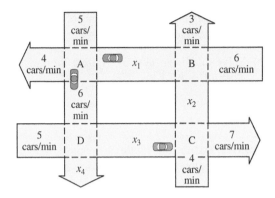

(a) The number of vehicles per minute entering an intersection equals the number exiting an intersection. Verify that the given system of linear equations describes the traffic flow.

A: $x_1 + 5 = 4 + 6$ B: $x_2 + 6 = x_1 + 3$
C: $x_3 + 4 = x_2 + 7$ D: $6 + 5 = x_3 + x_4$

(b) Write the system as $AX = B$ and solve using A^{-1}.

(c) Interpret your results.

73. Home Prices The table contains data on sales of three homes. Price P is measured in thousands of dollars, home size S is in square feet, and condition C is rated on a scale from 1 to 10, where 10 represents excellent condition. The variables were found to be related by the equation $P = a + bS + cC$.

P	S	C
122	1500	8
130	2000	5
158	2200	10

(a) Use the table to write a system of linear equations whose solution gives a, b, and c. Solve this system of linear equations.

(b) Estimate the selling price of a home with 1800 square feet and a condition of 7.

74. Tire Sales A study investigated the relationship among annual tire sales T in thousands, automobile registrations A in millions, and personal disposable income I in millions of dollars. Representative data for three different years are shown in the table. The data were modeled by $T = aA + bI + c$, where a, b, and c are constants. (*Source:* J. Jarrett, *Business Forecasting Methods.*)

T	A	I
10,170	113	308
15,305	133	622
21,289	155	1937

continued on next page

(a) Use the data to write a system of linear equations whose solution gives a, b, and c.

(b) Solve this linear system. Write a formula for T, as $T = aA + bI + c$.

(c) If $A = 118$ and $I = 311$, predict T. (The actual value for T was 11,314.)

75. Leontief Economic Model Suppose that a closed economic region has three industries: service, electrical power, and tourism. The service industry uses 20% of its own production, 40% of the electrical power, and 80% of the tourism. The power company uses 40% of the service industry, 20% of the electrical power, and 10% of the tourism. The tourism industry uses 40% of the service industry, 40% of the electrical power, and 10% of the tourism.

(a) Let S, E, and T be the numbers of units produced by the service, electrical, and tourism industries, respectively. The following system of linear equations can be used to determine the relative number of units each industry needs to produce. (This model assumes that all production is consumed by the region.)

$$0.2S + 0.4E + 0.8T = S$$
$$0.4S + 0.2E + 0.1T = E$$
$$0.4S + 0.4E + 0.1T = T$$

Solve the system and write the solution in terms of T.

(b) If tourism produces 60 units, how many units should the service and electrical industries produce?

76. Plate Glass Sales Plate glass sales G can be affected by the number of new building contracts B issued and the number of automobiles A produced, since plate glass is used in buildings and cars. To forecast sales, a plate glass company in California collected data for three consecutive years, shown in the table. All units are in millions. The data were modeled by $G = aA + bB + c$, where a, b, and c are constants. (*Source:* S. Makridakis and S. Wheelwright, *Forecasting Methods for Management.*)

G	A	B
603	5.54	37.1
657	6.93	41.3
779	7.64	45.6

(a) Write a system of linear equations whose solution gives a, b, and c.

(b) Solve this linear system. Write a formula for G.

(c) For the following year, it was estimated that $A = 7.75$ and $B = 47.4$. Predict G. (The actual value for G was 878.)

Writing about Mathematics

77. Discuss how to solve the matrix equation $AX = B$ if A^{-1} exists.

78. Give an example of a 2×2 matrix A with only nonzero elements that does not have an inverse. Explain what happens if one attempts to find A^{-1} symbolically.

CHECKING BASIC CONCEPTS FOR SECTIONS 9.5 AND 9.6

1. Perform the operations on the given matrices A and B.

$$A = \begin{bmatrix} 1 & 0 & 1 \\ -1 & 1 & 2 \\ 1 & 3 & 0 \end{bmatrix}, \quad B = \begin{bmatrix} -1 & 1 & 2 \\ 0 & 4 & 1 \\ 1 & -2 & 0 \end{bmatrix}$$

(a) $A + B$ **(b)** $2A - B$ **(c)** AB

2. Find the inverse of the matrix A by hand.

$$A = \begin{bmatrix} 0 & 0 & 1 \\ 1 & 1 & 0 \\ 1 & 0 & 1 \end{bmatrix}$$

3. Write each system of linear equations as a matrix equation $AX = B$. Solve the system utilizing A^{-1}.

(a) $\quad x - 2y = 13$
$\quad\quad 2x + 3y = 5$

(b) $\quad x - y + z = 2$
$\quad\quad -x + y + z = 4$
$\quad\quad\quad\quad y - z = -1$

(c) $\quad 3.1x - 5.3y = -2.682$
$\quad\quad -0.1x + 1.8y = 0.787$

4. Find A^{-1} if $A = \begin{bmatrix} 2 & -3 & 5 \\ 4 & -3 & 2 \\ 1 & 5 & -4 \end{bmatrix}$.

9.7 Determinants

- **Define and calculate determinants**
- **Apply Cramer's rule**
- **Use determinants to find areas of regions**

Introduction

Determinants are used in mathematics for theoretical purposes. However, they also are used to test if a matrix is invertible and to find the area of certain geometric figures, such as triangles. A *determinant* is a real number associated with a square matrix. We begin our discussion by defining a determinant for a 2 × 2 matrix.

Definition and Calculation of Determinants

Finding the determinant of a matrix with dimension 2 × 2 is a straightforward arithmetic calculation.

DETERMINANT OF A 2 × 2 MATRIX

The **determinant** of

$$A = \begin{bmatrix} a & b \\ c & d \end{bmatrix}$$

is a real number defined by

$$\det A = ad - cb.$$

Later we define determinants for any $n \times n$ matrix. The following theorem can be used to determine if a matrix has an inverse.

INVERTIBLE MATRIX

A square matrix A is invertible if and only if $\det A \neq 0$.

EXAMPLE 1 Determining if a 2 × 2 matrix is invertible

Determine if A^{-1} exists by computing the determinant of the matrix A.

(a) $A = \begin{bmatrix} 3 & -4 \\ -5 & 9 \end{bmatrix}$ (b) $A = \begin{bmatrix} 52 & -32 \\ 65 & -40 \end{bmatrix}$

SOLUTION

(a) The determinant of the 2 × 2 matrix A is calculated as follows.

$$\det A = \det \begin{bmatrix} 3 & -4 \\ -5 & 9 \end{bmatrix} = (3)(9) - (-5)(-4) = 7$$

Since $\det A = 7 \neq 0$, the matrix A is invertible and A^{-1} exists.

(b) Similarly,

$$\det A = \det \begin{bmatrix} 52 & -32 \\ 65 & -40 \end{bmatrix} = (52)(-40) - (65)(-32) = 0.$$

Since $\det A = 0$, A^{-1} does not exist. Try finding A^{-1}. What happens?

Now Try Exercises 1 and 3

We can use determinants of 2×2 matrices to find determinants of larger square matrices. In order to do this, we first define the concepts of a *minor* and a *cofactor*.

MINORS AND COFACTORS

The **minor**, denoted by M_{ij}, for element a_{ij} in the square matrix A is the real number computed by performing the following steps.

STEP 1: Delete the ith row and jth column from the matrix A.

STEP 2: Compute the determinant of the resulting matrix, which is equal to M_{ij}.

The **cofactor**, denoted A_{ij}, for a_{ij} is defined by $A_{ij} = (-1)^{i+j} M_{ij}$.

EXAMPLE 2 Calculating minors and cofactors

Find the following minors and cofactors for the matrix A.

$$A = \begin{bmatrix} 2 & -3 & 1 \\ -2 & 1 & 0 \\ 0 & -1 & 4 \end{bmatrix}$$

(a) M_{11} and M_{21} **(b)** A_{11} and A_{21}

SOLUTION

(a) To obtain the minor M_{11}, begin by crossing out the first row and first column of A.

$$A = \begin{bmatrix} 2 & -3 & 1 \\ -2 & 1 & 0 \\ 0 & -1 & 4 \end{bmatrix}$$

For M_{11}, cross out row **1** and column **1**.

The remaining elements form the 2×2 matrix

$$B = \begin{bmatrix} 1 & 0 \\ -1 & 4 \end{bmatrix}.$$

The minor M_{11} is equal to det $B = (1)(4) - (-1)(0) = 4$.

M_{21} is found by crossing out the second row and first column of A.

$$A = \begin{bmatrix} 2 & -3 & 1 \\ -2 & 1 & 0 \\ 0 & -1 & 4 \end{bmatrix}$$

For M_{21}, cross out row **2** and column **1**.

The resulting matrix is

$$B = \begin{bmatrix} -3 & 1 \\ -1 & 4 \end{bmatrix}.$$

Thus $M_{21} = \det B = (-3)(4) - (-1)(1) = -11$.

(b) Since $A_{ij} = (-1)^{i+j} M_{ij}$, A_{11} and A_{21} can be computed as follows.

$$A_{11} = (-1)^{1+1} M_{11} = (-1)^2(4) = 4$$
$$A_{21} = (-1)^{2+1} M_{21} = (-1)^3(-11) = 11$$

Now Try Exercise 5

Using the concept of a cofactor, we can calculate the determinant of *any* square matrix.

> ### DETERMINANT OF A SQUARE MATRIX USING COFACTORS
>
> For a square matrix A, multiply each element in any row or column of the matrix by its cofactor. The sum of the products is equal to the determinant of A.

To compute the determinant of a 3×3 matrix A, begin by selecting either a row or a column.

$$A = \begin{bmatrix} a_{11} & a_{12} & a_{13} \\ a_{21} & a_{22} & a_{23} \\ a_{31} & a_{32} & a_{33} \end{bmatrix}$$

For example, if the *second row* of A is selected, the elements are a_{21}, a_{22}, and a_{23}. Then

$$\det A = a_{21} A_{21} + a_{22} A_{22} + a_{23} A_{23}.$$

On the other hand, utilizing the elements of a_{11}, a_{21}, and a_{31} in the *first column* gives

$$\det A = a_{11} A_{11} + a_{21} A_{21} + a_{31} A_{31}.$$

Regardless of the row or column selected, the value of det A is the same. The calculation is easier if some elements in the selected row or column equal 0.

EXAMPLE 3   Evaluating the determinant of a 3×3 matrix

Find det A if

$$A = \begin{bmatrix} 2 & -3 & 1 \\ -2 & 1 & 0 \\ 0 & -1 & 4 \end{bmatrix}.$$

SOLUTION   To find the determinant of A, we can select any row or column. If we begin *expanding* about the first column of A, then

$$\det A = a_{11} A_{11} + a_{21} A_{21} + a_{31} A_{31}.$$

In the first column, $a_{11} = 2$, $a_{21} = -2$, and $a_{31} = 0$. In Example 2, the cofactors A_{11} and A_{21} were computed as 4 and 11, respectively. Since A_{31} is multiplied by $a_{31} = 0$, we do not need to calculate its value. Thus

$$\begin{aligned} \det &= a_{11} A_{11} + a_{21} A_{21} + a_{31} A_{31} \\ &= 2(4) + (-2)(11) + (0)A_{31} \qquad \text{First column of A} \\ &= -14. \end{aligned}$$

We could also have expanded about the second row.

$$\begin{aligned} \det A &= a_{21} A_{21} + a_{22} A_{22} + a_{23} A_{23} \\ &= (-2)A_{21} + (1)A_{22} + (0)A_{23} \qquad \text{Second row of A} \end{aligned}$$

CLASS DISCUSSION

If a row or column in matrix A contains only zeros, what is det A?

To complete this computation we need to determine only A_{22}, since A_{21} is known to be 11 and A_{23} is multiplied by 0. To compute A_{22}, delete the second row and column of A to obtain M_{22}.

$$M_{22} = \det \begin{bmatrix} 2 & 1 \\ 0 & 4 \end{bmatrix} = 8 \qquad \text{and} \qquad A_{22} = (-1)^{2+2}(8) = 8$$

Thus det $A = (-2)(11) + (1)(8) + (0)A_{23} = -14$. The same value for det A is obtained in both calculations.

Now Try Exercise 17

Instead of calculating $(-1)^{i+j}$ for each cofactor, we can use the following **sign matrix** to find determinants of 3×3 matrices. The checkerboard pattern can be expanded to include larger square matrices.

Sign Matrix

$$\begin{bmatrix} + & - & + \\ - & + & - \\ + & - & + \end{bmatrix}$$

For example, if

$$A = \begin{bmatrix} 2 & 3 & 7 \\ -3 & -2 & -1 \\ 4 & 0 & 2 \end{bmatrix},$$

we can compute det A by expanding about the second column to take advantage of the 0. The second column contains $-$, $+$, and $-$ signs. Therefore

$$\det A = -(3) \det \begin{bmatrix} -3 & -1 \\ 4 & 2 \end{bmatrix} + (-2) \det \begin{bmatrix} 2 & 7 \\ 4 & 2 \end{bmatrix} - (0) \det \begin{bmatrix} 2 & 7 \\ -3 & -1 \end{bmatrix}$$

$$= -3(-2) + (-2)(-24) - (0)(19)$$

$$= 54.$$

NOTE   We could have computed det A by expanding about *any* row or column. However, computation can be simplified by taking advantage of any 0's in the matrix. For the matrix above, the 0 can be used by expanding about either the second column or the third row.

Graphing calculators can evaluate determinants, as shown in the next example.

EXAMPLE 4   Using technology to find a determinant

Find the determinant of A.

(a) $A = \begin{bmatrix} 2 & -3 & 1 \\ -2 & 1 & 0 \\ 0 & -1 & 4 \end{bmatrix}$ (b) $A = \begin{bmatrix} 2 & -3 & 1 & 5 \\ 7 & 1 & -8 & 0 \\ 5 & 4 & 9 & 7 \\ -2 & 3 & 3 & 0 \end{bmatrix}$

SOLUTION

(a) The determinant of this matrix was calculated in Example 3 by hand. To use technology, enter the matrix and evaluate its determinant, as shown in Figure 9.68. The result is det $A = -14$, which agrees with our earlier calculation.

Calculator Help
To calculate a determinant, see
Appendix A (page AP-15).

Finding Determinants with a Calculator

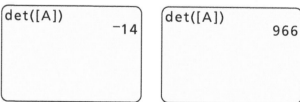

Figure 9.68   Figure 9.69

(b) The determinant of a 4×4 matrix can be computed using cofactors. However, it is considerably easier to use technology. From Figure 9.69 we see that det $A = 966$.

Now Try Exercises 23 and 24

Cramer's Rule

We can solve *linear* systems in two variables using determinants and a method called **Cramer's rule.** Cramer's rule for linear systems in *three* variables is discussed in the Extended and Discovery Exercises at the end of this section. Although Cramer's rule can be used to solve linear systems with more than three variables, it is not practical to do so.

CRAMER'S RULE FOR LINEAR SYSTEMS IN TWO VARIABLES

The solution to the linear system

$$a_1 x + b_1 y = c_1$$
$$a_2 x + b_2 y = c_2$$

is given by $x = \frac{E}{D}$ and $y = \frac{F}{D}$, where

$$E = \det \begin{bmatrix} c_1 & b_1 \\ c_2 & b_2 \end{bmatrix}, \quad F = \det \begin{bmatrix} a_1 & c_1 \\ a_2 & c_2 \end{bmatrix}, \quad \text{and} \quad D = \det \begin{bmatrix} a_1 & b_1 \\ a_2 & b_2 \end{bmatrix} \neq 0.$$

NOTE If $D = 0$, then the system does not have a unique solution. There are either no solutions or infinitely many solutions.

EXAMPLE 5 Using Cramer's rule to solve a linear system in two variables

Use Cramer's rule to solve the linear system

$$4x + y = 146$$
$$9x + y = \ \ 66.$$

SOLUTION In this system $a_1 = 4, b_1 = 1, c_1 = 146, a_2 = 9, b_2 = 1,$ and $c_2 = 66.$ By Cramer's rule, the solution can be found as follows.

$$E = \det \begin{bmatrix} c_1 & b_1 \\ c_2 & b_2 \end{bmatrix} = \det \begin{bmatrix} 146 & 1 \\ 66 & 1 \end{bmatrix} = (146)(1) - (66)(1) = 80$$

$$F = \det \begin{bmatrix} a_1 & c_1 \\ a_2 & c_2 \end{bmatrix} = \det \begin{bmatrix} 4 & 146 \\ 9 & 66 \end{bmatrix} = (4)(66) - (9)(146) = -1050$$

$$D = \det \begin{bmatrix} a_1 & b_1 \\ a_2 & b_2 \end{bmatrix} = \det \begin{bmatrix} 4 & 1 \\ 9 & 1 \end{bmatrix} = (4)(1) - (9)(1) = -5$$

The solution is

$$x = \frac{E}{D} = \frac{80}{-5} = -16 \quad \text{and} \quad y = \frac{F}{D} = \frac{-1050}{-5} = 210.$$

Now Try Exercise 25

Triangular Region

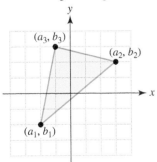

Figure 9.70

Area of Regions

Determinants may be used to find the area of a triangle. If a triangle has vertices $(a_1, b_1), (a_2, b_2),$ and $(a_3, b_3),$ as shown in Figure 9.70, then its area is equal to the *absolute value* of D, where

$$D = \frac{1}{2} \det \begin{bmatrix} a_1 & a_2 & a_3 \\ b_1 & b_2 & b_3 \\ 1 & 1 & 1 \end{bmatrix}.$$

If the vertices are entered into the columns of D in a *counterclockwise* direction, then D will be positive. (***Source:*** W. Taylor, *The Geometry of Computer Graphics.*)

EXAMPLE 6   Computing the area of a parallelogram

Use determinants to calculate the area of the parallelogram in Figure 9.71.

SOLUTION   To find the area of the parallelogram, we view the parallelogram as comprising two triangles. One triangle has vertices at $(0, 0)$, $(4, 2)$, and $(1, 2)$, and the other triangle has vertices at $(4, 2)$, $(5, 4)$, and $(1, 2)$. The area of the parallelogram is equal to the sum of the areas of the two triangles. Since these triangles are congruent, we can calculate the area of one triangle and double it. The area of one triangle is equal to D.

$$D = \frac{1}{2} \det \begin{bmatrix} 0 & 4 & 1 \\ 0 & 2 & 2 \\ 1 & 1 & 1 \end{bmatrix} = \frac{1}{2}(6) = 3$$

Since the vertices were entered in a counterclockwise direction, D is positive. The area of one triangle is equal to 3 square units. Therefore the area of the parallelogram is twice this value, or 6 square units.

Now Try Exercise 35

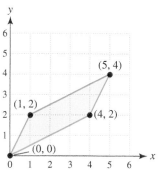

Figure 9.71

CLASS DISCUSSION

Suppose we are given three distinct vertices and $D = 0$. What must be true about the three points?

9.7 Putting It All Together

The determinant of a square matrix A is a real number, denoted det A. If det $A \neq 0$, then the matrix A is invertible. The following table summarizes the calculation of 2×2 and 3×3 determinants by hand.

DETERMINANTS OF 2 × 2 MATRICES

The determinant of a 2×2 matrix A is given by

$$\det A = \det \begin{bmatrix} a & b \\ c & d \end{bmatrix} = ad - cb.$$

Example: $\det \begin{bmatrix} 6 & -2 \\ 3 & 7 \end{bmatrix} = (6)(7) - (3)(-2) = 48$

DETERMINANTS OF 3 × 3 MATRICES

Finding the determinant of a 3×3 matrix A can be reduced to calculating the determinants of three 2×2 matrices. This calculation can be performed using cofactors.

$$\det A = \det \begin{bmatrix} a_1 & b_1 & c_1 \\ a_2 & b_2 & c_2 \\ a_3 & b_3 & c_3 \end{bmatrix}$$

$$= a_1 \det \begin{bmatrix} b_2 & c_2 \\ b_3 & c_3 \end{bmatrix} - a_2 \det \begin{bmatrix} b_1 & c_1 \\ b_3 & c_3 \end{bmatrix} + a_3 \det \begin{bmatrix} b_1 & c_1 \\ b_2 & c_2 \end{bmatrix}$$

Example: $\det \begin{bmatrix} 1 & -2 & 3 \\ 4 & 5 & -1 \\ -3 & 7 & 8 \end{bmatrix} = (1) \det \begin{bmatrix} 5 & -1 \\ 7 & 8 \end{bmatrix} - (4) \det \begin{bmatrix} -2 & 3 \\ 7 & 8 \end{bmatrix} + (-3) \det \begin{bmatrix} -2 & 3 \\ 5 & -1 \end{bmatrix}$

$$= (1)(47) - 4(-37) - 3(-13) = 234$$

9.7 Exercises

Calculating Determinants

Exercises 1–4: Determine if the matrix A is invertible by calculating det A.

1. $A = \begin{bmatrix} 4 & 3 \\ 5 & 4 \end{bmatrix}$

2. $A = \begin{bmatrix} 1 & -3 \\ 2 & 6 \end{bmatrix}$

3. $A = \begin{bmatrix} -4 & 6 \\ -8 & 12 \end{bmatrix}$

4. $A = \begin{bmatrix} 10 & -20 \\ -5 & 10 \end{bmatrix}$

Exercises 5–8: Find the specified minor and cofactor for A.

5. M_{12} and A_{12} if $A = \begin{bmatrix} 1 & -1 & 3 \\ 2 & 3 & -2 \\ 0 & 1 & 5 \end{bmatrix}$

6. M_{23} and A_{23} if $A = \begin{bmatrix} 1 & 2 & -1 \\ 4 & 6 & -3 \\ 2 & 3 & 9 \end{bmatrix}$

7. M_{22} and A_{22} if $A = \begin{bmatrix} 7 & -8 & 1 \\ 3 & -5 & 2 \\ 1 & 0 & -2 \end{bmatrix}$

8. M_{31} and A_{31} if $A = \begin{bmatrix} 0 & 0 & -1 \\ 6 & -7 & 1 \\ 8 & -9 & -1 \end{bmatrix}$

Exercises 9–12: Let A be the given matrix. Find det A by expanding about the first column. State whether A^{-1} exists.

9. $\begin{bmatrix} 1 & 4 & -7 \\ 0 & 2 & -3 \\ 0 & -1 & 3 \end{bmatrix}$

10. $\begin{bmatrix} 0 & 2 & 8 \\ -1 & 3 & 5 \\ 0 & 4 & 1 \end{bmatrix}$

11. $\begin{bmatrix} 5 & 1 & 6 \\ 0 & -2 & 0 \\ 0 & 4 & 0 \end{bmatrix}$

12. $\begin{bmatrix} 3 & 2 & 3 \\ 2 & 2 & 2 \\ 1 & 3 & 1 \end{bmatrix}$

Exercises 13–20: Let A be the given matrix. Find det A by using the method of cofactors.

13. $\begin{bmatrix} 2 & 0 & 0 \\ 0 & 3 & 0 \\ 0 & 0 & 5 \end{bmatrix}$

14. $\begin{bmatrix} 0 & 0 & 2 \\ 0 & 3 & 0 \\ 5 & 0 & 0 \end{bmatrix}$

15. $\begin{bmatrix} 0 & 0 & 0 \\ -8 & 3 & -9 \\ 15 & 5 & 9 \end{bmatrix}$

16. $\begin{bmatrix} 1 & 1 & 5 \\ -3 & -3 & 0 \\ 7 & 0 & 0 \end{bmatrix}$

17. $\begin{bmatrix} 3 & -1 & 2 \\ 0 & 5 & 7 \\ 1 & 0 & -1 \end{bmatrix}$

18. $\begin{bmatrix} 3 & 0 & -1 \\ 2 & 3 & -4 \\ 6 & -5 & 1 \end{bmatrix}$

19. $\begin{bmatrix} 1 & -5 & 2 \\ -7 & 1 & 3 \\ 0 & 4 & -2 \end{bmatrix}$

20. $\begin{bmatrix} 1 & -1 & 2 \\ -2 & 0 & 1 \\ 1 & 1 & -1 \end{bmatrix}$

Exercises 21–24: Let A be the given matrix. Use technology to calculate det A.

21. $\begin{bmatrix} 11 & -32 \\ 1.2 & 55 \end{bmatrix}$

22. $\begin{bmatrix} 17 & -4 & 3 \\ 11 & 5 & -15 \\ 7 & -9 & 23 \end{bmatrix}$

23. $\begin{bmatrix} 2.3 & 5.1 & 2.8 \\ 1.2 & 4.5 & 8.8 \\ -0.4 & -0.8 & -1.2 \end{bmatrix}$

24. $\begin{bmatrix} 1 & -1 & 3 & 7 \\ 9 & 2 & -7 & -4 \\ 5 & -7 & 1 & -9 \\ 7 & 1 & 3 & 6 \end{bmatrix}$

Cramer's Rule

Exercises 25–32: Use Cramer's rule to solve the system of linear equations.

25. $\begin{aligned} -x + 2y &= 5 \\ 3x + 3y &= 1 \end{aligned}$

26. $\begin{aligned} 2x + y &= -3 \\ -4x - 6y &= -7 \end{aligned}$

27. $\begin{aligned} -2x + 3y &= 8 \\ 4x - 5y &= 3 \end{aligned}$

28. $\begin{aligned} 5x - 3y &= 4 \\ -3x - 7y &= 5 \end{aligned}$

29. $\begin{aligned} 7x + 4y &= 23 \\ 11x - 5y &= 70 \end{aligned}$

30. $\begin{aligned} -7x + 5y &= 8.2 \\ 6x + 4y &= -0.4 \end{aligned}$

31. $\begin{aligned} 1.7x - 2.5y &= -0.91 \\ -0.4x + 0.9y &= 0.423 \end{aligned}$

32. $\begin{aligned} -2.7x + 1.5y &= -1.53 \\ 1.8x - 5.5y &= -1.68 \end{aligned}$

Calculating Area

Exercises 33–36: Use a determinant to find the area of the shaded region.

33.

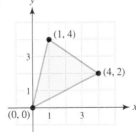

34.

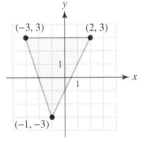

35.

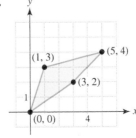

36.

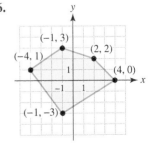

Applying a Concept

Exercises 37–40: Use the concept of the area of a triangle to determine if the three points are collinear.

37. $(1, 3), (-3, 11), (2, 1)$

38. $(3, 6), (-1, -6), (5, 11)$

39. $(-2, -5), (4, 4), (2, 3)$

40. $(4, -5), (-2, 10), (6, -10)$

Equations of Lines

Exercises 41–44: If a line passes through the points (x_1, y_1) and (x_2, y_2), then an equation of this line can be found by calculating the determinant.

$$\det \begin{bmatrix} x & y & 1 \\ x_1 & y_1 & 1 \\ x_2 & y_2 & 1 \end{bmatrix} = 0$$

Find the standard form $ax + by = c$ of the line passing through the given points.

41. $(2, 1)$ and $(-1, 4)$ **42.** $(-1, 3)$ and $(4, 2)$

43. $(6, -7)$ and $(4, -3)$ **44.** $(5, 1)$ and $(2, -2)$

Writing about Mathematics

45. Choose two matrices A and B with dimension 2×2. Calculate det A, det B, and det (AB). Repeat this process until you are able to discover how these three determinants are related. Summarize your results.

46. Calculate both det A and det A^{-1} for several different matrices. Compare the determinants. Try to generalize your results.

Extended and Discovery Exercises

Exercises 1–6: **Cramer's Rule** *Cramer's rule can be applied to systems of three linear equations in three variables. For the system of equations*

$$a_1 x + b_1 y + c_1 z = d_1$$
$$a_2 x + b_2 y + c_2 z = d_2$$
$$a_3 x + b_3 y + c_3 z = d_3,$$

the solution can be written as follows.

$$D = \det \begin{bmatrix} a_1 & b_1 & c_1 \\ a_2 & b_2 & c_2 \\ a_3 & b_3 & c_3 \end{bmatrix}, \quad E = \det \begin{bmatrix} d_1 & b_1 & c_1 \\ d_2 & b_2 & c_2 \\ d_3 & b_3 & c_3 \end{bmatrix}$$

$$F = \det \begin{bmatrix} a_1 & d_1 & c_1 \\ a_2 & d_2 & c_2 \\ a_3 & d_3 & c_3 \end{bmatrix}, \quad G = \det \begin{bmatrix} a_1 & b_1 & d_1 \\ a_2 & b_2 & d_2 \\ a_3 & b_3 & d_3 \end{bmatrix}$$

If $D \neq 0$, a unique solution exists and is given by

$$x = \frac{E}{D}, \quad y = \frac{F}{D}, \quad z = \frac{G}{D}.$$

Use Cramer's rule to solve the system of equations.

1.
$$x + y + z = 6$$
$$2x + y + 2z = 9$$
$$y + 3z = 9$$

2.
$$y + z = 1$$
$$2x - y - z = -1$$
$$x + y - z = 3$$

3.
$$x \quad + z = 2$$
$$x + y \quad = 0$$
$$y + 2z = 1$$

4.
$$x + y + 2z = 1$$
$$-x - 2y - 3z = -2$$
$$y - 3z = 5$$

5.
$$x \quad + 2z = 7$$
$$-x + y + z = 5$$
$$2x - y + 2z = 6$$

6.
$$x + 2y + 3z = -1$$
$$2x - 3y - z = 12$$
$$x + 4y - 2z = -12$$

Exercises 7–10: **Equations of Circles** *Given three distinct points on a circle (x_1, y_1), (x_2, y_2), and (x_3, y_3), we can find the equation of the circle by using the following determinant.*

$$\det \begin{bmatrix} x^2 + y^2 & x & y & 1 \\ x_1{}^2 + y_1{}^2 & x_1 & y_1 & 1 \\ x_2{}^2 + y_2{}^2 & x_2 & y_2 & 1 \\ x_3{}^2 + y_3{}^2 & x_3 & y_3 & 1 \end{bmatrix} = 0$$

Find the equation of the circle through the given points.

7. $(0, 2)$ $(2, 0)$, and $(-2, 0)$

8. $(0, 0)$, $(4, 0)$, and $(2, -2)$

9. $(0, 1)$, $(1, -1)$, and $(2, 2)$

10. $(1, 0)$, $(-1, 2)$, and $(3, 2)$

CHECKING BASIC CONCEPTS FOR SECTION 9.7

1. Find the determinant of the matrix A by using the method of cofactors. Is A invertible?

$$A = \begin{bmatrix} 1 & -1 & 2 \\ 2 & 3 & 1 \\ 0 & -2 & 5 \end{bmatrix}$$

2. Use Cramer's rule to solve the system of equations.
$$3x - 4y = 7$$
$$-4x + 3y = 5$$

9 Summary

CONCEPT	EXPLANATION AND EXAMPLES

Section 9.1 Functions and Systems of Equations in Two Variables

Functions of Two Variables

$z = f(x, y)$, where x and y are inputs to f

Example: $f(x, y) = 2x - 3y$
$f(4, -1) = 2(4) - 3(-1) = 11$

System of Linear Equations in Two Variables

General form: $a_1x + b_1y = c_1$
$a_2x + b_2y = c_2$

A linear system can have zero, one, or infinitely many solutions. A solution can be written as an ordered pair. A linear system may be solved symbolically, graphically, or numerically.

Example: $x - y = 2$
$2x + y = 7$ Solution: (3, 1)

Types of Linear Systems with Two Variables

Consistent system: Has either one solution (independent equations) or infinitely many solutions (dependent equations)

Inconsistent system: Has no solutions

One Solution

Consistent System
Independent Equations

Infinitely Many Solutions

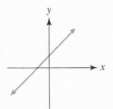

Consistent System
Dependent Equations

No Solution

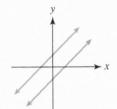

Inconsistent System

Method of Substitution for Two Equations

Can be used to solve systems of linear or nonlinear equations

Example: $x - y = -3$
$x + 4y = 17$

Solve the first equation for x to obtain $x = y - 3$. Substitute this result in the second equation and solve for y.

$(y - 3) + 4y = 17$ implies that $y = 4$.

Then $x = 4 - 3 = 1$ and the solution is $(1, 4)$.

Method of Elimination

Can be used to solve systems of linear or nonlinear equations

Example: $2x - 3y = 4$
$x + 3y = 11$
$\overline{3x \quad\quad = 15}$,   or $x = 5$ Add.

Substituting $x = 5$ in the first equation gives $y = 2$.
The solution is $(5, 2)$.

CONCEPT	EXPLANATION AND EXAMPLES

Section 9.1 Functions and Systems of Equations in Two Variables (CONTINUED)

Joint Variation

Let m and n be real numbers. Then z *varies jointly* with the mth power of x and the nth power of y if a nonzero real number k exists such that $z = kx^m y^n$.

Example: The area of a triangle varies jointly with the base b and the height h because $A = \frac{1}{2}bh$. Note that $k = \frac{1}{2}$, $m = 1$, and $n = 1$ in this example.

Section 9.2 Systems of Inequalities in Two Variables

System of Inequalities in Two Variables

The solution set is often a shaded region in the xy-plane.

Example:

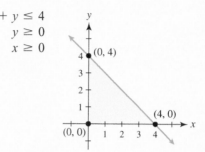

Linear Programming

Method for maximizing (or minimizing) an objective function subject to a set of constraints

Example: Maximize $P = 2x + 4y$, subject to

$$x + y \le 4, x \ge 0, y \ge 0.$$

The maximum of $P = 16$ occurs at the vertex $(0, 4)$, in the region of feasible solutions. See the figure above.

Section 9.3 Systems of Linear Equations in Three Variables

Solution to a System of Linear Equations in Three Variables

An ordered triple (x, y, z) that satisfies *every* equation

Example:
$$x - 2y + 3z = 6$$
$$-x + 3y + 4z = 17$$
$$3x + 4y - 5z = -4$$

The solution is $(1, 2, 3)$ because the values $x = 1$, $y = 2$, and $z = 3$ satisfy all three equations. (Check this fact.)

Elimination and Substitution

Systems of linear equations in three variables can be solved by using elimination and substitution. The following three steps outline this process.

STEP 1: Eliminate one variable, such as x, from two of the equations.

STEP 2: Apply the techniques discussed in Section 9.1 to solve the two equations in two variables resulting from Step 1. If x is eliminated, then solve these equations to find y and z.

If there are no solutions for y and z, then the given system has no solutions. If there are infinitely many solutions for y and z, then write y in terms of z and go to Step 3.

STEP 3: Substitute the values for y and z in one of the given equations to find x. The solution is (x, y, z). If possible, check your solution.

CONCEPT	EXPLANATION AND EXAMPLES

Section 9.4 Solutions to Linear Systems Using Matrices

Matrices and Systems of Linear Equations

An augmented matrix can be used to represent a system of linear equations.

Example:

$$\begin{aligned} x - 2y + z &= 0 \\ -x + 4y - z &= 4 \\ 2x + y - 3z &= -5 \end{aligned}$$

Augmented Matrix

$$\begin{bmatrix} 1 & -2 & 1 & | & 0 \\ -1 & 4 & -1 & | & 4 \\ 2 & 1 & -3 & | & -5 \end{bmatrix}$$

Row-Echelon Form

Examples:

$$\begin{bmatrix} 1 & 2 & -1 \\ 0 & 1 & 2 \end{bmatrix} \qquad \begin{bmatrix} 1 & 3 & -2 & | & 7 \\ 0 & 1 & 4 & | & 5 \\ 0 & 0 & 1 & | & -3 \end{bmatrix}$$

Gaussian Elimination with Backward Substitution

Gaussian elimination can be used to transform a matrix representing a system of linear equations into row-echelon form. Then backward substitution can be used to solve the resulting system of linear equations. (Graphing calculators can also be used to solve systems of equations.)

Section 9.5 Properties and Applications of Matrices

Operations on Matrices

Matrices can be added, subtracted, and multiplied, but there is *no* division of matrices.

Addition

$$\begin{bmatrix} 2 & 4 \\ 5 & 6 \end{bmatrix} + \begin{bmatrix} -2 & 1 \\ 7 & 3 \end{bmatrix} = \begin{bmatrix} 0 & 5 \\ 12 & 9 \end{bmatrix}$$

Subtraction

$$\begin{bmatrix} -3 & 0 \\ 4 & -4 \end{bmatrix} - \begin{bmatrix} 1 & 2 \\ 6 & -7 \end{bmatrix} = \begin{bmatrix} -4 & -2 \\ -2 & 3 \end{bmatrix}$$

Scalar Multiplication

$$3\begin{bmatrix} 5 & 1 & 6 & -1 \\ 0 & -2 & 3 & 2 \end{bmatrix} = \begin{bmatrix} 15 & 3 & 18 & -3 \\ 0 & -6 & 9 & 6 \end{bmatrix}$$

Multiplication

$$\begin{bmatrix} 2 & -1 \\ 0 & 3 \\ -7 & 1 \end{bmatrix}\begin{bmatrix} 1 & -1 & 0 \\ 3 & -5 & -4 \end{bmatrix} = \begin{bmatrix} -1 & 3 & 4 \\ 9 & -15 & -12 \\ -4 & 2 & -4 \end{bmatrix}$$

Section 9.6 Inverses of Matrices

Matrix Inverses

The inverse of an $n \times n$ matrix A, denoted A^{-1}, satisfies $A^{-1}A = I_n$ and $AA^{-1} = I_n$, where I_n is the $n \times n$ identity matrix. The inverse of a matrix can be found by hand or with technology.

Example:

$$A = \begin{bmatrix} 5 & 2 \\ 2 & 1 \end{bmatrix} \quad \text{and} \quad A^{-1} = \begin{bmatrix} 1 & -2 \\ -2 & 5 \end{bmatrix}$$

$$\begin{bmatrix} 5 & 2 \\ 2 & 1 \end{bmatrix}\begin{bmatrix} 1 & -2 \\ -2 & 5 \end{bmatrix} = \begin{bmatrix} 1 & 0 \\ 0 & 1 \end{bmatrix} = I_2$$

$$\begin{bmatrix} 1 & -2 \\ -2 & 5 \end{bmatrix}\begin{bmatrix} 5 & 2 \\ 2 & 1 \end{bmatrix} = \begin{bmatrix} 1 & 0 \\ 0 & 1 \end{bmatrix} = I_2$$

CONCEPT	EXPLANATION AND EXAMPLES

Section 9.6 Inverses of Matrices (CONTINUED)

Matrix Equations

A system of linear equations can be written as the matrix equation $AX = B$.

Example: $2x - 2y = 3$
$-3x + 4y = 2$

$$AX = \begin{bmatrix} 2 & -2 \\ -3 & 4 \end{bmatrix} \begin{bmatrix} x \\ y \end{bmatrix} = \begin{bmatrix} 3 \\ 2 \end{bmatrix} = B$$

The solution can be found as follows.

$$X = A^{-1}B = \begin{bmatrix} 2 & 1 \\ 1.5 & 1 \end{bmatrix} \begin{bmatrix} 3 \\ 2 \end{bmatrix} = \begin{bmatrix} 8 \\ 6.5 \end{bmatrix}$$

The solution is (8, 6.5).

Section 9.7 Determinants

Determinant of a 2 × 2 Matrix

$$\det A = \det \begin{bmatrix} a & b \\ c & d \end{bmatrix} = ad - cb$$

Example: $\det \begin{bmatrix} 1 & 4 \\ 3 & 5 \end{bmatrix} = (1)(5) - (3)(4) = -7$

Determinant of a 3 × 3 Matrix

Finding a 3 × 3 determinant can be reduced to calculating the determinants of three 2 × 2 matrices by using cofactors. If $\det A \neq 0$, then A^{-1} exists.

Example: $\det \begin{bmatrix} 3 & 1 & -1 \\ 2 & 2 & 0 \\ 0 & 1 & -3 \end{bmatrix}$

$$= 3 \begin{bmatrix} 2 & 0 \\ 1 & -3 \end{bmatrix} - 2 \begin{bmatrix} 1 & -1 \\ 1 & -3 \end{bmatrix} + 0 \begin{bmatrix} 1 & -1 \\ 2 & 0 \end{bmatrix}$$

$$= 3(-6) - 2(-2) + 0(2)$$

$$= -14$$

Cramer's Rule

Cramer's rule makes use of determinants to solve systems of linear equations. However, Gaussian elimination with backward substitution is usually more efficient.

---

9 | Review Exercises

Exercises 1 and 2: Evaluate the function for the inputs.

1. $A(3, 6)$, where $A(b, h) = \frac{1}{2}bh$

2. $V(2, 5)$, where $V(r, h) = \pi r^2 h$

Exercises 3 and 4: The figure in the next column shows the graph of a system of two linear equations. Use the graph to estimate the solution to the system of equations. Then solve the system symbolically.

3.

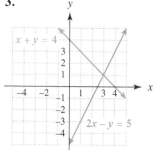

4.

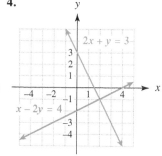

Exercises 5 and 6: Solve the system of equations
(a) graphically and   (b) symbolically.

5. $3x + y = 1$
$2x - 3y = 8$

6. $x^2 - y = 1$
$x + y = 1$

Exercises 7–10: Use the elimination method to solve each system of linear equations, if possible. Identify the system as consistent or inconsistent.

7. $2x + y = 7$
$x - 2y = -4$

8. $3x + 3y = 15$
$-x - y = -4$

9. $6x - 15y = 12$
$-4x + 10y = -8$

10. $3x - 4y = -10$
$4x + 3y = -30$

Exercises 11 and 12: Use elimination to solve the nonlinear system of equations.

11. $x^2 - 3y = 3$
$x^2 + 2y^2 = 5$

12. $2x - 3y = 1$
$2x^2 + y = 1$

Exercises 13 and 14: Graph the solution set to the inequality.

13. $y \geq -1$

14. $2x - y < 4$

Exercises 15 and 16: Graph the solution set to the system of inequalities. Use the graph to find one solution.

15. $x^2 + y^2 < 9$
$x + y > 3$

16. $x + 3y \geq 3$
$x + y \leq 4$

Exercises 17–20: If possible, solve the system.

17. $x - y + z = -2$
$x + 2y - z = 2$
$2y + 3z = 7$

18. $x - 3y + 2z = -10$
$2x - y + 3z = -9$
$-x - y + z = -1$

19. $-x + 2y + 2z = 9$
$x + y - 3z = 6$
$3y - z = 8$

20. $2x - y - 3z = -9$
$x - 8z = -23$
$-3x + 2y - 2z = -5$

Exercises 21–24: The augmented matrix represents a system of linear equations. Solve the system.

21. $\begin{bmatrix} 1 & 5 & | & 6 \\ 0 & 1 & | & 3 \end{bmatrix}$

22. $\begin{bmatrix} 1 & 2 & -2 & | & 8 \\ 0 & 1 & 1 & | & 5 \\ 0 & 0 & 0 & | & 0 \end{bmatrix}$

23. $\begin{bmatrix} 1 & 0 & 0 & | & -2 \\ 0 & 1 & 0 & | & 3 \\ 0 & 0 & 1 & | & 0 \end{bmatrix}$

24. $\begin{bmatrix} 1 & 0 & 0 & | & -5 \\ 0 & 1 & -4 & | & 1 \\ 0 & 0 & 0 & | & 5 \end{bmatrix}$

Exercises 25 and 26: Use Gaussian elimination with backward substitution to solve the system of linear equations.

25. $2x - y + 2z = 10$
$x - 2y + z = 8$
$3x - y + 2z = 11$

26. $x - 2y + z = 1$
$2x - 5y + 3z = 4$
$2x - 3y + z = 0$

Exercises 27 and 28: Let a_{ij} denote the general term for the matrix A. Find each of the following.
(a) $a_{12} + a_{22}$ (b) $a_{11} - 2a_{23}$

27. $A = \begin{bmatrix} -2 & 3 & -1 \\ 5 & 2 & 4 \end{bmatrix}$

28. $\begin{bmatrix} -1 & 2 & 5 \\ 1 & -3 & 7 \\ 0 & 7 & -2 \end{bmatrix}$

Exercises 29 and 30: Evaluate the following.
(a) $A + 2B$ (b) $A - B$ (c) $-4A$

29. $A = \begin{bmatrix} 1 & -3 \\ 2 & -1 \end{bmatrix}$, $B = \begin{bmatrix} 3 & 2 \\ -5 & 1 \end{bmatrix}$

30. $A = \begin{bmatrix} 4 & 0 & 1 \\ -2 & 8 & 9 \end{bmatrix}$, $B = \begin{bmatrix} -5 & 3 & 2 \\ -4 & 0 & 7 \end{bmatrix}$

Exercises 31–34: If possible, find AB and BA.

31. $A = \begin{bmatrix} 2 & 0 \\ -5 & 3 \end{bmatrix}$, $B = \begin{bmatrix} -1 & -2 \\ 4 & 7 \end{bmatrix}$

32. $A = \begin{bmatrix} 1 & -2 \\ 2 & 3 \end{bmatrix}$, $B = \begin{bmatrix} 1 & 0 & 2 \\ -1 & 3 & 4 \end{bmatrix}$

33. $A = \begin{bmatrix} 2 & -1 & 3 \\ 2 & 4 & 0 \end{bmatrix}$, $B = \begin{bmatrix} 1 & 0 \\ -1 & 2 \\ 0 & 3 \end{bmatrix}$

34. $A = \begin{bmatrix} 1 & -1 & 2 \\ 0 & 3 & 4 \\ 1 & 0 & 2 \end{bmatrix}$, $B = \begin{bmatrix} -1 & 0 & 0 \\ 2 & 0 & -1 \\ 1 & 4 & 2 \end{bmatrix}$

Exercises 35 and 36: Determine if B is the inverse matrix of A by evaluating AB and BA.

35. $A = \begin{bmatrix} 8 & 5 \\ 6 & 4 \end{bmatrix}$, $B = \begin{bmatrix} 2 & -2.5 \\ -3 & 4 \end{bmatrix}$

36. $A = \begin{bmatrix} -1 & 1 & 2 \\ 1 & 0 & -1 \\ 0 & 1 & 2 \end{bmatrix}$, $B = \begin{bmatrix} -1 & 0 & 1 \\ 2 & 2 & -1 \\ -1 & -1 & -1 \end{bmatrix}$

Exercises 37 and 38: Let A be the given matrix. Find A^{-1}.

37. $\begin{bmatrix} 1 & -2 \\ -1 & 1 \end{bmatrix}$

38. $\begin{bmatrix} 1 & 0 & 1 \\ 1 & 1 & 1 \\ 0 & 1 & -1 \end{bmatrix}$

Exercises 39 and 40: Complete the following.
(a) Write the system in the form $AX = B$.
(b) Solve the linear system by computing $X = A^{-1}B$.

39. $x - 3y = 4$
$2x - y = 3$

40. $x - 2y + z = 0$
$2x + y + 2z = 10$
$y + z = 3$

41. Solve the system using technology.

$$12x + 7y - 3z = 14.6$$
$$8x - 11y + 13z = -60.4$$
$$-23x \qquad + 9z = -14.6$$

42. If possible, graphically approximate the solution of each system of equations to the nearest thousandth. Identify each system as consistent or inconsistent. If the system is consistent, determine if the equations are dependent or independent.

(a) $3.1x + 4.2y = 6.4$
$1.7x - 9.1y = 1.6$

(b) $6.3x - 5.1y = 9.3$
$4.2x - 3.4y = 6.2$

(c) $0.32x - 0.64y = 0.96$
$-0.08x + 0.16y = -0.72$

Exercises 43 and 44: Let A be the given matrix. Find det A by using the method of cofactors.

43. $\begin{bmatrix} 2 & 1 & 3 \\ 0 & 3 & 4 \\ 1 & 0 & 5 \end{bmatrix}$ **44.** $\begin{bmatrix} 3 & 0 & 2 \\ 1 & 3 & 5 \\ -5 & 2 & 0 \end{bmatrix}$

Exercises 45 and 46: Let A be the given matrix. Use technology to find det A. State whether A is invertible.

45. $\begin{bmatrix} 13 & 22 \\ 55 & -57 \end{bmatrix}$ **46.** $\begin{bmatrix} 6 & -7 & -1 \\ -7 & 3 & -4 \\ 23 & 54 & 77 \end{bmatrix}$

Applications

47. Area and Perimeter Let l represent the length of a rectangle and w its width, where $l \geq w$. Then its area can be computed by $A(l, w) = lw$ and its perimeter by $P(l, w) = 2l + 2w$. Solve the system of equations determined by $A(l, w) = 77$ and $P(l, w) = 36$.

48. Cylinder Approximate the radius r and height h of a cylindrical container with a volume V of 30 cubic inches and a lateral (side) surface area S of 45 square inches.

49. Student Loans A student takes out two loans totaling $2000 to help pay for college expenses. One loan is at 7% interest, and the other is at 9%. Interest for both loans is compounded annually.
(a) If the combined total interest for the first year is $156, find the amount of each loan symbolically.

(b) Determine the amount of each loan graphically or numerically.

50. Dimensions of a Screen The screen of a rectangular television set is 3 inches wider than it is high. If the perimeter of the screen is 42 inches, find its dimensions by writing a system of linear equations and solving.

51. CD Prices A music store marks its compact discs A or B to indicate one of two selling prices. Each row in the table represents a purchase. Determine the cost of each type of CD by using a matrix inverse.

A	B	Total
1	2	$37.47
2	3	$61.95

52. Digital Photography Design a 3×3 matrix A that represents a digital photograph of the letter T in black on a white background. Find a matrix B such that adding B to A darkens only the white background by one gray level.

53. Area Use a determinant to find the area of the triangle whose vertices are $(0, 0)$, $(5, 2)$, and $(2, 5)$.

54. Voter Turnout The table shows the percent y of voter turnout in the United States for the presidential election in year x, where $x = 0$ corresponds to 1900. Find a quadratic function defined by $f(x) = ax^2 + bx + c$ that models these data. Graph f together with the data.

x	24	60	96
y	48.9	62.8	48.8

Source: Committee for the Study of the American Electorate.

55. Joint Variation Suppose P varies jointly with the square of x and the cube of y. If $P = 432$ when $x = 2$ and $y = 3$, find P when $x = 3$ and $y = 5$.

56. Linear Programming Find the maximum value of $P = 3x + 4y$ subject to the following constraints.

$$x + 3y \leq 12$$
$$3x + y \leq 12$$
$$x \geq 0, y \geq 0$$

Extended and Discovery Exercises

1. To form the **transpose** of a matrix A, denoted A^T, let the first row of A be the first column of A^T, the second row of A be the second column of A^T, and so on, for each row of A. The following are examples of A and A^T. If A has dimension $m \times n$, then A^T has dimension $n \times m$.

$$A = \begin{bmatrix} 3 & -3 & 7 \\ 1 & 6 & -2 \\ 4 & 2 & 5 \end{bmatrix}, \quad A^T = \begin{bmatrix} 3 & 1 & 4 \\ -3 & 6 & 2 \\ 7 & -2 & 5 \end{bmatrix}$$

$$A = \begin{bmatrix} 1 & 2 \\ 3 & 4 \\ 5 & 6 \end{bmatrix}, \quad A^T = \begin{bmatrix} 1 & 3 & 5 \\ 2 & 4 & 6 \end{bmatrix}$$

Find the transpose of each matrix A.

(a) $A = \begin{bmatrix} 3 & -3 \\ 2 & 6 \\ 4 & 2 \end{bmatrix}$ **(b)** $A = \begin{bmatrix} 0 & 1 & -2 \\ 2 & 5 & 4 \\ -4 & 3 & 9 \end{bmatrix}$

(c) $A = \begin{bmatrix} 5 & 7 \\ 1 & -7 \\ 6 & 3 \\ -9 & 2 \end{bmatrix}$

Exercises 2 and 3: **Least-Square Models**   *The table shows the average cost of tuition and fees y in dollars at 4-year public colleges. In this table $x = 0$ represents 1980 and $x = 20$ corresponds to 2000.*

x	0	5	10	15	20
y	804	1318	1908	2860	3487

Source: The College Board.

These data can be modeled by using linear regression. Ideally, we would like $f(x) = ax + b$ to satisfy the following five equations.

$$f(0) = a(0) + b = 804$$
$$f(5) = a(5) + b = 1318$$
$$f(10) = a(10) + b = 1908$$
$$f(15) = a(15) + b = 2860$$
$$f(20) = a(20) + b = 3487$$

Since the data points are not collinear, it is impossible for the graph of a line to pass through all five points. These five equations can be written as

$$AX = \begin{bmatrix} 0 & 1 \\ 5 & 1 \\ 10 & 1 \\ 15 & 1 \\ 20 & 1 \end{bmatrix} \begin{bmatrix} a \\ b \end{bmatrix} = \begin{bmatrix} 804 \\ 1318 \\ 1908 \\ 2860 \\ 3487 \end{bmatrix} = B.$$

The least-squares solution is found by solving the **normal equations**

$$A^{T}AX = A^{T}B$$

for X. The solution is $X = (A^{T}A)^{-1}A^{T}B$. Using technology, we find $a = 138.16$ and $b = 693.8$. Thus f is given by the formula $f(x) = 138.16x + 693.8$. The function f and the data can be graphed. See the figure.

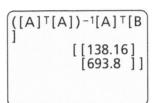

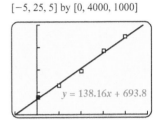

[−5, 25, 5] by [0, 4000, 1000]

Solve the normal equations to model the data with the line determined by $f(x) = ax + b$. Plot the data and f in the same viewing rectangle.

2. **Tuition and Fees**   The table shows average cost of tuition and fees y in dollars at private 4-year colleges. In this table $x = 0$ corresponds to 1980 and $x = 20$ to 2000.

x	0	5	10	15	20
y	3617	6121	9340	12,216	16,233

Source: The College Board.

3. **Early Satellite TV**   The table lists the number of satellite television subscribers y in millions. In this table $x = 0$ corresponds to 1995 and $x = 5$ to the year 2000.

x	0	1	2	3	4	5
y	2.2	4.5	7.9	10.5	13	15

Source: USA Today.

10 | Conic Sections

Throughout history, people have been fascinated by the universe around them and compelled to try to understand it. Conic sections have played an important role in gaining this understanding. In the sixteenth century Tycho Brahe, the greatest observational astronomer of the age, recorded precise data on planetary movement in the sky. In 1619, using Brahe's data, Johannes Kepler determined that planets move in elliptical orbits around the sun. Later, Newton used Kepler's work to show that elliptical orbits are the result of his famous theory of gravitation. We now know that all celestial objects—including planets, comets, asteroids, and satellites—travel in paths described by conic sections.

Parabolas, ellipses, and hyperbolas have had a profound influence on our understanding of ourselves and the cosmos around us. In this chapter we consider these age-old curves.

Source: Historical Topics for the Mathematics Classroom, Thirty-first Yearbook, NCTM.

> I want to put a ding in the universe.
>
> —Steve Jobs

10.1 Parabolas

- **Find equations of parabolas**
- **Graph parabolas**
- **Learn the reflective property of parabolas**
- **Translate parabolas**

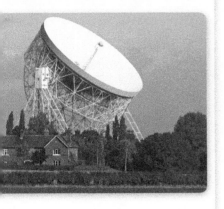

Introduction

Conic sections are named after the different ways in which a plane can intersect a cone. See Figure 10.1. Three basic conic sections are parabolas, ellipses, and hyperbolas. A circle is also an example of a conic section.

Examples of Conic Sections

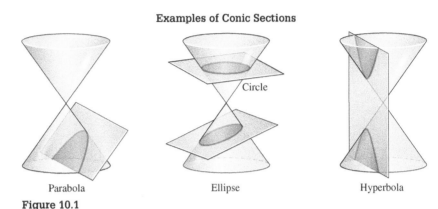

Parabola   Ellipse   Hyperbola

Figure 10.1

Conic sections can be graphed in the *xy*-plane as shown in Figures 10.2–10.4.

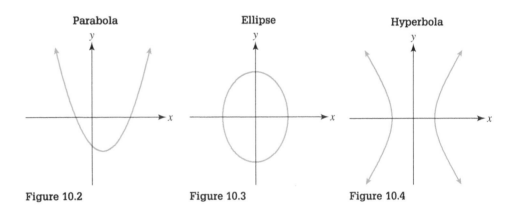

Parabola   Ellipse   Hyperbola

Figure 10.2   **Figure 10.3**   **Figure 10.4**

Ellipses will be discussed in Section 10.2 and hyperbolas will be discussed in Section 10.3. In this section we focus on parabolas.

Equations and Graphs of Parabolas

In Chapter 3 we saw that a parabola with vertex (0, 0) can be represented symbolically by the equation $y = ax^2$. With this representation, a parabola can open either upward when $a > 0$ or downward when $a < 0$. The following definition of a parabola allows it to open in *any* direction.

PARABOLA

A **parabola** is the set of points in a plane that are equidistant from a fixed point and a fixed line. The fixed point is called the **focus** and the fixed line is called the **directrix** of the parabola.

The following See the Concept shows some of the important features of parabolas. Note that the blue parabola in Figure 10.5 passes the vertical line test and can be represented by a function. However, the blue parabola in Figure 10.6 fails the vertical line test and cannot be represented by a function.

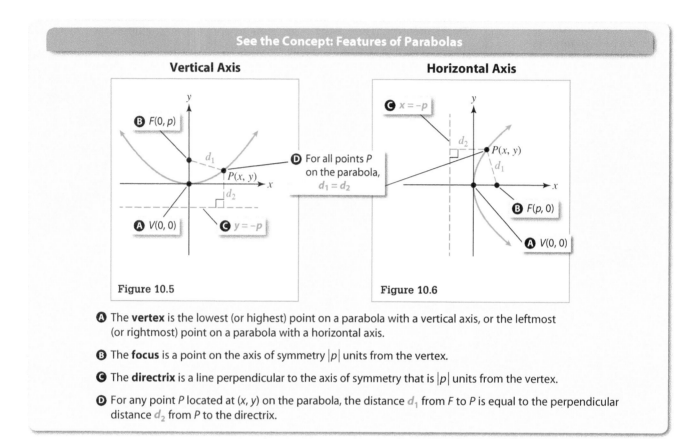

See the Concept: Features of Parabolas

Vertical Axis

Figure 10.5

Horizontal Axis

Figure 10.6

Ⓓ For all points P on the parabola, $d_1 = d_2$

Ⓐ The **vertex** is the lowest (or highest) point on a parabola with a vertical axis, or the leftmost (or rightmost) point on a parabola with a horizontal axis.

Ⓑ The **focus** is a point on the axis of symmetry $|p|$ units from the vertex.

Ⓒ The **directrix** is a line perpendicular to the axis of symmetry that is $|p|$ units from the vertex.

Ⓓ For any point P located at (x, y) on the parabola, the distance d_1 from F to P is equal to the perpendicular distance d_2 from P to the directrix.

> MAKING CONNECTIONS
>
> **Functions and Points**   In Figures 10.5 and 10.6, the point P is labeled $P(x, y)$. This notation resembles the notation for a function involving two inputs, since the point P is determined by x and y.

We can derive an equation of the parabola shown in Figure 10.5. Since $d_1 = d_2$, the distance formula can be used to express the variables x, y, and p in an equation.

$$d_1 = d_2$$
$$\sqrt{(x - 0)^2 + (y - p)^2} = \sqrt{(x - x)^2 + (y - (-p))^2} \qquad \text{Distance formula}$$
$$x^2 + (y - p)^2 = 0^2 + (y + p)^2 \qquad \text{Square each side.}$$
$$x^2 + y^2 - 2py + p^2 = y^2 + 2py + p^2 \qquad \text{Expand binomials.}$$
$$x^2 - 2py = 2py \qquad \text{Subtract } y^2 \text{ and } p^2.$$
$$x^2 = 4py \qquad \text{Add } 2py.$$

If the value of p is known, then the equation of a parabola with vertex $(0, 0)$ can be found using one of the following equations.

EQUATION OF A PARABOLA WITH VERTEX (0, 0)

Vertical Axis

The parabola with a focus at $(0, p)$ and directrix $y = -p$ has equation

$$x^2 = 4py.$$

The parabola opens upward if $p > 0$ and downward if $p < 0$.

Horizontal Axis

The parabola with a focus at $(p, 0)$ and directrix $x = -p$ has equation

$$y^2 = 4px.$$

The parabola opens to the right if $p > 0$ and to the left if $p < 0$.

EXAMPLE 1   Sketching graphs of parabolas

Sketch a graph of each parabola. Label the vertex, focus, and directrix.
(a) $x^2 = 8y$ **(b)** $y^2 = -2x$

SOLUTION
(a) The equation $x^2 = 8y$ is in the form $x^2 = 4py$, where $8 = 4p$. Therefore the parabola has a vertical axis with $p = 2$. Since $p > 0$, the parabola opens upward. The focus is $(0, 2)$ and the directrix is $y = -2$. See Figure 10.7.

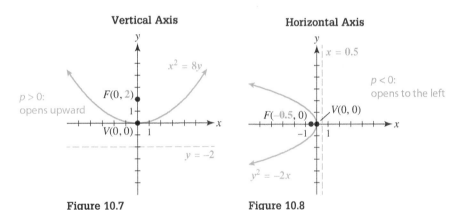

Figure 10.7   Figure 10.8

(b) The equation $y^2 = -2x$ has the form $y^2 = 4px$, where $-2 = 4p$. Therefore the parabola has a horizontal axis with $p = -0.5$. Since $p < 0$, the parabola opens to the left. The focus is $(-0.5, 0)$ and the directrix is $x = 0.5$. See Figure 10.8.

Now Try Exercises 23 and 27

EXAMPLE 2   Finding the equation of a parabola

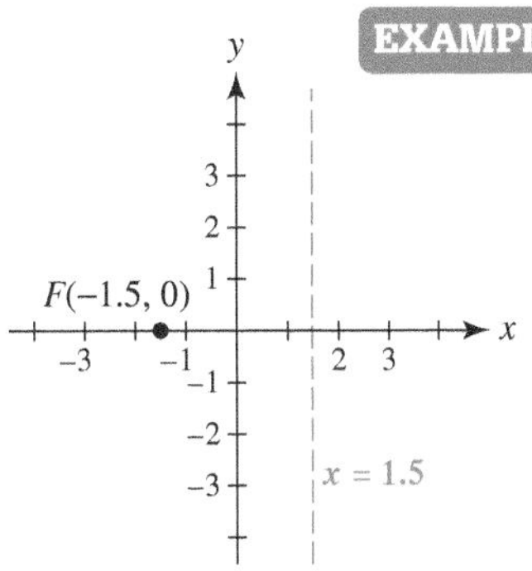

Find the equation of the parabola with focus $(-1.5, 0)$ and directrix $x = 1.5$, as shown in Figure 10.9. Sketch a graph of the parabola.

SOLUTION A parabola always *opens toward the focus* and *away from the directrix*. From Figure 10.9 we see that the parabola should open to the left. It follows that $p < 0$ in the equation $y^2 = 4px$. The distance between the focus at $(-1.5, 0)$ and the vertex at $(0, 0)$ is 1.5, and so $p = -1.5 < 0$. (Note that the vertex of the parabola is $(0, 0)$ because the vertex always lies *midway* between the focus and the directrix.) The equation of the parabola is $y^2 = 4(-1.5)x$, or $y^2 = -6x$, and a graph of the parabola is shown in Figure 10.10 at the top of the next page.

Figure 10.9

Horizontal Axis

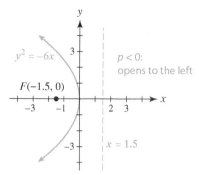

Figure 10.10

Now Try Exercise 35

Reflective Property of Parabolas

When a parabola is rotated about its axis, it sweeps out a shape called a **paraboloid**, as shown in Figure 10.11. Paraboloids have a special reflective property. When incoming, parallel rays of light from the sun or distant stars strike the surface of a paraboloid, each ray is reflected toward the focus. See Figure 10.12. This property of a paraboloid can also be used in reverse. If a light source is placed at the focus, then the light is reflected straight ahead, as shown in Figure 10.13. Searchlights, flashlights, and car headlights make use of this property.

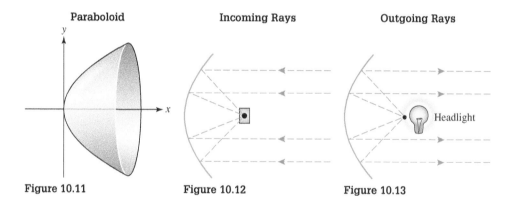

Paraboloid

Figure 10.11

Incoming Rays

Figure 10.12

Outgoing Rays

Figure 10.13

An Application   The next example illustrates how this reflective property is used in the construction of a telescope in the shape of a large parabolic dish.

Figure 10.14

EXAMPLE 3   Locating the receiver for a radio telescope

The giant Arecibo telescope in Puerto Rico has a parabolic dish with a diameter of 300 meters and a depth of 50 meters. See Figure 10.14. (*Source:* National Astronomy and Ionosphere Center, Arecibo Observatory.)

(a) Find an equation in the form $y = ax^2$ that describes a cross section of this dish.

(b) If the receiver is located at the focus, how far should it be from the vertex?

SOLUTION

(a) A parabola that passes through $(-150, 50)$ and $(150, 50)$, as shown in Figure 10.15, has a diameter of 300 meters and a depth of 50 meters. Substitute either point into $y = ax^2$.

Telescope Cross Section

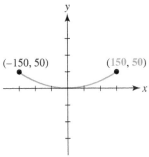

Figure 10.15

$$y = ax^2 \qquad \text{\textcolor{gray}{Equation of parabola}}$$
$$50 = a(150)^2 \qquad \text{\textcolor{gray}{Substitute.}}$$
$$a = \frac{50}{150^2} = \frac{1}{450} \quad \text{\textcolor{gray}{Solve for } a.}$$

The equation of the parabola is $y = \frac{1}{450}x^2$, where $-150 \le x \le 150$.

(b) The value of p represents the distance from the vertex to the focus. To determine p, write the equation in the form $x^2 = 4py$. Then

$$y = \frac{1}{450}x^2 \quad \text{is equivalent to} \quad x^2 = 450y.$$

It follows that $4p = 450$, or $p = 112.5$. Therefore the receiver should be located about 112.5 meters from the vertex.

Now Try Exercise 95

Translations of Parabolas

If the equation of a parabola is either $x^2 = 4py$ or $y^2 = 4px$, then its vertex is $(0, 0)$. We can use translations of graphs to find the equation of a parabola with vertex (h, k). This translation can be obtained by replacing x with $(x - h)$ and y with $(y - k)$.

$$(x - h)^2 = 4p(y - k) \qquad \text{\textcolor{gray}{Vertex } (h, k); \text{ vertical axis}}$$
$$(y - k)^2 = 4p(x - h) \qquad \text{\textcolor{gray}{Vertex } (h, k); \text{ horizontal axis}}$$

These two parabolas with $p > 0$ are shown in Figures 10.16 and 10.17, respectively.

Vertex (h, k); Vertical Axis

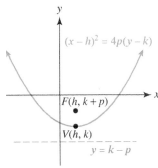

Figure 10.16

Vertex (h, k); Horizontal Axis

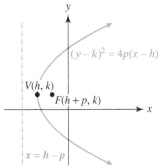

Figure 10.17

EQUATION OF A PARABOLA WITH VERTEX (h, k)

$(x - h)^2 = 4p(y - k)$ Vertical axis; vertex: (h, k)
           $p > 0$: opens upward; $p < 0$: opens downward
           Focus: $(h, k + p)$; directrix: $y = k - p$

$(y - k)^2 = 4p(x - h)$ Horizontal axis; vertex: (h, k)
           $p > 0$: opens to the right; $p < 0$: opens to the left
           Focus: $(h + p, k)$; directrix: $x = h - p$

EXAMPLE 4   Graphing a parabola with vertex (h, k)

Graph the parabola $x = -\frac{1}{8}(y + 3)^2 + 2$. Label the vertex, focus, and directrix.

Algebra Review
To review translations, or shifts, see
Section 3.5.

SOLUTION Rewrite the equation in the form $(y - k)^2 = 4p(x - h)$.

$$x = -\frac{1}{8}(y + 3)^2 + 2 \qquad \text{Given equation}$$

$$x - 2 = -\frac{1}{8}(y + 3)^2 \qquad \text{Subtract 2.}$$

$$-8(x - 2) = (y + 3)^2 \qquad \text{Multiply by } -8.$$

$$(y + 3)^2 = -8(x - 2) \qquad \text{Rewrite equation.}$$

$$(y - (-3))^2 = 4(-2)(x - 2) \qquad (y - k)^2 = 4p(x - h)$$

The vertex is $(2, -3)$, $p = -2$, and the parabola opens to the left. The focus is 2 units left of the vertex, and the directrix is 2 units right of the vertex. Thus the focus is $(0, -3)$, and the directrix is $x = 4$. See Figure 10.18.

Translated Parabola

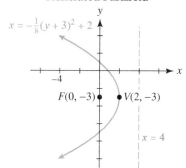

Figure 10.18

Now Try Exercise 61

EXAMPLE 5 Finding the equation of a parabola with vertex (h, k)

Find the equation of the parabola with focus $(3, -4)$ and directrix $y = 2$. Sketch a graph of the parabola. Label the focus, directrix, and vertex.

SOLUTION The focus and directrix are shown in Figure 10.19. The parabola opens downward $(p < 0)$, and its equation has the form $(x - h)^2 = 4p(y - k)$. The vertex is located midway between the focus and the directrix, so its coordinates are $(3, -1)$. The distance between the focus $(3, -4)$ and the vertex $(3, -1)$ is 3, so $p = -3$. The equation of the parabola is

$$(x - 3)^2 = -12(y + 1),$$

and its graph is shown in Figure 10.20.

Focus and Directrix

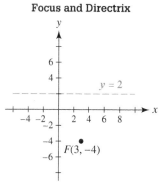

Figure 10.19

Translated Parabola

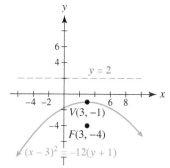

Figure 10.20

Now Try Exercise 67

EXAMPLE 6   Finding the equation of a parabola

Write $2x = y^2 + 4y + 12$ in the form $(y - k)^2 = a(x - h)$.

SOLUTION   Write the given equation in the required form by completing the square.

$$2x = y^2 + 4y + 12 \qquad \textit{Given equation}$$
$$2x - 12 = y^2 + 4y \qquad \textit{Subtract 12 from each side.}$$

CLASS DISCUSSION

Sketch a graph of the parabola in Example 6. Identify the vertex, focus, and directrix.

To complete the square on the right side of the equation, add $\left(\frac{4}{2}\right)^2 = 4$ to each side.

$$2x - 12 + 4 = y^2 + 4y + 4 \qquad \textit{Add 4 to each side.}$$
$$2x - 8 = (y + 2)^2 \qquad \textit{Perfect square trinomial}$$
$$2(x - 4) = (y + 2)^2 \qquad \textit{Factor out 2.}$$

The given equation is equivalent to $(y + 2)^2 = 2(x - 4)$.

Now Try Exercise 73

Using Technology   Graphing calculators can graph parabolas with horizontal axes, as illustrated in the next example.

EXAMPLE 7   Graphing a parabola with technology

Graph the equation $(y - 1)^2 = -0.5(x - 2)$ with a graphing calculator.

SOLUTION   Begin by solving the equation for y.

$$(y - 1)^2 = -0.5(x - 2) \qquad \textit{Given equation}$$
$$y - 1 = \pm \sqrt{-0.5(x - 2)} \qquad \textit{Square root property}$$
$$y = 1 \pm \sqrt{-0.5(x - 2)} \qquad \textit{Add 1.}$$

$[-4.7, 4.7, 1]$ by $[-3.1, 3.1, 1]$

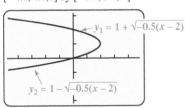

Let $y_1 = 1 + \sqrt{-0.5(x - 2)}$ and $y_2 = 1 - \sqrt{-0.5(x - 2)}$. The graph of y_1 creates the upper portion of the parabola, and the graph of y_2 creates the lower portion of the parabola, as shown in Figure 10.21.

Now Try Exercise 83

Figure 10.21

10.1 Putting It All Together

The following table summarizes some important concepts about parabolas.

CONCEPT	EQUATION	EXAMPLE
Parabola with vertex $(0, 0)$ and vertical axis	$x^2 = 4py$ $p > 0$: opens upward $p < 0$: opens downward Focus: $(0, p)$ Directrix: $y = -p$	$x^2 = -2y$ has $4p = -2$, or $p = -\frac{1}{2}$. The parabola opens downward with vertex $(0, 0)$, focus $\left(0, -\frac{1}{2}\right)$, and directrix $y = \frac{1}{2}$.

continued on next page

CONCEPT	EQUATION	EXAMPLE
Parabola with vertex $(0, 0)$ and horizontal axis	$y^2 = 4px$ $p > 0$: opens to the right $p < 0$: opens to the left Focus: $(p, 0)$ Directrix: $x = -p$	$y^2 = 4x$ has $4p = 4$, or $p = 1$. The parabola opens to the right with vertex $(0, 0)$, focus $(1, 0)$, and directrix $x = -1$.
Parabola with vertex (h, k) and vertical axis	$(x - h)^2 = 4p(y - k)$ $p > 0$: opens upward $p < 0$: opens downward Focus: $(h, k + p)$ Directrix: $y = k - p$	$(x - 1)^2 = 8(y - 3)$ has $p = 2$. The parabola opens upward with vertex $(1, 3)$, focus $(1, 5)$, and directrix $y = 1$.
Parabola with vertex (h, k) and horizontal axis	$(y - k)^2 = 4p(x - h)$ $p > 0$: opens to the right $p < 0$: opens to the left Focus: $(h + p, k)$ Directrix: $x = h - p$	$(y + 1)^2 = -2(x + 2)$ has $p = -\frac{1}{2}$. The parabola opens to the left with vertex $(-2, -1)$, focus $\left(-\frac{5}{2}, -1\right)$, and directrix $x = -\frac{3}{2}$.

10.1 Exercises

Basic Concepts

1. A parabola always opens toward its _____.

2. A parabola always opens away from its _____.

3. The parabola $x^2 = 4py$ opens _____ if $p > 0$ and it opens _____ if $p < 0$.

4. The parabola $y^2 = 4px$ opens _____ if $p > 0$ and it opens _____ if $p < 0$.

5. The parabola $x^2 = 4py$ has a __vertical/horizontal__ axis of symmetry.

6. The parabola $y^2 = 4px$ has a __vertical/horizontal__ axis of symmetry.

Parabolas with Vertex (0, 0)

Exercises 7–16: Sketch a graph of the parabola.

7. $x^2 = y$ **8.** $x^2 = -y$

9. $y^2 = -x$ **10.** $y^2 = x$

11. $4x^2 = -2y$ **12.** $y^2 = -3x$

13. $y^2 = -4x$ **14.** $x^2 = 4y$

15. $y^2 = -\frac{1}{2}x$ **16.** $8x = y^2$

Exercises 17–22: Match the equation with its graph (a–f).

17. $x^2 = 2y$ **18.** $x^2 = -2y$

19. $y^2 = -8x$ **20.** $y^2 = 4x$

21. $x = \frac{1}{2}y^2$ **22.** $y = -2x^2$

a.
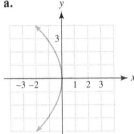

b.
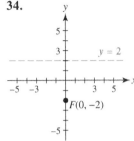

c.
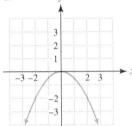

d.
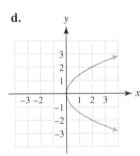

e.
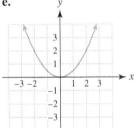

f.
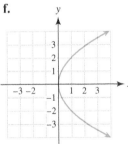

Exercises 23–32: Graph the parabola. Label the vertex, focus, and directrix.

23. $16y = x^2$ **24.** $y = -2x^2$

25. $x = \frac{1}{8}y^2$ **26.** $-y^2 = 6x$

27. $-4x = y^2$ **28.** $\frac{1}{2}y^2 = 3x$

29. $x^2 = -8y$ **30.** $x^2 = -4y$

31. $2y^2 = -8x$ **32.** $-3x = \frac{1}{4}y^2$

Exercises 33–36: Sketch a parabola with focus and directrix as shown in the figure. Find an equation of the parabola.

33.
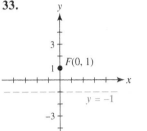

34.
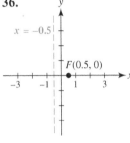

35.
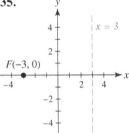

36.
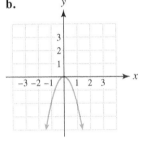

Exercises 37–46: Find an equation of the parabola with vertex $(0, 0)$ that satisfies the given conditions.

37. Focus $\left(0, \frac{3}{4}\right)$ **38.** Directrix $y = 2$

39. Directrix $x = 2$ **40.** Focus $(-1, 0)$

41. Focus $(1, 0)$ **42.** Focus $\left(0, -\frac{1}{2}\right)$

43. Directrix $x = \frac{1}{4}$ **44.** Directrix $y = -1$

45. Horizontal axis, passing through $(1, -2)$

46. Vertical axis, passing through $(-2, 3)$

Exercises 47–50: Find an equation of a parabola that satisfies the given conditions.

47. Focus $(0, -3)$ and directrix $y = 3$

48. Focus $(0, 2)$ and directrix $y = -2$

49. Focus $(-1, 0)$ and directrix $x = 1$

50. Focus $(3, 0)$ and directrix $x = -3$

Parabolas with Vertex (h, k)

Exercises 51–54: Sketch a graph of the parabola.

51. $(x - 1)^2 = (y - 2)$ **52.** $(x - 2)^2 = -(y + 1)$

53. $(y - 1)^2 = -(x + 1)$ **54.** $(y + 2)^2 = 2x$

Exercises 55–58: Match the equation with its graph (a–d).

55. $(x - 1)^2 = 4(y - 1)$ **56.** $(x + 1)^2 = -4(y - 2)$

57. $(y - 2)^2 = -8x$ **58.** $(y + 1)^2 = 8(x + 3)$

a.
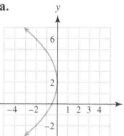

b.
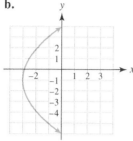

c.
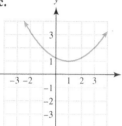

d.
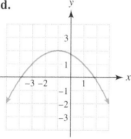

Exercises 59–64: Graph the parabola. Label the vertex, focus, and directrix.

59. $(x - 2)^2 = 8(y + 2)$ **60.** $\frac{1}{16}(x + 4)^2 = -(y - 4)$

61. $x = -\frac{1}{4}(y + 3)^2 + 2$ **62.** $x = 2(y - 2)^2 - 1$

63. $y = -\frac{1}{4}(x + 2)^2$ **64.** $-2(y + 1) = (x + 3)^2$

Exercises 65–68: Find an equation of a parabola that satisfies the given conditions. Sketch a graph of the parabola. Label the focus, directrix, and vertex.

65. Focus $(0, 2)$ and vertex $(0, 1)$

66. Focus $(-1, 2)$ and vertex $(3, 2)$

67. Focus $(0, 0)$ and directrix $x = -2$

68. Focus $(2, 1)$ and directrix $x = -1$

Exercises 69–72: Find an equation of a parabola that satisfies the given conditions.

69. Focus $(-1, 3)$ and directrix $y = 7$

70. Focus $(1, 2)$ and directrix $y = 4$

71. Horizontal axis, vertex $(-2, 3)$, passing through $(-4, 0)$

72. Horizontal axis, vertex $(-1, 2)$, passing through $(2, 3)$

Exercises 73–80: Write the given equation either in the form $(y - k)^2 = a(x - h)$ or in the form $(x - h)^2 = a(y - k)$.

73. $-2x = y^2 + 6x + 10$ **74.** $y^2 + 8x - 8 = 4x$

75. $x = 2y^2 + 4y - 1$ **76.** $x = 3y^2 - 6y - 2$

77. $x^2 - 3x + 4 = 2y$ **78.** $-3y = -x^2 + 4x - 6$

79. $4y^2 + 4y - 5 = 5x$ **80.** $-2y^2 + 5y + 1 = -x$

Graphing Parabolas with Technology

 Exercises 81–86: Graph the parabola.

81. $(y + 0.75)^2 = -3x$ **82.** $(y - 3)^2 = \frac{1}{7}x$

83. $(y - 0.5)^2 = 3.1(x + 1.3)$

84. $1.4(y - 1.5)^2 = 0.5(x + 2.1)$

85. $x = 2.3(y + 1)^2$

86. $(y - 2.5)^2 = 4.1(x + 1)$

Solving Nonlinear Systems

Exercises 87–92: Solve each system.

87. $x^2 = 2y$
$x^2 = y + 1$

88. $x^2 = -3y$
$-x^2 = 2y - 2$

89. $\frac{1}{3}y^2 = -3x$
$y^2 = x + 1$

90. $-2y^2 = x - 5$
$y^2 = 2x$

91. $(y - 1)^2 = x + 1$
$(y + 2)^2 = -x + 4$

92. $(y + 1)^2 = -x$
$-(y - 1)^2 = x + 4$

Applications

Exercises 93 and 94: **Satellite Dishes** *(Refer to Example 3.) Use the dimensions of a television satellite dish in the shape of a paraboloid to calculate how far from the vertex the receiver should be located.*

93. Six-foot diameter, nine inches deep

94. Nine-inch radius, two inches deep

95. Radio Telescope (Refer to Example 3.) The radio telescope shown in the figure has the shape of a parabolic dish with a diameter of 210 feet and a depth of 32 feet. (*Source:* J. Mar, *Structure Technology for Large Radio and Radar Telescope Systems.*)

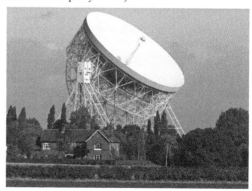

(a) Determine an equation of the form $y = ax^2$ with $a > 0$ describing a cross section of the dish.

(b) The receiver is placed at the focus. How far from the vertex is the receiver located?

96. Radio Telescope (Refer to Example 3.) A radio telescope is being designed in the shape of a parabolic dish with a diameter of 180 feet and a depth of 25 feet.
(a) Determine an equation of the form $x = ay^2$ with $a > 0$ describing a cross section of the dish.

(b) The receiver is placed at the focus. How far from the vertex should the receiver be located?

97. Comets A comet sometimes travels along a parabolic path as it passes the sun. In this case the sun is located at the focus of the parabola and the comet passes the sun once, rather than orbiting the sun. Suppose the path of a comet is given by $y^2 = 100x$, where units are in millions of miles.
(a) Find the coordinates of the sun.

(b) Find the minimum distance between the sun and the comet.

98. Headlight A headlight is being constructed in the shape of a paraboloid with a depth of 4 inches and a diameter of 5 inches, as illustrated in the figure. Find the distance d that the bulb should be from the vertex in order to have the beam of light shine straight ahead.

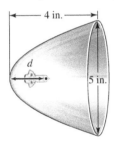

99. Solar Heater A solar heater is being designed to heat a pipe that will contain water, as illustrated in the figure. A cross section of the heater is described by the equation $x^2 = ky$, where k is a constant and all units are in feet. If the pipe is to be placed 18 inches from the vertex of this cross section, find the value of k.

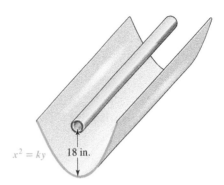

$x^2 = ky$ 18 in.

100. Solar Heater If the figure in Exercise 99 is rotated 90° clockwise, then the front edge of the reflector can be described by the equation $y^2 = kx$. If the pipe is placed 2 feet from the vertex of this cross section, find the value of k.

Writing about Mathematics

101. Explain how the distance between the focus and the vertex of a parabola affects the shape of the parabola.

102. Explain how to determine the direction that a parabola opens, given the focus and the directrix.

10.2 Ellipses

- **Find equations of ellipses**
- **Graph ellipses**
- **Learn the reflective property of ellipses**
- **Translate ellipses**
- **Solve nonlinear systems of equations and inequalities**

Introduction

When planets travel around the sun, they travel in elliptical orbits. This discovery by Johannes Kepler made it possible for astronomers to determine the precise positions of all types of celestial objects, such as asteroids, comets, and moons, and made it easier to predict both solar and lunar eclipses. Ellipses are also used in construction and medicine. In this section we examine the basic properties of ellipses.

Equations and Graphs of Ellipses

One method for sketching an ellipse is to tie a string to two nails driven into a flat board. If a pencil is placed inside the loop formed by the string, the curve it traces (shown in Figure 10.22 on the next page) is an ellipse. The sum of the distances d_1 and d_2 between the pencil and each of the nails is always fixed by the string. The locations of the nails correspond to the *foci* of the ellipse. If the two nails coincide, the ellipse becomes a circle. As the nails spread farther apart, the ellipse becomes more elongated, or *eccentric*.

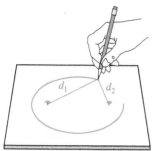

Figure 10.22

This method of sketching an ellipse suggests the following definition.

> **ELLIPSE**
>
> An **ellipse** is the set of points in a plane, the sum of whose distances from two fixed points is constant. Each fixed point is called a **focus** (plural, **foci**) of the ellipse.

The following See the Concept shows some of the important features of ellipses.

> **See the Concept: Features of Ellipses**
>
> **Horizontal Major Axis**   **Vertical Major Axis**
>
> **D** For all points P on the ellipse, $d_1 + d_2$ is a fixed value.
>
> **A** The **major axis** is the longer line segment connecting the **vertices** V_1 and V_2.
>
> **B** The **minor axis** is the shorter line segment connecting U_1 and U_2.
>
> **C** The **foci** F_1 and F_2 (singular, focus) are points located on the major axis of the ellipse.
>
> **D** For any point P located at (x, y) on the ellipse, the sum of the distances d_1 and d_2 is fixed.

> **NOTE** Since a vertical line can intersect the graph of an ellipse more than once, an ellipse cannot be described by a function.

Some ellipses can be represented by the following equations.

> **STANDARD EQUATIONS FOR ELLIPSES CENTERED AT (0, 0)**
>
> The ellipse with center at the origin, *horizontal* major axis, and equation
>
> $$\frac{x^2}{a^2} + \frac{y^2}{b^2} = 1 \qquad (a > b > 0)$$
>
> has vertices $(\pm a, 0)$, endpoints of the minor axis $(0, \pm b)$, and foci $(\pm c, 0)$, where $c^2 = a^2 - b^2$ and $c \geq 0$.
>
> The ellipse with center at the origin, *vertical* major axis, and equation
>
> $$\frac{x^2}{b^2} + \frac{y^2}{a^2} = 1 \qquad (a > b > 0)$$
>
> has vertices $(0, \pm a)$, endpoints of the minor axis $(\pm b, 0)$, and foci $(0, \pm c)$, where $c^2 = a^2 - b^2$ and $c \geq 0$.

> **NOTE** If $a = b$, then the ellipse becomes a circle with radius $r = a$ and center $(0, 0)$.

Figures 10.23 and 10.24 show two ellipses. The first has a horizontal major axis and the second has a vertical major axis. The coordinates of the vertices V_1 and V_2, foci F_1 and F_2, and endpoints of the minor axis U_1 and U_2 are labeled. In each figure $a > b > 0$.

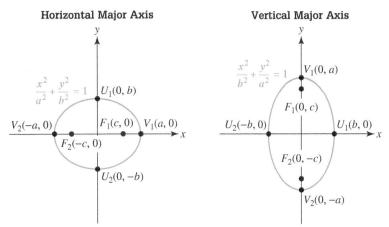

Horizontal Major Axis   **Vertical Major Axis**

Figure 10.23   **Figure 10.24**

NOTE   In every ellipse the major and minor axes are perpendicular bisectors of each other.

MAKING CONNECTIONS

Intercept Form of a Line and Standard Form for an Ellipse   If the equation of a line can be written as

$$\frac{x}{a} + \frac{y}{b} = 1, \qquad \text{Intercept form}$$

then the x-intercept is a and the y-intercept is b. If the equation of an ellipse centered at $(0, 0)$ can be written as

$$\frac{x^2}{a^2} + \frac{y^2}{b^2} = 1, \qquad \text{Standard form}$$

then the x-intercepts are $\pm a$ and the y-intercepts are $\pm b$. See Extended and Discovery Exercises 1–6 at the end of this section.

EXAMPLE 1   Sketching graphs of ellipses

Sketch a graph of each ellipse. Label the vertices, foci, and endpoints of the minor axis.

(a) $\dfrac{x^2}{9} + \dfrac{y^2}{4} = 1$ **(b)** $25x^2 + 16y^2 = 400$

SOLUTION

(a) The equation $\dfrac{x^2}{9} + \dfrac{y^2}{4} = 1$ can be written as $\dfrac{x^2}{3^2} + \dfrac{y^2}{2^2} = 1$ and describes an ellipse with $a = 3$ and $b = 2$. The ellipse has a horizontal major axis with vertices $(\pm 3, 0)$. The endpoints of the minor axis are $(0, \pm 2)$. To locate the foci, find c.

$$c^2 = a^2 - b^2 = 3^2 - 2^2 = 5, \quad \text{or} \quad c = \sqrt{5} \approx 2.24.$$

The foci are located on the major axis, with coordinates $\left(\pm \sqrt{5}, 0 \right)$. See Figure 10.25.

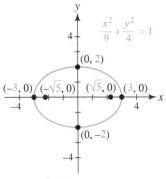

Figure 10.25

(b) The given equation can be written in standard form by dividing each side by 400.

$$25x^2 + 16y^2 = 400 \qquad \textit{Given equation}$$

$$\frac{25x^2}{400} + \frac{16y^2}{400} = \frac{400}{400} \qquad \textit{Divide each side by 400.}$$

$$\frac{x^2}{16} + \frac{y^2}{25} = 1 \qquad \textit{Simplify each fraction.}$$

$$\frac{x^2}{4^2} + \frac{y^2}{5^2} = 1 \qquad \textit{Rewrite the equation.}$$

This ellipse has a vertical major axis with $a = 5$ and $b = 4$. The value of c is given by

$$c^2 = 5^2 - 4^2 = 9, \qquad \text{or} \qquad c = 3.$$

The ellipse has foci $(0, \pm 3)$, vertices $(0, \pm 5)$, and endpoints of the minor axis located at $(\pm 4, 0)$. See Figure 10.26.

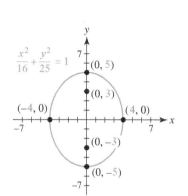

Figure 10.26

> **Now Try Exercises 5 and 9**

In the next two examples, we find standard equations for ellipses.

EXAMPLE 2 Finding the equation of an ellipse

Find the standard equation of the ellipse shown in Figure 10.27. Identify the coordinates of the vertices and the foci.

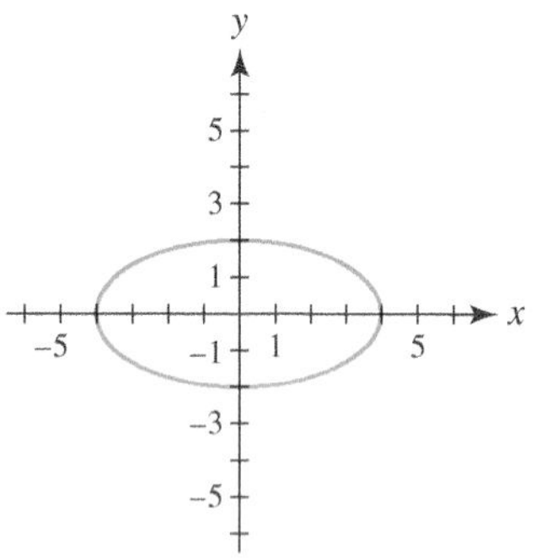

SOLUTION The ellipse is centered at $(0, 0)$ and has a horizontal major axis. Its standard equation has the form

$$\frac{x^2}{a^2} + \frac{y^2}{b^2} = 1.$$

The endpoints of the major axis are $(\pm 4, 0)$, and the endpoints of the minor axis are $(0, \pm 2)$. It follows that $a = 4$ and $b = 2$, and the standard equation is

$$\frac{x^2}{4^2} + \frac{y^2}{2^2} = 1 \qquad \text{or} \qquad \frac{x^2}{16} + \frac{y^2}{4} = 1.$$

The foci lie on the horizontal *major* axis and can be determined as follows.

$$c^2 = a^2 - b^2 = 4^2 - 2^2 = 12$$

Thus $c = \sqrt{12} \approx 3.46$, and the coordinates of the foci are $\left(\pm \sqrt{12}, 0 \right)$. A graph of the ellipse with the vertices and foci plotted is shown in Figure 10.28.

Figure 10.27

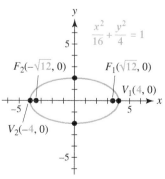

Figure 10.28

> **Now Try Exercise 17**

EXAMPLE 3 Finding the equation of an ellipse

Find the standard equation of the ellipse with foci $(0, \pm 1)$ and vertices $(0, \pm 3)$.

SOLUTION Since the foci and vertices lie on the y-axis, the ellipse has a vertical major axis. Its standard equation has the form

$$\frac{x^2}{b^2} + \frac{y^2}{a^2} = 1.$$

Because the foci are $(0, \pm 1)$ and the vertices are $(0, \pm 3)$, it follows that $c = 1$ and $a = 3$. The value of b^2 can be found by rewriting the equation $c^2 = a^2 - b^2$.

$$b^2 = a^2 - c^2 = 3^2 - 1^2 = 8 \qquad \text{or} \qquad b = \sqrt{8}$$

Thus the equation of the ellipse is $\frac{x^2}{(\sqrt{8})^2} + \frac{y^2}{3^2} = 1$ or $\frac{x^2}{8} + \frac{y^2}{9} = 1$. Its graph is shown in Figure 10.29.

Now Try Exercise 25

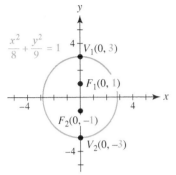

Figure 10.29

Eccentricity and Applications The planets travel around the sun in elliptical orbits. Although their orbits are nearly circular, many have a slight eccentricity to them. The **eccentricity** e of an ellipse is defined by

$$e = \frac{\sqrt{a^2 - b^2}}{a} = \frac{c}{a}. \qquad a > b > 0$$

Since the foci of an ellipse lie *inside* the ellipse, $0 < c < a$ and $0 < \frac{c}{a} < 1$. Therefore the eccentricity e of an ellipse satisfies $0 < e < 1$. If $a = b$, then $e = 0$ and the ellipse becomes a circle. See Figure 10.30. As e increases, the foci spread apart and the ellipse becomes more elongated. See Figures 10.31 and 10.32.

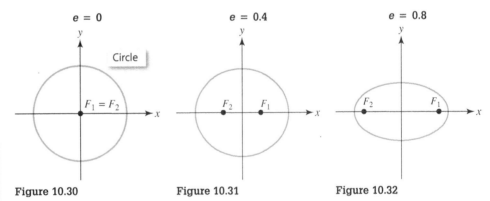

Figure 10.30   Figure 10.31   Figure 10.32

MAKING CONNECTIONS

The Number e and the Variable e Do not confuse the *variable e*, which is used to denote the eccentricity of an ellipse, with the irrational *number* $e \approx 2.72$, which is the base of the natural exponential function $f(x) = e^x$ and of the natural logarithmic function $g(x) = \ln x$.

Astronomers have measured values of a and e for the eight major planets and Pluto. With this information and the fact that the sun is located at one focus of the ellipse, the equations of their orbits can be found.

EXAMPLE 4 Finding the orbital equation for Pluto

Pluto has $a = 39.44$ and $e = 0.249$. (For Earth, $a = 1$.) Graph the orbit of Pluto and the position of the sun in $[-60, 60, 10]$ by $[-40, 40, 10]$. (**Source:** M. Zeilik, *Introductory Astronomy and Astrophysics.*)

SOLUTION Let the orbit of Pluto be given by $\frac{x^2}{a^2} + \frac{y^2}{b^2} = 1$. Then

$$e = \frac{c}{a} = 0.249 \qquad \text{implies} \qquad c = 0.249a = 0.249(39.44) \approx 9.821.$$

To find b, solve the equation $c^2 = a^2 - b^2$ for b.

$$b = \sqrt{a^2 - c^2}$$
$$= \sqrt{39.44^2 - 9.821^2} \approx 38.20$$

Pluto's orbit is modeled by $\dfrac{x^2}{39.44^2} + \dfrac{y^2}{38.20^2} = 1$. Since $c \approx 9.821$, the foci are $(\pm 9.821, 0)$. The sun could be located at either focus. We locate the sun at $(9.821, 0)$.

To graph this ellipse on a graphing calculator, we must solve the equation for y.

$$\frac{x^2}{39.44^2} + \frac{y^2}{38.20^2} = 1$$
$$\frac{y^2}{38.20^2} = 1 - \frac{x^2}{39.44^2}$$
$$\frac{y}{38.20} = \pm\sqrt{1 - \frac{x^2}{39.44^2}}$$
$$y = \pm 38.20\sqrt{1 - \frac{x^2}{39.44^2}}$$

See Figures 10.33 and 10.34.

Graphing Pluto's Orbit

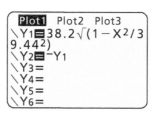

Figure 10.33

$[-60, 60, 10]$ by $[-40, 40, 10]$

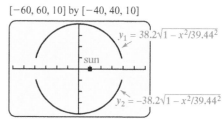

Figure 10.34

Now Try Exercise 93

Reflective Property of Ellipses

Like parabolas, ellipses also have an important reflective property. If an ellipse is rotated about the x-axis, an **ellipsoid** is formed, which resembles the shell of an egg, as illustrated in Figure 10.35. If a light source is placed at focus F_1, then every beam of light emanating from the light source, regardless of its direction, is reflected at the surface of the ellipsoid toward focus F_2. See Figure 10.36

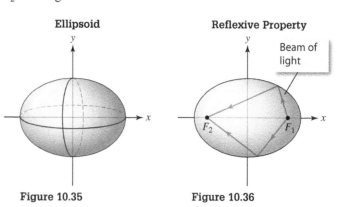

Figure 10.35

Figure 10.36

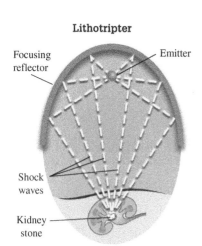

Figure 10.37

An Application   A *lithotripter* is a machine designed to break up kidney stones without surgery, by using the reflexive property of ellipses to focus powerful shock waves. See Figure 10.37. A patient is carefully positioned so that the kidney stone is at one focus, while the source of the shock waves is located at the other focus. The kidney stone absorbs all of the energy from the shock wave and is broken up without harming the patient. In Exercises 95 – 97 this reflective property of ellipses is applied.

Translations of Ellipses

If the equation of an ellipse is given by either $\frac{x^2}{a^2} + \frac{y^2}{b^2} = 1$ or $\frac{x^2}{b^2} + \frac{y^2}{a^2} = 1$, then the center of the ellipse is $(0, 0)$. We can use translations of graphs to find the equation of an ellipse centered at (h, k) by replacing x with $(x - h)$ and y with $(y - k)$.

STANDARD EQUATIONS FOR ELLIPSES CENTERED AT (h, k)

An ellipse with center (h, k) and either a horizontal or a vertical major axis satisfies one of the following equations, where $a > b > 0$ and $c^2 = a^2 - b^2$ with $c \geq 0$.

$$\frac{(x - h)^2}{a^2} + \frac{(y - k)^2}{b^2} = 1 \qquad \text{Horizontal major axis; foci: } (h \pm c, k);$$
$$\text{Vertices: } (h \pm a, k)$$

$$\frac{(x - h)^2}{b^2} + \frac{(y - k)^2}{a^2} = 1 \qquad \text{Vertical major axis; foci: } (h, k \pm c);$$
$$\text{Vertices: } (h, k \pm a)$$

EXAMPLE 5   Translating an ellipse

Translate the ellipse with equation $\frac{x^2}{9} + \frac{y^2}{4} = 1$ so that it is centered at $(-1, 2)$. Find the new equation and sketch its graph.

SOLUTION   To translate the center from $(0, 0)$ to $(-1, 2)$, replace x with $(x - (-1))$ or $(x + 1)$ and replace y with $(y - 2)$. The new equation is

$$\frac{(x + 1)^2}{9} + \frac{(y - 2)^2}{4} = 1.$$

The given ellipse is shown in Figure 10.38, and the translated ellipse is shown in Figure 10.39.

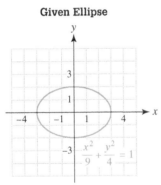

Given Ellipse

Figure 10.38

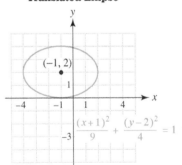

Translated Ellipse

Figure 10.39

Now Try Exercise 33

EXAMPLE 6   Graphing an ellipse with center (h, k)

Graph the ellipse given by $\frac{(x + 2)^2}{16} + \frac{(y - 2)^2}{25} = 1$. Label the vertices and the foci.

SOLUTION   The ellipse has a vertical major axis, and its center is $(-2, 2)$. Since $a^2 = 25$ and $b^2 = 16$, it follows that $c^2 = a^2 - b^2 = 25 - 16 = 9$. Thus $a = 5$, $b = 4$, and $c = 3$. The vertices are located 5 units above and below the center of the ellipse, and the foci are located 3 units above and below the center of the ellipse. That is, the vertices are $(-2, 2 \pm 5)$, or $(-2, 7)$ and $(-2, -3)$, and the foci are $(-2, 2 \pm 3)$, or $(-2, 5)$ and $(-2, -1)$. A graph of the ellipse is shown in Figure 10.40

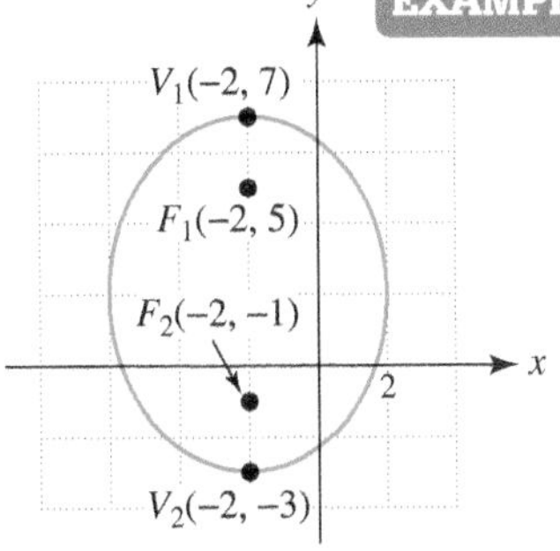

Now Try Exercise 47

Figure 10.40

EXAMPLE 7   Finding the standard equation of an ellipse

Write $4x^2 - 16x + 9y^2 + 54y + 61 = 0$ in the standard form for an ellipse centered at (h, k). Identify the center and the vertices.

SOLUTION   We can write the given equation in standard form by completing the square.

$$4x^2 - 16x + 9y^2 + 54y + 61 = 0 \qquad \textit{Given equation}$$
$$4(x^2 - 4x + \underline{}) + 9(y^2 + 6y + \underline{}) = -61 \qquad \textit{Distributive property}$$
$$4(x^2 - 4x + \underline{4}) + 9(y^2 + 6y + \underline{9}) = -61 + 16 + 81 \qquad \textit{Complete the square.}$$
$$4(x - 2)^2 + 9(y + 3)^2 = 36 \qquad \textit{Perfect square trinomials}$$
$$\frac{(x - 2)^2}{9} + \frac{(y + 3)^2}{4} = 1 \qquad \textit{Divide each side by 36.}$$

The center is $(2, -3)$. Because the major axis is horizontal and $a = 3$, the vertices of the ellipse are $(2 \pm 3, -3)$, or $(5, -3)$ and $(-1, -3)$.

Now Try Exercise 57

More Nonlinear Systems of Equations

In Sections 9.1 and 9.2 we discussed systems of equations and inequalities. In this and the next subsections we revisit these topics.

EXAMPLE 8   Solving a nonlinear system of equations

Use substitution to solve the following system of equations. Give graphical support.

$$9x^2 + 4y^2 = 36$$
$$12x^2 + y^2 = 12$$

SOLUTION

STEP 1: Begin by solving the second equation for y^2 to obtain $y^2 = 12 - 12x^2$.

STEP 2: Next, substitute $(12 - 12x^2)$ for y^2 in the first equation and solve for x.

$$9x^2 + 4y^2 = 36 \qquad \textit{First equation}$$
$$9x^2 + 4(12 - 12x^2) = 36 \qquad \textit{Let } y^2 = 12 - 12x^2.$$
$$9x^2 + 48 - 48x^2 = 36 \qquad \textit{Distributive property}$$
$$-39x^2 = -12 \qquad \textit{Subtract 48; simplify.}$$
$$x^2 = \frac{4}{13} \qquad \textit{Divide by } -39; \textit{ simplify.}$$
$$x = \pm\sqrt{\frac{4}{13}} \qquad \textit{Square root property}$$

Four Solutions

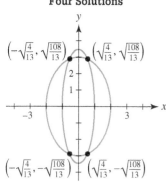

Figure 10.41

STEP 3: To determine the y-values, substitute $x^2 = \frac{4}{13}$ in $y^2 = 12 - 12x^2$.

$$y^2 = 12 - 12\left(\frac{4}{13}\right) = \frac{108}{13}, \quad \text{or} \quad y = \pm\sqrt{\frac{108}{13}}$$

There are four solutions: $\left(\pm\sqrt{\frac{4}{13}}, \pm\sqrt{\frac{108}{13}}\right)$.

To graph the system of equations by hand, put each equation in standard form by dividing the first given equation by 36 and the second given equation by 12.

$$\frac{x^2}{4} + \frac{y^2}{9} = 1 \qquad \text{and} \qquad x^2 + \frac{y^2}{12} = 1$$

The graphs of these ellipses and the four solutions are shown in Figure 10.41.

Now Try Exercise 71

NOTE The system of equations in Example 8 could also be solved by elimination. To do this, multiply the second equation by -4 and then add the equations.

More Nonlinear Systems of Inequalities

In the next example, we solve a nonlinear system of inequalities whose graph involves a parabola and an ellipse.

EXAMPLE 9   Solving a nonlinear inequality

Shade the region in the xy-plane that satisfies the system of inequalities.

$$36x^2 + 25y^2 \leq 900$$
$$x + (y + 2)^2 \leq 4$$

SOLUTION   Before sketching a graph, rewrite these two inequalities as follows.

First Inequality: $\dfrac{36}{900}x^2 + \dfrac{25}{900}y^2 \leq \dfrac{900}{900}$ Divide each term by 900.

$\dfrac{x^2}{25} + \dfrac{y^2}{36} \leq 1$ Simplify to standard form.

Second Inequality: $(y + 2)^2 \leq -x + 4$ Subtract x.

$(y + 2)^2 \leq -(x - 4)$ Distributive property

   The first inequality represents the region inside an ellipse, as shown in Figure 10.42. The second inequality represents the region left of a parabola that opens to the left with vertex $(4, -2)$, as shown in Figure 10.43. The solution set for the system, which satisfies both inequalities, is shaded in Figure 10.44. (To verify this, try the test point $(-2, -2)$.)

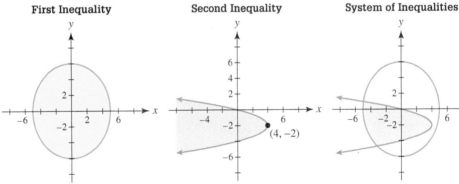

Figure 10.42   Figure 10.43   Figure 10.44

Now Try Exercise 87

Area Inside an Ellipse   The following formula can be used to calculate the area inside an ellipse.

CLASS DISCUSSION

Explain why the area formula for an ellipse is a generalization of the area formula for a circle.

AREA INSIDE AN ELLIPSE

The area A of the region contained inside an ellipse is given by $A = \pi ab$, where a and b are from the standard equation of the ellipse.

This formula is applied in the next example.

EXAMPLE 10 Finding the area inside an ellipse

Shade the region in the xy-plane that satisfies the inequality $x^2 + 4y^2 \leq 4$. Find the area of this region if units are in inches.

SOLUTION Begin by dividing each term in the given inequality by 4.

Elliptical Region

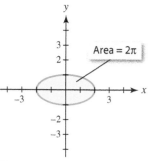

$$x^2 + 4y^2 \leq 4 \qquad \text{Given inequality}$$

$$\frac{x^2}{4} + \frac{4y^2}{4} \leq \frac{4}{4} \qquad \text{Divide by 4.}$$

$a = 2$
$b = 1$
$$\frac{x^2}{4} + \frac{y^2}{1} \leq 1 \qquad \text{Simplify the fractions.}$$

Figure 10.45

The boundary of the region is the ellipse $\frac{x^2}{4} + \frac{y^2}{1} = 1$. The region *inside* the ellipse satisfies the inequality. To verify this fact, note that the test point $(0, 0)$, which is located inside the ellipse, satisfies the inequality. The solution set is shaded in Figure 10.45. The area of this elliptical region with $a = 2$ and $b = 1$ is

$$A = \pi ab = \pi(2)(1) = 2\pi \approx 6.28 \text{ square inches.}$$

Now Try Exercise 89

10.2 Putting It All Together

The following table summarizes some important concepts about ellipses.

CONCEPT	EQUATION	EXAMPLE
Ellipse with center $(0, 0)$	Standard equation with $a > b > 0$ Horizontal major axis: $$\frac{x^2}{a^2} + \frac{y^2}{b^2} = 1$$ Vertical major axis: $$\frac{x^2}{b^2} + \frac{y^2}{a^2} = 1$$ See the box on page 808.	$\frac{x^2}{4} + \frac{y^2}{9} = 1; a = 3, b = 2$ Center: $(0, 0)$; major axis: vertical Vertices; $(0, \pm 3)$; foci: $\left(0, \pm \sqrt{5}\right)$ $\left(c^2 = a^2 - b^2 = 9 - 4 = 5, \text{ so } c = \sqrt{5}.\right)$

CONCEPT	EQUATION	EXAMPLE
Ellipse with center (h, k)	Standard equation with $a > b > 0$ Horizontal major axis: $$\frac{(x - h)^2}{a^2} + \frac{(y - k)^2}{b^2} = 1$$ Vertical major axis: $$\frac{(x - h)^2}{b^2} + \frac{(y - k)^2}{a^2} = 1$$ See the box on page 813.	$\frac{(x - 1)^2}{4} + \frac{(y + 1)^2}{9} = 1; a = 3, b = 2$ Center: $(1, -1)$; major axis: vertical Vertices: $(1, -1 \pm 3)$; foci: $\left(1, -1 \pm \sqrt{5}\right)$ $\left(c^2 = a^2 - b^2 = 9 - 4 = 5, \text{ so } c = \sqrt{5}.\right)$ 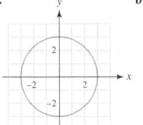
Area inside an ellipse	$A = \pi a b$	The area inside the ellipse given by $\frac{x^2}{49} + \frac{y^2}{9} = 1$ is $$A = \pi(7)(3) = 21\pi \text{ square units.}$$

10.2 Exercises

Basic Concepts

1. The endpoints of the major axis of an ellipse are called the _____ of the ellipse.

2. The foci of an ellipse are located on the _____ axis.

3. An ellipse with equation $\frac{x^2}{a^2} + \frac{y^2}{b^2} = 1$ $(a > b > 0)$ has a(n) <u>vertical/horizontal</u> major axis.

4. An ellipse with equation $\frac{x^2}{b^2} + \frac{y^2}{a^2} = 1$ $(a > b > 0)$ has a(n) <u>vertical/horizontal</u> major axis.

Ellipses with Center (0, 0)

Exercises 5–12: Graph the ellipse. Label the foci and the endpoints of each axis.

5. $\frac{x^2}{4} + \frac{y^2}{9} = 1$

6. $\frac{x^2}{9} + \frac{y^2}{4} = 1$

7. $\frac{x^2}{36} + \frac{y^2}{16} = 1$

8. $x^2 + \frac{y^2}{4} = 1$

9. $x^2 + 4y^2 = 400$

10. $9x^2 + 5y^2 = 45$

11. $25x^2 + 9y^2 = 225$

12. $5x^2 + 4y^2 = 20$

Exercises 13–16: Match the equation with its graph (a–d).

13. $\frac{x^2}{16} + \frac{y^2}{36} = 1$

14. $\frac{x^2}{4} + y^2 = 1$

15. $\frac{x^2}{16} + \frac{y^2}{4} = 1$

16. $\frac{x^2}{9} + \frac{y^2}{9} = 1$

a.
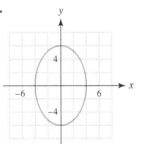

b.
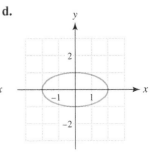

c.
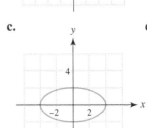

d.

Exercises 17–20: Find the standard equation of the ellipse shown in the figure. Identify the coordinates of the vertices, endpoints of the minor axis, and the foci.

17.

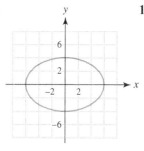

18.

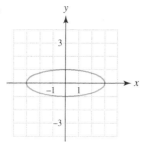

19.

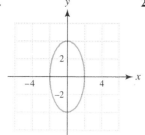

20.

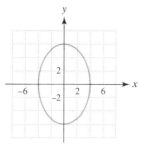

Exercises 21–24: The foci F_1 and F_2, vertices V_1 and V_2, and endpoints U_1 and U_2 of the minor axis of an ellipse are labeled in the figure. Graph the ellipse and find its standard equation. (The coordinates of V_1, V_2, F_1, and F_2 are integers.)

21.

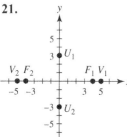

22.

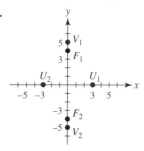

23.

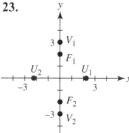

24.

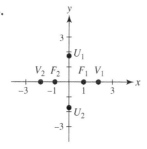

Exercises 25–32: Find an equation of the ellipse, centered at the origin, satisfying the conditions.

25. Foci $(0, \pm 2)$, vertices $(0, \pm 4)$

26. Foci $(0, \pm 3)$, vertices $(0, \pm 5)$

27. Foci $(\pm 5, 0)$, vertices $(\pm 6, 0)$

28. Foci $(\pm 4, 0)$, vertices $(\pm 6, 0)$

29. Horizontal major axis of length 8, minor axis of length 6

30. Vertical major axis of length 12, minor axis of length 8

31. Eccentricity $\frac{2}{3}$, horizontal major axis of length 6

32. Eccentricity $\frac{3}{4}$, vertices $(0, \pm 8)$

Ellipses with Center (h, k)

Exercises 33–36: Translate the ellipse with the given equation so that it is centered at the given point. Find the new equation and sketch its graph.

33. $\dfrac{x^2}{4} + \dfrac{y^2}{3} = 1; (2, -1)$ **34.** $\dfrac{x^2}{9} + \dfrac{y^2}{2} = 1; (-3, 7)$

35. $\dfrac{x^2}{2} + \dfrac{y^2}{9} = 1; (-3, -4)$ **36.** $\dfrac{x^2}{15} + \dfrac{y^2}{16} = 1; (5, -6)$

Exercises 37–42: Sketch a graph of the ellipse.

37. $\dfrac{(x-2)^2}{4} + \dfrac{(y-1)^2}{9} = 1$

38. $\dfrac{(x+1)^2}{16} + \dfrac{(y+3)^2}{9} = 1$

39. $\dfrac{(x+1)^2}{16} + \dfrac{(y+2)^2}{25} = 1$

40. $\dfrac{(x-4)^2}{9} + \dfrac{y^2}{4} = 1$ **41.** $\dfrac{(x+2)^2}{4} + y^2 = 1$

42. $x^2 + \dfrac{(y-3)^2}{4} = 1$

Exercises 43–46: Match the equation with its graph (a–d).

43. $\dfrac{(x-2)^2}{16} + \dfrac{(y+4)^2}{36} = 1$

44. $\dfrac{(x+1)^2}{4} + \dfrac{y^2}{9} = 1$

45. $\dfrac{(x+1)^2}{9} + \dfrac{(y-1)^2}{4} = 1$

46. $\dfrac{x^2}{25} + \dfrac{(y+1)^2}{10} = 1$

a.

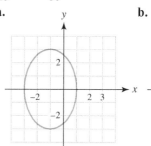

b.

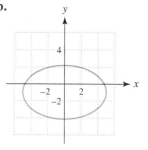

c.

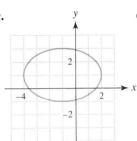

d.

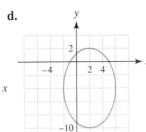

Exercises 47–50: Sketch a graph of the ellipse. Identify the foci and vertices.

47. $\dfrac{(x-1)^2}{9} + \dfrac{(y-1)^2}{25} = 1$

48. $\dfrac{(x+2)^2}{25} + \dfrac{(y+1)^2}{16} = 1$

49. $\dfrac{(x+4)^2}{16} + \dfrac{(y-2)^2}{9} = 1$

50. $\dfrac{x^2}{4} + \dfrac{(y-1)^2}{9} = 1$

Exercises 51–54: Find an equation of an ellipse that satisfies the given conditions.

51. Center $(2, 1)$, focus $(2, 3)$, and vertex $(2, 4)$

52. Center $(-3, -2)$, focus $(-1, -2)$, and vertex $(1, -2)$

53. Vertices $(\pm 3, 2)$ and foci $(\pm 2, 2)$

54. Vertices $(-1, \pm 3)$ and foci $(-1, \pm 1)$

Exercises 55 and 56: Find an (approximate) equation of the ellipse shown in the figure.

55.

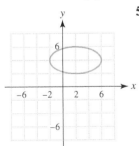

56.

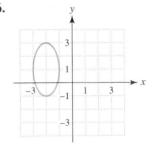

Exercises 57–64: (Refer to Example 7.) Write the equation in standard form for an ellipse centered at (h, k). Identify the center and the vertices.

57. $9x^2 + 18x + 4y^2 - 8y - 23 = 0$

58. $9x^2 - 36x + 16y^2 - 64y - 44 = 0$

59. $4x^2 + 8x + y^2 + 2y + 1 = 0$

60. $x^2 - 6x + 9y^2 = 0$

61. $4x^2 + 16x + 5y^2 - 10y + 1 = 0$

62. $2x^2 + 4x + 3y^2 - 18y + 23 = 0$

63. $16x^2 - 16x + 4y^2 + 12y = 51$

64. $16x^2 + 48x + 4y^2 - 20y + 57 = 0$

Graphing Ellipses with Technology

Exercises 65–68: Graph the ellipse.

65. $\dfrac{x^2}{15} + \dfrac{y^2}{10} = 1$

66. $\dfrac{(x-1.2)^2}{7.1} + \dfrac{y^2}{3.5} = 1$

67. $4.1x^2 + 6.3y^2 = 25$

68. $\frac{1}{2}x^2 + \frac{1}{3}y^2 = \frac{1}{6}$

Solving Equations and Inequalities

Exercises 69–74: Solve the system of equations. Give graphical support by making a sketch.

69. $\dfrac{x^2}{4} + \dfrac{y^2}{9} = 1$
$x + y = 3$

70. $\dfrac{x^2}{16} + \dfrac{y^2}{25} = 1$
$-2x + y = 5$

71. $4x^2 + 16y^2 = 64$
$x^2 + y^2 = 9$

72. $4x^2 + y^2 = 4$
$x^2 + y^2 = 2$

73. $x^2 + y^2 = 9$
$2x^2 + 3y^2 = 18$

74. $x^2 + y^2 = 4$
$(x-1)^2 + y^2 = 4$

Exercises 75–80: Solve the system of equations.

75. $\dfrac{x^2}{2} + \dfrac{y^2}{4} = 1$
$-x^2 + 2y = 4$

76. $x^2 + \frac{1}{9}y^2 = 1$
$x + y = 3$

77. $\dfrac{x^2}{2} + \dfrac{y^2}{4} = 1$
$\dfrac{x^2}{4} + \dfrac{y^2}{2} = 1$

78. $\dfrac{x^2}{5} + \dfrac{y^2}{10} = 1$
$\dfrac{x^2}{10} + \dfrac{y^2}{5} = 1$

79. $(x-2)^2 + y^2 = 9$
$x^2 + y^2 = 9$

80. $(x-2) - y^2 = 0$
$\dfrac{x^2}{4} + \dfrac{y^2}{9} = 1$

Exercises 81–88: Shade the solution set to the system.

81. $(x-1)^2 + (y+1)^2 < 4$
$(x+1)^2 + y^2 > 1$

82. $\dfrac{x^2}{16} + \dfrac{y^2}{25} < 1$
$\dfrac{x^2}{4} + \dfrac{y^2}{9} > 1$

83. $\dfrac{x^2}{4} + \dfrac{y^2}{9} \le 1$
$x + y \ge 2$

84. $\dfrac{x^2}{16} + \dfrac{y^2}{25} \le 1$
$-x + y \le 4$

85. $\quad x^2 + y^2 \le 4$
$\quad x^2 + (y - 2)^2 \le 4$

86. $x^2 + (y + 1)^2 \le 9$
$\quad (x + 1)^2 + y^2 \le 9$

87. $\quad x^2 + y^2 \le 4$
$\quad (x + 1)^2 - y \le 0$

88. $\quad 4x^2 + 9y^2 \le 36$
$\quad x - (y - 2)^2 \ge 0$

Exercises 89–92: (Refer to Example 10.) Shade the region in the xy-plane that satisfies the given inequality. Find the area of this region if units are in feet.

89. $4x^2 + 9y^2 \le 36$

90. $9x^2 + y^2 \le 9$

91. $\dfrac{(x - 1)^2}{25} + \dfrac{(y + 2)^2}{16} \le 1$

92. $\dfrac{(x + 3)^2}{4} + \dfrac{(y - 2)^2}{8} \le 1$

Applications

Exercises 93 and 94: **Orbits of Planets** *(Refer to Example 4.) Find an equation for the orbit of the planet. Graph its orbit and the location of the sun at a focus on the positive x-axis.*

93. Mercury: $e = 0.206, a = 0.387$

94. Mars: $e = 0.093, a = 1.524$

95. Lithotripter (Refer to the discussion in this section.) The source of a shock wave is placed at one focus of an ellipsoid with a major axis of 8 inches and a minor axis of 5 inches. Estimate, to the nearest thousandth of an inch, how far a kidney stone should be positioned from the source.

96. Shape of a Lithotripter A patient's kidney stone is placed 12 units away from the source of the shock waves of a lithotripter. The lithotripter is based on an ellipse with a minor axis that measures 16 units. Find the equation of an ellipse that would satisfy this situation.

97. Whispering Gallery A large room constructed in the shape of the upper half of an ellipsoid has a unique property. Any sound emanating from one focus is reflected directly toward the other focus. See the figure. If the foci are 100 feet apart and the maximum height of the ceiling is 40 feet, estimate the area of the floor of the room.

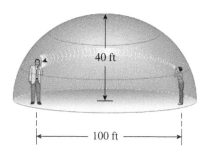

98. Halley's Comet Halley's comet travels in an elliptical orbit with $a = 17.95$ and $b = 4.44$ and passes by Earth roughly every 76 years. Note that each unit represents one astronomical unit, or 93 million miles. The comet most recently passed by Earth in February 1986. (*Source:* M. Zeilik, *Introductory Astronomy and Astrophysics.*)

(a) Write an equation for this orbit, centered at (0, 0) with major axis on the *x*-axis.

(b) If the sun lies (at the focus) on the positive *x*-axis, approximate its coordinates.

(c) Determine the maximum and minimum distances between Halley's comet and the sun.

99. The Roman Colosseum The perimeter of the Roman Colosseum is an ellipse with major axis 620 feet and minor axis 513 feet. Find the distance between the foci of this ellipse.

100. Orbit of Earth (Refer to Example 4.) Earth has a nearly circular orbit with $e \approx 0.0167$ and $a = 93$ million miles. Approximate the minimum and maximum distances between Earth and the sun. (*Source:* M. Zeilik, *Introductory Astronomy and Astrophysics.*)

101. Arch Bridge An elliptical arch under a bridge is constructed so that it is 60 feet wide and has a maximum height of 25 feet, as illustrated in the figure. Find the height of the arch 15 feet from the center of the arch.

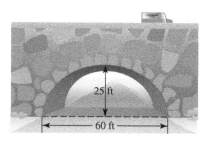

102. Perimeter of an Ellipse The perimeter P of an ellipse can be approximated by

$$P \approx 2\pi\sqrt{\dfrac{a^2 + b^2}{2}}.$$

(a) Approximate the distance in miles that Mercury travels in one orbit of the sun if $a = 36.0$, $b = 35.2$, and the units are in millions of miles.

(b) If a planet has a circular orbit, does this formula give the *exact* perimeter? Explain.

103. Satellite Orbit The orbit of *Explorer VII* and the outline of Earth's surface are shown in the figure at the top of the next column. This orbit can be described by the equation $\dfrac{x^2}{a^2} + \dfrac{y^2}{b^2} = 1$, where $a = 4464$ and $b = 4462$. The surface of Earth can be described by $(x - 164)^2 + y^2 = 3960^2$. Find the maximum and minimum heights of the satellite above Earth's surface if all units are in miles. (*Sources:* W. Loh; W. Thomson.)

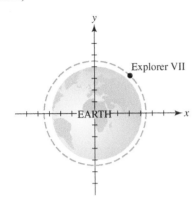

104. Orbital Velocity The maximum and minimum velocities in kilometers per second of a celestial body moving in an elliptical orbit can be calculated by

$$v_{max} = \frac{2\pi a}{P}\sqrt{\frac{1+e}{1-e}} \quad \text{and} \quad v_{min} = \frac{2\pi a}{P}\sqrt{\frac{1-e}{1+e}}.$$

In these equations, a is half the length of the major axis of the orbit in kilometers, P is the orbital period in seconds, and e is the eccentricity of the orbit. (*Source:* M. Zeilik.)

(a) Find v_{max} and v_{min} for Pluto if $a = 5.913 \times 10^9$ kilometers, the period is $P = 2.86 \times 10^{12}$ seconds, and the eccentricity is $e = 0.249$.

(b) If a planet has a circular orbit, what can be said about its orbital velocity?

Writing about Mathematics

105. Explain how the distance between the foci of an ellipse affects the shape of the ellipse.

106. Given the standard equation of an ellipse, explain how to determine the length of the major axis. How can you determine whether the major axis is vertical or horizontal?

Extended and Discovery Exercises

Exercises 1–4: (Refer to the first Making Connections in this Section.) Write in intercept form the equation of the line satisfying the given conditions. Then find the x- and y-intercepts of the line.

1. Passing through $(-2, 6)$ and $(4, -3)$

2. Passing through $(-6, -4)$ and $(3, 8)$

3. Slope -2, passing through $(3, -1)$

4. Slope 4, passing through $(-2, 1)$

Exercises 5 and 6: (Refer to the first Making Connections in this Section.) Find the x- and y-intercepts of the ellipse.

5. $\dfrac{x^2}{25} + \dfrac{y^2}{9} = 1$

6. Vertices $(0, \pm 13)$ and foci $(0, \pm 12)$

CHECKING BASIC CONCEPTS FOR SECTIONS 10.1 AND 10.2

1. Graph the parabola defined by $x = \frac{1}{2}y^2$. Include the focus and directrix.

2. Find an equation of the parabola with focus $(-1, 0)$ and directrix $y = 3$.

3. Graph the ellipse defined by $\frac{x^2}{36} + \frac{y^2}{100} = 1$. Include the foci and label the major and minor axes.

4. Find an equation of the ellipse centered at $(3, -2)$ with a vertical major axis of length 6 and minor axis of length 4. What are the coordinates of the foci?

5. A parabolic reflector for a searchlight has a diameter of 4 feet and a depth of 1 foot. How far from the vertex should the filament of the light bulb be located?

6. Solve the nonlinear system of equations.

$$x^2 + y^2 = 10$$
$$2x^2 + 3y^2 = 29$$

7. Write $x^2 - 4x + 4y^2 + 8y - 8 = 0$ in the standard form for an ellipse centered at (h, k). Identify the center and the vertices.

10.3 Hyperbolas

- **Find equations of hyperbolas**
- **Graph hyperbolas**
- **Learn the reflective property of hyperbolas**
- **Translate hyperbolas**

Introduction

Hyperbolas have several interesting properties. For example, if a comet passes by the sun with a high velocity, then the sun's gravity may not be strong enough to cause the comet to go into orbit; instead, the comet will pass by the sun just once and follow a trajectory that can be described by a hyperbola. Hyperbolas also have a reflective property, which is used in telescopes. In this section we look at some basic properties of hyperbolas.

Equations and Graphs of Hyperbolas

A third type of conic section is a hyperbola.

> **HYPERBOLA**
>
> A **hyperbola** is the set of points in a plane, the difference of whose distances from two fixed points is constant. Each fixed point is called a **focus** of the hyperbola.

The following See the Concept shows some of the important features of hyperbolas.

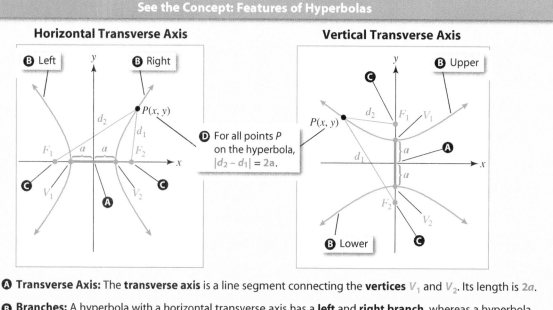

See the Concept: Features of Hyperbolas

Ⓐ Transverse Axis: The **transverse axis** is a line segment connecting the **vertices** V_1 and V_2. Its length is **2a**.

Ⓑ Branches: A hyperbola with a horizontal transverse axis has a **left** and **right branch**, whereas a hyperbola with a vertical transverse axis has an **upper** and **lower branch**.

Ⓒ Foci: The **foci** (singular focus) are points located on a line that is an extention of the transverse axis of the hyperbola.

Ⓓ For any point P located at (x, y) on the hyperbola, the difference $|d_2 - d_1|$ always equals **2a**.

Two hyperbolas are shown in Figures 10.46 and 10.47. The vertices, $(\pm a, 0)$ or $(0, \pm a)$, and foci, $(\pm c, 0)$ or $(0, \pm c)$, are labeled. A line segment connecting the points $(0, \pm b)$ in Figure 10.46 and $(\pm b, 0)$ in Figure 10.47 is the **conjugate axis**. The dashed lines $y = \pm \frac{b}{a}x$ and $y = \pm \frac{a}{b}x$ are **asymptotes** for the respective hyperbolas. They can be used as an aid in graphing. The dashed rectangle is called the **fundamental rectangle**.

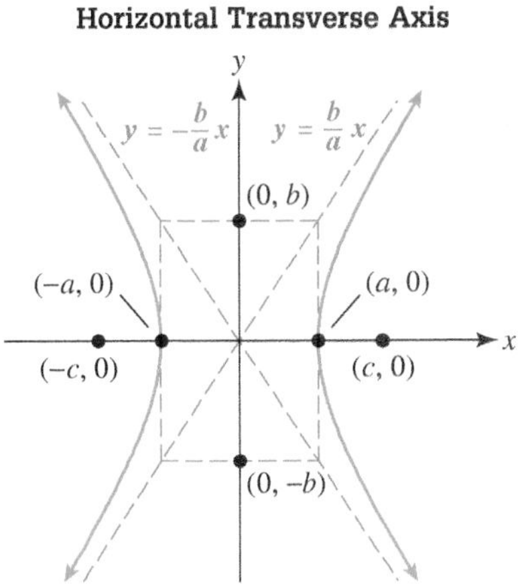

Horizontal Transverse Axis

Figure 10.46

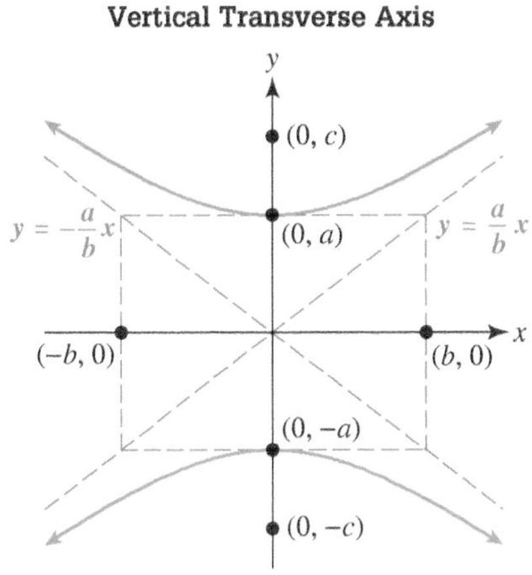

Vertical Transverse Axis

Figure 10.47

By the vertical line test, a hyperbola cannot be represented by a function, but many can be described by the following equations. The constants a, b, and c are *positive*.

STANDARD EQUATIONS FOR HYPERBOLAS CENTERED AT (0, 0)

The hyperbola with center at the origin, *horizontal* transverse axis, and equation

$$\frac{x^2}{a^2} - \frac{y^2}{b^2} = 1$$

has asymptotes $y = \pm \frac{b}{a}x$, vertices $(\pm a, 0)$, and foci $(\pm c, 0)$, where $c^2 = a^2 + b^2$. The hyperbola with center at the origin, *vertical* transverse axis, and equation

$$\frac{y^2}{a^2} - \frac{x^2}{b^2} = 1$$

has asymptotes $y = \pm \frac{a}{b}x$, vertices $(0, \pm a)$, and foci $(0, \pm c)$, where $c^2 = a^2 + b^2$.

EXAMPLE 1   Sketching the graph of a hyperbola

Sketch a graph of $\frac{x^2}{4} - \frac{y^2}{9} = 1$. Label the vertices, foci, and asymptotes.

SOLUTION   The equation is in standard form with $a = 2$ and $b = 3$. It has a horizontal transverse axis with vertices $(\pm 2, 0)$. The endpoints of the conjugate axis are $(0, \pm 3)$. To locate the foci, find c.

$$c^2 = a^2 + b^2 = 2^2 + 3^2 = 13, \quad \text{or} \quad c = \sqrt{13} \approx 3.61.$$

The foci are $\left(\pm \sqrt{13}, 0 \right)$. The asymptotes are $y = \pm \frac{b}{a}x$, or $y = \pm \frac{3}{2}x$. See Figure 10.48.

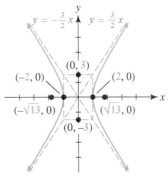

Figure 10.48

Now Try Exercise 5

NOTE A hyperbola consists of two solid (blue) curves, or branches. The asymptotes, foci, transverse axis, conjugate axis, and fundamental (dashed) rectangle are not part of the hyperbola, but are aids for sketching its graph.

An Application of Conic Sections One interpretation of an asymptote relates to trajectories of comets as they approach the sun. Comets travel in parabolic, elliptic, or hyperbolic trajectories. If the speed of a comet is too slow, the gravitational pull of the sun will capture the comet in an elliptical orbit. See Figure 10.49. If the speed of the comet is too fast, the comet will pass by the sun once in a hyperbolic trajectory; farther from the sun, gravity becomes weaker and the comet will eventually return to a straight-line trajectory that is determined by the *asymptote* of the hyperbola. See Figure 10.50. Finally, if the speed is neither too slow nor too fast, the comet will travel in a parabolic path. See Figure 10.51. In all three cases, the sun is located at a focus of the conic section.

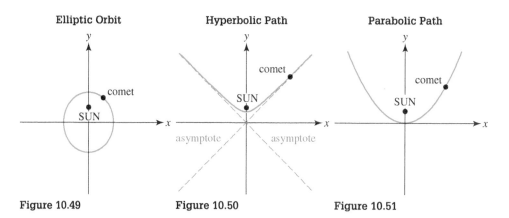

Figure 10.49   Figure 10.50   Figure 10.51

EXAMPLE 2 Finding the equation of a hyperbola

Find the equation of the hyperbola centered at the origin with a vertical transverse axis of length 6 and focus (0, 5). Also find the equations of its asymptotes.

SOLUTION Since the hyperbola is centered at the origin with a vertical transverse axis, its equation is $\frac{y^2}{a^2} - \frac{x^2}{b^2} = 1$. The transverse axis has length $6 = 2a$, so $a = 3$. Since one focus is located at (0, 5), it follows that $c = 5$. We can find b by using the following equation.

$$b^2 = c^2 - a^2$$
$$b = \sqrt{c^2 - a^2}$$
$$b = \sqrt{5^2 - 3^2} = 4$$

The standard equation of this hyperbola is $\frac{y^2}{9} - \frac{x^2}{16} = 1$. Its asymptotes are $y = \pm \frac{a}{b}x$, or $y = \pm \frac{3}{4}x$.

Now Try Exercise 23

EXAMPLE 3 Finding the equation of a hyperbola

Find the standard equation of the hyperbola shown in Figure 10.52. Identify the vertices, foci, and asymptotes.

SOLUTION

Getting Started Because the hyperbola is centered at (0, 0) with a horizontal transverse axis, its equation has the form

$$\frac{x^2}{a^2} - \frac{y^2}{b^2} = 1.$$

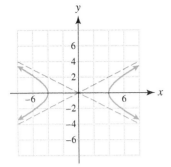

Figure 10.52

Sketch the fundamental rectangle first. Half of its length equals a, and half of its width equals b. ▶

In Figure 10.53 the fundamental rectangle is determined by the four points $(\pm 4, 0)$ and $(0, \pm 2)$, and its diagonals correspond to the asymptotes. It follows that $a = 4$ and $b = 2$. Thus the standard equation of the hyperbola is

$$\frac{x^2}{4^2} - \frac{y^2}{2^2} = 1 \quad \text{or} \quad \frac{x^2}{16} - \frac{y^2}{4} = 1.$$

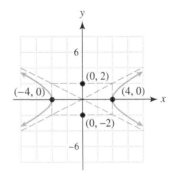

Figure 10.53

The vertices are $(\pm 4, 0)$, and the asymptotes are $y = \pm \frac{1}{2} x$. To find the foci, find c.

$$c^2 = a^2 + b^2 = 4^2 + 2^2 = 20, \quad \text{or} \quad c = \sqrt{20}.$$

The foci are $\left(\pm \sqrt{20}, 0 \right)$.

Now Try Exercise 41

Using Technology In the next example, a graphing calculator is used to graph a hyperbola.

EXAMPLE 4 Graphing a hyperbola with technology

Use a graphing calculator to graph $\frac{y^2}{4.2} - \frac{x^2}{8.4} = 1$.

SOLUTION Begin by solving the given equation for y.

$$\frac{y^2}{4.2} = 1 + \frac{x^2}{8.4} \qquad \text{Add } \tfrac{x^2}{8.4}.$$

$$y^2 = 4.2\left(1 + \frac{x^2}{8.4} \right) \qquad \text{Multiply by 4.2.}$$

$$y = \pm \sqrt{4.2\left(1 + \frac{x^2}{8.4} \right)} \qquad \text{Square root property}$$

Graph $Y_1 = \sqrt{(4.2(1 + X^\wedge 2/8.4))}$ and $Y_2 = -\sqrt{(4.2(1 + X^\wedge 2/8.4))}$. See Figures 10.54 and 10.55.

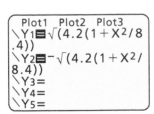

Figure 10.54

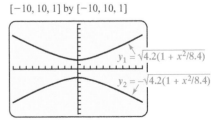

$[-10, 10, 1]$ by $[-10, 10, 1]$

Figure 10.55

Now Try Exercise 59

Reflective Property of Hyperbolas

Hyperbolas have an important reflective property. If a hyperbola is rotated about its transverse axis, a **hyperboloid** is formed, as illustrated in Figure 10.56. Any beam of light that is directed toward focus F_1 will be reflected by the hyperboloid toward focus F_2. See Figure 10.57.

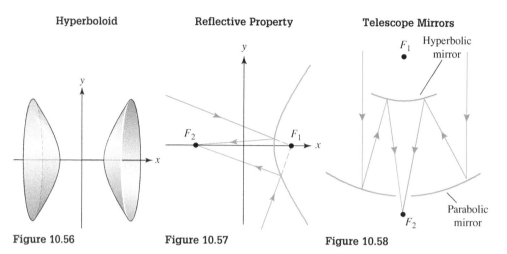

| Hyperboloid | Reflective Property | Telescope Mirrors |

Figure 10.56   Figure 10.57   Figure 10.58

An Application   Telescopes sometimes make use of both parabolic and hyperbolic mirrors, as shown in Figure 10.58. When parallel rays of light from distant stars strike the large parabolic (primary) mirror, they are reflected toward its focus, F_1. A smaller hyperbolic (secondary) mirror is placed so that its focus is also located at F_1. Light rays striking the hyperbolic mirror are reflected toward its other focus, F_2, through a small hole in the parabolic mirror, and into an eye piece. See Exercise 72.

Translations of Hyperbolas

If the equation of a hyperbola is either $\frac{x^2}{a^2} - \frac{y^2}{b^2} = 1$ or $\frac{y^2}{a^2} - \frac{x^2}{b^2} = 1$ then the center of the hyperbola is $(0, 0)$. We can use translations of graphs to find the equation of a hyperbola centered at (h, k) by replacing x with $(x - h)$ and y with $(y - k)$. The constants a, b, and c are positive.

STANDARD EQUATIONS FOR HYPERBOLAS CENTERED AT (h, k)

A hyperbola with center (h, k) and either a horizontal or a vertical transverse axis satisfies one of the following equations, where $c^2 = a^2 + b^2$.

$$\frac{(x - h)^2}{a^2} - \frac{(y - k)^2}{b^2} = 1$$

Transverse axis: horizontal
Vertices: $(h \pm a, k)$; foci: $(h \pm c, k)$
Asymptotes: $y = \pm \frac{b}{a}(x - h) + k$

$$\frac{(y - k)^2}{a^2} - \frac{(x - h)^2}{b^2} = 1$$

Transverse axis: vertical
Vertices: $(h, k \pm a)$; foci: $(h, k \pm c)$
Asymptotes: $y = \pm \frac{a}{b}(x - h) + k$

EXAMPLE 5   Graphing a hyperbola with center (h, k)

Graph the hyperbola whose equation is $\frac{(y + 2)^2}{9} - \frac{(x - 2)^2}{16} = 1$. Label the vertices, foci, and asymptotes.

SOLUTION   The hyperbola has a vertical transverse axis, and its center is $(2, -2)$. Since $a^2 = 9$ and $b^2 = 16$, it follows that $c^2 = a^2 + b^2 = 9 + 16 = 25$. Thus $a = 3$, $b = 4$,

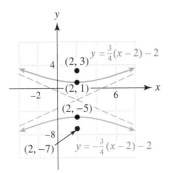

Figure 10.59

and $c = 5$. The vertices are located 3 units above and below the center of the hyperbola, and the foci are located 5 units above and below the center of the hyperbola. That is, the vertices are $(2, -2 \pm 3)$, or $(2, 1)$ and $(2, -5)$, and the foci are $(2, -2 \pm 5)$, or $(2, 3)$ and $(2, -7)$. The asymptotes are given by

$$y = \pm \frac{a}{b}(x - h) + k, \quad \text{or} \quad y = \pm \frac{3}{4}(x - 2) - 2.$$

A graph of the hyperbola is shown in Figure 10.59.

Now Try Exercise 45

EXAMPLE 6   Finding the standard equation of a hyperbola

Write $9x^2 - 18x - 4y^2 - 16y = 43$ in the standard form for a hyperbola centered at (h, k). Identify the center and the vertices.

SOLUTION   We can write the given equation in standard form by completing the square.

$$9x^2 - 18x - 4y^2 - 16y = 43 \qquad \text{Given equation}$$
$$9(x^2 - 2x + \underline{}) - 4(y^2 + 4y + \underline{}) = 43 \qquad \text{Distributive property}$$
$$9(x^2 - 2x + \underline{1}) - 4(y^2 + 4y + \underline{4}) = 43 + 9 - 16 \qquad \text{Complete the square.}$$
$$9(x - 1)^2 - 4(y + 2)^2 = 36 \qquad \text{Perfect square trinomials}$$
$$\frac{(x - 1)^2}{4} - \frac{(y + 2)^2}{9} = 1 \qquad \text{Divide each side by 36.}$$

The center is $(1, -2)$. Because $a = 2$ and the transverse axis is horizontal, the vertices of the hyperbola are $(h \pm a, k) = (1 \pm 2, -2)$.

Now Try Exercise 51

10.3 Putting It All Together

The following table summarizes some important concepts about hyperbolas.

CONCEPT	EQUATION	EXAMPLE
Hyperbola with center $(0, 0)$	Standard equation Transverse axis: horizontal $$\frac{x^2}{a^2} - \frac{y^2}{b^2} = 1$$ Transverse axis: vertical $$\frac{y^2}{a^2} - \frac{x^2}{b^2} = 1$$ See the box on page 823.	$\frac{y^2}{4} - \frac{x^2}{9} = 1; a = 2, b = 3$ Transverse axis: vertical Vertices: $(0, \pm 2)$; foci: $\left(0, \pm \sqrt{13}\right)$ $\left(c^2 = a^2 + b^2 = 4 + 9 = 13, \text{ so } c = \sqrt{13}.\right)$ Asymptotes: $y = \pm \frac{2}{3}x$

continued on next page

CONCEPT	EQUATION	EXAMPLE
Hyperbola with center (h, k)	Standard equation Transverse axis: horizontal $$\frac{(x - h)^2}{a^2} - \frac{(y - k)^2}{b^2} = 1$$ Transverse axis: vertical $$\frac{(y - k)^2}{a^2} - \frac{(x - h)^2}{b^2} = 1$$ See the box on page 826.	$\frac{(x - 1)^2}{4} - \frac{(y + 1)^2}{9} = 1; a = 2, b = 3$ Transverse axis: horizontal; center: $(1, -1)$ Vertices: $(1 \pm 2, -1)$; foci: $\left(1 \pm \sqrt{13}, -1\right)$ $\left(c^2 = a^2 + b^2 = 4 + 9 = 13, \text{ so } c = \sqrt{13}.\right)$ Asymptotes: $y = \pm\frac{3}{2}(x - 1) - 1$ 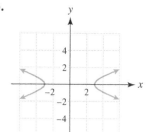

10.3 Exercises

Basic Concepts

1. The _____ are the endpoints of the transverse axis of a hyperbola.

2. The (dashed) rectangle used as an aid in graphing a hyperbola is called the _____ rectangle.

3. A hyperbola with an equation of the form $\frac{x^2}{a^2} - \frac{y^2}{b^2} = 1$

   has a(n) _vertical/horizontal_ transverse axis.

4. A hyperbola with an equation of the form $\frac{y^2}{a^2} - \frac{x^2}{b^2} = 1$

   has a(n) _vertical/horizontal_ transverse axis.

Hyperbolas with Center (0, 0)

Exercises 5–12: Sketch a graph of the hyperbola, including the asymptotes. Give the coordinates of the foci and vertices.

5. $\frac{x^2}{9} - \frac{y^2}{49} = 1$

6. $\frac{x^2}{16} - \frac{y^2}{4} = 1$

7. $\frac{y^2}{36} - \frac{x^2}{16} = 1$

8. $\frac{y^2}{4} - \frac{x^2}{4} = 1$

9. $x^2 - y^2 = 9$

10. $49y^2 - 25x^2 = 1225$

11. $9y^2 - 16x^2 = 144$

12. $4x^2 - 4y^2 = 100$

Exercises 13–16: Match the equation with its graph (a–d).

13. $\frac{x^2}{4} - \frac{y^2}{6} = 1$

14. $\frac{x^2}{9} - y^2 = 1$

15. $\frac{y^2}{9} - \frac{x^2}{16} = 1$

16. $\frac{y^2}{4} - \frac{x^2}{4} = 1$

a.
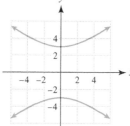

b.
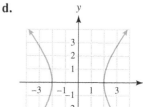

c.
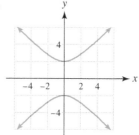

d.

Exercises 17–20: Sketch a graph of a hyperbola, centered at the origin, with the foci, vertices, and asymptotes shown in the figure. Find an equation of the hyperbola. (The coordinates of the foci and vertices are integers.)

17.
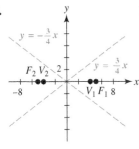

18.
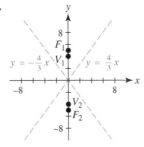

19.
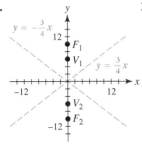

20.
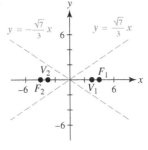

Exercises 21–30: Determine an equation of the hyperbola, centered at the origin, satisfying the conditions. Give the equations of its asymptotes.

21. Foci $(0, \pm 13)$, vertices $(0, \pm 12)$

22. Foci $(\pm 13, 0)$, vertices $(\pm 5, 0)$

23. Vertical transverse axis of length 4, foci $(0, \pm 5)$

24. Horizontal transverse axis of length 12, foci $(\pm 10, 0)$

25. Vertices $(\pm 3, 0)$, asymptotes $y = \pm \frac{2}{3}x$

26. Vertices $(0, \pm 4)$, asymptotes $y = \pm \frac{1}{2}x$

27. Endpoints of conjugate axis $(0, \pm 3)$, vertices $(\pm 4, 0)$

28. Endpoints of conjugate axis $(\pm 4, 0)$, vertices $(0, \pm 2)$

29. Vertices $\left(\pm \sqrt{10}, 0 \right)$, passing through $(10, 9)$

30. Vertices $\left(0, \pm \sqrt{5} \right)$, passing through $(4, 5)$

Hyperbolas with Center (h, k)

Exercises 31–36: Sketch a graph of the hyperbola. Identify the vertices, foci, and asymptotes.

31. $\dfrac{(x - 1)^2}{16} - \dfrac{(y - 2)^2}{4} = 1$

32. $\dfrac{(y + 1)^2}{16} - \dfrac{(x + 3)^2}{9} = 1$

33. $\dfrac{(y - 2)^2}{36} - \dfrac{(x + 2)^2}{4} = 1$

34. $\dfrac{(x + 1)^2}{4} - \dfrac{(y - 1)^2}{4} = 1$

35. $\dfrac{x^2}{4} - (y - 1)^2 = 1$

36. $(y + 1)^2 - \dfrac{(x - 3)^2}{4} = 1$

Exercises 37–40: Match the equation with its graph (a–d).

37. $\dfrac{(x - 2)^2}{4} - \dfrac{(y + 4)^2}{4} = 1$ **38.** $\dfrac{(x + 1)^2}{4} - \dfrac{y^2}{9} = 1$

39. $\dfrac{(y + 1)^2}{16} - \dfrac{(x - 2)^2}{16} = 1$ **40.** $\dfrac{y^2}{25} - \dfrac{(x + 1)^2}{9} = 1$

a.
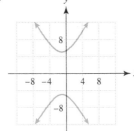

b.
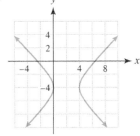

c.
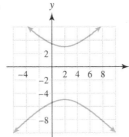

d.
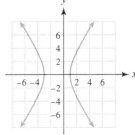

Exercises 41 and 42: Find an (approximate) equation of the hyperbola shown in the graph. Identify the vertices, foci, and asymptotes.

41.
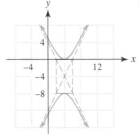

42.
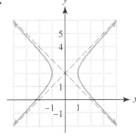

Exercises 43–46: Sketch a graph of the hyperbola, including the asymptotes. Give the coordinates of the vertices and foci.

43. $\dfrac{(x - 1)^2}{4} - \dfrac{(y - 1)^2}{4} = 1$

44. $\dfrac{(x+2)^2}{4} - \dfrac{(y+1)^2}{16} = 1$

45. $\dfrac{(y+1)^2}{16} - \dfrac{(x-1)^2}{9} = 1$

46. $y^2 - \dfrac{(x-2)^2}{4} = 1$

Exercises 47–50: Find the standard equation of a hyperbola with center (h, k) that satisfies the given conditions.

47. Center $(2, -2)$, focus $(4, -2)$, and vertex $(3, -2)$

48. Center $(-1, 1)$, focus $(-1, 4)$, and vertex $(-1, 3)$

49. Vertices $(-1, \pm 1)$ and foci $(-1, \pm 3)$

50. Vertices $(2 \pm 1, 1)$ and foci $(2 \pm 3, 1)$

Exercises 51–58: Write the standard form for a hyperbola centered at (h, k). Identify the center and the vertices.

51. $x^2 - 2x - y^2 + 2y = 4$

52. $y^2 + 4y - x^2 + 2x = 6$

53. $3y^2 + 24y - 2x^2 + 12x + 24 = 0$

54. $4x^2 + 16x - 9y^2 + 18y = 29$

55. $x^2 - 6x - 2y^2 + 7 = 0$

56. $y^2 + 8y - 3x^2 + 13 = 0$

57. $4y^2 + 32y - 5x^2 - 10x + 39 = 0$

58. $5x^2 + 10x - 7y^2 + 28y = 58$

Graphing Hyperbolas with Technology

Exercises 59–62: Graph the hyperbola.

59. $\dfrac{(y-1)^2}{11} - \dfrac{x^2}{5.9} = 1$

60. $\dfrac{x^2}{5.3} - \dfrac{y^2}{6.7} = 1$

61. $3y^2 - 4x^2 = 15$

62. $2.1x^2 - 6y^2 = 12$

Solving Equations

Exercises 63–70: Solve the system of equations.

63. $x^2 - y^2 = 4$
    $x^2 + y^2 = 9$

64. $x^2 - 4y^2 = 16$
    $x^2 + 4y^2 = 16$

65. $\dfrac{x^2}{4} - \dfrac{y^2}{9} = 1$
    $x + y = 2$

66. $x^2 - y^2 = 4$
    $x + y = 2$

67. $8x^2 - 6y^2 = 24$
    $5x^2 + 3y^2 = 24$

68. $3y^2 - 4x^2 = 12$
    $y^2 + 2x^2 = 34$

69. $\dfrac{y^2}{3} - \dfrac{x^2}{4} = 1$
    $3x - y = 0$

70. $x^2 - 4y^2 = 16$
    $y^2 - 4x^2 = 4$

Applications

71. **Satellite Orbits**   The trajectory of a satellite near Earth can trace a hyperbola, parabola, or ellipse. If the satellite follows either a hyperbolic or a parabolic path, it escapes Earth's gravitational influence after a single pass. The path that a satellite travels near Earth depends on both its velocity V in meters per second and its distance D in meters from the center of Earth. Its path is hyperbolic if $V > \dfrac{k}{\sqrt{D}}$, parabolic if $V = \dfrac{k}{\sqrt{D}}$, and elliptic if $V < \dfrac{k}{\sqrt{D}}$, where $k = 2.82 \times 10^7$ is a constant.   (**Sources:** W. Loh, *Dynamics and Thermodynamics of Planetary Entry;* W. Thomson, *Introduction to Space Dynamics.*)

   (a) When *Explorer IV* was at a maximum distance of 42.5×10^6 meters from Earth's center, it had a velocity of 2090 meters/second. Determine the shape of its trajectory.

   (b) If an orbiting satellite is to escape Earth's gravity so that it can travel to another planet, its velocity must be increased so that its trajectory changes from elliptic to hyperbolic. What range of velocities would allow *Explorer IV* to leave Earth's influence when it is at a maximum distance?

   (c) Explain why it is easier to change a satellite's trajectory from an ellipse to a hyperbola when D is maximum rather than minimum.

72. **Telescopes**   (Refer to Figure 10.58.) Suppose that the coordinates of F_1 are $(0, 5.2)$ and the coordinates of F_2 are $(0, -5.2)$. If the coordinates of the vertex of the hyperbolic mirror are $(0, 4.1)$, find the standard equation of a hyperbola whose upper branch coincides with the hyperbolic mirror.

Writing about Mathematics

73. Explain how the center, vertices, and asymptotes of a hyperbola are related to the fundamental rectangle.

74. Given the standard equation of a hyperbola, explain how to determine the length of the transverse axis. How can you determine whether the transverse axis is vertical or horizontal?

Extended and Discovery Exercises

1. **Structure of an Atom** In 1911, Ernest Rutherford discovered the basic structure of the atom by "shooting" positively charged alpha particles with a speed of 10^7 meter per second at a piece of gold foil 6×10^{-7} meter thick. Only a small percentage of the alpha particles struck a gold nucleus head on and were deflected directly back toward their source. The rest of the particles often followed a *hyperbolic* trajectory because they were repelled by positively charged gold nuclei. The figure shows the (blue) path of an alpha particle A initially approaching a gold nucleus N and being deflected at an angle $\theta = 90°$. N is located at a focus of the hyperbola, and the trajectory of A passes through a vertex of the hyperbola.   (**Source:** H. Semat and J. Albright, *Introduction to Atomic and Nuclear Physics*.)

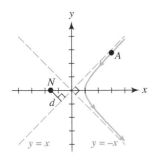

(a) Determine the equation of the trajectory of the alpha particle if $d = 5 \times 10^{-14}$ meter.

(b) What was the minimum distance between the centers of the alpha particle and the gold nucleus?

2. **Sound Detection** Microphones are placed at points $(-c, 0)$ and $(c, 0)$. An explosion occurs at point $P(x, y)$, which has a positive x-coordinate. See the figure.

   The sound is detected at the closer microphone t seconds before being detected at the farther microphone. Assume that sound travels at a speed of 330 meters per second, and show that P must be on the hyperbola

$$\frac{x^2}{330^2 t^2} - \frac{y^2}{4c^2 - 330^2 t^2} = \frac{1}{4}.$$

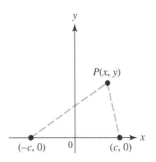

CHECKING BASIC CONCEPTS FOR SECTION 10.3

1. Use the graph to find the standard form of the hyperbola.

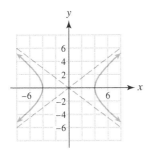

2. Graph the hyperbola defined by $\frac{x^2}{9} - \frac{y^2}{16} = 1$. Include the foci and asymptotes.

3. Find an equation of the hyperbola centered at $(1, 3)$ with a horizontal transverse axis of length 6 and a conjugate axis of length 4. Identify the foci.

4. Write $9y^2 - 54y - 16x^2 - 32x = 79$ in the standard form for a hyperbola centered at (h, k). Identify the center and the vertices.

10 Summary

CONCEPT	EXPLANATION AND EXAMPLES

Section 10.1 Parabolas

Conic Sections

Basic types: parabola, ellipse, circle, and hyperbola.

Parabolas with Vertex (0, 0)

Standard Forms

$x^2 = 4py$ (vertical axis)   or $y^2 = 4px$ (horizontal axis)

Meaning of p

Both the vertex–focus distance and the vertex–directrix distance are p. The sign of p determines if the parabola opens upward or downward—or left or right. The focus is either $(0, p)$ or $(p, 0)$, and the directrix is either $y = -p$ or $x = -p$. In the figures below $p > 0$, but $p < 0$ is also possible.

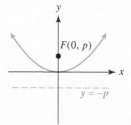

Vertical Axis: $x^2 = 4py$ Horizontal Axis: $y^2 = 4px$

Parabolas with Vertex (*h*, *k*)

$(x - h)^2 = 4p(y - k)$ Vertical axis; Focus: $(h, k + p)$
Directrix: $y = k - p$

$(y - k)^2 = 4p(x - h)$ Horizontal axis; Focus: $(h + p, k)$
Directrix: $x = h - p$

Section 10.2 Ellipses

Ellipses with Center (0, 0)

Standard Forms with a > b > 0

$\dfrac{x^2}{a^2} + \dfrac{y^2}{b^2} = 1$ (horizontal major axis)   or $\dfrac{x^2}{b^2} + \dfrac{y^2}{a^2} = 1$ (vertical major axis)

Meaning of a, b, and c

The distance from the center to a vertex is a, the distance from the center to an endpoint of the minor axis is b, and the distance from the center to a focus is c. The ratio $\frac{c}{a}$ equals the eccentricity e. The values of a, b, and c are related by $c^2 = a^2 - b^2$. The foci are either $(\pm c, 0)$ or $(0, \pm c)$, and the vertices are either $(\pm a, 0)$ or $(0, \pm a)$. If $a = b$, then the ellipse becomes a circle.

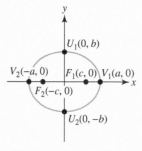

Horizontal Major Axis

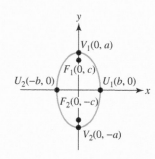

Vertical Major Axis

CONCEPT	EXPLANATION AND EXAMPLES

Section 10.2 Ellipses (CONTINUED)

Ellipses with Center (h, k)

$a > b > 0; c^2 = a^2 - b^2$

$$\frac{(x - h)^2}{a^2} + \frac{(y - k)^2}{b^2} = 1$$

Major axis: horizontal; Foci: $(h \pm c, k)$
Vertices: $(h \pm a, k)$

$$\frac{(x - h)^2}{b^2} + \frac{(y - k)^2}{a^2} = 1$$

Major axis: vertical; Foci: $(h, k \pm c)$
Vertices: $(h, k \pm a)$

Area Inside an Ellipse

The area A of the region contained inside an ellipse is given by $A = \pi ab$, where a and b are from the standard equation of the ellipse.

Section 10.3 Hyperbolas

Hyperbolas with Center (0, 0)

Standard Forms with both a and b positive

$$\frac{x^2}{a^2} - \frac{y^2}{b^2} = 1 \text{ (horizontal transverse axis)} \quad \text{or} \quad \frac{y^2}{a^2} - \frac{x^2}{b^2} = 1 \text{ (vertical transverse axis)}$$

Meaning of a, b, and c
The distance from the center to a vertex is a, and the distance from the center to a focus is c. The asymptotes are $y = \pm \frac{b}{a}x$ if the transverse axis is horizontal and $y = \pm \frac{a}{b}x$ if the transverse axis is vertical. The values of a, b, and c are related by $c^2 = a^2 + b^2$. The foci are either $(\pm c, 0)$ or $(0, \pm c)$, and the vertices are either $(\pm a, 0)$ or $(0, \pm a)$.

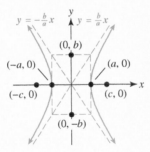

Horizontal Transverse Axis

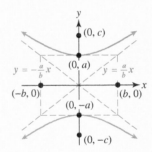

Vertical Transverse Axis

Hyperbolas with Center (h, k)

$a > 0, b > 0; c^2 = a^2 + b^2$

$$\frac{(x - h)^2}{a^2} - \frac{(y - k)^2}{b^2} = 1$$

Transverse axis: horizontal
Foci: $(h \pm c, k)$; Vertices: $(h \pm a, k)$
Asymptotes: $y = \pm \frac{b}{a}(x - h) + k$

$$\frac{(y - k)^2}{a^2} - \frac{(x - h)^2}{b^2} = 1$$

Transverse axis: vertical
Foci: $(h, k \pm c)$; Vertices: $(h, k \pm a)$
Asymptotes: $y = \pm \frac{a}{b}(x - h) + k$

10 Review Exercises

Exercises 1–6: Sketch a graph of the equation.

1. $-x^2 = y$

2. $y^2 = 2x$

3. $\dfrac{x^2}{25} + \dfrac{y^2}{49} = 1$

4. $\dfrac{y^2}{4} + \dfrac{x^2}{2} = 1$

5. $\dfrac{y^2}{4} - \dfrac{x^2}{9} = 1$

6. $x^2 - y^2 = 4$

Exercises 7–12: Match the equation with its graph (a–f).

7. $x^2 = 2y$

8. $y^2 = -3x$

9. $x^2 + y^2 = 4$

10. $\dfrac{x^2}{36} + \dfrac{y^2}{49} = 1$

11. $\dfrac{x^2}{4} - \dfrac{y^2}{9} = 1$

12. $\dfrac{y^2}{36} - \dfrac{x^2}{25} = 1$

a.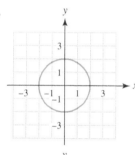

b.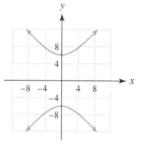

c.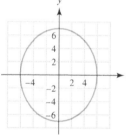

d.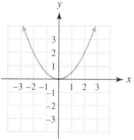

e.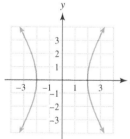

f.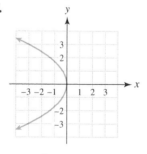

Exercises 13–18: Determine an equation of the conic section that satisfies the given conditions.

13. Parabola with focus (2, 0) and vertex (0, 0)

14. Parabola with vertex (5, 2) and focus (5, 0)

15. Ellipse with foci (± 4, 0) and vertices (± 5, 0)

16. Ellipse centered at the origin with vertical major axis of length 14 and minor axis of length 8

17. Hyperbola with foci (0, ± 10) and endpoints of the conjugate axis (± 6, 0)

18. Hyperbola with vertices (-2 ± 3, 3) and foci given by (-2 ± 4, 3)

Exercises 19–25: Sketch a graph of the conic section. Give the coordinates of any foci.

19. $-4y = x^2$

20. $y^2 = 8x$

21. $\dfrac{x^2}{25} + \dfrac{y^2}{4} = 1$

22. $49x^2 + 36y^2 = 1764$

23. $\dfrac{x^2}{16} - \dfrac{y^2}{9} = 1$

24. $\dfrac{y^2}{4} - x^2 = 1$

25. $(x - 3)^2 + (y + 1)^2 = 9$

Exercises 26–28: Sketch a graph of the conic section. Identify the coordinates of its center when appropriate.

26. $\dfrac{(y - 2)^2}{4} + \dfrac{(x + 1)^2}{16} = 1$

27. $\dfrac{(x - 1)^2}{4} - \dfrac{(y + 1)^2}{4} = 1$

28. $(x + 2) = 4(y - 1)^2$

29. Sketch a graph of $(y - 4)^2 = -8(x - 8)$. Include the focus and the directrix.

Exercises 30–32: Graph the equation.

30. $y^2 = \frac{3}{4}x$

31. $7.1x^2 + 8.2y^2 = 60$

32. $\dfrac{(y - 1.4)^2}{7} - \dfrac{(x + 2.3)^2}{11} = 1$

Exercises 33 and 34: Write the equation in the form given by $(y - k)^2 = a(x - h)$.

33. $-2x = y^2 + 8x + 14$

34. $2y^2 - 12y + 16 = x$

Exercises 35–38: Write the equation in standard form for an ellipse or a hyperbola centered at (h, k). Identify the center and the vertices.

35. $4x^2 + 8x + 25y^2 - 250y = -529$

36. $5x^2 + 20x + 2y^2 - 8y = -18$

37. $x^2 + 4x - 4y^2 + 24y = 36$

38. $4y^2 + 8y - 3x^2 + 6x = 11$

Exercises 39 and 40: Solve the system of equations.

39. $\dfrac{x^2}{4} + \dfrac{y^2}{4} = 1$

$\dfrac{x^2}{8} + \dfrac{y^2}{2} = 1$

40. $x^2 - y^2 = 1$

$x + y = 2$

Exercises 41 and 42: Shade the solution set to the system.

41. $\dfrac{x^2}{9} + \dfrac{y^2}{4} \le 1$

$x + y \le 3$

42. $y^2 - x^2 \le 9$

$y - x \le 0$

Applications

43. Comets A comet travels along an elliptical orbit around the sun. Its path can be described by the equation

$$\frac{x^2}{70^2} + \frac{y^2}{500^2} = 1,$$

where units are in millions of miles.

(a) What are the comet's minimum and maximum distances from the sun?

(b) Estimate the distance that the comet travels in one orbit around the sun. (Refer to Exercise 102 from Section 10.2.)

44. Searchlight A searchlight is constructed in the shape of a paraboloid with a depth of 7 inches and a diameter of 20 inches, as illustrated in the figure. Determine the distance d that the bulb should be from the vertex in order to have the beam of light shine straight ahead.

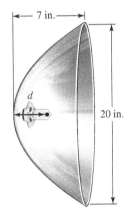

45. Arch Bridge An elliptical arch under a bridge is constructed so that it is 80 feet wide and has a maximum height of 30 feet, as illustrated in the figure. Find the height of the arch 10 feet from the center of the arch.

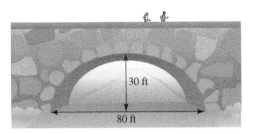

Extended and Discovery Exercises

Exercises 1–5: **Neptune and Pluto** *Both Neptune and Pluto travel around the sun in elliptical orbits. For Neptune's orbit, $a = 30.10$, and for Pluto's orbit, $a = 39.44$, where the variable a represents their average distances from the sun in astronomical units. (One astronomical unit equals 93 million miles.) The value of the variable a also corresponds to half the length of the major axis. Pluto has a highly eccentric orbit with $e = 0.249$, and Neptune has a nearly circular orbit with $e = 0.009$.*

1. Calculate the value of c for Neptune and Pluto.

2. Position the sun at the *origin* of the xy-plane. Find the coordinates of the center of Neptune's orbit and the coordinates of the center of Pluto's orbit. Assume that the centers lie on the positive x-axis.

3. Find equations for Neptune's orbit and for Pluto's orbit.

4. Graph both orbits in the same xy-plane.

5. Is Pluto always farther from the sun than Neptune? Explain.

11 Further Topics in Algebra

Mathematics permeates the fabric of modern society. It is the language of technology and allows society to quantify its experiences.

While technology and visualization provide new ways for us to investigate mathematical problems, they are *not* replacements for mathematical understanding. Computers and calculators are incapable of mathematical insight, but are excellent at performing arithmetic and other routine computation. Together, technology and the human mind can create amazing inventions.

In previous chapters we saw hundreds of examples of the use of mathematics to describe physical and social phenomena and events. Mathematics is diverse in its ability to adapt to new situations and solve complex problems. If any subject area is studied in enough detail, mathematics usually appears.

This chapter introduces further topics in mathematics. It represents only a small fraction of the topics found in mathematics. Although it may be difficult to predict exactly what the future will bring, one thing is certain—mathematics will continue to play a very important role.

> The art of asking the right questions in mathematics is more important than the art of solving them.
>
> —Georg Cantor

11.1 Sequences

- **Understand basic concepts about sequences**
- **Learn how to represent sequences**
- **Identify and use arithmetic sequences**
- **Identify and use geometric sequences**

Introduction

A sequence is a *function* that computes an ordered list. For example, the average person in the United States uses about 100 gallons of water each day. The function $f(n) = 100n$ generates the terms of the *sequence*

$$100, 200, 300, 400, 500, 600, 700, \ldots$$

when $n = 1, 2, 3, 4, 5, 6, 7, \ldots$. This *ordered list* represents the gallons of water used by the average person after n days. Sequences are a fundamental concept in mathematics and have many applications.

Basic Concepts

A second example of a sequence involves investing money. If $100 is deposited into a savings account paying 5% interest compounded annually, then the function defined by $g(n) = 100(1.05)^n$ calculates the account balance after n years, which is given by

$$g(1), g(2), g(3), g(4), g(5), g(6), g(7), \ldots$$

These terms can be approximated as

> Terms of the sequence

$$105, 110.25, 115.76, 121.55, 127.63, 134.01, 140.71, \ldots$$

We now define a sequence formally.

SEQUENCE

An **infinite sequence** is a function that has the set of natural numbers as its domain. A **finite sequence** is a function with domain $D = \{1, 2, 3, \ldots, n\}$ for some fixed natural number n.

Since sequences are functions, many of the concepts discussed in previous chapters apply to sequences. Instead of letting y represent the output, it is common to write $a_n = f(n)$, where n is a natural number in the domain of the sequence. The **terms** of a sequence are

$$a_1, a_2, a_3, \ldots, a_n, \ldots$$

The first term is $a_1 = f(1)$, the second term is $a_2 = f(2)$, and so on. The **nth term**, or **general term**, of a sequence is $a_n = f(n)$.

NOTE The nth term, a general term, and a symbolic representation (formula) of a sequence are equivalent concepts.

EXAMPLE 1 Finding terms of sequences

Write the first four terms $a_1, a_2, a_3,$ and a_4 of each sequence, where $a_n = f(n)$.

(a) $f(n) = 2n - 5$ **(b)** $f(n) = 4(2)^{n-1}$ **(c)** $f(n) = (-1)^n \left(\dfrac{n}{n+1} \right)$

SOLUTION
(a) Evaluate $f(n) = 2n - 5$ as follows.

$$a_1 = f(1) = 2(1) - 5 = -3$$

$$a_2 = f(2) = 2(2) - 5 = -1$$

In a similar manner, $a_3 = f(3) = 1$ and $a_4 = f(4) = 3$.

(b) Since $f(n) = 4(2)^{n-1}$,

$$a_1 = f(1) = 4(2)^{1-1} = 4.$$

Similarly, $a_2 = 8$, $a_3 = 16$, and $a_4 = 32$.

(c) Let $f(n) = (-1)^n \left(\frac{n}{n+1} \right)$, and substitute $n = 1, 2, 3,$ and 4.

$$a_1 = f(1) = (-1)^1 \left(\frac{1}{1+1} \right) = -\frac{1}{2}$$

$$a_2 = f(2) = (-1)^2 \left(\frac{2}{2+1} \right) = \frac{2}{3}$$

$$a_3 = f(3) = (-1)^3 \left(\frac{3}{3+1} \right) = -\frac{3}{4}$$

$$a_4 = f(4) = (-1)^4 \left(\frac{4}{4+1} \right) = \frac{4}{5}$$

> Note the alternating signs.

Note that the factor $(-1)^n$ causes the terms of the sequence to alternate signs.

Now Try Exercises 1, 3, and 9

Calculator Help

To learn how to generate a sequence, see Appendix A (page AP-15).

Graphing Calculators and Sequences Graphing calculators may be used to calculate the terms of a sequence. Figures 11.1–11.3 show the first four terms of each sequence in Example 1. The graphing calculator is in sequence mode.

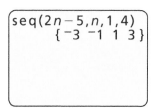

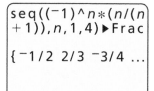

Figure 11.1   **Figure 11.2**   **Figure 11.3**

Recursive Sequences Some sequences are not defined using a general term. Instead they are defined *recursively*. With a **recursive sequence**, we must find terms a_1 through a_{n-1} before we can find a_n. For example, we need to find a_1 before we can find a_2, a_2 before we can find a_3, and so on.

EXAMPLE 2 Finding the terms of a recursive sequence

Find the first four terms of the recursive sequence that is defined by

$$a_n = 2a_{n-1} + 1; \qquad a_1 = 3.$$

SOLUTION The sequence is defined recursively, so we must find the terms in order.

> We substitute the value of a_1 to find the value of a_2.

$$a_1 = 3$$
$$a_2 = 2a_1 + 1 = 2(3) + 1 = 7$$
$$a_3 = 2a_2 + 1 = 2(7) + 1 = 15$$
$$a_4 = 2a_3 + 1 = 2(15) + 1 = 31$$

The first four terms are 3, 7, 15, and 31.

Now Try Exercise 15(a)

An Application A population model for an insect with a life span of 1 year can be described using a recursive sequence. Suppose each adult female insect produces r female offspring that survive to reproduce the following year. Let $f(n)$ calculate the female insect population during year n. Then the number of female insects is given recursively by

$$f(n) = rf(n-1) \quad \text{for } n > 1.$$

Females in year n ⟍   ⟋ Females in previous year

The number of female insects in the year n is equal to r times the number of female insects in the previous year $n - 1$. Note that this function f is defined in terms of *itself*. To evaluate $f(n)$, we evaluate $f(n-1)$. To evaluate $f(n-1)$, we evaluate $f(n-2)$, and so on. If we know the number of adult female insects during the first year, then we can determine the sequence. That is, if $f(1)$ is given, we can determine $f(n)$ by first computing

$$f(1), f(2), f(3), \ldots, f(n-1).$$

The next example illustrates a similar recursively defined sequence where $f(n)$ gives the female population density during year n. (***Source:*** D. Brown and P. Rothery, *Models in Biology: Mathematics, Statistics and Computing*.)

EXAMPLE 3 Modeling an insect population

Suppose that the initial density of adult female insects is 1000 per acre and $r = 1.1$. Then the density of female insects during year n is described by

$$f(1) = 1000$$
$$f(n) = 1.1f(n-1), \quad n > 1.$$

(a) Rewrite this symbolic representation in terms of a_n.
(b) Find a_4 and interpret the result. Is the density of female insects increasing or decreasing?
(c) A general term for this sequence is given by $f(n) = 1000(1.1)^{n-1}$. Use this representation to find a_4.

SOLUTION
(a) Since $a_n = f(n)$ for all n, $a_{n-1} = f(n-1)$. The sequence can be expressed as

$$a_1 = 1000$$
$$a_n = 1.1a_{n-1}, \quad n > 1.$$

CLASS DISCUSSION
How does the value of r in Example 3 affect the population density in future years?

(b) In order to calculate the fourth term, a_4, we must first determine $a_1, a_2,$ and a_3.

$$a_1 = 1000$$
$$a_2 = 1.1a_1 = 1.1(1000) = 1100$$
$$a_3 = 1.1a_2 = 1.1(1100) = 1210$$
$$a_4 = 1.1a_3 = 1.1(1210) = 1331$$

The fourth term is $a_4 = 1331$. The female population density is increasing and reaches 1331 per acre during the fourth year.
(c) Since $a_4 = f(4)$,

$$a_4 = 1000(1.1)^{4-1} = 1331.$$

It is less work to find a_n using a formula for a general term rather than a recursive formula—particularly if n is large.

Now Try Exercise 89

Representations of Sequences

Sequences are functions. Therefore they have graphical, numerical, and symbolic representations. In the next example we make a table of values and a graph for a sequence.

EXAMPLE 4 Representing a sequence numerically and graphically

Let a recursive sequence be defined as follows.

$$a_1 = 3$$
$$a_n = 2a_{n-1} - 2, \quad n > 1$$

(a) Give a numerical representation (list each term in a table) for $n = 1, 2, 3, 4, 5$.
(b) Graph the first five terms of this sequence.

SOLUTION
(a) *Numerical Representation* Start by calculating the first five terms of the sequence.

$$a_1 = 3$$
$$a_2 = 2a_1 - 2 = 2(3) - 2 = 4$$
$$a_3 = 2a_2 - 2 = 2(4) - 2 = 6$$
$$a_4 = 2a_3 - 2 = 2(6) - 2 = 10$$
$$a_5 = 2a_4 - 2 = 2(10) - 2 = \mathbf{18}$$

n	a_n
1	3
2	4
3	6
4	10
5	18

Table 11.1

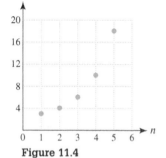

a_n

Figure 11.4

The first five terms are 3, 4, 6, 10, and 18. A numerical representation of the sequence is shown in Table 11.1.

(b) *Graphical Representation* To represent these terms graphically, plot the points $(1, 3)$, $(2, 4)$, $(3, 6)$, $(4, 10)$, and $(5, 18)$, as shown in Figure 11.4. Because the domain of a sequence contains only natural numbers, the graph of a sequence is a scatterplot.

Now Try Exercise 19

NOTE A graphing calculator set in sequence mode may be used to calculate the terms of the recursive sequence in Example 4. See Figures 11.5 and 11.6.

Table of a Sequence

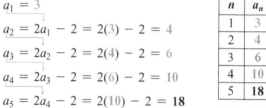

Figure 11.5

Graph of a Sequence
[0, 6, 1] by [0, 20, 4]

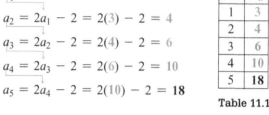

Figure 11.6 Dot Mode

Calculator Help
To make a table or graph of a sequence, see Appendix A (page AP-16).

An Application The next example illustrates numerical and graphical representations for a sequence involving population growth.

EXAMPLE 5 Representing a sequence numerically and graphically

Frequently the population of a particular insect does not continue to grow indefinitely, as it does in Example 3. Instead, the population grows rapidly at first and then levels off because of competition for limited resources. In one study, the population of the winter moth was modeled with a sequence similar to the following, where a_n represents the

population density in thousands per acre at the beginning of year n.   (*Source:* G. Varley and G. Gradwell, "Population models for the winter moth.")

$$a_1 = 1$$

$$a_n = 2.85a_{n-1} - 0.19a_{n-1}^2, \qquad n \geq 2$$

(a) Make a table of values for $n = 1, 2, 3, \ldots, 10$. Describe what happens to the population density of the winter moth.

(b) Use the table to graph the sequence.

SOLUTION

(a) *Numerical Representation* Evaluate $a_1, a_2, a_3, \ldots, a_{10}$ recursively. Since $a_1 = 1$,

$$a_2 = 2.85a_1 - 0.19a_1^2 = 2.85(1) - 0.19(1)^2 = 2.66 \qquad \text{and}$$

$$a_3 = 2.85a_2 - 0.19a_2^2 = 2.85(2.66) - 0.19(2.66)^2 \approx 6.24.$$

Approximate values for other terms are shown in Table 11.2. Figure 11.7 shows the sequence computed using a calculator, where the sequence is denoted $u(n)$ rather than a_n.

Calculating Table 11.2

n	$u(n)$
1	1
2	2.66
3	6.2366
4	10.384
5	9.1069
6	10.197
7	9.3056

$n = 1$

Figure 11.7

Winter Moth Population Density

n	1	2	3	4	5	6	7	8	9	10
a_n	1	2.66	6.24	10.4	9.11	10.2	9.31	10.1	9.43	9.98

Table 11.2

(b) *Graphical Representation* The graph of a sequence is a scatterplot. Plot the points

$$(1, 1), (2, 2.66), (3, 6.24), \ldots, (10, 9.98),$$

as shown in Figure 11.8. The insect population increases rapidly at first and then oscillates about the line $y = 9.7$. (See the Class Discussion in the margin.) The oscillations become smaller as n increases, indicating that the population density may stabilize near 9.7 thousand per acre. Some calculators can plot sequences, as shown in Figure 11.9. In this figure, the first 20 terms have been plotted in dot mode.

CLASS DISCUSSION

In Example 5, the insect population stabilizes near the value $k = 9.74$ thousand. This value of k can be found by solving the quadratic equation

$$k = 2.85k - 0.19k^2.$$

Try to explain why this is true.

Graphical Representations of an Insect Population

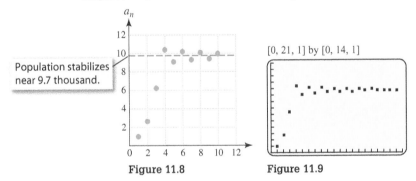

Population stabilizes near 9.7 thousand.

[0, 21, 1] by [0, 14, 1]

Figure 11.8

Figure 11.9

Now Try Exercise 91

Arithmetic Sequences

Suppose that a person receives a starting salary of $30,000 per year and a $1000 raise each year. The salary *after* n years of experience is represented by

$$f(n) = 1000n + 30,000, \quad \text{—— Linear Function}$$

where f is a linear function. After 10 years of experience, the annual salary would be

$$f(10) = 1000(10) + 30,000 = \$40,000.$$

If a sequence can be defined by a linear function, it is an *arithmetic sequence*. Its formula is given by $f(n) = dn + c$.

INFINITE ARITHMETIC SEQUENCE

An **infinite arithmetic sequence** is a linear function f whose domain is the set of natural numbers. The general term can be written as $a_n = dn + c$ where d and c are constants and $a_n = f(n)$.

An arithmetic sequence can be defined recursively by $a_n = a_{n-1} + d$, where d is a constant. Since $d = a_n - a_{n-1}$ for each valid n, d is called the **common difference**. If $d = 0$, then the sequence is a **constant sequence**. A **finite arithmetic sequence** is similar to an infinite arithmetic sequence except that its domain is $D = \{1, 2, 3, \ldots, n\}$, where n is a fixed natural number.

EXAMPLE 6 Determining arithmetic sequences

Figure 11.10

Determine if f is an arithmetic sequence for each situation.
(a) $f(n) = n^2 + 3n$
(b) f as graphed in Figure 11.10
(c) f as given in Table 11.3

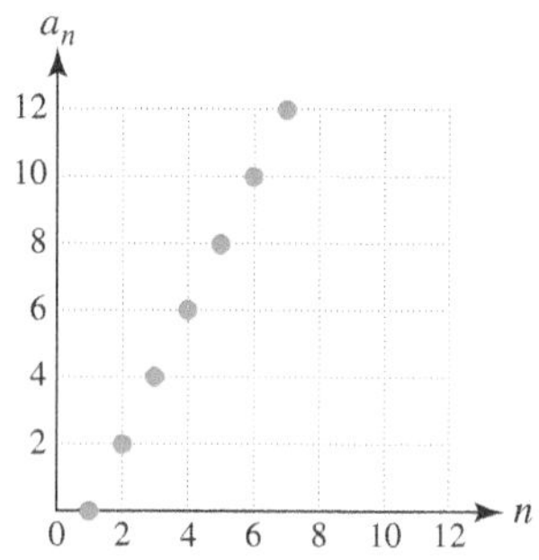

n	1	2	3	4	5	6	7
$f(n)$	-1.5	0	1.5	3	4.5	6	7.5

Table 11.3

SOLUTION

Getting Started The formula for an arithmetic sequence is given by $f(n) = dn + c$, its graph lies on a line with slope d, and consecutive terms in its numerical representation always change by a common difference d. ▶
(a) This sequence is not arithmetic because $f(n) = n^2 + 3n$ is nonlinear.
(b) The sequence in Figure 11.10 is an arithmetic sequence because the points lie on a line. A linear function could generate these points. Notice that the slope between points is always 2, which equals the common difference d.
(c) The successive terms, $-1.5, 0, 1.5, 3, 4.5, 6, 7.5$, increase by precisely 1.5. Therefore the common difference is $d = 1.5$. Since $a_n = a_{n-1} + 1.5$ for each valid n, the sequence is arithmetic.

> **Now Try Exercises 61, 65, and 67**

An arithmetic sequence is a linear function and can always be represented by $f(n) = dn + c$, where d is the common difference and c is a constant.

EXAMPLE 7 Finding general terms for arithmetic sequences

Find a general term $a_n = f(n)$ for each arithmetic sequence.
(a) $a_1 = 3$ and $d = -2$
(b) $a_3 = 4$ and $a_9 = 17$

SOLUTION
(a) Let $f(n) = dn + c$. Since $d = -2$, $f(n) = -2n + c$. Since $a_1 = 3$,

$$a_1 = f(1) = -2(1) + c = 3, \quad \text{or} \quad c = 5.$$

Thus $a_n = -2n + 5$.
(b) Since $a_3 = 4$ and $a_9 = 17$, we find a linear function $f(n) = dn + c$ that satisfies the equations $f(3) = 4$ and $f(9) = 17$. The common difference is equal to the slope between the points $(3, 4)$ and $(9, 17)$.

MAKING CONNECTIONS

Linear Functions and Arithmetic Sequences

In Chapter 2 we discussed several techniques for finding a formula for linear functions. These methods can be applied to finding a general term for arithmetic sequences. It is important to realize that the mathematical concept of linear functions is simply being applied to the new topic of sequences by restricting their domains to the natural numbers.

$$d = \frac{17 - 4}{9 - 3} = \frac{13}{6}$$ Common difference = slope

It follows that $f(n) = \frac{13}{6}n + c$.

$$a_3 = f(3) = \frac{13}{6}(3) + c = 4, \quad \text{or} \quad c = -\frac{5}{2}$$ Use one point and d to find c.

Thus $a_n = \frac{13}{6}n - \frac{5}{2}$.

Now Try Exercises 41 and 45

Finding the nth Term If a_1 is the first term of an arithmetic sequence and d is the common difference, then consecutive terms of the sequence are given by

$$a_2 \qquad\qquad = a_1 + d$$
$$a_3 = a_2 + d = a_1 + 1d + d = a_1 + 2d$$
$$a_4 = a_3 + d = a_1 + 2d + d = a_1 + 3d$$
$$a_5 = a_4 + d = a_1 + 3d + d = a_1 + 4d$$

$(n - 1)d$

and, in general, $a_n = a_1 + (n - 1)d$. This result is summarized in the following box.

nTH TERM OF AN ARITHMETIC SEQUENCE

In an arithmetic sequence with first term a_1 and common difference d, the nth term, a_n, is given by

$$a_n = a_1 + (n - 1)d.$$

EXAMPLE 8 Finding the nth term of an arithmetic sequence

(a) Find a symbolic representation for the nth term of the arithmetic sequence

$$9, 8.5, 8, 7.5, 7, 6.5, 6, \ldots.$$

(b) Find the 12th term in the sequence using your formula for a_n.

SOLUTION

(a) The first term is 9. Successive terms can be found by subtracting 0.5 from (or adding -0.5 to) the previous term. Therefore $a_1 = 9$ and $d = -0.5$, and it follows that

$$a_n = a_1 + (n - 1)d \qquad \text{General formula}$$
$$= 9 + (n - 1)(-0.5) \qquad \text{Substitute.}$$
$$= -0.5n + 9.5. \qquad \text{Simplify.}$$

(b) $a_{12} = -0.5(12) + 9.5 = 3.5$

Now Try Exercise 31(c)

Geometric Sequences

Suppose that a person with a starting salary of $30,000 per year receives a 5% raise each year. If $a_n = f(n)$ computes this salary at the *beginning* of the nth year, then

$$f(1) = 30,000$$
$$f(2) = 30,000(1.05) = 31,500$$
$$f(3) = 31,500(1.05) = 33,075$$
$$f(4) = 33,075(1.05) = 34,728.75.$$

Previous year's salary   Salary in year n

Terms of Geometric Sequences

c	r	a_1, a_2, a_3, a_4
1	2	1, 2, 4, 8
1	$\frac{1}{2}$	$1, \frac{1}{2}, \frac{1}{4}, \frac{1}{8}$
2	-4	2, -8, 32, -128
3	$\frac{1}{10}$	3, 0.3, 0.03, 0.003

Table 11.4

Each salary results from multiplying the previous salary by 1.05. A general term in the sequence can be written as

$$f(n) = 30{,}000(1.05)^{n-1}.$$

During the 10th year, the annual salary is

$$f(10) = 30{,}000(1.05)^{10-1} \approx \$46{,}540.$$

This type of sequence is a *geometric sequence* given by $f(n) = cr^{n-1}$, where c and r are constants, as shown in our example above. Geometric sequences are capable of either rapid growth or rapid decay. The first four terms from some geometric sequences are shown in Table 11.4. The corresponding values of c and r have been included.

The terms of a geometric sequence can be found by multiplying the previous term by r. In our example we multiplied the previous term by 1.05, indicating a 5% raise each year. We now define a geometric sequence formally.

INFINITE GEOMETRIC SEQUENCE

An **infinite geometric sequence** is a function defined by $f(n) = cr^{n-1}$, where c and r are nonzero constants. The domain of f is the set of natural numbers.

A geometric sequence can be defined recursively by $a_n = ra_{n-1}$, where $a_n = f(n)$ and the first term is $a_1 = c$. Since $r = \frac{a_n}{a_{n-1}}$ for each valid n, r is called the **common ratio**.

The next example illustrates how to recognize symbolic, graphical, and numerical representations of geometric sequences.

EXAMPLE 9 Determining geometric sequences

Decide which of the following represents a geometric sequence.
(a) The sequence defined by $a_n = 4(0.5)^n$
(b) The sequence a_n in Figure 11.11
(c) The sequence a_n in Table 11.5

Figure 11.11

n	1	2	3	4	5	6
a_n	1	-3	9	-27	81	-243

Table 11.5

SOLUTION

Getting Started The formula for a geometric sequence is given by $a_n = cr^{n-1}$, and consecutive terms on its graph change by a common ratio r, as do consecutive terms in its numerical representation. ▶

(a) The formula for a_n can be written as

$$a_n = 4(0.5)^n = 4(0.5)(0.5)^{n-1} = 2(0.5)^{n-1}.$$

Thus a_n represents a geometric sequence with $c = 2$ and $r = 0.5$.

(b) The points on the graph are (1, 2), (2, 4), (3, 7), and (4, 10). Thus $a_1 = 2$, $a_2 = 4$, $a_3 = 7$, and $a_4 = 10$. Taking ratios of successive terms results in

$$\frac{a_2}{a_1} = \frac{4}{2} = 2, \qquad \frac{a_3}{a_2} = \frac{7}{4}, \qquad \text{and} \qquad \frac{a_4}{a_3} = \frac{10}{7}.$$

Since these ratios are not equal, there is no *common* ratio. The sequence is *not* geometric.

(c) The terms in Table 11.5 are $a_1 = 1$, $a_2 = -3$, $a_3 = 9$, $a_4 = -27$, $a_5 = 81$, and $a_6 = -243$. Note that these terms result from multiplying the previous term by -3. This sequence can be written either as

MAKING CONNECTIONS

Exponential Functions and Geometric Sequences

If the domain of an exponential function $f(x) = Ca^x$ is restricted to the natural numbers, then f represents a geometric sequence. For example, $f(x) = 3(2)^x$ generates the geometric sequence

$$6, 12, 24, 48, 96, \ldots$$

when

$$x = 1, 2, 3, 4, 5, \ldots.$$

$$a_n = -3a_{n-1} \quad \text{with} \quad a_1 = 1$$

or as

$$a_n = (-3)^{n-1}.$$

Therefore the sequence is geometric.

Now Try Exercises 69, 73, and 75

EXAMPLE 10   Finding general terms for geometric sequences

Find a general term a_n for each geometric sequence.
(a) $a_1 = 5$ and $r = 1.12$ **(b)** $a_2 = 8$ and $a_5 = 512$

SOLUTION
(a) Since $a_1 = c = 5$ and the common ratio is $r = 1.12$, $a_n = 5(1.12)^{n-1}$.
(b) We need to find $a_n = cr^{n-1}$ so that $a_2 = 8$ and $a_5 = 512$. Start by determining the common ratio r. Since

$$\frac{a_5}{a_2} = \frac{cr^{5-1}}{cr^{2-1}} = \frac{r^4}{r^1} = r^3 \quad \text{and} \quad \frac{a_5}{a_2} = \frac{512}{8} = 64,$$

it follows that $r^3 = 64$, or $r = 4$. So $a_n = c(4)^{n-1}$. Now

$$a_2 = c(4)^{2-1} = 8, \quad \text{or} \quad c = 2.$$

Thus $a_n = 2(4)^{n-1}$.

Now Try Exercises 51 and 55

11.1 Putting It All Together

The following table summarizes some fundamental concepts about sequences.

CONCEPT	EXPLANATION	EXAMPLE
Infinite sequence	A function f whose domain is the set of natural numbers; denoted $a_n = f(n)$; the terms are $a_1, a_2, a_3, \ldots$.	$f(n) = n^2 - 2n$, where $a_n = f(n)$ The first three terms are $a_1 = 1^2 - 2(1) = -1$ $a_2 = 2^2 - 2(2) = 0$ $a_3 = 3^2 - 2(3) = 3$. Graphs of sequences are scatterplots.
Recursive sequence	Defined in terms of previous terms; a_1 through a_{n-1} must be calculated before a_n can be found.	$a_n = 2a_{n-1}, a_1 = 1$ $a_1 = 1, a_2 = 2, a_3 = 4$, and $a_4 = 8$. A new term is found by multiplying the previous term by 2.
Arithmetic sequence	A *linear* function whose domain is the natural numbers; $a_n = dn + c$ or $a_n = a_{n-1} + d$, with common difference d. General term is $a_n = a_1 + (n-1)d$.	$f(n) = 2n - 1$, where $a_n = f(n)$ $a_1 = 1, a_2 = 3, a_3 = 5$, and $a_4 = 7$. Consecutive terms increase by the common difference $d = 2$. The points on the graph of this sequence lie on a line with slope 2.
Geometric sequence	$f(n) = cr^{n-1}$, where c is a nonzero constant and r is the nonzero common ratio; may also be written as $a_n = ra_{n-1}$	$f(n) = 2(3)^{n-1}$, where $a_n = f(n)$ $a_1 = 2, a_2 = 6, a_3 = 18$, and $a_4 = 54$. Consecutive terms are found by multiplying the previous term by the common ratio $r = 3$.

11.1 Exercises

Finding Terms of Sequences

Exercises 1–12: Find the first four terms of the sequence.

1. $a_n = 2n + 1$

2. $a_n = 3(n - 1) + 5$

3. $a_n = 4(-2)^{n-1}$

4. $a_n = 2(3)^n$

5. $a_n = \dfrac{n}{n^2 + 1}$

6. $a_n = 5 - \dfrac{1}{n^2}$

7. $a_n = (-1)^n \left(\dfrac{1}{2}\right)^n$

8. $a_n = (-1)^n \left(\dfrac{1}{n}\right)$

9. $a_n = (-1)^{n-1}\left(\dfrac{2^n}{1 + 2^n}\right)$

10. $a_n = (-1)^{n-1}\left(\dfrac{1}{3^n}\right)$

11. $a_n = 2^n + n^2$

12. $a_n = \dfrac{1}{n} + \dfrac{1}{3n}$

Exercises 13 and 14: Use the graphical representation to list the terms of the sequence.

13.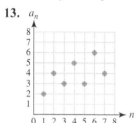

14.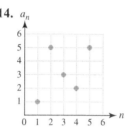

Exercises 15–28: Complete the following for the recursively defined sequence.

(a) Find the first four terms.
(b) Graph these terms.

15. $a_n = 2a_{n-1}; a_1 = 1$

16. $a_n = a_{n-1} + 5; a_1 = -4$

17. $a_n = a_{n-1} + 3; a_1 = -3$

18. $a_n = 2a_{n-1} + 1; a_1 = 1$

19. $a_n = 3a_{n-1} - 1; a_1 = 2$

20. $a_n = \frac{1}{2}a_{n-1}; a_1 = 16$

21. $a_n = a_{n-1} - a_{n-2}; a_1 = 2, a_2 = 5$

22. $a_n = 2a_{n-1} + a_{n-2}; a_1 = 0, a_2 = 1$

23. $a_n = a_{n-1}^2; a_1 = 2$

24. $a_n = \frac{1}{2}a_{n-1}^3 + 1; a_1 = 0$

25. $a_n = a_{n-1} + n; a_1 = 1$

26. $a_n = 3a_{n-1}^2; a_1 = 2$

27. $a_n = a_{n-1}a_{n-2}; a_1 = 2, a_2 = 3$

28. $a_n = 2a_{n-1}^2 + a_{n-2}; a_1 = 2, a_2 = 1$

Representations of Sequences

Exercises 29–34: The first five terms of an arithmetic sequence are given. Find

(a) numerical, (b) graphical, and (c) symbolic representations of the sequence. Include at least eight terms for the graphical and numerical representations.

29. 1, 3, 5, 7, 9

30. 4, 1, −2, −5, −8

31. 7.5, 6, 4.5, 3, 1.5

32. 5.1, 5.5, 5.9, 6.3, 6.7

33. $\frac{1}{2}, 2, \frac{7}{2}, 5, \frac{13}{2}$

34. 2, 4, 6, 8, 10

Exercises 35–40: The first five terms of a geometric sequence are given. Find

(a) numerical, (b) graphical, and (c) symbolic representations of the sequence. Include at least eight terms for the graphical and numerical representations.

35. $8, 4, 2, 1, \frac{1}{2}$

36. $32, -8, 2, -\frac{1}{2}, \frac{1}{8}$

37. $\frac{3}{4}, \frac{3}{2}, 3, 6, 12$

38. $\frac{1}{27}, \frac{1}{9}, \frac{1}{3}, 1, 3$

39. $-\frac{1}{4}, -\frac{1}{2}, -1, -2, -4$

40. $9, 6, 4, \frac{8}{3}, \frac{16}{9}$

Exercises 41–50: Find a general term a_n for the arithmetic sequence.

41. $a_1 = 5, d = -2$

42. $a_1 = -3, d = 5$

43. $a_3 = 1, d = 3$

44. $a_4 = 12, d = -10$

45. $a_2 = 5, a_6 = 13$ **46.** $a_3 = 22, a_{17} = -20$

47. $a_1 = 8, a_4 = 17$ **48.** $a_1 = -2, a_5 = 8$

49. $a_5 = -4, a_8 = -2.5$ **50.** $a_3 = 10, a_7 = -4$

Exercises 51–60: Find a general term a_n for the geometric sequence.

51. $a_1 = 2, r = \frac{1}{2}$ **52.** $a_1 = 0.8, r = -3$

53. $a_3 = \frac{1}{32}, r = -\frac{1}{4}$ **54.** $a_4 = 3, r = 3$

55. $a_3 = 2, a_6 = \frac{1}{4}$ **56.** $a_2 = 6, a_4 = 24, r > 0$

57. $a_1 = -5, a_3 = -125, r < 0$

58. $a_1 = 10, a_2 = 2$

59. $a_2 = -1, a_7 = -32$ **60.** $a_2 = \frac{9}{4}, a_4 = \frac{81}{4}, r < 0$

Identifying Types of Sequences

Exercises 61–68: Determine if f is an arithmetic sequence.

61. $f(n) = 4 - 3n^3$ **62.** $f(n) = 2(n - 1)$

63. $f(n) = 4n - (3 - n)$ **64.** $f(n) = n^2 - n + 2$

65.
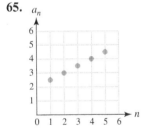

66.
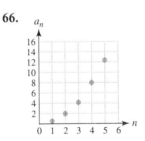

67.

n	1	2	3	4	5
$f(n)$	3	1	-1	-3	-5

68.

n	1	2	3	4	5
$f(n)$	1	4	9	16	25

Exercises 69–76: Determine if f is a geometric sequence.

69. $f(n) = 4(2)^{n-1}$ **70.** $f(n) = -3(0.25)^n$

71. $f(n) = -3(n)^2$ **72.** $f(n) = 2(n - 1)^n$

73.
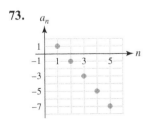

74.
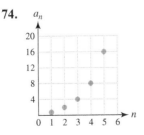

75.

n	1	2	3	4	5
$f(n)$	$\frac{1}{2}$	$\frac{3}{4}$	1	$\frac{5}{4}$	$\frac{5}{2}$

76.

n	1	2	3	4	5
$f(n)$	9	3	1	$\frac{1}{3}$	$\frac{1}{9}$

Exercises 77–82: Given the terms of a finite sequence, classify it as arithmetic, geometric, or neither.

77. $-5, 2, 9, 16, 23, 30$ **78.** $5, 2, -2, -6, -11$

79. $2, 8, 32, 128, 512$ **80.** $5.75, 5.5, 5.25, 5, 4.75, 4.5$

81. $100, 110, 130, 160, 200$

82. $0.7, 0.21, 0.063, 0.0189, 0.00567$

Exercises 83–86: Use the graph to determine if the sequence is arithmetic or geometric. If the sequence is arithmetic, state the sign of the common difference d and estimate its value. If the sequence is geometric, give the sign of the common ratio r and state if $|r| < 1$ or $|r| > 1$.

83.
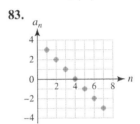

84.
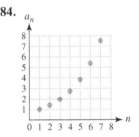

85.
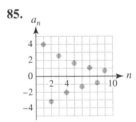

86.
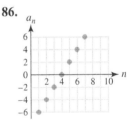

Modeling Insect and Bacteria Populations

Exercises 87 and 88: **Insect Population** *The annual population density of a species of insect after n years is modeled by a sequence. Use the graph to discuss trends in the insect population.*

87.
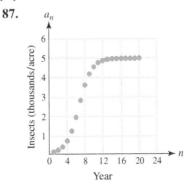

88.

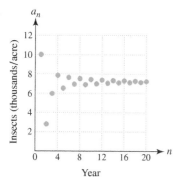

89. Insect Population (Refer to Example 3.) Suppose that the density of female insects during the first year is 500 per acre with $r = 0.8$.

(a) Write a recursive sequence that describes these data, where a_n denotes the female insect density during year n.

(b) Find the six terms $a_1, a_2, a_3, \ldots, a_6$. Interpret the results.

(c) Find a formula for a_n.

90. Bacteria Growth It is possible for some kinds of bacteria to double their size and then divide every 40 minutes. (*Source:* F. Hoppensteadt and C. Peskin, *Mathematics in Medicine and the Life Sciences.*)

(a) Write a recursive sequence that describes this growth where each value of n represents a 40-minute interval. Let $a_1 = 300$ represent the initial number of bacteria per milliliter. Find the first five terms.

(b) Determine the number of bacteria per milliliter after 10 hours have elapsed.

(c) Is this sequence arithmetic or geometric? Explain.

91. Insect Population (Refer to Example 5.) Suppose an insect population density in thousands per acre at the beginning of year n can be modeled by the following recursive sequence.

$$a_1 = 8$$
$$a_n = 2.9a_{n-1} - 0.2a_{n-1}^2, \qquad n > 1$$

(a) Find the population for $n = 1, 2, 3$.

(b) Graph the given sequence for $n = 1, 2, 3, \ldots, 20$. Interpret the graph.

92. Bacteria Growth (Refer to Exercise 90.) If bacteria are cultured in a medium with limited nutrients, competition ensues and growth slows. According to *Verhulst's model*, the number of bacteria at 40-minute intervals is given by

$$a_n = \left(\frac{2}{1 + a_{n-1}/K}\right)a_{n-1},$$

where K is a constant.

(a) Let $a_1 = 200$ and $K = 10,000$. Graph the sequence for $n = 1, 2, 3, \ldots, 20$.

(b) Describe the growth of these bacteria.

(c) Trace the graph of the sequence. Make a conjecture as to why K is called the **saturation constant**. Test your conjecture by changing the value of K.

Applications

93. Digital Waste On average, the United States throws out 100 million cell phones per year. Write a general term a_n for a sequence that gives the number of cell phones thrown out after n years. Find a_5 and interpret the result. (*Source:* EPA.)

94. Global Poverty Between 1981 and 2008, the percent of the world population living on less than $1.25 per day can be modeled by the function $f(n) = -1.1n + 53.1$, where $n = 1$ corresponds to 1981, $n = 2$ to 1982, and so on. (*Source:* World Bank.)

(a) Let $a_n = f(n)$. Find a_1 and interpret the result.

(b) Find a_{28} and interpret the result. Is the percentage of the population living on less than $1.25 per day increasing or decreasing?

95. Tablet Sales In 2011 there were about 100 million tablets sold, and that number was expected to increase by 94 million per year until 2015. (*Source:* Business Insider.)

(a) Write the five terms of the sequence that gives the number of tablets sold in each year from 2011 to 2015. What type of sequence is this?

(b) Give a graphical representation of these terms.

(c) Find a general term a_n.

96. Overweight in the U.S. In 2010, 68% of the U.S. population was overweight. This number is expected to increase by 0.7% per year until 2020. (*Source:* New York Times.)

(a) Write the first six terms of the sequence that gives the percentage of the population that was/will be overweight in each year from 2010 to 2015. What type of sequence is this?

(b) Find the general term a_n

97. Fibonacci Sequence The *Fibonacci sequence* dates back to 1202. It is one of the most famous sequences in mathematics and can be defined recursively.

$$a_1 = 1, a_2 = 1$$
$$a_n = a_{n-1} + a_{n-2} \quad \text{for } n > 2$$

(a) Find the first 12 terms of this sequence.

(b) Compute $\frac{a_n}{a_{n-1}}$ when $n = 2, 3, 4, \ldots, 12$. What happens to this ratio?

(c) Show that for $n = 2$, 3, and 4 the terms of the Fibonacci sequence satisfy the equation

$$a_{n-1} \cdot a_{n+1} - a_n{}^2 = (-1)^n.$$

98. Bouncing Ball If a tennis ball is dropped, it bounces, or rebounds, to 80% of its initial height.
(a) Write the first five terms of a sequence that gives the maximum height attained by the tennis ball on each rebound when it is dropped from an initial height of 5 feet. Let $a_1 = 5$. What type of sequence is this?

(b) Graph these terms.

(c) Find a general term a_n.

99. Salary Increases Suppose an employee's initial salary is \$30,000.
(a) If this person receives a \$2000 raise for each year of experience, determine a sequence that gives the salary at the beginning of the nth year. What type of sequence is this?

(b) Suppose another employee has the same starting salary and receives a 5% raise after each year. Find a sequence that computes the salary at the beginning of the nth year. What type of sequence is this?

(c) Which salary is higher at the beginning of the 10th year and the 20th year?

(d) Graph both sequences in the same viewing rectangle. Compare the two salaries.

100. Area A sequence of smaller squares is formed by connecting the midpoints of the sides of a larger square, as shown in the figure. If the area of the largest square is one square unit, give the first five terms of a sequence that describes the area of each successive square. What type of sequence is this? Write an expression for the area of the nth square.

Exercises 101–104: **Computing Square Roots** *The following recursively defined sequence can be used to compute $\sqrt{k}$ for any positive number k.*

$$a_1 = k; \; a_n = \frac{1}{2}\left(a_{n-1} + \frac{k}{a_{n-1}}\right)$$

This sequence was known to Sumerian mathematicians 4000 years ago, but it is still used today. Use this sequence to approximate the given square root by finding a_6. Compare your result with the actual value. (***Source:*** P. Heinz-Otto, *Chaos and Fractals.*)

101. $\sqrt{2}$ **102.** $\sqrt{11}$

103. $\sqrt{21}$ **104.** $\sqrt{41}$

105. Suppose that a_n and b_n represent arithmetic sequences. Show that their sum, $c_n = a_n + b_n$, is also an arithmetic sequence.

106. Explain why the sequence

$$\log 2, \log 4, \log 8, \log 16, \ldots$$

is an arithmetic sequence.

Writing about Mathematics

107. Explain how we can distinguish between an arithmetic and a geometric sequence. Give examples.

108. Compare a sequence whose nth term is given by $a_n = f(n)$ to a sequence that is defined recursively. Give examples. Which symbolic representation for defining a sequence is usually more convenient to use? Explain why.

11.2 Series

- Understand basic concepts about series
- Identify and find the sum of arithmetic series
- Identify and find the sum of geometric series
- Learn to use summation notation

Introduction

Although the terms *sequence* and *series* are sometimes used interchangeably in everyday English, they represent different mathematical concepts. In mathematics, a sequence is an *ordered list* (a function whose domain is the set of natural numbers), whereas a series is a summation of the terms in a sequence. Series have played a central role in the development of modern mathematics. Today series are often used to approximate functions that are too complicated to have simple formulas. Series are also instrumental in calculating approximations of numbers like π and e.

Basic Concepts

Suppose a person has a starting salary of $30,000 per year and receives a $2000 raise each year. Then

A Finite Sequence

$$30{,}000, \; 32{,}000, \; 34{,}000, \; 36{,}000, \; 38{,}000$$

| 5 terms of a sequence |

are terms of the finite sequence that describe this person's salaries over a 5-year period. The total amount earned is given by the finite *series*

A Finite Series

$$30{,}000 \, + \, 32{,}000 \, + \, 34{,}000 \, + \, 36{,}000 \, + \, 38{,}000,$$

| Sum of 5 terms of a sequence |

whose sum is $170,000. Any sequence can be used to define a series. For example, the *infinite sequence*

An Infinite Sequence

$$1, \frac{1}{3}, \frac{1}{9}, \frac{1}{27}, \frac{1}{81}, \frac{1}{243}, \cdots$$

defines the terms of the *infinite series*

An Infinite Series

Add the terms of a sequence to define a series.

$$1 + \frac{1}{3} + \frac{1}{9} + \frac{1}{27} + \frac{1}{81} + \frac{1}{243} + \cdots .$$

Finite Series   We now define the concept of a finite series, where $a_1, a_2, a_3, \ldots, a_n$ represent terms of a sequence.

> **FINITE SERIES**
>
> A **finite series** is the sum of the first n terms of a sequence and can be written as
>
> $$a_1 + a_2 + a_3 + \cdots + a_n.$$

EXAMPLE 1   Writing sequences and series

Complete the following.
(a) Write a sequence that is the first 5 even natural numbers.
(b) Write a series that sums the terms of the sequence in part (a).
(c) Find the sum of the series in part (b).

SOLUTION
(a) A sequence is a list of values, so the terms are 2, 4, 6, 8, 10.
(b) The corresponding series is $2 + 4 + 6 + 8 + 10$.
(c) Because $2 + 4 + 6 + 8 + 10 = 30$, the sum of the series is 30.

Now Try Exercise 1

See the Concept: Sequences and Series

A Sequence	1, 3, 5, 7, 9, 11, 13	**A** A sequence is an ordered list.
B Series	1 + 3 + 5 + 7 + 9 + 11 + 13	**B** A series is the sum of the terms of a sequence.
C Sum of the series	49	**C** When we evaluate the sum in **B**, we say that we are finding the "sum of the series."

Infinite Series and Partial Sums In the following box we define an infinite series.

> **INFINITE SERIES**
>
> An **infinite series** is the sum of the terms of an infinite sequence and can be written as
> $$a_1 + a_2 + a_3 + \cdots + a_n + \cdots .$$

An infinite series contains infinitely many terms. Since a series represents a sum, we must define what is meant by finding the sum of an *infinite* series. Let the following be a **sequence of partial sums**.

$$S_1 = a_1 \qquad\qquad \text{Sum of the first term}$$

$$S_2 = a_1 + a_2 \qquad\qquad \text{Sum of the first two terms}$$

$$S_3 = a_1 + a_2 + a_3 \qquad\qquad \text{Sum of the first three terms}$$

$$\vdots$$

$$S_n = a_1 + a_2 + a_3 + \cdots + a_n \qquad \text{Sum of the first } n \text{ terms}$$

If the sequence of partial sums $S_1, S_2, S_3, \ldots, S_n$ approaches a real number S as $n \to \infty$, then the sum of the infinite series is S.

For example, let $S_1 = 0.3$, $S_2 = 0.3 + 0.03$, $S_3 = 0.3 + 0.03 + 0.003$, and so on. Then, as $n \to \infty$, $S_n \to \frac{1}{3}$. We say that the infinite series

As the number of terms n approaches infinity, the sum approaches $\frac{1}{3}$.

$$0.3 + 0.03 + 0.003 + 0.0003 + \cdots = 0.3333\ldots = 0.\overline{3}$$

has sum $\frac{1}{3}$. Some infinite series do not have a sum S. For example, the series given by $1 + 2 + 3 + 4 + 5 + \cdots$ would have an **unbounded**, or "infinite," sum.

EXAMPLE 2 Finding partial sums

For each a_n, calculate S_4.
(a) $a_n = 2n + 1$ **(b)** $a_n = n^2$

SOLUTION
(a) Because $S_4 = a_1 + a_2 + a_3 + a_4$, start by calculating the first four terms of the sequence $a_n = 2n + 1$.

$$a_1 = 2(1) + 1 = 3; \qquad a_2 = 2(2) + 1 = 5;$$

$$a_3 = 2(3) + 1 = 7; \qquad a_4 = 2(4) + 1 = 9$$

Thus $S_4 = \underbrace{3 + 5 + 7 + 9}_{4 \text{ terms}} = 24$.

(b) $a_1 = 1^2 = 1; \qquad a_2 = 2^2 = 4; \qquad a_3 = 3^2 = 9; \qquad a_4 = 4^2 = 16$

Thus $S_4 = 1 + 4 + 9 + 16 = 30$.

Now Try Exercises 7 and 11

Calculating π Since π is an irrational number, it cannot be represented exactly by a fraction. Its decimal expansion neither repeats nor has a discernible pattern. The ability to compute π was essential to the development of every modern society, because π appears in formulas used in construction, surveying, and geometry. It was not until the discovery of series that exceedingly accurate decimal approximations of π were possible. In 2002, after 400 hours of supercomputer time, π was computed to 1.24 trillion digits. Why would anyone want to compute π to so many decimal places? One practical reason is to test electrical circuits in new computers. If a computer has a small defect in its hardware, there is a good chance that an error will appear after trillions of arithmetic calculations are performed during the computation of π. (***Sources:*** P. Beckmann, *A History of PI;* P. Heinz-Otto, *Chaos and Fractals.*)

EXAMPLE 3 Computing π with a series

The infinite series given by

$$\frac{\pi^4}{90} = \frac{1}{1^4} + \frac{1}{2^4} + \frac{1}{3^4} + \frac{1}{4^4} + \frac{1}{5^4} + \cdots + \frac{1}{n^4} + \cdots$$

can be used to estimate π.
(a) Approximate π by finding the sum of the first four terms.
(b) Use technology to approximate π by summing the first 50 terms. Compare the result to the actual value of π.

SOLUTION
(a) Summing the first four terms results in the following approximation.

$$\frac{\pi^4}{90} \approx \frac{1}{1^4} + \frac{1}{2^4} + \frac{1}{3^4} + \frac{1}{4^4} \approx 1.078751929$$

This approximation can be solved for π by multiplying by 90 and then taking the fourth root. Thus

$$\pi \approx \sqrt[4]{90(1.078751929)} \approx 3.139.$$

```
sum(seq(1/n^4,n,
1,50))
          1.082320646
(90*Ans)^(1/4)
          3.141590776
π
          3.141592654
```

Figure 11.12

(b) Some calculators are capable of summing the terms of a sequence, as shown in Figure 11.12. (Summing the terms of a sequence is equivalent to finding the sum of a series.) The first 50 terms of the series provide an approximation of $\pi \approx 3.141590776$. This computation matches the actual value of π for the first five decimal places.

Now Try Exercise 107

Calculator Help
To find the sum of a series, see Appendix A (page AP-17).

Arithmetic Series

Summing the terms of an arithmetic sequence results in an **arithmetic series**. For example, the sequence defined by $a_n = 2n - 1$ for $n = 1, 2, 3, \ldots, 7$ is the arithmetic sequence

$$1, 3, 5, 7, 9, 11, 13. \qquad \text{Arithmetic sequence}$$

The corresponding arithmetic series is

$$1 + 3 + 5 + 7 + 9 + 11 + 13. \qquad \text{Arithmetic series}$$

The following formula can be used to sum a finite arithmetic series. (For a proof, see Exercise 3 in the Extended and Discovery Exercises at the end of this chapter.)

SUM OF A FINITE ARITHMETIC SERIES

The sum of the first n terms of an arithmetic series, denoted S_n, is found by averaging the first and nth terms and then multiplying by n. That is,

$$S_n = a_1 + a_2 + a_3 + \cdots + a_n = n\left(\frac{a_1 + a_n}{2}\right).$$

From Section 11.1, the general term a_n for an arithmetic sequence can be written as $a_n = a_1 + (n - 1)d$, so S_n can also be written as follows.

$$S_n = n\left(\frac{a_1 + a_n}{2}\right)$$

$$= \frac{n}{2}(a_1 + a_1 + (n - 1)d)$$

$$= \frac{n}{2}(2a_1 + (n - 1)d) \quad\longrightarrow\quad \text{Sum of a finite arithmetic series with } n \text{ terms}$$

EXAMPLE 4 Finding the sum of a finite arithmetic series

Use a formula to find the sum of the arithmetic series

$$2 + 4 + 6 + 8 + \cdots + 100.$$

SOLUTION The series $2 + 4 + 6 + 8 + \cdots + 100$ has $n = 50$ terms with $a_1 = 2$ and $a_{50} = 100$. We can use the formula

$$S_n = n\left(\frac{a_1 + a_n}{2}\right)$$

to find its sum.

$$S_{50} = 50\left(\frac{2 + 100}{2}\right) = 2550$$

We can also use the formula

$$S_n = \frac{n}{2}(2a_1 + (n - 1)d)$$

with common difference $d = 2$ to find this sum.

$$S_{50} = \frac{50}{2}(2(2) + (50 - 1)2) = 2550$$

The two answers agree, as expected.

Now Try Exercise 15

EXAMPLE 5 Finding the sum of a finite arithmetic series

A person has a starting annual salary of \$30,000 and receives a \$1500 raise each year.
(a) Calculate the total amount earned over 10 years.
(b) Verify this value using a calculator.

SOLUTION
(a) The arithmetic sequence describing the salary during year n is computed by

$$a_n = 30{,}000 + 1500(n - 1).$$

Because $a_n = 30{,}000 + 1500(n - 1)$, the first and tenth year's salaries are

$$a_1 = 30{,}000 + 1500(1 - 1) = 30{,}000$$

$$a_{10} = 30{,}000 + 1500(10 - 1) = 43{,}500.$$

Thus the total amount earned during this 10-year period is

$$S_{10} = 10\left(\frac{30{,}000 + 43{,}500}{2}\right) = \$367{,}500.$$

This sum can also be found using $S_n = \frac{n}{2}(2a_1 + (n - 1)d)$.

$$S_{10} = \frac{10}{2}(2 \cdot 30{,}000 + (10 - 1)1500) = \$367{,}500$$

(b) To verify this result with a calculator, compute the sum

$$a_1 + a_2 + a_3 + \cdots + a_{10},$$

where $a_n = 30{,}000 + 1500(n - 1)$. This calculation is shown in Figure 11.13. The result of 367,500 agrees with part (a).

Now Try Exercise 95

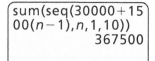

```
sum(seq(30000+15
00(n−1),n,1,10))
            367500
```

Figure 11.13

EXAMPLE 6 Finding a term of an arithmetic series

The sum of an arithmetic series with 15 terms is 285. If $a_{15} = 40$, find a_1.

SOLUTION To find a_1, we apply the sum formula

$$S_n = n\left(\frac{a_1 + a_n}{2}\right) = a_1 + a_2 + a_3 + \cdots + a_n$$

with $n = 15$ and $a_{15} = 40$.

Apply the formula and solve for a_1.

$$15\left(\frac{a_1 + 40}{2}\right) = 285$$

$$15(a_1 + 40) = 570 \qquad \text{Multiply by 2.}$$

$$a_1 + 40 = 38 \qquad \text{Divide by 15.}$$

$$a_1 = -2 \qquad \text{Subtract 40.}$$

Now Try Exercise 23

CLASS DISCUSSION

Explain why a formula for the sum of an infinite arithmetic series is not given.

Geometric Series

What will happen if we attempt to find the sum of an infinite geometric series? For example, suppose that a person walked 1 mile on the first day, $\frac{1}{2}$ mile the second day, $\frac{1}{4}$ mile the third day, and so on. How far down the road would this person travel? This distance is described by the infinite series

$$1 + \frac{1}{2} + \frac{1}{4} + \frac{1}{8} + \frac{1}{16} + \frac{1}{32} + \frac{1}{64} + \cdots . \qquad \text{Total distance traveled}$$

Does the sum of an infinite number of positive values always become infinitely large? We answer this question later in Example 9.

Finite Geometric Series In a manner similar to the way an arithmetic series was defined, a **geometric series** is defined as the sum of the terms of a geometric sequence.

In order to calculate sums of infinite geometric series, we begin by finding sums of finite geometric series. Any finite geometric sequence can be written as

Geometric Sequence

$$a_1, a_1r, a_1r^2, a_1r^3, \ldots, a_1r^{n-1}.$$

The summation of these n terms is a finite geometric series. Its sum S_n is expressed by

Geometric Series

$$S_n = a_1 + a_1r + a_1r^2 + a_1r^3 + \cdots + a_1r^{n-1}. \qquad \text{Equation 1}$$

To find the value of S_n, multiply this equation by r.

$$rS_n = a_1r + a_1r^2 + a_1r^3 + \cdots + a_1r^{n-1} + a_1r^n \qquad \text{Equation 2}$$

Subtracting equation 2 from equation 1 results in

$$S_n - rS_n = a_1 - a_1r^n$$

$$S_n(1 - r) = a_1(1 - r^n)$$

Sum of a finite geometric series with n terms — $S_n = a_1\left(\dfrac{1 - r^n}{1 - r}\right), \qquad$ provided $r \neq 1$.

SUM OF A FINITE GEOMETRIC SERIES

If a geometric sequence has first term a_1 and common ratio r, then the sum of the first n terms is given by

$$S_n = a_1\left(\frac{1 - r^n}{1 - r}\right), \qquad r \neq 1.$$

EXAMPLE 7 Finding the sums of finite geometric series

Approximate the sum S_n for the given values of n.
(a) $1 + \frac{1}{2} + \frac{1}{4} + \cdots + \left(\frac{1}{2}\right)^{n-1}$; $n = 5, 10,$ and 20
(b) $3 - 6 + 12 - 24 + 48 - \cdots + 3(-2)^{n-1}$; $n = 3, 8,$ and 13

SOLUTION
(a) This geometric series has $a_1 = 1$ and $r = \frac{1}{2} = 0.5$.

$$S_5 = 1\left(\frac{1 - 0.5^5}{1 - 0.5}\right) = 1.9375$$

$$S_{10} = 1\left(\frac{1 - 0.5^{10}}{1 - 0.5}\right) \approx 1.998047$$

$$S_{20} = 1\left(\frac{1 - 0.5^{20}}{1 - 0.5}\right) \approx 1.999998$$

(b) This geometric series has $a_1 = 3$ and $r = -2$.

$$S_3 = 3\left(\frac{1 - (-2)^3}{1 - (-2)}\right) = 9$$

$$S_8 = 3\left(\frac{1 - (-2)^8}{1 - (-2)}\right) = -255$$

$$S_{13} = 3\left(\frac{1 - (-2)^{13}}{1 - (-2)}\right) = 8193$$

Now Try Exercises 41 and 43

Annuities With an **annuity**, an individual often makes a sequence of deposits at equal time intervals. Suppose A_0 dollars is deposited at the end of each year into an account that pays an annual interest rate i compounded annually. At the end of the first year, the account contains A_0 dollars. At the end of the second year, A_0 dollars would be deposited again. In addition, the first deposit of A_0 dollars would have received interest during the second year. Therefore the value of the annuity after 2 years is

1st year deposit plus interest

$$A_0 + A_0(1 + i).$$

2nd year deposit

After 3 years the balance is

By the end of the 3rd year the 1st year deposit has earned 2 years of interest.

$$A_0 + A_0(1 + i) + A_0(1 + i)^2,$$

and after n years this amount is given by

$$A_0 + A_0(1 + i) + A_0(1 + i)^2 + \cdots + A_0(1 + i)^{n-1}.$$

This is a geometric series with first term $a_1 = A_0$ and common ratio $r = (1 + i)$. The sum of the first n terms is given by

$$S_n = A_0\left(\frac{1 - (1 + i)^n}{1 - (1 + i)}\right) = A_0\left(\frac{(1 + i)^n - 1}{i}\right). \qquad S_n = a_1\left(\frac{1 - r^n}{1 - r}\right)$$

EXAMPLE 8 Finding the future value of an annuity

Suppose that a 20-year-old worker deposits $1000 into an account at the end of each year until age 65. If the interest rate is 4%, find the future value of the annuity.

SOLUTION Let $A_0 = 1000$, $i = 0.04$, and $n = 45$. The future value of the annuity is

$$S_n = A_0\left(\frac{(1 + i)^n - 1}{i}\right)$$

$$= 1000\left(\frac{(1 + 0.04)^{45} - 1}{0.04}\right)$$

$$\approx \$121,029.39.$$

Now Try Exercise 97

Infinite Geometric Series The absolute value of r affects the sum of a finite geometric series.

- If $|r| > 1$, then $|r^n|$ becomes large as n increases and the sum of the series S_n also becomes large in *absolute value*. See Example 7, part (b) where $r = -2$.
- If $|r| < 1$, then $|r^n|$ becomes closer to 0. So as n increases, S_n approaches a number

$$S_n = a_1\left(\frac{1 - r^n}{1 - r}\right) \approx a_1\left(\frac{1 - 0}{1 - r}\right) = \frac{a_1}{1 - r}.$$

See Example 7, part (a), where $r = \frac{1}{2}$ and the values appear to approach 2. This result is summarized in the following box.

SUM OF AN INFINITE GEOMETRIC SERIES

The sum of the infinite geometric series with first term a_1 and common ratio r is given by

$$S = \frac{a_1}{1 - r},$$

provided $|r| < 1$. If $|r| \geq 1$, then this sum does not exist.

Infinite series can be used to describe repeating decimals. For example, the fraction $\frac{1}{3}$ can be written as the repeating decimal $0.333333\ldots$. This decimal can be expressed as an infinite series.

Writing a Fraction as a Series

$$\frac{1}{3} = 0.3 + 0.03 + 0.003 + 0.0003 + \cdots + 0.3(0.1)^{n-1} + \cdots$$

In this series $a_1 = 0.3$ and $r = 0.1$. Since $|r| < 1$, the sum exists and is given by

Summing the Series

$$S = \frac{0.3}{1 - 0.1} = \frac{3}{9} = \frac{1}{3}$$

as expected.

We are now able to answer the question concerning how far a person will walk if he or she travels 1 mile on the first day, $\frac{1}{2}$ mile the second day, $\frac{1}{4}$ mile the third day, and so on.

EXAMPLE 9 Finding the sum of an infinite geometric series

Find the sum of the infinite geometric series

$$1 + \frac{1}{2} + \frac{1}{4} + \frac{1}{8} + \cdots.$$

SOLUTION In this series, the first term is $a_1 = 1$ and the common ratio is $\frac{1}{2} = 0.5$. Its sum is

$$S = \frac{a_1}{1 - r} = \frac{1}{1 - 0.5} = 2.$$

If it were possible to walk in the prescribed manner, the total distance traveled after many days would always be slightly less than 2 miles.

Now Try Exercise 45

Summation Notation

Summation notation is used to write series efficiently. The symbol Σ, the uppercase Greek letter *sigma*, indicates a sum.

SUMMATION NOTATION

$$\sum_{k=1}^{n} a_k = a_1 + a_2 + a_3 + \cdots + a_n$$

The letter k is called the **index of summation**. The numbers 1 and n represent the subscripts of the first and last terms in the series. They are called the **lower limit** and **upper limit** of the summation, respectively.

EXAMPLE 10 Using summation notation

Evaluate each series.

(a) $\displaystyle\sum_{k=1}^{5} k^2$ (b) $\displaystyle\sum_{k=1}^{4} 5$ (c) $\displaystyle\sum_{k=3}^{6} (2k - 5)$

SOLUTION

(a) $\displaystyle\sum_{k=1}^{5} k^2 = 1^2 + 2^2 + 3^2 + 4^2 + 5^2 = 55$ $k = 1, 2, 3, 4, 5$

(b) $\displaystyle\sum_{k=1}^{4} 5 = 5 + 5 + 5 + 5 = 20$ $k = 1, 2, 3, 4$

(c) $\displaystyle\sum_{k=3}^{6} (2k - 5) = (2(3) - 5) + (2(4) - 5) + (2(5) - 5) + (2(6) - 5)$

                               $k = 3$ $k = 4$ $k = 5$ $k = 6$

$$= 1 + 3 + 5 + 7 = 16$$

Now Try Exercise 61, 63, and 67

EXAMPLE 11   Writing a series in summation notation

Write the series using summation notation. Let the lower limit equal 1.

(a) $\dfrac{1}{2^3} + \dfrac{1}{3^3} + \dfrac{1}{4^3} + \dfrac{1}{5^3} + \dfrac{1}{6^3} + \dfrac{1}{7^3} + \dfrac{1}{8^3}$

(b) $\dfrac{1}{2} + \dfrac{2}{3} + \dfrac{3}{4} + \dfrac{4}{5} + \dfrac{5}{6} + \dfrac{6}{7} + \dfrac{7}{8}$

SOLUTION

(a) The terms of the series can be written as $\dfrac{1}{(k + 1)^3}$ for $k = 1, 2, 3, \ldots, 7$. Thus

$$\frac{1}{2^3} + \frac{1}{3^3} + \frac{1}{4^3} + \frac{1}{5^3} + \frac{1}{6^3} + \frac{1}{7^3} + \frac{1}{8^3} = \sum_{k=1}^{7} \frac{1}{(k + 1)^3}.$$

(b) The terms of the series can be written as $\dfrac{k}{k + 1}$ for $k = 1, 2, 3, \ldots, 7$. Thus

$$\frac{1}{2} + \frac{2}{3} + \frac{3}{4} + \frac{4}{5} + \frac{5}{6} + \frac{6}{7} + \frac{7}{8} = \sum_{k=1}^{7} \frac{k}{k + 1}.$$

Now Try Exercises 69 and 71

MAKING CONNECTIONS

Notation   The expressions

$$\sum_{k=1}^{n} a_k \text{ and } \Sigma_{k=1}^{n}\, a_k$$

are equivalent.

EXAMPLE 12   Shifting the index of a series

Rewrite each summation so that the index starts with $n = 1$.

(a) $\displaystyle\sum_{k=4}^{7} k^2$ **(b)** $\displaystyle\sum_{k=8}^{30} (2k - 3)$

SOLUTION

(a) Getting Started Because $\sum_{k=4}^{7} k^2 = 4^2 + 5^2 + 6^2 + 7^2$, the summation has four terms. Instead of letting $k = 4, 5, 6, 7$, we must rewrite the sum so that $n = 1, 2, 3, 4$. It follows that $n + 3 = k$, so substitute $n + 3$ for k in the expression. ▶

$$\sum_{k=4}^{7} k^2 = \sum_{n=1}^{4} (n + 3)^2$$

$$= (1 + 3)^2 + (2 + 3)^2 + (3 + 3)^2 + (4 + 3)^2$$

$$= 4^2 + 5^2 + 6^2 + 7^2$$

(b) Instead of letting $k = 8, 9, 10, \ldots, 30$, we must rewrite the given sum so that $n = 1, 2, 3, \ldots, 23$. Thus $n + 7 = k$.

$$\sum_{k=8}^{30} (2k - 3) = \sum_{n=1}^{23} (2(n + 7) - 3)$$

$$= \sum_{n=1}^{23} (2n + 11)$$

Now Try Exercises 75 and 77

The following box lists properties for summation notation.

PROPERTIES FOR SUMMATION NOTATION

Let $a_1, a_2, a_3, \ldots, a_n$ and $b_1, b_2, b_3, \ldots, b_n$ be sequences, and c be a constant.

1. $\displaystyle\sum_{k=1}^{n} ca_k = c\sum_{k=1}^{n} a_k$

2. $\displaystyle\sum_{k=1}^{n} (a_k + b_k) = \sum_{k=1}^{n} a_k + \sum_{k=1}^{n} b_k$

3. $\displaystyle\sum_{k=1}^{n} (a_k - b_k) = \sum_{k=1}^{n} a_k - \sum_{k=1}^{n} b_k$

4. $\displaystyle\sum_{k=1}^{n} c = nc$

5. $\displaystyle\sum_{k=1}^{n} k = \frac{n(n+1)}{2}$

6. $\displaystyle\sum_{k=1}^{n} k^2 = \frac{n(n+1)(2n+1)}{6}$

These properties can be used to find sums, as illustrated in the next example.

EXAMPLE 13 Applying summation notation

Use properties for summation notation to find each sum.

(a) $\displaystyle\sum_{k=1}^{40} 5$

(b) $\displaystyle\sum_{k=1}^{22} 2k$

(c) $\displaystyle\sum_{k=1}^{14} (2k^2 - 3)$

SOLUTION

(a)
$$\sum_{k=1}^{40} 5 = 40(5) = 200$$
Property 4 with $n = 40$ and $c = 5$

(b)
$$\sum_{k=1}^{22} 2k = 2\sum_{k=1}^{22} k$$
Property 1 with $c = 2$ and $a_k = k$
$$= 2 \cdot \frac{22(22 + 1)}{2}$$
Property 5 with $n = 22$
$$= 506$$
Simplify.

(c)
$$\sum_{k=1}^{14} (2k^2 - 3) = \sum_{k=1}^{14} 2k^2 - \sum_{k=1}^{14} 3$$
Property 3 with $a_k = 2k^2$ and $b_k = 3$
$$= 2\sum_{k=1}^{14} k^2 - \sum_{k=1}^{14} 3$$
Property 1 with $c = 2$ and $a_k = k^2$
$$= 2 \cdot \frac{14(14 + 1)(2 \cdot 14 + 1)}{6} - 14(3)$$
Properties 6 and 4
$$= 1988$$
Simplify.

Now Try Exercises 81, 83, and 89

NOTE The infinite series $a_1 + a_2 + a_3 + \ldots + a_k + \ldots$ is sometimes written in summation notation as

$$\sum_{k=1}^{\infty} a_k, \text{ where the upper limit is infinity.}$$

11.2 Putting It All Together

$\mathbf{T}$he following table summarizes concepts related to series.

CONCEPT	EXPLANATION	EXAMPLE
Series	A series is the summation of the terms of a sequence. A finite series always has a sum, but an infinite series may not have a sum.	$2 + 4 + 6 + 8 + \cdots + 20$ $S_4 = a_1 + a_2 + a_3 + a_4$ (partial sum) $\quad = 2 + 4 + 6 + 8$ $\quad = 20$
Arithmetic series	An arithmetic series is the summation of the terms of an arithmetic sequence. The sum of the first n terms is given by $$S_n = n\left(\frac{a_1 + a_n}{2}\right)$$ or $$S_n = \frac{n}{2}(2a_1 + (n-1)d).$$	$1 + 4 + 7 + 10 + 13 + 16 + 19$ (7 terms) $$S_7 = 7\left(\frac{a_1 + a_7}{2}\right) = 7\left(\frac{1 + 19}{2}\right) = 70 \quad \text{or}$$ $$S_7 = \frac{7}{2}(2a_1 + 6d) = \frac{7}{2}(2(1) + 6(3)) = 70$$
Geometric series	A geometric series is the summation of the terms of a geometric sequence. The sum of the first n terms is given by $$S_n = a_1\left(\frac{1 - r^n}{1 - r}\right).$$ If $|r| < 1$, then an infinite geometric series has the sum $$S = \frac{a_1}{1 - r}.$$	$3 + 6 + 12 + 24 + 48 + 96$ (6 terms) $$S_6 = 3\left(\frac{1 - 2^6}{1 - 2}\right) = 189$$ The infinite geometric series $$1 + \frac{1}{4} + \frac{1}{16} + \frac{1}{64} + \cdots$$ has a sum $$S = \frac{1}{1 - \frac{1}{4}} = \frac{4}{3}.$$
Summation notation	The series $a_1 + a_2 + \cdots + a_n$ can be written with summation notation as $$\sum_{k=1}^{n} a_k.$$	$1^2 + 2^2 + 3^2 + 4^2 + \cdots + 10^2$ can be written as $$\sum_{k=1}^{10} k^2.$$

Exercises

Concepts

Exercises 1–4: Complete the following.

(a) *Write the described sequence.*
(b) *Write a series that sums the terms of the sequence in part (a).*
(c) *Find the sum of the series in part (b).*

1. The counting numbers from 1 to 5

2. The first seven positive odd integers

3. The integers counting down from 1 to -3

4. The integers counting down from 10 to 6

Exercises 5 and 6: Let A_n represent the number of U.S. AIDS deaths reported n years after 2000.

5. Write a series whose sum gives the cumulative number of AIDS deaths from 2005 to 2009.

6. Explain what S_6 represents.

Finding Sums of Series

Exercises 7–14: For the given a_n, calculate S_5.

7. $a_n = 3n$

8. $a_n = n + 4$

9. $a_n = 2n - 1$

10. $a_n = 4n + 1$

11. $a_n = n^2 + 1$

12. $a_n = 2n^2$

13. $a_n = \dfrac{n}{n + 1}$

14. $a_n = \dfrac{1}{2n}$

Exercises 15–22: Use a formula to find the sum of the arithmetic series.

15. $3 + 5 + 7 + 9 + 11 + 13 + 15 + 17$

16. $7.5 + 6 + 4.5 + 3 + 1.5 + 0 + (-1.5)$

17. $1 + 2 + 3 + 4 + \cdots + 50$

18. $1 + 3 + 5 + 7 + \cdots + 97$

19. $-7 + (-4) + (-1) + 2 + 5 + \cdots + 98 + 101$

20. $89 + 84 + 79 + 74 + \cdots + 9 + 4$

21. The first 40 terms of the series defined by $a_n = 5n$

22. The first 50 terms of the series defined by $a_n = 1 - 3n$

23. The sum of an arithmetic series with 15 terms is 255. If $a_1 = 3$, find a_{15}.

24. The sum of an arithmetic series with 20 terms is 610. If $a_{20} = 59$, find a_1.

Exercises 25–34: Use a formula to find the sum of the first 20 terms for the arithmetic sequence.

25. $a_1 = 4, d = 2$

26. $a_1 = -3, d = \frac{2}{3}$

27. $a_1 = 10, d = -\frac{1}{2}$

28. $a_1 = 0, d = -4$

29. $a_1 = 4, a_{20} = 190.2$

30. $a_1 = -4, a_{20} = 15$

31. $a_1 = -2, a_{11} = 50$

32. $a_1 = 6, a_5 = -30$

33. $a_2 = 6, a_{12} = 31$

34. $a_8 = 4, a_{10} = 14$

Exercises 35–40: Use a formula to find the sum of the finite geometric series.

35. $1 + 2 + 4 + 8 + 16 + 32 + 64 + 128$

36. $2 + \frac{1}{2} + \frac{1}{8} + \frac{1}{32} + \frac{1}{128} + \frac{1}{512}$

37. $0.5 + 1.5 + 4.5 + 13.5 + 40.5 + 121.5 + 364.5$

38. $0.6 + 0.3 + 0.15 + 0.075 + 0.0375$

39. The first 20 terms of the series defined by $a_n = 3(2)^{n-1}$

40. The first 15 terms of the series defined by $a_n = 2\left(\frac{1}{3}\right)^n$

Exercises 41–44: Use a formula to approximate the sum for $n = 4, 7,$ and 10.

41. $1 - \frac{1}{2} + \frac{1}{4} - \frac{1}{8} + \cdots + \left(-\frac{1}{2}\right)^{n-1}$

42. $3 - 1 + \frac{1}{3} - \frac{1}{9} + \cdots + 3\left(-\frac{1}{3}\right)^{n-1}$

43. $\frac{1}{3} + \frac{2}{3} + \frac{4}{3} + \frac{8}{3} + \cdots + \frac{1}{3}(2)^{n-1}$

44. $4 + \frac{8}{3} + \frac{16}{9} + \frac{32}{27} + \cdots + 4\left(\frac{2}{3}\right)^{n-1}$

Exercises 45–50: Find the sum of the infinite geometric series.

45. $1 + \frac{1}{3} + \frac{1}{9} + \frac{1}{27} + \frac{1}{81} + \cdots$

46. $5 + \frac{5}{2} + \frac{5}{4} + \frac{5}{8} + \frac{5}{16} + \cdots$

47. $6 - 4 + \frac{8}{3} - \frac{16}{9} + \frac{32}{27} - \frac{64}{81} + \cdots$

48. $-2 + \frac{1}{2} - \frac{1}{8} + \frac{1}{32} - \frac{1}{128} + \cdots$

49. $1 - \frac{1}{10} + \frac{1}{100} - \frac{1}{1000} + \cdots + \left(-\frac{1}{10}\right)^{n-1} + \cdots$

50. $25 - 5 + 1 - \frac{1}{5} + \cdots + 25\left(-\frac{1}{5}\right)^{n-1} + \cdots$

Decimal Numbers and Geometric Series

Exercises 51–56: Write each rational number in the form of an infinite geometric series.

51. $\frac{2}{3}$ **52.** $\frac{1}{9}$

53. $\frac{9}{11}$ **54.** $\frac{14}{33}$

55. $\frac{1}{7}$ **56.** $\frac{23}{99}$

Exercises 57–60: Write the sum of each geometric series as a rational number.

57. $0.8 + 0.08 + 0.008 + 0.0008 + \cdots$

58. $0.9 + 0.09 + 0.009 + 0.0009 + \cdots$

59. $0.45 + 0.0045 + 0.000045 + \cdots$

60. $0.36 + 0.0036 + 0.000036 + \cdots$

Summation Notation

Exercises 61–68: Write out the terms of the series and then evaluate it.

61. $\sum_{k=1}^{4}(k + 1)$ **62.** $\sum_{k=1}^{6}(3k - 1)$

63. $\sum_{k=1}^{8}4$ **64.** $\sum_{k=2}^{6}(5 - 2k)$

65. $\sum_{k=1}^{7}k^3$ **66.** $\sum_{k=1}^{4}5(2)^{k-1}$

67. $\sum_{k=4}^{5}(k^2 - k)$ **68.** $\sum_{k=1}^{5}\log k$

Exercises 69–74: Write the series with summation notation. Let the lower limit equal 1.

69. $1^4 + 2^4 + 3^4 + 4^4 + 5^4 + 6^4$

70. $1 + \frac{1}{5} + \frac{1}{25} + \frac{1}{125} + \frac{1}{625}$

71. $1 + \frac{4}{3} + \frac{6}{4} + \frac{8}{5} + \frac{10}{6} + \frac{12}{7} + \frac{14}{8}$

72. $2 + \frac{5}{8} + \frac{10}{27} + \frac{17}{64} + \frac{26}{125} + \frac{37}{216}$

73. $1 + \frac{1}{2^2} + \frac{1}{3^2} + \frac{1}{4^2} + \frac{1}{5^2} + \cdots$

74. $1 + \frac{1}{10} + \frac{1}{100} + \frac{1}{1000} + \frac{1}{10,000} + \cdots$

Exercises 75–80: (Refer to Example 12.) Rewrite each summation so that the index starts with $n = 1$.

75. $\sum_{k=6}^{9}k^3$ **76.** $\sum_{k=5}^{10}(k^2 - 2)$

77. $\sum_{k=9}^{32}(3k - 2)$ **78.** $\sum_{k=8}^{21}(4k + 1)$

79. $\sum_{k=16}^{52}(k^2 - 3k)$ **80.** $\sum_{k=25}^{59}(k^2 + 4k)$

Exercises 81–92: (Refer to Example 13.) Use properties for summation notation to find the sum.

81. $\sum_{k=1}^{60}9$ **82.** $\sum_{k=1}^{43}-4$

83. $\sum_{k=1}^{15}5k$ **84.** $\sum_{k=1}^{22}-2k$

85. $\sum_{k=1}^{31}(3k - 3)$ **86.** $\sum_{k=1}^{17}(1 - 4k)$

87. $\sum_{k=1}^{25}k^2$ **88.** $\sum_{k=1}^{12}3k^2$

89. $\sum_{k=1}^{16}(k^2 - k)$ **90.** $\sum_{k=1}^{18}(k^2 - 4k + 3)$

91. $\sum_{k=5}^{24}k$ **92.** $\sum_{k=7}^{19}(k^2 + 1)$

93. Verify the formula $\sum_{k=1}^{n} k = \frac{n(n + 1)}{2}$ by using the formula for the sum of the first n terms of a finite arithmetic sequence.

94. Use Exercise 93 to find the sum of the series $\sum_{k=1}^{200} k$.

Applications

Exercises 95 and 96: **Salaries** *A person has the given starting salary S and receives a raise R each year thereafter.*

(a) Use a formula to calculate the total amount earned over 15 years.

(b) Use a calculator to verify this value.

95. $S = \$42,000$, $R = \$1800$

96. $S = \$35,000$, $R = \$2500$

Exercises 97–100: **Annuities** *(Refer to Example 8.) Determine the future value of each annuity.*

97. $A_0 = \$2000,$ $i = 0.08, n = 20$

98. $A_0 = \$500,$ $i = 0.15, n = 10$

99. $A_0 = \$10,000,$ $i = 0.11, n = 5$

100. $A_0 = \$3000,$ $i = 0.19, n = 45$

101. Stacking Logs Logs are stacked in layers, with one fewer log in each layer. See the figure. If the top layer has 7 logs and the bottom layer has 15 logs, what is the total number of logs in the pile? Use a formula to find the sum.

102. Stacking Logs (Refer to Exercise 101.) Suppose a stack of logs has 13 logs in the top layer and a total of 7 layers. How many logs are in the stack?

103. Filter Suppose that one filter removes half of the impurities in a water supply.

   (a) Find a series that represents the amount of impurities removed by a sequence of n filters. Express your answer in summation notation.

   (b) How many filters would be necessary to remove all of the impurities?

104. Walking Suppose that a person walks 1 mile on the first day, $\frac{1}{3}$ mile on the second day, $\frac{1}{9}$ mile on the third day, and so on. Assuming that a person could walk each distance precisely, estimate how far the person would have traveled after a very long time.

105. Area (Refer to Exercise 100, Section 11.1.) Use a geometric series to find the sum of the areas of the squares if they continue indefinitely.

106. Perimeter (Refer to Exercise 100, Section 11.1.) Use a geometric series to find the sum of the perimeters of the squares if they continue indefinitely.

Exercises 107 and 108: **The Natural Exponential Function** *The following series can be used to estimate the value of e^a for any real number a:*

$$e^a \approx 1 + a + \frac{a^2}{2!} + \frac{a^3}{3!} + \cdots + \frac{a^n}{n!},$$

where $n! = 1 \cdot 2 \cdot 3 \cdot 4 \cdots \cdot n$. Use the first eight terms of this series to approximate the given expression. Compare this estimate with the actual value.

107. e **108.** e^{-1}

Computing Partial Sums

Exercises 109–112: Use a_k and n to find $S_n = \sum_{k=1}^{n} a_k$. (Refer to Example 7.) Then evaluate the infinite geometric series $S = \sum_{k=1}^{\infty} a_k$. Compare S to the values for S_n.

109. $a_k = \left(\frac{1}{3}\right)^{k-1}; n = 2, 4, 8, 16$

110. $a_k = 3\left(\frac{1}{2}\right)^{k-1}; n = 5, 10, 15, 20$

111. $a_k = 4\left(-\frac{1}{10}\right)^{k-1}; n = 1, 2, 3, 4, 5, 6$

112. $a_k = 2(-0.02)^{k-1}; n = 1, 2, 3, 4, 5, 6$

Writing about Mathematics

113. Discuss the difference between a sequence and a series. Give examples.

114. Under what circumstances can we find the sum of a geometric series? Give examples.

115. Explain how to write the series

$$\log 1 + \log 2 + \log 3 + \cdots + \log n$$

as one term.

116. Explain how to write the series

$$\log 2 - \log 4 + \log 6 - \log 8 + \cdots + (-1)^{n-1}\log 2n$$

as one term. Assume n is even.

CHECKING BASIC CONCEPTS FOR SECTIONS 11.1 AND 11.2

1. Give graphical and numerical representations of the sequence defined by $a_n = -2n + 3$, where $a_n = f(n)$. Include the first six terms.

2. Determine if the sequence is arithmetic or geometric. If it is arithmetic, state the common difference; if it is geometric, give the common ratio.
   (a) $2, -4, 8, -16, 32, -64, 128, \ldots$
   (b) $-3, 0, 3, 6, 9, 12, \ldots$
   (c) $4, 2, 1, \frac{1}{2}, \frac{1}{4}, \frac{1}{8}, \frac{1}{16}, \ldots$

3. Determine if the series is arithmetic or geometric. Use a formula to find its sum.
   (a) $1 + 5 + 9 + 13 + \cdots + 37$
   (b) $3 + 1 + \frac{1}{3} + \frac{1}{9} + \frac{1}{27} + \frac{1}{81}$

   (c) $2 + \frac{1}{2} + \frac{1}{8} + \frac{1}{32} + \cdots$
   (d) $0.9 + 0.09 + 0.009 + 0.0009 + \cdots$

4. Write each series in Exercise 3 in summation notation.

5. Use properties of summation notation to find the sum.
   (a) $\sum_{k=1}^{15} (k + 2)$ (b) $\sum_{k=1}^{21} 2k^2$

6. **Bouncing Ball** A ball is dropped from a height of 6 feet. On each bounce the ball returns to $\frac{2}{3}$ of its previous height. How far does the ball travel (up and down) before it comes to rest?

11.3 Counting

- Apply the fundamental counting principle
- Calculate and apply permutations
- Calculate and apply combinations

Introduction

The notion of *counting* in mathematics includes much more than simply counting from 1 to 100. It also includes determining the number of ways that an event can occur. For example, how many ways are there to answer a true-false quiz with ten questions? The answer involves counting the different ways that a student could answer such a quiz. Counting is an important concept that is used to calculate probabilities. Probability is discussed in Section 11.6.

Fundamental Counting Principle

Suppose that a quiz has only two questions. The first is a multiple-choice question with four choices, A, B, C, or D, and the second is a true-false (T-F) question. The **tree diagram** in Figure 11.14 can be used to count the ways that this quiz can be answered.

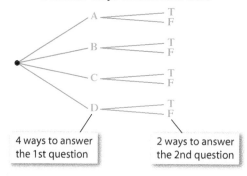

Different Ways to Answer a Quiz

4 ways to answer the 1st question

2 ways to answer the 2nd question

Figure 11.14

A tree diagram is a systematic way of listing every possibility. From Figure 11.14 we can see that there are eight ways to answer the quiz. They are

AT, AF, BT, BF, CT, CF, DT, and DF.   8 ways to answer the quiz

For instance, CF indicates a quiz with answers of C on the first question and F on the second question.

A tree diagram is not always practical, because it can quickly become very large. For this reason mathematicians have developed more efficient ways of counting. Since the multiple-choice question has four possible answers, after which the true-false question has two possible answers, there are $4 \cdot 2 = 8$ possible ways of answering the test. This is an application of the *fundamental counting principle*, which applies to independent events. Two events are **independent** if neither event influences the outcome of the other.

FUNDAMENTAL COUNTING PRINCIPLE

Let $E_1, E_2, E_3, \ldots, E_n$ be a sequence of n independent events. If event E_k can occur m_k ways for $k = 1, 2, 3, \ldots, n$, then there are

$$m_1 \cdot m_2 \cdot m_3 \cdot \cdots \cdot m_n$$

ways for all n events to occur.

EXAMPLE 1 Counting ways to answer an exam

An exam contains four true-false questions and six multiple-choice questions. Each multiple-choice question has five possible answers. Count the number of ways that the exam can be answered.

SOLUTION

Getting Started Answering these ten questions can be thought of as a sequence of ten independent events. There are two ways to answer each of the first four questions and five ways of answering each of the next six questions. ▶

The number of ways to answer the exam is

Each factor represents the number of ways to answer the given question.

$$\underbrace{2 \cdot 2 \cdot 2 \cdot 2}_{\text{4 factors}} \cdot \underbrace{5 \cdot 5 \cdot 5 \cdot 5 \cdot 5 \cdot 5}_{\text{6 factors}} = 2^4 5^6 = 250{,}000.$$

> Now Try Exercise 3

In the next example, we count the number of different license plates possible with a given format.

EXAMPLE 2 Counting license plates

Sometimes a license plate is limited to three uppercase letters (A through Z) followed by three digits (0 through 9). For example, ABB 112 would be a valid license plate. Would this format provide enough license plates for a state with 8 million vehicles?

SOLUTION Since there are 26 letters of the alphabet, it follows that there are 26 ways to choose each of the first three letters of the license plate. Similarly, there are 10 digits, so there are 10 ways to choose each of the three digits in the license plate. By the fundamental counting principle, there are

$$26 \cdot 26 \cdot 26 \cdot 10 \cdot 10 \cdot 10 = 17{,}576{,}000$$

unique license plates that could be issued. This format for license plates could accommodate more than 8 million vehicles.

> Now Try Exercise 5

An Application At one time, toll-free numbers always began with 800. Because there were not enough toll-free 800 numbers to meet demand, phone companies started to use toll-free numbers that began with 888 and 877. In the next example, we count the number of valid 800 numbers. (*Source:* Database Services Management.)

EXAMPLE 3 Counting toll-free telephone numbers

Count the total number of 800 numbers if the local portion of a telephone number (the last seven digits) does not start with a 0 or 1.

SOLUTION A toll-free 800 number assumes the following form.

We can think of choosing the remaining digits for the local number as seven independent events. Since the local number cannot begin with a 0 or 1, there are eight possibilities (2 to 9) for the first digit. The remaining six digits can be any number from 0 to 9, so there are ten possibilities for each of these digits. The total is given by

$$8 \cdot \underbrace{10 \cdot 10 \cdot 10 \cdot 10 \cdot 10 \cdot 10}_{\text{Last 6 digits}} = 8 \cdot 10^6 = 8{,}000{,}000.$$

First digit

Now Try Exercise 47

Permutations

A **permutation** is an *ordering* or *arrangement*. For example, suppose that three students are scheduled to give speeches in a class. The different arrangements in which these speeches can be ordered are called permutations. Initially, any one of the three students could give the first speech. After the first speech, there are two students remaining for the second speech. For the third speech there is only one possibility. By the fundamental counting principle, the total number of permutations is equal to

$$3 \cdot 2 \cdot 1 = 6. \quad\text{—— Six possible orderings}$$

If the students are denoted as A, B, and C, then these six permutations are ABC, ACB, BAC, BCA, CAB, and CBA. In a similar manner, if there were ten students scheduled to give speeches, the number of permutations would increase to

Ten possible choices to go first ── $10 \cdot 9 \cdot 8 \cdot 7 \cdot 6 \cdot 5 \cdot 4 \cdot 3 \cdot 2 \cdot 1 = 3{,}628{,}800.$

A more efficient way of writing the previous two products is to use *factorial notation*. The number $n!$ (read "n-factorial") is defined as follows.

Calculator Help

To calculate $n!$, see Appendix A (page AP-17).

n-FACTORIAL

For any natural number n,

$$n! = n(n-1)(n-2)\cdots(3)(2)(1)$$

and

$$0! = 1.$$

EXAMPLE 4 Calculating factorials

Compute $n!$ for $n = 0, 1, 2, 3, 4,$ and 5 by hand. Use a calculator to find 8!, 13!, and 25!.

```
8!
             40320
13!
        6227020800
25!
    1.551121004E25
```

Figure 11.15

SOLUTION The values for $n!$ can be calculated as

$$0! = 1, \quad 1! = 1, \quad 2! = 2 \cdot 1 = 2, \quad 3! = 3 \cdot 2 \cdot 1 = 6,$$

$$4! = 4 \cdot 3 \cdot 2 \cdot 1 = 24, \quad \text{and} \quad 5! = 5 \cdot 4 \cdot 3 \cdot 2 \cdot 1 = 120.$$

Figure 11.15 shows the values of 8!, 13!, and 25!. The value for 25! is an approximation. Notice how rapidly $n!$ increases.

Now Try Exercise 27

A Famous Unsolved Problem One of the most famous unanswered questions in computing today is called the *traveling salesperson problem*. It is a relatively simple problem to state, but if someone could design a procedure to solve this problem *efficiently*, he or she would not only become famous but also provide a valuable way for businesses to save millions of dollars on scheduling problems, such as assigning bus routes and truck deliveries.

One example of the traveling salesperson problem can be stated as follows. A salesperson must begin and end at home and travel to three cities. Assuming that the salesperson can travel between any pair of cities, what route would minimize the salesperson's mileage? In Figure 11.16, the four cities are labeled A, B, C, and D. Let the salesperson live in city A. There are six routes that could be tried. They are listed in Table 11.6 with the appropriate mileage for each.

Traveling Salesperson Problem

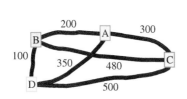

Figure 11.16

Route	Mileage
A B C D A	200 + 480 + 500 + 350 = 1530
A B D C A	200 + 100 + 500 + 300 = 1100
A C B D A	300 + 480 + 100 + 350 = 1230
A C D B A	300 + 500 + 100 + 200 = 1100
A D B C A	350 + 100 + 480 + 300 = 1230
A D C B A	350 + 500 + 480 + 200 = 1530

Minimum Distance

Table 11.6

The shortest route of 1100 miles occurs when the salesperson either (1) starts at A and travels through B, D, and C and back to A or (2) reverses this route. Currently, this method of listing all possible routes to find the minimum distance is the only known way to consistently find the optimal solution for any general map containing *n* cities. In fact, people have not been able to determine whether a *significantly* faster method even exists.

Counting the number of routes involves the fundamental counting principle. At the first step, the salesperson can travel to any one of three cities. Once this city has been selected, there are two possible cities to choose, and then one. Finally the salesperson returns home. The total number of routes is given by

$$3! = 3 \cdot 2 \cdot 1 = 6.$$

If the salesperson must travel to 30 cities, then there are

$$30! \approx 2.7 \times 10^{32}$$

routes to check, far too many to check even with the largest supercomputers.

Next suppose that a salesperson must visit three of eight possible cities. At first there are eight cities to choose. After the first city has been visited, there are seven cities to select. Since the salesperson travels to only three of the eight cities, there are

$$8 \cdot 7 \cdot 6 = 336$$

possible routes. This number of permutations is denoted $P(8, 3)$. It represents the number of arrangements that can be made using three elements taken from a sample of eight.

PERMUTATIONS OF *n* ELEMENTS TAKEN *r* AT A TIME

If $P(n, r)$ denotes the number of permutations of *n* elements taken *r* at a time, with $r \le n$, then

$$P(n, r) = \frac{n!}{(n - r)!} = \underbrace{n(n - 1)(n - 2) \cdots (n - r + 1)}_{r \text{ factors}}.$$

Calculator Help
To calculate $P(n, r)$, see Appendix A (page AP-17).

EXAMPLE 5 Calculating $P(n, r)$

Calculate each of the following by hand. Then support your answers by using a calculator.
(a) $P(7, 3)$ **(b)** $P(100, 2)$

SOLUTION
(a) $P(7, 3) = \underbrace{7 \cdot 6 \cdot 5}_{3 \text{ factors}} = 210$

Permutations: $P(n, r)$

```
7 nPr 3
              210
100 nPr 2
             9900
```

Figure 11.17

(b) $P(100, 2) = 100 \cdot 99 = 9900$. We also can compute this number as follows.

$$P(100, 2) = \frac{100!}{(100 - 2)!} = \frac{100 \cdot 99 \cdot 98!}{98!} = 100 \cdot 99 = 9900$$

In this case, it is helpful to cancel 98! before performing the arithmetic. Both of these computations are performed by a calculator in Figure 11.17.

Now Try Exercise 31 and 37

EXAMPLE 6 Calculating permutations

For a class of 30 students, how many arrangements are there in which 4 students each give a speech?

SOLUTION The number of permutations of 30 elements taken 4 at a time is given by

$$P(30, 4) = \underbrace{30 \cdot 29 \cdot 28 \cdot 27}_{4 \text{ factors}} = 657{,}720.$$

Thus there are 657,720 ways to arrange the four speeches.

Now Try Exercise 43

In the next example, we determine the number of ways that four people can have *different* birthdays. For example, if the birthdays of four people are February 29, May 2, June 30, and July 11, then these dates would be one way that four people could have different birthdays.

EXAMPLE 7 Counting birthdays

Count the possible ways that four people can have different birthdays.

SOLUTION Counting February 29, there are 366 possible birthdays. The first person could have any of the 366 possible birthdays. The second person could have any of 365 birthdays, because the first person's birthday cannot be duplicated. Similarly, the third person could have any of 364 birthdays, and the fourth person could have any of 363 birthdays. The total number of ways that four people could have different birthdays equals

$$P(366, 4) = \underbrace{366 \cdot 365 \cdot 364 \cdot 363}_{4 \text{ factors}} \approx 1.77 \times 10^{10}.$$

Now Try Exercise 53

CLASS DISCUSSION

Count the number of arrangements of 52 cards in a standard deck. Is it likely that there are arrangements that no one has ever shuffled at any time in the history of the world? Explain.

Combinations

Unlike a permutation, a **combination** is not an ordering or arrangement, but rather a subset of a set of elements. Order is unimportant in finding combinations. For example, suppose we want to select a tennis team of two players from four people. The order in which the selection is made does not affect the final team of two players. From a set of four people, we select a subset of two players. The number of possible subsets, or combinations, is denoted either $C(4, 2)$ or $\binom{4}{2}$.

To calculate $C(4, 2)$, we first consider $P(4, 2)$. If we denote the four players by the letters A, B, C, and D, there are $P(4, 2) = 4 \cdot 3 = 12$ permutations given by

Equivalent teams AB, BA, AC, CA, AD, DA, BC, CB, BD, DB, CD, DC.

However, the team that comprises person A and person B is equivalent to the team with person B and person A. The sets {AB} and {BA} are equal. The valid combinations are the following two-element subsets of {A, B, C, D}.

$$\{AB\} \quad \{AC\} \quad \{AD\} \quad \{BC\} \quad \{BD\} \quad \{CD\}$$

That is, $C(4, 2) = \frac{P(4, 2)}{2!} = 6$. The relationship between $P(n, r)$ and $C(n, r)$ is given below.

COMBINATIONS OF n ELEMENTS TAKEN r AT A TIME

If $C(n, r)$ denotes the number of combinations of n elements taken r at a time, with $r \le n$, then

$$C(n, r) = \frac{P(n, r)}{r!} = \frac{n!}{(n - r)!\, r!}.$$

Calculator Help

To calculate $C(n, r)$, see Appendix A (page AP-17).

EXAMPLE 8 Calculating $C(n, r)$

Calculate each of the following. Support your answers by using a calculator.

(a) $C(7, 3)$ **(b)** $\binom{50}{47}$

SOLUTION

(a) $C(7, 3) = \dfrac{7!}{\underbrace{(7 - 3)!}_{n-r}3!} = \dfrac{7!}{4!3!} = \dfrac{7 \cdot 6 \cdot 5 \cdot 4!}{4!3!} = \dfrac{7 \cdot 6 \cdot 5}{3!} = \dfrac{210}{6} = 35$

   $\underset{n\ r}{\underbrace{|\ |}}$

(b) The notation $\binom{50}{47}$ is equivalent to $C(50, 47)$.

$$\binom{50}{47} = \frac{50!}{(50 - 47)!\, 47!} = \frac{50!}{3!\, 47!} = \frac{50 \cdot 49 \cdot 48 \cdot 47!}{3!\, 47!}$$

$$= \frac{50 \cdot 49 \cdot 48}{3!} = \frac{117{,}600}{6} = 19{,}600$$

These computations are performed by a calculator in Figure 11.18.

Combinations: $C(n, r)$

```
7 nCr 3
                35
50 nCr 47
             19600
```

Figure 11.18

Now Try Exercise 59 and 65

EXAMPLE 9 Counting combinations

A college student has five courses left in her major and plans to take two of them this semester. Assuming that this student has the prerequisites for all five courses, determine how many ways these two courses can be selected.

SOLUTION The order in which the courses are selected is unimportant. From a set of five courses, the student selects a subset of two courses. The number of subsets is

$$C(5, 2) = \frac{5!}{(5 - 2)!\, 2!} = \frac{5!}{3!\, 2!} = 10.$$

There are 10 ways to select two courses from a set of five.

Now Try Exercise 67

EXAMPLE 10 Calculating the number of ways to play the lottery

To win the jackpot in a lottery, a person must select five different numbers from 1 to 59 and then pick the powerball, which has a number from 1 to 35. Count the ways to play the game. (**Source:** Minnesota State Lottery.)

SOLUTION From 59 numbers a player picks five numbers. There are $C(59, 5)$ ways of doing this. There are 35 ways to choose the powerball. By the fundamental counting principle, the number of ways to play the game equals $C(59, 5) \cdot 35 = 175{,}223{,}510$.

> **Now Try Exercise 71**

MAKING CONNECTIONS

Permutations and Combinations

Permutation: An arrangement (or list) in which ordering of the objects *is* important. For example, $P(20, 9)$ would give the number of possible batting orders for 9 players from a team of 20.

Combination: A subset of a set of objects where the ordering of the objects *is not* important. For example, $C(20, 9)$ would give the number of committees possible when 9 people are selected from a group of 20. The order in which members are selected does not affect the resulting committee.

EXAMPLE 11 Counting committees

How many committees of six people can be selected from six women and three men if a committee must have at least two men?

SOLUTION

Getting Started Because there are three men and each committee must have at least two men, a committee can include either two or three men. The order of selection is not important. Therefore we need to consider combinations of committee members rather than permutations. ▶

Two Men: This committee would consist of four women and two men. We can select two men from a group of three in $C(3, 2) = 3$ ways. Four women can be selected from a group of six in $C(6, 4) = 15$ ways. By the fundamental counting principle, a total of

$$C(3, 2) \cdot C(6, 4) = 3 \cdot 15 = 45$$

committees have two men.

Three Men: This committee would have three women and three men. We can select three men from a group of three in $C(3, 3) = 1$ way. We can select three women from a group of six in $C(6, 3) = 20$ ways. By the fundamental counting principle, a total of

$$C(3, 3) \cdot C(6, 3) = 1 \cdot 20 = 20$$

committees have three men.

The total number of possible committees would be $45 + 20 = 65$.

> **Now Try Exercise 69**

11.3 Putting It All Together

The fundamental counting principle can be used to determine the number of ways a sequence of independent events can occur. Permutations are arrangements or listings, whereas combinations are subsets of a set of events.

The following table summarizes some concepts related to counting in mathematics.

NOTATION	EXPLANATION	EXAMPLES
n-factorial: $n!$	$n!$ represents the product $$n(n - 1) \cdots (3)(2)(1).$$	$6! = 6 \cdot 5 \cdot 4 \cdot 3 \cdot 2 \cdot 1 = 720$ $0! = 1$
$P(n, r) = \dfrac{n!}{(n - r)!}$	$P(n, r)$ represents the number of permutations of n elements taken r at a time.	The number of two-letter strings that can be formed using the four letters A, B, C, and D with no letter repeated is given by $$P(4, 2) = \frac{4!}{(4 - 2)!} = \frac{4!}{2!} = 12,$$ or $P(4, 2) = 4 \cdot 3 = 12$.
$C(n, r) = \dfrac{n!}{(n - r)!r!}$	$C(n, r)$ represents the number of combinations of n elements taken r at a time.	The number of committees of three people that can be formed from five people is $$C(5, 3) = \frac{5!}{(5 - 3)! \, 3!} = \frac{5!}{2!3!} = 10.$$

11.3 Exercises

Counting

Exercises 1–4: **Exam Questions** *Count the number of ways that the questions on an exam could be answered.*

1. Ten true-false questions

2. Ten multiple-choice questions with five choices each

3. Five true-false questions and ten multiple-choice questions with four choices each

4. One question involving matching ten items in one column with ten items in another column, using a one-to-one correspondence

Exercises 5–8: **License Plates** *Count the number of possible license plates with the given constraints.*

5. Three digits followed by three letters

6. Two letters followed by four digits

7. Three letters followed by three digits or letters

8. Two letters followed by either three or four digits

Exercises 9–12: **Counting Strings** *Count the number of five-letter strings that can be formed with the given letters, assuming a letter can be used more than once.*

9. A, B, C

10. W, X, Y, Z

11. D, E, F, G, H

12. A, C

Exercises 13–16: **Counting Strings** *Count the number of strings that can be formed with the given letters, assuming each letter is used exactly once.*

13. A, B

14. A, B, C

15. W, X, Y, Z

16. V, W, X, Y, Z

17. **Combination Lock** A briefcase has two locks. The combination to each lock consists of a three-digit number, in which digits may be repeated. See the figure. How many combinations are possible? (*Hint:* The word *combination* is a misnomer. Lock combinations are permutations in which the arrangement of the numbers is important.)

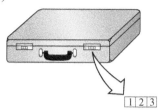

18. **Combination Lock** A typical combination for a padlock consists of three numbers from 0 to 39. Count the combinations possible with this type of lock if a number may be repeated.

19. **Garage Door Openers** The code for some garage door openers consists of 12 electrical switches that can be set to either 0 or 1 by the owner. With this type of opener, how many codes are possible? (*Source:* Promax.)

20. **Lottery** To win the jackpot in a lottery game, a person must pick three numbers from 0 to 9 in the correct order. If a number can be repeated, how many ways are there to play the game?

21. **Radio Stations** Call letters for a radio station usually begin with either a K or a W, followed by three letters. In 2012, there were 14,952 radio stations on the air. Is there any shortage of call letters for new radio stations? (*Source:* M. Street Corporation.)

22. **Access Codes** An ATM access code often consists of a four-digit number. How many codes are possible without giving two accounts the same access code?

23. **Computer Package** A computer store offers a package in which buyers choose one of two monitors, one of three printers, and one of four types of software. How many different packages can be purchased?

24. **Dice** A red die and a blue die are thrown. How many ways are there for both dice to show an even number?

25. **Telephone Numbers** How many different 7-digit telephone numbers are possible if the first digit cannot be a 0 or a 1?

26. **Dinner Choices** A menu offers 5 different salads, 10 different entrées, and 4 different desserts. How many ways are there to order a salad, an entrée, and a dessert?

Exercises 27–30: Evaluate the expression.

27. 6!   28. 0!

29. 10!   30. 7!

Permutations

Exercises 31–40: Evaluate the expression.

31. $P(5, 3)$ 32. $P(10, 2)$

33. $P(8, 1)$ 34. $P(6, 6)$

35. $P(7, 3)$ 36. $P(12, 3)$

37. $P(25, 2)$ 38. $P(20, 1)$

39. $P(10, 4)$ 40. $P(34, 2)$

41. **Standing in Line** How many ways can four people stand in a line?

42. **Books on a Shelf** How many arrangements are there of six different books on a shelf?

43. **Giving a Speech** In how many arrangements can 3 students from a class of 15 each give a speech?

44. **Introductions** How many ways could five basketball players be introduced at a game?

45. **Traveling Salesperson** (Refer to the discussion after Example 4.) A salesperson must travel to three of seven cities. Direct travel is possible between every pair of cities. How many arrangements are there in which the salesperson could visit these three cities? Assume that traveling a route in reverse order constitutes a different arrangement.

46. **Traveling Salesperson** A salesperson must start at city A, stop in each city once, and then return to city A. Use the figure to find the route with the least mileage.

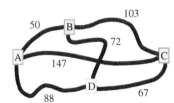

47. **Phone Numbers** How many seven-digit phone numbers are there if the first three numbers must be 387, 388, or 389?

48. **Keys** How many distinguishable ways can four keys be put on a key ring?

49. **Sitting at a Round Table** How many ways can seven people sit at a round table? (For a way to be different, at least one person must be sitting next to someone different.)

50. **Batting Orders** A softball team has 10 players. How many batting orders are possible?

51. **Baseball Positions** In how many ways can nine players be assigned to the nine positions on a baseball team, assuming that any player can play any position?

52. **Musical Chairs Seating** In a game of musical chairs, seven children will sit in six chairs arranged in a circle. One child will be left out. How many (different) ways can the children sit in the chairs? (For a way to be different, at least one child must be sitting next to someone different.)

53. **Birthdays** In how many ways can five people have different birthdays?

54. **Course Schedule** A scheduling committee has one room in which to offer five mathematics courses. In how many ways can the committee arrange the five courses over the day?

55. **Telephone Numbers** How many 10-digit telephone numbers are there if the first digit and the fourth digit cannot be a 0 or a 1?

56. **Car Designs** There are 10 basic colors available for a new car, along with 5 basic styles of trim. In how many ways can a person pick the color and trim?

Combinations

Exercises 57–66: Evaluate the expression.

57. $C(3, 1)$

58. $C(4, 3)$

59. $C(6, 3)$

60. $C(7, 5)$

61. $C(5, 0)$

62. $C(10, 2)$

63. $\binom{8}{2}$

64. $\binom{9}{4}$

65. $\binom{20}{18}$

66. $\binom{100}{2}$

67. **Lottery** To win the jackpot in a lottery, one must select five different numbers from 1 to 39. How many ways are there to play this game?

68. **Selecting a Committee** How many ways can a committee of five be selected from eight people?

69. **Selecting a Coed Team** How many teams of four people can be selected from five women and three men if a team must have two people of each sex on it?

70. **Essay Questions** On a test with six essay questions, students are asked to answer four questions. How many ways can the essay questions be selected?

71. **Test Questions** A test consists of two parts. In the first part a student must choose three of five essay questions, and in the second part a student must choose four of five essay questions. How many ways can the essay questions be selected?

72. **Cards** How many ways are there to draw a 5-card hand from a 52-card deck?

73. **Selecting Marbles** How many ways are there to draw 3 red marbles and 2 blue marbles from a jar that contains 10 red marbles and 12 blue marbles?

74. **Book Arrangements** A professor has three copies of an algebra book and four copies of a calculus text. How many distinguishable ways can the books be placed on a shelf?

75. **Peach Samples** How many samples of 3 peaches can be drawn from a crate of 24 peaches? (Assume that the peaches are distinguishable.)

76. **Flower Samples** A bouquet of flowers contains three red roses, four yellow roses, and five white roses. In how many ways can a person choose one flower of each type? (Assume that the flowers are distinguishable.)

77. **Permutations** Show that $P(n, n - 1) = P(n, n)$. Give an example that supports your result.

78. **Combinations** Show that $\binom{n}{r} = \binom{n}{n - r}$. Give an example that supports your result.

Writing about Mathematics

79. Explain the difference between a permutation and a combination. Give examples.

80. Explain what counting is, as presented in this section.

11.4 The Binomial Theorem

- Derive the binomial theorem
- Use the binomial theorem
- Apply Pascal's triangle

Introduction

In this section we discuss how to expand expressions in the form $(a + b)^n$, where n is a natural number. Some examples include the following.

$$(a + b)^2, (a + b)^5, (2x + 1)^3, \text{ and } (x - y)^4$$

These expressions occur in statistics, finite mathematics, computer science, and calculus.

Derivation of the Binomial Theorem

Combinations play a central role in the development of the binomial theorem. The binomial theorem can be used to expand expressions of the form $(a + b)^n$. Before stating the binomial theorem, we begin by counting the number of strings of a given length that can be formed with only the variables a and b.

EXAMPLE 1 Calculating distinguishable strings

Count the number of distinguishable strings that can be formed with the given number of a's and b's. List these strings.
(a) Two a's, one b **(b)** Two a's, three b's   **(c)** Four a's, no b's

SOLUTION
(a) Using two a's and one b, we can form strings of length three. Once the b has been positioned, the string is determined. For example, if the b is placed in the middle position,

$$\boxed{}\boxed{b}\boxed{},$$

then the string must be *aba*. From a set of three slots, we choose one slot in which to place the b. This is computed by $C(3, 1) = 3$. The strings are *aab*, *aba*, and *baa*.
(b) With two a's and three b's we can form strings of length five. Once the locations of the three b's have been selected, the string is determined. For instance, if the b's are placed in the first, third, and fifth positions,

$$\boxed{b}\boxed{}\boxed{b}\boxed{}\boxed{b}$$

then the string becomes *babab*. From a set of five slots, we select three in which to place the b's. This is computed by $C(5, 3) = 10$. The 10 strings are

bbbaa, *bbaba*, *bbaab*, *babba*, *babab*, *baabb*, *abbba*, *abbab*, *ababb*, and *aabbb*.

(c) There is only one string of length four that contains no b's. This is *aaaa* and is computed by

$$C(4, 0) = \frac{4!}{(4 - 0)!0!} = \frac{24}{24(1)} = 1.$$

Now Try Exercise 9, 11, and 13

Next we expand $(a + b)^n$ for a few values of n, without simplifying.

$$(a + b)^1 = a + b$$

$$(a + b)^2 = (a + b)(a + b)$$

$$= aa + ab + ba + bb$$

$$(a + b)^3 = (a + b)(a + b)^2$$

$$= (a + b)(aa + ab + ba + bb)$$

$$= aaa + aab + aba + abb + baa + bab + bba + bbb$$

Notice that $(a + b)^1$ is the sum of all possible strings of length one that can be formed using a and b. The only possibilities are a and b. The expression $(a + b)^2$ is the sum of all possible strings of length two using a and b. The strings are aa, ab, ba, and bb. Similarly, $(a + b)^3$ is the sum of all possible strings of length three using a and b. This pattern continues for higher powers of $(a + b)$.

Strings with equal numbers of a's and equal numbers of b's can be combined into one term. For example, in $(a + b)^2$ the terms ab and ba can be combined as $2ab$. Notice that there are $C(2, 1) = 2$ distinguishable strings of length two containing one b. Similarly, in the expansion of $(a + b)^3$, the terms containing one a and two b's can be combined as

$$abb + bab + bba = 3ab^2.$$

There are $C(3, 2) = 3$ strings of length three that contain two b's.

We can use these concepts to expand $(a + b)^4$. The expression $(a + b)^4$ consists of the sum of all strings of length four using only the letters a and b: $C(4, 0) = 1$ string containing no b's, $C(4, 1) = 4$ strings containing one b, and so on, up to $C(4, 4) = 1$ string containing four b's. Thus

$$(a + b)^4 = \binom{4}{0}a^4b^0 + \binom{4}{1}a^3b^1 + \binom{4}{2}a^2b^2 + \binom{4}{3}a^1b^3 + \binom{4}{4}a^0b^4$$

$$= a^4 + 4a^3b + 6a^2b^2 + 4ab^3 + b^4.$$

These results are summarized by the **binomial theorem**.

BINOMIAL THEOREM

For any positive integer n and numbers a and b,

$$(a + b)^n = \binom{n}{0}a^n + \binom{n}{1}a^{n-1}b^1 + \cdots + \binom{n}{n-1}a^1b^{n-1} + \binom{n}{n}b^n.$$

We can use the binomial theorem to expand $(a + b)^n$. For example,

$$(a + b)^3 = \binom{3}{0}a^3 + \binom{3}{1}a^2b^1 + \binom{3}{2}a^1b^2 + \binom{3}{3}b^3$$

$$= 1a^3 + 3a^2b + 3ab^2 + 1b^3$$

$$= a^3 + 3a^2b + 3ab^2 + b^3.$$

Since $\binom{n}{r} = C(n, r)$, we can use the combination formula $C(n, r) = \frac{n!}{(n-r)!\,r!}$ to evaluate the binomial coefficients.

EXAMPLE 2 Applying the binomial theorem

Use the binomial theorem to expand the expression $(2a + 1)^5$.

SOLUTION Using the binomial theorem, we arrive at the following result.

$$(2a + 1)^5 = \binom{5}{0}(2a)^5 + \binom{5}{1}(2a)^41^1 + \binom{5}{2}(2a)^31^2 + \binom{5}{3}(2a)^21^3 + \binom{5}{4}(2a)^11^4 + \binom{5}{5}1^5$$

$$= \frac{5!}{5!0!}(32a^5) + \frac{5!}{4!1!}(16a^4) + \frac{5!}{3!2!}(8a^3) + \frac{5!}{2!3!}(4a^2) + \frac{5!}{1!4!}(2a) + \frac{5!}{0!5!}$$

$$= 32a^5 + 80a^4 + 80a^3 + 40a^2 + 10a + 1$$

Now Try Exercise 19

Pascal's Triangle

Pascal's Triangle

```
            1
          1   1
        1   2   1
      1   3   3   1
    1   4   6   4   1
  1   5  10  10   5   1
```

Figure 11.19

Expanding $(a + b)^n$ for increasing values of n gives the following results.

$(a + b)^0 =$ $\qquad$ 1

$(a + b)^1 =$ $\qquad$ $1a + 1b$

$(a + b)^2 =$ $\qquad$ $1a^2 + 2ab + 1b^2$

$(a + b)^3 =$ $\qquad$ $1a^3 + 3a^2b + 3ab^2 + 1b^3$

$(a + b)^4 =$ $\qquad$ $1a^4 + 4a^3b + 6a^2b^2 + 4ab^3 + 1b^4$

$(a + b)^5 =$ $\qquad$ $1a^5 + 5a^4b + 10a^3b^2 + 10a^2b^3 + 5ab^4 + 1b^5$

| Exponent on a decreases by 1 each term. | Exponent on b increases by 1 each term. |

Notice that $(a + b)^1$ has two terms starting with a and ending with b, $(a + b)^2$ has three terms starting with a^2 and ending with b^2, and in general $(a + b)^n$ has $n + 1$ terms starting with a^n and ending with b^n. The exponent on a decreases by 1 each successive term, and the exponent on b increases by 1 each successive term.

The triangle formed by the highlighted numbers is called **Pascal's triangle**. It can be used to efficiently compute the binomial coefficients, $C(n, r)$. The triangle consists of 1's along the sides. Each element inside the triangle is the sum of the two numbers above it. Pascal's triangle is usually written without variables, as in Figure 11.19. It can be extended to include as many rows as needed.

We can use this triangle to expand powers of binomials in the form $(a + b)^n$, where n is a natural number. For example, the expression $(m + n)^4$ consists of five terms written as follows.

```
            1
          1   1
        1   2   1
      1   3   3   1
    1   4   6   4   1
  1   5  10  10   5   1
```

$$(m + n)^4 = \_\, m^4 + \_\, m^3n^1 + \_\, m^2n^2 + \_\, m^1n^3 + \_\, n^4$$

Because there are five terms, the coefficients can be found in the fifth row of Pascal's triangle, which from the figure in the margin is

$$1 \quad 4 \quad 6 \quad 4 \quad 1.$$

Thus

$$(m + n)^4 = \underline{1}\, m^4 + \underline{4}\, m^3n^1 + \underline{6}\, m^2n^2 + \underline{4}\, m^1n^3 + \underline{1}\, n^4$$

$$= m^4 + 4m^3n + 6m^2n^2 + 4mn^3 + n^4.$$

EXAMPLE 3 Expanding expressions with Pascal's triangle

Expand each of the following.
(a) $(2x + 1)^5$ $\qquad$ **(b)** $(3x - y)^3$

SOLUTION
(a) To expand $(2x + 1)^5$, let $a = 2x$ and $b = 1$ in the binomial theorem. We can use the sixth row of Pascal's triangle to obtain the coefficients 1, 5, 10, 10, 5, and 1. Compare this solution with the solution for Example 2.

$$(2x + 1)^5 = 1(2x)^5 + 5(2x)^4(1)^1 + 10(2x)^3(1)^2 + 10(2x)^2(1)^3 + 5(2x)^1(1)^4 + 1(1)^5$$

$$= 32x^5 + 80x^4 + 80x^3 + 40x^2 + 10x + 1$$

(b) Let $a = 3x$ and $b = -y$ in the binomial theorem. Use the coefficients 1, 3, 3, and 1 from the fourth row of Pascal's triangle.

$$(3x - y)^3 = 1(3x)^3 + 3(3x)^2(-y)^1 + 3(3x)^1(-y)^2 + 1(-y)^3$$

$$= 27x^3 - 27x^2y + 9xy^2 - y^3$$

Now Try Exercise 33 and 35

Finding the kth Term   The binomial theorem gives *all* of the terms of $(a + b)^n$. However, we can find any individual term by noting that the $(r + 1)$st term in the binomial expansion for $(a + b)^n$ is given by the formula $\binom{n}{r}a^{n-r}b^r$ for $0 \le r \le n$. The next example shows how to use this formula to find the $(r + 1)$st term of $(a + b)^n$.

EXAMPLE 4   Finding the kth term in a binomial expansion

Find the third term of $(x - y)^5$.

SOLUTION   In this example the $(r + 1)$st term is the *third* term in the expansion of $(x - y)^5$. That is, $r + 1 = 3$, or $r = 2$. Also, the exponent in the expression is $n = 5$. To get this binomial into the form $(a + b)^n$, we note that the first term in the binomial is $a = x$ and that the second term in the binomial is $b = -y$. Substituting the values for r, n, a, and b in the formula for the $(r + 1)$st term yields

$$\binom{5}{2}(x)^{5-2}(-y)^2 = 10x^3y^2. \qquad \binom{n}{r}a^{n-r}b^r$$

The third term in the binomial expansion of $(x - y)^5$ is $10x^3y^2$.

Now Try Exercise 45

11.4 Putting It All Together

The following table summarizes topics related to the binomial theorem.

NOTATION	EXPLANATION	EXAMPLES
Binomial coefficient	$$\binom{n}{r} = C(n, r) = \frac{n!}{(n - r)!\, r!}$$	$$\binom{5}{3} = \frac{5!}{(5 - 3)!\, 3!} = \frac{120}{2 \cdot 6} = 10$$ $$\binom{4}{0} = \frac{4!}{(4 - 0)!\, 0!} = \frac{24}{24 \cdot 1} = 1$$
Binomial theorem	$(a + b)^n =$ $$\binom{n}{0}a^n + \binom{n}{1}a^{n-1}b + \cdots + \binom{n}{n}b^n$$ for any positive integer n and real numbers a and b.	$$(a + b)^3 = \binom{3}{0}a^3 + \binom{3}{1}a^2b + \binom{3}{2}ab^2 + \binom{3}{3}b^3$$ $$= a^3 + 3a^2b + 3ab^2 + b^3$$ The binomial coefficients can also be found using the fourth row of Pascal's triangle, which is shown below.
Pascal's triangle	A triangle of numbers that can be used to find the binomial coefficients needed to expand an expression of the form $(a + b)^n$. To expand $(a + b)^n$, use row $n + 1$ of Pascal's triangle.	1 1 1 1 2 1 1 3 3 1 1 4 6 4 1 1 5 10 10 5 1
Finding the $(r + 1)$st term of $(a + b)^n$	The $(r + 1)$st term of $(a + b)^n$ is given by $$\binom{n}{r}a^{n-r}b^r$$ for $0 \le r \le n$.	To find the fifth term of $(x + y)^6$, let $r + 1 = 5$, or $r = 4$, and $n = 6$. $$\binom{n}{r}a^{n-r}b^r = \binom{6}{4}x^{6-4}y^4$$ $$= 15x^2y^4$$

11.4 Exercises

Binomial Coefficients

Exercises 1–8: Evaluate the expression.

1. $\binom{5}{4}$ 2. $\binom{6}{2}$

3. $\binom{4}{0}$ 4. $\binom{4}{2}$

5. $\binom{6}{5}$ 6. $\binom{6}{3}$

7. $\binom{3}{3}$ 8. $\binom{5}{2}$

Binomial Theorem

Exercises 9–16: (Refer to Example 1.) Calculate the number of distinguishable strings that can be formed with the given number of a's and b's.

9. Three a's, two b's   10. Five a's, three b's

11. Four a's, four b's   12. One a, five b's

13. Five a's, no b's   14. No a's, three b's

15. Four a's, one b 16. Four a's, two b's

Exercises 17–30: Use the binomial theorem to expand each expression.

17. $(x + y)^2$ 18. $(x + y)^4$

19. $(m + 2)^3$ 20. $(m + 2n)^5$

21. $(2x - 3)^3$ 22. $(x + y^2)^3$

23. $(p - q)^6$ 24. $(p^2 - 3)^4$

25. $(2m + 3n)^3$ 26. $(3a - 2b)^5$

27. $(1 - x^2)^4$ 28. $(2 + 3x^2)^3$

29. $(2p^3 - 3)^3$ 30. $(2r + 3t)^4$

Pascal's Triangle

Exercises 31–44: Use Pascal's triangle to help expand the expression.

31. $(x + y)^2$ 32. $(m + n)^3$

33. $(3x + 1)^4$ 34. $(2x - 1)^4$

35. $(2 - x)^5$ 36. $(2a + 3b)^3$

37. $(x^2 + 2)^4$ 38. $(5 - x^2)^3$

39. $(4x - 3y)^4$ 40. $(3 - 2x)^5$

41. $(m + n)^6$

42. $(2m - n)^4$

43. $(2x^3 - y^2)^3$

44. $(3x^2 + y^3)^4$

Finding the *k*th Term

Exercises 45–52: Find the specified term.

45. The fourth term of $(a + b)^9$

46. The second term of $(m - n)^9$

47. The fifth term of $(x + y)^8$

48. The third term of $(a + b)^7$

49. The fourth term of $(2x + y)^5$

50. The eighth term of $(2a - b)^9$

51. The sixth term of $(3x - 2y)^6$

52. The seventh term of $(2a + b)^9$

Writing about Mathematics

53. Explain how to find the numbers in Pascal's triangle.

54. Compare the expansion of $(a + b)^n$ with the expansion of $(a - b)^n$. Give an example.

CHECKING BASIC CONCEPTS FOR SECTIONS 11.3 AND 11.4

1. Count the ways to answer a quiz that consists of eight true-false questions.

2. Count the number of 5-card poker hands that can be dealt using a standard deck of 52 cards.

3. How many distinct license plates could be made using a letter followed by five digits or letters?

4. Expand each expression.
   (a) $(2x + 1)^4$ (b) $(4 - 3x)^3$

11.5 Mathematical Induction

- Learn basic concepts about mathematical induction
- Use mathematical induction to prove statements
- Apply the generalized principle of mathematical induction

Introduction

The brilliant mathematician Carl Friedrich Gauss (1777–1855) proved the fundamental theorem of algebra at age 20. When he was a young child, he amazed his teacher by showing that

$$1 + 2 + 3 + 4 + \cdots + 100 = \frac{100(101)}{2}.$$

With *mathematical induction* we will be able to show, more generally, that

$$1 + 2 + 3 + 4 + \cdots + n = \frac{n(n + 1)}{2}.$$

Mathematical induction is a powerful method of proof. It is used not only in mathematics; it is also used in computer science to prove that programs and basic concepts are correct.

Mathematical Induction

Many results in mathematics are claimed true for every positive integer. Any of these results could be checked for $n = 1, n = 2, n = 3$, and so on, but since the set of positive integers is infinite, it would be impossible to check every number. For example, let S_n represent the statement that the sum of the first n positive integers is $\frac{n(n + 1)}{2}$; that is,

$$S_n: 1 + 2 + 3 + \cdots + n = \frac{n(n + 1)}{2}.$$

The truth of this statement can be checked quickly for the first few values of n.

If $n = 1, S_1$ is	$1 = \frac{1(1 + 1)}{2}$, a true statement, since $1 = 1$.
If $n = 2, S_2$ is	$1 + 2 = \frac{2(2 + 1)}{2}$, a true statement, since $3 = 3$.
If $n = 3, S_3$ is	$1 + 2 + 3 = \frac{3(3 + 1)}{2}$, a true statement, since $6 = 6$.
If $n = 4, S_4$ is $1 + 2 + 3 + 4 = \frac{4(4 + 1)}{2}$, a true statement, since $10 = 10$.	

Since the statement is true for $n = 1, 2, 3, 4$, can we conclude that the statement is true for all positive integers? The answer is *no*. To prove that such a statement is true for every positive integer, we use the following principle.

PRINCIPLE OF MATHEMATICAL INDUCTION

Let S_n be a statement concerning the positive integer n. Suppose that

1. S_1 is true;
2. for any positive integer k, if S_k is true, then S_{k+1} is also true.

Then S_n is true for every positive integer n.

A proof by mathematical induction can be explained as follows. By assumption (1), the statement is true when $n = 1$. By assumption (2), the fact that the statement is true for $n = 1$ implies that it is true for $n = 1 + 1 = 2$. Using (2) again, the statement is thus true for $2 + 1 = 3$, for $3 + 1 = 4$, for $4 + 1 = 5$, and so on. Continuing in this way shows that the statement must be true for *every* positive integer.

The situation is similar to that of an infinite number of dominoes lined up. If the first domino is pushed over, it pushes the next, which pushes the next, and so on, indefinitely.

Another example of the principle of mathematical induction might be an infinite ladder. Suppose the rungs are spaced so that, whenever you are on a rung, you know you can move to the next rung. Then *if* you can get to the first rung, you can go as high up the ladder as you wish.

Two separate steps are required for a proof by mathematical induction.

PROOF BY MATHEMATICAL INDUCTION

STEP 1: Prove that the statement is true for $n = 1$.

STEP 2: Show that for any positive integer k, if S_k is true, then S_{k+1} is also true.

Proving Statements

Mathematical induction is used in the next example to prove the statement S_n discussed earlier.

EXAMPLE 1 Proving an equality statement

Let S_n represent the statement

$$1 + 2 + 3 + \cdots + n = \frac{n(n + 1)}{2}.$$

Prove that S_n is true for every positive integer n.

SOLUTION The proof by mathematical induction is as follows.

STEP 1: Show that the statement is true when $n = 1$. If $n = 1$, S_1 becomes

$$1 = \frac{1(1 + 1)}{2},$$

which is true.

STEP 2: Show that if S_k is true, then S_{k+1} is also true, where S_k is the statement

Statement S_k $\quad 1 + 2 + 3 + \cdots + k = \dfrac{k(k + 1)}{2}$

and S_{k+1} is the statement

Statement S_{k+1} $\quad 1 + 2 + 3 + \cdots + k + (k + 1) = \dfrac{(k + 1)[(k + 1) + 1]}{2}.$

Start with S_k and assume it is a true statement.

$$1 + 2 + 3 + \cdots + k = \frac{k(k + 1)}{2} \qquad S_k \text{ is true.}$$

Add $k + 1$ to each side of equation S_k and simplify to obtain S_{k+1}.

$$1 + 2 + 3 + \cdots + k + (k + 1) = \frac{k(k + 1)}{2} + (k + 1)$$

$$= (k + 1)\left(\frac{k}{2} + 1\right) \qquad \text{Factor out } k + 1.$$

$$= (k + 1)\left(\frac{k + 2}{2}\right)$$

Statement S_{k+1} is true.

$$= \frac{(k + 1)[(k + 1) + 1]}{2}$$

This final result is the statement S_{k+1}. Therefore, if S_k is true, then S_{k+1} is also true. The two steps required for a proof by mathematical induction have been completed, so the statement S_n is true for every positive integer n.

Now Try Exercise 1

EXAMPLE 2 Proving an equality statement

Let S_n represent the statement

$$2^1 + 2^2 + 2^3 + 2^4 + \cdots + 2^n = 2^{n+1} - 2.$$

Prove that S_n is true for every positive integer n.

SOLUTION

STEP 1: Show that the statement S_1 is true, where S_1 is

$$2^1 = 2^{1+1} - 2.$$

Since $2 = 4 - 2$, S_1 is a true statement.

STEP 2: Show that if S_k is true, then S_{k+1} is also true, where S_k is

Statement S_k $$2^1 + 2^2 + 2^3 + \cdots + 2^k = 2^{k+1} - 2$$

and S_{k+1} is

Statement S_{k+1} $$2^1 + 2^2 + 2^3 + \cdots + 2^k + 2^{k+1} = 2^{(k+1)+1} - 2.$$

Start with the given equation S_k and add 2^{k+1} to each side of this equation. Then algebraically change the right side to look like the right side of S_{k+1}.

$$2^1 + 2^2 + 2^3 + \cdots + 2^k + 2^{k+1} = 2^{k+1} - 2 + 2^{k+1}$$

Statement S_{k+1} is true.

$$= 2 \cdot 2^{k+1} - 2$$
$$= 2^{(k+1)+1} - 2$$

The final result is the statement S_{k+1}. Therefore, if S_k is true, then S_{k+1} is also true. The two steps required for a proof by mathematical induction have been completed, so the statement S_n is true for every positive integer n.

Now Try Exercise 5

EXAMPLE 3 Proving an inequality statement

Prove that if x satisfies $0 < x < 1$, then for every positive integer n,

$$0 < x^n < 1.$$

SOLUTION

STEP 1: Here S_1 is the statement

$$\text{if } 0 < x < 1, \text{ then } 0 < x^1 < 1,$$

which is true.

STEP 2: S_k is the statement

$$\text{if } 0 < x < 1, \text{ then } 0 < x^k < 1. \quad \text{Statement } S_k$$

To show that S_k implies that S_{k+1} is true, multiply all three parts of $0 < x^k < 1$ by x to get

$$x \cdot 0 < x \cdot x^k < x \cdot 1.$$

(Here the fact that $0 < x$ is used. Why?) Simplify to obtain

$$0 < x^{k+1} < x.$$

Because $x < 1$,

$$0 < x^{k+1} < 1, \quad \underline{\quad} \begin{array}{l} \text{Statement } S_{k+1} \\ \text{is true.} \end{array}$$

which implies that S_{k+1} is true. Therefore, if S_k is true, then S_{k+1} is true. Since both steps for a proof by mathematical induction have been completed, the given statement is true for every positive integer n.

Now Try Exercise 23

Generalized Principle of Mathematical Induction

Some statements S_n are not true for the first few values of n, but are true for all values of n that are greater than or equal to some fixed integer j. The following slightly generalized form of the principle of mathematical induction addresses these cases.

GENERALIZED PRINCIPLE OF MATHEMATICAL INDUCTION

Let S_n be a statement concerning the positive integer n. Let j be a fixed positive integer. Suppose that

1. S_j is true;
2. for any positive integer k, $k \geq j$, S_k implies S_{k+1}.

Then S_n is true for all positive integers n, where $n \geq j$.

EXAMPLE 4 Using the generalized principle

Let S_n represent the statement $2^n > 2n + 1$. Show that S_n is true for all values of n such that $n \geq 3$.

SOLUTION (Check that S_n is false for $n = 1$ and $n = 2$.)

STEP 1: Show that S_n is true for $n = 3$. If $n = 3$, then S_3 is

$$2^3 > 2 \cdot 3 + 1, \quad \text{or}$$

$$8 > 7.$$

Thus S_3 is true.

STEP 2: Now show that S_k implies S_{k+1} for $k \geq 3$, where

$$S_k \text{ is } 2^k > 2k + 1 \qquad \text{and} \qquad \text{\textit{Assume } } S_k \text{ \textit{ is true.}}$$

$$S_{k+1} \text{ is } 2^{k+1} > 2(k+1) + 1. \qquad \text{\textit{Show } } S_{k+1} \text{ \textit{ is true.}}$$

Multiply each side of $2^k > 2k + 1$ by 2, obtaining

$$2 \cdot 2^k > 2(2k + 1), \quad \text{or}$$

$$2^{k+1} > 4k + 2.$$

Rewrite $4k + 2$ as $2(k + 1) + 2k$, to get

$$2^{k+1} > 2(k+1) + 2k.$$

Since k is a positive integer greater than or equal to 3,

$$2k > 1.$$

It follows that

$$2^{k+1} > 2(k+1) + 2k > 2(k+1) + 1, \quad \text{or}$$

$$\begin{array}{l} \text{Statement } S_{k+1} \\ \text{is true.} \end{array} \underline{\quad} \quad 2^{k+1} > 2(k+1) + 1,$$

as required. Thus S_k implies S_{k+1}, and this, together with the fact that S_3 is true, shows that S_n is true for every positive integer n greater than or equal to 3.

Now Try Exercise 27

11.5 Putting It All Together

$\mathbf{S}$ome important concepts about mathematical induction are summarized in the following table.

CONCEPT	EXPLANATION
Principle of mathematical induction	Let S_n be a statement concerning the positive integer n. Suppose that **1.** S_1 is true; **2.** for any positive integer k, if S_k is true, then S_{k+1} is also true. Then S_n is true for every positive integer n.
Proof by mathematical induction	**STEP 1:** Prove that the statement is true for $n = 1$. **STEP 2:** Show that for any positive integer k, if S_k is true, then S_{k+1} is also true.
Generalized principle of mathematical induction	Let S_n be a statement concerning the positive integer n. Let j be a fixed positive integer. Suppose that **1.** S_j is true; **2.** for any positive integer k, $k \geq j$, S_k implies S_{k+1}. Then S_n is true for all positive integers n, where $n \geq j$.

11.5 Exercises

Mathematical Induction

Exercises 1–14: Use mathematical induction to prove the statement. Assume that n is a positive integer.

1. $3 + 6 + 9 + \cdots + 3n = \dfrac{3n(n + 1)}{2}$

2. $1 + 3 + 5 + \cdots + (2n - 1) = n^2$

3. $5 + 10 + 15 + \cdots + 5n = \dfrac{5n(n + 1)}{2}$

4. $4 + 7 + 10 + \cdots + (3n + 1) = \dfrac{n(3n + 5)}{2}$

5. $3 + 3^2 + 3^3 + \cdots + 3^n = \dfrac{3(3^n - 1)}{2}$

6. $1^2 + 2^2 + 3^2 + \cdots + n^2 = \dfrac{n(n + 1)(2n + 1)}{6}$

7. $1^3 + 2^3 + 3^3 + \cdots + n^3 = \dfrac{n^2(n + 1)^2}{4}$

8. $5 \cdot 6 + 5 \cdot 6^2 + 5 \cdot 6^3 + \cdots + 5 \cdot 6^n = 6(6^n - 1)$

9. $\dfrac{1}{1 \cdot 2} + \dfrac{1}{2 \cdot 3} + \dfrac{1}{3 \cdot 4} + \cdots + \dfrac{1}{n(n + 1)} = \dfrac{n}{n + 1}$

10. $7 \cdot 8 + 7 \cdot 8^2 + 7 \cdot 8^3 + \cdots + 7 \cdot 8^n = 8(8^n - 1)$

11. $\dfrac{4}{5} + \dfrac{4}{5^2} + \dfrac{4}{5^3} + \cdots + \dfrac{4}{5^n} = 1 - \dfrac{1}{5^n}$

12. $\dfrac{1}{2} + \dfrac{1}{2^2} + \dfrac{1}{2^3} + \cdots + \dfrac{1}{2^n} = 1 - \dfrac{1}{2^n}$

13. $\dfrac{1}{1 \cdot 4} + \dfrac{1}{4 \cdot 7} + \cdots + \dfrac{1}{(3n - 2)(3n + 1)} = \dfrac{n}{3n + 1}$

14. $x^{2n} + x^{2n-1}y + \cdots + xy^{2n-1} + y^{2n} = \dfrac{x^{2n+1} - y^{2n+1}}{x - y}$

Exercises 15–18: Find all positive integers n for which the given statement is not true.

15. $3^n > 6n$ **16.** $3^n > 2n + 1$

17. $2^n > n^2$ **18.** $n! > 2n$

Exercises 19–28: Prove the statement by mathematical induction.

19. $(a^m)^n = a^{mn}$ (Assume a and m are constants.)

20. $(ab)^n = a^n b^n$ (Assume a and b are constants.)

21. $2^n > 2n$ if $n \geq 3$

22. $3^n > 2n + 1$, if $n \geq 2$

23. If $a > 1$, then $a^n > 1$.

24. If $a > 1$, then $a^n > a^{n-1}$.

25. If $0 < a < 1$, then $a^n < a^{n-1}$.

26. $2^n > n^2$ for $n > 4$

27. If $n \geq 4$, then $n! > 2^n$, where

$$n! = n(n - 1)(n - 2) \cdots (3)(2)(1).$$

28. $4^n > n^4$ for $n \geq 5$

Applications

29. Number of Handshakes Suppose that each of the n ($n \geq 2$) people in a room shakes hands with everyone else, but not with himself. Show that the number of handshakes is $\frac{n^2 - n}{2}$.

30. Sides of a Polygon The series of sketches starts with an equilateral triangle having sides of length 1. In the following steps, equilateral triangles are constructed on each side of the preceding figure. The length of the sides of each new triangle is $\frac{1}{3}$ the length of the sides of the preceding triangles. Develop a formula for the number of sides of the nth figure. Use mathematical induction to prove your answer.

31. Perimeter Find the perimeter of the nth figure in Exercise 30.

32. Area Show that the area of the nth figure in Exercise 30 is given by

$$\sqrt{3}\left[\frac{2}{5} - \frac{3}{20}\left(\frac{4}{9}\right)^{n-1}\right].$$

33. Tower of Hanoi A pile of n rings, each ring smaller than the one below it, is on a peg. Two other pegs are attached to the same board as this peg. In a game called the *Tower of Hanoi* puzzle, all the rings must be moved to a different peg, with only one ring moved at a time and with no ring ever placed on top of a smaller ring. Find the least number of moves required. Prove your result with mathematical induction.

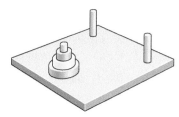

Writing about Mathematics

34. Explain the principle of mathematical induction.

35. Explain how the generalized principle of mathematical induction differs from the principle of mathematical induction.

36. When using mathematical induction, why is it important to prove that the statement holds for $n = 1$?

11.6 Probability

- Learn the basic concepts about probability
- Calculate the probability of compound events
- Calculate the probability of independent and dependent events

Introduction

Questions of chance have no doubt engaged the minds of people since antiquity. However, the mathematical treatment of probability did not begin until the 15th century. The birth of probability theory as a mathematical discipline occurred in the 17th century with the work of Blaise Pascal and Pierre Fermat. Today probability pervades society. It is used not only to determine outcomes in gambling, but also to predict weather, genetic outcomes, and the risk involved with various types of substances and behaviors.

Probability provides us with a measure of the likelihood that an event will occur. Risk is the chance, or probability, that a harmful event will occur. The following activities increase the annual risk of death by one chance in a million: flying 1000 miles in a jet, traveling 300 miles in a car, riding 10 miles on a bicycle, smoking 1.4 cigarettes, living 2 days in New York City, having one chest X-ray, or living 2 months with a cigarette smoker. Knowledge about probability allows individuals to make informed decisions about their lives. (*Sources:* NCTM, *Historical Topics for the Mathematics Classroom, Thirty-first Yearbook;* J. Rodricks, *Calculated Risk.*)

Definition of Probability

In the study of probability, experiments often are performed. The following explains terminology about experiments and gives an example.

Experiment Terminology	Example: Rolling a Die
Outcome: A result from an experiment	*Outcome*: The number showing on the die
Sample Space: The set of all possible outcomes S	*Sample Space*: $S = \{1, 2, 3, 4, 5, 6\}$
	Two outcomes in E Six outcomes in S
Event: Any subset E of a sample space	*Event*: $E = \{1, 6\}$ contains the outcomes of either 1 or 6 showing on the die

If $n(E)$ and $n(S)$ denote the number of outcomes in E and S, then $n(E) = 2$ and $n(S) = 6$ in the above experiment of rolling a die. The probability of rolling a 1 or a 6 is given by $P(E) = \frac{2}{6}$. That is, the likelihood of event E occurring is two chances in six. These concepts are summarized in the following box.

PROBABILITY OF AN EVENT

If the outcomes of a finite sample space S are equally likely and if E is an event in S, then the **probability of E** is given by

$$P(E) = \frac{n(E)}{n(S)},$$

where $n(E)$ and $n(S)$ represent the number of outcomes in E and S, respectively.

Since $n(E) \leq n(S)$, the probability of an event E satisfies $0 \leq P(E) \leq 1$. If $P(E) = 1$, then event E is *certain* to occur. If $P(E) = 0$, then event E is *impossible*.

EXAMPLE 1   Drawing a card

One card is drawn at random from a standard deck of 52 cards. Find the probability that the card is an ace.

SOLUTION The sample space S consists of 52 outcomes that correspond to drawing any one of 52 cards. Each outcome is equally likely. Let E represent the event of drawing

an ace. There are four aces in the deck, so event E contains four outcomes. Therefore $n(S) = 52$ and $n(E) = 4$. The probability of drawing an ace is given by

$$P(E) = \frac{n(E)}{n(S)} = \frac{4}{52} = \frac{1}{13}.$$

Now Try Exercise 15

EXAMPLE 2 Estimating probability of organ transplants

In 2012, there were 114,448 patients waiting for an organ transplant. Table 11.7 lists the numbers of patients waiting for the *most common types* of transplants. None of these people need two or more transplants. Approximate the probability that a transplant patient chosen at random will need
(a) a kidney or a heart,   **(b)** neither a kidney nor a heart.

Waiting List

Heart	3186
Kidney	92,346
Liver	16,082
Lung	1645

Table 11.7

Source: UNOS.

SOLUTION

(a) Let each patient represent an outcome in a sample space S. The event E of a transplant patient needing either a kidney or a heart contains $92,346 + 3186 = 95,532$ outcomes. The desired probability is

$$P(E) = \frac{n(E)}{n(S)} = \frac{95,532}{114,448} \approx 0.83.$$

In 2012, about 83% of transplant patients needed either a kidney or a heart.

(b) Let F be the event of a patient waiting for an organ other than a kidney or a heart. Then

$$n(F) = n(S) - n(E) = 114,448 - 95,532 = 18,916.$$

The probability of F is

$$P(F) = \frac{n(F)}{n(S)} = \frac{18,916}{114,448} \approx 0.17, \quad \text{or} \quad 17\%.$$

Now Try Exercise 43

Union and Intersection The **union** of set A and set B is the set of elements that belong to either A or B, and is denoted $A \cup B$ and sometimes read "A or B". For example, if

$$A = \{1, 2, 3\} \text{ and } B = \{3, 4, 5\}, \text{ then}$$
$$A \cup B = \{1, 2, 3, 4, 5\}.$$

Appears in both A and B, but is only listed once

The **intersection** of A and B is the set of elements that belong to *both A and B*, and is denoted $A \cap B$ and sometimes read "A and B." Using the sets A and B above,

$$A \cap B = \{3\}, \text{ as it is the only element that is in both } A \text{ and } B.$$

Notice that $P(E) + P(F) = 1$ in Example 2. The events E and F are **complements** because $E \cap F = \varnothing$ and $E \cup F = S$, where $\varnothing$ denotes the *empty set*. That is, a transplant patient is either waiting for a kidney or a heart (event E) or not waiting for a kidney or a heart (event F). The complement of E may be denoted by E'.

Venn Diagrams Probability concepts can be illustrated using **Venn diagrams**. In Figure 11.20 the sample space S of an experiment is the union of the disjoint sets E and its complement E'. That is, $E \cup E' = S$ and $E \cap E' = \varnothing$.

If $P(E)$ is known, then $P(E')$ can be calculated as follows.

$$P(E') = \frac{n(E')}{n(S)} = \frac{n(S) - n(E)}{n(S)} = 1 - \frac{n(E)}{n(S)} = 1 - P(E)$$

Complements E and E'

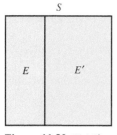

Figure 11.20 $E \cup E' = S$

In Example 2(b), the probability of $F = E'$ could also have been calculated by using

$$P(F) = 1 - P(E) \approx 1 - 0.83 = 0.17.$$

PROBABILITY OF A COMPLEMENT

Let E be an event and E' be its complement. If the probability of E is $P(E)$, then the probability of its complement is given by

$$P(E') = 1 - P(E).$$

EXAMPLE 3   Finding probabilities of human eye color

In 1865, Gregor Mendel performed important research in genetics. His work led to a better understanding of dominant and recessive genetic traits. According to Mendel's research, brown eye color B is dominant over blue eye color b. A person receives one gene (B or b) from each parent. If a person has the genotype BB, Bb, or bB, he or she will have brown eyes. The genotype bb will result in blue eyes. Table 11.8 shows how these two genes can be paired.   (**Source:** H. Lancaster, *Quantitative Methods in Biology and Medical Sciences.*)
(a) Assuming that each genotype is equally likely, find the probability of blue eyes.
(b) What is the probability that a person has brown eyes?

Eye Color Outcomes

	B	b
B	BB	Bb
b	bB	bb

Table 11.8

SOLUTION
(a) The sample space S consists of four equally likely outcomes denoted BB, Bb, bB, and bb. The event E of blue eye color (bb) occurs once. Therefore

$$P(E) = \frac{n(E)}{n(S)} = \frac{1}{4} = 0.25.$$

(b) In Table 11.8 brown eyes are the complement of blue eyes. The probability of brown eyes is

$$1 - P(\text{blue eyes}) = P(\text{brown eyes})$$
$$P(E') = 1 - P(E) = 1 - 0.25 = 0.75.$$

This probability also could be computed as

$$P(E') = \frac{n(E')}{n(S)} = \frac{3}{4} = 0.75,$$

since there are three genotypes that result in brown eye color.

Now Try Exercise 47

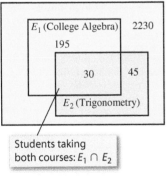

Student Enrollment

E_1 (College Algebra)   2230
195
30   45
E_2 (Trigonometry)

Students taking
both courses: $E_1 \cap E_2$

Figure 11.21

Compound Events

Frequently the probability of more than one event is needed. For example, suppose a college with a total of 2500 students has 225 students enrolled in college algebra, 75 in trigonometry, and 30 in both. Let E_1 denote the event that a student is enrolled in college algebra and E_2 the event that a student is enrolled in trigonometry. Then the Venn diagram in Figure 11.21 visually describes the situation.

In this Venn diagram, it is important that the 30 students taking both courses not be counted twice. Set E_1 has a total of $195 + 30 = 225$ students, and set E_2 contains $45 + 30 = 75$ students.

EXAMPLE 4   Calculating the probability of a union

In the preceding scenario, suppose a student is selected at random. What is the probability that this student is enrolled in college algebra, trigonometry, or both?

Student Enrollment

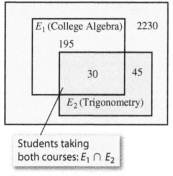

Students taking both courses: $E_1 \cap E_2$

Figure 11.21 (Repeated)

SOLUTION We would like to find the probability $P(E_1$ or $E_2)$, which is usually denoted $P(E_1 \cup E_2)$. Since $n(E_1 \cup E_2) = 195 + 30 + 45 = 270$ and $n(S) = 2500$,

$$P(E_1 \cup E_2) = \frac{n(E_1 \cup E_2)}{n(S)} = \frac{270}{2500} = 0.108.$$

There is a 10.8% chance that a student selected at random will be taking college algebra, trigonometry, or both.

> **Now Try Exercise 41**

In the previous example, it would have been incorrect to simply add the probability of a student taking algebra and the probability of a student taking trigonometry. Their sum would be

$$P(E_1) + P(E_2) = \frac{n(E_1)}{n(S)} + \frac{n(E_2)}{n(S)}$$

$$= \frac{225}{2500} + \frac{75}{2500}$$

$$= \frac{300}{2500}$$

$$= 0.12, \quad \text{or} \quad 12\%. \ ✗$$

This sum is greater than $P(E_1 \cup E_2)$ because the 30 students taking both courses are counted *twice* in this calculation. In order to find the correct probability for $P(E_1 \cup E_2)$, **we must subtract the probability of the intersection $E_1 \cap E_2$.**

$$P(E_1 \cup E_2) = P(E_1) + P(E_2) - \mathbf{P(E_1 \cap E_2)}$$

$$= \frac{n(E_1)}{n(S)} + \frac{n(E_2)}{n(S)} - \frac{n(E_1 \cap E_2)}{n(S)}$$

$$= \frac{225}{2500} + \frac{75}{2500} - \frac{30}{2500}$$

$$= \frac{270}{2500}$$

$$= 0.108, \quad \text{or} \quad 10.8\% \ ✓$$

This is the same result obtained in Example 4 and suggests the following property.

PROBABILITY OF THE UNION OF TWO EVENTS

For any two events E_1 and E_2,

$$P(E_1 \cup E_2) = P(E_1) + P(E_2) - P(E_1 \cap E_2).$$

EXAMPLE 5 Rolling dice

Suppose two dice are rolled. Find the probability that the dice show either a sum of 8 or a pair.

SOLUTION In Table 11.9 the roll of the dice is represented by an ordered pair. For example, the ordered pair (3, 6) repre4sents the first die showing 3 and the second die 6.

Possibilities when Rolling Two Dice

(1, 1)	(1, 2)	(1, 3)	(1, 4)	(1, 5)	(1, 6)
(2, 1)	**(2, 2)**	(2, 3)	(2, 4)	(2, 5)	**(2, 6)**
(3, 1)	(3, 2)	**(3, 3)**	(3, 4)	**(3, 5)**	(3, 6)
(4, 1)	(4, 2)	(4, 3)	**(4, 4)**	(4, 5)	(4, 6)
(5, 1)	(5, 2)	**(5, 3)**	(5, 4)	**(5, 5)**	(5, 6)
(6, 1)	**(6, 2)**	(6, 3)	(6, 4)	(6, 5)	**(6, 6)**

Table 11.9

Because each die can show six different outcomes, there are a total of $6 \cdot 6 = 36$ outcomes in the sample space S. Let E_1 denote the event of rolling a sum of 8 and E_2 the event of rolling a pair. Then

> 5 possible ways to roll a sum of 8

$$E_1 = \{(6, 2), (5, 3), (4, 4), (3, 5), (2, 6)\} \quad \text{and}$$

$$E_2 = \{(1, 1), (2, 2), (3, 3), (4, 4), (5, 5), (6, 6)\}.$$

> 6 possible ways to roll a pair

The intersection of E_1 and E_2 is

$$E_1 \cap E_2 = \{(4, 4)\}.$$

Since $n(S) = 36$, $n(E_1) = 5$, $n(E_2) = 6$, and $n(E_1 \cap E_2) = 1$, the following can be computed.

> Subtract the probability of the intersection.

$$P(E_1 \cup E_2) = P(E_1) + P(E_2) - P(E_1 \cap E_2)$$

$$= \frac{n(E_1)}{n(S)} + \frac{n(E_2)}{n(S)} - \frac{n(E_1 \cap E_2)}{n(S)}$$

$$= \frac{5}{36} + \frac{6}{36} - \frac{1}{36}$$

$$= \frac{10}{36}, \quad \text{or} \quad \frac{5}{18}$$

This result can be verified by counting the number of boldfaced outcomes in Table 11.9. Of the 36 possible outcomes, 10 satisfy the conditions, so the probability is $\frac{10}{36}$, or $\frac{5}{18}$.

> **Now Try Exercise 49**

Mutually Exclusive Events   If $E_1 \cap E_2 = \varnothing$, then the events E_1 and E_2 are **mutually exclusive**. Mutually exclusive events have no outcomes in common, so $P(E_1 \cap E_2) = 0$. In this case, $P(E_1 \cup E_2) = P(E_1) + P(E_2)$.

EXAMPLE 6   Drawing cards

Find the probability of drawing either an ace or a king from a standard deck of 52 cards.

SOLUTION   The event E_1 of drawing an ace and the event E_2 of drawing a king are mutually exclusive. No card can be both an ace and a king. Therefore $P(E_1 \cap E_2) = 0$. The probability of drawing an ace is $P(E_1) = \frac{4}{52}$, since there are 4 aces in 52 cards. Similarly, the probability of drawing a king is $P(E_2) = \frac{4}{52}$.

$$P(E_1 \cup E_2) = P(E_1) + P(E_2)$$

$$= \frac{4}{52} + \frac{4}{52}$$

$$= \frac{8}{52}, \quad \text{or} \quad \frac{2}{13}$$

Thus the probability of drawing either an ace or a king is $\frac{2}{13}$.   **Now Try Exercise 51**

The next example uses concepts from both counting and probability.

EXAMPLE 7 Drawing a poker hand

A standard deck of cards contains 52 cards, consisting of 13 different cards from each of four suits: hearts, diamonds, spades, and clubs. A poker hand consists of 5 cards drawn from a standard deck of cards, and a flush occurs when the 5 cards are all from the same suit. Find an expression for the probability of drawing 5 cards of the same suit in one try. Assume that the cards are not replaced.

SOLUTION Let E be the event of drawing 5 cards of the same suit. To determine $n(E)$, start by calculating the number of ways to draw a flush in a particular suit, such as hearts. From a set of 13 hearts, 5 hearts need to be drawn. There are $\binom{13}{5}$ ways to draw this hand. Because there are 4 suits, there are $4\binom{13}{5}$ ways to draw 5 cards of the same suit. Thus $n(E) = 4\binom{13}{5}$. The sample space S consists of all 5-card poker hands that can be drawn from a deck of 52 cards. There are $\binom{52}{5}$ different poker hands. Thus $n(S) = \binom{52}{5}$. The probability of a flush can now be calculated as follows.

Calculator Help

To calculate $C(n, r)$, see Appendix A (page AP-17).

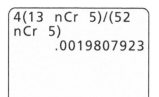

Figure 11.22

$$P(E) = \frac{n(E)}{n(S)} = \frac{4\binom{13}{5}}{\binom{52}{5}}$$

— Number of ways to draw a flush

— Number of ways to draw any 5-card poker hand

In Figure 11.22, we see that $P(E) \approx 0.00198$. Thus there is about a 0.2% chance of drawing 5 cards of the same suit (in one try) from a standard deck of 52 cards.

Now Try Exercise 37

Independent Events

Two events are **independent** if they do not influence each other. Otherwise they are **dependent**. An example of independent events would be one coin being tossed twice. The result of the first toss does not affect the second toss. The following shows how to calculate the probability of two independent events both occurring.

INDEPENDENT EVENTS

If E_1 and E_2 are independent events, then

$$P(E_1 \cap E_2) = P(E_1) \cdot P(E_2).$$

EXAMPLE 8 Tossing a coin

Suppose a coin is tossed twice. Determine the probability that the result is two heads.

SOLUTION Let E_1 be the event of a head on the first toss, and let E_2 be the event of a head on the second toss. Then $P(E_1) = P(E_2) = \frac{1}{2}$. The two events are independent. The probability of two heads occurring is

$$P(E_1 \cap E_2) = P(E_1) \cdot P(E_2) = \frac{1}{2} \cdot \frac{1}{2} = \frac{1}{4}.$$

This probability of $\frac{1}{4}$ also can be found using a tree diagram, as shown in Figure 11.23. There are four equally likely outcomes. Tosses resulting in two heads occur once.

Now Try Exercise 27

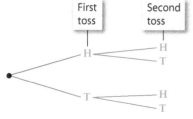

Figure 11.23

EXAMPLE 9   Rolling dice

What is the probability of rolling a sum of 12 with two dice?

SOLUTION   The roll of one die does not influence the roll of the other. They are independent events. To obtain a sum of 12, both dice must show a 6. Let E_1 be the event of rolling a 6 with the first die and E_2 the event of rolling a 6 with the second die. Then $P(E_1) = P(E_2) = \frac{1}{6}$. The probability of rolling a 12 is

$$P(E_1 \cap E_2) = P(E_1) \cdot P(E_2) = \frac{1}{6} \cdot \frac{1}{6} = \frac{1}{36}.$$

___CLASS DISCUSSION___

When a pair of dice are rolled, what sum is most likely to appear?

This result can be verified by using Table 11.9. There is only 1 outcome out of 36 that results in a sum of 12.

Now Try Exercise 31

Conditional Probability and Dependent Events

The **conditional probability** of an event E_2 is the probability that the event will occur, given the knowledge that event E_1 already occurred. For example, we might want to find the probability of attending college, given that graduating from high school already occurred. $P(E_2, \text{given } E_1 \text{ occurred})$ is called the conditional probability of E_2, given E_1.

When events E_1 and E_2 are independent, $P(E_2, \text{given that } E_1 \text{ occurred}) = P(E_2)$, as event E_1 does not influence event E_2. For example, $P(\text{tossing heads given that the last toss was tails})$ is simply $P(\text{tossing heads}) = \frac{1}{2}$, since two separate coin flips are independent events. However, we often use conditional probability to find the probability of dependent events.

If events E_1 and E_2 influence each other, they are *dependent*. The probability of dependent events both occurring is given as follows.

___PROBABILITY OF DEPENDENT EVENTS___

If E_1 and E_2 are dependent events, then

$$P(E_1 \cap E_2) = P(E_1) \cdot P(E_2, \text{given that } E_1 \text{ occurred}).$$

EXAMPLE 10   Drawing cards

Find the probability of drawing two hearts from a standard deck of 52 cards when the first card is
(a) replaced before drawing the second card,   **(b)** not replaced.

SOLUTION
(a) Let E_1 denote the event of the first card being a heart and E_2 the event of the second card being a heart. If the first card is replaced before the second card is drawn, the two events are *independent*. Since there are 13 hearts in a standard deck of 52 cards, the probability of two hearts being drawn is

$$P(E_1 \cap E_2) = P(E_1) \cdot P(E_2) = \frac{13}{52} \cdot \frac{13}{52} = \frac{1}{16}.$$

(b) If the first card is not replaced, then the outcome for the second card is influenced by the first card. Therefore the events E_1 and E_2 are dependent and we need to find the conditional probability of E_2, given E_1. The probability of drawing a second heart, given that the first card is a heart, is $P(E_2, \text{given } E_1 \text{ has occurred}) = \frac{12}{51}$. That is, if the first card drawn were a heart and removed from the deck, then there would be 12 hearts in a sample space of 51 cards.

$$P(E_1 \cap E_2) = P(E_1) \cdot P(E_2, \text{ given that } E_1 \text{ occurred}) = \frac{13}{52} \cdot \frac{12}{51} = \frac{1}{17}$$

Thus the probability of drawing two hearts is slightly less if the first card is not replaced.

Now Try Exercise 61

EXAMPLE 11 Calculating the probability of dependent events

Table 11.10 shows the number of students (by gender) registered for either a Spanish class or a French class. No student is taking both languages.

	Spanish	French	Totals
Females	20	25	45
Males	40	25	65
Totals	60	50	110

Table 11.10

If one student is selected at random, calculate each of the following.
(a) The probability that the student is female
(b) The probability that the student is taking Spanish, given that the student is female
(c) The probability that the student is female and taking Spanish

SOLUTION
(a) Let F represent the event that the student is female. Since 45 of the 110 students are female, $P(F) = \frac{45}{110} = \frac{9}{22}$.
(b) Let S be the event that the student is taking Spanish. The probability that the student is taking Spanish, given that the student is female, is $P(S, \text{ given } F) = \frac{20}{45} = \frac{4}{9}$, because 20 of the 45 female students are taking Spanish.
(c) The probability that the student is female *and* taking Spanish is calculated by

$$P(F \cap S) = P(F) \cdot P(S, \text{ given } F) = \frac{45}{110} \cdot \frac{20}{45} = \frac{2}{11}.$$

Table 11.10 shows that 20 of the 110 students are female and taking Spanish. Thus the required probability is $\frac{20}{110} = \frac{2}{11}$, which is in agreement with our previous calculation.

Now Try Exercise 71

EXAMPLE 12 Analyzing a polygraph test

Suppose there is a 6% chance that a polygraph test will incorrectly say a person is lying when he or she is actually telling the truth. If a person tells the truth 95% of the time, what percentage of the time will the polygraph test incorrectly indicate a lie for this person?

SOLUTION Let E_1 be the event that the person is telling the truth and E_2 be the event that the polygraph test is incorrect. Then

$$P(E_1 \cap E_2) = P(E_1) \cdot P(E_2, \text{ given the person is telling the truth)}$$

$$= (0.95)(0.06)$$

$$= 0.057, \quad \text{or} \quad 5.7\%.$$

Now Try Exercise 67

11.6 Putting It All Together

The following table summarizes some concepts about probability. In this table, S denotes a finite sample space of equally likely outcomes, and E, E_1, and E_2 denote events in the sample space S.

CONCEPT	EXPLANATION	EXAMPLE
Probability P	A number P satisfying $0 \leq P \leq 1$	$P(E) = 1$ indicates that an event E is certain to occur, $P(E) = 0$ indicates that an event E is impossible, and $P(E) = 0.3$ indicates that an event E has a 30% chance of occurring.
Probability of an event	The probability of event E is $$P(E) = \frac{n(E)}{n(S)},$$ where $n(E)$ and $n(S)$ denote the number of equally likely outcomes in E and S, respectively.	The probability of rolling two dice and their sum being 3 is $\frac{2}{36}$. This is because there are $6 \cdot 6 = 36$ ways to roll two dice and only 2 ways to roll a sum of 3. (They are 1 and 2 or 2 and 1.)
Probability of a complement	If E and E' are complementary events, then $E \cap E' = \varnothing$, $E \cup E' = S$, and $P(E') = 1 - P(E)$.	The probability of rolling a 6 with one die is $\frac{1}{6}$. Therefore the probability of *not* rolling a 6 is $1 - \frac{1}{6} = \frac{5}{6}$.
Probability of the union of two events	The probability of E_1 or E_2 (or both) occurring is $P(E_1 \cup E_2) = P(E_1) + P(E_2) - P(E_1 \cap E_2)$.	If $P(E_1) = 0.5$, $P(E_2) = 0.2$, and $P(E_1 \cap E_2) = 0.1$, then $P(E_1 \cup E_2) = 0.5 + 0.2 - 0.1 = 0.6$.
Probability of independent events	Two events E_1 and E_2 are independent if they do not influence one another. $$P(E_1 \cap E_2) = P(E_1) \cdot P(E_2)$$	If E_1 represents a head on the first toss of a coin and E_2 represents a tail on the second toss, then E_1 and E_2 are independent events and $$P(E_1 \cap E_2) = \frac{1}{2} \cdot \frac{1}{2} = \frac{1}{4}.$$
Conditional probability	The conditional probability of E_2 is the probability the event will occur, given that E_1 already occurred. $P(E_2$, given that E_1 occurred)	An example would be the probability of rain, given that it's cloudy.
Probability of dependent events	Two events E_1 and E_2 are dependent if they are not independent. $P(E_1 \cap E_2) = P(E_1) \cdot P(E_2$, given that E_1 occurred)	Drawing two hearts without replacement from a standard deck of cards is an example of dependent events. See Example 10.

11.6 Exercises

Probability of an Event

Exercises 1–8: Does the number represent a probability?

1. $\frac{11}{13}$ 2. 0.995

3. 2.5   4. 1

5. 0   6. 110%

7. −0.375   8. $\frac{9}{8}$

Exercises 9–18: Find the probability of each event.

9. Tossing a head with a fair coin

10. Tossing a tail with a fair coin

11. Rolling a 2 with a fair die

12. Rolling a 5 or 6 with a fair die

13. Guessing the correct answer to a true-false question

14. Guessing the correct answer to a multiple-choice question with five choices

15. Randomly drawing a king from a standard deck of 52 cards

16. Randomly drawing a club from a standard deck of 52 cards

17. Randomly guessing a four-digit ATM access code

18. Randomly picking the winning team at a basketball game

19. The following table shows people's favorite pizza toppings.

Pepperoni	43%
Sausage	19%
Mushrooms	14%
Vegetables	13%

Source: USA Today

(a) If a person is selected at random, what is the probability that pepperoni is not his or her favorite topping?

(b) Find the probability that a person's favorite topping is either mushrooms or sausage.

20. (Refer to Example 2.) Find the probability that a transplant patient in 2012 was waiting for the following.
(a) A lung

(b) A heart or a liver

Union and Intersection

Exercises 21–26: Find the union and the intersection of events A and B.

21. $A = \{10, 25, 26\}$; $B = \{25, 26, 35\}$

22. $A = \{100, 200, 300\}$; $B = \{100, 500, 1000\}$

23. $A = \{1, 3, 5, 7\}$; $B = \{9, 11\}$

24. $A = \{2, 4, 6\}$; $B = \{2, 4, 6, 8\}$

25. $A = \{\text{Heads}\}$; $B = \{\text{Tails}\}$

26. $A = \{\text{Rain}\}$; $B = \{\text{No rain}\}$

Probability of Compound Events

Exercises 27–36: Find the probability of the compound event.

27. Tossing a coin twice with the outcomes of two tails

28. Tossing a coin three times with the outcomes of three heads

29. Rolling a die three times and obtaining a 5 or 6 on each roll

30. Rolling a sum of 7 with two dice

31. Rolling a sum of 2 with two dice

32. Rolling a sum other than 7 with two dice

33. Rolling a die four times without obtaining a 6

34. Rolling a die four times and obtaining at least one 6

35. Drawing four consecutive aces from a standard deck of 52 cards without replacement

36. Drawing a pair (two cards with the same value) from a standard deck of 52 cards without replacement

37. **Poker Hands** (Refer to Example 7.) Calculate the probability of drawing 3 hearts and 2 diamonds in a 5-card poker hand. Assume that drawn cards are not replaced and that the 5 cards are drawn only once.

38. **Poker Hands** (Refer to Example 7.) Calculate the probability of drawing 3 kings and 2 queens in a 5-card poker hand. Assume that drawn cards are not replaced and that the 5 cards are drawn only once.

39. **Quality Control** A quality-control experiment involves selecting 1 string of decorative lights from a box of 20.

If the string is defective, the entire box of 20 is rejected. Suppose the box contains 4 defective strings of lights. What is the probability of rejecting the box?

40. **Quality Control** (Refer to Exercise 39.) Suppose 3 strings of lights are tested. If any of the strings are defective, the entire box of 20 is rejected. What is the probability of rejecting a box if there are 4 defective strings of lights in the box? (*Hint:* Start by finding the probability that the box is not rejected.)

41. **Entrance Exams** A group of students is preparing for college entrance exams. It is estimated that 50% need help with mathematics, 45% with English, and 25% with both.
    (a) Draw a Venn diagram representing these data.

    (b) Use this diagram to find the probability that a student needs help with mathematics, English, or both.

    (c) Solve part (b) symbolically by applying a probability formula.

42. **College Classes** In a college of 5500 students, 950 students are enrolled in English classes, 1220 in business classes, and 350 in both. If a student is chosen at random, find the probability that he or she is enrolled in an English class, a business class, or both.

43. **Pinterest Categories** The table shows the most popular Pinterest categories in 2012 and the percentage of total pins associated with them. Find the probability that a randomly selected pin will be as specified.

Home	18%
Arts/Crafts	11%
Food	11%
Style/Fashion	11%
Inspiration/Education	9%
Holiday/Seasonal	4%

Source: Analytics by RJ Metrics

    (a) In the Home category

    (b) In none of the categories in the table

    (c) In neither the Home nor the Style/Fashion category

44. **Death Rates** In 2012, the U.S. death rate per 100,000 people was 838. What is the probability that a person selected at random died during 2012? (*Source:* Department of Health and Human Services.)

45. **Death Rates** In 2010, the death rate per 100,000 females was 634. What is the probability that a person

selected at random from this gender group died during 2010? (*Source:* Department of Health and Human Services.)

46. **Tossing a Coin** Find the probability of tossing a coin n times and obtaining n heads. What happens to this probability as n increases? Does this agree with your intuition? Explain.

47. **U.S. HIV** By 2008, a total of 679,590 people were living with an HIV diagnoses. The table lists HIV cases diagnosed in certain cities. Estimate the probability that a person diagnosed with HIV satisfied the following conditions.

New York	223,508
Los Angeles	65,947
San Francisco	44,422
Miami	64,573

Source: Department of Health and Human Services.

    (a) Resided in New York

    (b) Did not reside in New York

    (c) Resided in Los Angeles or Miami

48. **Rolling Dice** Find the probability of rolling a die five times and obtaining a 6 on the first two rolls, a 5 on the third roll, and a 1, 2, 3, or 4 on the last two rolls.

49. **Rolling Dice** (Refer to Example 5.) Two dice are rolled. Find the probability that the dice show either a pair or a sum of 6.

50. **Rolling Dice** Two dice are rolled. Find the probability that the dice show a sum other than 7 or 11.

51. **Drawing Cards** (Refer to Example 6.) Find the probability of drawing a 2, 3, or 4 from a standard deck of 52 playing cards.

52. **Drawing Cards** Find the probability of drawing two cards, neither of which is an ace or a queen.

53. **Unfair Die** Suppose a die is not fair, but instead the probability P of each number n is as listed in the table. Find the probability of each event.

n	1	2	3	4	5	6
P	0.1	0.1	0.1	0.2	0.2	0.3

    (a) Rolling a number that is 4 or higher

    (b) Rolling a 6 twice on consecutive rolls

54. Unfair Coin Suppose a coin is not fair, but instead the probability of obtaining a head (H) is $\frac{3}{4}$ and a tail (T) is $\frac{1}{4}$. What is the probability of each event?

(a) HT   (b) HH

(c) HHT   (d) THT

55. Dice Suppose there are two dice, one red and one blue, having the probabilities shown in the table in Exercise 53. If both dice are rolled, find the probability of the given sum.

(a) 12   (b) 11

56. Garage Door Code The code for some garage door openers consists of 12 electrical switches that can be set to either 0 or 1 by the owner. Each setting represents a different code. What is the probability of guessing someone's code at random? (*Source:* Promax.)

57. Lottery To win a lottery, a person must pick three numbers from 0 to 9 in the correct order. If a number may be repeated, what is the probability of winning this game with one play?

58. Lottery To win the jackpot in a lottery, a person must pick five numbers from 1 to 59 and then pick the powerball, which has a number from 1 to 35. If the numbers are picked at random, what is the probability of winning this game with one play?

59. Marbles A jar contains 22 red marbles, 18 blue marbles, and 10 green marbles. If a marble is drawn from the jar at random, find the probability that the color is the following.

(a) Red   (b) Not red

(c) Blue or green

60. Marbles A jar contains 55 red marbles and 45 blue marbles. If 2 marbles are drawn from the jar at random without replacement, find the probability that the marbles satisfy the following.

(a) Both are blue

(b) Neither is blue

(c) The first marble is red and the second marble is blue

Conditional Probability and Dependent Events

61. Drawing a Card Find the probability of drawing a queen from a standard deck of cards given that one card, a queen, has already been drawn and not replaced.

62. Drawing a Card Find the probability of drawing a king from a standard deck of cards given that two cards, both kings, have already been drawn and not replaced.

63. Drawing a Card A card is drawn from a standard deck of 52 cards. Given that the card is a face card, what is the probability that the card is a king? (*Hint:* A face card is a jack, queen, or king.)

64. Drawing a Card Three cards are drawn from a deck without replacement. Find the probability that the three cards are an ace, king, and queen in that order.

65. Drawing Marbles A jar initially contains 10 red marbles and 23 blue marbles. What is the probability of drawing a blue marble, given that 2 red marbles and 4 blue marbles have already been drawn?

66. Tennis Serve The probability that the first serve of a tennis ball is out of bounds is 0.3, and the probability that the second serve of a tennis ball is in bounds, given that the first serve was out of bounds, is 0.8. Find the probability that the first serve is out of bounds and the second serve is in bounds.

67. Cloudy and Windy The probability of a day being cloudy is 30%, and the probability of it being cloudy and windy is 12%. Given that the day is cloudy, what is the probability that it will be windy?

68. Rainy and Windy The probability of a day being rainy is 80%, and the probability of it being windy and rainy is 72%. Given that the day is rainy, what is the probability that it will be windy?

69. Rolling Dice Two dice are rolled. If the first die shows a 2, find the probability that the sum of the dice is 7 or more.

70. Rolling Dice Three dice are rolled. If the first die shows a 4, find the probability that the sum of the three dice is less than 12.

71. Defective Parts The table shows numbers of automobile parts that are either defective or not defective.

	Type A	Type B	Totals
Defective	7	11	18
Not defective	123	94	217
Totals	130	105	235

If one part is selected at random, calculate each of the following.

(a) The probability that the part is defective

(b) The probability that the part is type A, given that it is defective

(c) The probability that the part is type A and defective

72. **Health** The table shows numbers of patients with two different diseases by gender. (Assume that a person does not have both diseases.)

	Disease A	Disease B	Totals
Females	145	851	996
Males	256	355	611
Totals	401	1206	1607

If one patient is selected at random, find the probability that the patient is female and has disease B.

73. **Prime Numbers** Suppose a number from 1 to 15 is selected at random. Find the probability of each event.
   (a) The number is odd

   (b) The number is even

   (c) The number is prime (*Hint:* A natural number greater than 1 that has only itself and 1 as factors is called a **prime number**.)

(d) The number is prime and odd

(e) The number is prime and even

74. **Students and Classes** (Refer to Example 11.) If one student is selected at random, use Table 11.10 to calculate each of the following.
   (a) The probability that the student is male

   (b) The probability that the student is taking French, given that the student is male

   (c) The probability that the student is male and taking French

Writing about Mathematics

75. What values are possible for a probability? Interpret different probabilities and give examples.

76. Discuss the difference between dependent and independent events. How are their probabilities calculated?

CHECKING BASIC CONCEPTS FOR SECTIONS 11.5 AND 11.6

1. Use mathematical induction to prove that
$$4 + 8 + 12 + 16 + \cdots + 4n = 2n(n + 1).$$

2. Use mathematical induction to prove that $n^2 \leq 2^n$ for $n \geq 4$.

3. Find the probability of tossing a coin four times and obtaining a head every time.

4. Find the probability of rolling a sum of 11 with two dice.

5. Find the probability of drawing four aces and a queen from a standard deck of 52 cards.

6. **Electronic Waste** Worldwide electronic waste is increasing at about 40 million tons per year, with China producing 2.6 million tons per year. Estimate the probability that a given ton of electronic waste is *not* produced by China. (*Source:* EPA)

---

11 Summary

CONCEPT	EXPLANATION AND EXAMPLES

Section 11.1 Sequences

Sequences

An infinite sequence is a function whose domain is the natural numbers. Its graph is a scatterplot.

Example: $a_n = \frac{1}{2}n^2 - 2$; the first 4 terms a_1, a_2, a_3, a_4 are as follows.

$$a_1 = \frac{1}{2}(1)^2 - 2 = -\frac{3}{2}, \qquad a_2 = \frac{1}{2}(2)^2 - 2 = 0$$

$$a_3 = \frac{1}{2}(3)^2 - 2 = \frac{5}{2}, \qquad a_4 = \frac{1}{2}(4)^2 - 2 = 6$$

CONCEPT	EXPLANATION AND EXAMPLES

Section 11.1 Sequences (CONTINUED)

Arithmetic Sequence

Recursive Definition:

$a_n = a_{n-1} + d$, where d is the common difference

Function Definition:

$f(n) = dn + c$, or equivalently, $f(n) = a_1 + d(n - 1)$, where $a_n = f(n)$ and d is the common difference

Example: $a_n = a_{n-1} + 3$, $a_1 = 4$ and $f(n) = 3n + 1$ describe the same sequence. The common difference is $d = 3$. The terms of the sequence are

$$4, 7, 10, 13, 16, 19, 22, \ldots.$$

Geometric Sequence

Recursive Definition:

$a_n = ra_{n-1}$, where r is the common ratio

Function Definition:

$f(n) = cr^{n-1}$, where $c = a_1$ and r is the common ratio

Example: $a_n = -2a_{n-1}$, $a_1 = 3$ and $f(n) = 3(-2)^{n-1}$ describe the same sequence. The common ratio is $r = -2$. The terms of the sequence are

$$3, -6, 12, -24, 48, -96, 192, \ldots.$$

Section 11.2 Series

Series

A series is the summation of the terms of a sequence.

Examples: $1 + \dfrac{1}{2} + \dfrac{1}{4} + \dfrac{1}{8} + \cdots + \dfrac{1}{2^{n-1}} + \cdots$ Infinite series

$\displaystyle\sum_{k=1}^{5} 2k = 2 + 4 + 6 + 8 + 10$ Finite series

Arithmetic Series

Finite Arithmetic Series:

$$\sum_{k=1}^{n} a_k = a_1 + a_2 + a_3 + \cdots + a_n,$$

where $a_k = dk + c$ for some constants c and d and d is the common difference. Summing the terms of an arithmetic *sequence* results in an arithmetic *series*.

Sum of the First n Terms:

$$S_n = n\left(\frac{a_1 + a_n}{2}\right) \quad \text{or} \quad S_n = \frac{n}{2}(2a_1 + (n - 1)d)$$

Example: The series $4 + 7 + 10 + 13 + 16 + 19 + 22$ is defined by $a_k = 3k + 1$. Its sum is $S_7 = 7\left(\frac{4 + 22}{2}\right) = 91$.

CONCEPT	EXPLANATION AND EXAMPLES

Section 11.2 Series (CONTINUED)

Geometric Series

Infinite Geometric Series:

$$\sum_{k=1}^{\infty} a_k = a_1 + a_2 + a_3 + \cdots + a_n + \cdots,$$

where $a_k = a_1 r^{k-1}$ for some nonzero constants a_1 and r.
Summing the terms of a geometric *sequence* results in a geometric *series*.

Sum of First n Terms:
$S_n = a_1\left(\frac{1 - r^n}{1 - r}\right)$, where a_1 is the first term and r is the common ratio

Example: The series $3 + 6 + 12 + 24 + 48 + 96$ has $a_1 = 3$ and $r = 2$.
Its sum is $S_6 = 3\left(\frac{1 - 2^6}{1 - 2}\right) = 189$.

Sum of Infinite Geometric Series:
$S = \frac{a_1}{1 - r}$, if $|r| < 1$. The sum S does not exist if $|r| \geq 1$.

Example: $4 + 1 + \frac{1}{4} + \frac{1}{16} + \frac{1}{64} + \cdots$ has sum $S = \dfrac{4}{1 - \frac{1}{4}} = \dfrac{16}{3}$.

Section 11.3 Counting

Fundamental Counting Principle

Let E_1 and E_2 be independent events. If event E_1 can occur m_1 ways and if event E_2 can occur m_2 ways, then there are $m_1 \cdot m_2$ ways for both events to occur.

Example: If two multiple-choice questions have 5 choices each, then there are $5 \cdot 5 = 25$ ways to answer the two questions.

Factorial Notation

$n! = n(n - 1)(n - 2) \cdots (3)(2)(1)$

Examples: $0! = 1$; $1! = 1$; $5! = 5 \cdot 4 \cdot 3 \cdot 2 \cdot 1 = 120$

Permutations

$P(n, r) = \frac{n!}{(n - r)!}$ represents the number of permutations, or arrangements, of n elements taken r at a time. Order is important in calculating a permutation.

Example: $P(5, 3) = \dfrac{5!}{(5 - 3)!} = \dfrac{120}{2} = 60$

Combinations

$C(n, r) = \binom{n}{r} = \frac{n!}{(n - r)!\, r!}$ represents the number of combinations of n elements taken r at a time. Order is unimportant in calculating a combination.

Example: $C(5, 3) = \dbinom{5}{3} = \dfrac{5!}{(5 - 3)!3!} = \dfrac{120}{2 \cdot 6} = 10$

CONCEPT	EXPLANATION AND EXAMPLES

Section 11.4 The Binomial Theorem

Binomial Theorem

$$(a + b)^n = \binom{n}{0}a^n + \binom{n}{1}a^{n-1}b + \cdots + \binom{n}{n-1}ab^{n-1} + \binom{n}{n}b^n$$

Example: $(x + y)^4 = 1x^4 + 4x^3y + 6x^2y^2 + 4xy^3 + 1y^4$

The coefficients can also be found in the fifth row of Pascal's triangle.

Pascal's Triangle

Pascal's triangle can be used to calculate the binomial coefficients when expanding the expression $(a + b)^n$.

$$1$$
$$1 \quad 1$$
$$1 \quad 2 \quad 1$$
$$1 \quad 3 \quad 3 \quad 1$$
$$1 \quad 4 \quad 6 \quad 4 \quad 1$$
$$1 \quad 5 \quad 10 \quad 10 \quad 5 \quad 1$$

Section 11.5 Mathematical Induction

Principle of Mathematical Induction

Let S_n be a statement concerning the positive integer n. Suppose that

1. S_1 is true;
2. for any positive integer k, if S_k is true, then S_{k+1} is also true.

Then S_n is true for every positive integer n.

Section 11.6 Probability

Probability

$P(E) = \frac{n(E)}{n(S)}$, where $n(E)$ is the number of outcomes in event E and $n(S)$ is the number of equally likely outcomes in the finite sample space S. Note that $0 \le P(E) \le 1$.

Compound Events

Probability of either E_1 or E_2 (or both) occurring:

$$P(E_1 \cup E_2) = P(E_1) + P(E_2) - P(E_1 \cap E_2)$$

If E_1 and E_2 are *mutually exclusive*, then $E_1 \cap E_2 = \varnothing$ and

$$P(E_1 \cup E_2) = P(E_1) + P(E_2).$$

Probability of *both* E_1 and E_2 occurring:
If E_1 and E_2 are *independent*, then

$$P(E_1 \cap E_2) = P(E_1) \cdot P(E_2).$$

If E_1 and E_2 are *dependent*, then

$$P(E_1 \cap E_2) = P(E_1) \cdot P(E_2, \text{ given that } E_1 \text{ occurred}),$$

where $P(E_2, \text{ given that } E_1 \text{ occurred})$ is called the ***conditional probability*** of event E_2, given E_1.

11 Review Exercises

Exercises 1–4: Find the first four terms of the sequence.

1. $a_n = -3n + 2$

2. $a_n = n^2 + n$

3. $a_n = 2a_{n-1} + 1; a_1 = 0$

4. $a_n = a_{n-1} + 2a_{n-2}; a_1 = 1, a_2 = 4$

Exercises 5 and 6: Use the graphical representation to identify the terms of the finite sequence.

5.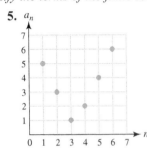

6.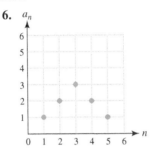

Exercises 7 and 8: The first five terms of an infinite arithmetic or geometric sequence are given. Find

  (a) numerical, (b) graphical, and (c) symbolic

representations of the sequence. Include at least the first eight terms of the sequence in your table and graph.

7. $3, 1, -1, -3, -5$

8. $1.5, -3, 6, -12, 24$

9. Find a general term a_n for the arithmetic sequence with $a_3 = -3$ and $d = 4$.

10. Find a general term a_n for the geometric sequence with $a_1 = 2.5$ and $a_6 = -80$.

Exercises 11–14: Determine if the sequence is arithmetic, geometric, or neither.

11. $f(n) = 5 - 2n$

12. $f(n) = 3n^2$

13. $f(n) = 3(2)^n$

14. $f(n) = n + \left(\frac{1}{2}\right)^{n-1}$

Exercises 15 and 16: For the given a_n, calculate S_5.

15. $a_n = 4n + 1$

16. $a_n = 3(4)^{n-1}$

Exercises 17–20: Use a formula to find the sum of the series.

17. $-2 + 1 + 4 + 7 + 10 + 13 + 16 + 19 + 22$

18. $2 + 4 + 6 + 8 + \cdots + 98 + 100$

19. $1 + 3 + 9 + 27 + 81 + 243 + 729 + 2187$

20. $64 + 16 + 4 + 1 + \frac{1}{4} + \frac{1}{16}$

Exercises 21 and 22: Find the sum of the infinite geometric series.

21. $4 - \frac{4}{3} + \frac{4}{9} - \frac{4}{27} + \frac{4}{81} - \frac{4}{243} + \cdots$

22. $0.2 + 0.02 + 0.002 + 0.0002 + 0.00002 + \cdots$

Exercises 23 and 24: Write out the terms of the series.

23. $\sum_{k=1}^{5}(5k + 1)$ **24.** $\sum_{k=1}^{4}(2 - k^2)$

Exercises 25 and 26: Write the series using summation notation.

25. $1^3 + 2^3 + 3^3 + 4^3 + 5^3 + 6^3$

26. $1 + \frac{1}{10} + \frac{1}{100} + \frac{1}{1000} + \frac{1}{10,000}$

Exercises 27 and 28: Use a formula to find the sum of the first 30 terms of the arithmetic sequence.

27. $a_1 = 5, d = -3$ **28.** $a_1 = -2, a_{10} = 16$

29. Write $\frac{2}{11}$ as an infinite geometric series.

30. Write the infinite series

$$0.23 + 0.0023 + 0.000023 + \cdots$$

as a rational number.

Exercises 31 and 32: Evaluate the expression.

31. $P(6, 3)$ **32.** $C(7, 4)$

Exercises 33 and 34: Use mathematical induction to prove that the statement is true for every positive integer.

33. $1 + 3 + 5 + 7 + \cdots + (2n - 1) = n^2$

34. $2 + 2^2 + 2^3 + \cdots + 2^n = 2(2^n - 1)$

Exercises 35 and 36: Find the probability of each event.

35. A 1, 2, or 3 appears when a die is rolled

36. Tossing three heads in a row using a fair coin

Applications

37. Standing in Line In how many arrangements can five people stand in a line?

38. Giving a Speech How many arrangements are possible in which 4 students out of a class of 15 each give a speech?

39. Exam Questions Count the ways that an exam, consisting of 20 multiple-choice questions with four choices each, could be answered.

40. License Plates Count the different license plates having four numeric digits followed by two letters.

41. Combination Lock A combination lock consists of four numbers from 0 to 49. If a number may be repeated, find the number of possible combinations.

42. Dice A red die and a blue die are rolled. How many ways are there for the sum to equal 4?

43. Height of a Ball When a Ping-Pong ball is dropped, it rebounds to 90% of its initial height.
   (a) Write the first five terms of a sequence that gives the maximum height attained by the ball on each rebound when it is dropped from an initial height of 4 feet. Let $a_1 = 4$. What type of sequence describes these maximum heights?

   (b) Give a graphical representation of this sequence for the first five terms.

   (c) Find a formula for a_n.

44. Falling Object If air resistance is ignored, an object falls 16, 48, 80, and 112 feet during each successive 1-second interval.
   (a) What type of sequence describes these distances?

   (b) Determine how far an object falls during the sixth second.

   (c) Find a formula for the nth term of this sequence.

45. Committees In how many ways can a committee of three be selected from six people?

46. Committees Find the number of committees with three women and three men that can be selected from a group of seven women and five men.

47. Test Questions On a test with 10 essay questions, students are asked to answer 6 questions. How many ways can the essay questions be selected?

48. Binomial Theorem Use the binomial theorem to expand the expression $(2x - y)^4$.

49. Quality Control A quality-control experiment involves selecting 2 batteries from a pack of 16. If either battery is defective, the entire pack of 16 is rejected. Suppose a pack contains 2 defective batteries. What is the probability that this pack will not be rejected?

50. Venn Diagram Of a group of 82 students, 19 are enrolled in music, 22 in art, and 10 in both.
   (a) Draw a Venn diagram representing these data.

   (b) Use this diagram to determine the probability that a student selected at random is enrolled in music, art, or both.

   (c) Solve part (b) symbolically by applying a probability formula.

51. Marbles A jar contains 13 red, 27 blue, and 20 green marbles. If a marble is drawn from the jar at random, find the probability that the marble is the following.
   (a) Blue

   (b) Not blue

   (c) Red

52. Cards Find the probability of drawing 2 diamonds from a standard deck of 52 cards without replacing the first card.

53. Insect Populations The monthly density of an insect population, measured in thousands per acre, is described by the recursive sequence

$$a_1 = 100; \quad a_n = \frac{2a_{n-1}}{1 + (a_{n-1}/4000)}, \quad n > 1.$$

Use your calculator to graph the sequence in the window $[0, 16, 1]$ by $[0, 5000, 1000]$. Include the first 15 terms and discuss any trends illustrated by the graph.

Extended and Discovery Exercises

Exercises 1 and 2: **Antibiotic Resistance** *Because of the frequent use of antibiotics in society, many strains of bacteria are becoming resistant. Some types of haploid bacteria contain genetic material called plasmids. Plasmids are capable of making a strain of bacterium resistant to antibiotic drugs. Genetic engineers want to predict the resistance of various bacteria after many generations.*

1. Suppose a strain of bacterium contains two plasmids R_1 and R_2. Plasmid R_1 is resistant to the antibiotic ampicillin, whereas plasmid R_2 is resistant to the antibiotic tetracycline. When bacteria reproduce through cell division, the type of plasmids passed on to each new cell is random. For example, a daughter cell could have two plasmids of type R_1 and no plasmid of type R_2, one of each type, or no plasmid of type R_1 and two plasmids of type R_2. The probability $P_{k,j}$ that a mother cell with k plasmids of type R_1 produces a daughter cell with j plasmids of type R_1 can be calculated by the formula

$$P_{k,j} = \frac{\binom{2k}{j}\binom{4 - 2k}{2 - j}}{\binom{4}{2}}.$$

(*Source:* F. Hoppensteadt and C. Peskin, *Mathematics in Medicine and the Life Sciences.*)
   (a) Compute $P_{k,j}$ for $0 \le k, j \le 2$. Assume that $\binom{0}{0} = 1$ and $\binom{k}{j} = 0$ whenever $k < j$. Record your results in the matrix

$$P = \begin{bmatrix} P_{00} & P_{01} & P_{02} \\ P_{10} & P_{11} & P_{12} \\ P_{20} & P_{21} & P_{22} \end{bmatrix}.$$

(b) Which elements in P are the greatest? Interpret the result.

2. (Continuation of Exercise 1.) The genetic makeup of future generations of the haploid bacterium can be modeled using matrices. Let $A = [a_1, a_2, a_3]$ be a 1×3 matrix containing three probabilities. The value of a_1 is the probability that it has two R_1 plasmids and no R_2 plasmid; a_2 is the probability that it has one R_1 plasmid and one R_2 plasmid; a_3 is the probability that it has no R_1 plasmid and two R_2 plasmids. If an entire generation of the bacterium has one plasmid of each type, then $A_1 = [0, 1, 0]$. In this case the bacterium is resistant to both antibiotics. The probabilities A_n for plasmids R_1 and R_2 in the nth generation of the bacterium can be calculated with the matrix recurrence equation $A_n = A_{n-1}P$, where $n > 1$ and P is the 3×3 matrix determined in Exercise 1. The resulting phenomenon

was not well understood until recently. It is now used in the genetic engineering of plasmids.
(a) If an entire strain of the bacterium is resistant to both the antibiotics ampicillin and tetracycline, make a conjecture as to the drug resistance of future generations of this bacterium.

(b) Test your conjecture by repeatedly computing the matrix product $A_n = A_{n-1}P$. Let $A_1 = [0, 1, 0]$ and $n = 2, 3, \dots, 12$. Interpret the result. (It may surprise you.)

3. The sum of the first n terms of an arithmetic series is given by $S_n = n\left(\frac{a_1 + a_n}{2}\right)$. Justify this formula using a geometric discussion. (*Hint:* Start by graphing an arithmetic sequence where n is an odd number.)*

1-11 Cumulative Review Exercises

1. Write 34,500 in scientific notation and 1.52×10^{-4} in standard form.

2. Evaluate $\dfrac{5 - \sqrt[3]{4}}{\pi^2 - (\sqrt{3} + 1)}$. Round your answer to the nearest hundredth.

3. Find the exact distance between $(-4, 2)$ and $(1, -2)$.

4. Graph f.
  (a) $f(x) = 4x - 2$ **(b)** $f(x) = |2x - 1|$
  (c) $f(x) = x^2 + 2x$ **(d)** $f(x) = \sqrt{x - 1}$
  (e) $f(x) = \dfrac{1}{x + 2}$ **(f)** $f(x) = x^3 - 2$
  (g) $f(x) = \log_2 x$ **(h)** $f(x) = 3\left(\frac{1}{2}\right)^x$

Exercises 5 and 6: Complete the following.
(a) Evaluate $f(-3)$ and $f(a + 1)$.
(b) Determine the domain of f.

5. $f(x) = \sqrt{1 - x}$ **6.** $f(x) = \dfrac{1}{x^2 - 4}$

7. Find the average rate of change of $f(x) = x^3 - 4$ from $x = -2$ to $x = -1$.

8. Find the difference quotient for $f(x) = x^2 - 3x$.

Exercises 9 and 10: Write an equation of a line satisfying the conditions. Use slope-intercept form whenever possible.

9. Passing through $(2, -4)$ and $(-3, 2)$

10. Passing through the point $(-1, 3)$ and perpendicular to the line $y = -\frac{3}{4}x + 1$

11. The graph of a linear function f is shown.
  (a) Identify the slope, y-intercept, and x-intercept.
  (b) Write a formula for f.
  (c) Find any zeros of f.

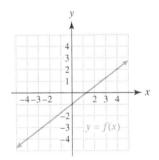

12. Determine the x- and y-intercepts on the graph of $-3x + 4y = 12$. Graph the equation.

13. Solve each equation.
  (a) $4(x - 2) + 1 = 3 - \frac{1}{2}(2x + 3)$
  (b) $6x^2 = 13x + 5$ **(c)** $x^2 - x - 3 = 0$
  (d) $x^3 + x^2 = 4x + 4$ **(e)** $x^4 - 4x^2 + 3 = 0$
  (f) $\dfrac{1}{x - 3} = \dfrac{4}{x + 5}$ **(g)** $3e^{2x} - 5 = 23$
  (h) $2\log(x + 1) - 1 = 2$
  (i) $\sqrt{x + 3} + 4 = x + 1$
  (j) $|3x - 1| = 5$

14. Solve each inequality. Write your answer in set-builder or interval notation.

(a) $3x - 5 < x + 1$ (b) $x^2 - 4x - 5 \leq 0$

(c) $(x + 1)(x - 2)(x - 3) > 0$

(d) $\dfrac{2}{x - 1} < 0$ (e) $|3x - 5| \leq 4$

(f) $|4 - x| > 0$ (g) $\dfrac{3}{4} \leq \dfrac{1 - 2x}{3} < \dfrac{5}{2}$

15. Graph f. Is f continuous on its domain?

$$f(x) = \begin{cases} 2x + 3 & \text{if } -3 \leq x < -1 \\ x^2 & \text{if } -1 \leq x < 1 \\ 2 - x & \text{if } 1 \leq x \leq 3 \end{cases}$$

16. Solve $-2.3x + 3.4 = \sqrt{2x^2 - 1}$ graphically. Round your answers to the nearest tenth.

17. The graph of a nonlinear function f is shown. Solve each equation or inequality. Write the solution set to each inequality in set-builder or interval notation.

(a) $f(x) = 0$ (b) $f(x) > 0$ (c) $f(x) \leq 0$

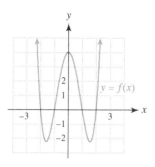

18. Write $f(x) = 3x^2 + 24x + 43$ in the vertex form given by $f(x) = a(x - h)^2 + k$.

19. Find the vertex on the graph of $f(x) = -3x^2 + 9x + 1$.

20. Use the given graph of $y = f(x)$ to sketch a graph of each equation.

(a) $y = f(x - 1) + 2$ (b) $y = \frac{1}{2}f(x)$

(c) $y = -f(x)$ (d) $y = f(2x)$

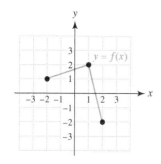

21. Use the graph of f to estimate each of the following.

(a) Intervals where f is increasing or decreasing

(b) The zeros of f

(c) The coordinates of any turning points

(d) Any local extrema

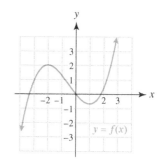

22. Determine if the function defined by $f(x) = x^3 - 5x$ is even, odd, or neither.

23. Divide each expression.

(a) $\dfrac{6x^4 - 2x^2 + 1}{2x^2}$ (b) $\dfrac{2x^4 - 3x^3 - x + 2}{x + 1}$

24. A degree 4 function f has zeros -2, -1, 1, and 2 and leading coefficient 6. Write the complete factored form of $f(x)$.

25. A degree 3 function f with real coefficients has leading coefficient 3 and zeros -1 and $3i$. Write $f(x)$ in complete factored form and expanded form.

26. Write $(2 - i)(2 + 3i)$ in standard form.

27. Find all solutions, real or imaginary, to the quadratic equation $x^2 + 2x + 5 = 0$.

28. State the domain of $f(x) = \frac{2x - 5}{x + 5}$. Find any vertical or horizontal asymptotes for the graph of f.

29. Write $\sqrt[5]{(x + 1)^3}$ using rational exponents. Evaluate the expression for $x = 31$.

30. Use the tables to evaluate each expression, if possible.

x	0	1	2	3
$f(x)$	1	2	4	5

x	0	1	2	3
$g(x)$	4	3	2	1

(a) $(f - g)(1)$ (b) $(f/g)(2)$

(c) $(g \circ f)(3)$ (d) $(g \circ f^{-1})(5)$

31. Use the graphs of f and g to complete the following.

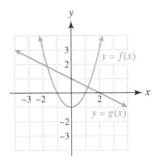

(a) $(f + g)(2)$ **(b)** $(fg)(0)$

(c) $(g \circ f)(1)$ **(d)** $(g^{-1} \circ f)(-2)$

32. Let $f(x) = \frac{1}{x + 2}$ and $g(x) = x^2 + x - 4$. Find each of the following.

(a) $(f - g)(0)$ **(b)** $(g \circ f)(-1)$

(c) $(fg)(x)$ **(d)** $(g \circ f)(x)$

33. Find $f^{-1}(x)$ if $f(x) = \frac{x}{x + 1}$.

34. Graph $f(x) = x^3 - 1$, $y = x$, and $y = f^{-1}(x)$ on the same axes.

35. Find either a linear or an exponential function f that models the data in the table.

x	0	1	2	3
$f(x)$	2	6	18	54

36. There are initially 1000 bacteria in a sample, and the number doubles every 2 hours.
(a) Find C and a so that $f(x) = Ca^x$ models the number of bacteria after x hours.

(b) Estimate the number of bacteria after 5.2 hours.

(c) When are there 9000 bacteria in the sample?

37. Five hundred dollars is deposited in an account that pays 6% annual interest compounded quarterly. Find the amount in the account after 15 years.

38. Simplify each logarithm by hand.
(a) $\log_2 \frac{1}{16}$ **(b)** $\log \sqrt{10}$

(c) $\ln e^4$ **(d)** $\log_4 2 + \log_4 32$

39. Find the domain and range of each function f.
(a) $f(x) = x^2 - 2x + 1$

(b) $f(x) = 10^x$ **(c)** $f(x) = \ln x$

(d) $f(x) = \frac{1}{x}$

40. Expand the expression $\log \sqrt{\frac{x + 1}{yz}}$.

41. Write $2 \log x + 3 \log y - \frac{1}{3} \log z$ as a logarithm of a single expression.

42. Approximate $\log_4 52$ to three decimal places.

43. Graph $y = f(x)$.
(a) $f(x) = \csc x$

(b) $f(x) = -2 \sin \frac{1}{2} x$

(c) $f(x) = 3 \cos \left(2 \left(x - \frac{\pi}{2} \right) \right)$

(d) $f(x) = \tan (\pi x)$

44. Find the domain of $f(x) = \sec 2x$.

45. Solve each equation for all real numbers t.
(a) $\cos t = -\frac{\sqrt{3}}{2}$

(b) $\tan^2 t - 1 = 0$

(c) $\sin^2 t + \frac{1}{2} \sin t = 0$

(d) $\cos 2t = -1$

46. Find the complementary angle α and the supplementary angle β to $54°35'12''$.

47. Convert $5.54°$ to degrees, minutes, and seconds.

48. Convert $135°$ to radians.

49. Convert $\frac{5\pi}{4}$ radians to degrees.

50. Approximate $\cot \frac{2\pi}{9}$ to the nearest hundredth.

51. Find the values of the six trigonometric functions of an angle θ in standard position having its terminal side pass through the point $(-7, 24)$,

52. Find the exact values of the six trigonometric functions of $\theta = \frac{5\pi}{6}$.

53. Find the values of the six trigonometric functions of θ if $\cos \theta = -\frac{11}{61}$ and $\cos \theta < 0$.

54. Evaluate $\cos^{-1}\left(\frac{1}{2}\right)$.

55. Solve the right triangle shown in the figure.

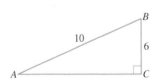

56. Simplify $(\sec t - 1)(\sec t + 1)$.

57. Verify the identity.
$$1 - \sin^2 \theta + \cot^2 \theta - \sin^2 \theta \cot^2 \theta = \cot^2 \theta$$

58. Solve $2 \sin 2x = \ln x$ graphically for $0 \le x < 2\pi$.

59. Solve triangle ABC. Approximate values to the nearest tenth.
  (a) $\beta = 42°, \gamma = 31°, a = 22$

  (b) $\gamma = 50°, c = 7, b = 8$

  (c) $\alpha = 44°, b = 7, c = 8$

  (d) $a = 10, b = 11, c = 12$

60. Find the area of a triangle with $\alpha = 30°, b = 15$ feet, and $c = 20$ feet.

61. Let $\mathbf{a} = \langle 3, -4 \rangle$ and $\mathbf{b} = \langle -5, 12 \rangle$. Find the following.
  (a) $\|\mathbf{a}\|$

  (b) $4\mathbf{b} - 2\mathbf{a}$

  (c) $\mathbf{a} \cdot \mathbf{b}$

  (d) The angle between $\mathbf{a}$ and $\mathbf{b}$

62. Graph the parametric equations $x = 2\cos t, y = 2\sin t$ for $0 \le t \le 2\pi$.

63. Graph the polar equation given by $r = 1 + \sin\theta$ for $0 \le \theta < 2\pi$.

64. Find the two square roots of $-16i$.

65. Solve the system of equations.
  (a) $\begin{aligned} 2x + 3y &= 4 \\ 2x - 5y &= -12 \end{aligned}$
  (b) $\begin{aligned} -2x + \tfrac{1}{2}y &= 1 \\ 4x - y &= -2 \end{aligned}$

  (c) $\begin{aligned} x^2 + y^2 &= 16 \\ 2x^2 - y^2 &= 11 \end{aligned}$
  (d) $\begin{aligned} x + y - 2z &= -6 \\ 2x - y - 3z &= -18 \\ 3y - z &= 6 \end{aligned}$

66. The variable z varies inversely with the square of x. If $z = 8$ when $x = 50$, find z when $x = 36$.

67. Graph the solution set to each inequality or system of inequalities.*
  (a) $-2x + 3y < 6$
  (b) $\begin{aligned} x + y &\le 4 \\ x - 2y &> 6 \end{aligned}$

68. Find $2A + B$ and AB if
$$A = \begin{bmatrix} -1 & 0 & 2 \\ 1 & -3 & 1 \\ 0 & -3 & 4 \end{bmatrix} \quad \text{and} \quad B = \begin{bmatrix} 1 & 5 & 1 \\ -2 & 2 & 1 \\ 0 & 1 & -2 \end{bmatrix}.$$

69. Find A^{-1} if $A = \begin{bmatrix} 1 & -2 \\ -3 & 4 \end{bmatrix}$.

70. Solve by using A^{-1}.
$$\begin{aligned} x - y - 2z &= 5 \\ -x + 2y + 3z &= -7 \\ 2y + z &= -2 \end{aligned}$$

71. Calculate the determinant of each matrix.
  (a) $\begin{bmatrix} -1 & 4 \\ 2 & 3 \end{bmatrix}$
  (b) $\begin{bmatrix} 2 & 3 & -1 \\ 3 & -1 & 5 \\ 0 & 0 & -2 \end{bmatrix}$

72. Sketch a graph of each equation. Label any foci.
  (a) $y^2 = 2x$
  (b) $\dfrac{x^2}{9} + \dfrac{y^2}{25} = 1$

  (c) $9x^2 - 18x + 4y^2 + 16y + 25 = 36$

  (d) $\dfrac{(x + 1)^2}{16} - \dfrac{(y - 2)^2}{9} = 1$

73. Find an equation of a parabola with vertex $(0, 0)$ and focus $\left(\tfrac{3}{4}, 0\right)$.

74. Find an equation of an ellipse with vertices $(\pm 3, 1)$ and foci $(\pm 2, 1)$.

75. Find an equation of a hyperbola with foci $(0, \pm 13)$ and vertices $(0, \pm 5)$.

76. Find the first four terms of each sequence.
  (a) $a_n = (-1)^{n-1}(3)^n$

  (b) $a_n = a_{n-1}a_{n-2}; a_1 = 2, a_2 = 3$

77. Find a general term for the arithmetic sequence given that $a_1 = 4$ and $a_3 = 12$.

78. Find a general term for the geometric sequence given that $a_2 = 6$ and $r = \tfrac{1}{2}$.

79. Use a formula to find the sum of each series.
  (a) $2 + 5 + 8 + 11 + \cdots + 74$

  (b) $0.2 + 0.02 + 0.002 + 0.0002 + \cdots$

80. Find the sum $\sum_{k=1}^{7}(k^2 + k)$.

81. Count the number of license plates that can be formed by three letters followed by four digits.

82. Evaluate $P(4, 2)$ and $\binom{6}{3}$.

83. Expand $(2x - 1)^4$.

84. Use mathematical induction to show that
$$5 + 7 + 9 + 11 + \cdots + (2n + 3) = n(n + 4).$$

85. Find the probability of drawing a heart or an ace from a standard deck of 52 cards.

86. Find the probability of rolling a sum of 7 with two dice.

87. A number from 1 to 20 is drawn at random. Find the probability that the number is prime.

88. The probability of a day being cloudy is 40%, and the probability of it being cloudy *and* windy is 15%. Given that the day is cloudy, what is the probability that it will be windy?

Applications

89. Distance At noon, car A is traveling north at 50 miles per hour and is located 30 miles north of car B. Car B is traveling east at 50 miles per hour. Approximate the distance between the cars at 1:45 P.M. to the nearest tenth of a mile.

90. Distance from Home A driver is initially 240 miles from home, traveling toward home on a straight interstate at 60 miles per hour.
   (a) Write a formula for a linear function D that models the distance between the driver and home after x hours.

   (b) What is an appropriate domain for D?

   (c) Graph D.

   (d) Identify the x- and y-intercepts. Interpret each.

91. Running An athlete traveled 10.5 miles in 1.3 hours, jogging at 7 miles per hour and 9 miles per hour. How long did the athlete run at each speed?

92. Average Rate of Change The total distance D in feet traveled by a racehorse after t seconds is given by $D(t) = 3t^2$ for $0 \leq t \leq 5$.
   (a) Find the average rate of change of D from 0 to 1 and 3 to 4.

   (b) Interpret these average rates of change.*

93. Working Together Suppose one person can mow a lawn in 5 hours and another person can mow the same lawn in 4 hours. How long will it take to mow the lawn if they work together?

94. Maximum Height A stone is shot upward with a slingshot. Its height s in feet after t seconds is given by $s(t) = -16t^2 + 96t + 4$. Find its maximum height.

95. Airline Tickets Tickets for a charter flight are regularly $400, but for each additional ticket bought the cost of each ticket is reduced by $5.
   (a) Write a quadratic function C that gives the total cost of buying x tickets.

   (b) Solve $C(x) = 7000$ and interpret the result.

   (c) Find the absolute maximum for C and interpret your result. Assume that x is an integer.

96. Dimensions of a Rectangle A rectangle has a perimeter of 48 inches and an area of 143 square inches. Find its dimensions.

97. Satellite Dish A parabolic satellite dish has a 3-foot diameter and is 6 inches deep. How far from the vertex should the receiver be so that it is located at the focus?

98. Bouncing Ball A Ping-Pong ball is dropped from 4 feet. Each time the ball bounces, it rebounds to 75% of its previous height. Use an infinite geometric series to estimate the *total* distance that the ball travels before coming to rest on the floor.

99. Marbles A jar contains 15 red, 28 blue, and 34 green marbles. If a marble is drawn at random, find the probability that the marble is not blue.

Appendix A: Using the Graphing Calculator

Overview of the Appendix

The intent of this appendix is to provide instruction in the TI-83, TI-83 Plus, and TI-84 Plus graphing calculators that may be used in conjunction with this textbook. It includes specific keystrokes needed to work several examples from the text. Students are also advised to consult the *Graphing Calculator Guidebook* provided by the manufacturer.

The following is a listing of the topics covered in this appendix.

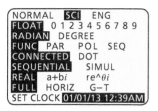

Figure A.1

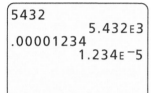

Figure A.2

$$4.2 \text{E}^{-3}$$
$$\qquad\qquad .0042$$
$$4.2*10^{\wedge}(^{-3})$$
$$\qquad\qquad .0042$$

Figure A.3 Normal Mode

Displaying Numbers in Scientific Notation

To display numbers in scientific notation when the calculator is in normal mode, set the graphing calculator in scientific mode (SCI) by using the following keystrokes. See Figure A.1.

$$\boxed{\text{MODE}}\ \boxed{\triangleright}\ \boxed{\text{ENTER}}\ \boxed{\text{2nd}}\ \boxed{\text{MODE [QUIT]}}$$

Figure A.2 shows the numbers 5432 and 0.00001234 displayed in scientific notation.

> **SUMMARY: SETTING SCIENTIFIC MODE**
>
> If your calculator is in normal mode, it can be set in scientific mode by pressing
>
> $$\boxed{\text{MODE}}\ \boxed{\triangleright}\ \boxed{\text{ENTER}}\ \boxed{\text{2nd}}\ \boxed{\text{MODE [QUIT]}}.$$
>
> These keystrokes return the graphing calculator to the home screen.

Entering Numbers in Scientific Notation

Numbers can be entered in scientific notation. For example, to enter 4.2×10^{-3} in scientific notation, use the following keystrokes. (Be sure to use the negation key (−) rather than the subtraction key.)

Use the negation key not the subtraction key.

$$\boxed{4}\ \boxed{.}\ \boxed{2}\ \boxed{\text{2nd}}\ \boxed{,\text{[EE]}}\ \boxed{(\text{--})}\ \boxed{3}$$

This number can also be entered using the following keystrokes. See Figure A.3.

$$\boxed{4}\ \boxed{.}\ \boxed{2}\ \boxed{\times}\ \boxed{1}\ \boxed{0}\ \boxed{\wedge}\ \boxed{(}\ \boxed{(\text{--})}\ \boxed{3}\ \boxed{)}$$

> **SUMMARY: ENTERING NUMBERS IN SCIENTIFIC NOTATION**
>
> One way to enter a number in scientific notation is to use the keystrokes
>
> $$\boxed{\text{2nd}}\ \boxed{,\text{[EE]}}$$
>
> to access an exponent (EE) of 10.

Entering Mathematical Expressions

Several expressions are evaluated in Example 7, Section 1.1. To evaluate $\sqrt[3]{131}$, use the following keystrokes from the home screen.

$$\boxed{\text{MATH}}\ \boxed{4}\ \boxed{1}\ \boxed{3}\ \boxed{1}\ \boxed{)}\ \boxed{\text{ENTER}}$$

To calculate $\pi^3 + 1.2^2$, use the following keystrokes. (Do *not* use 3.14 for π.)

$$\boxed{\text{2nd}}\ \boxed{^{\wedge}[\pi]}\ \boxed{^{\wedge}}\ \boxed{3}\ \boxed{+}\ \boxed{1}\ \boxed{.}\ \boxed{2}\ \boxed{x^2}\ \boxed{\text{ENTER}}$$

To calculate $|\sqrt{3} - 6|$, use the following keystrokes.

$$\boxed{\text{MATH}}\ \boxed{\triangleright}\ \boxed{1}\ \boxed{\text{2nd}}\ \boxed{x^2[\sqrt{\ }]}\ \boxed{3}\ \boxed{)}\ \boxed{-}\ \boxed{6}\ \boxed{)}\ \boxed{\text{ENTER}}$$

> **SUMMARY: ENTERING COMMON MATHEMATICAL EXPRESSIONS**
>
> To calculate a cube root, use the keystrokes $\boxed{\text{MATH}}\ \boxed{4}$.
>
> To access the number π, use the keystrokes $\boxed{\text{2nd}}\ \boxed{^{\wedge}[\pi]}$.
>
> To access the absolute value, use the keystrokes $\boxed{\text{MATH}}\ \boxed{\triangleright}\ \boxed{1}$.
>
> To access the square root, use the keystrokes $\boxed{\text{2nd}}\ \boxed{x^2[\sqrt{\ }]}$.

Setting the Viewing Rectangle

In Example 12, Section 1.2, there are at least two ways to set the standard viewing rectangle to $[-10, 10, 1]$ by $[-10, 10, 1]$. The first method involves pressing (ZOOM) followed by (6). (See Figure A.4.) The second method is to press (WINDOW) and enter the following keystrokes. (See Figure A.5.)

Use the negation key.

(Be sure to use the negation key $(-)$ rather than the subtraction key.) The viewing rectangle $[-30, 40, 10]$ by $[-400, 800, 100]$ can be set in a similar manner, as shown in Figure A.6. To see the viewing rectangle, press (GRAPH).

SUMMARY: SETTING THE VIEWING RECTANGLE

To set the standard viewing rectangle, press (ZOOM) (6). To set any viewing rectangle, press (WINDOW) and enter the necessary values. To see the viewing rectangle, press (GRAPH).

Note: You do not need to change "Xres".

Making a Scatterplot or a Line Graph

In Example 13, Section 1.2, we are asked to make a scatterplot with $(-5, -5)$, $(-2, 3)$, $(1, -7)$, and $(4, 8)$. Begin this task by following these steps.

1. Press (STAT) followed by (1).
2. If list L1 is not empty, use the arrow keys to place the cursor on L1, as shown in Figure A.7. Then press (CLEAR) followed by (ENTER). This deletes all elements in the list. Similarly, if L2 is not empty, clear the list.
3. Input each x-value into list L1, followed by (ENTER). Input each y-value into list L2, followed by (ENTER). See Figure A.8.

It is essential that both lists have the same number of values—otherwise an error message will appear when a scatterplot is attempted. Before these four points can be plotted, STATPLOT must be turned on. It is accessed by pressing

(2nd) (Y=[STAT PLOT])

as shown in Figure A.9.

There are three possible STATPLOTS, numbered 1, 2, and 3. Any one of the three can be selected. The first plot is selected by pressing (1). Next, place the cursor over "On" and press (ENTER) to turn Plot1 on. There are six types of plots that can be selected. The first type is a *scatterplot* and the second type is a *line graph*, so place the cursor over the first type of plot and press (ENTER) to select a scatterplot. (To make the line graph in Example 14, Section 1.2, be sure to select the line graph.) The x-values are stored in list L1, so select L1 for "Xlist" by pressing (2nd) (1). Similarly, press (2nd) (2) for "Ylist," since the y-values are stored in list L2. Finally, there are three styles of marks that can be used to show data points in the graph. We usually use the first, because it is largest and shows up the best. Make the screen appear as in Figure A.10. Before plotting the four data points, be sure to set an appropriate viewing rectangle. Then press (GRAPH). The data points will appear as in Figure A.11 on the next page.

NOTE 1 A fast way to set the viewing rectangle for any scatterplot is to select the ZOOMSTAT feature by pressing (ZOOM) (9). This feature automatically scales the viewing rectangle so that all data points are shown.

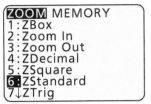

Figure A.4

```
WINDOW
 Xmin=-10
 Xmax=10
 Xscl=1
 Ymin=-10
 Ymax=10
 Yscl=1
 Xres=1
```

Figure A.5

```
WINDOW
 Xmin=-30
 Xmax=40
 Xscl=10
 Ymin=-400
 Ymax=800
 Yscl=100
 Xres=1
```

Figure A.6

Figure A.7

Figure A.8

Figure A.9

Figure A.10

[−10, 10, 1] by [−10, 10, 1]

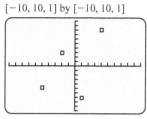

Figure A.11

NOTE 2 If an equation has been entered into the (Y =) menu and selected, it will be graphed with the data. Throughout this textbook, this feature is used frequently in modeling data.

NOTE 3 When the error message "ERR: DIM MISMATCH" appears, it usually means that there are not equal numbers of x-values and y-values in lists L1 and L2.

SUMMARY: MAKING A SCATTERPLOT OR A LINE GRAPH

The following are basic steps necessary to make either a scatterplot or a line graph.

STEP 1: Use (STAT)(1) to access lists L1 and L2.

STEP 2: If list L1 is not empty, place the cursor on L1 and press (CLEAR)(ENTER). Repeat for list L2 if it is not empty.

STEP 3: Enter the x-values into list L1 and the y-values into list L2.

STEP 4: Use (2nd)(Y = [STAT PLOT]) to set the appropriate parameters for the scatterplot or line graph.

STEP 5: Either set an appropriate viewing rectangle or press (ZOOM)(9). This feature automatically sets the viewing rectangle and plots the data.

Note: (ZOOM)(9) *cannot* be used to set a viewing rectangle for the graph of a function.

Deleting and Inserting a List A list, such as L2, can be deleted. Press (STAT)(1) and then place the cursor on L2 and press (DEL). If you want to insert a deleted list, press (STAT)(1) and then place the cursor where you want to insert the list. For example, to insert L2, place the cursor on L3. Press (2nd)(DEL [INS])(2nd)(2[L2])(ENTER).

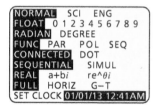

Figure A.12

Entering a Formula for a Function

To enter the formula for a function f, press (Y =). For example, use the following keystrokes after "Y₁ = " to enter $f(x) = 2x^2 - 3x + 7$. See Figure A.12.

(Y =)(CLEAR)(2)(X,T,θ,n)(^)(2)(−)(3)(X,T,θ,n)(+)(7)

Note that there is a built-in key for entering the variable X. If "Y₁ = " does not appear after you press (Y =), press (MODE) and make sure the calculator is set in function mode, denoted "Func". See Figure A.13.

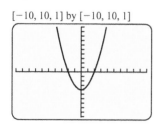

Figure A.13

SUMMARY: ENTERING A FORMULA FOR A FUNCTION

To enter the formula for a function, press (Y =). To delete an existing formula, press (CLEAR). Then enter the symbolic representation for the function.

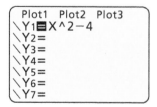

Figure A.14

[−10, 10, 1] by [−10, 10, 1]

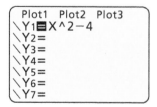

Figure A.15

Graphing a Function

To graph a function such as $f(x) = x^2 - 4$, start by pressing (Y =) and then enter Y₁ = X^2 − 4. If there is an equation already entered, remove it by pressing (CLEAR). The equals sign in "Y₁ = " should be in reverse video (a dark rectangle surrounding a white equals sign), which indicates that the equation will be graphed. If the equals sign is not in reverse video, place the cursor over it and press (ENTER). Set an appropriate viewing rectangle and then press (GRAPH). The graph of f will appear in the specified viewing rectangle. See Figures A.14 and A.15.

NOTE If the error message "ERR: DIM MISMATCH" appears when you try to graph a function, check to see if one of the STATPLOTS is turned on. If it is, turn it off and then try graphing the function.

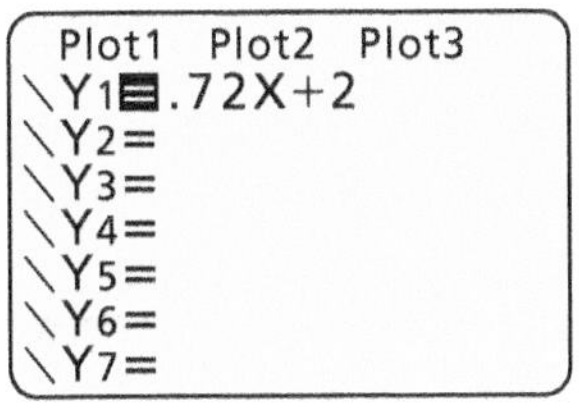

```
Plot1  Plot2  Plot3
\Y1■.72X+2
\Y2=
\Y3=
\Y4=
\Y5=
\Y6=
\Y7=
```

Figure A.16

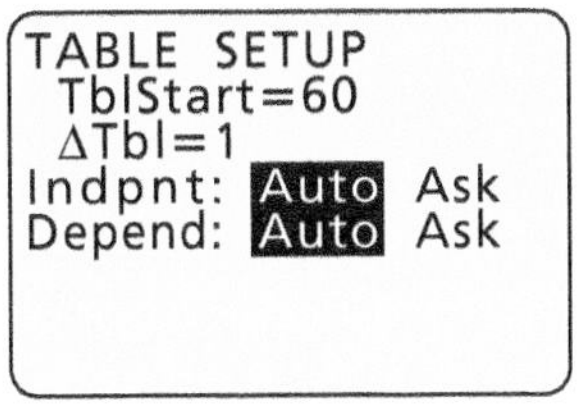

```
TABLE SETUP
 TblStart=60
 ΔTbl=1
Indpnt: Auto  Ask
Depend: Auto  Ask
```

Figure A.17

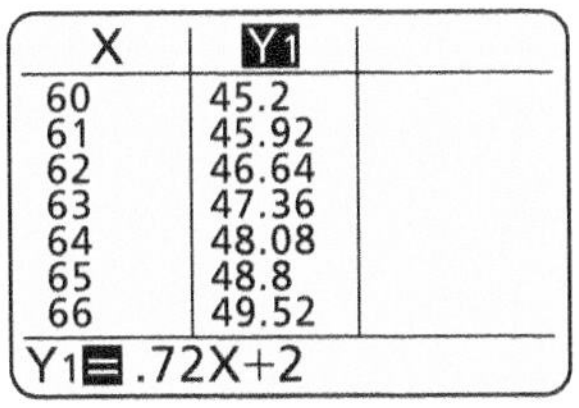

```
  X   │  Y1  │
 60   │ 45.2 │
 61   │ 45.92│
 62   │ 46.64│
 63   │ 47.36│
 64   │ 48.08│
 65   │ 48.8 │
 66   │ 49.52│
Y1■.72X+2
```

Figure A.18

```
ZOOM MEMORY
1:ZBox
2:Zoom In
3:Zoom Out
4:ZDecimal
5:ZSquare
6:ZStandard
7↓ZTrig
```

Figure A.19

SUMMARY: GRAPHING A FUNCTION

Use the $(Y=)$ menu to enter the formula for the function and the $(WINDOW)$ menu to set an appropriate viewing rectangle. Then press $(GRAPH)$.

ZoomFit The ZoomFit feature can be used to find an appropriate window when graphing a function. ZoomFit leaves the current Xmin and Xmax settings unchanged and adjusts the current Ymin and Ymax values so that they are equal to the smallest and largest y-values on the graph of the function between Xmin and Xmax. To use ZoomFit, press $(ZOOM)\ (0)$.

Making a Table

To make a table of values for a function, such as $f(x) = 0.72x + 2$, start by pressing $(Y=)$ and then entering the formula $Y_1 = .72X + 2$, as shown in Figure A.16. To set the table parameters, use the following keystrokes. (See Figure A.17.)

$$(2nd)\ (WINDOW\ [TBLSET])\ (6)\ (0)\ (ENTER)\ (1)$$

These keystrokes specify a table that starts at $x = 60$ and increments the x-values by 1. Therefore the values of Y_1 at $x = 60, 61, 62, \ldots$ appear in the table. To create this table, press the following keys.

$$(2nd)\ (GRAPH\ [TABLE])$$

One can scroll through x- and y-values by using the arrow keys. See Figure A.18. Note that there is no first or last x-value in the table.

SUMMARY: MAKING A TABLE OF A FUNCTION

Enter the formula for the function using $(Y=)$. Then press

$$(2nd)\ (WINDOW\ [TBLSET])$$

to set the starting x-value and the increment between x-values appearing in the table. Create the table by pressing

$$(2nd)\ (GRAPH\ [TABLE]).$$

Squaring a Viewing Rectangle

In a square viewing rectangle, the graph of $y = x$ is a line that makes a 45° angle with the positive x-axis, a circle appears circular, and all sides of a square have the same length. An approximately square viewing rectangle can be set if the distance along the x-axis is 1.5 times the distance along the y-axis. Examples of viewing rectangles that are (approximately) square include

$$[-6, 6, 1] \text{ by } [-4, 4, 1] \quad \text{and} \quad [-9, 9, 1] \text{ by } [-6, 6, 1].$$

Square viewing rectangles can be set automatically by pressing either

$$(ZOOM)\ (4) \quad \text{or} \quad (ZOOM)\ (5).$$

ZOOM 4 provides a decimal window, which is discussed later. See Figure A.19.

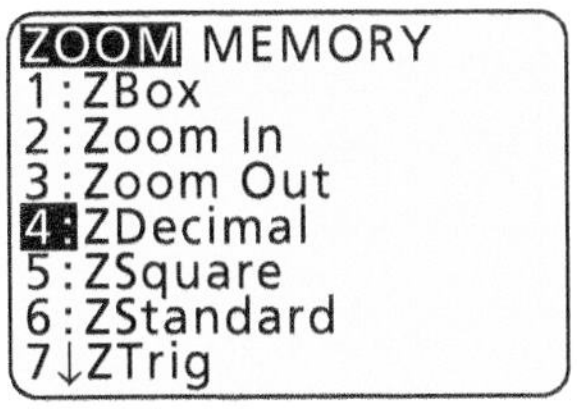

SUMMARY: SQUARING A VIEWING RECTANGLE

Either $(ZOOM)\ (4)$ or $(ZOOM)\ (5)$ may be used to produce a square viewing rectangle. An (approximately) square viewing rectangle has the form

$$[-1.5k, 1.5k, 1] \text{ by } [-k, k, 1],$$

where k is a positive number.

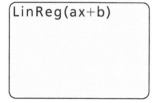

Figure A.20

Plotting Data and an Equation

In Example 3, Section 2.4, we are asked to plot data and graph a modeling function in the same xy-plane. (You may want to refer to the subsection on making a scatterplot and line graph in this appendix.) Start by entering the x-values into list L1 and the y-values into list L2, as shown in Figure A.20. Then press $\boxed{Y=}$ and enter the formula $Y_1 = .65X$ for $f(x)$. Make sure that STATPLOT is on, and set an appropriate viewing rectangle. See Figures A.21 and A.22, and note that Figure A.21 shows "Plot1" in reverse video, which indicates that the scatterplot is on. Now press $\boxed{GRAPH}$ to have both the scatterplot and the graph of Y_1 appear in the same viewing rectangle, as shown in Figure A.23.

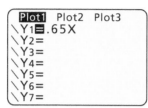

Figure A.21

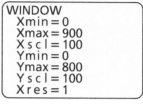

Figure A.22

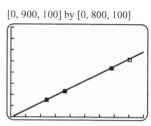

Figure A.23

SUMMARY: PLOTTING DATA AND AN EQUATION

STEP 1: Enter the x-values into list L1 and the y-values into list L2 using the STAT EDIT menu. Turn on Plot1 so that the scatterplot appears.

STEP 2: Use the $\boxed{Y=}$ menu to enter the equation to be graphed.

STEP 3: Use $\boxed{WINDOW}$ or $\boxed{ZOOM}$ to set an appropriate viewing rectangle.

STEP 4: Press $\boxed{GRAPH}$ to graph both the scatterplot and the equation in the same viewing rectangle.

Figure A.24

Accessing the Greatest Integer Function

To access the greatest integer function, enter the following keystrokes from the home screen.

$$\boxed{MATH}\ \boxed{\triangleright}\ \boxed{5}$$

See Figure A.24.

SUMMARY: ACCESSING THE GREATEST INTEGER FUNCTION

STEP 1: Press $\boxed{MATH}$.

STEP 2: Position the cursor over "NUM".

STEP 3: Press $\boxed{5}$ to select the greatest integer function, which is denoted "int(".

Finding the Line of Least-Squares Fit

In Example 11, Section 2.1, the line of least-squares fit for the points (1, 1), (2, 3), and (3, 4) is found. Begin by entering the points in the same way as for a scatterplot. See Figure 2.14, where the x-values are in list L1 and the y-values are in list L2.

After the data have been entered, perform the following keystrokes from the home screen.

$$\boxed{CLEAR}\ \boxed{STAT}\ \boxed{\triangleright}\ \boxed{4}$$

(See Figure 2.15.) This causes "LinReg(ax+b)" to appear on the home screen, as shown in Figure A.25. The graphing calculator assumes that the x-values are in list L1 and the y-values are in list L2. Now press $\boxed{ENTER}$. The result is shown in Figure 2.16.

Figure A.25

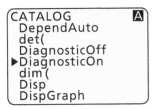

Figure A.26

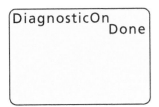

Figure A.27

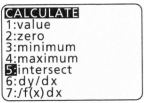

Figure A.28

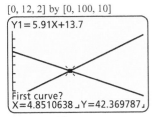

Figure A.29

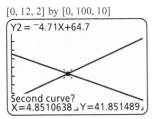

Figure A.30

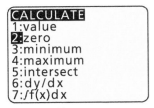

Figure A.31

Figure A.32

If the correlation coefficient r does not appear, enter the keystrokes

$$\boxed{\text{2nd}}\ \boxed{\text{0 [CATALOG]}}$$

and scroll down until you find "DiagnosticsOn". Press $\boxed{\text{ENTER}}$ twice. See Figures A.26 and A.27. The graphs of the data and the least-squares regression line are shown in Figure 2.17.

SUMMARY: LINEAR LEAST-SQUARES FIT

STEP 1: Enter the data using $\boxed{\text{STAT}}\ \boxed{1}$, as is done for a scatterplot. Input the x-values into list L1 and the y-values into list L2.

STEP 2: Press $\boxed{\text{STAT}}\ \boxed{\triangleright}\ \boxed{4}$ from the home screen to access the least-squares regression line. Press $\boxed{\text{ENTER}}$ to start the computation. See page AP-11 to learn how to copy a regression equation into Y_1.

Locating a Point of Intersection

In Example 8, Section 2.2, we are asked to find the point of intersection for two lines. To find the point of intersection for the graphs of

$$f(x) = 5.91x + 13.7 \quad \text{and} \quad g(x) = -4.71x + 64.7,$$

start by entering Y_1 and Y_2, as shown in Figure A.28. Set the viewing rectangle to $[0, 12, 2]$ by $[0, 100, 10]$, and graph both equations in the same viewing rectangle, as shown in Figure 2.24. Then press the following keys to find the intersection point.

$$\boxed{\text{2nd}}\ \boxed{\text{TRACE [CALC]}}\ \boxed{5}$$

See Figure A.29, where the intersect utility is being selected. The calculator prompts for the first curve, as shown in Figure A.30. Use the arrow keys to locate the cursor near the point of intersection and press $\boxed{\text{ENTER}}$. Repeat these steps for the second curve, as shown in Figure A.31. Finally the calculator prompts for a guess. For each of the three prompts, place the free-moving cursor near the point of intersection and press $\boxed{\text{ENTER}}$. The approximate coordinates of the point of intersection are shown in Figure 2.25.

SUMMARY: FINDING A POINT OF INTERSECTION

STEP 1: Graph the two functions in an appropriate viewing rectangle.

STEP 2: Press $\boxed{\text{2nd}}\ \boxed{\text{TRACE [CALC]}}\ \boxed{5}$.

STEP 3: Use the arrow keys to select an approximate location for the point of intersection. Press $\boxed{\text{ENTER}}$ to make the three selections for "First curve?", "Second curve?", and "Guess?". (If the cursor is near the point of intersection, you usually do not need to move the cursor for each selection. Just press $\boxed{\text{ENTER}}$ three times.)

Locating a Zero of a Function

In Example 4, Section 2.3, we are asked to locate an x-intercept, or *zero*, of the function f given by $f(x) = 1 - x - \frac{1}{2}x + 2$. Start by entering $Y_1 = 1 - X - .5X + 2$ into the $\boxed{Y=}$ menu. Set the viewing rectangle to $[-6, 6, 1]$ by $[-4, 4, 1]$ and graph Y_1. Afterwards, press the following keys to invoke the zero finder. (See Figure A.32.)

$$\boxed{\text{2nd}}\ \boxed{\text{TRACE [CALC]}}\ \boxed{2}$$

The calculator prompts for a left bound. Use the arrow keys to set the cursor to the left of the x-intercept and press $\boxed{\text{ENTER}}$. The calculator then prompts for a right bound. Set the cursor to the right of the x-intercept and press $\boxed{\text{ENTER}}$. Finally the calculator prompts for a guess. Set the cursor roughly at the x-intercept and press $\boxed{\text{ENTER}}$. See Figures A.33–A.35 on the next page. The calculator then approximates the x-intercept, or zero, automatically, as shown in Figure 2.35(b).

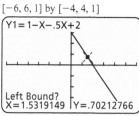

[−6, 6, 1] by [−4, 4, 1]

Y1=1−X−.5X+2

Left Bound?
X=1.5319149 Y=.70212766

Figure A.33

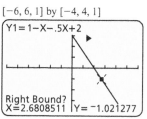

[−6, 6, 1] by [−4, 4, 1]

Y1=1−X−.5X+2

Right Bound?
X=2.6808511 Y=−1.021277

Figure A.34

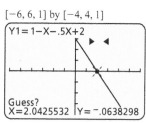

[−6, 6, 1] by [−4, 4, 1]

Y1=1−X−.5X+2

Guess?
X=2.0425532 Y=−.0638298

Figure A.35

SUMMARY: LOCATING A ZERO OF A FUNCTION

STEP 1: Graph the function in an appropriate viewing rectangle.

STEP 2: Press (2nd) (TRACE [CALC]) (2).

STEP 3: Select the left and right bounds, followed by a guess. Press (ENTER) after each selection. The calculator then approximates the zero.

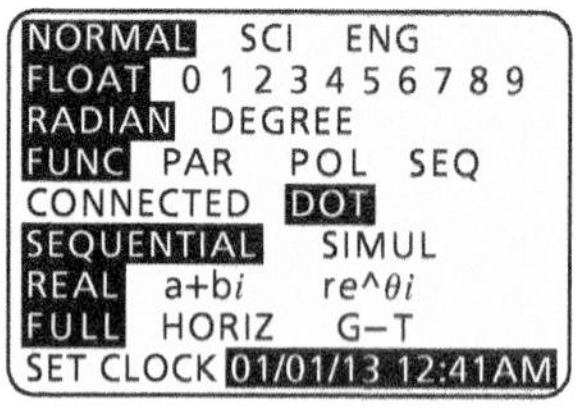

NORMAL SCI ENG
FLOAT 0 1 2 3 4 5 6 7 8 9
RADIAN DEGREE
FUNC PAR POL SEQ
CONNECTED DOT
SEQUENTIAL SIMUL
REAL a+b*i* re^*θi*
FULL HORIZ G−T
SET CLOCK 01/01/13 12:41AM

Figure A.36

Setting Connected and Dot Mode

In Figure 2.48 of Section 2.4 a form of the greatest integer function is graphed in dot mode, and in Figure 2.49 it is graphed in connected mode. To set your graphing calculator in dot mode, press (MODE), position the cursor over "Dot", and press (ENTER). See Figure A.36. Graphs will now appear in dot mode rather than connected mode.

SUMMARY: SETTING CONNECTED OR DOT MODE

STEP 1: Press (MODE).

STEP 2: Position the cursor over "Connected" or "Dot". Press (ENTER).

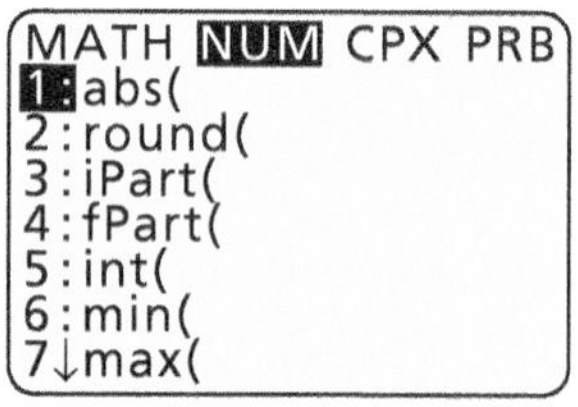

MATH NUM CPX PRB
1:abs(
2:round(
3:iPart(
4:fPart(
5:int(
6:min(
7↓max(

Figure A.37

Accessing the Absolute Value

In Example 1, Section 2.5, the absolute value is used to graph $f(x) = |x + 2|$. To graph f, begin by entering $Y_1 = $ abs$(X + 2)$. The absolute value (abs) is accessed by pressing

(MATH) (▷) (1).

See Figure A.37.

SUMMARY: ACCESSING THE ABSOLUTE VALUE

STEP 1: Press (MATH).

STEP 2: Position the cursor over "NUM".

STEP 3: Press (1) to select the absolute value.

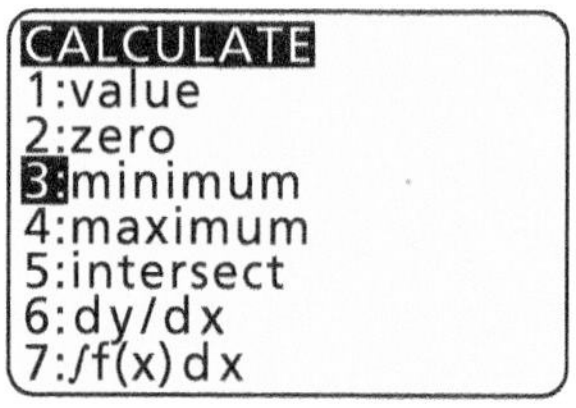

CALCULATE
1:value
2:zero
3:minimum
4:maximum
5:intersect
6:dy/dx
7:∫f(x)dx

Figure A.38

Finding Extrema (Minima and Maxima)

To find a minimum point (or vertex) on a graph, such as $f(x) = 1.5x^2 − 6x + 4$, start by entering $Y_1 = 1.5X^2 − 6X + 4$ into the (Y =) menu. Set the viewing rectangle to [−4.7, 4.7, 1] by [−3.1, 3.1, 1] by entering (ZOOM) (4). Then perform the following keystrokes to find the minimum y-value.

(2nd) (TRACE [CALC]) (3)

See Figure A.38.

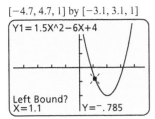

Figure A.39

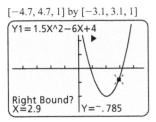

Figure A.40

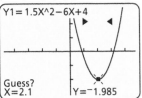

Figure A.41

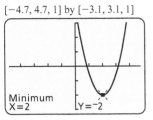

Figure A.42

The calculator prompts for a left bound. Use the arrow keys to position the cursor to the left of the vertex and press (ENTER). Similarly, position the cursor to the right of the vertex for the right bound and press (ENTER). Finally the calculator asks for a guess between the left and right bounds. Place the cursor near the minimum point and press (ENTER). See Figures A.39–A.41. The minimum point (or vertex) is shown in Figure A.42.

To find a maximum of the function f on an interval, use a similar approach, except enter

$$\boxed{\text{2nd}}\ \boxed{\text{TRACE [CALC]}}\ \boxed{4}.$$

The calculator prompts for left and right bounds, followed by a guess. Press (ENTER) after the cursor has been located appropriately for each prompt. An example of a maximum point is displayed in Figure 3.17 in Section 3.1.

SUMMARY: FINDING EXTREMA (MAXIMA AND MINIMA)

STEP 1: Graph the function in an appropriate viewing rectangle.

STEP 2: Press (2nd) (TRACE [CALC]) (3) to find a minimum point or (2nd) (TRACE [CALC]) (4) to find a maximum point.

STEP 3: Use the arrow keys to locate the left and right x-bounds, followed by a guess. Press (ENTER) to select each position of the cursor.

Using the Ask Table Feature

In Example 10, Section 3.1, a table with x-values of 0, 2, 4, 6, and 8 is created. Start by entering $Y_1 = 1.875(X - 8)^2 + 80$. To obtain the table shown in Figure 3.20, use the Ask feature rather than the Auto feature for the independent variable (Indpnt:). Press (2nd) (GRAPH [TABLE]). Whenever an x-value is entered, the corresponding y-value is calculated automatically. See Figures A.43 and A.44.

SUMMARY: USING THE ASK FEATURE FOR A TABLE

STEP 1: Enter the formula for $f(x)$ into Y_1 by using the (Y =) menu.

STEP 2: Press (2nd) (WINDOW [TBLSET]) to access "TABLE SETUP" and then select "Ask" for the independent variable (Indpnt:). "TblStart" and "ΔTbl" do not need to be set.

STEP 3: Enter x-values of your choice. The corresponding y-values will be calculated automatically.

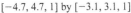

Figure A.43

Figure A.44

Finding a Nonlinear Function of Least-Squares Fit

In Example 11, Section 3.1, a quadratic function of least-squares fit is found in a manner similar to the way a linear function of least-squares fit is found. To solve Example 11, start by pressing (STAT) (1) and then enter the data points from Table 3.4, as shown in Figure 3.22. Input the x-values into list L1 and the y-values into list L2. To find the equation for a quadratic polynomial of least-squares fit, perform the following keystrokes from the home screen.

$$\boxed{\text{CLEAR}}\ \boxed{\text{STAT}}\ \boxed{\triangleright}\ \boxed{5}$$

This causes "Quadreg" to appear on the home screen. The calculator assumes that the x-values are in list L1 and the y-values are in list L2, unless otherwise designated. Press (ENTER) to obtain the quadratic regression equation, as shown in Figure 3.24. Graphs of the data and the regression equation are shown in Figure 3.25.

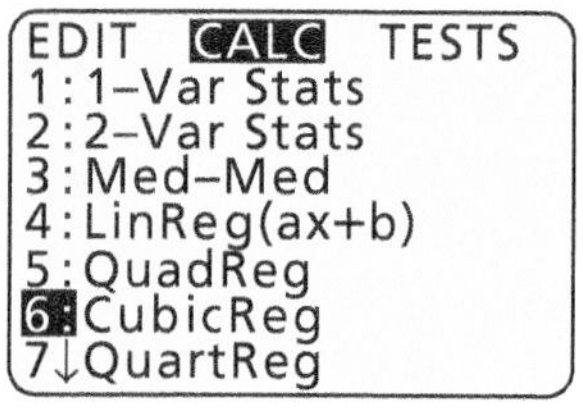

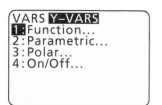

Figure A.45

Other types of regression equations, such as cubic, quartic, power, and exponential, can be selected from the STAT CALC menu. See Figure A.45.

> **SUMMARY: NONLINEAR LEAST-SQUARES FIT**
>
> **STEP 1:** Enter the data using $\boxed{\text{STAT}}\ \boxed{1}$. Input the x-values into list L1 and the y-values into list L2, as is done for a scatterplot.
>
> **STEP 2:** From the home screen, press $\boxed{\text{STAT}}\ \boxed{\triangleright}$ and select a type of least-squares modeling function from the menu. Press $\boxed{\text{ENTER}}$ to initiate the computation.

Evaluating Complex Arithmetic

Complex arithmetic can be performed in much the same way as other arithmetic expressions are evaluated. The imaginary unit i is obtained by entering

$$\boxed{\text{2nd}}\ \boxed{.\,[i]}$$

from the home screen. For example, to add the numbers $(-2 + 3i) + (4 - 6i)$, perform the following keystrokes on the home screen.

$$\boxed{(}\ \boxed{1}\ \boxed{(-)}\ \boxed{2}\ \boxed{+}\ \boxed{3}\ \boxed{\text{2nd}}\ \boxed{.\,[i]}\ \boxed{)}\ \boxed{+}\ \boxed{(}\ \boxed{4}\ \boxed{-}\ \boxed{6}\ \boxed{\text{2nd}}\ \boxed{.\,[i]}\ \boxed{)}\ \boxed{\text{ENTER}}$$

The result is shown in the first two lines of Figure 3.37 in Section 3.3. Other complex arithmetic operations are done similarly.

> **SUMMARY: EVALUATING COMPLEX ARITHMETIC**
>
> Enter a complex expression in the same way as any other arithmetic expression. To obtain the complex number i, use $\boxed{\text{2nd}}\ \boxed{.\,[i]}$.

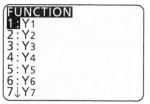

Figure A.46

Accessing the Variable Y_1

In Figure 3.78, Section 3.5, the expressions $-Y_1$ and $Y_1(-X)$ in the $\boxed{Y=}$ menu are used to graph reflections. The Y_1 variable can be found by pressing the following keys. (See Figures A.46 and A.47.)

$$\boxed{\text{VARS}}\ \boxed{\triangleright}\ \boxed{1}\ \boxed{1}$$

> **SUMMARY: ACCESSING THE VARIABLE Y_1**
>
> **STEP 1:** Press $\boxed{\text{VARS}}$.
>
> **STEP 2:** Position the cursor over "Y-VARS".
>
> **STEP 3:** Press $\boxed{1}$ twice.
>
> These keystrokes will make Y_1 appear on the screen.

Figure A.47

Shading between Two Graphs

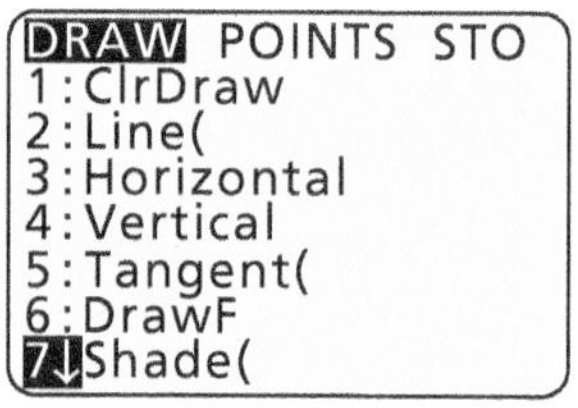

In Example 9, Section 3.5, the region below the graph of $f(x) = -0.4x^2 + 4$ is shaded to make it look like a mountain, as illustrated in Figure 3.97. One way to shade below the graph of f is to begin by entering $Y_1 = -.4X^2 + 4$ after pressing $\boxed{Y=}$. Then use the following keystrokes from the home screen.

$$\boxed{\text{2nd}}\ \boxed{\text{PRGM [DRAW]}}\ \boxed{7}\ \boxed{(-)}\ \boxed{5}\ \boxed{,}\ \boxed{\text{VARS}}\ \boxed{\triangleright}\ \boxed{1}\ \boxed{1}\ \boxed{)}$$

Figure A.48

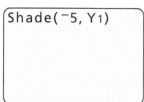

Figure A.49

The expression $\text{Shade}(-5, Y_1)$ should appear on your home screen. See Figures A.48 and A.49. The shading utility, accessed from the DRAW menu, requires a lower function and then an upper function, separated by a comma. When $\boxed{\text{ENTER}}$ is pressed, the graphing calculator shades between the graph of the lower function and the graph of the upper function.

For the lower function we have arbitrarily selected $y = -5$ because its graph lies below the graph of f and does not appear in the viewing rectangle in Figure 3.97. Instead of entering the variable Y_1, we could enter the formula $-.4X^\wedge 2 + 4$ for the upper function.

SUMMARY: SHADING A GRAPH

STEP 1: Press (2nd) (PRGM [DRAW]) (7) from the home screen.

STEP 2: Enter a formula or a variable such as Y_1 for the lower function, followed by a comma.

STEP 3: Enter a formula or a variable such as Y_2 for the upper function, followed by a right parenthesis.

STEP 4: Set an appropriate viewing rectangle.

STEP 5: Press (ENTER). The region between the two graphs will be shaded.

Copying a Regression Equation into $Y_1 =$

In Example 8, Section 4.2, we are asked to use cubic regression to model real data. The resulting formula for the cubic function, shown in Figure 4.54, is quite complicated and tedious to enter into $Y_1 =$ by hand. A graphing calculator has the capability to copy this equation into Y_1 automatically. To do this, clear the equation for $Y_1 =$. Then enter Y_1 after "CubicReg", as shown in Figure A.50. When (ENTER) is pressed, the regression equation will be calculated and then copied into $Y_1 =$, as shown in Figure A.51. The following keystrokes may be used from the home screen. (Be sure to enter the data into lists L1 and L2.)

(STAT) (▷) (6) (VARS) (▷) (1) (1) (ENTER)

SUMMARY: COPYING A REGRESSION EQUATION INTO $Y_1 =$

STEP 1: Clear Y_1 in the (Y=) menu if an equation is present. Return to the home screen.

STEP 2: Select a type of regression from the STAT CALC menu.

STEP 3: Press (VARS) (▷) (1) (1) (ENTER).

Setting a Decimal Window

In Example 1, Section 4.7, a decimal (or friendly) window is used to trace the graph of f. With a decimal window, the cursor stops on convenient x-values. In the decimal window $[-9.4, 9.4, 1]$ by $[-6.2, 6.2, 1]$, the cursor stops on x-values that are multiples of 0.2. If we reduce the viewing rectangle to $[-4.7, 4.7, 1]$ by $[-3.1, 3.1, 1]$, the cursor stops on x-values that are multiples of 0.1. To set this smaller window automatically, press (ZOOM) (4). See Figure A.52. Decimal windows are useful when graphing rational functions with asymptotes in connected mode.

SUMMARY: SETTING A DECIMAL WINDOW

Press (ZOOM) (4) to set the viewing rectangle $[-4.7, 4.7, 1]$ by $[-3.1, 3.1, 1]$. A convenient larger decimal window is $[-9.4, 9.4, 1]$ by $[-6.2, 6.2, 1]$.

Graphing an Inverse Function

In Example 7, Section 5.2, the inverse function of $f(x) = x^3 + 2$ is graphed. A graphing calculator can graph the inverse of a function without a formula for $f^{-1}(x)$. Begin by entering $Y_1 = X^\wedge 3 + 2$ into the (Y=) menu. Then return to the home screen by pressing

(2nd) (MODE [QUIT]).

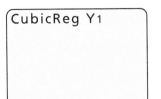

Figure A.50

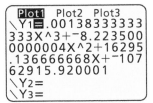

Figure A.51

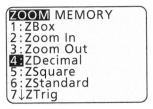

Figure A.52

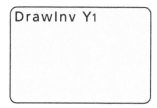

Figure A.53

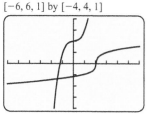

$[-6, 6, 1]$ by $[-4, 4, 1]$

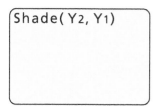

Figure A.54

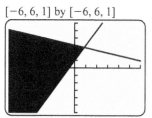

Figure A.55

$[-6, 6, 1]$ by $[-6, 6, 1]$

Figure A.56

The DrawInv utility may be accessed by pressing

$$\boxed{\text{2nd}}\ \boxed{\text{PRGM [DRAW]}}\ \boxed{8},$$

followed by

$$\boxed{\text{VARS}}\ \boxed{\triangleright}\ \boxed{1}\ \boxed{1}$$

to obtain the variable Y_1. See A.53. Pressing $\boxed{\text{ENTER}}$ causes both Y_1 and its inverse to be graphed, as shown in A.54.

SUMMARY: GRAPHING AN INVERSE FUNCTION

STEP 1: Enter the formula for $f(x)$ into Y_1 using the $\boxed{\text{Y =}}$ menu.

STEP 2: Set an appropriate viewing rectangle by pressing $\boxed{\text{WINDOW}}$.

STEP 3: Return to the home screen by pressing $\boxed{\text{2nd}}\ \boxed{\text{MODE [QUIT]}}$.

STEP 4: Press $\boxed{\text{2nd}}\ \boxed{\text{PRGM [DRAW]}}\ \boxed{8}\ \boxed{\text{VARS}}\ \boxed{\triangleright}\ \boxed{1}\ \boxed{1}\ \boxed{\text{ENTER}}$ to create the graphs of f and f^{-1}.

Shading a System of Inequalities

In Example 2(b), Section 9.2, we are asked to shade the solution set for the system of linear inequalities $x + 3y \le 9$, $2x - y \le -1$. Begin by solving each system for y to obtain $y \le -\frac{1}{3}x + 3$ and $y \ge 2x + 1$. Then let $Y_1 = -X/3 + 3$ and $Y_2 = 2X + 1$, as shown in Figure 9.30. Position the cursor to left of Y_1 and press $\boxed{\text{ENTER}}$ three times. The triangle that appears indicates that the calculator will shade the region below the graph of Y_1. Next locate the cursor to the left of Y_2 and press $\boxed{\text{ENTER}}$ twice. This triangle indicates that the calculator will shade the region above the graph of Y_2. After setting the viewing rectangle to $[-6, 6, 1]$ by $[-6, 6, 1]$, press $\boxed{\text{GRAPH}}$. The result is shown in Figure 9.31. The solution set could also be shaded using Shade(Y_2, Y_1) from the home screen. See Figures A.55 and A.56.

SUMMARY: SHADING A SYSTEM OF INEQUALITIES

STEP 1: Solve each inequality for y.

STEP 2: Enter the formulas as Y_1 and Y_2 in the $\boxed{\text{Y =}}$ menu.

STEP 3: Locate the cursor to the left of Y_1 and press $\boxed{\text{ENTER}}$ two or three times, to shade either above or below the graph of Y_1. Repeat for Y_2.

STEP 4: Set an appropriate viewing rectangle.

STEP 5: Press $\boxed{\text{GRAPH}}$.

Note: The Shade utility under the DRAW menu can also be used to shade the region *between* two graphs.

Entering the Elements of a Matrix

In Example 9, Section 9.4, the augmented matrix A is given by

$$A = \begin{bmatrix} 2 & 1 & 2 & | & 10 \\ 1 & 0 & 2 & | & 5 \\ 1 & -2 & 2 & | & 1 \end{bmatrix}.$$

On the TI-83 Plus and TI-84 Plus, use the following keystrokes to define a matrix A with dimension 3×4. (On the TI-83 graphing calculator, the matrix menu is found by pressing $\boxed{\text{MATRIX}}$.)

$$\boxed{\text{2nd}}\ \boxed{x^{-1} \text{ [MATRIX]}}\ \boxed{\triangleright}\ \boxed{\triangleright}\ \boxed{1}\ \boxed{3}\ \boxed{\text{ENTER}}\ \boxed{4}\ \boxed{\text{ENTER}}$$

See Figures 9.41 and 9.42. Then input the 12 elements of the matrix A, row by row, as shown in Figure 9.42. Finish each entry by pressing (ENTER). After these elements have been entered, press

$$\boxed{\text{2nd}}\ \boxed{\text{MODE [QUIT]}}$$

to return to the home screen. To display the matrix A, press

$$\boxed{\text{2nd}}\ \boxed{x^{-1}\ [\text{MATRIX}]}\ \boxed{1}\ \boxed{\text{ENTER}}.$$

See Figure 9.43.

SUMMARY: ENTERING THE ELEMENTS OF A MATRIX A

STEP 1: Begin by accessing the matrix A by pressing $\boxed{\text{2nd}}\ \boxed{x^{-1}\ [\text{MATRIX}]}\ \boxed{\triangleright}\ \boxed{\triangleright}\ \boxed{1}$.

STEP 2: Enter the dimension of A by pressing $\boxed{m}\ \boxed{\text{ENTER}}\ \boxed{n}\ \boxed{\text{ENTER}}$, where the dimension of the matrix is $m \times n$.

STEP 3: Input each element of the matrix, row by row. Finish each entry by pressing $\boxed{\text{ENTER}}$. Use $\boxed{\text{2nd}}\ \boxed{\text{MODE [QUIT]}}$ to return to the home screen.

Note: On the TI-83, replace the keystrokes $\boxed{\text{2nd}}\ \boxed{x^{-1}\ [\text{MATRIX}]}$ with $\boxed{\text{MATRIX}}$.

Reduced Row-Echelon Form

In Example 9, Section 9.4, the reduced row-echelon form of a matrix is found. To find this reduced row-echelon form on the TI-83 Plus and TI-84 Plus, use the following keystrokes from the home screen. (See Figure 9.44.)

$$\boxed{\text{2nd}}\ \boxed{x^{-1}\ [\text{MATRIX}]}\ \boxed{\triangleright}\ \boxed{\text{ALPHA}}\ \boxed{\text{APPS [B]}}\ \boxed{\text{2nd}}\ \boxed{x^{-1}\ [\text{MATRIX}]}\ \boxed{1}\ \boxed{)}\ \boxed{\text{ENTER}}$$

The resulting matrix is shown in Figure 9.45. On the TI-83 graphing calculator, use the following keystrokes to find the reduced row-echelon form.

$$\boxed{\text{MATRIX}}\ \boxed{\triangleright}\ \boxed{\text{ALPHA}}\ \boxed{\text{MATRIX [B]}}\ \boxed{\text{MATRIX}}\ \boxed{1}\ \boxed{)}\ \boxed{\text{ENTER}}$$

SUMMARY: FINDING THE REDUCED ROW-ECHELON FORM OF A MATRIX

STEP 1: To make rref([A]) appear on the home screen, use the following keystrokes.

$$\boxed{\text{2nd}}\ \boxed{x^{-1}\ [\text{MATRIX}]}\ \boxed{\triangleright}\ \boxed{\text{ALPHA}}\ \boxed{\text{APPS [B]}}\ \boxed{\text{2nd}}\ \boxed{x^{-1}\ [\text{MATRIX}]}\ \boxed{1}\ \boxed{)}\ \boxed{\text{ENTER}}$$

STEP 2: Press $\boxed{\text{ENTER}}$ to calculate the reduced row-echelon form. Use arrow keys to access elements that do not appear on the screen.

Note: On the TI-83, replace the keystrokes $\boxed{\text{2nd}}\ \boxed{x^{-1}\ [\text{MATRIX}]}$ with $\boxed{\text{MATRIX}}$ and $\boxed{\text{APPS [B]}}$ with $\boxed{\text{MATRIX [B]}}$.

Performing Arithmetic Operations on Matrices

In Example 10, Section 9.5, the matrices A and B are multiplied. Begin by entering the elements for the matrices A and B. The following keystrokes can be used to define a matrix A with dimension 3×3.

$$\boxed{\text{2nd}}\ \boxed{x^{-1}\ [\text{MATRIX}]}\ \boxed{\triangleright}\ \boxed{\triangleright}\ \boxed{1}\ \boxed{3}\ \boxed{\text{ENTER}}\ \boxed{3}\ \boxed{\text{ENTER}}$$

Next input the 9 elements in the matrix A, row by row. Finish each entry by pressing $\boxed{\text{ENTER}}$. See Figure 9.59. Repeat this process to define a matrix B with dimension 3×3.

$$\boxed{\text{2nd}}\ \boxed{x^{-1}\ [\text{MATRIX}]}\ \boxed{\triangleright}\ \boxed{\triangleright}\ \boxed{2}\ \boxed{3}\ \boxed{\text{ENTER}}\ \boxed{3}\ \boxed{\text{ENTER}}$$

Enter the 9 elements in B. See Figure 9.60. After the elements of A and B have been entered, press

$$\boxed{\text{2nd}}\ \boxed{\text{MODE [QUIT]}}$$

to return to the home screen. To multiply the expression AB, use the following keystrokes from the home screen.

$$\boxed{\text{2nd}}\ \boxed{x^{-1}\ \text{[MATRIX]}}\ \boxed{1}\ \boxed{\times}\ \boxed{\text{2nd}}\ \boxed{x^{-1}\ \text{[MATRIX]}}\ \boxed{2}\ \boxed{\text{ENTER}}$$

The result is shown in Figure 9.61.

SUMMARY: PERFORMING ARITHMETIC OPERATIONS ON MATRICES

STEP 1: Enter the elements of each matrix, beginning with the keystrokes

$$\boxed{\text{2nd}}\ \boxed{x^{-1}\ \text{[MATRIX]}}\ \boxed{\triangleright}\ \boxed{\triangleright}\ \boxed{k}\ \boxed{m}\ \boxed{\text{ENTER}}\ \boxed{n}\ \boxed{\text{ENTER}},$$

where k is the menu number of the matrix and the dimension of the matrix is $m \times n$.

STEP 2: Return to the home screen by pressing $\boxed{\text{2nd}}\ \boxed{\text{MODE [QUIT]}}$.

STEP 3: Enter the matrix expression, followed by $\boxed{\text{ENTER}}$. Use the keystrokes

$$\boxed{\text{2nd}}\ \boxed{x^{-1}\ \text{[MATRIX]}}\ \boxed{k}$$

to access the matrix with menu number k.

Note: On the TI-83, replace the keystrokes $\boxed{\text{2nd}}\ \boxed{x^{-1}\ \text{[MATRIX]}}$ with $\boxed{\text{MATRIX}}$.

Finding the Inverse of a Matrix

```
MATRIX[A]   3 ×3
[ 1      3     ⁻1    ]
[ 0     ⁻2     1     ]
[ ⁻1     1    ⁻3     ]
```

Figure A.57

In Example 8, Section 9.6, the inverse of A, denoted A^{-1}, is displayed in Figure 9.65. To calculate A^{-1}, start by entering the elements of the matrix A, as shown in Figure A.57. To compute A^{-1}, perform the following keystrokes from the home screen.

$$\boxed{\text{2nd}}\ \boxed{x^{-1}\ \text{[MATRIX]}}\ \boxed{1}\ \boxed{x^{-1}}\ \boxed{\text{ENTER}}$$

The results are shown in Figure 9.65.

SUMMARY: FINDING THE INVERSE OF A SQUARE MATRIX

STEP 1: Enter the elements of the square matrix A.

STEP 2: Return to the home screen by pressing

$$\boxed{\text{2nd}}\ \boxed{\text{MODE [QUIT]}}.$$

STEP 3: Perform the following keystrokes from the home screen to display A^{-1}.

$$\boxed{\text{2nd}}\ \boxed{x^{-1}\ \text{[MATRIX]}}\ \boxed{1}\ \boxed{x^{-1}}\ \boxed{\text{ENTER}}$$

Note: On the TI-83, replace the keystrokes $\boxed{\text{2nd}}\ \boxed{x^{-1}\ \text{[MATRIX]}}$ with $\boxed{\text{MATRIX}}$.

Solving a Linear System with a Matrix Inverse

In Example 8, Section 9.6, the solution to a system of equations is found. The matrix equation $AX = B$ has the solution $X = A^{-1}B$, provided A^{-1} exists, and is given by

$$AX = \begin{bmatrix} 1 & 3 & -1 \\ 0 & -2 & 1 \\ -1 & 1 & -3 \end{bmatrix} \begin{bmatrix} x \\ y \\ z \end{bmatrix} = \begin{bmatrix} 6 \\ -2 \\ 4 \end{bmatrix} = B.$$

To solve this equation, start by entering the elements of the matrices A and B. To compute the solution $A^{-1}B$, perform the following keystrokes from the home screen.

$$\boxed{\text{2nd}}\ \boxed{x^{-1}\ [\text{MATRIX}]}\ \boxed{1}\ \boxed{x^{-1}}\ \boxed{\times}\ \boxed{\text{2nd}}\ \boxed{x^{-1}\ [\text{MATRIX}]}\ \boxed{2}\ \boxed{\text{ENTER}}$$

The results are shown in Figure 9.66.

SUMMARY: SOLVING A LINEAR SYSTEM WITH A MATRIX INVERSE

STEP 1: Write the system of equations as $AX = B$.

STEP 2: Enter the elements of the matrices A and B.

STEP 3: Return to the home screen by pressing

$$\boxed{\text{2nd}}\ \boxed{\text{MODE [QUIT]}}.$$

STEP 4: Perform the following keystrokes.

$$\boxed{\text{2nd}}\ \boxed{x^{-1}\ [\text{MATRIX}]}\ \boxed{1}\ \boxed{x^{-1}}\ \boxed{\times}\ \boxed{\text{2nd}}\ \boxed{x^{-1}\ [\text{MATRIX}]}\ \boxed{2}\ \boxed{\text{ENTER}}$$

Note: On the TI-83, replace the keystrokes with $\boxed{\text{2nd}}\ \boxed{x^{-1}\ [\text{MATRIX}]}$ with $\boxed{\text{MATRIX}}$.

Evaluating a Determinant

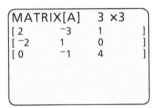

Figure A.58

In Example 4(a), Section 9.7, a graphing calculator is used to evaluate a determinant of a matrix. Start by entering the 9 elements of the 3×3 matrix A, as shown in Figure A.58. To compute det A, perform the following keystrokes from the home screen.

$$\boxed{\text{2nd}}\ \boxed{x^{-1}\ [\text{MATRIX}]}\ \boxed{\triangleright}\ \boxed{1}\ \boxed{\text{2nd}}\ \boxed{x^{-1}\ [\text{MATRIX}]}\ \boxed{1}\ \boxed{)}\ \boxed{\text{ENTER}}$$

The results are shown in Figure 9.68.

SUMMARY: EVALUATING A DETERMINANT OF A SQUARE MATRIX

STEP 1: Enter the elements of the matrix A.

STEP 2: Return to the home screen by pressing

$$\boxed{\text{2nd}}\ \boxed{\text{MODE [QUIT]}}.$$

STEP 3: Perform the following keystrokes.

$$\boxed{\text{2nd}}\ \boxed{x^{-1}\ [\text{MATRIX}]}\ \boxed{\triangleright}\ \boxed{1}\ \boxed{\text{2nd}}\ \boxed{x^{-1}\ [\text{MATRIX}]}\ \boxed{1}\ \boxed{)}\ \boxed{\text{ENTER}}$$

Note: On the TI-83, replace the keystrokes $\boxed{\text{2nd}}\ \boxed{x^{-1}\ [\text{MATRIX}]}$ with $\boxed{\text{MATRIX}}$.

Creating a Sequence

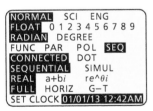

Figure A.59

A graphing calculator can be used to calculate the terms of the sequence given by $f(n) = 2n - 5$ for $n = 1, 2, 3, 4$. See Example 1(a), Section 11.1. Start by setting the mode of the calculator to sequence ("Seq") using the following keystrokes. (See Figure A.59.)

$$\boxed{\text{MODE}}\ \boxed{\triangledown}\ \boxed{\triangledown}\ \boxed{\triangledown}\ \boxed{\triangleright}\ \boxed{\triangleright}\ \boxed{\triangleright}\ \boxed{\text{ENTER}}\ \boxed{\text{2nd}}\ \boxed{\text{MODE [QUIT]}}$$

Then enter the following from the home screen.

$$\boxed{\text{2nd}}\ \boxed{\text{STAT [LIST]}}\ \boxed{\triangleright}\ \boxed{5}$$

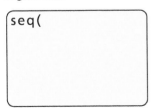

Figure A.60

On the home screen, "seq(" will appear, as shown in Figure A.60. This sequence utility requires that four things be entered—all separated by commas. They are the formula, the variable, the subscript of the first term, and the subscript of the last term. Use the following keystrokes to obtain the first four terms (a_1, a_2, a_3, a_4) of the sequence $a_n = 2n - 5$, as shown in Figure 11.1.

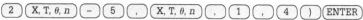

SUMMARY: CREATING A SEQUENCE

STEP 1: To create a sequence, use the keystrokes

$$\boxed{\text{2nd}} \ \boxed{\text{STAT [LIST]}} \ \boxed{\triangleright} \ \boxed{5}.$$

STEP 2: Enter the formula, the variable, the subscript of the first term, and the subscript of the last term—all separated by commas. For example, if you want the first 10 terms ($a_1, a_2, a_3, \ldots, a_{10}$) of $a_n = n^2$, enter seq ($n^2, n, 1, 10$). Be sure to set your calculator in sequence mode.

STEP 3: Press $\boxed{\text{ENTER}}$ to get the terms of the sequence to appear.

Entering, Tabling, and Graphing a Sequence

In Example 5, Section 11.1, a table and a graph of a sequence are created with a graphing calculator. The calculator should be set to sequence mode by entering the following keystrokes.

$$\boxed{\text{MODE}} \ \boxed{\triangledown} \ \boxed{\triangledown} \ \boxed{\triangledown} \ \boxed{\triangleright} \ \boxed{\triangleright} \ \boxed{\triangleright} \ \boxed{\text{ENTER}}$$

```
Plot1  Plot2  Plot3
 nMin=1
∴u(n)▪2.85u(n−1)
 −.19u(n−1)^2
 u(nMin)▪{1}
\v(n)=
 v(nMin)=
\w(n)=
```

Figure A.61

To enter the formula for a sequence, press $\boxed{\text{Y=}}$. See Figure A.61. Let nMin $= 1$, since the initial value of n is equal to 1. To enter $a_n = 2.85a_{n-1} - .19a_{n-1}^2$, use the following keystrokes, after clearing out any old formula. (Notice that the graphing calculator uses u instead of a to denote a term of the sequence.)

$$\boxed{2} \ \boxed{.} \ \boxed{8} \ \boxed{5} \ \boxed{\text{2nd}} \ \boxed{7[u]} \ \boxed{(} \ \boxed{X, T, \theta, n} \ \boxed{-} \ \boxed{1} \ \boxed{)} \ \boxed{-} \ \boxed{.} \ \boxed{1} \ \boxed{9}$$

$$\boxed{\text{2nd}} \ \boxed{7[u]} \ \boxed{(} \ \boxed{X, T, \theta, n} \ \boxed{-} \ \boxed{1} \ \boxed{)} \ \boxed{\wedge} \ \boxed{2} \ \boxed{\text{ENTER}}$$

Since $a_1 = 1$, let $u(n\text{Min}) = \{1\}$. This can be done as follows. See Figure A.61.

$$\boxed{\text{CLEAR}} \ \boxed{\text{2nd}} \ \boxed{(} \ \boxed{1} \ \boxed{\text{2nd}} \ \boxed{)}$$

```
TABLE SETUP
 TblStart=1
 ΔTbl=1
Indpnt: ▊Auto▊ Ask
Depend: ▊Auto▊ Ask
```

Figure A.62

To create a table for this sequence, starting with a_1 and incrementing n by 1, perform the following keystrokes. See Figure A.62 and Figure 11.7.

$$\boxed{\text{2nd}} \ \boxed{\text{WINDOW [TBLSET]}} \ \boxed{1} \ \boxed{\text{ENTER}} \ \boxed{1} \ \boxed{\text{2nd}} \ \boxed{\text{GRAPH [TABLE]}}$$

```
WINDOW
 nMin=1
 nMax=20
 PlotStart=1
 PlotStep=1
 Xmin=0
 Xmax=21
↓Xscl=1
```

Figure A.63

To graph the first 20 terms of this sequence, start by selecting $\boxed{\text{WINDOW}}$. Since we want the first 20 terms plotted, let nMin $= 1$, nMax $= 20$, PlotStart $= 1$, and PlotStep $= 1$. The window can be set as [0, 21, 1] by [0, 14, 1]. See Figure A.63. To graph the sequence, press $\boxed{\text{GRAPH}}$. The resulting graph uses dot mode and is shown in Figure 11.9.

SUMMARY: ENTERING, TABLING, AND GRAPHING A SEQUENCE

STEP 1: Set the mode to "Seq" by using the $\boxed{\text{MODE}}$ menu.

STEP 2: Enter the formula for the sequence by pressing $\boxed{\text{Y=}}$.

STEP 3: To create a table of a sequence, set the start and increment values with

$$\boxed{\text{2nd}} \ \boxed{\text{WINDOW [TBLSET]}}$$

and then press

$$\boxed{\text{2nd}} \ \boxed{\text{GRAPH [TABLE]}}.$$

STEP 4: To graph a sequence, set the viewing rectangle by using $\boxed{\text{WINDOW}}$ and then press $\boxed{\text{GRAPH}}$. Be sure to use dot mode.

Summing a Series

In Example 3, Section 11.2, the sum of the series $\sum_{n=1}^{50}\left(\frac{1}{n^4}\right)$ is found by using a graphing calculator. Use the following keystrokes from the home screen.

The results are shown in the first three lines of Figure 11.12.

> **SUMMARY: SUMMING A SERIES**
>
> **STEP 1:** Use (2nd) (STAT [LIST]) (▷) (▷) (5) to access the sum utility.
>
> **STEP 2:** Use (2nd) (STAT [LIST]) (▷) (5) to access the sequence utility. (To use the sequence utility, see "Creating a Sequence" in this appendix.)

Calculating Factorial Notation

In Example 4, Section 11.3, factorial notation is evaluated with a graphing calculator. The factorial utility is found under the MATH PRB menus. To calculate 8!, use the following keystrokes from the home screen.

(8) (MATH) (▷) (▷) (▷) (4) (ENTER)

The results are shown in the first two lines of Figure 11.15.

> **SUMMARY: CALCULATING FACTORIAL NOTATION**
>
> To calculate n factorial, use the following keystrokes.
>
> (n) (MATH) (▷) (▷) (▷) (4) (ENTER)
>
> The value of n should be entered as a number, not a variable.

Calculating Permutations and Combinations

In Example 5(a), Section 11.3, the permutation $P(7, 3)$ is evaluated. To perform this calculation, use the following keystrokes from the home screen.

(7) (MATH) (▷) (▷) (▷) (2) (3) (ENTER)

The results are shown in the first two lines of Figure 11.17.

In Example 8(a), Section 11.3, the combination $C(7, 3)$ can be calculated by using the following keystrokes.

(7) (MATH) (▷) (▷) (▷) (3) (3) (ENTER)

The results are shown in the first two lines of Figure 11.18.

> **SUMMARY: CALCULATING PERMUTATIONS AND COMBINATIONS**
>
> **STEP 1:** To calculate $P(n, r)$, use (MATH) and select "PRB" followed by (2).
>
> **STEP 2:** To calculate $C(n, r)$, use (MATH) and select "PRB" followed by (3).

Graphing Parametric Equations

In Figure 8.72, Section 8.4, the parametric equations $x = t + 3$, $y = t^2$ for $-3 \le t \le 3$ are graphed. To set your graphing calculator in parametric mode, press $\boxed{\text{MODE}}$, position the cursor over "Par", and press $\boxed{\text{ENTER}}$. See Figure A.64. Next Press $\boxed{\text{Y}=}$ and enter the equations for x and y, as shown in Figure A.65.

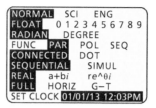

Figure A.64

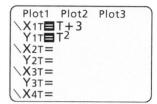

Figure A.65

To set a viewing rectangle, press $\boxed{\text{WINDOW}}$. In addition to setting Xmin, Xmax, Xscl, Ymin, Ymax, and Yscl, you must set values for Tmin, Tmax, and Tstep. Tmin refers to the minimum value of t in the graph, and Tmax refers to the maximum value of t. It is given that $-3 \le t \le 3$, so it follows that Tmin $= -3$ and Tmax $= 3$. However, when an interval for t is not given, it may take a little experimentation to determine an appropriate interval for t. Tstep represents the increment between consecutive t-values on the graph. If Tstep is too large, the graph appears more like a line graph than a smooth curve. If Tstep is too small, the graphing calculator will take a long time to create the graph. Many times a reasonable value is Tstep $= 0.1$. See Figure 8.70. A parametric graph can be created by pressing $\boxed{\text{GRAPH}}$.

Tables for parametric equations can be created. Press

$$\boxed{\text{2nd}}\;\boxed{\text{WINDOW [TBLSET]}}$$

and proceed in the usual manner. Note that the variables TblStart and ΔTbl refer to t and not x. See Figure 8.71.

SUMMARY: GRAPHING PARAMETRIC EQUATIONS

1. Press $\boxed{\text{MODE}}$, move the cursor to "Par", and press $\boxed{\text{ENTER}}$.
2. Press $\boxed{\text{Y}=}$ and enter the equations for x and y.
3. Press $\boxed{\text{WINDOW}}$ and set the viewing rectangle. Be sure to set Tmin, Tmax, and Tstep. When in doubt, let Tstep $= 0.1$.
4. To make the graph appear, press $\boxed{\text{GRAPH}}$.

Graphing in Polar Coordinates

In Figure 8.102, Section 8.5, the polar equation $r = 2 + 2\cos\theta$ for $0° \le \theta \le 360°$ is graphed. To set your graphing calculator in polar coordinate mode, press $\boxed{\text{MODE}}$, position the cursor over "Pol", and press $\boxed{\text{ENTER}}$. See Figure A.66. Polar equations can be graphed in either degree or radian mode. To set your calculator in degree mode, position the cursor over "Degree" and press $\boxed{\text{ENTER}}$. See Figure A.67. Next press $\boxed{\text{Y}=}$ and enter the equation for "$r_1 = $", as shown in Figure A.68. Note that the polar equation must be solved for the variable r.

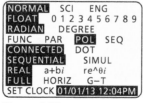

Figure A.66

Figure A.67

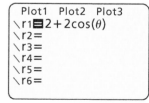

Figure A.68

```
WINDOW
 θmin=0
 θmax=360
 θstep=7.5
 Xmin=-6
 Xmax=6
 Xscl=1
↓Ymin=-4
```

Figure A.69 Degree Mode

To set a viewing rectangle, press (WINDOW). In addition to setting Xmin, Xmax, Xscl, Ymin, Ymax, and Yscl, you must set values for θmin, θmax, and θstep. The variable θmin refers to the minimum value of θ, and θmax refers to the maximum value of θ. Since $\cos\theta$ is periodic with 360°, the entire graph will appear if we let $0° \leq \theta \leq 360°$. Let θmin = 0 and θmax = 360. The variable θstep represents the increment between consecutive θ-values on the polar graph. If θstep is too large, the graph appears more like a line graph than a smooth curve. If θstep is too small, the graphing calculator will take a long time to create the graph. In degree mode a reasonable value for θstep is 7.5°, and in radian mode a reasonable value for θstep is 0.1 radian. See Figure A.69. A polar graph can be created by pressing (GRAPH).

Tables for polar coordinates can be created. Press

(2nd) (WINDOW [TBLSET])

and proceed in the usual manner. Note that the variables TblStart and ΔTbl refer to θ and not x. See Figure 8.101.

> **SUMMARY: GRAPHING IN POLAR COORDINATES**
>
> 1. Press (MODE), move the cursor to "Pol", and press (ENTER). Set the calculator to either degree or radian mode.
> 2. Press (Y=) and enter the polar equation.
> 3. Press (WINDOW) and set the viewing rectangle. Be sure to set θmin, θmax, and θstep. When in doubt, let θstep = 7.5 in degree mode and θstep = 0.1 in radian mode.
> 4. To make the graph appear, press (GRAPH).

Appendix B:
A Library of Functions

Basic Functions

The following are symbolic, numerical, and graphical representations of several functions used in algebra and trigonometry. Their domains D and ranges R are given.

Identity Function: $f(x) = x$

x	-2	-1	0	1	2
$y = x$	-2	-1	0	1	2

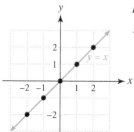

$D = (-\infty, \infty)$
$R = (-\infty, \infty)$

Absolute Value Function: $f(x) = |x|$

x	-2	-1	0	1	2
$y = |x|$	2	1	0	1	2

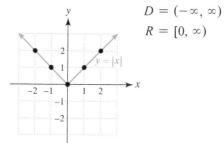

$D = (-\infty, \infty)$
$R = [0, \infty)$

Square Function: $f(x) = x^2$

x	-2	-1	0	1	2
$y = x^2$	4	1	0	1	4

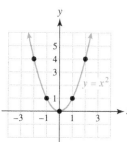

$D = (-\infty, \infty)$
$R = [0, \infty)$

Cube Function: $f(x) = x^3$

x	-2	-1	0	1	2
$y = x^3$	-8	-1	0	1	8

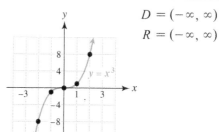

$D = (-\infty, \infty)$
$R = (-\infty, \infty)$

Square Root Function: $f(x) = \sqrt{x}$

x	0	1	4	9
$y = \sqrt{x}$	0	1	2	3

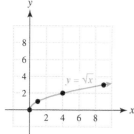
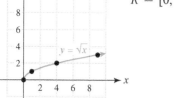

$D = [0, \infty)$
$R = [0, \infty)$

Cube Root Function: $f(x) = \sqrt[3]{x}$

x	-8	-1	0	1	8
$y = \sqrt[3]{x}$	-2	-1	0	1	2

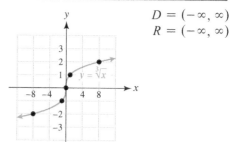

$D = (-\infty, \infty)$
$R = (-\infty, \infty)$

Greatest Integer Function: $f(x) = [\![x]\!]$

x	-2.5	-1.5	0	1.5	2.5
$y = [\![x]\!]$	-3	-2	0	1	2

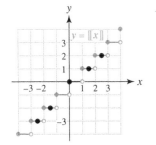

$D = (-\infty, \infty)$
$R = $ Integers

Reciprocal Function: $f(x) = \frac{1}{x}$

x	-2	-1	0	1	2
$y = \frac{1}{x}$	$-\frac{1}{2}$	-1	—	1	$\frac{1}{2}$

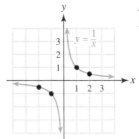

$D = (-\infty, 0) \cup (0, \infty)$
$R = (-\infty, 0) \cup (0, \infty)$

Base-2 Exponential Function: $f(x) = 2^x$

x	-2	-1	0	1	2
$y = 2^x$	$\frac{1}{4}$	$\frac{1}{2}$	1	2	4

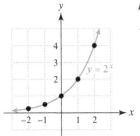

$D = (-\infty, \infty)$
$R = (0, \infty)$

Natural Exponential Function: $f(x) = e^x$

x	-2	-1	0	1	2
$y = e^x$	e^{-2}	e^{-1}	1	e^1	e^2

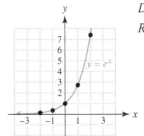

$D = (-\infty, \infty)$
$R = (0, \infty)$

Common Logarithmic Function: $f(x) = \log x$

x	0.1	1	4	7	10
$y = \log x$	-1	0	$\log 4$	$\log 7$	1

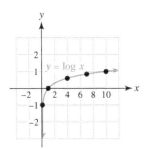

$D = (0, \infty)$
$R = (-\infty, \infty)$

Natural Logarithmic Function: $f(x) = \ln x$

x	$\frac{1}{2}$	1	2	e	e^2
$y = \ln x$	$\ln \frac{1}{2}$	0	$\ln 2$	1	2

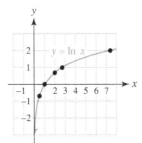

$D = (0, \infty)$
$R = (-\infty, \infty)$

Sine Function: $f(x) = \sin x$

x	0	$\frac{\pi}{2}$	π	$\frac{3\pi}{2}$	2π
$y = \sin x$	0	1	0	−1	0

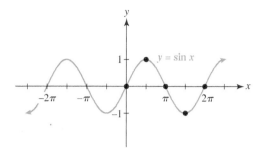

$D = (-\infty, \infty), R = [-1, 1]$

Cosine Function: $f(x) = \cos x$

x	0	$\frac{\pi}{2}$	π	$\frac{3\pi}{2}$	2π
$y = \cos x$	1	0	−1	0	1

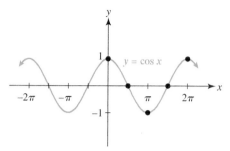

$D = (-\infty, \infty), R = [-1, 1]$

Tangent Function: $f(x) = \tan x$

x	$-\frac{\pi}{3}$	$-\frac{\pi}{4}$	0	$\frac{\pi}{4}$	$\frac{\pi}{3}$
$y = \tan x$	$-\sqrt{3}$	−1	0	1	$\sqrt{3}$

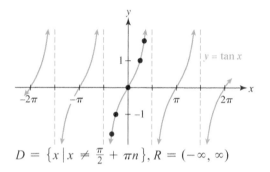

$D = \left\{ x \mid x \neq \frac{\pi}{2} + \pi n \right\}, R = (-\infty, \infty)$

Cotangent Function: $f(x) = \cot x$

x	$\frac{\pi}{6}$	$\frac{\pi}{4}$	$\frac{\pi}{2}$	$\frac{3\pi}{4}$	$\frac{5\pi}{6}$
$y = \cot x$	$\sqrt{3}$	1	0	−1	$-\sqrt{3}$

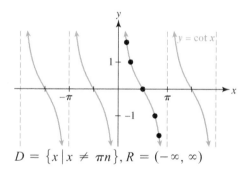

$D = \left\{ x \mid x \neq \pi n \right\}, R = (-\infty, \infty)$

Cosecant Function: $f(x) = \csc x$

x	$\frac{\pi}{6}$	$\frac{\pi}{4}$	$\frac{\pi}{2}$	$\frac{3\pi}{4}$	$\frac{5\pi}{6}$
$y = \csc x$	2	$\sqrt{2}$	1	$\sqrt{2}$	2

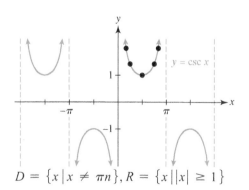

$D = \left\{ x \mid x \neq \pi n \right\}, R = \left\{ x \mid |x| \geq 1 \right\}$

Secant Function: $f(x) = \sec x$

x	$-\frac{\pi}{3}$	$-\frac{\pi}{4}$	0	$\frac{\pi}{4}$	$\frac{\pi}{3}$
$y = \sec x$	2	$\sqrt{2}$	1	$\sqrt{2}$	2

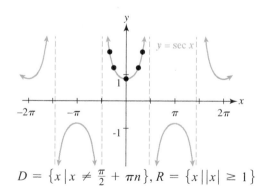

$D = \left\{ x \mid x \neq \frac{\pi}{2} + \pi n \right\}, R = \left\{ x \mid |x| \geq 1 \right\}$

Families of Functions

This subsection shows the formulas and graphs of some families of functions, such as linear, quadratic, and exponential. Notice that the appearance of the graphs of these functions depends on the value of k, m, or a.

Constant Functions: $f(x) = k$

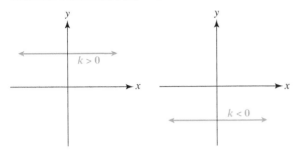

Linear Functions: $f(x) = mx + b$

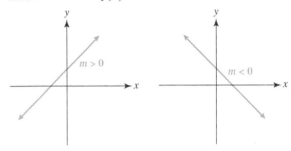

Quadratic Functions: $f(x) = ax^2 + bx + c$

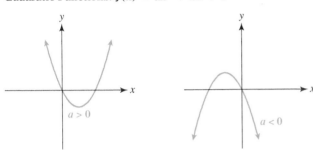

Cubic Functions: $f(x) = ax^3 + bx^2 + cx + d$

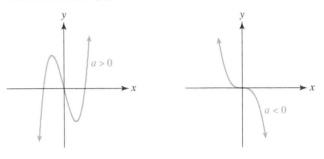

Power Functions: $f(x) = x^a$, $x > 0$

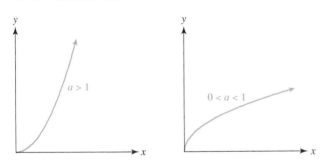

Sinusoidal Functions: $f(x) = a \sin (b(x - c)) + d$ or
$f(x) = a \cos (b(x - c)) + d$

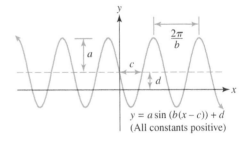

Exponential Functions: $f(x) = Ca^x$, $C > 0$

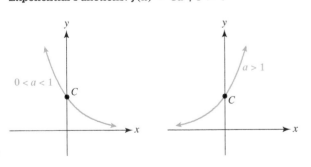

Logarithmic Functions: $f(x) = \log_a x$

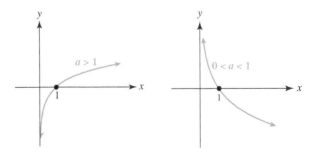

C

Appendix C: Partial Fractions

Decomposition of Rational Expressions

The sums of rational expressions are found by combining two or more rational expressions into one rational expression. Here, the reverse process is considered: given one rational expression, express it as the sum of two or more rational expressions. A special type of sum of rational expressions is called the **partial fraction decomposition**; each term in the sum is a **partial fraction**. The technique of finding partial fraction decompositions can be accomplished by using the following steps.

PARTIAL FRACTION DECOMPOSITION OF $\dfrac{f(x)}{g(x)}$

STEP 1: If $\dfrac{f(x)}{g(x)}$ is not a proper fraction (a fraction with the numerator of lower degree than the denominator), divide $f(x)$ by $g(x)$. For example,

$$\frac{x^4 - 3x^3 + x^2 + 5x}{x^2 + 3} = x^2 - 3x - 2 + \frac{14x + 6}{x^2 + 3}.$$

Then apply the following steps to the remainder, which is a proper fraction.

STEP 2: Factor $g(x)$ completely into factors of the form $(ax + b)^m$ or $(cx^2 + dx + e)^n$, where $cx^2 + dx + e$ is *irreducible* and m and n are positive integers.

STEP 3: **(a)** For each distinct linear factor $(ax + b)$, include in the decomposition the term

$$\frac{A}{ax + b}.$$

(b) For each repeated linear factor $(ax + b)^m$, include in the decomposition the terms

$$\frac{A_1}{ax + b} + \frac{A_2}{(ax + b)^2} + \cdots + \frac{A_m}{(ax + b)^m}.$$

STEP 4: **(a)** For each distinct quadratic factor $(cx^2 + dx + e)$, include in the decomposition the term

$$\frac{Bx + C}{cx^2 + dx + e}.$$

(b) For each repeated quadratic factor $(cx^2 + dx + e)^n$, include in the decomposition the terms

$$\frac{B_1x + C_1}{cx^2 + dx + e} + \frac{B_2x + C_2}{(cx^2 + dx + e)^2} + \cdots + \frac{B_nx + C_n}{(cx^2 + dx + e)^n}.$$

STEP 5: Use algebraic techniques to solve for the constants in the numerators.

To find the constants in Step 5, the goal is to get a system of equations with as many equations as there are unknowns in the numerators. One method for finding these equations is to substitute values for x on each side of the rational equation formed in Steps 3 and 4.

Distinct Linear Factors

EXAMPLE 1 Finding a partial fraction decomposition

Find the partial fraction decomposition of

$$\frac{2x^4 - 8x^2 + 5x - 2}{x^3 - 4x}.$$

SOLUTION The given fraction is not a proper fraction; the numerator has higher degree than the denominator. Perform the following division.

$$
\begin{array}{r}
2x \\
x^3 - 4x\overline{)2x^4 - 8x^2 + 5x - 2} \\
\underline{2x^4 - 8x^2} \\
5x - 2
\end{array}
$$

Algebra Review
To review clearing fractions from rational equations, see chapter R (page R-33).

The result is $2x + \dfrac{5x - 2}{x^3 - 4x}$. Now work with the remainder fraction. Factor the denominator as $x^3 - 4x = x(x + 2)(x - 2)$. Since the factors are distinct linear factors, use Step 3(a) to write the decomposition as

$$\frac{5x - 2}{x^3 - 4x} = \frac{A}{x} + \frac{B}{x + 2} + \frac{C}{x - 2}, \qquad \text{Equation 1}$$

where A, B, and C are constants that need to be found. Multiply each side of equation 1 by $x(x + 2)(x - 2)$ to clear fractions and get

$$5x - 2 = A(x + 2)(x - 2) + Bx(x - 2) + Cx(x + 2). \qquad \text{Equation 2}$$

Equation 1 is an identity, since both sides represent the same rational expression. Thus equation 2 is also an identity. Equation 1 holds for all values of x except 0, -2, and 2. However, equation 2 holds for all values of x. In particular, substituting 0 for x in equation 2 gives $-2 = -4A$, so $A = \frac{1}{2}$. Similarly, choosing $x = -2$ gives $-12 = 8B$, so $B = -\frac{3}{2}$. Finally, choosing $x = 2$ gives $8 = 8C$, so $C = 1$. The remainder rational expression can be written as the sum of partial fractions

$$\frac{5x - 2}{x^3 - 4x} = \frac{1}{2x} + \frac{-3}{2(x + 2)} + \frac{1}{x - 2},$$

and the given rational expression can be written as

Partial fractions

$$\frac{2x^4 - 8x^2 + 5x - 2}{x^3 - 4x} = 2x + \frac{1}{2x} + \frac{-3}{2(x + 2)} + \frac{1}{x - 2}.$$

Partial fraction decomposition

Check the work by combining the terms on the right.

Now Try Exercise 11

Repeated Linear Factors

EXAMPLE 2 Finding a partial fraction decomposition

Find the partial fraction decomposition of

$$\frac{2x}{(x-1)^3}.$$

SOLUTION This is a proper fraction. The denominator is already factored with repeated linear factors. We write the decomposition as shown, using Step 3(b).

$$\frac{2x}{(x-1)^3} = \frac{A}{x-1} + \frac{B}{(x-1)^2} + \frac{C}{(x-1)^3}$$

We clear denominators by multiplying each side of this equation by $(x-1)^3$.

$$2x = A(x-1)^2 + B(x-1) + C$$

Substituting 1 for x leads to $C = 2$, so

$$2x = A(x-1)^2 + B(x-1) + 2. \qquad \text{Equation 1}$$

We found C and we still need to find values for A and B. *Any* number can be substituted for x. For example, when we choose $x = -1$ (because it is easy to substitute), equation 1 becomes

$$-2 = 4A - 2B + 2$$
$$-4 = 4A - 2B$$
$$-2 = 2A - B. \qquad \text{Equation 2}$$

Substituting 0 for x in equation 1 gives

$$0 = A - B + 2$$
$$2 = -A + B. \qquad \text{Equation 3}$$

Now we solve the system of equations 2 and 3 to get $A = 0$ and $B = 2$. Since $A = 0$, the term $\frac{A}{x-1}$ is not used. The partial fraction decomposition is

$$\frac{2x}{(x-1)^3} = \frac{2}{(x-1)^2} + \frac{2}{(x-1)^3}.$$

We needed three substitutions because there were three constants to find: A, B, and C. To check this result, we could combine the terms on the right.

Now Try Exercise 13

Distinct Linear and Quadratic Factors

EXAMPLE 3 Finding a partial fraction decomposition

Find the partial fraction decomposition of

$$\frac{x^2 + 3x - 1}{(x+1)(x^2+2)}.$$

SOLUTION This denominator has distinct linear and quadratic factors, neither of which is repeated. Since $x^2 + 2$ cannot be factored, it is *irreducible*. The partial fraction decomposition is

$$\frac{x^2 + 3x - 1}{(x+1)(x^2+2)} = \frac{A}{x+1} + \frac{Bx + C}{x^2+2}.$$

Multiply each side by $(x + 1)(x^2 + 2)$ to get

$$x^2 + 3x - 1 = A(x^2 + 2) + (Bx + C)(x + 1). \qquad \text{Equation 1}$$

First substitute -1 for x to get

$$(-1)^2 + 3(-1) - 1 = A((-1)^2 + 2) + 0$$
$$-3 = 3A$$
$$A = -1.$$

Replace A with -1 in equation 1 and substitute any value for x. If $x = 0$, then

$$0^2 + 3(0) - 1 = -1(0^2 + 2) + (B \cdot 0 + C)(0 + 1)$$
$$-1 = -2 + C$$
$$C = 1.$$

Now, letting $A = -1$ and $C = 1$, substitute again in equation 1, using another number for x. For $x = 1$,

$$3 = -3 + (B + 1)(2)$$
$$6 = 2B + 2$$
$$B = 2.$$

With $A = -1$, $B = 2$, and $C = 1$, the partial fraction decomposition is

$$\frac{x^2 + 3x - 1}{(x + 1)(x^2 + 2)} = \frac{-1}{x + 1} + \frac{2x + 1}{x^2 + 2}.$$

This work can be checked by combining terms on the right. **Now Try Exercise 21**

For fractions with denominators that have quadratic factors, another method is often more convenient. The system of equations is formed by equating coefficients of like terms on each side of the partial fraction decomposition. For instance, in Example 3, after each side was multiplied by the common denominator, equation 1 was

$$x^2 + 3x - 1 = A(x^2 + 2) + (Bx + C)(x + 1). \qquad \text{Equation 1}$$

Multiplying on the right and collecting like terms, we have

$$x^2 + 3x - 1 = Ax^2 + 2A + Bx^2 + Bx + Cx + C$$
$$x^2 + 3x - 1 = (A + B)x^2 + (B + C)x + (C + 2A).$$

Now equating the coefficients of like powers of x gives three equations:

$$1 = A + B$$
$$3 = B + C$$
$$-1 = C + 2A.$$

Solving this system of equations for A, B, and C would give the partial fraction decomposition. The next example uses a combination of the two methods.

Repeated Quadratic Factors

EXAMPLE 4 Finding a partial fraction decomposition

Find the partial fraction decomposition of

$$\frac{2x}{(x^2 + 1)^2 (x - 1)}.$$

SOLUTION This expression has both a linear factor and a repeated quadratic factor. By Steps 3(a) and 4(b),

$$\frac{2x}{(x^2 + 1)^2(x - 1)} = \frac{Ax + B}{x^2 + 1} + \frac{Cx + D}{(x^2 + 1)^2} + \frac{E}{x - 1}.$$

Multiplying each side by $(x^2 + 1)^2(x - 1)$ leads to

$$2x = (Ax + B)(x^2 + 1)(x - 1) + (Cx + D)(x - 1) + E(x^2 + 1)^2. \qquad \text{Equation 1}$$

If $x = 1$, equation 1 reduces to $2 = 4E$, or $E = \frac{1}{2}$. Substituting $\frac{1}{2}$ for E in equation 1 and combining terms on the right gives

$$2x = \left(A + \frac{1}{2}\right)x^4 + (-A + B)x^3 + (A - B + C + 1)x^2$$

$$+ (-A + B + D - C)x + \left(-B - D + \frac{1}{2}\right). \qquad \text{Equation 2}$$

To get additional equations involving the unknowns, equate the coefficients of like powers of x on each side of equation 2. Setting corresponding coefficients of x^4 equal gives $0 = A + \frac{1}{2}$, or $A = -\frac{1}{2}$. From the corresponding coefficients of x^3, $0 = -A + B$, which means that since $A = -\frac{1}{2}$, $B = -\frac{1}{2}$. From the coefficients of x^2, $0 = A - B + C + 1$. Since $A = -\frac{1}{2}$ and $B = -\frac{1}{2}$, it follows that $C = -1$. Finally, from the coefficients of x, $2 = -A + B + D - C$. Substituting for A, B, and C gives $D = 1$. With

$$A = -\frac{1}{2}, \quad B = -\frac{1}{2}, \quad C = -1, \quad D = 1, \quad \text{and} \quad E = \frac{1}{2},$$

the given fraction has the partial fraction decomposition

$$\frac{2x}{(x^2 + 1)^2(x - 1)} = \frac{-\frac{1}{2}x - \frac{1}{2}}{x^2 + 1} + \frac{-x + 1}{(x^2 + 1)^2} + \frac{\frac{1}{2}}{x - 1},$$

or

$$\frac{2x}{(x^2 + 1)^2(x - 1)} = \frac{-(x + 1)}{2(x^2 + 1)} + \frac{-x + 1}{(x^2 + 1)^2} + \frac{1}{2(x - 1)}.$$

Now Try Exercise 25

In summary, to solve for the constants in the numerators of a partial fraction decomposition, use either of the following methods or a combination of the two.

TECHNIQUES FOR DECOMPOSITION INTO PARTIAL FRACTIONS

Method 1 for Linear Factors

STEP 1: Multiply each side of the rational expression by the common denominator.

STEP 2: Substitute the zero of each factor in the resulting equation. For repeated linear factors, substitute as many other numbers as necessary to find all the constants in the numerators. The number of substitutions required will equal the number of constants.

Method 2 for Quadratic Factors

STEP 1: Multiply each side of the rational expression by the common denominator.

STEP 2: Collect terms on the right side of the resulting equation.

STEP 3: Equate the coefficients of like terms to get a system of equations.

STEP 4: Solve the system to find the constants in the numerators.

C   Exercises

Exercises 1–30: Find the partial fraction decomposition for the rational expression.

1. $\dfrac{5}{3x(2x + 1)}$

2. $\dfrac{3x - 1}{x(x + 1)}$

3. $\dfrac{4x + 2}{(x + 2)(2x - 1)}$

4. $\dfrac{x + 2}{(x + 1)(x - 1)}$

5. $\dfrac{x}{x^2 + 4x - 5}$

6. $\dfrac{5x - 3}{(x + 1)(x - 3)}$

7. $\dfrac{2x}{(x + 1)(x + 2)^2}$

8. $\dfrac{2}{x^2(x + 3)}$

9. $\dfrac{4}{x(1 - x)}$

10. $\dfrac{4x^2 - 4x^3}{x^2(1 - x)}$

11. $\dfrac{4x^2 - x - 15}{x(x + 1)(x - 1)}$

12. $\dfrac{2x + 1}{(x + 2)^3}$

13. $\dfrac{x^2}{x^2 + 2x + 1}$

14. $\dfrac{3}{x^2 + 4x + 3}$

15. $\dfrac{2x^5 + 3x^4 - 3x^3 - 2x^2 + x}{2x^2 + 5x + 2}$

16. $\dfrac{6x^5 + 7x^4 - x^2 + 2x}{3x^2 + 2x - 1}$

17. $\dfrac{x^3 + 4}{9x^3 - 4x}$

18. $\dfrac{x^3 + 2}{x^3 - 3x^2 + 2x}$

19. $\dfrac{-3}{x^2(x^2 + 5)}$

20. $\dfrac{2x + 1}{(x + 1)(x^2 + 2)}$

21. $\dfrac{3x - 2}{(x + 4)(3x^2 + 1)}$

22. $\dfrac{3}{x(x + 1)(x^2 + 1)}$

23. $\dfrac{1}{x(2x + 1)(3x^2 + 4)}$

24. $\dfrac{x^4 + 1}{x(x^2 + 1)^2}$

25. $\dfrac{3x - 1}{x(2x^2 + 1)^2}$

26. $\dfrac{3x^4 + x^3 + 5x^2 - x + 4}{(x - 1)(x^2 + 1)^2}$

27. $\dfrac{-x^4 - 8x^2 + 3x - 10}{(x + 2)(x^2 + 4)^2}$

28. $\dfrac{x^2}{x^4 - 1}$

29. $\dfrac{5x^5 + 10x^4 - 15x^3 + 4x^2 + 13x - 9}{x^3 + 2x^2 - 3x}$

30. $\dfrac{3x^6 + 3x^4 + 3x}{x^4 + x^2}$

Percent Change and Exponential Functions

Percentages and Percent Change

Percentages A percentage can be written either in **percent form** or in **decimal form**. For example, the percent form of 15% can also be written in decimal form as 0.15. To change a percent form $R\%$ to a decimal form r we divide R by 100. That is, $r = \frac{R}{100}$.

EXAMPLE 1 Writing percentages as decimals

Write each percentage as a decimal.
(a) 45%   **(b)** 0.03%   **(c)** 420%   **(d)** -1.45% **(e)** $\frac{2}{5}\%$

SOLUTION
(a) Let $R = 45$. Then $r = \frac{45}{100} = 0.45$.
(b) Let $R = 0.03$. Then $r = \frac{0.03}{100} = 0.0003$.
(c) Let $R = 420$. Then $r = \frac{420}{100} = 4.2$.
(d) Let $R = -1.45$. Then $r = \frac{-1.45}{100} = -0.0145$. A negative percentage generally corresponds to a quantity decreasing rather than increasing.

(e) Let $R = \frac{2}{5}$. Then $r = \frac{\frac{2}{5}}{100} = \frac{2}{500} = 0.004$.

Now Try Exercise 1

NOTE Dividing a number by 100 is equivalent to moving the decimal point two places to the *left*.

In a similar manner a decimal form r can be changed to a percent form R by using the formula $R = 100r$. For example, the decimal form 0.047 has the percent form

$$R = 100r = 100(0.047) = 4.7\%.$$

In this calculation the decimal point is moved 2 places to the *right*.

Percent Change When an amount A_1 changes to a new amount A_2, then the **percent change** is

$$\frac{A_2 - A_1}{A_1} \times 100. \qquad \textit{Percent change}$$

We multiply by 100 to change decimal form to percent form.

EXAMPLE 2 Finding percent change

Complete the following.
(a) Find the percent change if an account increases from $1200 to $1500.
(b) Find the percent change if an account decreases from $1500 to $1200.
(c) Comment on your results from parts (a) and (b).

SOLUTION

(a) Let $A_1 = 1200$ and $A_2 = 1500$.

$$\frac{1500 - 1200}{1200} \times 100 = \frac{300}{1200} \times 100$$

$$= \frac{1}{4} \times 100$$

$$= 25\%$$

The percent change (increase) is 25%.

(b) Let $A_1 = 1500$ and $A_2 = 1200$.

$$\frac{1200 - 1500}{1500} \times 100 = -\frac{300}{1500} \times 100$$

$$= -\frac{1}{5} \times 100$$

$$= -20\%$$

The percent change (decrease) is −20%.

(c) Notice that the account increased by 25% and then decreased by 20% to return to its initial value. Because the initial amount of $A_1 = \$1500$ in part (b) is larger than the initial amount $A_1 = \$1200$ in part (a), the amount of $1500 only needs to decrease by 20% or $300, to return to the original $1200.

> **Now Try Exercise 9**

Suppose a child's weight increases from 20 pounds to 60 pounds over a period of years. The percent increase is

$$\frac{60 - 20}{20} \times 100 = 2 \times 100 = 200\%.$$

Notice that the child's weight *tripled* and the percent change is 200%, *not* 300%. The actual *increase* in weight is 40 pounds and can be found by taking 200% of 20 pounds.

$$200\% \text{ of } 20 = 2.00 \times 20 = 40 \text{ pounds} \qquad \textit{Change 200\% to decimal form.}$$

If we want to find the percent change, expressed in *decimal form*, of an amount A_1 changing to an amount A_2, then we do not need to multiply by 100. Thus

$$r = \frac{A_2 - A_1}{A_1}.$$

We can solve this equation for A_2.

$$r = \frac{A_2 - A_1}{A_1} \qquad \textit{Percent change in decimal form}$$

$$rA_1 = A_2 - A_1 \qquad \textit{Multiply each side by } A_1.$$

$$A_1 + rA_1 = A_2 \qquad \textit{Add } A_1 \textit{ to each side.}$$

$$A_2 = A_1 + rA_1 \qquad \textit{Rewrite the equation.}$$

Thus, if the percent increase in an amount A_1 is given by r in *decimal form*, then the *increase* (or *decrease*) in A_1 is given by rA_1 and the *final amount* is given by $A_1 + rA_1$, or $A_1(1 + r)$. The initial amount A_1 changes by the *factor* $1 + r$.

For example, if a $100,000 budget decreases by 12%, then

$$rA_1 = -0.12(100,000) = -\$12,000$$

and the budget decrease is $12,000. Also,

$$A_1 + rA_1 = 100,000 + (-0.12)(100,000) = \$88,000$$

and the new budget decreased to \$88,000. The budget changed by a factor of

$$1 + r = 1 + (-0.12) = 0.88,$$

or the budget is now 88% of the original budget.

EXAMPLE 3 Analyzing the increase in an account

An account that contains \$5000 increases in value by 150%.
(a) Find the increase in value of the account.
(b) Find the final value of the account.
(c) By what factor did the account increase?

SOLUTION
(a) Let $A_1 = 5000$ and $r = 1.50$ (150% in decimal form). The increase is

$$rA_1 = 1.50(5000) = 7500.$$

The account increased in value by \$7500.
(b) The final value of the account is $A_1 + rA_1 = 5000 + 7500 = \$12,500$.
(c) The account increased in value by a factor of $1 + r = 1 + 1.50 = 2.5$. Note that $5000(2.5) = 12,500$.

Now Try Exercise 15

More Exponential Functions and Models

Section 5.3 discussed how an exponential function results when the *initial value C* is multiplied by a *constant factor a* for each unit increase in x. For example, if an initial value of $C = 3$ is multiplied by a *constant growth factor* of $a = 2$ for each unit increase in x, then the exponential function

$$f(x) = 3(2)^x \qquad \text{Initial value} = 3, \text{growth factor} = 2$$

models this growth. This concept can be used to describe exponential functions and models in terms of *constant percent change*.

Suppose that an initial population of a country is $P_0 = 10$ million and the population increases by 1.2% in 1 year. Then the increase is

$$rP_0 = 0.012(10) = 0.12 \text{ million}, \qquad \text{1.2\% equals 0.012 in decimal form.}$$

and after 1 year the new population is

$$P_0(1 + r)^1 = 10(1.012)^1 = 10.12 \text{ million}.$$

After 1 year the population has increased by a *growth factor* of $1 + r$, or 1.012. If the rate of growth were to remain constant in future years, then after x years the population would be

$$P_0(1 + r)^x = 10(1.012)^x$$

with initial value $C = 10$ and *growth* factor $a = 1.012$.

EXAMPLE 4 Finding exponential models

A sample of 10,000 insects is decreasing in number by 8% per week. Find an exponential model $f(x)$ that describes this population after x weeks.

SOLUTION The initial value is $C = 10,000$, the rate of decrease is $r = -0.08$, and the *decay* factor is

$$a = 1 + r = 1 + (-0.08) = 0.92.$$

Thus the sample of insects contains

$$f(x) = 10{,}000(0.92)^x$$

insects after x weeks.

Now Try Exercise 21

These concepts are summarized in the following box.

PERCENT CHANGE AND EXPONENTIAL FUNCTIONS

Suppose that an amount A changes by R percent (or r expressed in decimal form) for each unit increase in x. Then the following hold.

1. $r = \dfrac{R}{100}$ and $R = 100r$.
2. If $r > 0$, the **constant growth factor** is $a = 1 + r$ and $a > 1$.
3. If $r < 0$, the **constant decay factor** is $a = 1 + r$ and $0 < a < 1$.
4. If the initial amount is C, then the amount A after an x-unit increase in time is given by the exponential model

$$A(x) = C(1 + r)^x, \quad \text{or} \quad A(x) = Ca^x.$$

EXAMPLE 5 Analyzing constant percent change

For each $f(x)$, give the initial value, the growth or decay factor, and percent change for each unit increase in x.
(a) $f(x) = 5(1.034)^x$ (b) $f(x) = 10(0.45)^x$ (c) $f(x) = 3^x$

SOLUTION
(a) For $f(x) = 5(1.034)^x$ the initial value is $C = 5$ and the growth factor is $a = 1.034$. Because $a = 1 + r$, it follows that

$$r = a - 1 = 1.034 - 1 = 0.034.$$

The percent change for each unit increase in x is 3.4%.
(b) For $f(x) = 10(0.45)^x$ the initial value is $C = 10$ and the decay factor is $a = 0.45$. The percent change for each unit increase in x is

$$r = a - 1 = 0.45 - 1 = -0.55, \text{ or } -55\%.$$

(c) For $f(x) = 3^x$ the initial value is $C = 1$ and the growth factor is $a = 3$. The percent change for each unit increase in x is $r = a - 1 = 3 - 1 = 2$, or 200%.

Now Try Exercises 27, 29, and 31

Growth and Decay Models If an initial quantity A_0 either grows or decays by a factor of b each k units of time, then the amount A after t units of time is given by the exponential model

$$A(t) = Ab^{t/k}.$$

For example, if 700 bacteria triple every 5 days, the formula

$$A(t) = 700(3)^{t/5}$$

gives the number of bacteria after t days.

EXAMPLE 6 Applying an exponential model

The population of a city is currently 239,000 and is increasing at a constant rate of 8.5% every 4 years. Find the population of this city after 7 years.

SOLUTION The population of the city is 239,000 and increasing by a factor of 1.085 every 4 years. Thus $A_0 = 239,000$, $b = 1.085$, $k = 4$, and

$$A(t) = 239,000(1.085)^{t/4}.$$

After 7 years the population is

$$A(7) = 239,000(1.085)^{7/4} \approx 275,677.$$

Now Try Exercise 37

Rule of 70 The **rule of 70** can be used to quickly estimate the number of years it takes for an investment to double. If R is the interest rate (in percent form) and T is the number of years for a quantity to double, then

$$RT = 70. \quad \text{Rule of 70}$$

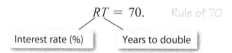

This formula is most accurate for continuous compounding, but it can also be applied to other types of compound interest. For example, if we deposit an amount of money at 5% interest compounded continuously, then it will require about

$$T = \frac{70}{R} = \frac{70}{5} = 14 \text{ years}$$

to double. Similarly, if a city's population doubles in 35 years, then its annual growth rate is about

$$R = \frac{70}{T} = \frac{70}{35} = 2\%.$$

See Exercises 45–50.

D Exercises

Percentages

Exercises 1–4: Write each percentage in decimal form.

1. (a) 35%   (b) −0.07%   (c) 721%   (d) $\frac{3}{10}$%

2. (a) 95%   (b) 0.321%   (c) −175%   (d) $\frac{4}{5}$%

3. (a) −5.5%   (b) −1.54%   (c) 120%   (d) $\frac{3}{20}$%

4. (a) −4.7%   (b) −0.01%   (c) 500%   (d) $\frac{1}{40}$%

Exercises 5–8: Write each decimal form in percent form.

5. (a) 0.37   (b) −0.095   (c) 1.9   (d) $\frac{7}{20}$

6. (a) 0.97   (b) −0.04   (c) 10   (d) $\frac{9}{10}$

7. (a) −0.121   (b) 1.4   (c) 3.2   (d) $-\frac{1}{4}$

8. (a) 0.001   (b) 12   (c) 1.01   (d) $-\frac{1}{8}$

Percent Change

Exercises 9–14: For the given amounts A and B, find each of the following. Round values to the nearest hundredth when appropriate.

(a) The percent change if A changes to B
(b) The percent change if B changes to A

9. $A = \$500, B = \$1000$ **10.** $A = \$500, B = \$200$

11. $A = \$1.27, B = \$1.30$ **12.** $A = 15, B = 5$

13. $A = 45, B = 65$ **14.** $A = 75, B = 50$

Exercises 15–20: An account that initially contains A dollars increases/decreases by R percent. For each A and R, complete the following.

(a) Find the increase/decrease in value of the account.
(b) Find the final value of the account.
(c) By what factor did the account value increase/decrease?

15. $A = \$1500, R = 120\%$

16. $A = \$3500, R = 210\%$

17. $A = \$4000, R = -55\%$

18. $A = \$6000, R = -75\%$

19. $A = \$7500, R = -60\%$

20. $A = \$9000, R = 85\%$

Exponential Models

Exercises 21–26: Find an exponential model $f(x)$ that describes each situation.

21. A sample of 9500 insects decreases in number by 35% per week

22. A sample of 5000 insects increases in number by 120% per day

23. A sample of 2500 fish increases in number by 5% per month

24. A sample of 152 birds decreases in number by 3.4% per week

25. A mutual fund account contains $1000 and decreases by 6.5% per year

26. A mutual fund account contains $2500 and increases by 2.1% per year

Exercises 27–36: For the given $f(x)$, state the initial value, the growth or decay factor, and percent change for each unit increase in x.

27. $f(x) = 8(1.12)^x$ **28.** $f(x) = 9(1.005)^x$

29. $f(x) = 1.5(0.35)^x$

30. $f(x) = 100(1.23)^x$

31. $f(x) = 0.55^x$

32. $f(x) = 0.4^x$

33. $f(x) = 7e^x$

34. $f(x) = 91e^{x/2}$

35. $f(x) = 6(3^{-x})$

36. $f(x) = 9(4^{-x})$

Exercises 37–44: (Refer to Example 6.) Write a formula for $f(t)$ that models the situation and then answer the question.

37. The population of a city is currently 35,000 and is increasing at a constant rate of 9.8% every 2 years. What is the population after 5 years?

38. A savings account contains $2500 and increases by 10% in 3 years. How much is in the account after 8 years?

39. A sample of 1000 bacteria triples in number every 7 hours. How many bacteria are there after 11 hours?

40. A sample of 5 million insects decreases in number by $\frac{2}{3}$ every 10 days. In millions, how many insects are there after 65 days?

41. The intensity I_0 of a light passing through colored glass decreases by $\frac{1}{3}$ for each 2 millimeters in thickness of the glass. What is the intensity of the light in terms of I_0 after passing through 4.3 millimeters of colored glass?

42. The intensity I_0 of a sound passing through the atmosphere decreases 20% for each 100 feet of distance. What is the intensity of the sound in terms of I_0 after traveling a distance of 450 feet?

43. An investment of $5000 will quadruple every 35 years. How much is the investment worth after 8 years?

44. An investment of $2500 increases by a factor of 1.2 every 4 years. How much is the investment worth after 9 years?

*Exercises 45–50: **Rule of 70** Use the rule of 70 to estimate the time required for the given principal P to double at the annual percent interest rate R. Check your answer by using the continuously compounded interest formula.*

45. $P = \$2000, R = 7\%$ **46.** $P = \$1200, R = 14\%$

47. $P = \$500, R = 20\%$ **48.** $P = \$9000, R = 10\%$

49. $P = \$1500, R = 25\%$ **50.** $P = \$5000, R = 8\%$

*Exercises 51–56: **Rule of 70** Use the rule of 70 to estimate the annual percent rate of growth for a city whose population P doubles in time T.*

51. $P = 150,000, T = 40$ years

52. $P = 400,000, T = 25$ years

53. $P = 1,500,000$, $T = 35$ years

54. $P = 20,000$, $T = 10$ years

55. $P = 750,000$, $T = 70$ years

56. $P = 80,000$, $T = 50$ years

Applications

57. Bacteria Growth A population of bacteria increases by 6% every 8 hours. By what percentage does the sample increase in 3 hours?

58. Bacteria Growth A population of bacteria decreases by 40% every 4 hours. By what percentage does the sample decrease in 7 hours?

59. Percent Change The number of cell phone subscribers to a company increases by 25% during the first year and then decreases by 20% the second year. Compare the number of subscribers at the beginning of the first year with the number of subscribers at the end of the second year.

60. Wage Increase If your wages are $8 per hour and you receive a 300% raise for excellent work, determine your new wages.

61. Wages If a wage of $9.81 decreases by 9% each year, what is the new wage after 3 years?

62. Pollution A pollutant in a river has an initial concentration of 3 parts per million and degrades at a rate of 3% every 2 years. Approximate its concentration after 20 years.

63. Radioactive Half-Life A radioactive element decays to 40% of its original amount every 2 years. Approximate the percentage that remains after 8 years.

64. Radioactive Half-Life A radioactive element decays to 80% of its original amount every 3 years. Approximate the percentage that remains after 8 years.

Appendix E: Rotation of Axes

Derivation of Rotation Equations

If we begin with an xy-coordinate system having origin O and rotate the axes about O through an angle θ, the new coordinate system is called a **rotation** of the xy-system. Trigonometric identities can be used to obtain equations for converting the coordinates of a point from the xy-system to the rotated $x'y'$-system. Let P be any point other than the origin, with coordinates (x, y) in the xy-system and (x', y') in the $x'y'$-system. See Figure E.1. Let $OP = r$, and let α represent the angle made by OP and the x'-axis. As shown in Figure E.1,

Rotation of *xy*-Plane

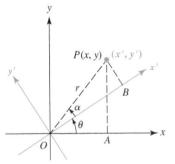

Figure E.1

$$\cos(\theta + \alpha) = \frac{OA}{r} = \frac{x}{r}, \quad \sin(\theta + \alpha) = \frac{AP}{r} = \frac{y}{r},$$

$$\cos \alpha = \frac{OB}{r} = \frac{x'}{r}, \quad \sin \alpha = \frac{BP}{r} = \frac{y'}{r}.$$

These four statements can be rewritten as

$$x = r\cos(\theta + \alpha), \quad y = r\sin(\theta + \alpha), \quad x' = r\cos \alpha, \quad y' = r\sin \alpha.$$

Using the trigonometric identity for the cosine of the sum of two angles gives

$$x = r\cos(\theta + \alpha)$$

$$= r(\cos \theta \cos \alpha - \sin \theta \sin \alpha)$$

$$= (r\cos \alpha)\cos \theta - (r\sin \alpha)\sin \theta$$

$$= x'\cos \theta - y'\sin \theta.$$

Using the identity for the sine of the sum of two angles in the same way gives $y = x'\sin \theta + y'\cos \theta$. This proves the following result.

> **ROTATION EQUATIONS**
>
> If the rectangular coordinate axes are rotated about the origin through an angle θ and if the coordinates of a point P are (x, y) and (x', y') with respect to the xy-system and the $x'y'$-system, respectively, then the rotation equations are
>
> $$x = x'\cos \theta - y'\sin \theta \quad \text{and} \quad y = x'\sin \theta + y'\cos \theta.$$

Applying a Rotation Equation

EXAMPLE 1   Finding an equation after a rotation

The equation of a curve is $x^2 + y^2 + 2xy + 2\sqrt{2}x - 2\sqrt{2}y = 0$. Find the resulting equation if the axes are rotated $45°$. Graph the equation.

SOLUTION If $\theta = 45°$, then $\sin\theta = \dfrac{\sqrt{2}}{2}$ and $\cos\theta = \dfrac{\sqrt{2}}{2}$, and the rotation equations become

$$x = \frac{\sqrt{2}}{2}x' - \frac{\sqrt{2}}{2}y' \qquad \text{and} \qquad y = \frac{\sqrt{2}}{2}x' + \frac{\sqrt{2}}{2}y'.$$

Substituting these values into the given equation yields

$$x^2 + y^2 + 2xy + 2\sqrt{2}x - 2\sqrt{2}y = 0$$

$$\left(\frac{\sqrt{2}}{2}x' - \frac{\sqrt{2}}{2}y'\right)^2 + \left(\frac{\sqrt{2}}{2}x' + \frac{\sqrt{2}}{2}y'\right)^2$$

$$+ 2\left(\frac{\sqrt{2}}{2}x' - \frac{\sqrt{2}}{2}y'\right)\left(\frac{\sqrt{2}}{2}x' + \frac{\sqrt{2}}{2}y'\right)$$

$$+ 2\sqrt{2}\left(\frac{\sqrt{2}}{2}x' - \frac{\sqrt{2}}{2}y'\right) - 2\sqrt{2}\left(\frac{\sqrt{2}}{2}x' + \frac{\sqrt{2}}{2}y'\right) = 0.$$

Expanding these terms yields

$$\frac{1}{2}x'^2 - x'y' + \frac{1}{2}y'^2 + \frac{1}{2}x'^2 + x'y' + \frac{1}{2}y'^2 + x'^2 - y'^2$$

$$+ 2x' - 2y' - 2x' - 2y' = 0.$$

Collecting terms gives

$$2x'^2 - 4y' = 0$$

$$x'^2 - 2y' = 0 \qquad \text{Divide by 2.}$$

or, finally,

$$x'^2 = 2y',$$

the equation of a parabola. The graph is shown in Figure E.2.

Now Try Exercise 13

Rotation of a Parabola

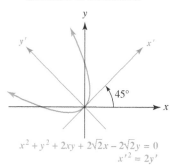

$x^2 + y^2 + 2xy + 2\sqrt{2}x - 2\sqrt{2}y = 0$
$x'^2 = 2y'$

Figure E.2

We have graphed equations written in the form $Ax^2 + Cy^2 + Dx + Ey + F = 0$. As we saw in the preceding example, the rotation of axes eliminated the xy-term. Thus, to graph by hand an equation that has an xy-term, it is necessary to find an appropriate **angle of rotation** to eliminate the xy-term. The necessary angle of rotation can be determined by using the following result. The proof is quite lengthy and is not presented here.

ANGLE OF ROTATION

The xy-term is removed from the general equation

$$Ax^2 + Bxy + Cy^2 + Dx + Ey + F = 0$$

by a rotation of the axes through an angle θ, $0° < \theta < 90°$, where

$$\cot 2\theta = \frac{A - C}{B}.$$

This result can be used to find the appropriate angle of rotation, θ. To find the rotation equations, first find $\sin\theta$ and $\cos\theta$. The following example illustrates a way to obtain $\sin\theta$ and $\cos\theta$ from $\cot 2\theta$ without first identifying the angle θ.

EXAMPLE Rotating and graphing

Rotate the axes and graph $52x^2 - 72xy + 73y^2 = 200$.

SOLUTION Here $A = 52$, $B = -72$, and $C = 73$. By substitution,

$$\cot 2\theta = \frac{52 - 73}{-72} = \frac{-21}{-72} = \frac{7}{24}.$$

To find $\sin \theta$ and $\cos \theta$, use the trigonometric identities

$$\sin \theta = \sqrt{\frac{1 - \cos 2\theta}{2}} \quad \text{and} \quad \cos \theta = \sqrt{\frac{1 + \cos 2\theta}{2}}.$$

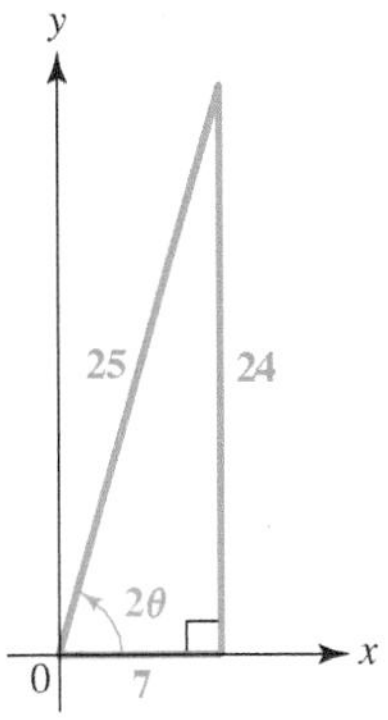

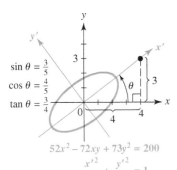

Figure E.3

Sketch a right triangle and label it as in Figure E.3, to see that $\cos 2\theta = \frac{7}{25}$. (Recall that in the two quadrants with which we are concerned, $0° \leq 2\theta \leq 180°$, cosine and cotangent have the same sign.) Then

$$\sin \theta = \sqrt{\frac{1 - \frac{7}{25}}{2}} = \sqrt{\frac{9}{25}} = \frac{3}{5} \quad \text{and} \quad \cos \theta = \sqrt{\frac{1 + \frac{7}{25}}{2}} = \sqrt{\frac{16}{25}} = \frac{4}{5}.$$

Use these values for $\sin \theta$ and $\cos \theta$ to obtain

$$x = \frac{4}{5}x' - \frac{3}{5}y' \quad \text{and} \quad y = \frac{3}{5}x' + \frac{4}{5}y'.$$

Substituting these expressions for x and y into the original equation yields

$$52\left(\frac{4}{5}x' - \frac{3}{5}y'\right)^2 - 72\left(\frac{4}{5}x' - \frac{3}{5}y'\right)\left(\frac{3}{5}x' + \frac{4}{5}y'\right) + 73\left(\frac{3}{5}x' + \frac{4}{5}y'\right)^2 = 200.$$

This becomes

$$52\left(\frac{16}{25}x'^2 - \frac{24}{25}x'y' + \frac{9}{25}y'^2\right) - 72\left(\frac{12}{25}x'^2 + \frac{7}{25}x'y' - \frac{12}{25}y'^2\right)$$
$$+ 73\left(\frac{9}{25}x'^2 + \frac{24}{25}x'y' + \frac{16}{25}y'^2\right) = 200.$$

Combining terms gives

$$25x'^2 + 100y'^2 = 200.$$

Divide each side by 200 to get

$$\frac{x'^2}{8} + \frac{y'^2}{2} = 1, \quad \boxed{\text{New equation after rotation}}$$

an equation of an ellipse having x'-intercepts $\pm\sqrt{8}$ and y'-intercepts $\pm\sqrt{2}$. The graph is shown in Figure E.4. To find θ, use the fact that

$$\frac{\sin \theta}{\cos \theta} = \frac{\frac{3}{5}}{\frac{4}{5}} = \frac{3}{4} = \tan \theta,$$

from which $\theta = \tan^{-1}\frac{3}{4} \approx 37°$.

$\sin \theta = \frac{3}{5}$
$\cos \theta = \frac{4}{5}$
$\tan \theta = \frac{3}{4}$

$52x^2 - 72xy + 73y^2 = 200$
$\frac{x'^2}{8} + \frac{y'^2}{2} = 1$

Figure E.4

Now Try Exercise 17

Summary of Conics with an xy-Term

The following summary enables us to use the general equation to decide on the type of graph to expect.

EQUATIONS OF CONICS WITH AN XY-TERM

If the general second-degree equation

$$Ax^2 + Bxy + Cy^2 + Dx + Ey + F = 0$$

has a graph, it will be one of the following:

(a) a circle or an ellipse (or a point) if $B^2 - 4AC < 0$;
(b) a parabola (or one line or two parallel lines) if $B^2 - 4AC = 0$;
(c) a hyperbola (or two intersecting lines) if $B^2 - 4AC > 0$;
(d) a straight line if $A = B = C = 0$ and $D \neq 0$ or $E \neq 0$.

E Exercises

Exercises 1–6: Use the summary in this section to predict the graph of the second-degree equation.

1. $4x^2 + 3y^2 + 2xy - 5x = 8$

2. $x^2 + 2xy - 3y^2 + 2y = 12$

3. $2x^2 + 3xy - 4y^2 = 0$

4. $x^2 - 2xy + y^2 + 4x - 8y = 0$

5. $4x^2 + 4xy + y^2 + 15 = 0$

6. $-x^2 + 2xy - y^2 + 16 = 0$

Exercises 7–12: Find the angle of rotation θ that will remove the xy-term in the equation.

7. $2x^2 + \sqrt{3}xy + y^2 + x = 5$

8. $4\sqrt{3}x^2 + xy + 3\sqrt{3}y^2 = 10$

9. $3x^2 + \sqrt{3}xy + 4y^2 + 2x - 3y = 12$

10. $4x^2 + 2xy + 2y^2 + x - 7 = 0$

11. $x^2 - 4xy + 5y^2 = 18$

12. $3\sqrt{3}x^2 - 2xy + \sqrt{3}y^2 = 25$

Exercises 13–16: Use the given angle of rotation to remove the xy-term and graph the equation.

13. $x^2 - xy + y^2 = 6; \theta = 45°$

14. $2x^2 - xy + 2y^2 = 25; \theta = 45°$

15. $8x^2 - 4xy + 5y^2 = 36; \sin\theta = \dfrac{2}{\sqrt{5}}$

16. $5y^2 + 12xy = 10; \sin\theta = \dfrac{3}{\sqrt{13}}$

Exercises 17–24: Remove the xy-term from the equation by performing a suitable rotation. Graph the equation.

17. $3x^2 - 2xy + 3y^2 = 8$ **18.** $x^2 + xy + y^2 = 3$

19. $x^2 - 4xy + y^2 = -5$

20. $x^2 + 2xy + y^2 + 4\sqrt{2}x - 4\sqrt{2}y = 0$

21. $7x^2 + 6\sqrt{3}xy + 13y^2 = 64$

22. $7x^2 + 2\sqrt{3}xy + 5y^2 = 24$

23. $3x^2 - 2\sqrt{3}xy + y^2 - 2x - 2\sqrt{3}y = 0$

24. $2x^2 + 2\sqrt{3}xy + 4y^2 = 5$

Exercises 25–30: In the equation, remove the xy-term by rotation. Then translate the axes and sketch the graph.

25. $x^2 + 3xy + y^2 - 5\sqrt{2}y = 15$

26. $x^2 - \sqrt{3}xy + 2\sqrt{3}x - 3y - 3 = 0$

27. $4x^2 + 4xy + y^2 - 24x + 38y - 19 = 0$

28. $12x^2 + 24xy + 19y^2 - 12x - 40y + 31 = 0$

29. $16x^2 + 24xy + 9y^2 - 130x + 90y = 0$

30. $9x^2 - 6xy + y^2 - 12\sqrt{10}x - 36\sqrt{10}y = 0$

Bibliography

Acker, A., and C. Jaschek. *Astronomical Methods and Calculations.* New York: John Wiley and Sons, 1986.

Battan, L. *Weather in Your Life.* San Francisco: W. H. Freeman, 1983.

Beckmann, P. *A History of Pi.* New York: Barnes and Noble, 1993.

Bell, D. *Fundamentals of Electric Circuits,* Reston. Va.: Reston Publishing Company. 1981.

Benade, A. *Fundamentals of Musical Acoustics.* New York: Oxford University Press, 1976.

Beni, G., and S. Hackwood. *Recent Advances in Robotics.* New York: John Wiley and Sons, 1985.

Beranek, L. *Noise and Vibration Control.* Washington, D.C.: Institute of Noise Control Engineering, 1988.

Brearley, J., and A. Nicholas. *This Is the Bichon Frise.* Hong Kong: TFH Publication, 1973.

Brown, D., and P. Rothery. *Models in Biology: Mathematics, Statistics and Computing.* West Sussex, England: John Wiley and Sons, 1993.

Brown, F., J. Hastings, and J. Palmer. *The Biological Clock.* New York: Academic Press, 1970.

Carlson, T. "Über Geschwindigkeit und Grösse der Hefevermehrung in Würze." *Biochem. A.* 57:313–334.

Cheney, W., and D. Kincaid. *Numerical Mathematics and Computing.* 3rd ed. Pacific Grove, Calif.: Brooks/Cole Publishing Company, 1994.

Clime, W. *The Economics of Global Warming.* Washington, D.C.: Institute for International Economics, 1992.

Cole, F. *Introduction to Meteorology.* New York: Wiley, 1980.

Cooper, J., and R. Glassow. *Kinesiology.* 2nd ed. St. Louis: The C. V. Mosby Company, 1968.

Cotton, W., and R. Pielke. *Human Impacts on Weather and Climate.* Geophysical Science Series, vol. 2. Fort Collins, Colo.: *ASTeR Press, 1992.

Craig, J. *Introduction to Robotics: Mechanics and Control.* Reading, Mass.: Addison-Wesley Publishing Company, 1989.

Crownover, R. *Introduction to Fractals and Chaos.* Boston: Jones and Bartlett, 1995.

Duffet-Smith, P. *Practical Astronomy with Your Calculator.* New York: Cambridge University Press, 1988.

Eves, H. *An Introduction to the History of Mathematics.* 5th ed. Philadelphia: Saunders College Publishing, 1983.

Fletcher, N., and T. Rossing. *The Physics of Musical Instruments.* New York: Springer-Verlag, 1991.

Foley, J., A. van Dam, S. Feiner, J. Hughes, and R. Phillips. *Introduction to Computer Graphics.* Reading, Mass.: Addison-Wesley Publishing Company, 1994.

Foster, R., and J. Bates. "Use of mussels to monitor point source industrial discharges." *Environ. Sci. Technol.* 12:958–962.

Freebury, H. *A History of Mathematics.* New York: Macmillan, 1961.

Freedman, B. *Environmental Ecology: The Ecological Effects of Pollution, Disturbance, and Other Stresses.* 2nd ed. San Diego: Academic Press, 1995.

Garber, N., and L. Hoel. *Traffic and Highway Engineering.* Boston, Mass.: PWS Publishing Co., 1997.

Good, I. J. "What is the most amazing approximate integer in the universe?" *Pi Mu Epsilon Journal* 5 (1972): 314–315.

Grigg, D. *The World Food Problem.* Oxford: Blackwell Publishers, 1993.

Haber-Schaim, U., J. Cross, G. Abegg, J. Dodge, and J. Walter. *Introductory Physical Science.* Englewood Cliffs, N.J.: Prentice Hall, 1972.

Haefner, L. *Introduction to Transportation Systems.* New York: Holt, Rinehart and Winston, 1986.

Harker, J. *The Physiology of Diurnal Rhythms.* New York: Cambridge University Press, 1964.

Harrison, F., F. Hills, J. Paterson, and R. Saunders. "The measurement of liver blood flow in conscious calves." *Quarterly Journal of Experimental Physiology* 71:235–247.

Hartman, D. *Global Physical Climatology.* San Diego: Academic Press, 1994.

Heinz-Otto, P., H. Jürgens, and D. Saupe. *Chaos and Fractals: New Frontiers in Science.* New York: Springer-Verlag, 1993.

Hibbeler, R. *Structural Analysis.* Englewood Cliffs, N.J.: Prentice-Hall, 1995.

Hill, F. *Computer Graphics.* New York: Macmillan Publishing Company, 1990.

Hines, A., T. Ghosh, S. Loyalka, and R. Warder, Jr. *Indoor Air Quality and Control.* Englewood Cliffs, N.J.: Prentice-Hall, 1993.

Hoggar, S. *Mathematics for Computer Graphics.* New York: Cambridge University Press, 1993.

Hoppensteadt, F., and C. Peskin. *Mathematics in Medicine and the Life Sciences.* New York: Springer-Verlag, 1992.

Hosmer, D., and S. Lemeshow. *Applied Logistic Regression.* New York: John Wiley and Sons, 1989.

Howatson, A. *Electrical Circuits and Systems.* New York: Oxford University Press, 1996.

Howells, G. *Acid Rain and Acid Waters.* 2nd ed. New York: Ellis Horwood, 1995.

Huffman, R. *Atmospheric Ultraviolet Remote Sensing.* San Diego: Academic Press, 1992.

Huxley, J. *Problems of Relative Growth.* London: Methuen and Co., 1932.

Jarrett, J. *Business Forecasting Methods.* Oxford: Basil Blackwell, 1991.

Karttunen, H., P. Kroger, H. Oja, M. Poutanen, and K. Donner, eds. *Fundamental Astronomy.* 2nd ed. New York: Springer-Verlag, 1994.

Kerlow, I. *The Art of 3-D Computer Animation and Imaging.* New York: Van Nostrand Riehold, 1996.

Kissam, P. *Surveying Practice.* 3rd ed. New York: McGraw-Hill, 1978.

Kline, M. *The Loss of Certainty.* New York: Oxford University Press, 1980.

Kraljic, M. *The Greenhouse Effect.* New York: The H. W. Wilson Company, 1992.

Kress, S. *Bird Life—A Guide to the Behavior and Biology of Birds.* Racine, Wisc.: Western Publishing Company, 1991.

Lack, D. *The Life of a Robin.* London: Collins, 1965.

Lancaster, H. *Quantitative Methods in Biological and Medical Sciences: A Historical Essay.* New York: Springer-Verlag, 1994.

Loh, W. *Dynamics and Thermodynamics of Planetary Entry.* Englewood Cliffs, N.J.: Prentice-Hall, 1963.

Makridakis, S., and S. Wheelwright. *Forecasting Methods for Management.* New York: John Wiley and Sons, 1989.

Mandelbrot, B. *The Fractal Geometry of Nature.* New York: W. H. Freeman Company, 1982.

Mannering, F., and W. Kilareski. *Principles of Highway Engineering and Traffic Analysis.* New York: John Wiley and Sons, 1990.

Mar, J., and H. Liebowitz. *Structure Technology for Large Radio and Radar Telescope Systems.* Cambridge, Mass.: The MIT Press, 1969.

Mason, C. *Biology of Freshwater Pollution.* New York: Longman and Scientific and Technical, John Wiley and Sons, 1991.

Meeus, J. *Astronomical Algorithms.* Richmond, Va.: Willman-Bell, 1991.

Mehrotra, A. *Cellular Radio: Analog and Digital Systems.* Boston: Artech House, 1994.

Metcalf, H. *Topics in Classical Biophysics.* Englewood Cliffs, N.J.: Prentice-Hall, 1980.

Miller, A., and J. Thompson. *Elements of Meteorology.* 2nd ed. Columbus, Ohio: Charles E. Merrill Publishing Company, 1975.

Miller, A., and R. Anthes. *Meteorology.* 5th ed. Columbus, Ohio: Charles E. Merrill Publishing Company, 1985.

Moffitt, F. *Photogrammetry.* Scranton, Pa.: International Textbook Company, 1967.

Mortenson, M. *Computer Graphics: An Introduction to Mathematics and Geometry.* New York: Industrial Press Inc., 1989.

Motz, L., and J. Weaver. *The Story of Mathematics.* New York: Plenum Press, 1993.

Mueller, I., and K. Ramsayer. *Introduction to Surveying.* New York: Frederick Ungar Publishing Company, 1979.

National Council of Teachers of Mathematics. *Historical Topics for the Mathematics Classroom, Thirty-first Yearbook*, 1969.

Navarra, J. *Atmosphere, Weather and Climate.* Philadelphia: W. B. Saunders, 1979.

Nilsson, A. *Greenhouse Earth.* New York: John Wiley and Sons, 1992.

Pennycuick, C. *Newton Rules Biology.* New York: Oxford University Press, 1992.

Pielou, E. *Population and Community Ecology: Principles and Methods.* New York: Gordon and Breach Science Publishers, 1974.

Pierce, J. *The Science of Musical Sound.* New York: W. H. Freeman, 1992.

Pokorny, C., and C. Gerald. *Computer Graphics: The Principles behind the Art and Science.* Irvine, Calif.: Franklin, Beedle, and Associates, 1989.

Raggett, G. "Modeling the Eyam plague." *The Institute of Mathematics and Its Applications* 18: 221–226.

Resnikoff, H., and R. Wells, Jr. *Mathematics in Civilization.* New York: Dover Publications, Inc., 1984.

Riley, W., L. Sturges, and D. Morris. *Statics and Mechanics of Materials: An Integrated Approach.* New York: John Wiley and Sons, Inc., 1995.

Rist, Curtis. "The Physics of Foul Shots." *Discover*, October 2000.

Robert Wood Johnson Foundation. *Chronic Care in America: A 21st Century Challenge*, 1996.

Rodricks, J. *Calculated Risk.* New York: Cambridge University Press, 1992.

Roederer, J. *Introduction to the Physics and Psychophysics of Music.* New York: Springer-Verlag, 1973.

Rogers, E., and T. Kostigen. *The Green Book.* New York: Random House, 2007.

Ronan, C. *The Natural History of the Universe.* New York: MacMillan Publishing Company, 1991.

Ryan, B., B. Joiner, and T. Ryan. *Minitab Handbook.* Boston: Duxbury Press, 1985.

Sanders, D. *Statistics: A First Course.* 5th ed. New York: McGraw-Hill, 1995.

Schlosser, W. *Challenges of Astronomy.* New York: Springer-Verlag, 1991.

Semat, H., and J. Albright. *Introduction to Atomic and Nuclear Physics.* Austin, Tex.: Holt, Rinehart and Winston, 1972.

Sharov, A., and I. Novikov. *Edwin Hubble: The Discoverer of the Big Bang Universe.* New York: Cambridge University Press, 1993.

Sinkov, A. *Elementary Cryptanalysis: A Mathematical Approach.* New York: Random House, 1968.

Smith, R., and R. Dorf. *Circuits, Devices and Systems.* 5th ed. New York: John Wiley and Sons, Inc., 1992.

Socolow, R., and S. Pacala. "A Plan to Keep Carbon in Check." *Scientific American*, September 2006.

Stadler, W. *Analytical Robotics and Mechatronics.* New York: McGraw-Hill, Inc., 1995.

Stent, G. S. *Molecular Biology of Bacterial Viruses.* San Francisco: W. H. Freeman, 1963.

Thomas, D. *Swimming Pool Operators Handbook.* Washington, D.C.: National Swimming Pool Foundation, 1972.

Thomas, R. *The Old Farmer's 2012 Almanac.* Dublin, N.H.: The Old Farmer's Almanac, 2011.

Thomas, V. *Science and Sport.* London: Faber and Faber, 1970.

Thomson, W. *Introduction to Space Dynamics.* New York: John Wiley and Sons, 1961.

Triola, M. *Elementary Statistics.* Pearson Education, 2012.

Tucker, A., A. Bernat, W. Bradley, R. Cupper, and G. Scragg. *Fundamentals of Computing 1. Logic: Problem Solving, Programs, and Computers.* New York: McGraw-Hill, 1995.

Turner, R. K., D. Pierce, and I. Bateman. *Environmental Economics: An Elementary Approach.* Baltimore: The Johns Hopkins University Press, 1993.

Van Sickle, J. *GPS for Land Surveyors.* Chelsea, Mich.: Ann Arbor Press, 1996.

Varley, G., and G. Gradwell. "Population models for the winter moth." *Symposium of the Royal Entomological Society of London* 4:132–142.

Walker, A. *Observation and Inference: An Introduction to the Methods of Epidemiology.* Newton Lower Falls, Mass.: Epidemiology Resources, 1991.

Wang, Z. "Self-Powered Nanotech." *Scientific American,* January 2008.

Watt, A. *3D Computer Graphics.* Reading, Mass.: Addison-Wesley Publishing Company, 1993.

Webb, T. *Celestial Objects for Common Telescopes.* New York: Dover Publications Inc., 1962.

Weidner, R., and R. Sells. *Elementary Classical Physics,* vol. 2. Boston: Allyn and Bacon, 1965.

Wilcox, G., and C. Hesselberth. *Electricity for Engineering Technology.* Boston: Allyn and Bacon, 1970.

Williams, J. *The Weather Almanac 1995.* New York: Vintage Books, 1994.

Winter, C. *Solar Power Plants.* New York: Springer-Verlag, 1991.

Wolff, R., and L. Yaeger. *Visualization of Natural Phenomena.* New York: Springer-Verlag, 1993.

Wuebbles, D., and J. Edmonds. *Primer on Greenhouse Gases.* Chelsea, Mich.: Lewis Publishers, 1991.

Zeilik, M., S. Gregory, and D. Smith. *Introductory Astronomy and Astrophysics.* 3rd ed. Philadelphia: Saunders College Publishers, 1992.

Zhao, Y. *Vehicle Location and Navigation Systems.* Boston, Mass.: Artech House, 1997.

Answers to Selected Exercises

SECTION 6.1 (pp. 462–465)

1. (a)   **(b)**

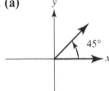

(c)   **(d)**

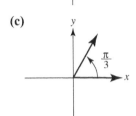

3. Answers may vary.   **5.**

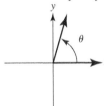

7. Answers may vary.   **9.** Answers may vary.

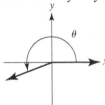

11. (a) $\frac{1}{4}$ **(b)** $\frac{1}{12}$ **(c)** $\frac{1}{6}$ **(d)** $\frac{1}{8}$
13. $510°, -210°$ (answers may vary)
15. $288°, -432°$ (answers may vary)
17. $\frac{5\pi}{2}, -\frac{3\pi}{2}$ (answers may vary)
19. $\frac{9\pi}{5}, -\frac{11\pi}{5}$ (answers may vary)
21. $125.25°$ **23.** $108.76°$ **25.** $125°18'$
27. $51°21'36''$ **29.** $\alpha = 34.1°, \beta = 124.1°$
31. $\alpha = 4°36'15'', \beta = 94°36'15''$
33. $\alpha = 66°19'25'', \beta = 156°19'25''$
35. $\theta = 2$ radians; $\theta \approx 114.6°$
37. $\theta = 1.3$ radians; $\theta \approx 74.5°$

39. (a) $\frac{\pi}{4}$ **(b)** $\frac{3\pi}{4}$ **(c)** $-\frac{2\pi}{3}$ **(d)** $-\frac{7\pi}{6}$
41. (a) $\frac{37\pi}{180}$ **(b)** 2.15 **(c)** -1.61 **(d)** 4.02
43. (a) $30°$ **(b)** $12°$ **(c)** $-300°$ **(d)** $-210°$

45. (a) $45°$ **(b)** $25.71°$ **(c)** $177.62°$ **(d)** $-143.24°$
47. $s = \frac{2\pi}{3}$ in. **49.** $\theta = \frac{12}{5}$ radians **51.** $r = \frac{5}{\pi}$ ft
53. $\frac{\pi}{4}$ m **55.** π ft **57.** $\frac{7\pi}{360}$ mi **59.** 2π in.; $\frac{2\pi}{15}$ in./min
61. 10π in.; $\frac{2\pi}{15}$ in./min **63.** 1.5π in^2 **65.** 4.5π in^2
67. $\frac{17{,}161\pi}{3000} \approx 5.72\pi$ cm^2 **69.** $\frac{3\pi}{16} \approx 0.59$ ft^2
71. 240π in^2 **73.** 4292π cm^2 **75.** 16.25 ft/sec
77. (a) $\frac{\pi}{210} \approx 0.015$ radian/sec **(b)** $\frac{\pi}{3} \approx 1.05$ ft/sec
79. (a) $1000\pi \approx 3141.6$ radians/min
(b) $15{,}000\pi \approx 47{,}123.89$ in./min, or about 65.4 ft/sec
81. 810 mi **83.** About 69 ft/sec **85.** 14.5 in.
87. (a) 2.5 revolutions **(b)** $\frac{65\pi}{6} \approx 34$ ft/sec
89. (a) $78{,}370$ mi/hr **(b)** $66{,}630$ mi/hr
(c) $29{,}250$ mi/hr **(d)** $12{,}160$ mi/hr
Planets farther from the sun have slower orbital velocities.
91. 137.2 m **93. (a)** 388.8 m **(b)** 881.8 m

6.1 EXTENDED AND DISCOVERY EXERCISES (p. 465)

1. $s = r\theta\left(\frac{\pi}{180°}\right)$, where θ is in degrees. The formula for radian measure is simpler.

SECTION 6.2 (pp. 475–479)

1.   **3.**

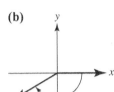

5.

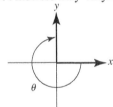

7. $\frac{\sqrt{3}}{2}$ **9.** $\frac{\sqrt{3}}{2}$ **11.** 2 **13.** 1 **15.** 1 **17.** $\frac{1}{\sqrt{2}}$
19. $\sin\theta = \frac{4}{5}, \cos\theta = \frac{3}{5}, \tan\theta = \frac{4}{3},$
  $\csc\theta = \frac{5}{4}, \sec\theta = \frac{5}{3}, \cot\theta = \frac{3}{4}$
21. $\sin\theta = \frac{12}{13}, \cos\theta = \frac{5}{13}, \tan\theta = \frac{12}{5},$
  $\csc\theta = \frac{13}{12}, \sec\theta = \frac{13}{5}, \cot\theta = \frac{5}{12}$
23. $\sin 60° \approx 0.866, \cos 60° = 0.5, \tan 60° \approx 1.732,$
  $\csc 60° \approx 1.155, \sec 60° = 2, \cot 60° \approx 0.577$
25. $\sin 25° \approx 0.423, \cos 25° \approx 0.906, \tan 25° \approx 0.466,$
  $\csc 25° \approx 2.366, \sec 25° \approx 1.103, \cot 25° \approx 2.145$
27. $\sin 5°35' \approx 0.097, \cos 5°35' \approx 0.995,$
  $\tan 5°35' \approx 0.098, \csc 5°35' \approx 10.278,$
  $\sec 5°35' \approx 1.005, \cot 5°35' \approx 10.229$
29. $\sin 13°45'30'' \approx 0.238, \cos 13°45'30'' \approx 0.971,$
  $\tan 13°45'30'' \approx 0.245, \csc 13°45'30'' \approx 4.205,$
  $\sec 13°45'30'' \approx 1.030, \cot 13°45'30'' \approx 4.084$

31. $\sin 1.05° \approx 0.018$, $\cos 1.05° \approx 1.000$,
    $\tan 1.05° \approx 0.018$, $\csc 1.05° \approx 54.570$,
    $\sec 1.05° \approx 1.000$, $\cot 1.05° \approx 54.561$

33. 3   **35.** $\frac{13}{12}$ **37.** $\frac{24}{7}$ **39.** $a \approx 13.86$, $b = 8$

41. $b \approx 5.03$, $c \approx 7.83$ **43.** $a \approx 5.25$, $b \approx 6.04$

45. $a \approx 16.82$, $c \approx 23.28$

47. $a = 12$, $b = 12\sqrt{3}$, $c = 12\sqrt{6}$, $d = 12\sqrt{3}$

49. $a = \frac{14\sqrt{3}}{3}$, $b = \frac{7\sqrt{3}}{3}$, $c = \frac{14\sqrt{3}}{3}$, $d = \frac{14\sqrt{6}}{3}$

51. $a \approx 20.78$ **53.** $c \approx 168.98$

55. (a) $\cos 20° \approx 0.9397$ **(b)** $\sin 50° \approx 0.7660$

57. (a) $\sec 41° \approx 1.3250$ **(b)** $\csc 27° \approx 2.2027$

59. $1500 \tan 37°30' \approx 1151$ ft   **61.** 7.8 ft

63. 39.2 ft   **65.** 52,000 ft   **67.** About 128.2 ft

69. About 194.5 ft   **71.** 19,600 ft   **73.** 114 ft

75. Barnard's Star: 3.5×10^{13} mi, 5.9 light-years;
Sirius: 5.1×10^{13} mi, 8.6 light-years;
61 Cygni: 6.6×10^{13} mi, 11.1 light-years;
Procyon: 6.7×10^{13} mi, 11.3 light-years

77. Min: 2.9×10^7 mi; max: 4.4×10^7 mi

79. 12,534 mi

81. (a) About 704 ft   **(b)** About 595 ft
    (c) Increasing θ decreases r.

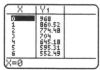

83. $d = 625\left(\frac{1}{\cos 54°} - 1\right) \approx 438$ ft   **85.** $A = \frac{\sqrt{3}}{4} s^2$

CHECKING BASIC CONCEPTS FOR SECTIONS 6.1 AND 6.2 (p. 480)

1. (a) $\frac{\pi}{4}$ **(b)** $\frac{5\pi}{12}$ **3.** $s = 2\pi$ in.; $A = 12\pi$ in^2

5. $\sin \theta = \frac{5}{13}$, $\cos \theta = \frac{12}{13}$, $\tan \theta = \frac{5}{12}$, $\csc \theta = \frac{13}{5}$,
    $\sec \theta = \frac{13}{12}$, $\cot \theta = \frac{12}{5}$

SECTION 6.3 (pp. 494–497)

1. (a) 13   **(b)** $\sin \theta = \frac{5}{13}$, $\cos \theta = \frac{12}{13}$

3. (a) 17   **(b)** $\sin \theta = \frac{8}{17}$, $\cos \theta = -\frac{15}{17}$

5. $\sin \theta = \frac{3}{5}$, $\cos \theta = \frac{4}{5}$

7. $\sin \theta = -\frac{2}{\sqrt{5}}$, $\cos \theta = \frac{1}{\sqrt{5}}$

9. $\sin \theta = \frac{2}{\sqrt{5}}$, $\cos \theta = \frac{1}{\sqrt{5}}$

11. $\sin \theta = -\frac{3}{\sqrt{10}}$, $\cos \theta = \frac{1}{\sqrt{10}}$

13. $\sin 45° = \frac{1}{\sqrt{2}}$, $\cos 45° = \frac{1}{\sqrt{2}}$

15. $\sin(-30°) = -\frac{1}{2}$, $\cos(-30°) = \frac{\sqrt{3}}{2}$

17. $\sin 225° = -\frac{1}{\sqrt{2}}$, $\cos 225° = -\frac{1}{\sqrt{2}}$

19. $\sin(-420°) = -\frac{\sqrt{3}}{2}$, $\cos(-420°) = \frac{1}{2}$

21. $\sin \frac{\pi}{3} = \frac{\sqrt{3}}{2}$, $\cos \frac{\pi}{3} = \frac{1}{2}$

23. $\sin\left(-\frac{\pi}{2}\right) = -1$, $\cos\left(-\frac{\pi}{2}\right) = 0$

25. $\sin \frac{7\pi}{6} = -\frac{1}{2}$, $\cos \frac{7\pi}{6} = -\frac{\sqrt{3}}{2}$

27. $\sin\left(-\frac{9\pi}{4}\right) = -\frac{1}{\sqrt{2}}$, $\cos\left(-\frac{9\pi}{4}\right) = \frac{1}{\sqrt{2}}$

29. $\sin 93.2° \approx 0.9984$, $\cos 93.2° \approx -0.0558$

31. $\sin 123°50' \approx 0.8307$, $\cos 123°50' \approx -0.5568$

33. $\sin(-4) \approx 0.7568$, $\cos(-4) \approx -0.6536$

35. $\sin \frac{11\pi}{7} \approx -0.9749$, $\cos \frac{11\pi}{7} \approx 0.2225$

37. $\sin \theta = \frac{3}{5}$, $\cos \theta = \frac{4}{5}$

39. $\sin \theta = -\frac{5}{13}$, $\cos \theta = \frac{12}{13}$

41. $\sin \frac{\pi}{2} = 1$, $\cos \frac{\pi}{2} = 0$

43. $\sin \frac{7\pi}{6} = -\frac{1}{2}$, $\cos \frac{7\pi}{6} = -\frac{\sqrt{3}}{2}$

45. $\sin\left(-\frac{3\pi}{4}\right) = -\frac{1}{\sqrt{2}}$, $\cos\left(-\frac{3\pi}{4}\right) = -\frac{1}{\sqrt{2}}$

47. $\sin \frac{5\pi}{2} = 1$, $\cos \frac{5\pi}{2} = 0$

49. $\sin\left(-\frac{\pi}{3}\right) = -\frac{\sqrt{3}}{2}$, $\cos\left(-\frac{\pi}{3}\right) = \frac{1}{2}$

51. $(-1, 0)$ **53.** $(1, 0)$ **55.** $(0, -1)$ **57.** $(0, -1)$

59. $\left(-\frac{1}{\sqrt{2}}, -\frac{1}{\sqrt{2}}\right)$ **61.** $\left(-\frac{1}{\sqrt{2}}, \frac{1}{\sqrt{2}}\right)$ **63.** $\left(\frac{\sqrt{3}}{2}, -\frac{1}{2}\right)$

65. $\left(\frac{1}{2}, -\frac{\sqrt{3}}{2}\right)$ **67.** $\sin 3\pi = 0$, $\cos 3\pi = -1$

69. $\sin(-2\pi) = 0$, $\cos(-2\pi) = 1$

71. $\sin \frac{3\pi}{2} = -1$, $\cos \frac{3\pi}{2} = 0$

73. $\sin\left(-\frac{5\pi}{2}\right) = -1$, $\cos\left(-\frac{5\pi}{2}\right) = 0$

75. $\sin \frac{5\pi}{4} = -\frac{1}{\sqrt{2}}$, $\cos \frac{5\pi}{4} = -\frac{1}{\sqrt{2}}$

77. $\sin\left(-\frac{5\pi}{4}\right) = \frac{1}{\sqrt{2}}$, $\cos\left(-\frac{5\pi}{4}\right) = -\frac{1}{\sqrt{2}}$

79. $\sin \frac{11\pi}{6} = -\frac{1}{2}$, $\cos \frac{11\pi}{6} = \frac{\sqrt{3}}{2}$

81. $\sin\left(-\frac{7\pi}{3}\right) = -\frac{\sqrt{3}}{2}$, $\cos\left(-\frac{7\pi}{3}\right) = \frac{1}{2}$

83.

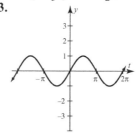

85. (a) $[-2\pi, 2\pi, \pi/2]$ by $[-4, 4, 1]$

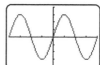

$R = \{y \mid -3 \le y \le 3\}$; $f\left(\frac{3\pi}{2}\right) = -3$

(b) $[-2\pi, 2\pi, \pi/2]$ by $[-4, 4, 1]$

$R = \{y \mid -1 \le y \le 1\}$; $f\left(\frac{3\pi}{2}\right) = 1$

87. (a) $[-2\pi, 2\pi, \pi/2]$ by $[-4, 4, 1]$

$R = \{y \mid -1 \le y \le 3\}$; $f\left(\frac{3\pi}{2}\right) = 1$

(b) $[-2\pi, 2\pi, \pi/2]$ by $[-4, 4, 1]$

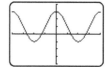

$R = \{y \mid -2 \le y \le 0\}$; $f\left(\frac{3\pi}{2}\right) = -2$

89. (a) 3%   **(b)** $25{,}000\left(\frac{3}{\sqrt{10{,}009}}\right) \approx 750$ lb

91. First quarter: $\frac{\pi}{2} + 2\pi n$

93. (a) [0, 24, 2] by [0, 100, 10]

(b) 6:00 P.M.   **(c)** 6:00 A.M.

95. (a) V is sinusoidal and varies between -310 volts and 310 volts.   **(b)** $V(1/120) = 0$; after $1/120$ second, the voltage is 0.   **(c)** $310/\sqrt{2} \approx 219$ volts

97. (a) 201 ft   **(b)** 258 ft   **(c)** It is easier to stop going uphill ($\theta > 0$) than downhill ($\theta < 0$).

99. (a) 31.4 ft   **(b)** 78.3 ft   **(c)** When the speed limit is higher, more land needs to be cleared on the inside of the curve.

101. (a) [0, 13, 1] by [3, 8, 1]   **(b)** [0, 13, 1] by [3, 8, 1]

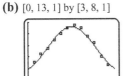

From the close data fit shown, we may conclude that flying squirrels become active near sunset.

6.3 EXTENDED AND DISCOVERY EXERCISES (p. 497)

1. $[-2\pi, 2\pi, \pi/2]$ by $[-2, 2, 1]$

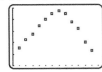

The translated graph and the graph of g are identical.

SECTION 6.4 (pp. 510–513)

1. $\sin \theta = \frac{12}{13}$, $\cos \theta = \frac{5}{13}$, $\tan \theta = \frac{12}{5}$, $\csc \theta = \frac{13}{12}$, $\sec \theta = \frac{13}{5}$, $\cot \theta = \frac{5}{12}$ **3.** $\sin \theta = -\frac{24}{25}$, $\cos \theta = \frac{7}{25}$, $\tan \theta = -\frac{24}{7}$, $\csc \theta = -\frac{25}{24}$, $\sec \theta = \frac{25}{7}$, $\cot \theta = -\frac{7}{24}$

5. $\sin 90° = 1$, $\cos 90° = 0$, $\tan 90°$ is undefined, $\csc 90° = 1$, $\sec 90°$ is undefined, $\cot 90° = 0$

7. $\sin(-45°) = -\frac{1}{\sqrt{2}}$, $\cos(-45°) = \frac{1}{\sqrt{2}}$, $\tan(-45°) = -1$, $\csc(-45°) = -\sqrt{2}$, $\sec(-45°) = \sqrt{2}$, $\cot(-45°) = -1$

9. $\sin \pi = 0$, $\cos \pi = -1$, $\tan \pi = 0$, $\csc \pi$ is undefined, $\sec \pi = -1$, $\cot \pi$ is undefined

11. $\sin\left(-\frac{\pi}{3}\right) = -\frac{\sqrt{3}}{2}$, $\cos\left(-\frac{\pi}{3}\right) = \frac{1}{2}$, $\tan\left(-\frac{\pi}{3}\right) = -\sqrt{3}$, $\csc\left(-\frac{\pi}{3}\right) = -\frac{2}{\sqrt{3}}$, $\sec\left(-\frac{\pi}{3}\right) = 2$, $\cot\left(-\frac{\pi}{3}\right) = -\frac{1}{\sqrt{3}}$

13. $\sin\left(-\frac{\pi}{2}\right) = -1$, $\cos\left(-\frac{\pi}{2}\right) = 0$, $\tan\left(-\frac{\pi}{2}\right)$ is undefined, $\csc\left(-\frac{\pi}{2}\right) = -1$, $\sec\left(-\frac{\pi}{2}\right)$ is undefined, $\cot\left(-\frac{\pi}{2}\right) = 0$

15. $\sin 360° = 0$, $\cos 360° = 1$, $\tan 360° = 0$, $\csc 360°$ is undefined, $\sec 360° = 1$, $\cot 360°$ is undefined

17. $\sin \frac{\pi}{6} = \frac{1}{2}$, $\cos \frac{\pi}{6} = \frac{\sqrt{3}}{2}$, $\tan \frac{\pi}{6} = \frac{1}{\sqrt{3}}$, $\csc \frac{\pi}{6} = 2$, $\sec \frac{\pi}{6} = \frac{2}{\sqrt{3}}$, $\cot \frac{\pi}{6} = \sqrt{3}$

19. $\sin \frac{4\pi}{3} = -\frac{\sqrt{3}}{2}$, $\cos \frac{4\pi}{3} = -\frac{1}{2}$, $\tan \frac{4\pi}{3} = \sqrt{3}$, $\csc \frac{4\pi}{3} = -\frac{2}{\sqrt{3}}$, $\sec \frac{4\pi}{3} = -2$, $\cot \frac{4\pi}{3} = \frac{1}{\sqrt{3}}$

21. $\sin(-225°) = \frac{1}{\sqrt{2}}$, $\cos(-225°) = -\frac{1}{\sqrt{2}}$, $\tan(-225°) = -1$, $\csc(-225°) = \sqrt{2}$, $\sec(-225°) = -\sqrt{2}$, $\cot(-225°) = -1$

23. $\sin\left(-\frac{13\pi}{6}\right) = -\frac{1}{2}$, $\cos\left(-\frac{13\pi}{6}\right) = \frac{\sqrt{3}}{2}$, $\tan\left(-\frac{13\pi}{6}\right) = -\frac{1}{\sqrt{3}}$, $\csc\left(-\frac{13\pi}{6}\right) = -2$, $\sec\left(-\frac{13\pi}{6}\right) = \frac{2}{\sqrt{3}}$, $\cot\left(-\frac{13\pi}{6}\right) = -\sqrt{3}$

25. $\sin \theta = \frac{4}{\sqrt{17}}$, $\cos \theta = -\frac{1}{\sqrt{17}}$, $\tan \theta = -4$, $\csc \theta = \frac{\sqrt{17}}{4}$, $\sec \theta = -\sqrt{17}$, $\cot \theta = -\frac{1}{4}$
The slope of the line equals $\tan \theta$.

27. $\sin \theta = -\frac{6}{\sqrt{37}}$, $\cos \theta = -\frac{1}{\sqrt{37}}$, $\tan \theta = 6$, $\csc \theta = -\frac{\sqrt{37}}{6}$, $\sec \theta = -\sqrt{37}$, $\cot \theta = \frac{1}{6}$
The slope of the line equals $\tan \theta$.

29. $\tan \theta = \frac{3}{4}$, $\cot \theta = \frac{4}{3}$, $\csc \theta = \frac{5}{3}$, $\sec \theta = \frac{5}{4}$

31. $\sin \theta = -\frac{15}{17}$, $\cos \theta = -\frac{8}{17}$, $\tan \theta = \frac{15}{8}$, $\cot \theta = \frac{8}{15}$

33. $\sin \theta = \frac{5}{13}$, $\csc \theta = \frac{13}{5}$, $\cot \theta = \frac{12}{5}$, $\sec \theta = \frac{13}{12}$

35. $\cos \theta = \frac{4}{5}$, $\tan \theta = -\frac{3}{4}$, $\csc \theta = -\frac{5}{3}$, $\sec \theta = \frac{5}{4}$, $\cot \theta = -\frac{4}{3}$

37. $\sin \theta = -\frac{3}{5}$, $\tan \theta = \frac{3}{4}$, $\csc \theta = -\frac{5}{3}$, $\sec \theta = -\frac{5}{4}$, $\cot \theta = \frac{4}{3}$

39. $\sin(-7\pi) = 0$, $\cos(-7\pi) = -1$, $\tan(-7\pi) = 0$, $\csc(-7\pi)$ is undefined, $\sec(-7\pi) = -1$, $\cot(-7\pi)$ is undefined

41. $\sin \frac{7\pi}{2} = -1$, $\cos \frac{7\pi}{2} = 0$, $\tan \frac{7\pi}{2}$ is undefined, $\csc \frac{7\pi}{2} = -1$, $\sec \frac{7\pi}{2}$ is undefined, $\cot \frac{7\pi}{2} = 0$

43. $\sin\left(-\frac{3\pi}{4}\right) = -\frac{1}{\sqrt{2}}$, $\cos\left(-\frac{3\pi}{4}\right) = -\frac{1}{\sqrt{2}}$, $\tan\left(-\frac{3\pi}{4}\right) = 1$, $\csc\left(-\frac{3\pi}{4}\right) = -\sqrt{2}$, $\sec\left(-\frac{3\pi}{4}\right) = -\sqrt{2}$, $\cot\left(-\frac{3\pi}{4}\right) = 1$

45. $\sin \frac{7\pi}{6} = -\frac{1}{2}$, $\cos \frac{7\pi}{6} = -\frac{\sqrt{3}}{2}$, $\tan \frac{7\pi}{6} = \frac{1}{\sqrt{3}}$, $\csc \frac{7\pi}{6} = -2$, $\sec \frac{7\pi}{6} = -\frac{2}{\sqrt{3}}$, $\cot \frac{7\pi}{6} = \sqrt{3}$

47. $\sin \theta = \frac{1}{\sqrt{2}}$, $\cos \theta = \frac{1}{\sqrt{2}}$, $\tan \theta = 1$, $\csc \theta = \sqrt{2}$, $\sec \theta = \sqrt{2}$, $\cot \theta = 1$

49. $\sin \theta = -\frac{12}{13}$, $\cos \theta = \frac{5}{13}$, $\tan \theta = -\frac{12}{5}$, $\csc \theta = -\frac{13}{12}$, $\sec \theta = \frac{13}{5}$, $\cot \theta = -\frac{5}{12}$

51. -1 **53.** 2   **55.** $\frac{2}{\sqrt{3}}$

57. $\sin \frac{9\pi}{2} = 1$, $\cos \frac{9\pi}{2} = 0$, $\tan \frac{9\pi}{2}$ is undefined, $\csc \frac{9\pi}{2} = 1$, $\sec \frac{9\pi}{2}$ is undefined, $\cot \frac{9\pi}{2} = 0$

59. $\sin(-\pi) = 0$, $\cos(-\pi) = -1$, $\tan(-\pi) = 0$, $\csc(-\pi)$ is undefined, $\sec(-\pi) = -1$, $\cot(-\pi)$ is undefined

61. $\sin \frac{4\pi}{3} = -\frac{\sqrt{3}}{2}$, $\cos \frac{4\pi}{3} = -\frac{1}{2}$, $\tan \frac{4\pi}{3} = \sqrt{3}$, $\csc \frac{4\pi}{3} = -\frac{2}{\sqrt{3}}$, $\sec \frac{4\pi}{3} = -2$, $\cot \frac{4\pi}{3} = \frac{1}{\sqrt{3}}$

63. (a) 0.9984   **(b)** 1.0016   **65. (a)** 1.4045   **(b)** 0.7120

67. (a) -0.8637 **(b)** -1.1578

69. (a) 0.2225   **(b)** 4.4940

71. 0.900   **73.** 0.527

75. Origin symmetry

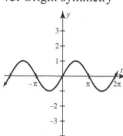

77. Origin symmetry

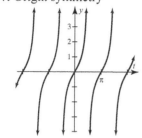

79. y-axis symmetry

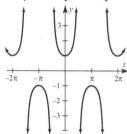

81. D = all real numbers, $R = \{y | -1 \le y \le 1\}$, period = 2π

83. $D = \{t | t \ne \pm\frac{\pi}{2}, \pm\frac{3\pi}{2}, \pm\frac{5\pi}{2}, \dots\}$, R = all real numbers, period = π

85. $D = \{t | t \ne \pm\frac{\pi}{2}, \pm\frac{3\pi}{2}, \pm\frac{5\pi}{2}, \dots\}$, $R = \{y | |y| \ge 1\}$, period = 2π

87. (a)

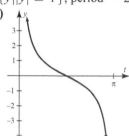

(b) Just after sunrise ($t = 0$), the shadow is very long. As the elevation of the sun increases, the shadow decreases in length until it is 0 when $t = \pi/2$. In the afternoon, the shadow increases in length in the opposite direction until sunset ($t = \pi$).

89. About 1300 ft **91.** About 17.95″; $\theta = \frac{57.3 \sin \alpha}{\cos \alpha}$

93. About 41%

95. As θ increases, the values of y_1 and y_2 become closer together. When $\theta = 20°$, the difference is only about 0.02, or 2%.

97. [0, 20000, 5000] by [0, 4000, 1000]

(a) About (7612, 2197)   **(b)** About 15,223 ft

6.4 EXTENDED AND DISCOVERY EXERCISE (p. 513)

1. Using the small right triangle yields
$\sin \theta = \frac{\text{Opp.}}{\text{Hyp.}} = \frac{\text{Opp.}}{1}$ = Opposite side. Similarly,
$\cos \theta = \frac{\text{Adj.}}{\text{Hyp.}} = \frac{\text{Adj.}}{1}$ = Adjacent side.
Then using the large right triangle yields
$\tan \theta = \frac{\text{Opp.}}{\text{Adj.}} = \frac{\text{Opp.}}{1}$ = Opposite side. Similarly,
$\sec \theta = \frac{\text{Hyp.}}{\text{Adj.}} = \frac{\text{Hyp.}}{1}$ = Hypotenuse.

CHECKING BASIC CONCEPTS FOR SECTIONS 6.3 AND 6.4 (p. 513)

1. $\sin \theta = \frac{6}{\sqrt{85}}$, $\cos \theta = -\frac{7}{\sqrt{85}}$, $\tan \theta = -\frac{6}{7}$,
$\csc \theta = \frac{\sqrt{85}}{6}$, $\sec \theta = -\frac{\sqrt{85}}{7}$, $\cot \theta = -\frac{7}{6}$

3. Sine   Cosine

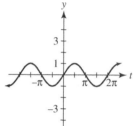 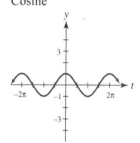

Tangent

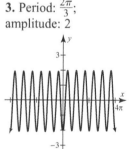

SECTION 6.5 (pp. 524–529)

1. Period: 4π; amplitude: 3

3. Period: $\frac{2\pi}{3}$; amplitude: 2

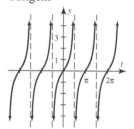 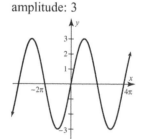

5. Period: 2; amplitude: $\frac{1}{2}$

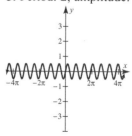

7. Shorten the period of the sine graph to π, increase the amplitude to 3, and shift the graph downward 1 unit.

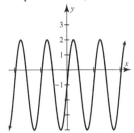

9. Shift the cosine graph $\frac{\pi}{2}$ units to the left, increase the amplitude to 2, and reflect the graph across the x-axis.

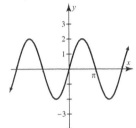

11. Shift the cosine graph $\frac{1}{\pi}$ unit to the right, shorten the period to 2, and decrease the amplitude to $\frac{1}{2}$.

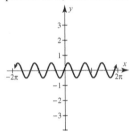

13. Amplitude: 3; period: $\frac{\pi}{2}$; phase shift: $\frac{\pi}{4}$; vertical shift: -4
15. Amplitude: 4; period: 4; phase shift: 1; vertical shift: 6
17. Amplitude: 20; period: 3π; phase shift: $-\frac{3\pi}{2}$; vertical shift: 2
19. $a = 3, b = 2$
21. Amplitude: 3; period: 4π; phase shift: 0
23. c **25.** d **27.** a **29.** $y = 3 \sin\left(\frac{1}{2}x\right)$
31. Amplitude: 2; period: 2π; phase shift: 0
33. Amplitude: 1; period: 4π; phase shift: 0

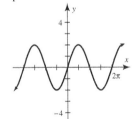 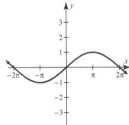

35. Amplitude: 1; period: 2π; phase shift: 0

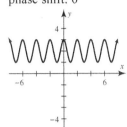

37. Amplitude: 1; period: 2; phase shift: 0

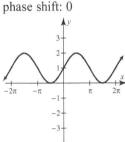

39. Amplitude: 1; period: π; phase shift: $-\pi$

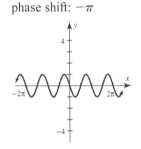

41. Amplitude: 1; period: 2π; phase shift: $\frac{\pi}{2}$

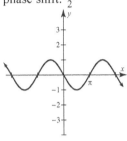

43. Amplitude: $\frac{1}{2}$; period: π; phase shift: 0

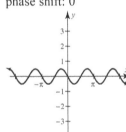

45. Amplitude: 2; period: π; phase shift: $-\frac{\pi}{4}$

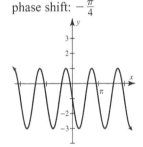

47. Amplitude: 1; period: π; phase shift: $\frac{\pi}{2}$

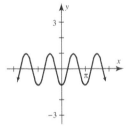

49. Amplitude $= 2$; period $= \pi$; phase shift $= 0$
$[-2\pi, 2\pi, \pi/2]$ by $[-4, 4, 1]$

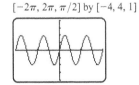

51. Amplitude $= \frac{1}{2}$; period $= \frac{2\pi}{3}$; phase shift $= -\frac{\pi}{3}$
$[-2\pi, 2\pi, \pi/2]$ by $[-4, 4, 1]$

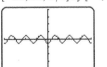

53. Amplitude $= 2.5$;
period $= \pi$;
phase shift $= -\frac{\pi}{4}$
$[-2\pi, 2\pi, \pi/2]$ by $[-4, 4, 1]$

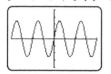

55. Amplitude $= 2$;
period $= 1$;
phase shift $= -\frac{1}{8}$
$[-2\pi, 2\pi, \pi/2]$ by $[-4, 4, 1]$

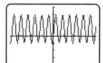

57. Period $= \frac{\pi}{2}$; phase shift $= 0$
Asymptotes: $x = \pm\frac{\pi}{4}, \pm\frac{3\pi}{4}, \pm\frac{5\pi}{4}, \pm\frac{7\pi}{4}$

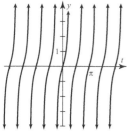

59. Period $= \pi$; phase shift $= \frac{\pi}{2}$
Asymptotes: $x = 0, \pm\pi, \pm 2\pi$

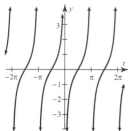

61. Period $= \frac{\pi}{2}$; phase shift $= 0$
Asymptotes: $x = 0, \pm\frac{\pi}{2}, \pm\pi, \pm\frac{3\pi}{2}, \pm 2\pi$

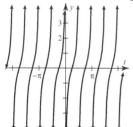

63. Period $= \frac{\pi}{2}$; phase shift $= \frac{\pi}{4}$
Asymptotes: $x = \pm\frac{\pi}{4}, \pm\frac{3\pi}{4}, \pm\frac{5\pi}{4}, \pm\frac{7\pi}{4}$

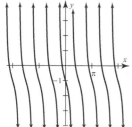

65. Period $= 4\pi$; phase shift $= 0$
Asymptotes: $x = \pm\pi$

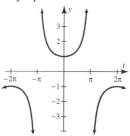

67. Period $= 2\pi$; phase shift $= \pi$
Asymptotes: $x = 0, \pm\pi, \pm 2\pi$

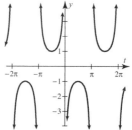

69. Period $= 6\pi$; phase shift $= \frac{\pi}{6}$
Asymptotes: $x = -\frac{4\pi}{3}, \frac{5\pi}{3}$

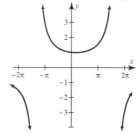

71. (a) $s(t) = 2\cos(4\pi t)$ **(b)** $s(1) = 2$. The weight is moving neither upward nor downward. At $t = 1$ the motion of the weight is changing from up to down.
73. (a) $s(t) = -3\cos(2.5\pi t)$ **(b)** $s(1) = 0$. The weight is moving upward.
75. $a = 0.21, b = 55\pi$; $Y_1 = 0.21\cos(55\pi X)$
$[0, 0.05, 0.01]$ by $[-0.3, 0.3, 0.1]$

77. $a = 0.14, b = 110\pi$; $Y_1 = 0.14\cos(110\pi X)$
$[0, 0.05, 0.01]$ by $[-0.3, 0.3, 0.1]$

79. (a) $P(x) = 40\sin\left(\frac{\pi}{12}x\right) + 50$ **(b)** Noon
(c) Midnight
81. (a) $40°F, -40°F$ **(b)** Amplitude $= 40$, half the difference between the maximum and minimum monthly average temperatures; period $= 12$ means that the temperature pattern repeats every 12 months.   **(c)** The months when the average temperature is $0°F$

83. (a) Amplitude = 34; period = 12; phase shift = 4.3
(b) $f(5) \approx 12.2°F$; $f(12) \approx -26.4°F$ **(c)** About 0°F
85. (a) [0, 25, 2] by [0, 80, 10]

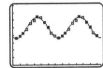

(b) $f(x) = 14 \sin\left(\frac{\pi}{6}(x-4)\right) + 50$
(c) [0, 25, 2] by [0, 80, 10]

87. (a) $f(x) = 17 \cos\left(\frac{\pi}{6}(x-7)\right) + 75$
(b) Yes. The period of the graph is 12, so, for example, the phase shift could be $c = 7 + 12 = 19$ or $c = 7 - 12 = -5$.
89. (a) About 18.5 hr; June 21   **(b)** About 6 hr; December 21   **(c)** The amplitude represents half the difference in daylight between the longest and shortest day; the period represents one year (answers may vary).
91. (a) Max $\approx$ 8 in.; min $\approx$ 0.5 in.   **(b)** Amp $\approx$ 3.75. The amplitude represents half the difference between the maximum and minimum monthly average precipitations.
(c) $f(x) = 3.75 \cos\left(\frac{\pi}{6}x\right) + 4.25$
93. (a) $f(t) = 2 \cos\left(\frac{\pi}{6}(t-1)\right) + 4$
(b) $f(1) = 6$, $f(7) = 2$
95. (a) [0, 25, 2] by [60, 90, 5]

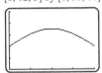

(b) $f(x) = 6.5 \sin\left(\frac{\pi}{6}(x-4)\right) + 78.5$
97. [0, 12, 3] by [0, 50, 10]

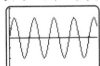

At 9:00 A.M. the outdoor temperature is 20°C. The temperature increases to a maximum of 35°C at 3:00 P.M. Then it begins to fall until it reaches 20°C again at 9:00 P.M.
99. (a) [0, 1/100, 1/880] by [-1.5, 1.5, 0.5]

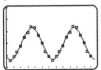

(b) $\frac{1}{440} \approx 0.00227$ sec   **(c)** 440 cycles per second
101. $y \approx 13.2 \sin(0.524x - 2.18) + 49.7$
[0, 25, 2] by [30, 80, 10]

103. $y \approx 16.9 \sin(0.522x - 2.09) + 75.4$
[0, 25, 2] by [50, 100, 10]

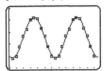

SECTION 6.6 (pp. 540–543)

1. one-to-one   **3.** π **5.** 0   **7.** $\frac{\pi}{2}$ **9.** $-\frac{\pi}{4}$ **11.** $\frac{2\pi}{3}$
13. (a) $\frac{\pi}{2}$, or 90°   **(b)** Undefined   **(c)** $-\frac{\pi}{3}$, or $-60°$
15. (a) $\frac{\pi}{2}$, or 90°   **(b)** π, or 180°   **(c)** $\frac{\pi}{3}$, or 60°
17. (a) $\frac{\pi}{4}$, or 45°   **(b)** $-\frac{\pi}{4}$, or $-45°$ **(c)** $\frac{\pi}{3}$, or 60°
19. (a) Undefined   **(b)** 1.47, or 84.3°   **(c)** 1.82, or 104.5°
21. (a) β **(b)** α **(c)** β **23.** 1   **25.** $\frac{3\pi}{4}$ **27.** -3
29. (a) 90°   **(b)** 90°   **(c)** 90°; $\sin^{-1} x + \cos^{-1} x = 90°$ whenever $-1 \leq x \leq 1$.
31. *Verbal:* Determine the angle (or real number) θ such that $\sin \theta = 2x$ and $-\frac{\pi}{2} \leq \theta \leq \frac{\pi}{2}$.
Numerical: *Graphical:*
[-1, 1, 1] by [-2, 2, 1]

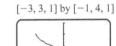

33. *Verbal:* Determine the angle (or real number) θ such that $\cos \theta = \frac{1}{2}x$ and $0 \leq \theta \leq \pi$.
Numerical: *Graphical:*
[-3, 3, 1] by [-1, 4, 1]

35. $\tan \theta = \frac{x}{\sqrt{1 - x^2}}$ **37.** $\cos \theta = \frac{1}{\sqrt{1 + x^2}}$
39. $\sqrt{1 - u^2}$ **41.** $\frac{\sqrt{1 - u^2}}{u}$ **43.** u
45. $\alpha = \tan^{-1}\frac{7}{24} \approx 16.3°$, $\beta = \tan^{-1}\frac{24}{7} \approx 73.7°$, $c = 25$
47. $\alpha = \sin^{-1}\frac{6}{10} \approx 36.9°$, $\beta = \cos^{-1}\frac{6}{10} \approx 53.1°$, $b = 8$
49. $\beta = 35°$, $b = \frac{5}{\tan 55°} \approx 3.5$, $c = \frac{5}{\sin 55°} \approx 6.1$
51. 90°   **53.** 45°   **55.** 90°   **57.** 82.8°   **59.** 80.5°
61. 68.9°   **63.** -0.197 **65.** 1.102   **67.** -0.282
69. 1.369, 1.772   **71.** π **73.** $-\frac{\pi}{4}$ **75.** $\frac{3\pi}{4}$ **77.** 1.231
79. 0.197   **81.** 0.588   **83.** $\tan^{-1}\frac{50}{85} \approx 30.5°$
85. (a) 4.6°   **(b)** 2.1°   **(c)** $-2.9°$ **87.** $\tan^{-1}\frac{4}{10} \approx 21.8°$
89. (a) $\tan^{-1}\frac{3}{12} \approx 14.0°$ **(b)** $\tan^{-1}\frac{4}{12} \approx 18.4°$
(c) $\tan^{-1}\frac{6}{12} \approx 26.6°$ **(d)** 45°
91. $\theta \approx 41.9°$ **93. (a)** 14.9 hr   **(b)** 13.8 hr   **(c)** 14.6 hr
95. $\theta_1 \approx 35.8°$, $\theta_2 \approx 54.2°$
97. Let α and β represent the angles of elevation from the shrub to the shorter and taller buildings, respectively. The distance from the shrub to the shorter building is $100 - x$; thus $\alpha = \arctan\frac{75}{100 - x}$. Similarly, $\beta = \arctan\frac{150}{x}$. Because the angles α, θ, and β form a straight angle,

$\theta = \pi - \alpha - \beta$. That is,
$\theta = \pi - \arctan \frac{75}{100 - x} - \arctan \frac{150}{x}$.

6.6 EXTENDED AND DISCOVERY EXERCISE (p. 543)

1. The maximum value of θ is 38.7° when $x \approx 6.24$.
[0, 50, 10] by [0, 50, 10]

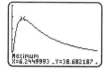

CHECKING BASIC CONCEPTS FOR SECTIONS 6.5 AND 6.6 (p. 543)

1. Amplitude = 3; period = $\frac{2\pi}{2} = \pi$; phase shift = $\frac{\pi}{4}$

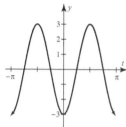

3. (a) $\sin^{-1} 0 = 0°$ **(b)** $\cos^{-1}(-1) = 180°$
(c) $\tan^{-1}(-1) = -45°$ **(d)** $\sin^{-1} \frac{1}{2} = 30°$
(e) $\tan^{-1} \sqrt{3} = 60°$ **(f)** $\cos^{-1} \frac{1}{2} = 60°$
5. (a) $\sin^{-1} 0.55 \approx 0.582$ **(b)** $\cos^{-1}(-0.35) \approx 1.93$
(c) $\tan^{-1}(-2.9) \approx -1.24$

CHAPTER 6 REVIEW EXERCISES (pp. 547–549)

1. (a) **(b)**

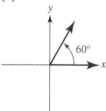 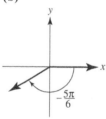

3. (a) 60° **(b)** 5° **(c)** −150° **(d)** −315°
5. 2π ft **7.** $\frac{1}{2}$ **9.** $\frac{1}{\sqrt{3}}$ **11.** $\sqrt{2}$
13. $\sin \theta = \frac{8}{\sqrt{145}}$, $\cos \theta = \frac{9}{\sqrt{145}}$, $\tan \theta = \frac{8}{9}$,
$\csc \theta = \frac{\sqrt{145}}{8}$, $\sec \theta = \frac{\sqrt{145}}{9}$, $\cot \theta = \frac{9}{8}$
15. $\csc \theta = 3$
17. $\sin 25° \approx 0.423$, $\cos 25° \approx 0.906$, $\tan 25° \approx 0.466$,
$\csc 25° \approx 2.366$, $\sec 25° \approx 1.103$, $\cot 25° \approx 2.145$
19. $\sin \theta = -\frac{2}{\sqrt{5}}$, $\cos \theta = \frac{1}{\sqrt{5}}$, $\tan \theta = -2$,
$\csc \theta = -\frac{\sqrt{5}}{2}$, $\sec \theta = \sqrt{5}$, $\cot \theta = -\frac{1}{2}$
21. $\sin \theta = \frac{\sqrt{3}}{2}$, $\cos \theta = -\frac{1}{2}$, $\tan \theta = -\sqrt{3}$,
$\csc \theta = \frac{2}{\sqrt{3}}$, $\sec \theta = -2$, $\cot \theta = -\frac{1}{\sqrt{3}}$
23. −1 **25.** 0
27. $\tan \theta = -\frac{4}{3}$, $\csc \theta = -\frac{5}{4}$, $\sec \theta = \frac{5}{3}$, $\cot \theta = -\frac{3}{4}$

29. Amplitude = 3; period = π; phase shift = 0

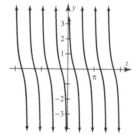

31. Amplitude = 3; period = 4π; phase shift = π

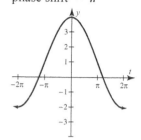

33. $a = 2$, $b = 3$
35. Period = $\frac{\pi}{2}$; phase shift = 0

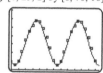

37. (a) $-\frac{\pi}{2}$, or −90° **(b)** $\frac{\pi}{3}$, or 60° **(c)** $\frac{\pi}{4}$, or 45°
39. (a) −0.64, or −36.9° **(b)** 1.37, or 78.7°
(c) 1.45, or 83.1°
41. $\alpha = \tan^{-1} \frac{5}{3} \approx 59.0°$, $\beta = \tan^{-1} \frac{3}{5} \approx 31.0°$, $c = \sqrt{34}$
43. 30° **45.** 78.5° **47.** −0.6435
49. (a) $\frac{\pi}{25}$ radian/sec **(b)** $\pi \approx 3.14$ ft/sec
51. 89 ft **53. (a)** $\sin^{-1} \frac{350}{6000} \approx 3.3°$ **(b)** $\sin^{-1} \frac{160}{4500} \approx 2.0°$
55. 161 mi
57. (a) [0, 25, 2] by [0, 70, 10] **(c)** [0, 25, 2] by [0, 70, 10]

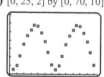

(b) $f(x) = 26 \cos \left(\frac{\pi}{6}(x - 7) \right) + 32$

CHAPTER 6 EXTENDED AND DISCOVERY EXERCISES (p. 549)

1. (a) $x_Q = d \sin \theta + x_p$ and $y_Q = d \cos \theta + y_p$
(b) Approximately (233.9, 377.2)
3. (a) $f(x) = 12.5 \cos \left(\frac{\pi}{6}(x - 1) \right) + 61.5$
(b) [0, 25, 2] by [40, 80, 10]

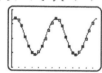

Answers may vary.
(c) The high temperatures occur in January in the Southern Hemisphere as opposed to July in the Northern Hemisphere. This affects the phase shift of f.

CHAPTERS 1–6 CUMULATIVE REVIEW EXERCISES
(pp. 550–552)

1. 1.25×10^5; 0.00467

3. (a) 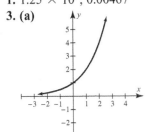   **(b)**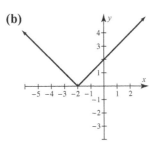

(c) 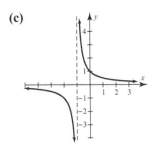   **(d)**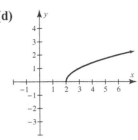

5. (a) $D = \{x \mid x \neq 2, x \neq -2\}$
(b) $f(-1) = \frac{1}{4}$; $f(2a) = \frac{1}{8(a + 1)}$
7. 90   **9.** $y = -\frac{2}{3}x - \frac{5}{3}$
11. (a) $-\frac{4}{5}, \frac{12}{5}$ **(b)** $\ln 14 \approx 2.64$ **(c)** 0, 1, 2
(d) 5   **(e)** $-1, 2$ **(f)** 65,535
13. (a) $\left(-\infty, \frac{9}{5}\right)$ **(b)** $\left(-\frac{2}{3}, \frac{7}{3}\right]$ **(c)** $\left(-\infty, -\frac{3}{2}\right] \cup [3, \infty)$
(d) $[1, 4]$ **(e)** $(-1, 0) \cup (1, \infty)$
15. $\frac{-2 \pm \sqrt{6}}{2}$
17. (a) Increasing: $(-2, 0), (2, \infty)$; decreasing:
$(-\infty, -2), (0, 2)$ **(b)** $-2.8, 0, 2.8$ (approximate)
(c) $(-2, -4), (0, 0), (2, -4)$ **(d)** Local minimum: -4;
local maximum: 0
19. (a) $\frac{5a^2}{2} - 1 + \frac{2}{a^2}$ **(b)** $x - 3 + \frac{4}{x^2 + 1}$
21. $D = \left\{x \mid x \neq \frac{7}{3}\right\}$; vertical: $x = \frac{7}{3}$; horizontal: $y = \frac{2}{3}$
23. (a) 5   **(b)** Undefined   **(c)** 2   **(d)** 0
25. (a) 8   **(b)** 0   **(c)** $(f - g)(x) = x^2 + 2x$
(d) $(f \circ g)(x) = x^2 - x - 4$ **27.** $C = \frac{1}{2}, a = 2$
29. (a) 2   **(b)** 4   **(c)** -2 **(d)** 2   **31.** 4.395
33. $\frac{5\pi}{6}$ **35.** $\frac{\pi}{4} \approx 0.79$ ft   **37.** $\frac{9}{\tan 30°} \approx 15.6$
39. $\sin \theta = -\frac{1}{\sqrt{2}}$, $\cos \theta = -\frac{1}{\sqrt{2}}$, $\tan \theta = 1$,
$\csc \theta = -\sqrt{2}$, $\sec \theta = -\sqrt{2}$, $\cot \theta = 1$
41. $\sin \theta = -\frac{12}{13}$, $\cos \theta = \frac{5}{13}$, $\tan \theta = -\frac{12}{5}$,
$\csc \theta = -\frac{13}{12}$, $\sec \theta = \frac{13}{5}$, $\cot \theta = -\frac{5}{12}$
43. (a) 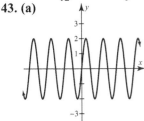   **(b)**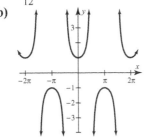

(c)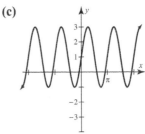

45. $\alpha \approx 33.4°$; $\beta \approx 56.6°$; $b \approx 16.7$ **47.** 24 lb
49. (a) $f^{-1}(x) = \frac{9}{5}x + 32$
(b) f^{-1} converts degrees Celsius to degrees Fahrenheit.
51. (a) $N(t) = 200{,}000 e^{0.135t}$
(b) $N(5) \approx 392{,}807$; after 5 hours, there are about 393,000
bacteria per mL.   **(c)** About 6.8 hours
53. $f(x) \approx 14.5 \sin\left(\frac{\pi}{6}(x - 4)\right) + 75.5$

CHAPTER 7: Trigonometric Identities and Equations

SECTION 7.1 (pp. 563–565)

1. $\cot \theta = 2$ **3.** $\sec \theta = \frac{7}{2}$ **5.** $\cos \theta = -\frac{1}{4}$
7. Undefined   **9.** $\frac{\sin^2 \theta}{\cos^2 \theta}$ **11.** $\cos^2 \theta$ **13.** $\sin \theta + \cos \theta$
15. $\tan \theta = -\frac{3}{4}$, $\csc \theta = \frac{5}{3}$, $\sec \theta = -\frac{5}{4}$, $\cot \theta = -\frac{4}{3}$
17. $\cos \theta = -\frac{7}{25}$, $\tan \theta = \frac{24}{7}$, $\csc \theta = -\frac{25}{24}$, $\sec \theta = -\frac{25}{7}$
19. $\tan \theta = \frac{60}{11}$, $\cot \theta = \frac{11}{60}$, $\csc \theta = -\frac{61}{60}$, $\sec \theta = -\frac{61}{11}$
21. $\sin \theta = \frac{1}{\sqrt{2}}$, $\cos \theta = -\frac{1}{\sqrt{2}}$, $\tan \theta = -1$, $\cot \theta = -1$
23. 1   **25.** 1   **27.** 1   **29.** $\cos^2 \theta$ **31.** $\tan^2 \theta$
33. $-\tan \theta$ **35.** $\sec \theta$ **37.** $\tan^2 \theta$ **39.** $\cos x$ **41.** 1
43. $\sec x - \csc x$ **45.** Yes   **47.** No   **49.** Quadrant IV
51. Quadrant III   **53.** Quadrant II
55. $\sin \theta = -\frac{\sqrt{3}}{2}$, $\tan \theta = -\sqrt{3}$, $\csc \theta = -\frac{2}{\sqrt{3}}$, $\sec \theta = 2$,
$\cot \theta = -\frac{1}{\sqrt{3}}$
57. $\sin \theta = -\frac{11}{61}$, $\cos \theta = \frac{60}{61}$, $\cot \theta = -\frac{60}{11}$, $\csc \theta = -\frac{61}{11}$,
$\sec \theta = \frac{61}{60}$
59. $\cos \theta = \frac{24}{25}$, $\tan \theta = \frac{7}{24}$, $\cot \theta = \frac{24}{7}$, $\csc \theta = \frac{25}{7}$,
$\sec \theta = \frac{25}{24}$
61. $\cos \theta = -\frac{\sqrt{8}}{3}$, $\tan \theta = \frac{1}{\sqrt{8}}$, $\cot \theta = \sqrt{8}$, $\csc \theta = -3$,
$\sec \theta = -\frac{3}{\sqrt{8}}$
63. $\sin \theta = -\frac{35}{37}$, $\cos \theta = \frac{12}{37}$, $\tan \theta = -\frac{35}{12}$,
$\csc \theta = -\frac{37}{35}$, $\cot \theta = -\frac{12}{35}$
65. $\sin \theta = \frac{3}{7}$, $\cos \theta = -\frac{\sqrt{40}}{7}$, $\tan \theta = -\frac{3}{\sqrt{40}}$,
$\sec \theta = -\frac{7}{\sqrt{40}}$, $\cot \theta = -\frac{\sqrt{40}}{3}$
67. $\sin x = \sqrt{1 - \cos^2 x}$; $\tan x = \frac{\sqrt{1 - \cos^2 x}}{\cos x}$
69. $\sin x = -\frac{\tan x}{\sqrt{1 + \tan^2 x}}$; $\sec x = -\sqrt{1 + \tan^2 x}$
71. $\cot x = -\sqrt{\csc^2 x - 1}$; $\cos x = -\frac{\sqrt{\csc^2 x - 1}}{\csc x}$
73. $\cos \theta = \sqrt{1 - x^2}$, 0.8586
75. $\sin \theta = -\frac{1}{\sqrt{1 + x^2}}$, -0.8899 **77.** $\tan \theta = \frac{x}{\sqrt{1 - x^2}}$
79. $-\sin 13°$ **81.** $-\tan \frac{\pi}{11}$ **83.** $\sec \frac{2\pi}{5}$

85. (a) I is a maximum when $\theta = 0$.

[-90, 90, 45] by [-1, 2, 1]

(b) $I = k(1 - \sin^2\theta)$

87. (a) The sum of L and C equals 3.

[0, 10^{-6}, 10^{-7}] by [-1, 4, 1]

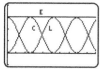

(b) Let $Y_1 = L(t)$, $Y_2 = C(t)$, and $Y_3 = E(t)$.
$E(t) = 3$ for all inputs

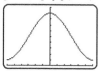

(c) $E(t) = L(t) + C(t)$
$= 3\cos^2(6{,}000{,}000t) + 3\sin^2(6{,}000{,}000t)$
$= 3(\cos^2(6{,}000{,}000t) + \sin^2(6{,}000{,}000t))$
$= 3(1) = 3$

89. (a) The graph has y-axis symmetry. The monthly high temperatures x months before and x months after July are equal.

[-6, 6, 1] by [0, 100, 10]   **(b)** f is even.

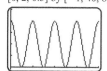

(c) $f(-x) = f(x)$

91. (a) $P = 16k\cos^2(2\pi t)$

(b) Let $Y_1 = 32(\cos(2\pi X))^2$. Y_1 has a maximum value of 32 when $t = 0, 0.5, 1, 1.5, 2.0$, and Y_1 has a minimum value of 0 when $t = 0.25, 0.75, 1.25, 1.75$. The spring is either stretched or compressed the most when Y_1 is maximum.

[0, 2, 0.5] by [-1, 40, 8]

(c) $P = 16k(1 - \sin^2(2\pi t))$

SECTION 7.2 (pp. 571–572)

1. (a) $1 - x^2$ **(b)** $\cos^2\theta$
3. (a) $x^2 - x$ **(b)** $\sec^2\theta - \sec\theta$ **5. (a)** y **(b)** $\sin\theta$
7. (a) $(x + 1)(x + 1)$ **(b)** $(\cos\theta + 1)(\cos\theta + 1)$
9. (a) $x(x - 2)$ **(b)** $\sec t(\sec t - 2)$
11. (a) $x(1 + x^2)$ **(b)** $\tan\theta\sec^2\theta$
13. (a) $\dfrac{2}{1 - x^2}$ **(b)** $2\csc^2\theta$
15. (a) $\dfrac{x^2 + y^2}{xy}$ **(b)** $\sec t\csc t$ **17. (a)** $y^2 + x^2$ **(b)** 1
19. (a) x **(b)** $\cos\theta$ **21.** $\sin\theta$ **23.** $\sin\theta - \sec\theta$
25. $2\tan t + \sec^2 t$ **27.** $\cos^2\theta$
29. $(1 - \tan\theta)(1 + \tan\theta)$ **31.** $(\sec t - 3)(\sec t + 2)$

33. $\sec^2\theta(\tan^2\theta + 2)$
35. $\csc^2\theta - \cot^2\theta = 1 + \cot^2\theta - \cot^2\theta = 1$
37. $(1 - \sin t)^2 = 1 - 2\sin t + \sin^2 t$ (FOIL)
39. $\dfrac{\sin t + \cos t}{\sin t} = \dfrac{\sin t}{\sin t} + \dfrac{\cos t}{\sin t} = 1 + \cot t$
41. $\sec^2\theta - 1 = (1 + \tan^2\theta) - 1$
$= \tan^2\theta$
43. $\dfrac{\tan^2 t}{\sec t} = \dfrac{\sec^2 t - 1}{\sec t}$
$= \sec t - \dfrac{1}{\sec t}$
$= \sec t - \cos t$
45. $\cot x + 1 = \dfrac{\cos x}{\sin x} + \dfrac{\sin x}{\sin x}$
$= \dfrac{1}{\sin x}(\cos x + \sin x)$
$= \csc x(\cos x + \sin x)$
47. $\dfrac{\sec t}{1 + \sec t} = \dfrac{\sec t}{1 + \sec t} \cdot \dfrac{\cos t}{\cos t}$
$= \dfrac{1}{\cos t + 1}$
49. $(\sec t - 1)(\sec t + 1) = \sec^2 t - 1$
$= \tan^2 t$
51. $\dfrac{1 - \sin^2\theta}{\cos\theta} = \dfrac{\cos^2\theta}{\cos\theta} = \cos\theta$
53. $\dfrac{\sec t}{\tan t} - \dfrac{\tan t}{\sec t} = \dfrac{\sec^2 t - \tan^2 t}{\sec t\tan t}$
$= \dfrac{(1 + \tan^2 t) - \tan^2 t}{\sec t\tan t}$
$= \dfrac{1}{\sec t\tan t}$
$= \cos t\cot t$
55. $\dfrac{\cot^2 t}{\csc t + 1} = \dfrac{\csc^2 t - 1}{\csc t + 1}$
$= \dfrac{(\csc t + 1)(\csc t - 1)}{\csc t + 1}$
$= \csc t - 1$
57. $\dfrac{\cot t}{\cot t + 1} = \dfrac{\cot t}{\cot t + 1} \cdot \dfrac{\tan t}{\tan t}$
$= \dfrac{\cot t\tan t}{\cot t\tan t + \tan t}$
$= \dfrac{1}{1 + \tan t}$
59. $\dfrac{1}{1 - \sin t} + \dfrac{1}{1 + \sin t} = \dfrac{(1 + \sin t) + (1 - \sin t)}{(1 - \sin t)(1 + \sin t)}$
$= \dfrac{2}{1 - \sin^2 t}$
$= \dfrac{2}{\cos^2 t}$
$= 2\sec^2 t$
61. $\dfrac{\csc t + \cot t}{\csc t - \cot t} = \dfrac{\csc t + \cot t}{\csc t - \cot t} \cdot \dfrac{\csc t + \cot t}{\csc t + \cot t}$
$= \dfrac{(\csc t + \cot t)^2}{\csc^2 t - \cot^2 t}$
$= \dfrac{(\csc t + \cot t)^2}{\csc^2 t - (\csc^2 t - 1)}$
$= (\csc t + \cot t)^2$
63. $\dfrac{\cos^2 t}{1 - \sin t} = \dfrac{\cos^2 t}{1 - \sin t} \cdot \dfrac{1 + \sin t}{1 + \sin t}$
$= \dfrac{\cos^2 t(1 + \sin t)}{1 - \sin^2 t}$
$= \dfrac{\cos^2 t(1 + \sin t)}{\cos^2 t}$
$= 1 + \sin t$
65. $\dfrac{1}{1 + \sin\theta} = \dfrac{1}{1 + \sin\theta} \cdot \dfrac{1 - \sin\theta}{1 - \sin\theta}$
$= \dfrac{1 - \sin\theta}{1 - \sin^2\theta}$
$= \dfrac{1 - \sin\theta}{\cos^2\theta}$
67. $\sqrt{1 - \sin^2\theta} = \sqrt{\cos^2\theta}$
$= |\cos\theta|$
$= \cos\theta$, where θ is acute

69. $\dfrac{1 + 2\sin x + \sin^2 x}{\cos^2 x} = \dfrac{(1 + \sin x)^2}{1 - \sin^2 x}$

$= \dfrac{(1 + \sin x)(1 + \sin x)}{(1 - \sin x)(1 + \sin x)}$

$= \dfrac{1 + \sin x}{1 - \sin x}$

71. $(1 - \cos^2 x)(1 + \cos^2 x) = \sin^2 x\,(1 + (1 - \sin^2 x))$

$= \sin^2 x\,(2 - \sin^2 x)$

$= 2\sin^2 x - \sin^4 x$

73. $\cot\theta\,\sin\theta = \dfrac{\cos\theta}{\sin\theta}\cdot\sin\theta$

$= \cos\theta$

75. $(1 - \cos^2\theta)(1 + \tan^2\theta) = \sin^2\theta\,\sec^2\theta$

$= \dfrac{\sin^2\theta}{\cos^2\theta}$

$= \tan^2\theta$

77. $\cos t(\tan t - \sec t) = \cos t\left(\dfrac{\sin t}{\cos t} - \dfrac{1}{\cos t}\right)$

$= \sin t - 1$

79. $\dfrac{\tan(-\theta)}{\sin(-\theta)} = \dfrac{-\tan\theta}{-\sin\theta}$

$= \dfrac{1}{\cos\theta}$

$= \sec\theta$

81. (a) $W(t) = 5(1 - \sin^2(120\pi t));\ W = 0$
(b) Whenever there is a peak or valley on the graph of V, the graph of W intersects the x-axis, which corresponds to a zero of W.

$[0, 1/15, 1/60]$ by $[-30, 30, 10]$

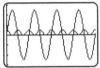

CHECKING BASIC CONCEPTS FOR SECTIONS 7.1 AND 7.2 (p. 572)

1. Quadrant III   **3. (a)** $\cos^2\theta$ **(b)** $\tan^2 t$
5. (a) $(1 - \sin^2\theta)(1 + \cot^2\theta) = \cos^2\theta\,\csc^2\theta$

$= \dfrac{\cos^2\theta}{\sin^2\theta} = \cot^2\theta$

(b) $\dfrac{\cot^2 t}{\csc t} = \dfrac{\csc^2 t - 1}{\csc t}$

$= \dfrac{\csc^2 t}{\csc t} - \dfrac{1}{\csc t}$

$= \csc t - \sin t$

SECTION 7.3 (pp. 583–586)

1. $60°$ **3.** $85°$ **5.** $65°$ **7.** $\frac{\pi}{6}$ **9.** $\frac{\pi}{3}$ **11.** $\frac{\pi}{4}$
13. (a) $90°; \frac{\pi}{2}$ **(b)** $270°; \frac{3\pi}{2}$
15. (a) $60°, 240°; \frac{\pi}{3}, \frac{4\pi}{3}$ **(b)** $120°, 300°; \frac{2\pi}{3}, \frac{5\pi}{3}$
17. (a) $60°, 300°; \frac{\pi}{3}, \frac{5\pi}{3}$ **(b)** $120°, 240°; \frac{2\pi}{3}, \frac{4\pi}{3}$
19. (a) No solutions   **(b)** No solutions
21. (a) $\frac{\pi}{6} + 2\pi n, \frac{5\pi}{6} + 2\pi n$ **(b)** $\frac{7\pi}{6} + 2\pi n, \frac{11\pi}{6} + 2\pi n$
23. (a) $\frac{\pi}{4} + \pi n$ **(b)** $\frac{3\pi}{4} + \pi n$
25. (a) $\frac{\pi}{3} + 2\pi n, \frac{5\pi}{3} + 2\pi n$ **(b)** $\frac{2\pi}{3} + 2\pi n, \frac{4\pi}{3} + 2\pi n$
27. $\frac{\pi}{4}, \frac{5\pi}{4}$ **29.** $\frac{\pi}{3}, \frac{5\pi}{3}$ **31. (a)** $\frac{1}{2}$ **(b)** $30°, 150°$
33. (a) $0, 1$ **(b)** $0°, 90°, 180°$
35. (a) $-1, 1$ **(b)** $\frac{\pi}{4}, \frac{3\pi}{4}, \frac{5\pi}{4}, \frac{7\pi}{4}$
37. (a) $-2, 1$ **(b)** 0 **39.** $\frac{\pi}{3}, \frac{2\pi}{3}, \frac{4\pi}{3}, \frac{5\pi}{3}$ **41.** No solutions

43. $\frac{\pi}{2}, \frac{3\pi}{2}$ **45.** $\frac{\pi}{4}, \frac{5\pi}{4}$ **47.** $\frac{\pi}{6}, \frac{5\pi}{6}, \frac{7\pi}{6}, \frac{11\pi}{6}$ **49.** $0, \frac{\pi}{2}, \pi, \frac{3\pi}{2}$
51. $\frac{\pi}{3}, \frac{5\pi}{3}$ **53.** 0 **55.** $\frac{\pi}{4} + \pi n$ **57.** $\frac{\pi}{6} + 2\pi n, \frac{5\pi}{6} + 2\pi n$
59. $\frac{\pi}{6} + 2\pi n, \frac{5\pi}{6} + 2\pi n, \frac{\pi}{2} + 2\pi n$
61. $\frac{2\pi}{3} + 2\pi n, \frac{4\pi}{3} + 2\pi n, \pi + 2\pi n$ **63.** $\frac{\pi}{4} + \frac{\pi n}{2}$
65. No solutions   **67.** πn **69.** $\frac{\pi}{4} + \pi n$ **71.** $\frac{\pi n}{2}$
73. $2\pi n, \frac{\pi}{2} + 2\pi n$ **75.** $\frac{\pi}{18} + \frac{2\pi}{3}n, \frac{5\pi}{18} + \frac{2\pi}{3}n$
77. $\frac{5\pi}{24} + \frac{\pi}{2}n, \frac{7\pi}{24} + \frac{\pi}{2}n$ **79.** $\frac{\pi}{20} + \frac{\pi}{5}n$
81. $\frac{7\pi}{24} + \frac{\pi}{2}n, \frac{11\pi}{24} + \frac{\pi}{2}n$ **83.** $\frac{3\pi}{16} + \frac{\pi}{2}n, \frac{5\pi}{16} + \frac{\pi}{2}n$
85. $\frac{\pi}{16} + \frac{\pi}{4}n$ **87.** $\frac{\pi}{16} + \frac{\pi}{4}n$
89. $0.456 + \frac{2\pi}{3}n, 1.638 + \frac{2\pi}{3}n$
91. $0.170 + \pi n, 1.401 + \pi n$ **93.** $1.085, 5.198$
95. $0.737, 2.404$ **97.** $0.659, 2.483, 3.801, 5.624$
99. $0, 4.49$ **101.** $0.39, 1.96$ **103.** 3.60
105. $30°, 210°; 30° + 180° \cdot n$ **107.** 1
109. $-\dfrac{\sqrt{3}}{2} \approx -0.866$ **111.** -1 **113.** 0
115. $\dfrac{1}{\sqrt{2}} \approx 0.707$ **117.** $60° + 360° \cdot n, 300° + 360° \cdot n$
119. About $9.1°$
121. $2.6, 10.7$; near February 17 and October 22
123. $2.6, 10.7$; near February 17 and October 22
125. (a) $f(x) = 122.3\sin(0.524x - 1.7) + 367$ (answers may vary)
(b) $2.98 \le x \le 9.51$ (approximately). At $50°$N latitude, the maximum number of monthly hours of sunshine is greater than or equal to 350 hours roughly from March through September.
127. 0.26
129. (a) $[0, 0.01, 0.005]$ by $[-0.005, 0.005, 0.001]$ $[0, 0.01, 0.005]$ by $[-0.005, 0.005, 0.001]$

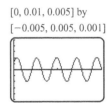

$[0, 0.01, 0.005]$ by $[-0.005, 0.005, 0.001]$

(b) Maximum: $P \approx 0.004$
(c) No; the maximum of P_1 is 0.003, and the maximum of P_2 is 0.002.

SECTION 7.4 (pp. 595–597)

1. $\dfrac{\sqrt{6} - \sqrt{2}}{4}$ **3.** $2 - \sqrt{3}$ **5.** $\dfrac{\sqrt{6} - \sqrt{2}}{4}$ **7.** $\dfrac{\sqrt{6} - \sqrt{2}}{4}$
9. $\dfrac{\sqrt{6} + \sqrt{2}}{4}$ **11. (a)** The graphs of $y = \sin\left(t + \frac{\pi}{2}\right)$ and $y = \cos t$ are the same.
(b) $\sin\left(t + \frac{\pi}{2}\right) = \sin t\cos\frac{\pi}{2} + \cos t\sin\frac{\pi}{2}$

$= \sin t\,(0) + \cos t\,(1)$

$= \cos t$

13. (a) The graphs of $y = \cos(t + \pi)$ and $y = -\cos t$ are the same.
(b) $\cos(t + \pi) = \cos t\cos\pi - \sin t\sin\pi$

$= \cos t\,(-1) - \sin t\,(0)$

$= -\cos t$

15. (a) The graphs of $y = \sec\left(t - \frac{\pi}{2}\right)$ and $y = \csc t$ are the same.

(b) $\sec\left(t - \frac{\pi}{2}\right) = \dfrac{1}{\cos\left(t - \frac{\pi}{2}\right)}$

$= \dfrac{1}{\cos t \cos\frac{\pi}{2} + \sin t \sin\frac{\pi}{2}}$

$= \dfrac{1}{\cos t (0) + \sin t (1)}$

$= \dfrac{1}{\sin t}$

$= \csc t$

17. $\sin\left(\frac{\pi}{2} - t\right) = \sin\frac{\pi}{2}\cos t - \cos\frac{\pi}{2}\sin t$

$= (1)\cos t - (0)\sin t$

$= \cos t$

19. $\sec\left(\frac{\pi}{2} - t\right) = \dfrac{1}{\cos\left(\frac{\pi}{2} - t\right)}$

$= \dfrac{1}{\cos\frac{\pi}{2}\cos t + \sin\frac{\pi}{2}\sin t}$

$= \dfrac{1}{(0)\cos t + (1)\sin t}$

$= \dfrac{1}{\sin t}$

$= \csc t$

21. (a) $\frac{56}{65}$ **(b)** $\frac{33}{65}$ **(c)** $\frac{56}{33}$ **(d)** I

23. (a) $-\frac{988}{1037}$ **(b)** $\frac{315}{1037}$ **(c)** $-\frac{988}{315}$ **(d)** IV

25. (a) $-\frac{33}{65}$ **(b)** $-\frac{56}{65}$ **(c)** $\frac{33}{56}$ **(d)** III

27. (a) $-\frac{775}{793}$ **(b)** $-\frac{168}{793}$ **(c)** $\frac{775}{168}$ **(d)** III

29. $\cos\left(t - \frac{\pi}{4}\right) = \cos t \cos\frac{\pi}{4} + \sin t \sin\frac{\pi}{4}$

$= \cos t\left(\frac{\sqrt{2}}{2}\right) + \sin t\left(\frac{\sqrt{2}}{2}\right)$

$= \frac{\sqrt{2}}{2}(\cos t + \sin t)$

31. $\tan\left(t + \frac{\pi}{4}\right) = \dfrac{\tan t + \tan\frac{\pi}{4}}{1 - \tan t \tan\frac{\pi}{4}}$

$= \dfrac{\tan t + 1}{1 - \tan t (1)}$

$= \dfrac{1 + \tan t}{1 - \tan t}$

33. $\dfrac{\cos(x - y)}{\cos(x + y)} = \dfrac{\cos x \cos y + \sin x \sin y}{\cos x \cos y - \sin x \sin y}$

$= \dfrac{\frac{\cos x \cos y}{\cos x \cos y} + \frac{\sin x \sin y}{\cos x \cos y}}{\frac{\cos x \cos y}{\cos x \cos y} - \frac{\sin x \sin y}{\cos x \cos y}}$

$= \dfrac{1 + \tan x \tan y}{1 - \tan x \tan y}$

35. $\dfrac{\cos(\alpha - \beta)}{\cos\alpha \sin\beta} = \dfrac{\cos\alpha \cos\beta + \sin\alpha \sin\beta}{\cos\alpha \sin\beta}$

$= \dfrac{\cos\alpha \cos\beta}{\cos\alpha \sin\beta} + \dfrac{\sin\alpha \sin\beta}{\cos\alpha \sin\beta}$

$= \dfrac{\cos\beta}{\sin\beta} + \dfrac{\sin\alpha}{\cos\alpha}$

$= \cot\beta + \tan\alpha$

$= \tan\alpha + \cot\beta$

37. $\sin 2t = \sin(t + t)$

$= \sin t \cos t + \cos t \sin t$

$= 2\sin t \cos t$

39. $\sin(\alpha + \beta) + \sin(\alpha - \beta)$

$= \sin\alpha \cos\beta + \cos\alpha \sin\beta + \sin\alpha \cos\beta$

$\quad - \cos\alpha \sin\beta$

$= \sin\alpha \cos\beta + \sin\alpha \cos\beta$

$= 2\sin\alpha \cos\beta$

41. $\tan(\pi - \theta) = \dfrac{\tan\pi - \tan\theta}{1 + \tan\pi \tan\theta}$

$= \dfrac{0 - \tan\theta}{1 + (0)\tan\theta}$

$= -\tan\theta$

43. $\tan(x - y) - \tan(y - x)$

$= \dfrac{\tan x - \tan y}{1 + \tan x \tan y} - \dfrac{\tan y - \tan x}{1 + \tan y \tan x}$

$= \dfrac{\tan x - \tan y - \tan y + \tan x}{1 + \tan x \tan y}$

$= \dfrac{2(\tan x - \tan y)}{1 + \tan x \tan y}$

45. $\dfrac{\sin(x + y)}{\cos x \cos y} = \dfrac{\sin x \cos y + \cos x \sin y}{\cos x \cos y}$

$= \dfrac{\sin x \cos y}{\cos x \cos y} + \dfrac{\cos x \sin y}{\cos x \cos y}$

$= \dfrac{\sin x}{\cos x} + \dfrac{\sin y}{\cos y}$

$= \tan x + \tan y$

47. $\frac{7}{79}$

49. $\tan\theta = \tan(\beta - \alpha)$

$= \dfrac{\tan\beta - \tan\alpha}{1 + \tan\alpha \tan\beta}$

$= \dfrac{m_2 - m_1}{1 + m_1 m_2}$

51. $\theta = \tan^{-1}\frac{7}{11} \approx 32.5°$

53. (a) $F \approx 409$ lb **(b)** About 0.81, or 46.2°

55. (a) $[0, 0.02, 0.001]$ by $[-6, 6, 1]$

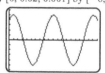

(b) $a = 5, k \approx 0.9272$

(c) $5\sin(220\pi t + 0.9272)$

$= 5(\sin(220\pi t)\cos(0.9272)$

$\quad + \cos(220\pi t)\sin(0.9272))$

$\approx 5(0.6\sin(220\pi t) + 0.8\cos(220\pi t))$

$= 3\sin(220\pi t) + 4\cos(220\pi t)$

7.4 EXTENDED AND DISCOVERY EXERCISES (p. 597)

1. (a) $[0.15, 1.15, 0.05]$ by $[-0.01, 0.01, 0.001]$

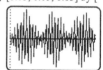

There are 3 beats in 1 second.

(b) $[0.15, 1.15, 0.05]$ by $[-0.01, 0.01, 0.001]$

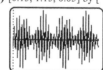

There are 4 beats in 1 second.

(c) When the frequencies are F_1 and F_2, the rate of beats per second is given by $|F_2 - F_1|$.

3. $[0.2, 1.2, 0.05]$ by $[-0.01, 0.01, 0.001]$

There are 3 beats in 1 second.

CHECKING BASIC CONCEPTS FOR SECTIONS 7.3 AND 7.4 (p. 597)

1. (a) $45°$ **(b)** $\frac{\pi}{6}$

3. (a) $\frac{3\pi}{4} + \pi n$ **(b)** $\frac{2\pi}{3} + 2\pi n$; $\frac{4\pi}{3} + 2\pi n$; $2\pi n$

5. $\sin(t - \pi) = \sin t \cos \pi - \cos t \sin \pi$
$= \sin t(-1) - \cos t(0)$
$= -\sin t$

SECTION 7.5 (pp. 609–612)

1. $\frac{1 - \cos 20t}{2}$ **3.** $\frac{1 - \cos 10t}{1 + \cos 10t}$

5. $2 \sin 10x \cos 10x$ **7.** $\frac{1 - \cos 10x}{\sin 10x}$

9. (a) 1 **(b)** $\frac{\sqrt{3}}{2}$; not equal

11. (a) 1 **(b)** $-\frac{1}{2}$; not equal

13. (a) 2 **(b)** Undefined; not equal

15. *Graphical:* Graphs of $y = \tan 2\theta$ and $y = 2 \tan \theta$ are not the same.
Symbolic: $\tan 2\theta = \frac{2 \tan \theta}{1 - \tan^2 \theta} \neq 2 \tan \theta$,
unless $\tan \theta = 0$.

17. $\sin 2\theta = \frac{24}{25}$, $\cos 2\theta = \frac{7}{25}$, $\tan 2\theta = \frac{24}{7}$

19. $\sin 2\theta = -\frac{336}{625}$, $\cos 2\theta = -\frac{527}{625}$, $\tan 2\theta = \frac{336}{527}$

21. $\sin 2\theta = -\frac{1320}{3721}$, $\cos 2\theta = \frac{3479}{3721}$, $\tan 2\theta = -\frac{1320}{3479}$

23. $\sin 2\theta = \frac{336}{625}$, $\cos 2\theta = \frac{527}{625}$, $\tan 2\theta = \frac{336}{527}$

25. 0 **27.** $\frac{527}{625}$ **29.** $\frac{828}{2197}$ **31.** $\frac{2x}{x^2 + 1}$ **33.** $\frac{24}{25}$

35. $\sin 2\theta$ **37.** $\frac{1}{2} \sin 2\theta$ **39.** $\cos 4\theta$ **41.** 1

43. $\cot^2 5x$ **45.** $\frac{2 + \sqrt{2}}{4}$ **47.** $\frac{2 + \sqrt{3}}{2 - \sqrt{3}}$

49. (a) $\frac{\sqrt{2 + \sqrt{3}}}{2}$

(b) $-\sqrt{\frac{2 - \sqrt{3}}{2 + \sqrt{3}}}$, or $-\frac{1}{2 + \sqrt{3}}$, or $\sqrt{3} - 2$

51. (a) $\sqrt{\frac{2 - \sqrt{2}}{2 + \sqrt{2}}}$, or $\frac{\sqrt{2}}{2 + \sqrt{2}}$, or $\sqrt{2} - 1$

(b) $-\frac{\sqrt{2 - \sqrt{2}}}{2}$

53. $\sin 30°$ **55.** $\cos 25°$ **57.** $\tan 20°$

59. $\sin \frac{\theta}{2} = \frac{1}{\sqrt{10}}$, $\cos \frac{\theta}{2} = \frac{3}{\sqrt{10}}$, $\tan \frac{\theta}{2} = \frac{1}{3}$

61. $\sin \frac{\theta}{2} = -\frac{1}{\sqrt{26}}$, $\cos \frac{\theta}{2} = \frac{5}{\sqrt{26}}$, $\tan \frac{\theta}{2} = -\frac{1}{5}$

63. $\sin \frac{\theta}{2} = \frac{4}{5}$, $\cos \frac{\theta}{2} = \frac{3}{5}$, $\tan \frac{\theta}{2} = \frac{4}{3}$

65. $4 \sin 2x = 4(2 \sin x \cos x)$
$= 8 \sin x \cos x$

67. $\frac{2 - \sec^2 x}{\sec^2 x} = \frac{2}{\sec^2 x} - 1$
$= 2 \cos^2 x - 1$
$= \cos 2x$

69. $\sec 2x = \frac{1}{\cos 2x}$
$= \frac{1}{1 - 2 \sin^2 x}$

71. $\sin 3\theta = \sin(2\theta + \theta)$
$= \sin 2\theta \cos \theta + \cos 2\theta \sin \theta$
$= (2 \sin \theta \cos \theta) \cos \theta + (1 - 2 \sin^2 \theta) \sin \theta$
$= 2 \sin \theta \cos^2 \theta + \sin \theta - 2 \sin^3 \theta$
$= 2 \sin \theta(1 - \sin^2 \theta) + \sin \theta - 2 \sin^3 \theta$
$= 2 \sin \theta - 2 \sin^3 \theta + \sin \theta - 2 \sin^3 \theta$
$= 3 \sin \theta - 4 \sin^3 \theta$

73. $\sin 4\theta = 2 \sin 2\theta \cos 2\theta$
$= 2(2 \sin \theta \cos \theta) \cos 2\theta$
$= 4 \sin \theta \cos \theta \cos 2\theta$

75. $\frac{\sin 2\theta}{\sin \theta} = \frac{2 \sin \theta \cos \theta}{\sin \theta}$
$= 2 \cos \theta$

77. $2 \cos^2 \frac{\theta}{2} = 2\left(\frac{1 + \cos \theta}{2}\right)$
$= 1 + \cos \theta$

79. $\cos^4 \theta - \sin^4 \theta = (\cos^2 \theta - \sin^2 \theta)(\cos^2 \theta + \sin^2 \theta)$
$= (\cos 2\theta)(1)$
$= \cos 2\theta$

81. $\csc 2t = \frac{1}{\sin 2t}$
$= \frac{1}{2 \sin t \cos t}$
$= \frac{\csc t}{2 \cos t}$

83. $\tan \frac{x}{2} = \frac{\sin \frac{x}{2}}{\cos \frac{x}{2}}$
$= \frac{2 \sin \frac{x}{2} \cos \frac{x}{2}}{2 \cos \frac{x}{2} \cos \frac{x}{2}}$
$= \frac{\sin x}{2 \cos^2 \frac{x}{2}}$
$= \frac{\sin x}{1 + \cos x}$

85. (a) $\frac{1}{2}(\sin 70° - \sin 30°)$ **(b)** $\frac{1}{2}(\cos 3x + \cos x)$

87. (a) $\frac{1}{2}(\sin 10\theta + \sin 4\theta)$ **(b)** $\frac{1}{2}(\cos 4x - \cos 12x)$

89. (a) $2 \sin 35° \cos 5°$ **(b)** $2 \cos 40° \cos 5°$

91. (a) $2 \cos 5\theta \cos \theta$ **(b)** $2 \sin \frac{11x}{2} \cos \frac{3x}{2}$ **93.** $0°, 180°$

95. $90°, 210°, 270°, 330°$ **97.** π **99.** $\frac{\pi}{2}, \frac{3\pi}{2}$

101. $\frac{\pi}{12} + \pi n, \frac{11\pi}{12} + \pi n$ **103.** $\pi n, \frac{2\pi}{3} + 2\pi n, \frac{4\pi}{3} + 2\pi n$

105. $\frac{\pi}{3} + 4\pi n, \frac{5\pi}{3} + 4\pi n$

107. $\frac{\pi}{6} + 2\pi n, \frac{5\pi}{6} + 2\pi n, \frac{3\pi}{2} + 2\pi n$

109. $\frac{\pi}{8} + \pi n, \frac{5\pi}{8} + \pi n$, or equivalently, $\frac{\pi}{8} + \frac{\pi n}{2}$

111. $\frac{2\pi}{3} + 4\pi n, \frac{10\pi}{3} + 4\pi n$

113. $\frac{\pi}{8} + \pi n, \frac{5\pi}{8} + \pi n$, or equivalently, $\frac{\pi}{8} + \frac{\pi n}{2}$

115. $\frac{\pi}{12} + \pi n, \frac{5\pi}{12} + \pi n, \frac{3\pi}{4} + \pi n$ **117.** $0.333, 4.379$

119. (a) $[0, 0.04, 0.01]$ by $[-500, 2500, 500]$

(b) $a = -1085, k = 240, d = 1085$

121. $\frac{1}{720} + \frac{n}{60}$, $\frac{5}{720} + \frac{n}{60}$ sec

123. (a) $d = 600\left(1 - \cos \frac{80°}{2}\right) \approx 140.4$ ft

(b) *Hint:* First show that $r = d + r \cos \frac{\beta}{2}$. See Student's Solutions Manual.

(c) No, since $\cos \frac{\beta}{2} \neq \frac{1}{2} \cos \beta$ in general

125. Let $f(t)$ model the tone for the number 3 and $g(t)$ model the tone for number 4.

(a) $f(t) = \cos(1394\pi t) + \cos(2954\pi t)$
$g(t) = \cos(1540\pi t) + \cos(2418\pi t)$

(b) $f(t) = 2 \cos(2174\pi t) \cos(780\pi t)$
$g(t) = 2 \cos(1979\pi t) \cos(439\pi t)$

CHECKING BASIC CONCEPTS FOR SECTION 7.5 (p. 612)

1. $\sin 2\theta = -\frac{336}{625}$, $\cos 2\theta = -\frac{527}{625}$

3. $\sin \frac{\theta}{2} = \frac{1}{\sqrt{5}}$, $\cos \frac{\theta}{2} = \frac{2}{\sqrt{5}}$ **5.** $\frac{\pi}{2}, \frac{3\pi}{2}$

CHAPTER 7 REVIEW EXERCISES (pp. 616–618)

1. Quadrant II

3. $\tan\theta = -\frac{3}{4}$, $\csc\theta = \frac{5}{3}$, $\sec\theta = -\frac{5}{4}$, $\cot\theta = -\frac{4}{3}$

5. $\sin\theta = -\frac{7}{25}$, $\csc\theta = -\frac{25}{7}$, $\sec\theta = \frac{25}{24}$, $\cot\theta = -\frac{24}{7}$

7. $-\sin 13°$ **9.** $\sec\frac{3\pi}{7}$ **11.** 1 **13.** 1 **15.** $\cos\theta$

17. $\sin\theta \approx 0.7776$, $\cos\theta \approx 0.6288$, $\csc\theta \approx 1.2860$, $\sec\theta \approx 1.5904$, $\cot\theta \approx 0.8086$

19. $\sin\theta \approx 0.8908$, $\tan\theta \approx -1.9604$, $\csc\theta \approx 1.1226$, $\sec\theta \approx -2.2007$, $\cot\theta \approx -0.5101$

21. $(\sin\theta + 1)(\sin\theta + 1)$ **23.** $(\tan\theta + 3)(\tan\theta - 3)$

25. $(\sec\theta - 1)(\sec\theta + 1) = \sec^2\theta - 1$
$= (1 + \tan^2\theta) - 1$
$= \tan^2\theta$

27. $(1 + \tan t)^2 = 1 + 2\tan t + \tan^2 t$
$= \sec^2 t + 2\tan t$

29. $\sin(x - \pi) = \sin x \cos\pi - \cos x \sin\pi$
$= \sin x(-1) - \cos x(0)$
$= -\sin x$

31. $\sin 8x = \sin(2 \cdot 4x)$
$= 2\sin 4x \cos 4x$

33. $\sec 2x = \frac{1}{\cos 2x}$
$= \frac{1}{2\cos^2 x - 1}$

35. $\cos^4 x \sin^3 x = \cos^4 x \sin^2 x \sin x$
$= \cos^4 x(1 - \cos^2 x)\sin x$
$= (\cos^4 x - \cos^6 x)\sin x$

37. $\sec^4\theta - \tan^4\theta = (\sec^2\theta - \tan^2\theta)(\sec^2\theta + \tan^2\theta)$
$= (1)(1 + \tan^2\theta + \tan^2\theta)$
$= 1 + 2\tan^2\theta$

39. $60°$ **41.** $\frac{2\pi}{7}$ **43.** $\frac{\pi}{2}, \frac{3\pi}{2}$

45. (a) $60°, 240°$ (b) $150°, 330°$

47. $\frac{\pi}{3}, \frac{5\pi}{3}$ **49.** $\frac{\pi}{2}$ **51.** $\frac{\pi}{4}, \frac{5\pi}{4}$

53. $\frac{\pi}{6} + \pi n, -\frac{\pi}{6} + \pi n$; $30° + 180° \cdot n, -30° + 180° \cdot n$

55. $\frac{\pi}{2} + \pi n$; $90° + 180° \cdot n$

57. $-\frac{\sqrt{2 - \sqrt{3}}}{2}$ **59.** $-4.43, 1.13, 4.53$

61. (a) $\sin(\alpha + \beta) = \frac{63}{65}$ (b) $\cos(\alpha + \beta) = \frac{16}{65}$,
(c) $\tan(\alpha + \beta) = \frac{63}{16}$ (d) Quadrant I

63. $\sin 2\theta = -\frac{24}{25}$, $\cos 2\theta = -\frac{7}{25}$, $\tan 2\theta = \frac{24}{7}$

65. $\sin\frac{\theta}{2} = \sqrt{\frac{3}{8}}$, $\cos\frac{\theta}{2} = \sqrt{\frac{5}{8}}$, $\tan\frac{\theta}{2} = \sqrt{\frac{3}{5}}$

67. $\frac{3479}{3721}$ **69.** $x = 4.7, 8.7$, about April 21 and August 22

71. (a) $[0, 0.06, 0.01]$ by $[-0.012, 0.012, 0.002]$

(b) $a = 0.01$, $k \approx 0.6435$

(c) $0.01\sin(100\pi t + 0.6435)$
$= 0.01(\sin(100\pi t)\cos(0.6435)$
$+ \cos(100\pi t)\sin(0.6435))$
$\approx 0.01(0.8\sin(100\pi t) + 0.6\cos(100\pi t))$
$\approx 0.008\sin(100\pi t) + 0.006\cos(100\pi t)$

73. $W(t) = 7 - 7\sin^2(240\pi t)$; when V is maximum or minimum, $W = 0$.

75. $\theta \approx 30.11°$, or 0.53 radian

CHAPTER 7 EXTENDED AND DISCOVERY EXERCISES (p. 618)

1. (a) **i.** $[0, 0.01, 0.002]$ by
$[-0.005, 0.005, 0.001]$

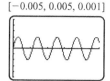

ii. $[0, 0.01, 0.002]$ by
$[-0.005, 0.005, 0.001]$

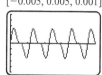

iii. $[0, 0.01, 0.002]$ by
$[-0.005, 0.005, 0.001]$

iv. $[0, 0.01, 0.002]$ by
$[-0.005, 0.005, 0.001]$

v. $[0, 0.01, 0.002]$ by $[-0.005, 0.005, 0.001]$

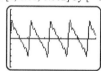

(b) The graph approximates a saw-tooth shape.
(c) The maximum pressure of P is approximately 0.00317.
(d) The pure tone is modeled by a smooth graph, whereas the piano tone is modeled by a saw-tooth shape.

3. (a) $[0, 1, 0.1]$ by $[-0.15, 0.15, 0.05]$

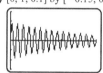

(b) These graphs bound the changing amplitude of A.
$[0, 1, 0.1]$ by $[-0.15, 0.15, 0.05]$

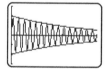

(c) $t \approx 0.55$ second (answers may vary slightly)

CHAPTER 8: Further Topics in Trigonometry

SECTION 8.1 (PP. 628–632)

1. $\beta = 60°$, $a \approx 5.5$, $b \approx 4.9$

3. $\beta = 35°$, $a \approx 15.1$, $c \approx 7.4$

5. $\gamma = 80°$, $a \approx 6.5$, $b \approx 8.8$

7. $\beta = 115°$, $b \approx 20.8$, $c \approx 14.8$

9. $\alpha = 79.1°$, $b \approx 3.6$, $c \approx 4.9$

11. $\beta = 104°$, $a \approx 31.3$, $c \approx 52.1$

13. No **15.** No **17.** Yes **19.** Yes

21. $\beta_1 \approx 57.1°$, $\gamma_1 \approx 76.9°$, $c_1 \approx 8.1$
$\beta_2 \approx 122.9°$, $\gamma_2 \approx 11.1°$, $c_2 \approx 1.6$

23. There are no solutions.

25. $\beta_1 \approx 67°13'$, $\gamma_1 \approx 62°35'$, $c_1 \approx 11.6$
$\beta_2 \approx 112°48'$, $\gamma_2 \approx 17°0'$, $c_2 \approx 3.8$

27. $\gamma = 93°$, $a \approx 7.8$, $c \approx 14.6$

29. $\beta_1 \approx 26.1°, \gamma_1 \approx 133.9°, c_1 \approx 14.7$
$\beta_2 \approx 153.9°, \gamma_2 \approx 6.1°, c_2 \approx 2.2$
31. $\gamma = 90°, \alpha = 60°, a = 10\sqrt{3} \approx 17.3$
33. $\alpha \approx 52.9°, \beta \approx 25.1°, b \approx 22.4$
35. $\beta = 10°, a \approx 92.2, c \approx 101.9$
37. There are no solutions.   **39.** There are no solutions.
41. $\alpha_1 \approx 60°56', \gamma_1 \approx 72°19', c_1 \approx 6.5$
$\alpha_2 \approx 119°4', \gamma_2 \approx 14°11', c_2 \approx 1.7$
43. $\gamma = 99°45', a \approx 84.6, b \approx 40.9$ **45.** 3629 ft
47. The calculated distance to the moon changes to about
343,000 km, a difference of about 76,000 km. A small error
in measuring the lunar angle could result in large errors in
calculating the distance to the moon.
49. $d \approx 7.2$ mi   **51.** About 28.8 ft
53. About 118.0 m   **55.** About 3.86 mi
57. About 0.49 mi   **59.** $AB \approx 105.4$ ft
61. (a) 3.57 mi   **(b)** 48°   **63.** 630 ft

SECTION 8.2 (pp. 639–642)

1. (a) SAS   **(b)** Law of cosines
3. (a) SSA   **(b)** Law of sines
5. (a) ASA   **(b)** Law of sines
7. (a) ASA   **(b)** Law of sines
9. 7   **11.** 55.8°   **13.** $a \approx 5.4, \beta \approx 40.7°, \gamma \approx 78.3°$
15. $\alpha \approx 22.3°, \beta \approx 108.2°, \gamma \approx 49.5°$
17. $\alpha \approx 33.6°, \beta \approx 50.7°, \gamma \approx 95.7°$
19. $c \approx 28.8, \alpha \approx 116.5°, \beta \approx 28.5°$
21. $\alpha \approx 101.0°, \beta \approx 44.0°, \gamma \approx 34.9°$
Angles do not sum to 180° because of rounding.
23. $a \approx 9.0, \beta \approx 150.9°, \gamma \approx 18.6°$
25. $\alpha \approx 23.1°, \beta \approx 107.2°, \gamma \approx 49.7°$
27. $b \approx 30.7, \alpha \approx 33°26', \gamma \approx 24°24'$
29. $\alpha \approx 45.1°, \beta \approx 63.5°, \gamma \approx 71.5°$
Angles do not sum to 180° because of rounding.
31. No, since $a + b < c$
33. No, since $89° + 112° > 180°$
35. Yes, since we are given ASA and $\alpha + \gamma < 180°$
37. 86.8   **39.** 5.3   **41.** 50.9   **43.** 18.3   **45.** 2.1   **47.** 18.3
49. 66   **51.** 160.4   **53.** 169 ft   **55.** About 29.8 mi
57. 4.4 ft; 7.7 ft   **59.** A to B: 76°; B to C: 309°
61. (a) $\alpha \approx 75.1°, \beta \approx 65.6°, \gamma \approx 39.4°$
Angles do not sum to 180° because of rounding.
(b) 6299 ft^2
63. $\theta \approx 40.5°$ **65.** 302 mi   **67.** About 1452 ft
69. About 745 mi   **71.** 147.8 ft^2
73. (a) $9\sqrt{3} \approx 15.6$ in^2 **(b)** The results are equal.
75. 149,429 ft^2 **77.** 21,309 ft^2

8.2 EXTENDED AND DISCOVERY EXERCISES (p. 643)

1. About 2000 km

CHECKING BASIC CONCEPTS FOR SECTIONS 8.1 AND 8.2 (p. 643)

1. $\beta = 74°, b \approx 16.6, c \approx 15.3$
3. (a) $b \approx 7.1, \alpha \approx 63.0°, \gamma \approx 66.0°$
(b) $\alpha \approx 110.7°, \beta \approx 37.0°, \gamma \approx 32.3°$

SECTION 8.3 (pp. 655–659)

1. (a) $a_1 \approx 3, a_2 \approx 4$ **(b)** $\|\mathbf{v}\| = 5$
3. (a) $a_1 \approx -5, a_2 \approx -12$ **(b)** $\|\mathbf{v}\| = 13$
5. (a) ↓ v (20 mi/hr)   **(b)** $\mathbf{v} = \langle 0, -20 \rangle$

(c) $2\mathbf{v} = \langle 0, -40 \rangle$; this represents a 40-mi/hr north wind.
$-\frac{1}{2}\mathbf{v} = \langle 0, 10 \rangle$; this represents a 10-mi/hr south wind.
7. (a) ↘ v (5 mi/hr)

(b) $\mathbf{v} = \langle \frac{5}{\sqrt{2}}, -\frac{5}{\sqrt{2}} \rangle$, or $\langle \frac{5}{2}\sqrt{2}, -\frac{5}{2}\sqrt{2} \rangle$
(c) $2\mathbf{v} = \langle \frac{10}{\sqrt{2}}, -\frac{10}{\sqrt{2}} \rangle$, or $\langle 5\sqrt{2}, -5\sqrt{2} \rangle$; this represents a
10-mi/hr northwest wind. $-\frac{1}{2}\mathbf{v} = \langle -\frac{5}{4}\sqrt{2}, \frac{5}{4}\sqrt{2} \rangle$; this
represents a 2.5-mi/hr southeast wind.
9. (a) ↑ v (30 lb)   **(b)** $\mathbf{v} = \langle 0, 30 \rangle$

(c) $2\mathbf{v} = \langle 0, 60 \rangle$; this represents a 60-lb force upward.
$-\frac{1}{2}\mathbf{v} = \langle 0, -15 \rangle$; this represents a 15-lb force downward.
11. (a) Horizontal = 1, vertical = 1
(b) $\|\mathbf{v}\| = \sqrt{2}$; $\mathbf{v}$ is not a unit vector.
(c) $\|\mathbf{v}\|$ represents the length of $\mathbf{v}$.

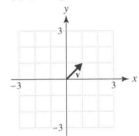

13. (a) Horizontal = 3, vertical = −4
(b) $\|\mathbf{v}\| = 5$; $\mathbf{v}$ is not a unit vector.
(c) $\|\mathbf{v}\|$ represents the length of $\mathbf{v}$.

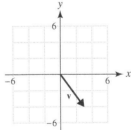

15. (a) Horizontal = 1, vertical = 0
(b) $\|\mathbf{v}\| = 1$; $\mathbf{v}$ is a unit vector.
(c) $\|\mathbf{v}\|$ represents the length of $\mathbf{v}$.

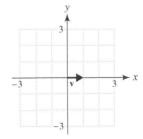

17. (a) Horizontal = 5, vertical = 12
(b) $\|\mathbf{v}\| = 13$; $\mathbf{v}$ is not a unit vector.
(c) $\|\mathbf{v}\|$ represents the length of $\mathbf{v}$.

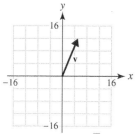

19. $3; 0°$ **21.** $\sqrt{2}; 135°$ **23.** $2; 330°$ **25.** $13; 247.4°$
27. $85; 278.8°$ **29.** $29; 133.6°$ **31.** $-4, 0$ **33.** $-1, 1$
35. $13.5, 18.6$ **37.** $22.8, -25.3$ **39.** $\langle 3\sqrt{3}, 3 \rangle$
41. $\langle -\frac{9\sqrt{2}}{2}, -\frac{9\sqrt{2}}{2} \rangle$ **43.** $\langle 3.06, 2.57 \rangle$ **45.** $\langle 4.10, -2.87 \rangle$
47. (a)

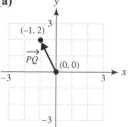

(b) $\overrightarrow{PQ} = \langle -1, 2 \rangle$
(c) $\|\overrightarrow{PQ}\| = \sqrt{5}$
49. (a)

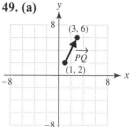

(b) $\overrightarrow{PQ} = \langle 2, 4 \rangle$
(c) $\|\overrightarrow{PQ}\| = \sqrt{20}$
51. (a)

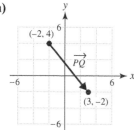

(b) $\overrightarrow{PQ} = \langle 5, -6 \rangle$ **(c)** $\|\overrightarrow{PQ}\| = \sqrt{61}$
53. 94.2 lb **55.** 24.4 lb **57.** $\mathbf{F} = -5\mathbf{i} + 12\mathbf{j}, \|\mathbf{F}\| = 13$
59. $\mathbf{F} = \langle 9, -22 \rangle, \|\mathbf{F}\| = \sqrt{565}$
61. $\mathbf{F} = -\mathbf{i} - 5\mathbf{j}, \|\mathbf{F}\| = \sqrt{26}$
63. (a) $\langle 3, 2 \rangle$ **(b)** $\langle -3, 2 \rangle$
65. (a) $3\mathbf{i} - \mathbf{j}$ **(b)** $\mathbf{i} + 3\mathbf{j}$
67. (a) $\langle 0, -\frac{1}{4} \rangle$ **(b)** $\langle -2\sqrt{2}, \frac{5}{4} \rangle$
69. (a) $\frac{\sqrt{2}}{2}\mathbf{i} + \frac{\sqrt{2}+2}{2}\mathbf{j}$ **(b)** $\frac{\sqrt{2}}{2}\mathbf{i} + \frac{\sqrt{2}-2}{2}\mathbf{j}$

71. (a) $\langle -4, 16 \rangle$ **(b)** $\langle -12, 0 \rangle$ **(c)** $\langle 8, -8 \rangle$
73. (a) $\langle 8, 0 \rangle$ **(b)** $\langle 0, 16 \rangle$ **(c)** $\langle -4, -8 \rangle$
75. (a) $\langle 0, 12 \rangle$ **(b)** $\langle -16, -4 \rangle$ **(c)** $\langle 8, -4 \rangle$
77. (a) 2 **(b)** $4\mathbf{i}$ **(c)** $7\mathbf{i} + 3\mathbf{j}$
79. (a) $\sqrt{5}$ **(b)** $\langle -2, 4 \rangle$ **(c)** $\langle 7, 4 \rangle$
81. (a) $-21\mathbf{i} + 10\mathbf{j}$ **(b)** $17\mathbf{i} - 10\mathbf{j}$
83. (a) $\langle -13, 24 \rangle$ **(b)** $\langle 11, -23 \rangle$
85. (a) $\langle 43, -2 \rangle$ **(b)** $\langle -41, -1 \rangle$
87. (a) 1 **(b)** $81.9°$ **(c)** Neither
89. (a) 0 **(b)** $90°$ **(c)** Perpendicular
91. (a) 122 **(b)** $0°$ **(c)** Parallel, same direction
93. (a) -4 **(b)** $143.1°$ **(c)** Neither
95. 150 ft-lb **97.** $100,000$ ft-lb
99. Work = 590 ft-lb, $\|\mathbf{F}\| = \sqrt{500} \approx 22.4$ lb
101. Work = 27 ft-lb, $\|\mathbf{F}\| = \sqrt{34} \approx 5.8$ lb
103. 24 **105.** 4
107. $\mathbf{v} = \langle 2, 3 \rangle$, speed = $\sqrt{13} \approx 3.6$ mi/hr
109. $\mathbf{v} \approx \langle -364.6, -35.4 \rangle$, groundspeed ≈ 366.3 mi/hr,
bearing $\approx 264.5°$
111. Ground speed ≈ 431.3 mi/hr, bearing $\approx 159.1°$
113. Airspeed ≈ 149.3 mi/hr, groundspeed ≈ 154.6 mi/hr
115. (a) $\|\mathbf{R}\| = \sqrt{5} \approx 2.2, \|\mathbf{A}\| = \sqrt{1.25} \approx 1.1$. About
2.2 inches of rain fell. The area of the opening of the rain
gauge is about 1.1 square inches.
(b) $V = 1.5$; the volume of rain collected in the gauge was
1.5 cubic inches. **(c)** $\mathbf{R}$ and $\mathbf{A}$ must be parallel and point in
opposite directions.
117. (a) $\mathbf{c} = \mathbf{a} + \mathbf{b} = \langle 1, 4 \rangle$ **(b)** $\sqrt{17} \approx 4.1$ ft
(c) $3\mathbf{a} + \frac{1}{2}\mathbf{b} = \langle 8, 7 \rangle$
119. (a) $(2, 2)$ **(b)**

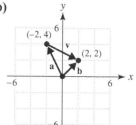

121. $W \approx 297,228$ ft-lb
123. Speed ≈ 180 mi/hr, bearing $\approx 128.2°$

8.3 EXTENDED AND DISCOVERY EXERCISES
(pp. 659–660)

1. Blue **3. (a)** Blue **(b)** White

SECTION 8.4 (pp. 667–669)

1. (a)

t	0	1	2	3
x	-1	0	1	2
y	0	2	4	6

(b)

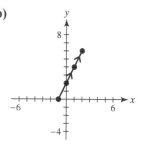

(c) Line segment

3. (a)

t	0	1	2	3
x	2	3	4	5
y	4	1	0	1

(b)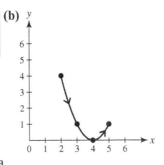

(c) Lower portion of a parabola

5. (a)

t	0	1	2	3
x	3	$\sqrt{8}$	$\sqrt{5}$	0
y	0	1	2	3

(b)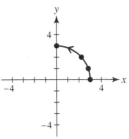

(c) Portion of a circle with radius 3

7. (a)

t	0	1	2	3
x	0	1	2	3
y	3	$\sqrt{8}$	$\sqrt{5}$	0

(b)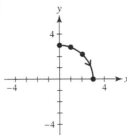

(c) Portion of a circle with radius 3

9. $y = \frac{1}{3}x - 1$; line

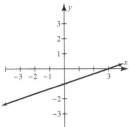

11. $x = 3(y - 1)^2$; parabola

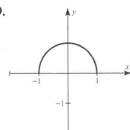

13. $x = \sqrt{1 - y^2}$; portion of a circle with radius 1

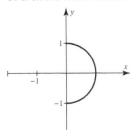

15. $y = \frac{1}{2}x^2$; portion of a parabola

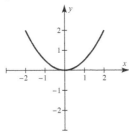

17. $y = x^2 + 4x + 5$; portion of a parabola

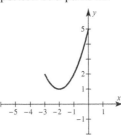

19. $x^2 + y^2 = 9$; circle with radius 3

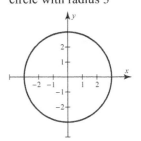

21. $x^2 + y^2 = 4$; circle with radius 2

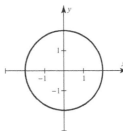

23. $x^2 + y^2 = 9$; circle with radius 3

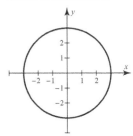

25.

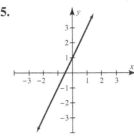

27.

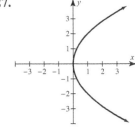

29.

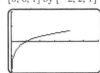

31.

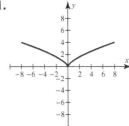

33. $[0, 6, 1]$ by $[-2, 2, 1]$

35. $[-2, 20, 2]$ by $[-1, 3, 1]$

37. $[-4.7, 4.7, 1]$ by $[-3.1, 3.1, 1]$

39. $[-1.5, 1.5, 0.5]$ by $[-1, 1, 0.5]$

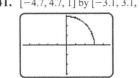

41. $[-4.7, 4.7, 1]$ by $[-3.1, 3.1, 1]$

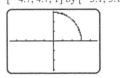

43. $x = t, y = 4 - 2t$ **45.** $x = t, y = 4 - t^2$
47. $x = t^2 + t - 3, y = t$ **49.** $x = 2 \cos t, y = 2 \sin t$
51. $x = t, y = e^{0.1t^2}$ **53.** $x = t^2 - 2t + 1, y = t$
55. (a) The curve traces a   **(b)** The curve traces a circle
circle of radius 3 once.   of radius 3 twice.

$[-4.7, 4.7, 1]$ by $[-3.1, 3.1, 1]$ $[-4.7, 4.7, 1]$ by $[-3.1, 3.1, 1]$

   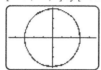

57. (a) The curve traces a circle of radius 3 once counterclockwise, starting at (3, 0).

$[-4.7, 4.7, 1]$ by $[-3.1, 3.1, 1]$

(b) The curve traces a circle of radius 3 once clockwise,
starting at (0, 3).

$[-4.7, 4.7, 1]$ by $[-3.1, 3.1, 1]$

59. (a) Circle of radius 1   **(b)** Circle of radius 1
centered at $(-1, 2)$ centered at $(1, 2)$

$[-4.7, 4.7, 1]$ by $[-3.1, 3.1, 1]$ $[-4.7, 4.7, 1]$ by $[-3.1, 3.1, 1]$

   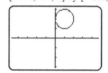

61. F   **63.** D

$[0, 6, 1]$ by $[0, 4, 1]$ $[0, 6, 1]$ by $[0, 4, 1]$

   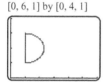

65. $x_1 = 0, y_1 = 2t; x_2 = t, y_2 = 0; 0 \le t \le 1$
67. $x_1 = \sin t, y_1 = \cos t; x_2 = 0, y_2 = t - 2; 0 \le t \le \pi$
69. Answers may vary.
71. The ball hit at 35° travels about 128 feet. The ball hit at
50° travels about 134 feet.
73. Yes **75.** About 285 feet
77. $[-6, 6, 1]$ by $[-4, 4, 1]$ **79.** $[-6, 6, 1]$ by $[-4, 4, 1]$

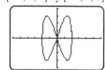   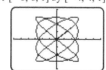

8.4 EXTENDED AND DISCOVERY
EXERCISES (p. 669)

1. $F_2 = 100$ **3.** $F_2 = 300$

CHECKING BASIC CONCEPTS FOR SECTIONS 8.3
AND 8.4 (p. 669)

1. (a) $\mathbf{v} = \langle 4, 4 \rangle$ **(b)** $\|\mathbf{v}\| = 4\sqrt{2}$ **(c)** $\langle 0, 0 \rangle$
3. (a) -9 **(b)** $142.1°$

SECTION 8.5 (pp. 679–680)

1.   **3.**

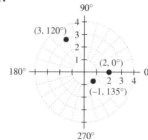   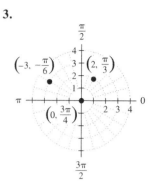

5. Yes **7.** No **9.** Yes
11. $\left(\dfrac{3}{\sqrt{2}}, \dfrac{3}{\sqrt{2}} \right)$, or $\left(\dfrac{3\sqrt{2}}{2}, \dfrac{3\sqrt{2}}{2} \right)$
13. $(0, 10)$ **15.** $(5, 0)$
17. $\left(-\dfrac{3}{2}, -\dfrac{3\sqrt{3}}{2} \right)$ **19.** $(0, -2)$
21. (a) $(3, 90°)$ **(b)** $(-3, -90°)$
23. (a) $(2, 240°)$ **(b)** $(-2, 60°)$
25. (a) $(\sqrt{18}, 315°)$ **(b)** $(-\sqrt{18}, 135°)$
27. $(25, 1.29)$ **29.** $(13, 1.97)$
31.

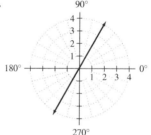

33. (a)   **(b)**

θ	0°	90°	180°	270°
r	2	2	2	2

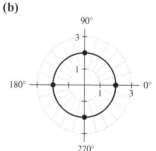

35. (a)   **(b)**

θ	0°	90°	180°	270°
r	0	3	0	−3

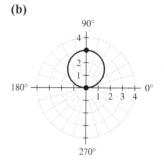

37. (a)

θ	0°	90°	180°	270°
r	2	4	2	0

(b)

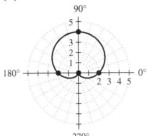

39. (a)

θ	0°	90°	180°	270°
r	1	2	3	2

(b)

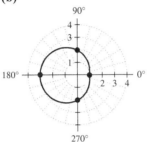

41.

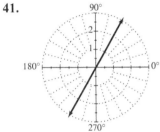

43.

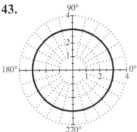

45.

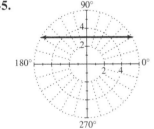

47.

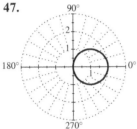

49.

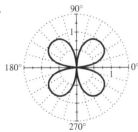

51.

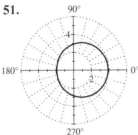

53.

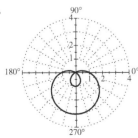

55.

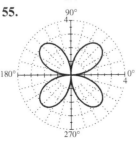

57.

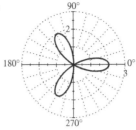

59. $r = 3 \csc \theta$ **61.** $\theta = \frac{\pi}{4}$ **63.** $r = 3$
65. $r = 2 \cos \theta$ **67.** $x^2 + y^2 = 9$ **69.** $x = 2$
71. $2x + 4y = 3$ **73.** $x^2 + y^2 = x$

75.

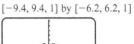
[−9.4, 9.4, 1] by [−6.2, 6.2, 1]

77.

[−9.4, 9.4, 1] by [−6.2, 6.2, 1]

79.

[−9.4, 9.4, 1] by [−6.2, 6.2, 1]

81.

[−9.4, 9.4, 1] by [−6.2, 6.2, 1]

83.   [−4.7, 4.7, 1] by [−3.1, 3.1, 1]

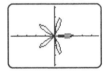

85. Use radian mode
with $0 \le \theta \le \frac{9\pi}{2}$.
[−9.4, 9.4, 1] by [−6.2, 6.2, 1]

87. Let $r_1 = \sqrt{2 \sin (2\theta)}$
and $r_2 = -\sqrt{2 \sin (2\theta)}$.
[−3, 3, 1] by [−2, 2, 1]

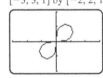

89. 30°, 150°   **91.** 210°, 330°   **93.** 30°, 150°

95. [−30, 30, 5] by [−20, 20, 5]

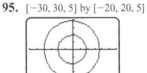

97. [−3, 3, 1] by [−2, 2, 1]

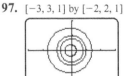

99. The radio signal can be received inside the "figure eight." This region is generally in an east–west direction from the two towers, with a maximum distance of 200 miles.

[−300, 300, 100] by [−200, 200, 100]

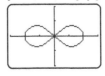

8.5 EXTENDED AND DISCOVERY EXERCISES (p. 681)

1.
$$y = x \tan (\ln (x^2 + y^2))$$
$$\frac{y}{x} = \tan (\ln r^2)$$
$$\tan \theta = \tan (\ln r^2)$$
$$\theta = \ln r^2$$
$$\theta = 2 \ln r$$
$$\frac{\theta}{2} = \ln r$$
$$e^{\theta/2} = r$$

SECTION 8.6 (pp. 689–691)

1.
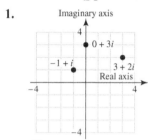

3.
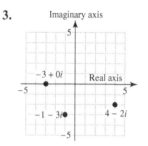

5. $\sqrt{2}$ **7.** 13   **9.** 6   **11.** $\sqrt{13}$
13. $\sqrt{2} (\cos 135° + i \sin 135°)$
15. $5(\cos 0° + i \sin 0°)$ **17.** $4(\cos 90° + i \sin 90°)$
19. $2(\cos 120° + i \sin 120°)$ **21.** $2(\cos 30° + i \sin 30°)$
23. $2(\cos \pi + i \sin \pi)$ **25.** $\sqrt{8} \left(\cos \frac{3\pi}{4} + i \sin \frac{3\pi}{4} \right)$
27. -5 **29.** $\sqrt{2} + i\sqrt{2}$ **31.** $\sqrt{3} + i$ **33.** 3
35. $z_1 z_2 = \frac{27}{2} + \frac{27\sqrt{3}}{2} i, \frac{z_1}{z_2} = \frac{3\sqrt{3}}{2} + \frac{3}{2}i$
37. $z_1 z_2 = -6, \frac{z_1}{z_2} = 6i$
39. $z_1 z_2 = \frac{\sqrt{3}}{2} - \frac{1}{2}i, \frac{z_1}{z_2} = \frac{1}{2} + \frac{\sqrt{3}}{2}i$ **41.** $8i$ **43.** 1
45. $-\frac{25}{2} + \frac{25\sqrt{3}}{2}i$ **47.** $-2 + 2i$ **49.** $-16\sqrt{3} + 16i$
51. $1 + i\sqrt{3}, -1 - i\sqrt{3}$ **53.** $-1, \frac{1}{2} + \frac{\sqrt{3}}{2}i, \frac{1}{2} - \frac{\sqrt{3}}{2}i$
55. $\frac{\sqrt{2}}{2} + \frac{\sqrt{2}}{2}i, -\frac{\sqrt{2}}{2} - \frac{\sqrt{2}}{2}i$ **57.** $-2, 1 + i\sqrt{3}, 1 - i\sqrt{3}$
59. $-4i, 2\sqrt{3} + 2i, -2\sqrt{3} + 2i$
61. $\pm 3, \pm 3i$ **63.** Yes   **65.** No
67. (a) $Z = 110 + 32i$ **(b)** $\sqrt{13,124} \approx 114.6$ ohms

8.6 EXTENDED AND DISCOVERY EXERCISES (p. 691)

1. (a) $\langle 2 \cos 30°, 2 \sin 30° \rangle$ **(b)** $(2, 30°)$
(c) $2(\cos 30° + i \sin 30°)$
3. (a) $\langle 5 \cos 323.1°, 5 \sin 323.1° \rangle$ **(b)** $(5, 323.1°)$
(c) $5(\cos 323.1° + i \sin 323.1°)$

CHECKING BASIC CONCEPTS FOR SECTIONS 8.5 AND 8.6 (p. 691)

1.
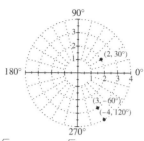

3.
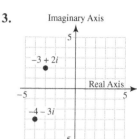

5. $\frac{\sqrt{3}}{2} + \frac{1}{2}i, -\frac{\sqrt{3}}{2} + \frac{1}{2}i, -i$

CHAPTER 8 REVIEW EXERCISES (pp. 694–696)

1. $\gamma = 70°, a = 10.1, b \approx 6.9$
3. $a \approx 5.5, \beta \approx 59.1°, \gamma \approx 78.9°$
5. $\gamma = 115°, a \approx 5.9, c \approx 16.4$
7. $\beta \approx 14.4°, \alpha \approx 145.6°, a \approx 18.2$
9. $c \approx 13.2, \beta \approx 93.6°, \alpha \approx 51.4°$
11. 53.0   **13.** 891.4
15. (a) Horizontal $= 3$, vertical $= 4$ **(b)** $\|v\| = 5$
(c) $\|v\|$ represents the length of **v**.

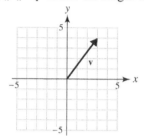

17. (a)

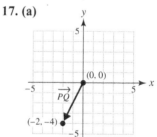

(b) $\overrightarrow{PQ} = -2\mathbf{i} - 4\mathbf{j}$ **(c)** $\|\overrightarrow{PQ}\| = \sqrt{20}$
19. (a) $2\mathbf{a} = \langle 6, -4 \rangle$ **(b)** $\mathbf{a} - 3\mathbf{b} = \langle 0, -5 \rangle$
(c) $\mathbf{a} \cdot \mathbf{b} = 1$ **(d)** $\theta \approx 78.7°$
21. (a) $2\mathbf{a} = 4\mathbf{i} + 4\mathbf{j}$ **(b)** $\mathbf{a} - 3\mathbf{b} = -\mathbf{i} - \mathbf{j}$
(c) $\mathbf{a} \cdot \mathbf{b} = 4$ **(d)** $\theta = 0°$
23. About 207.1 lb
25. $[-4.7, 4.7, 1]$ by $[-3.1, 3.1, 1]$ **27.** $[-4.7, 4.7, 1]$ by $[-3.1, 3.1, 1]$

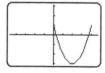

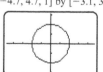

29.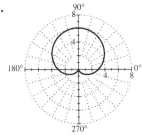

31.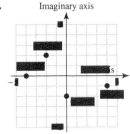

33.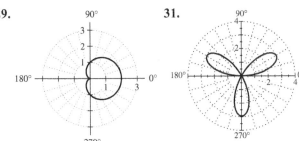

35.

Imaginary axis

37. $z_1 z_2 = -8$, $\frac{z_1}{z_2} = -1 + i\sqrt{3}$

39. $\sqrt{3} + i$, $-\sqrt{3} - i$ **41.** About 701.6 mi

43. 7204 ft **45.** 15,600 ft^2

47. (a) $60\mathbf{i} + 10\mathbf{j}$ **(b)** 60.8 cm **(c)** $80\mathbf{i} + 40\mathbf{j}$

49. About 78.1 ft

CHAPTER 8 EXTENDED AND DISCOVERY EXERCISES (pp. 696–697)

1. (a) About 56 miles per second

(b) About 87 miles per second

3. (a) 6.02 in. **(b)** About 7470 ft

5. $\|\mathbf{a} - \mathbf{b}\|^2 = \|\mathbf{a}\|^2 + \|\mathbf{b}\|^2 - 2\|\mathbf{a}\|\,\|\mathbf{b}\|\cos\theta$

$\Rightarrow \|\mathbf{a} - \mathbf{b}\|^2 - \|\mathbf{a}\|^2 - \|\mathbf{b}\|^2 = -2\|\mathbf{a}\|\,\|\mathbf{b}\|\cos\theta$

$\Rightarrow \left(\sqrt{(a_1 - b_1)^2 + (a_2 - b_2)^2}\right)^2 - \left(\sqrt{a_1{}^2 + a_2{}^2}\right)^2$

$\quad - \left(\sqrt{b_1{}^2 + b_2{}^2}\right)^2 = -2\|\mathbf{a}\|\,\|\mathbf{b}\|\cos\theta$

$\Rightarrow (a_1 - b_1)^2 + (a_2 - b_2)^2$

$\quad - (a_1{}^2 + a_2{}^2) - (b_1{}^2 + b_2{}^2) = -2\|\mathbf{a}\|\,\|\mathbf{b}\|\cos\theta$

$\Rightarrow a_1{}^2 - 2a_1 b_1 + b_1{}^2 + a_2{}^2 - 2a_2 b_2$

$\quad + b_2{}^2 - a_1{}^2 - a_2{}^2 - b_1{}^2 - b_2{}^2 = -2\|\mathbf{a}\|\,\|\mathbf{b}\|\cos\theta$

$\Rightarrow -2a_1 b_1 - 2a_2 b_2 = -2\|\mathbf{a}\|\,\|\mathbf{b}\|\cos\theta$

$\Rightarrow a_1 b_1 + a_2 b_2 = \|\mathbf{a}\|\,\|\mathbf{b}\|\cos\theta$

$\Rightarrow \mathbf{a}\cdot\mathbf{b} = \|\mathbf{a}\|\,\|\mathbf{b}\|\cos\theta$

CHAPTERS 1–8 CUMULATIVE REVIEW EXERCISES (pp. 698–699)

1. $\sqrt{65}$ **3.** $\{x \mid x \le 4\}$; 3 **5.** $8x + 4h$

7. x-intercept: -3; y-intercept: -4

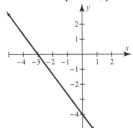

9. (a) $-\frac{1}{2}, \frac{11}{2}$ **(b)** $-4, \frac{1}{3}$ **(c)** $-1, 0, 1$

(d) $\pm i, \pm\sqrt{3}$ **(e)** $\frac{\ln(51/2)}{3} \approx 1.08$ **(f)** 8 **(g)** $\frac{\pi}{6}, \frac{5\pi}{6}$

(h) $\frac{\pi}{3} + \frac{\pi}{2}n$ **(i)** $\frac{\pi}{3} + 2\pi n, \pi + 2\pi n, \frac{5\pi}{3} + 2\pi n$

11. (a) $\left(\frac{13}{5}, \infty\right)$ **(b)** $[-1, 2]$

(c) $(-\infty, -1) \cup (3, \infty)$ **(d)** $(-2, 0) \cup (2, \infty)$

(e) $[0, 1)$ **(f)** $\left[-\frac{8}{3}, \frac{8}{3}\right]$

13. (a) $3x^2 - 6x + 11 + \frac{-20}{x + 2}$ **(b)** $x^2 - x + \frac{-1}{2x - 1}$

15. $D = \left\{x \mid x \ne \frac{2}{3}\right\}$; vertical asymptote: $x = \frac{2}{3}$; horizontal asymptote: $y = -1$

17. $f^{-1}(x) = \frac{x + 2}{3}$ **19.** $C = 5000$; $a = 2^{2/3}$

21. (a) -3 **(b)** -3 **(c)** $\frac{1}{3}$ **(d)** 3 **23.** $\frac{5\pi}{4}$

25. $\sin\theta = \frac{5}{13}$, $\cos\theta = \frac{12}{13}$, $\tan\theta = \frac{5}{12}$, $\csc\theta = \frac{13}{5}$, $\sec\theta = \frac{13}{12}$, $\cot\theta = \frac{12}{5}$

27. $\sin\theta = -\frac{7}{25}$, $\cos\theta = -\frac{24}{25}$, $\tan\theta = \frac{7}{24}$, $\csc\theta = -\frac{25}{7}$, $\sec\theta = -\frac{25}{24}$, $\cot\theta = \frac{24}{7}$

29. $c = 13$, $\theta \approx 22.6°$, $\beta \approx 67.4°$ **31.** $(\cot\theta - 1)^2$

33. (a) $\beta = 96°$, $a \approx 7.8$, $c \approx 12.0$

(b) $\beta \approx 25.4°$, $\gamma \approx 123.6°$, $c \approx 9.7$

(c) $\alpha \approx 47.0°$, $\gamma \approx 77.0°$, $b \approx 6.8$

(d) $\alpha \approx 46.6°$, $\beta \approx 57.9°$, $\gamma \approx 75.5°$

35. (a) 25 **(b)** $\langle -31, 96 \rangle$ **(c)** -323

(d) About 173.6°

37.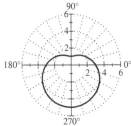

39. 15 by 19 inches

41. 12 by 6 by 4 inches or 7.4 by 3.7 by 10.5 inches

43. 2.5 feet **45.** 56.2°

47. (a) About 247 feet **(b)** About 18,988 ft^2

CHAPTER 9: Systems of Equations and Inequalities

SECTION 9.1 (pp. 714–719)

1. 20; the area of a triangle with base 5 and height 8 is 20.

3. 13 **5.** -18 **7.** $\frac{4}{5}$ **9.** $f(x, y) = y + 2x$

11. $f(x, y) = \frac{xy}{1 + x}$ **13.** $x = \frac{4y + 7}{3}$; $y = \frac{3x - 7}{4}$

15. $x = y^2 + 5$; $y = \pm\sqrt{x - 5}$ **17.** $x = 2y$; $y = \frac{x}{2}$

19. $(2, 1)$; linear **21.** $(4, -3)$; nonlinear **23.** $(2, 2)$

25. $\left(\frac{1}{2}, -2\right)$ **27.** Consistent with solution $(2, 2)$

29. Inconsistent; no solutions

31.

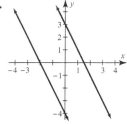

No solutions; inconsistent

33.

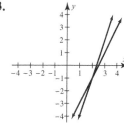

$(2, -1)$; consistent, independent

35.

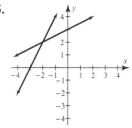

$(-2, 2)$; consistent, independent

37.

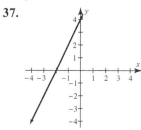

$\{(x, y) \mid 2x - y = -4\}$; consistent, dependent

39. $(-2, 1)$ **41.** $\left(\frac{1}{2}, 2\right)$ **43.** $(6, 8)$
45. $\{(x, y) \mid 3x - 2y = 5\}$ **47.** No solutions **49.** $(4, 3)$
51. $(-2, 4), (0, 0)$ **53.** $(2, 4), (4, 2)$ **55.** $(2, 4), (-2, -4)$
57. No real solutions **59.** $\{(x, y) \mid 2x^2 - y = 5\}$
61. $(-2, 0), (2, 0)$ **63.** $(-2, -2), (0, 0), (2, 2)$
65. $x - y = 2, 2x + 2y = 38$, where x is width and y is height; 10.5 in. wide, 8.5 in. high
67. $x + y = 75, 4x + 7y = 456$, where x is the number of child tickets and y is the number of adult tickets; 23 child tickets, 52 adult tickets **69.** $l = 7, w = 5$ **71.** $(14, 6)$; consistent, independent **73.** $(1, 3)$; consistent, independent
75. $\{(x, y) \mid x + y = 500\}$; consistent, dependent
77. No solutions; inconsistent
79. $\left(-\frac{11}{7}, \frac{12}{7}\right)$; consistent, independent
81. $(2, -4)$ **83.** $\{(x, y) \mid 7x - 3y = -17\}$
85. No solutions **87.** $(10, 20)$ **89.** $(2, 1)$
91. $(-5, -4)$ **93.** $(3, 3), (-3, 3)$
95. $(4, 3), (-4, 3), (3, 4), (-3, 4)$ **97.** $(2, 0), (-2, 0)$
99. $(-\sqrt{8}, -\sqrt{8}), (\sqrt{8}, \sqrt{8})$ **101.** $(6, 2), (-2, -6)$
103. $(1, -1)$ **105.** $(1, 2)$
107. $(-1.588, 0.239), (0.164, 1.487), (1.924, -0.351)$
109. $(1.220, 0.429)$ **111.** $(0.714, -0.169)$
113. (a) $x + y = 670, x - y = 98$
(b) $(384, 286)$ **(c)** Consistent; independent
115. $W_1 = \dfrac{300}{1 + \sqrt{3}} \approx 109.8$ lb,

$W_2 = \dfrac{300\sqrt{3}}{\sqrt{6} + \sqrt{2}} \approx 134.5$ lb
117. $r \approx 1.538$ in., $h \approx 6.724$ in.
119. 12 by 12 by 4 in. or 9.10 by 9.10 by 6.96 in.
121. (a) $x + y = 11,693, x - y = 437$
(b) & (c) $(6065, 5628)$
123. (a) $x + y = 3000, 0.08x + 0.10y = 264$
(b) $1800 at 8%; $1200 at 10%

125. There are no solutions. If loans totaling $3000 are at 10%, then the interest must be $300.
127. Airplane: 520 mi/hr; wind speed: 40 mi/hr
129. (a) $l = 13$ ft, $w = 7$ ft **(b)** $A = 20w - w^2$
(c) 100 ft^2; a square pen will provide the largest area.
131. (a) First model: about 245 lb; second model: about 253 lb **(b)** Models agree when $h \approx 65.96$ in.
(c) First model: 7.46 lb; second model: 7.93 lb
133. About 1.77 m^2 **135.** $S(60, 157.48) \approx 1.6$ m^2
137. 0.51 **139.** 32.4 **141.** Approximately 10,823 watts
143. Approximately 2.54 cords
145. $S(w, h) = 0.0101w^{0.425}h^{0.725}$

SECTION 9.2 (pp. 727–730)

1.

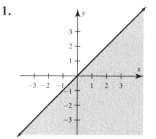

3.

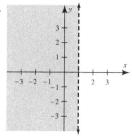

5.

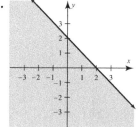

7.

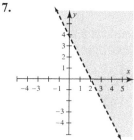

9.

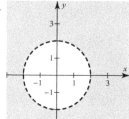

11.

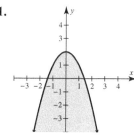

13. c; $(2, 3)$ (answers may vary)
15. d; $(-1, -1)$ (answers may vary)
17. $(0, 2)$ **19.** $(0, 0)$
(answers may vary)   (answers may vary)

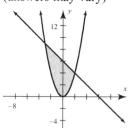

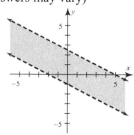

21. $(-1, 1)$
(answers may vary)

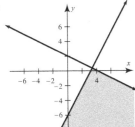

23. $(2, 1)$
(answers may vary)

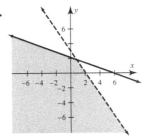

25.

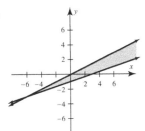

27.

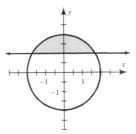

29.

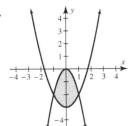

31.

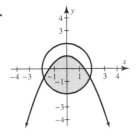

33.

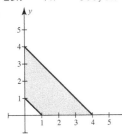

35.

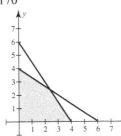

37. Jitters **39.** 180 pounds or more
41. $x = 300, y = 350$
43. This individual weighs less than recommended for his or her height.
45. $25h - 7w \leq 800, 5h - w \geq 170$

47.

49.

51. Maximum: 65; minimum: 8
53. Maximum: 66; minimum: 3
55. Maximum: 100; minimum: 0
57. $x + y \leq 4, x \geq 0, y \geq 0$
59. Minimum: 6
61. Maximum: $z = 56$; minimum: $z = 24$

63. 25 radios, 30 CD players
65. 2.4 units of Brand A, 1.2 units of Brand B
67. $600 **69.** Part X: 9, part Y: 4

CHECKING BASIC CONCEPTS FOR SECTIONS 9.1 AND 9.2 (p. 730)

1. $d(13, 18) = 20$ **3.** $y = \pm \sqrt{z - x^2}$
5.

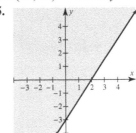

7. (a) $x + y = 220, 4.5x - y = 0$
(b) $(40, 180)$; in 2010 40 million HDTVs were sold with plasma screens and 180 million were sold with LCD screens.

SECTION 9.3 (pp. 736–737)

1. No **3.** 2 **5.** Dependent
7. $(0, 2, -2)$ is not, but $(-1, 3, -2)$ is a solution.
9. Both are solutions. **11.** $(1, 2, 3)$ **13.** $(1, 0, 1)$
15. $\left(\frac{1}{2}, \frac{1}{2}, -2\right)$ **17.** $\left(\frac{z + 3}{2}, \frac{-z + 3}{2}, z\right)$
19. No solutions **21.** $\left(-\frac{5}{2}, -2, 4\right)$ **23.** No solutions
25. $\left(-\frac{1}{2}, \frac{1}{2}, -\frac{1}{2}\right)$ **27.** $\left(\frac{-5z + 18}{13}, \frac{-6z + 19}{13}, z\right)$
29. $\left(8, -11, -\frac{1}{2}\right)$ **31.** $(2, 3, -4)$
33. 120 child, 280 student, and 100 adult tickets
35. No solutions; at least one student was charged incorrectly.
37. (a) $\begin{aligned} x + y + z &= 180 \\ x \quad\ - z &= 25 \\ -x + y + z &= 30 \end{aligned}$
(b) $75°, 55°, 50°$
39. $2500 at 5%, $7500 at 7%, $10,000 at 10%
41. (a) $\begin{aligned} N + P + K &= 80 \\ N + P - K &= 8 \\ 9P - K &= 0 \end{aligned}$
(b) $(40, 4, 36)$; 40 lb of nitrogen, 4 lb of phosphorus, 36 lb of potassium

SECTION 9.4 (pp. 750–753)

1. 3×1 **3.** 2×2 **5.** 3×2
7. Dimension: 2×3
$$\begin{bmatrix} 5 & -2 & | & 3 \\ -1 & 3 & | & -1 \end{bmatrix}$$

9. Dimension: 3×4
$$\begin{bmatrix} -3 & 2 & 1 & | & -4 \\ 5 & 0 & -1 & | & 9 \\ 1 & -3 & -6 & | & -9 \end{bmatrix}$$

11. $\begin{aligned} 3x + 2y &= 4 \\ y &= 5 \end{aligned}$

13. $3x + y + 4z = 0$
$5y + 8z = -1$
$-7z = 1$

15. (a) Yes **(b)** No **(c)** Yes **17.** $(5, -1)$ **19.** $(2, 0)$

21. $(2, 3, 1)$ **23.** $(3 - 3z, 1 + 2z, z)$ **25.** No solutions

27. $\begin{bmatrix} 1 & -2 & 3 & | & 5 \\ -3 & 5 & 3 & | & 2 \\ 1 & 2 & 1 & | & -2 \end{bmatrix}$ **29.** $\begin{bmatrix} 1 & -1 & 1 & | & 2 \\ 0 & 1 & -1 & | & 2 \\ 0 & 8 & -1 & | & 3 \end{bmatrix}$

31. $(-17, 10)$ **33.** $(0, 2, -1)$ **35.** $(-1, 2, 4)$

37. $(3, 2, 1)$ **39.** No solutions

41. $\left(-1 - z, \frac{9 - 5z}{2}, z\right)$ **43.** $(1, 1, 1)$

45. $\left(\frac{1}{2}, -\frac{1}{2}, 4\right)$ **47.** $(-2, 5, -1)$

49. No solutions **51.** $(-1, -2, 3)$

53. $\left(\frac{3z + 1}{7}, \frac{11z - 15}{7}, z\right)$ **55.** $(12, 3)$

57. $\left(-2, 4, \frac{1}{2}\right)$ **59.** $(4 - 2z, z - 3, z)$

61. No solutions **63.** $(3, 2)$ **65.** $(-2, 1, 3)$

67. $(-2, 5, 7)$ **69.** No solutions

71. $(-9.226, -9.167, 2.440)$

73. $(5.211, 3.739, -4.655)$

75. $(7.993, 1.609, -0.401)$

77. Pump 1: 12 hours; pumps 2 and 3: 24 hours

79. (a) $F = 0.5714N + 0.4571R - 2014$ **(b)** $5700

81. $(3.53, 1.62, 1.91)$

83. (a) $x + y + z = 5000$
$ x + y - z = 0$
$0.08x + 0.11y + 0.14z = 595,$

where x is amount invested at 8%, y is amount invested at 11%, and z is amount invested at 14%

(b) $1000 at 8%; $1500 at 11%; $2500 at 14%

85. (a) At intersection A, incoming traffic is equal to $x + 5$. The outgoing traffic is given by $y + 7$. Therefore, $x + 5 = y + 7$. The other equations can be justified in a similar way.

(b) The three equations can be written as
$x - y = 2$
$x - z = 3$
$y - z = 1$
The solution can be written as $\{(z + 3, z + 1, z) | z \geq 0\}$.

(c) There are infinitely many solutions, since some cars could be driving around the block continually.

87. (a) $a + b + c = 3$
$25a + 5b + c = 29$
$36a + 6b + c = 40$

(b) $f(x) = 0.9x^2 + 1.1x + 1$

(c) $[-0.5, 10, 1]$ by $[-5, 90, 10]$

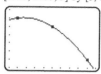

(d) After 9 quarters predicted sales are $f(9) = 83.8$ million (answers may vary).

89. (a) $1990^2a + 1990b + c = 11$
$2010^2a + 2010b + c = 10$
$2030^2a + 2030b + c = 6$

(b) $f(x) = -0.00375x^2 + 14.95x - 14,889.125$

(c) $[1985, 2035, 5]$ by $[5, 12, 1]$

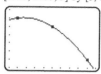

(d) In 2015 the predicted ratio is $f(2015) \approx 9.3$ (answers may vary).

9.4 EXTENDED AND DISCOVERY EXERCISES (p. 753)

1. $(1, -1, 2, 0)$

CHECKING BASIC CONCEPTS FOR SECTIONS 9.3 AND 9.4 (p. 753)

1. (a) $(3, 2, -1)$ **(b)** $\left(\frac{4 - 5z}{3}, \frac{5 - z}{3}, z\right)$ **(c)** No solutions

3. $(2, -1, 0)$

SECTION 9.5 (pp. 764–768)

1. (a) $a_{12} = 3, b_{32} = 1, b_{22} = 0$ **(b)** -2 **(c)** $x = 3$

3. $x = 1, y = 1$ **5.** Not possible

7. (a) $A + B = \begin{bmatrix} 3 & 3 \\ 3 & 3 \end{bmatrix}$ **(b)** $B + A = \begin{bmatrix} 3 & 3 \\ 3 & 3 \end{bmatrix}$

(c) $A - B = \begin{bmatrix} 5 & -5 \\ -5 & 5 \end{bmatrix}$

9. (a) $A + B = \begin{bmatrix} 14 & 9 & -3 \\ 4 & -10 & 14 \\ 4 & 11 & 16 \end{bmatrix}$

(b) $B + A = \begin{bmatrix} 14 & 9 & -3 \\ 4 & -10 & 14 \\ 4 & 11 & 16 \end{bmatrix}$

(c) $A - B = \begin{bmatrix} -8 & -1 & 1 \\ -4 & 4 & -10 \\ -8 & -1 & 4 \end{bmatrix}$

11. (a) $A + B = \begin{bmatrix} 1 & -6 \\ 1 & 4 \end{bmatrix}$ **(b)** $3A = \begin{bmatrix} 6 & -18 \\ 9 & 3 \end{bmatrix}$

(c) $2A - 3B = \begin{bmatrix} 7 & -12 \\ 12 & -7 \end{bmatrix}$

13. (a) $A + B$ is undefined.

(b) $3A = \begin{bmatrix} 3 & -3 & 0 \\ 3 & 15 & 27 \\ -12 & 24 & -15 \end{bmatrix}$

(c) $2A - 3B$ is undefined.

15. (a) $A + B = \begin{bmatrix} 0 & -2 \\ -2 & 2 \\ 9 & -8 \end{bmatrix}$ **(b)** $3A = \begin{bmatrix} -6 & -3 \\ -15 & 3 \\ 6 & -9 \end{bmatrix}$

(c) $2A - 3B = \begin{bmatrix} -10 & 1 \\ -19 & -1 \\ -17 & 9 \end{bmatrix}$

17. $\begin{bmatrix} 0 & 2 \\ 13 & -5 \\ 0 & 1 \end{bmatrix}$ **19.** $\begin{bmatrix} 2 & 6 \\ 11 & -9 \end{bmatrix}$

21. $\begin{bmatrix} 7 & 4 & 7 \\ 4 & 7 & 7 \\ 4 & 7 & 7 \end{bmatrix}$ **23.** $A = \begin{bmatrix} 1 & 2 & 1 \\ 1 & 2 & 1 \\ 1 & 2 & 1 \end{bmatrix}$

25. $B = \begin{bmatrix} -1 & 1 & -1 \\ -1 & 1 & -1 \\ -1 & 1 & -1 \end{bmatrix}, A + B = \begin{bmatrix} 0 & 3 & 0 \\ 0 & 3 & 0 \\ 0 & 3 & 0 \end{bmatrix}$

27. $AB = \begin{bmatrix} -3 & 1 \\ -4 & 6 \end{bmatrix}, BA = \begin{bmatrix} 4 & 2 \\ 5 & -1 \end{bmatrix}$

29. AB and BA are undefined.

31. $AB = \begin{bmatrix} -15 & 22 & -9 \\ -2 & 5 & -3 \\ -32 & 18 & 6 \end{bmatrix}, BA = \begin{bmatrix} 5 & 14 \\ 20 & -9 \end{bmatrix}$

33. AB is undefined. $BA = \begin{bmatrix} -1 & -3 & 19 \\ -1 & 1 & -39 \end{bmatrix}$

35. AB and BA are undefined.

37. $AB = \begin{bmatrix} -1 & 15 & -2 \\ 0 & 1 & 3 \\ -1 & 14 & -5 \end{bmatrix}, BA = \begin{bmatrix} 0 & 6 & 0 \\ 6 & -5 & 9 \\ 0 & 1 & 0 \end{bmatrix}$

39. $AB = \begin{bmatrix} -1 \\ 6 \end{bmatrix}, BA$ is undefined.

41. $AB = \begin{bmatrix} -7 & 8 & 7 \\ 18 & -32 & -8 \end{bmatrix}, BA$ is undefined.

43. $AB = \begin{bmatrix} -5 \\ 10 \\ 17 \end{bmatrix}, BA$ is undefined.

45. $\begin{bmatrix} -19 & 19 & 11 \\ 21 & -7 & -48 \\ -22 & 23 & -58 \end{bmatrix}$ **47.** $\begin{bmatrix} 83 & 32 & 92 \\ 10 & -63 & -8 \\ 210 & 56 & 93 \end{bmatrix}$

49. They both equal $\begin{bmatrix} 36 & 36 & 8 \\ -15 & -38 & -4 \\ -11 & 13 & 10 \end{bmatrix}$. The distributive

property appears to hold for matrices.

51. They both equal $\begin{bmatrix} 50 & 3 & 12 \\ -6 & 55 & 8 \\ 27 & -3 & 29 \end{bmatrix}$. Matrices appear to

conform to rules of algebra except that $AB \neq BA$.

53. $\begin{bmatrix} 0 & 0 & 1 & 1 \\ 1 & 0 & 0 & 0 \\ 1 & 0 & 0 & 1 \\ 1 & 1 & 1 & 0 \end{bmatrix}$

55. Person 2

57.

59. No one likes Person 4.

61. $B = \begin{bmatrix} 3 & 3 & 3 \\ 3 & 3 & 3 \\ 3 & 3 & 3 \end{bmatrix}, B - A = \begin{bmatrix} 3 & 0 & 3 \\ 3 & 0 & 3 \\ 3 & 0 & 3 \end{bmatrix}$

63. $A = \begin{bmatrix} 3 & 3 & 3 & 3 \\ 3 & 0 & 0 & 0 \\ 3 & 3 & 3 & 0 \\ 3 & 0 & 0 & 0 \\ 3 & 0 & 0 & 0 \end{bmatrix}$

65. (a) One possibility is $A = \begin{bmatrix} 3 & 3 & 3 & 3 \\ 0 & 0 & 3 & 0 \\ 0 & 3 & 0 & 0 \\ 3 & 3 & 3 & 3 \end{bmatrix}$.

(b) $B = \begin{bmatrix} 3 & 3 & 3 & 3 \\ 3 & 3 & 3 & 3 \\ 3 & 3 & 3 & 3 \\ 3 & 3 & 3 & 3 \end{bmatrix}$

67. (a) One possibility is $A = \begin{bmatrix} 3 & 0 & 0 & 0 \\ 3 & 0 & 0 & 0 \\ 3 & 0 & 0 & 0 \\ 3 & 3 & 3 & 3 \end{bmatrix}$.

(b) $B = \begin{bmatrix} 3 & 3 & 3 & 3 \\ 3 & 3 & 3 & 3 \\ 3 & 3 & 3 & 3 \\ 3 & 3 & 3 & 3 \end{bmatrix}$

69. (a) $A = \begin{bmatrix} 12 & 4 \\ 8 & 7 \end{bmatrix}, B = \begin{bmatrix} 55 \\ 70 \end{bmatrix}$

(b) $AB = \begin{bmatrix} 940 \\ 930 \end{bmatrix}$. Tuition for Student 1 is \$940, and

tuition for Student 2 is \$930.

71. (a) $A = \begin{bmatrix} 10 & 5 \\ 9 & 8 \\ 11 & 3 \end{bmatrix}, B = \begin{bmatrix} 60 \\ 70 \end{bmatrix}$

(b) $AB = \begin{bmatrix} 950 \\ 1100 \\ 870 \end{bmatrix}$. Tuition for Student 1 is \$950, for

Student 2 it is \$1100, and for Student 3 it is \$870.

73. $AB = \begin{bmatrix} 350 \\ 230 \end{bmatrix}$. The total cost of order 1 is \$350, and

the total cost of order 2 is \$230.

75. $\begin{bmatrix} 0 & 0 & 1 & 1 \\ 1 & 0 & 0 & 1 \\ 0 & 0 & 0 & 1 \\ 0 & 0 & 1 & 0 \end{bmatrix}$ **77.** $\begin{bmatrix} 0 & 0 & 1 & 1 \\ 0 & 0 & 2 & 1 \\ 0 & 0 & 1 & 0 \\ 0 & 0 & 0 & 1 \end{bmatrix}$

79. There are two different 2-click paths from Page 2
to Page 3

**9.5 EXTENDED AND DISCOVERY
EXERCISES (p. 768)**

1. Aquamarine is represented by (0.369, 0, 0.067) in CMY.

3. $\begin{bmatrix} R \\ G \\ B \end{bmatrix} = \begin{bmatrix} 1 \\ 1 \\ 1 \end{bmatrix} - \begin{bmatrix} C \\ M \\ Y \end{bmatrix}$

SECTION 9.6 (pp. 777–780)

1. Yes **3.** Yes **5.** No **7.** $k = 1$ **9.** $k = 2.5$ **11.** A **13.** A

15. $\begin{bmatrix} 3 & -2 \\ -1 & 1 \end{bmatrix}$ **17.** $\begin{bmatrix} 5 & 2 \\ 3 & 1 \end{bmatrix}$ **19.** $\begin{bmatrix} -\frac{1}{2} & \frac{5}{2} \\ 1 & -4 \end{bmatrix}$

21. $\begin{bmatrix} 0 & 1 & 0 \\ 0 & 0 & 1 \\ 1 & 0 & 0 \end{bmatrix}$ **23.** $\begin{bmatrix} -2 & 1 & -1 \\ -5 & 2 & -1 \\ 3 & -1 & 1 \end{bmatrix}$

25. $\begin{bmatrix} -10 & 3 & -5 \\ 4 & -1 & 2 \\ -3 & 1 & -1 \end{bmatrix}$ **27.** $\begin{bmatrix} -1 & -1 & -1 \\ -\frac{2}{5} & -\frac{1}{5} & -\frac{4}{5} \\ \frac{1}{5} & \frac{3}{5} & \frac{2}{5} \end{bmatrix}$

29. $\begin{bmatrix} -10 & 30 \\ -4 & 10 \end{bmatrix}$ **31.** $\begin{bmatrix} 0.2 & 0 & 0.4 \\ 0.4 & 0 & -0.2 \\ 1.4 & -1 & -1.2 \end{bmatrix}$

33. $\begin{bmatrix} 0.5 & 0.2 & 2.1 \\ 0 & 0.2 & 1.6 \\ 0 & 0 & -1 \end{bmatrix}$ **35.** $\begin{bmatrix} 0.5 & 0.25 & 0.25 \\ 0.25 & 0.5 & 0.25 \\ 0.25 & 0.25 & 0.5 \end{bmatrix}$

37. $\begin{bmatrix} 1.2\overline{6} & 0.2\overline{6} & 0.0\overline{6} & 0.0\overline{6} \\ 0.2\overline{6} & 0.2\overline{6} & 0.0\overline{6} & 0.0\overline{6} \\ 0.0\overline{6} & 0.0\overline{6} & 0.2\overline{6} & 0.2\overline{6} \\ 0.0\overline{6} & 0.0\overline{6} & 0.2\overline{6} & 1.2\overline{6} \end{bmatrix}$

39. $AX = \begin{bmatrix} 2 & -3 \\ -3 & -4 \end{bmatrix}\begin{bmatrix} x \\ y \end{bmatrix} = \begin{bmatrix} 7 \\ 9 \end{bmatrix} = B$

41. $AX = \begin{bmatrix} \frac{1}{2} & -\frac{3}{2} \\ -1 & 2 \end{bmatrix}\begin{bmatrix} x \\ y \end{bmatrix} = \begin{bmatrix} \frac{1}{4} \\ 5 \end{bmatrix} = B$

43. $AX = \begin{bmatrix} 1 & -2 & 1 \\ 0 & 3 & -1 \\ 5 & -4 & -7 \end{bmatrix}\begin{bmatrix} x \\ y \\ z \end{bmatrix} = \begin{bmatrix} 5 \\ 6 \\ 0 \end{bmatrix} = B$

45. $AX = \begin{bmatrix} 4 & -1 & 3 \\ 1 & 2 & 5 \\ 2 & -3 & 0 \end{bmatrix}\begin{bmatrix} x \\ y \\ z \end{bmatrix} = \begin{bmatrix} -2 \\ 11 \\ -1 \end{bmatrix} = B$

47. (a) $AX = \begin{bmatrix} 1 & 2 \\ 1 & 3 \end{bmatrix}\begin{bmatrix} x \\ y \end{bmatrix} = \begin{bmatrix} 3 \\ 6 \end{bmatrix} = B$ **(b)** $X = \begin{bmatrix} -3 \\ 3 \end{bmatrix}$

49. (a) $AX = \begin{bmatrix} -1 & 2 \\ 3 & -5 \end{bmatrix}\begin{bmatrix} x \\ y \end{bmatrix} = \begin{bmatrix} 5 \\ -2 \end{bmatrix} = B$

(b) $X = \begin{bmatrix} 21 \\ 13 \end{bmatrix}$

51. (a) $AX = \begin{bmatrix} 1 & 0 & 1 \\ 2 & 1 & 3 \\ -1 & 1 & 1 \end{bmatrix}\begin{bmatrix} x \\ y \\ z \end{bmatrix} = \begin{bmatrix} -7 \\ -13 \\ -4 \end{bmatrix} = B$

(b) $X = \begin{bmatrix} 5 \\ 13 \\ -12 \end{bmatrix}$

53. (a) $AX = \begin{bmatrix} 1 & 2 & -1 \\ 2 & 5 & 0 \\ -1 & -1 & 2 \end{bmatrix}\begin{bmatrix} x \\ y \\ z \end{bmatrix} = \begin{bmatrix} 2 \\ -1 \\ 0 \end{bmatrix} = B$

(b) $X = \begin{bmatrix} -23 \\ 9 \\ -7 \end{bmatrix}$

55. (a) $AX = \begin{bmatrix} 1.5 & 3.7 \\ -0.4 & -2.1 \end{bmatrix}\begin{bmatrix} x \\ y \end{bmatrix} = \begin{bmatrix} 0.32 \\ 0.36 \end{bmatrix} = B$

(b) $X = \begin{bmatrix} 1.2 \\ -0.4 \end{bmatrix}$

57. (a) $AX = \begin{bmatrix} 0.08 & -0.7 \\ 1.1 & -0.05 \end{bmatrix}\begin{bmatrix} x \\ y \end{bmatrix} = \begin{bmatrix} -0.504 \\ 0.73 \end{bmatrix} = B$

(b) $X = \begin{bmatrix} 0.7 \\ 0.8 \end{bmatrix}$

59. (a) $AX = \begin{bmatrix} 3.1 & 1.9 & -1 \\ 6.3 & 0 & -9.9 \\ -1 & 1.5 & 7 \end{bmatrix}\begin{bmatrix} x \\ y \\ z \end{bmatrix} = \begin{bmatrix} 1.99 \\ -3.78 \\ 5.3 \end{bmatrix} = B$

(b) $X = \begin{bmatrix} 0.5 \\ 0.6 \\ 0.7 \end{bmatrix}$

61. (a) $AX = \begin{bmatrix} 3 & -1 & 1 \\ 5.8 & -2.1 & 0 \\ -1 & 0 & 2.9 \end{bmatrix}\begin{bmatrix} x \\ y \\ z \end{bmatrix} = \begin{bmatrix} 4.9 \\ -3.8 \\ 3.8 \end{bmatrix} = B$

(b) $X \approx \begin{bmatrix} 9.26 \\ 27.39 \\ 4.50 \end{bmatrix}$

63. (a) $(2, 4)$ **(b)** It will translate $(2, 4)$ to the left 2 units and downward 3 units, back to $(0, 1)$;

$A^{-1} = \begin{bmatrix} 1 & 0 & -2 \\ 0 & 1 & -3 \\ 0 & 0 & 1 \end{bmatrix}$ **(c)** I_3

65. $A = \begin{bmatrix} 1 & 0 & -3 \\ 0 & 1 & -5 \\ 0 & 0 & 1 \end{bmatrix}$ and $A^{-1} = \begin{bmatrix} 1 & 0 & 3 \\ 0 & 1 & 5 \\ 0 & 0 & 1 \end{bmatrix}$.

A^{-1} will translate a point 3 units to the right and 5 units upward.

67. (a) $BX = \begin{bmatrix} -2 \\ 0 \\ 1 \end{bmatrix} = Y$ **(b)** $B^{-1}Y = \begin{bmatrix} -\sqrt{2} \\ -\sqrt{2} \\ 1 \end{bmatrix} = X$.

B^{-1} rotates the point represented by Y counterclockwise $45°$ about the origin.

69. (a) $ABX = \begin{bmatrix} 2 \\ 2 \\ 1 \end{bmatrix} = Y$ **(b)** The net result of A and B is to translate a point 1 unit to the right and 1 unit upward.

$AB = \begin{bmatrix} 1 & 0 & 1 \\ 0 & 1 & 1 \\ 0 & 0 & 1 \end{bmatrix}$. **(c)** Yes **(d)** Since AB translates a point 1 unit right and 1 unit upward, the inverse of AB would translate a point 1 unit left and 1 unit downward. Therefore

$$(AB)^{-1} = \begin{bmatrix} 1 & 0 & -1 \\ 0 & 1 & -1 \\ 0 & 0 & 1 \end{bmatrix}.$$

71. A: $10.99; B: $12.99; C: $14.99
73. (a)
$$\begin{aligned} a + 1500b + 8c &= 122 \\ a + 2000b + 5c &= 130 \\ a + 2200b + 10c &= 158 \\ a = 30,\ b &= 0.04,\ c = 4 \end{aligned}$$

(b) $130,000 **75. (a)** $\left(\frac{17}{12}T, \frac{5}{6}T, T\right)$
(b) Service: 85 units; electrical: 50 units

CHECKING BASIC CONCEPTS FOR SECTIONS 9.5 AND 9.6 (p. 780)

1. (a) $A + B = \begin{bmatrix} 0 & 1 & 3 \\ -1 & 5 & 3 \\ 2 & 1 & 0 \end{bmatrix}$

(b) $2A - B = \begin{bmatrix} 3 & -1 & 0 \\ -2 & -2 & 3 \\ 1 & 8 & 0 \end{bmatrix}$

(c) $AB = \begin{bmatrix} 0 & -1 & 2 \\ 3 & -1 & -1 \\ -1 & 13 & 5 \end{bmatrix}$

3. (a) $AX = \begin{bmatrix} 1 & -2 \\ 2 & 3 \end{bmatrix}\begin{bmatrix} x \\ y \end{bmatrix} = \begin{bmatrix} 13 \\ 5 \end{bmatrix} = B;\ X = \begin{bmatrix} 7 \\ -3 \end{bmatrix}$

(b) $AX = \begin{bmatrix} 1 & -1 & 1 \\ -1 & 1 & 1 \\ 0 & 1 & -1 \end{bmatrix}\begin{bmatrix} x \\ y \\ z \end{bmatrix} = \begin{bmatrix} 2 \\ 4 \\ -1 \end{bmatrix} = B;\ X = \begin{bmatrix} 1 \\ 2 \\ 3 \end{bmatrix}$

(c) $AX = \begin{bmatrix} 3.1 & -5.3 \\ -0.1 & 1.8 \end{bmatrix}\begin{bmatrix} x \\ y \end{bmatrix} = \begin{bmatrix} -2.682 \\ 0.787 \end{bmatrix} = B;$

$X = \begin{bmatrix} -0.13 \\ 0.43 \end{bmatrix}$

SECTION 9.7 (pp. 787–788)

1. det $A = 1 \neq 0$. A is invertible.
3. det $A = 0$. A is not invertible.
5. $M_{12} = 10,\ A_{12} = -10$
7. $M_{22} = -15,\ A_{22} = -15$
9. det $A = 3 \neq 0$. A^{-1} exists.
11. det $A = 0$. A^{-1} does not exist.
13. 30 **15.** 0 **17.** -32 **19.** 0
21. 643.4 **23.** -4.484 **25.** $\left(-\frac{13}{9}, \frac{16}{9}\right)$ **27.** $\left(\frac{49}{2}, 19\right)$
29. $(5, -3)$ **31.** $(0.45, 0.67)$ **33.** 7 square units
35. 6.5 square units **37.** The points are collinear.
39. The points are not collinear.
41. $x + y = 3$ **43.** $2x + y = 5$

9.7 EXTENDED AND DISCOVERY EXERCISES (p. 788)

1. $(1, 3, 2)$ **3.** $(1, -1, 1)$ **5.** $(-1, 0, 4)$
7. $x^2 + y^2 - 4 = 0$ **9.** $5x^2 + 5y^2 - 15x - 5y = 0$

CHECKING BASIC CONCEPTS FOR SECTION 9.7 (p. 788)

1. det $A = 19$; A is invertible.

CHAPTER 9 REVIEW EXERCISES (pp. 792–794)

1. $A(3, 6) = 9$ **3.** $(3, 1)$ **5.** $(1, -2)$
7. $(2, 3)$; consistent
9. $\{(x, y) \mid 2x - 5y = 4\}$; consistent
11. $\left(\frac{3\sqrt{2}}{2}, \frac{1}{2}\right), \left(-\frac{3\sqrt{2}}{2}, \frac{1}{2}\right)$

13.

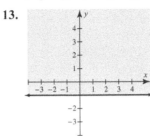

15. $(2, 2)$ (answers may vary)

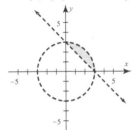

17. $(-1, 2, 1)$ **19.** No solutions **21.** $(-9, 3)$ **23.** $(-2, 3, 0)$
25. $(1, -2, 3)$ **27. (a)** 5 **(b)** -10

29. (a) $A + 2B = \begin{bmatrix} 7 & 1 \\ -8 & 1 \end{bmatrix}$

(b) $A - B = \begin{bmatrix} -2 & -5 \\ 7 & -2 \end{bmatrix}$ **(c)** $-4A = \begin{bmatrix} -4 & 12 \\ -8 & 4 \end{bmatrix}$

31. $AB = \begin{bmatrix} -2 & -4 \\ 17 & 31 \end{bmatrix}, BA = \begin{bmatrix} 8 & -6 \\ -27 & 21 \end{bmatrix}$

33. $AB = \begin{bmatrix} 3 & 7 \\ -2 & 8 \end{bmatrix}, BA = \begin{bmatrix} 2 & -1 & 3 \\ 2 & 9 & -3 \\ 6 & 12 & 0 \end{bmatrix}$ **35.** Yes

37. $\begin{bmatrix} -1 & -2 \\ -1 & -1 \end{bmatrix}$

39. (a) $AX = \begin{bmatrix} 1 & -3 \\ 2 & -1 \end{bmatrix}\begin{bmatrix} x \\ y \end{bmatrix} = \begin{bmatrix} 4 \\ 3 \end{bmatrix} = B$

(b) $X = \begin{bmatrix} 1 \\ -1 \end{bmatrix}$

41. $(-0.5, 1.7, -2.9)$
43. det $A = 25$ **45.** det $A = -1951 \neq 0$. A is invertible.
47. $l = 11,\ w = 7$
49. Both methods yield $1200 at 7%, $800 at 9%.
51. A: $11.49; B: $12.99
53. 10.5 square units **55.** 4500

CHAPTER 9 EXTENDED AND DISCOVERY EXERCISES (pp. 794–795)

1. (a) $A^T = \begin{bmatrix} 3 & 2 & 4 \\ -3 & 6 & 2 \end{bmatrix}$ **(b)** $A^T = \begin{bmatrix} 0 & 2 & -4 \\ 1 & 5 & 3 \\ -2 & 4 & 9 \end{bmatrix}$

(c) $A^T = \begin{bmatrix} 5 & 1 & 6 & -9 \\ 7 & -7 & 3 & 2 \end{bmatrix}$

3. $f(x) = 2.6314x + 2.2714$
$[-1, 6, 1]$ by $[0, 18, 2]$

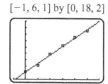

CHAPTER 10: Conic Sections

SECTION 10.1 (pp. 804–807)

1. focus **3.** upward; downward **5.** vertical

7.
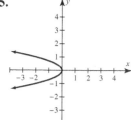

9.
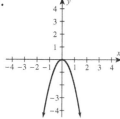

11.
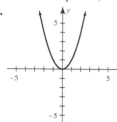

13.
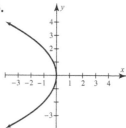

15.
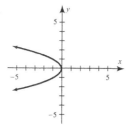

17. e **19.** a **21.** d

23. Vertex: $V(0, 0)$;
focus: $F(0, 4)$;
directrix: $y = -4$

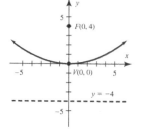

25. Vertex: $V(0, 0)$;
focus: $F(2, 0)$;
directrix: $x = -2$

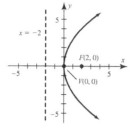

27. Vertex: $V(0, 0)$;
focus: $F(-1, 0)$;
directrix: $x = 1$

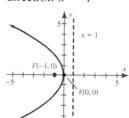

29. Vertex: $V(0, 0)$;
focus: $F(0, -2)$;
directrix: $y = 2$

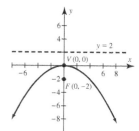

31. Vertex: $V(0, 0)$;
focus: $F(-1, 0)$;
directrix: $x = 1$

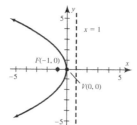

33. $x^2 = 4y$

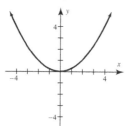

35. $y^2 = -12x$

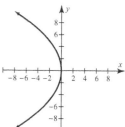

37. $x^2 = 3y$ **39.** $y^2 = -8x$ **41.** $y^2 = 4x$
43. $y^2 = -x$ **45.** $y^2 = 4x$ **47.** $x^2 = -12y$
49. $y^2 = -4x$

51.
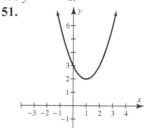

53.
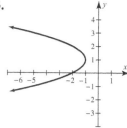

55. c **57.** a

59. Vertex: $V(2, -2)$;
focus: $F(2, 0)$;
directrix; $y = -4$

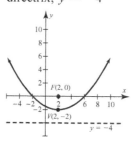

61. Vertex: $V(2, -3)$;
focus: $F(1, -3)$;
directrix: $x = 3$

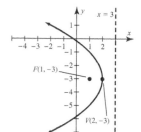

63. Vertex: $V(-2, 0)$; focus: $F(-2, -1)$; directrix: $y = 1$

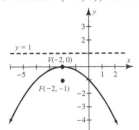

65. $x^2 = 4(y - 1)$

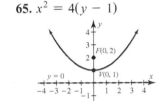

67. $y^2 = 4(x + 1)$

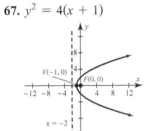

69. $(x + 1)^2 = -8(y - 5)$ **71.** $(y - 3)^2 = -\frac{9}{2}(x + 2)$
73. $(y - 0)^2 = -8\left(x + \frac{5}{4}\right)$ **75.** $(y + 1)^2 = \frac{1}{2}(x + 3)$
77. $\left(x - \frac{3}{2}\right)^2 = 2\left(y - \frac{7}{8}\right)$ **79.** $\left(y + \frac{1}{2}\right)^2 = \frac{5}{4}\left(x + \frac{6}{5}\right)$
81. $[-6, 6, 1]$ by $[-4, 4, 1]$ **83.** $[-9, 9, 1]$ by $[-6, 6, 1]$

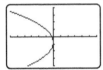
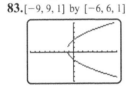

Note: If a break in the graph appears near the vertex, it should not be there. It is a result of the low resolution of the graphing calculator screen.
85. $[-6, 6, 1]$ by $[-4, 4, 1]$

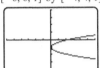

87. $\left(\pm\sqrt{2}, 1\right)$ **89.** $\left(-0.1, \pm\sqrt{0.9}\right)$
91. $(0, 0), (3, -1)$ **93.** $p = 3$ ft
95. (a) $y = \frac{32}{11{,}025}x^2$ **(b)** About 86.1 ft
97. (a) $(25, 0)$ **(b)** 25 million mi   **99.** $k = 6$

SECTION 10.2 (pp. 817–821)

1. vertices   **3.** horizontal
5. Foci: $F\left(0, \pm\sqrt{5}\right)$;
vertices: $V(0, \pm3)$;
endpoints of the
minor axis: $U(\pm2, 0)$

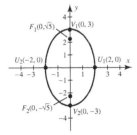

7. Foci: $F\left(\pm\sqrt{20}, 0\right)$;
vertices: $V(\pm6, 0)$;
endpoints of the
minor axis: $U(0, \pm4)$

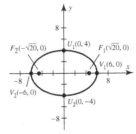

9. Foci: $F\left(\pm\sqrt{300}, 0\right)$;
vertices: $V(\pm20, 0)$;
endpoints of the
minor axis: $U(0, \pm10)$

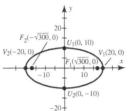

11. Foci: $F(0, \pm4)$;
vertices: $V(0, \pm5)$;
endpoints of the
minor axis: $U(\pm3, 0)$

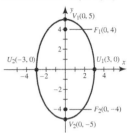

13. b   **15.** c
17. $\frac{x^2}{36} + \frac{y^2}{16} = 1$; vertices: $V(\pm6, 0)$; endpoints of the minor axis: $U(0, \pm4)$; foci: $F\left(\pm\sqrt{20}, 0\right)$
19. $\frac{x^2}{4} + \frac{y^2}{16} = 1$; vertices: $V(0, \pm4)$; endpoints of the minor axis: $U(\pm2, 0)$; foci: $F\left(0, \pm\sqrt{12}\right)$
21. $\frac{x^2}{25} + \frac{y^2}{9} = 1$ **23.** $\frac{x^2}{5} + \frac{y^2}{9} = 1$

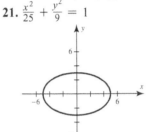

25. $\frac{x^2}{12} + \frac{y^2}{16} = 1$ **27.** $\frac{x^2}{36} + \frac{y^2}{11} = 1$
29. $\frac{x^2}{16} + \frac{y^2}{9} = 1$ **31.** $\frac{x^2}{9} + \frac{y^2}{5} = 1$
33. $\frac{(x - 2)^2}{4} + \frac{(y + 1)^2}{3} = 1$ **35.** $\frac{(x + 3)^2}{2} + \frac{(y + 4)^2}{9} = 1$

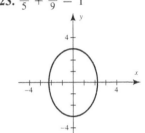

37.

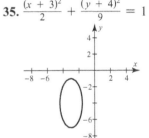

39.

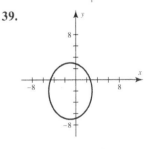

41.

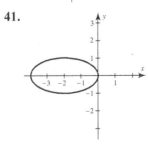

43. d   **45.** c

47. Foci: $F(1, 1 \pm 4)$;
vertices: $V(1, 1 \pm 5)$

49. Foci: $F(-4 \pm \sqrt{7}, 2)$;
vertices: $V(-4 \pm 4, 2)$

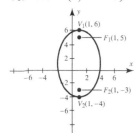

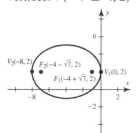

51. $\dfrac{(x-2)^2}{5} + \dfrac{(y-1)^2}{9} = 1$ **53.** $\dfrac{x^2}{9} + \dfrac{(y-2)^2}{5} = 1$

55. $\dfrac{(x-2)^2}{16} + \dfrac{(y-4)^2}{4} = 1$

57. $\dfrac{(x+1)^2}{4} + \dfrac{(y-1)^2}{9} = 1$; center: $C(-1, 1)$;
vertices: $V(-1, -2), V(-1, 4)$

59. $\dfrac{(x+1)^2}{1} + \dfrac{(y+1)^2}{4} = 1$; center: $C(-1, -1)$;
vertices: $V(-1, -3), V(-1, 1)$

61. $\dfrac{(x+2)^2}{5} + \dfrac{(y-1)^2}{4} = 1$; center: $C(-2, 1)$;
vertices: $V\left(-2 - \sqrt{5}, 1\right), V\left(-2 + \sqrt{5}, 1\right)$

63. $\dfrac{\left(x - \frac{1}{2}\right)^2}{4} + \dfrac{\left(y + \frac{3}{2}\right)^2}{16} = 1$; center: $C\left(\frac{1}{2}, -\frac{3}{2}\right)$;
vertices: $V\left(\frac{1}{2}, \frac{5}{2}\right), V\left(\frac{1}{2}, -\frac{11}{2}\right)$

65. $[-6, 6, 1]$ by $[-4, 4, 1]$

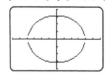

67. $[-4.7, 4.7, 1]$ by $[-3.1, 3.1, 1]$

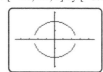

69. $(0, 3), \left(\dfrac{24}{13}, \dfrac{15}{13}\right)$

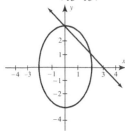

71. Four solutions:
$\left(\pm\sqrt{\dfrac{20}{3}}, \pm\sqrt{\dfrac{7}{3}}\right)$

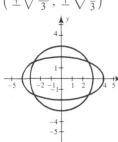

73. $(3, 0), (-3, 0)$

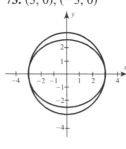

75. $(0, 2)$ **77.** Four solutions: $\left(\pm\sqrt{\dfrac{4}{3}}, \pm\sqrt{\dfrac{4}{3}}\right)$
79. $\left(1, \sqrt{8}\right), \left(1, -\sqrt{8}\right)$

81.

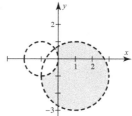

83.

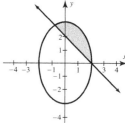

85.

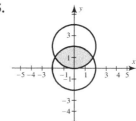

87.

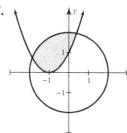

89. $A = 6\pi \approx 18.85$ ft^2

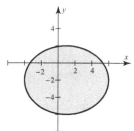

91. $A = 20\pi \approx 62.83$ ft^2

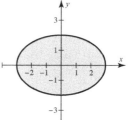

93. $\dfrac{x^2}{0.387^2} + \dfrac{y^2}{0.379^2} = 1$; sun: $(0.0797, 0)$
$[-0.6, 0.6, 0.1]$ by $[-0.4, 0.4, 0.1]$

95. 6.245 in.   **97.** $A = \pi(64.03)(40) \approx 8046.25$ ft^2
99. 348.2 ft   **101.** About 21.65 ft
103. Maximum: 668 mi; minimum: 340 mi

10.2 EXTENDED AND DISCOVERY EXERCISES (p. 821)
1. $\dfrac{x}{2} + \dfrac{y}{3} = 1$; x-int: 2, y-int: 3
3. $\dfrac{x}{2.5} + \dfrac{y}{5} = 1$; x-int: 2.5, y-int: 5
5. x-int: ± 5, y-int: ± 3

**CHECKING BASIC CONCEPTS FOR SECTIONS 10.1
AND 10.2 (p. 821)**

1. Focus: $F\left(\frac{1}{2}, 0\right)$;
directrix: $x = -\frac{1}{2}$

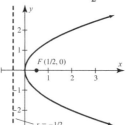

3. Foci: $F(0, \pm 8)$;
vertices: $V(0, \pm 10)$;
endpoints of the
minor axis: $U(\pm 6, 0)$

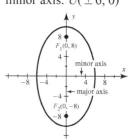

5. 1 ft   **7.** $\dfrac{(x-2)^2}{16}+\dfrac{(y+1)^2}{4}=1$; center: $C(2,-1)$;
vertices: $V(-2,-1)$, $V(6,-1)$

SECTION 10.3 (pp. 828–830)

1. vertices   **3.** horizontal
5. Asymptotes: $y=\pm\frac{7}{3}x$;
$F\left(\pm\sqrt{58},0\right)$; $V(\pm3,0)$

7. Asymptotes: $y=\pm\frac{3}{2}x$;
$F\left(0,\pm\sqrt{52}\right)$; $V(0,\pm6)$

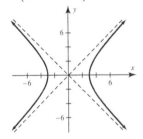
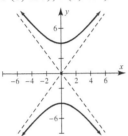

9. Asymptotes: $y=\pm x$;
$F\left(\pm\sqrt{18},0\right)$; $V(\pm3,0)$

11. Asymptotes: $y=\pm\frac{4}{3}x$;
$F(0,\pm5)$; $V(0,\pm4)$

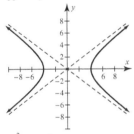
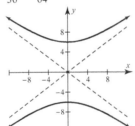

13. d   **15.** a
17. $\dfrac{x^2}{16}-\dfrac{y^2}{9}=1$

19. $\dfrac{y^2}{36}-\dfrac{x^2}{64}=1$

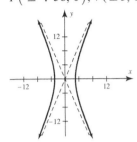

21. $\dfrac{y^2}{144}-\dfrac{x^2}{25}=1$; asymptotes: $y=\pm\frac{12}{5}x$
23. $\dfrac{y^2}{4}-\dfrac{x^2}{21}=1$; asymptotes: $y=\pm\dfrac{2}{\sqrt{21}}x$
25. $\dfrac{x^2}{9}-\dfrac{y^2}{4}=1$; asymptotes: $y=\pm\frac{2}{3}x$
27. $\dfrac{x^2}{16}-\dfrac{y^2}{9}=1$; asymptotes: $y=\pm\frac{3}{4}x$
29. $\dfrac{x^2}{10}-\dfrac{y^2}{9}=1$; asymptotes: $y=\pm\dfrac{3}{\sqrt{10}}x$

31. Vertices: $V(1\pm4,2)$; foci: $F\left(1\pm\sqrt{20},2\right)$;
asymptotes: $y=\pm\frac{1}{2}(x-1)+2$

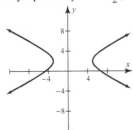

33. Vertices: $V(-2,2\pm6)$; foci: $F\left(-2,2\pm\sqrt{40}\right)$;
asymptotes: $y=\pm3(x+2)+2$

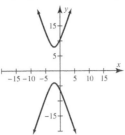

35. Vertices: $V(\pm2,1)$; foci: $F\left(\pm\sqrt{5},1\right)$;
asymptotes: $y=\pm\frac{1}{2}x+1$

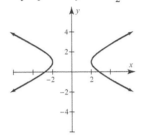

37. b   **39.** c
41. $\dfrac{(y+4)^2}{16}-\dfrac{(x-4)^2}{4}=1$; vertices: $V(4,-4\pm4)$;
foci: $F\left(4,-4\pm\sqrt{20}\right)$; asymptotes: $y=\pm2(x-4)-4$
43. Vertices: $V(1\pm2,1)$; foci: $F\left(1\pm\sqrt{8},1\right)$;
asymptotes: $y=\pm(x-1)+1$

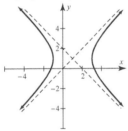

45. Vertices: $V(1,-1\pm4)$; foci: $F(1,-1\pm5)$;
asymptotes: $y=\pm\frac{4}{3}(x-1)-1$

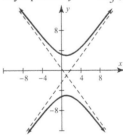

47. $(x-2)^2-\dfrac{(y+2)^2}{3}=1$ **49.** $y^2-\dfrac{(x+1)^2}{8}=1$
51. $\dfrac{(x-1)^2}{4}-\dfrac{(y-1)^2}{4}=1$; center: $C(1,1)$;
vertices: $V(-1,1)$, $V(3,1)$
53. $\dfrac{(y+4)^2}{2}-\dfrac{(x-3)^2}{3}=1$; center: $C(3,-4)$;
vertices: $V\left(3,-4-\sqrt{2}\right)$, $V\left(3,-4+\sqrt{2}\right)$
55. $\dfrac{(x-3)^2}{2}-\dfrac{(y-0)^2}{1}=1$; center: $C(3,0)$;
vertices: $V\left(3-\sqrt{2},0\right)$, $V\left(3+\sqrt{2},0\right)$

57. $\frac{(y+4)^2}{5} - \frac{(x+1)^2}{4} = 1$; center: $C(-1, -4)$;
vertices: $V\left(-1, -4 - \sqrt{5}\right)$, $V\left(-1, -4 + \sqrt{5}\right)$

59. $[-15, 15, 5]$ by $[-10, 10, 5]$ **61.** $[-9, 9, 1]$ by $[-6, 6, 1]$

63. Four solutions: $\left(\pm\sqrt{\frac{13}{2}}, \pm\sqrt{\frac{5}{2}}\right)$

65. $(2, 0)$, $(-5.2, 7.2)$ **67.** Four solutions: $\left(\pm 2, \pm\frac{2}{\sqrt{3}}\right)$

69. $\left(\frac{2}{\sqrt{11}}, \frac{6}{\sqrt{11}}\right), \left(-\frac{2}{\sqrt{11}}, -\frac{6}{\sqrt{11}}\right)$

71. (a) Elliptic   **(b)** Its speed should be 4326 m/sec or
greater.   **(c)** If D is larger, then $\frac{k}{\sqrt{D}}$ is smaller, so smaller
values for V satisfy $V > \frac{k}{\sqrt{D}}$.

**10.3 EXTENDED AND DISCOVERY EXERCISES
(p. 831)**

1. (a) $x = \sqrt{y^2 + 2.5 \times 10^{-27}}$; this equation represents
the right half of the hyperbola.   **(b)** About 1.2×10^{-13} m

**CHECKING BASIC CONCEPTS FOR SECTION 10.3
(p. 831)**

1. $\frac{x^2}{16} - \frac{y^2}{9} = 1$

3. $\frac{(x-1)^2}{9} - \frac{(y-3)^2}{4} = 1$; $F\left(1 \pm \sqrt{13}, 3\right)$

CHAPTER 10 REVIEW EXERCISES (pp. 834–835)

1.

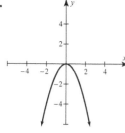

3.

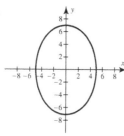

5.

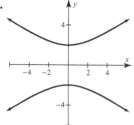

7. d   **9.** a   **11.** e

13. $y^2 = 8x$ **15.** $\frac{x^2}{25} + \frac{y^2}{9} = 1$ **17.** $\frac{y^2}{64} - \frac{x^2}{36} = 1$

19. $F(0, -1)$ **21.** $F\left(\pm\sqrt{21}, 0\right)$

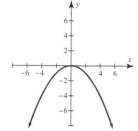   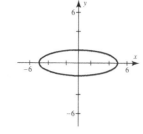

23. $F(\pm 5, 0)$

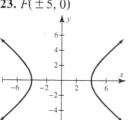

25. Both foci are located at $(3, -1)$.

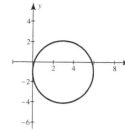

27. Center: $C(1, -1)$

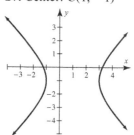

29.

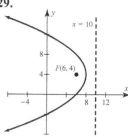

31. $[-5, 5, 1]$ by $[-5, 5, 1]$

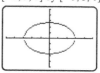

Note: If breaks in the graph appear near the vertices, they
should not be there. It is a result of the low resolution of the
graphing calculator screen.

33. $(y - 0)^2 = -10\left(x + \frac{7}{5}\right)$

35. $\frac{(x+1)^2}{25} + \frac{(y-5)^2}{4} = 1$; center: $C(-1, 5)$;
vertices: $V(-6, 5)$, $V(4, 5)$

37. $\frac{(x+2)^2}{4} - \frac{(y-3)^2}{1} = 1$; center: $C(-2, 3)$;
vertices: $V(-4, 3)$, $V(0, 3)$

39. Four solutions: $\left(\pm\sqrt{\frac{8}{3}}, \pm\sqrt{\frac{4}{3}}\right)$

41.

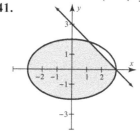

43. (a) Minimum: 4.92 million mi; maximum:
995.08 million mi   **(b)** $2\pi\sqrt{\frac{500^2 + 70^2}{2}} \approx 2243$ million
miles, or 2.243 billion miles   **45.** About 29.05 ft

**CHAPTER 10 EXTENDED AND DISCOVERY
EXERCISES (p. 835)**

1. Neptune: 0.271; Pluto: 9.82

3. Neptune: $\frac{(x - 0.271)^2}{30.10^2} + \frac{y^2}{30.10^2} = 1$;

Pluto: $\frac{(x - 9.82)^2}{39.44^2} + \frac{y^2}{38.20^2} = 1$

5. No. Because Pluto's orbit is so eccentric, there is a period
of time when Pluto is not farther from the sun. However, its
average distance a from the sun is greater.

CHAPTER 11: Further Topics in Algebra

SECTION 11.1 (pp. 846–849)

1. $a_1 = 3, a_2 = 5, a_3 = 7, a_4 = 9$
3. $a_1 = 4, a_2 = -8, a_3 = 16, a_4 = -32$
5. $a_1 = \frac{1}{2}, a_2 = \frac{2}{5}, a_3 = \frac{3}{10}, a_4 = \frac{4}{17}$
7. $a_1 = -\frac{1}{2}, a_2 = \frac{1}{4}, a_3 = -\frac{1}{8}, a_4 = \frac{1}{16}$
9. $a_1 = \frac{2}{3}, a_2 = -\frac{4}{5}, a_3 = \frac{8}{9}, a_4 = -\frac{16}{17}$
11. $a_1 = 3, a_2 = 8, a_3 = 17, a_4 = 32$
13. 2, 4, 3, 5, 3, 6, 4
15. **(a)** $a_1 = 1, a_2 = 2,$ $a_3 = 4, a_4 = 8$
(b) [0, 5, 1] by [0, 9, 1]

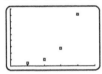

17. **(a)** $a_1 = -3, a_2 = 0,$ $a_3 = 3, a_4 = 6$
(b) [0, 5, 1] by [−4, 7, 1]

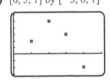

19. **(a)** $a_1 = 2, a_2 = 5,$ $a_3 = 14, a_4 = 41$
(b) [0, 5, 1] by [0, 45, 5]

21. **(a)** $a_1 = 2, a_2 = 5,$ $a_3 = 3, a_4 = -2$
(b) [0, 5, 1] by [−3, 6, 1]

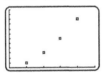

23. **(a)** $a_1 = 2, a_2 = 4,$ $a_3 = 16, a_4 = 256$
(b) [0, 5, 1] by [0, 300, 50]

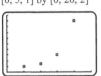

25. **(a)** $a_1 = 1, a_2 = 3,$ $a_3 = 6, a_4 = 10$
(b) [0, 5, 1] by [0, 12, 1]

27. **(a)** $a_1 = 2, a_2 = 3,$ $a_3 = 6, a_4 = 18$
(b) [0, 5, 1] by [0, 20, 2]

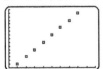

29. **(a)**

n	1	2	3	4	5	6	7	8
a_n	1	3	5	7	9	11	13	15

(b) [0, 10, 1] by [0, 16, 1]   **(c)** $a_n = 2n - 1$

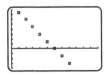

31. **(a)**

n	1	2	3	4	5	6	7	8
a_n	7.5	6	4.5	3	1.5	0	−1.5	−3

(b) [0, 12, 1] by [−4, 8, 1]   **(c)** $a_n = -1.5n + 9$

33. **(a)**

n	1	2	3	4	5	6	7	8
a_n	$\frac{1}{2}$	2	$\frac{7}{2}$	5	$\frac{13}{2}$	8	$\frac{19}{2}$	11

(b) [0, 9, 1] by [0, 12, 1]   **(c)** $a_n = \frac{3}{2}n - 1$

35. **(a)**

n	1	2	3	4	5	6	7	8
a_n	8	4	2	1	$\frac{1}{2}$	$\frac{1}{4}$	$\frac{1}{8}$	$\frac{1}{16}$

(b) [0, 10, 1] by [−1, 9, 1]   **(c)** $a_n = 8\left(\frac{1}{2}\right)^{n-1}$

37. **(a)**

n	1	2	3	4	5	6	7	8
a_n	$\frac{3}{4}$	$\frac{3}{2}$	3	6	12	24	48	96

(b) [0, 10, 1] by [−10, 110, 10]   **(c)** $a_n = \frac{3}{4}(2)^{n-1}$

39. **(a)**

n	1	2	3	4	5	6	7	8
a_n	$-\frac{1}{4}$	$-\frac{1}{2}$	−1	−2	−4	−8	−16	−32

(b) [0, 9, 1] by [−36, 4, 4]   **(c)** $a_n = -\frac{1}{4}(2)^{n-1}$

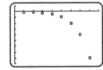

41. $a_n = -2n + 7$ **43.** $a_n = 3n - 8$
45. $a_n = 2n + 1$ **47.** $a_n = 3n + 5$
49. $a_n = 0.5n - 6.5$ **51.** $a_n = 2\left(\frac{1}{2}\right)^{n-1}$
53. $a_n = \frac{1}{2}\left(-\frac{1}{4}\right)^{n-1}$ **55.** $a_n = 8\left(\frac{1}{2}\right)^{n-1}$
57. $a_n = -5(-5)^{n-1}$ **59.** $a_n = -\frac{1}{2}(2)^{n-1}$
61. No   **63.** Yes   **65.** Yes   **67.** Yes
69. Yes   **71.** No   **73.** No   **75.** No
77. Arithmetic   **79.** Geometric   **81.** Neither
83. Arithmetic, $d < 0, d = -1$
85. Geometric, $r < 0, |r| < 1$
87. The insect population density increases rapidly and then levels off near 5000 per acre.
89. **(a)** $a_n = 0.8a_{n-1}, a_1 = 500$ **(b)** $a_1 = 500,$ $a_2 = 400, a_3 = 320, a_4 = 256, a_5 = 204.8,$ and $a_6 = 163.84.$ The population density decreases by 20% each year.   **(c)** $a_n = 500(0.8)^{n-1}$
91. **(a)** $a_1 = 8, a_2 = 10.4, a_3 = 8.528$
(b) [0, 21, 1] by [0, 14, 1]

The population density oscillates above and below approximately 9.5.

93. $a_n = 100n$; $a_5 = 500$; after 5 years, 500 million cell phones have been thrown out.

95. (a) 100, 194, 288, 382, 476; arithmetic

(b) [0, 6, 1] by [0, 500, 100]

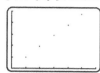

(c) $a_n = 94(n - 1) + 100$

97. (a) 1, 1, 2, 3, 5, 8, 13, 21, 34, 55, 89, 144

(b) $\frac{a_2}{a_1} = 1$, $\frac{a_3}{a_2} = 2$, $\frac{a_4}{a_3} = 1.5$, $\frac{a_5}{a_4} = \frac{5}{3} \approx 1.6667$,

$\frac{a_6}{a_5} = \frac{8}{5} = 1.6$, $\frac{a_7}{a_6} = \frac{13}{8} = 1.625$, $\frac{a_8}{a_7} = \frac{21}{13} \approx 1.6154$,

$\frac{a_9}{a_8} = \frac{34}{21} \approx 1.6190$, $\frac{a_{10}}{a_9} = \frac{55}{34} \approx 1.6176$,

$\frac{a_{11}}{a_{10}} = \frac{89}{55} \approx 1.6182$, and $\frac{a_{12}}{a_{11}} = \frac{144}{89} \approx 1.6180$.

The ratio appears to approach a number near 1.618.

(c) $n = 2$: $a_1 \cdot a_3 - a_2^2 = (1)(2) - (1)^2 = 1 = (-1)^2$

$n = 3$: $a_2 \cdot a_4 - a_3^2 = (1)(3) - (2)^2 = -1 = (-1)^3$

$n = 4$: $a_3 \cdot a_5 - a_4^2 = (2)(5) - (3)^2 = 1 = (-1)^4$

99. (a) $a_n = 2000n + 28{,}000$, or

$a_n = 30{,}000 + 2000(n - 1)$; arithmetic

(b) $b_n = 30{,}000(1.05)^{n-1}$; geometric

(c) Since $a_{10} = \$48{,}000 > b_{10} \approx \$46{,}540$, the first salary is higher after 10 years. Since $a_{20} = \$68{,}000 < b_{20} \approx \$75{,}809$, the second salary is higher after 20 years.

(d) With time, the geometric sequence with $r > 1$ overtakes the arithmetic sequence.

[0, 30, 10] by [0, 150000, 50000]

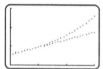

101. $a_6 \approx 1.414213562$, $\sqrt{2} \approx 1.414213562$

103. $a_6 = 4.582581971$, $\sqrt{21} \approx 4.582575695$

105. By definition,

$a_n = a_1 + (n - 1)d_1$ and $b_n = b_1 + (n - 1)d_2$.

Then $c_n = a_n + b_n$

$\quad = [a_1 + (n - 1)d_1] + [b_1 + (n - 1)d_2]$

$\quad = (a_1 + b_1) + [(n - 1)d_1 + (n - 1)d_2]$

$\quad = (a_1 + b_1) + (n - 1)(d_1 + d_2)$

$\quad = c_1 + (n - 1)d$,

where $c_1 = a_1 + b_1$ and $d = d_1 + d_2$.

SECTION 11.2 (pp. 861–863)

1. (a) 1, 2, 3, 4, 5 **(b)** $1 + 2 + 3 + 4 + 5$ **(c)** 15

3. (a) 1, 0, -1, -2, -3

(b) $1 + 0 + (-1) + (-2) + (-3)$ **(c)** -5

5. $A_5 + A_6 + A_7 + A_8 + A_9$

7. 45 **9.** 25 **11.** 60 **13.** $\frac{71}{20}$ **15.** 80 **17.** 1275

19. 1739 **21.** 4100 **23.** 31 **25.** 460 **27.** 105

29. 1942 **31.** 948 **33.** 545 **35.** 255 **37.** 546.5

39. 3,145,725 **41.** 0.625; 0.671875; 0.666015625

43. 5; 42.333333333; 341

45. $\frac{3}{2}$ **47.** $\frac{18}{5}$ **49.** $\frac{10}{11}$

51. $\frac{2}{3} = 0.6 + 0.06 + 0.006 + 0.0006 + \cdots$

53. $\frac{9}{11} = 0.81 + 0.0081 + 0.000081 + \cdots$

55. $\frac{1}{7} = 0.142857 + 0.000000142857 + \cdots$

57. $\frac{8}{9}$ **59.** $\frac{5}{11}$ **61.** $2 + 3 + 4 + 5 = 14$

63. $4 + 4 + 4 + 4 + 4 + 4 + 4 + 4 = 32$

65. $1 + 8 + 27 + 64 + 125 + 216 + 343 = 784$

67. $12 + 20 = 32$

69. $\sum_{k=1}^{6} k^4$ **71.** $\sum_{k=1}^{7} \left(\frac{2k}{k+1}\right)$

73. $\sum_{k=1}^{\infty} \left(\frac{1}{k^2}\right)$ **75.** $\sum_{n=1}^{4} (n + 5)^3$ **77.** $\sum_{n=1}^{24} (3n + 22)$

79. $\sum_{n=1}^{37} (n^2 + 27n + 180)$

81. 540 **83.** 600 **85.** 1395 **87.** 5525

89. 1360 **91.** 290

93. $\sum_{k=1}^{n} k = 1 + 2 + 3 + \cdots + n$ is an arithmetic series with $a_1 = 1$ and $a_n = n$. Its sum equals

$S_n = n\left(\frac{a_1 + a_n}{2}\right) = n\left(\frac{1 + n}{2}\right) = \frac{n(n + 1)}{2}$.

95. (a) & (b) $\$819{,}000$ **97.** $\$91{,}523.93$ **99.** $\$62{,}278.01$

101. $S_9 = 9\left(\frac{7 + 15}{2}\right) = 99$ logs

103. (a) $\sum_{k=1}^{n} 0.5(0.5)^{k-1}$ **(b)** Infinitely many filters

105. 2

107. $1 + 1 + \frac{1}{2} + \frac{1}{6} + \frac{1}{24} + \frac{1}{120} + \frac{1}{720} + \frac{1}{5040}$

≈ 2.718254; $e \approx 2.718282$

109. $S_2 = \frac{4}{3} \approx 1.3333$, $S_4 = \frac{40}{27} \approx 1.4815$, $S_8 \approx 1.49977$,

$S_{16} \approx 1.49999997$; $S = 1.5$. As n increases, the partial sums approach S.

111. $S_1 = 4$, $S_2 = 3.6$, $S_3 = 3.64$, $S_4 = 3.636$,

$S_5 = 3.6364$, $S_6 = 3.63636$; $S = \frac{40}{11} = 3.\overline{63}$.

As n increases, the partial sums approach S.

CHECKING BASIC CONCEPTS FOR SECTIONS 11.1 AND 11.2 (p. 864)

1. [0, 7, 1] by [-10, 2, 1]

3. (a) Arithmetic; $S_{10} = 190$

(b) Geometric; $S_6 = \frac{364}{81} \approx 4.494$

(c) Geometric; $S = \frac{8}{3} \approx 2.667$ **(d)** Geometric; $S = 1$

5. (a) 150 **(b)** 6622

SECTION 11.3 (pp. 871–873)

1. $2^{10} = 1024$

3. $2^5 4^{10} = 33{,}554{,}432$

5. $10^3 \cdot 26^3 = 17{,}576{,}000$

7. $26^3 \cdot 36^3 = 820{,}025{,}856$

9. $3^5 = 243$ **11.** $5^5 = 3125$ **13.** 2 **15.** 24

17. 1,000,000 **19.** $2^{12} = 4096$

21. No; there are 35,152 call letters possible.

23. 24 **25.** 8,000,000 **27.** 720 **29.** 3,628,800

31. 60 **33.** 8 **35.** 210 **37.** 600 **39.** 5040

41. 24   **43.** 2730   **45.** 210   **47.** 30,000
49. 360   **51.** 362,880   **53.** About 6.39×10^{12}
55. 6,400,000,000   **57.** 3   **59.** 20   **61.** 1
63. 28   **65.** 190   **67.** 575,757   **69.** 30
71. 50   **73.** 7920   **75.** 2024
77. $P(n, n-1) = \dfrac{n!}{(n-(n-1))!} = \dfrac{n!}{1} = n!$ and
$P(n, n) = \dfrac{n!}{(n-n)!} = \dfrac{n!}{0!} = \dfrac{n!}{1} = n!$. For example,
$P(7, 6) = 5040 = P(7, 7)$.

SECTION 11.4 (p. 878)

1. 5   **3.** 1   **5.** 6   **7.** 1   **9.** 10   **11.** 70   **13.** 1   **15.** 5
17. $x^2 + 2xy + y^2$ **19.** $m^3 + 6m^2 + 12m + 8$
21. $8x^3 - 36x^2 + 54x - 27$
23. $p^6 - 6p^5q + 15p^4q^2 - 20p^3q^3 + 15p^2q^4 - 6pq^5 + q^6$
25. $8m^3 + 36m^2n + 54mn^2 + 27n^3$
27. $1 - 4x^2 + 6x^4 - 4x^6 + x^8$
29. $8p^9 - 36p^6 + 54p^3 - 27$
31. $x^2 + 2xy + y^2$
33. $81x^4 + 108x^3 + 54x^2 + 12x + 1$
35. $32 - 80x + 80x^2 - 40x^3 + 10x^4 - x^5$
37. $x^8 + 8x^6 + 24x^4 + 32x^2 + 16$
39. $256x^4 - 768x^3y + 864x^2y^2 - 432xy^3 + 81y^4$
41. $m^6 + 6m^5n + 15m^4n^2 + 20m^3n^3 + 15m^2n^4 + 6mn^5 + n^6$
43. $8x^9 - 12x^6y^2 + 6x^3y^4 - y^6$
45. $84a^6b^3$ **47.** $70x^4y^4$ **49.** $40x^2y^3$ **51.** $-576xy^5$

CHECKING BASIC CONCEPTS FOR SECTIONS 11.3 AND 11.4 (p. 878)

1. $2^8 = 256$ **3.** $26 \cdot 36^5 = 1,572,120,576$

SECTION 11.5 (pp. 883–884)

1. $3 + 6 + 9 + \cdots + 3n = \dfrac{3n(n+1)}{2}$
(i) Show that the statement is true for $n = 1$:
$3(1) = \dfrac{3(1)(2)}{2}$
$\quad 3 = 3$
(ii) Assume that S_k is true:
$3 + 6 + 9 + \cdots + 3k = \dfrac{3k(k+1)}{2}$
Show that S_{k+1} is true:
$3 + 6 + \cdots + 3(k+1) = \dfrac{3(k+1)(k+2)}{2}$
Add $3(k+1)$ to each side of S_k:
$3 + 6 + 9 + \cdots + 3k + 3(k+1)$
$= \dfrac{3k(k+1)}{2} + 3(k+1)$
$= \dfrac{3k(k+1) + 6(k+1)}{2}$
$= \dfrac{(k+1)(3k+6)}{2}$
$= \dfrac{3(k+1)(k+2)}{2}$
Since S_k implies S_{k+1}, the statement is true for every positive integer n.
3–13. See the Student's Solutions Manual.
15. 1, 2   **17.** 2, 3, 4
19. $(a^m)^n = a^{mn}$
(i) Show that the statement is true for $n = 1$:
$(a^m)^1 = a^{m \cdot 1}$
$a^m = a^m$

(ii) Assume that S_k is true:
$(a^m)^k = a^{mk}$
Show that S_{k+1} is true:
$(a^m)^{k+1} = a^{m(k+1)}$
Multiply each side of S_k by a^m:
$(a^m)^k \cdot (a^m)^1 = a^{mk} \cdot a^m$
$(a^m)^{k+1} = a^{mk+m}$
$(a^m)^{k+1} = a^{m(k+1)}$
Since S_k implies S_{k+1}, the statement is true for every positive integer n.
21–29. See the Student's Solutions Manual.
31. $P = 3\left(\dfrac{4}{3}\right)^{n-1}$ **33.** $2^n - 1$

SECTION 11.6 (pp. 894–897)

1. Yes   **3.** No   **5.** Yes   **7.** No   **9.** $\dfrac{1}{2}$ **11.** $\dfrac{1}{6}$
13. $\dfrac{1}{2}$ **15.** $\dfrac{4}{52} = \dfrac{1}{13}$ **17.** $\dfrac{1}{10,000}$
19. (a) 0.57, or 57%   **(b)** 0.33, or 33%
21. $A \cup B = \{10, 25, 26, 35\}$; $A \cap B = \{25, 26\}$
23. $A \cup B = \{1, 3, 5, 7, 9, 11\}$; $A \cap B = \varnothing$
25. $A \cup B = \{\text{Heads, Tails}\}$; $A \cap B = \varnothing$
27. $\dfrac{1}{4}$ **29.** $\dfrac{1}{27}$ **31.** $\dfrac{1}{36}$ **33.** $\dfrac{625}{1296} \approx 0.482$ **35.** $\dfrac{1}{270,725}$
37. $\dfrac{\binom{13}{3} \cdot \binom{13}{2}}{\binom{52}{5}} \approx 0.0086$, or a 0.86% chance
39. $\dfrac{4}{20} = 0.2$
41. (a)

(b) 0.7, or 70%
(c) Let M denote the event of needing help with math and E the event of needing help with English. Then $P(M \cup E) = P(M) + P(E) - P(M \cap E)$
$= 0.5 + 0.45 - 0.25 = 0.7$.
43. (a) $\dfrac{9}{50}$ **(b)** $\dfrac{9}{25}$ **(c)** $\dfrac{71}{100}$
45. $\dfrac{634}{100,000} = 0.00634$
47. (a) $\dfrac{223,508}{679,590} \approx 0.329$ **(b)** $\dfrac{456,082}{679,590} \approx 0.671$
(c) $\dfrac{130,520}{679,590} \approx 0.192$
49. $\dfrac{10}{36} = \dfrac{5}{18}$ **51.** $\dfrac{12}{52} = \dfrac{3}{13}$ **53. (a)** 0.7   **(b)** 0.09
55. (a) 0.09   **(b)** 0.12   **57.** $\dfrac{1}{1000}$
59. (a) $\dfrac{22}{50} = 0.44$ **(b)** $\dfrac{28}{50} = 0.56$ **(c)** $\dfrac{28}{50} = 0.56$
61. $\dfrac{3}{51} = \dfrac{1}{17}$ **63.** $\dfrac{1}{3}$ **65.** $\dfrac{19}{27}$ **67.** 40%   **69.** $\dfrac{1}{3}$
71. (a) $\dfrac{18}{235}$ **(b)** $\dfrac{7}{18}$ **(c)** $\dfrac{7}{235}$
73. (a) $\dfrac{8}{15}$ **(b)** $\dfrac{7}{15}$ **(c)** $\dfrac{2}{5}$ **(d)** $\dfrac{1}{3}$ **(e)** $\dfrac{1}{15}$

CHECKING BASIC CONCEPTS FOR SECTIONS 11.5 AND 11.6 (p. 897)

1. $4 + 8 + 12 + \cdots + 4n = 2n(n+1)$
(i) Show that the statement is true for $n = 1$:
$4(1) = 2(1)(1+1)$
$\quad 4 = 4$

(ii) Assume that S_k is true:
$$4 + 8 + 12 + \cdots + 4k = 2k(k + 1)$$
Show that S_{k+1} is true:
$$4 + 8 + \cdots + 4(k + 1) = 2(k + 1)(k + 2)$$
Add $4(k + 1)$ to each side of S_k:
$$4 + 8 + 12 + \cdots + 4k + 4(k + 1)$$
$$= 2k(k + 1) + 4(k + 1)$$
$$= 2k^2 + 6k + 4$$
$$= 2(k + 1)(k + 2)$$
Since S_k implies S_{k+1}, the statement is true for every positive integer n.

3. $\frac{1}{16}$ **5.** $\dfrac{\binom{4}{4} \cdot \binom{4}{1}}{\binom{52}{5}} = \dfrac{4}{2,598,960} \approx 0.0000015$

CHAPTER 11: REVIEW EXERCISES (pp. 901–902)

1. $-1, -4, -7, -10$ **3.** $0, 1, 3, 7$
5. $5, 3, 1, 2, 4, 6$
7. (a)

n	1	2	3	4	5	6	7	8
a_n	3	1	-1	-3	-5	-7	-9	-11

(b) $[0, 10, 1]$ by $[-12, 4, 1]$

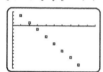

(c) $a_n = -2n + 5$
9. $a_n = 4n - 15$ **11.** Arithmetic   **13.** Geometric
15. 65   **17.** 90   **19.** 3280   **21.** 3
23. $6 + 11 + 16 + 21 + 26$

25. $\displaystyle\sum_{k=1}^{6} k^3$ **27.** -1155

29. $0.18 + 0.0018 + 0.000018 + \cdots$
31. 120
33. $1 + 3 + 5 + \cdots + (2n - 1) = n^2$
(i) Show that the statement is true for $n = 1$:
$$2(1) - 1 = 1^2$$
$$1 = 1$$
(ii) Assume that S_k is true:
$$1 + 3 + 5 + \cdots + (2k - 1) = k^2$$
Show that S_{k+1} is true:
$$1 + 3 + \cdots + (2(k + 1) - 1) = (k + 1)^2$$
Add $2k + 1$ to each side of S_k:
$$1 + 3 + 5 + \cdots + (2k - 1) + (2k + 1)$$
$$= k^2 + 2k + 1$$
$$= (k + 1)^2$$
Since S_k implies S_{k+1}, the statement is true for every positive integer n.
35. $\frac{1}{2}$ **37.** 120   **39.** $4^{20} \approx 1.1 \times 10^{12}$ **41.** 6,250,000
43. (a) $4, 3.6, 3.24, 2.916, 2.6244$; geometric
(b) $[0, 6, 1]$ by $[0, 6, 1]$ **(c)** $a_n = 4(0.9)^{n-1}$

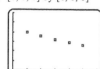

45. 20   **47.** 210   **49.** $\frac{91}{120} \approx 0.758$

51. (a) $\frac{27}{60} = 0.45$ **(b)** $\frac{33}{60} = 0.55$ **(c)** $\frac{13}{60} \approx 0.217$
53. The population density grows slowly initially, then increases rapidly, and finally levels off near 4,000,000 per acre.
$[0, 16, 1]$ by $[0, 5000, 1000]$

CHAPTER 11 EXTENDED AND DISCOVERY EXERCISES (pp. 902–903)

1. (a) $P = \begin{bmatrix} 1 & 0 & 0 \\ \frac{1}{6} & \frac{2}{3} & \frac{1}{6} \\ 0 & 0 & 1 \end{bmatrix}$

(b) The greatest probabilities lie on the main diagonal: $1, \frac{2}{3}, 1$; this means that a mother cell is most likely to produce a daughter cell like itself (answers will vary).
3. The quantity $\dfrac{a_1 + a_n}{2}$ represents not only the average of a_1 and a_n but also the average of the terms $a_1, a_2, a_3, \ldots, a_n$. This is true whether n is odd or even. The total sum is equal to n times the average of the terms.

CHAPTERS 1–11 CUMULATIVE REVIEW EXERCISES (pp. 903–907)

1. 3.45×10^4; 0.000152 **3.** $\sqrt{41}$
5. (a) 2; $\sqrt{-a}$ **(b)** $D = \{x \mid x \leq 1\}$, or $(-\infty, 1]$
7. 7   **9.** $y = -\frac{6}{5}x - \frac{8}{5}$
11. (a) $\frac{3}{4}$; -1; $\frac{4}{3}$ **(b)** $f(x) = \frac{3}{4}x - 1$ **(c)** $\frac{4}{3}$
13. (a) $\frac{17}{10}$ **(b)** $-\frac{1}{3}, \frac{5}{2}$ **(c)** $\frac{1 \pm \sqrt{13}}{2}$ **(d)** $-2, -1, 2$
(e) $\pm\sqrt{3}$, ± 1 **(f)** $\frac{17}{3}$ **(g)** $\dfrac{\ln(28/3)}{2} \approx 1.117$
(h) $10^{3/2} - 1 \approx 30.623$ **(i)** 6   **(j)** $-\frac{4}{3}, 2$
15. f is continuous.

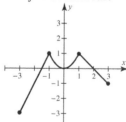

17. (a) $-2, -1, 1, 2$
(b) $\{x \mid x < -2 \text{ or } -1 < x < 1 \text{ or } x > 2\}$, or $(-\infty, -2) \cup (-1, 1) \cup (2, \infty)$
(c) $\{x \mid -2 \leq x \leq -1 \text{ or } 1 \leq x \leq 2\}$, or $[-2, -1] \cup [1, 2]$
19. $\left(\frac{3}{2}, \frac{31}{4}\right)$
21. (a) Incr: $\{x \mid x < -2\}$, $\{x \mid x > 1\}$, or $(-\infty, -2)$, $(1, \infty)$; decr: $\{x \mid -2 < x < 1\}$, or $(-2, 1)$
(b) $-3.3, 0, 1.8$ **(c)** $(-2, 2), (1, -0.7)$
(d) Local minimum: -0.7, local maximum: 2
23. (a) $3x^2 - 1 + \frac{1}{2x^2}$
(b) $2x^3 - 5x^2 + 5x - 6 + \frac{8}{x + 1}$

25. $f(x) = 3(x + 1)(x - 3i)(x + 3i)$;
$f(x) = 3x^3 + 3x^2 + 27x + 27$
27. $-1 \pm 2i$ **29.** $(x + 1)^{3/5}$; 8
31. (a) 3   **(b)** -1 **(c)** 1   **(d)** -4
33. $f^{-1}(x) = -\dfrac{x}{x - 1}$ **35.** $f(x) = 2(3)^x$
37. \$1221.61
39. (a) $D = \{x \mid -\infty < x < \infty\}$, or $(-\infty, \infty)$;
$R = \{x \mid x \geq 0\}$, or $[0, \infty)$
(b) $D = \{x \mid -\infty < x < \infty\}$, or $(-\infty, \infty)$;
$R = \{x \mid x > 0\}$, or $(0, \infty)$
(c) $D = \{x \mid x > 0\}$, or $(0, \infty)$;
$R = \{x \mid -\infty < x < \infty\}$, or $(-\infty, \infty)$
(d) $D = \{x \mid x \neq 0\}$, or $(-\infty, 0) \cup (0, \infty)$;
$R = \{x \mid x \neq 0\}$, or $(-\infty, 0) \cup (0, \infty)$
41. $\log \dfrac{x^2 y^3}{\sqrt[3]{z}}$
43. (a)

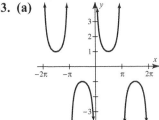

(b)

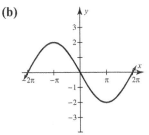

(c)

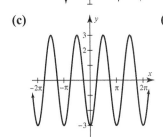

(d)

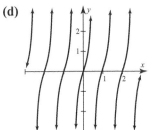

45. (a) $\dfrac{5\pi}{6} + 2\pi n, \dfrac{7\pi}{6} + 2\pi n$ **(b)** $\dfrac{\pi}{4} + \dfrac{\pi}{2}n$
(c) $\pi n, \dfrac{7\pi}{6} + 2\pi n, \dfrac{11\pi}{6} + 2\pi n$ **(d)** $\dfrac{\pi}{2} + \pi n$
47. $5°32'24''$ **49.** $225°$
51. $\sin\theta = \dfrac{24}{25}, \cos\theta = -\dfrac{7}{25}, \tan\theta = -\dfrac{24}{7}, \csc\theta = \dfrac{25}{4},$
$\sec\theta = -\dfrac{25}{7}, \cot\theta = -\dfrac{7}{24}$
53. $\sin\theta = -\dfrac{60}{61}, \cos\theta = -\dfrac{11}{61}, \tan\theta = \dfrac{60}{11}, \csc\theta = -\dfrac{61}{60},$
$\sec\theta = -\dfrac{61}{11}, \cot\theta = \dfrac{11}{60}$
55. $b = 8; \alpha \approx 36.9°; \beta \approx 53.1°$
57. $1 - \sin^2\theta + \cot^2\theta - \sin^2\theta \cot^2\theta$
$= 1 - \sin^2\theta - \sin^2\theta \cot^2\theta + \cot^2\theta$
$= 1 - \sin^2\theta(1 + \cot^2\theta) + \cot^2\theta$
$= 1 - \sin^2\theta(\csc^2\theta) + \cot^2\theta$
$= 1 - 1 + \cot^2\theta$
$= \cot^2\theta$
59. (a) $b \approx 15.4; c \approx 11.8; \alpha = 107°$
(b) $a_1 \approx 8.5; \alpha_1 \approx 68.9°; \beta_1 \approx 61.1°$ or
$a_2 \approx 1.8; \alpha_2 \approx 11.1°; \beta_2 \approx 118.9°$
(c) $a \approx 5.7; \beta \approx 58.6°; \gamma \approx 77.4°$
(d) $\alpha \approx 51.3°; \beta \approx 59.2°; \gamma \approx 69.5°$

61. (a) 5   **(b)** $\langle -26, 56 \rangle$ **(c)** -63
(d) About $165.75°$
63.

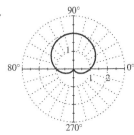

65. (a) $(-1, 2)$ **(b)** $\{(x, y) \mid 4x - y = -2\}$
(c) Four solutions: $(\pm 3, \pm\sqrt{7})$ **(d)** $\left(\dfrac{5z - 24}{3}, \dfrac{z + 6}{3}, z\right)$
67. (a)   **(b)**

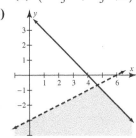

69. $\begin{bmatrix} -2 & -1 \\ -1.5 & -0.5 \end{bmatrix}$
71. (a) -11 **(b)** 22   **73.** $y^2 = 3x$
75. $\dfrac{y^2}{25} - \dfrac{x^2}{144} = 1$ **77.** $a_n = 4n$
79. (a) 950   **(b)** $\dfrac{2}{9}$ **81.** 175,760,000
83. $16x^4 - 32x^3 + 24x^2 - 8x + 1$
85. $\dfrac{16}{52} = \dfrac{4}{13}$ **87.** $\dfrac{8}{20} = \dfrac{2}{5}$ **89.** 146.5 mi
91. 0.6 hr at 7 mi/hr; 0.7 hr at 9 mi/hr
93. $\dfrac{20}{9} \approx 2.22$ hr
95. (a) $C(x) = x(405 - 5x)$ **(b)** 25 or 56; the cost is
\$7000 when 25 or 56 tickets are purchased.
(c) \$8200; the cost is \$8200 when 40 or 41 tickets are
purchased.
97. 1.125 ft   **99.** $\dfrac{49}{77} = \dfrac{7}{11}$

APPENDIX C: Partial Fractions (p. AP-29)

1. $\dfrac{5}{3x} + \dfrac{-10}{3(2x + 1)}$ **3.** $\dfrac{6}{5(x + 2)} + \dfrac{8}{5(2x - 1)}$
5. $\dfrac{5}{6(x + 5)} + \dfrac{1}{6(x - 1)}$
7. $\dfrac{-2}{x + 1} + \dfrac{2}{x + 2} + \dfrac{4}{(x + 2)^2}$ **9.** $\dfrac{4}{x} + \dfrac{4}{1 - x}$
11. $\dfrac{15}{x} + \dfrac{-5}{x + 1} + \dfrac{-6}{x - 1}$ **13.** $1 + \dfrac{-2}{x + 1} + \dfrac{1}{(x + 1)^2}$
15. $x^3 - x^2 + \dfrac{-1}{3(2x + 1)} + \dfrac{2}{3(x + 2)}$
17. $\dfrac{1}{9} + \dfrac{-1}{x} + \dfrac{25}{18(3x + 2)} + \dfrac{29}{18(3x - 2)}$
19. $\dfrac{-3}{5x^2} + \dfrac{3}{5(x^2 + 5)}$ **21.** $\dfrac{-2}{7(x + 4)} + \dfrac{6x - 3}{7(3x^2 + 1)}$
23. $\dfrac{1}{4x} + \dfrac{-8}{19(2x + 1)} + \dfrac{-9x - 24}{76(3x^2 + 4)}$
25. $\dfrac{-1}{x} + \dfrac{2x}{2x^2 + 1} + \dfrac{2x + 3}{(2x^2 + 1)^2}$
27. $\dfrac{-1}{x + 2} + \dfrac{3}{(x^2 + 4)^2}$
29. $5x^2 + \dfrac{3}{x} + \dfrac{-1}{x + 3} + \dfrac{2}{x - 1}$

APPENDIX D: Percent Change and Exponential Functions
(pp. AP-34–AP-36)

1. (a) 0.35 (b) −0.0007 (c) 7.21 (d) 0.003
3. (a) −0.055 (b) −0.0154 (c) 1.2 (d) 0.0015
5. (a) 37% (b) −9.5% (c) 190% (d) 35%
7. (a) −12.1% (b) 140% (c) 320% (d) −25%
9. (a) 100% (b) −50%
11. (a) 2.36% (b) −2.31%
13. (a) 44.44% (b) −30.77%
15. (a) $1800 (b) $3300 (c) 2.2
17. (a) −$2200 (b) $1800 (c) 0.45
19. (a) −$4500 (b) $3000 (c) 0.4
21. $f(x) = 9500(0.65)^x$ 23. $f(x) = 2500(1.05)^x$
25. $f(x) = 1000(0.935)^x$
27. $C = 8, a = 1.12, r = 0.12$ or 12%
29. $C = 1.5, a = 0.35, r = -0.65$ or −65%
31. $C = 1, a = 0.55, r = -0.45$ or −45%
33. $C = 7, a = e, r = e - 1$ or about 171.8%
35. $C = 6, a = \frac{1}{3}, r = -\frac{2}{3}$ or about −66.7%
37. $f(t) = 35,000(1.098)^{t/2}$; about 44,215
39. $f(t) = 1000(3)^{t/7}$; about 5620
41. $f(t) = I_0\left(\frac{2}{3}\right)^{t/2}$; about $0.418I_0$
43. $f(t) = 5000(4)^{t/35}$; $6864.10
45. 10 years; $4027.51 47. 3.5 years; $1006.88
49. 2.8 years; $3020.63 51. 1.75% 53. 2% 55. 1%
57. About 2.21% 59. They are equal. 61. $7.39
63. About 2.56%

APPENDIX E: Rotation of Axes (p. AP-40)

1. Circle or ellipse or a point
3. Hyperbola or two intersecting lines
5. Parabola or one line or two parallel lines
7. 30° 9. 60° 11. 22.5°

13.
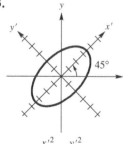
$$\frac{x'^2}{12} + \frac{y'^2}{4} = 1$$

15.
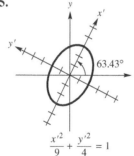
$$\frac{x'^2}{9} + \frac{y'^2}{4} = 1$$

17.
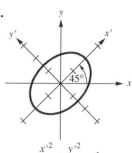
$$\frac{x'^2}{4} + \frac{y'^2}{2} = 1$$

19.
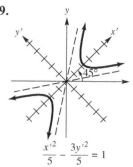
$$\frac{x'^2}{5} - \frac{3y'^2}{5} = 1$$

21.
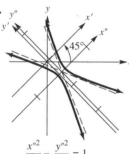
$$\frac{x'^2}{4} + \frac{y'^2}{16} = 1$$

23.
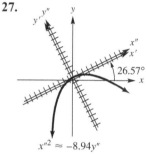
$$y'^2 = x'$$

25.
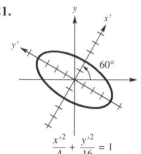
$$\frac{x''^2}{2} - \frac{y''^2}{10} = 1$$

27.
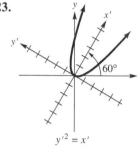
$$x''^2 \approx -8.94y''$$

29.
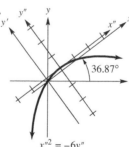
$$x''^2 = -6y''$$

Photo Credits

First front endsheet: **upper left,** Pixelbully/Alamy **upper right,** Frio Canyon Photography/Alamy **lower left,** Shutterstock **lower right,** Peter Dean/Alamy *Second front endsheet:* **upper left,** Fotoflirt Creative/Alamy **upper right,** Corbis Premium RF/Alamy **lower left,** Shutterstock **lower right,** Fotolia **iv,** Sommai/Shutterstock **1,** PCN Photography/Alamy **2,** Sandy Young/Alamy **4,** Courtesy of Wendy Rockswold **10,** Courtesy of Wendy Rockswold **11 (top),** Courtesy of Wendy Rockswold **11 (bottom),** Pressmaster/Fotolia **12,** Courtesy of Wendy Rockswold **13,** Steve Hamblin/Alamy **26,** Leonid Tit/Fotolia **42,** David Pearson/Alamy **45,** Marc Xavier/Fotolia **65,** U.S. Fish and Wildlife Service **66,** Andrew Watson/Fotolia **67,** Fotolia **68,** Stefan Sollfors/Alamy **71,** Kevin Foy/Alamy **76,** Iain Masterton/Alamy **86,** Fotolia **104,** Frio Canyon Photography/Alamy **110,** Courtesy of Wendy Rockswold **111,** Courtesy of Wendy Rockswold **116 (left),** Vera Bogaerts/Shutterstock **116 (right),** EPA European Pressphoto Agency B.V./Alamy **118,** Fotolia **121,** Corbis Premium RF/Alamy **122,** Courtesy of Wendy Rockswold **124,** Courtesy of Wendy Rockswold **134,** Peter Dean/Alamy **140,** Stanca Sanda/Alamy **155 (top),** Tannen Maury/Newscom **155 (bottom),** Walter Iooss Jr./NBAE/Getty Images **156,** ZUMA Wire Service/Alamy **165,** Alex Segre/Alamy **172,** Fotolia **178,** Fotolia **185,** Paul Sakuma/AP Images **188,** Shutterstock **197,** Shutterstock **205,** Fotolia **206,** Ilene MacDonald/Alamy **212,** Shutterstock **217,** Shutterstock **231,** Fotolia **232,** Courtesy of Wendy Rockswold **235,** Shutterstock **243,** Shutterstock **251,** Shutterstock **260,** Shutterstock **267,** Shutterstock **283,** Shutterstock **289,** Shutterstock **291,** Jeff Greenberg/Alamy **306,** Corbis Premium RF/Alamy **321,** NASA **322,** Shutterstock **325,** Shutterstock **326,** Fotolia **327,** Courtesy of Wendy Rockswold **348,** Newscom **349,** Keith Shuttlewood/Alamy **352,** UpperCut Images/Alamy **357,** Courtesy of Wendy Rockswold **365,** Cultura Creative/Alamy **380,** Muskopf Photography/Alamy **383,** Shutterstock **391,** Fotoflirt Creative/Alamy **399,** Shutterstock **415,** NASA **423,** Shutterstock **424,** Shutterstock **425,** Alex Segre/Alamy **432,** Shutterstock **435,** Courtesy of Wendy Rockswold **452,** Jeremy Sutton-Hibbert/Alamy **453,** Elise Amendola/AP Images **466,** Fotolia **480,** Fotolia **492,** Alan Pappe/Stockbyte/Getty Images **496,** Fotolia **498,** Fotolia **513,** Courtesy of Wendy Rockswold **520,** Darren Baker/Shutterstock **526,** Fotolia **529,** Fotolia **553,** Zuma Press/Newscom **554,** Fotolia **565,** Fotolia **573,** Elena Elisseeva/Shutterstock **579,** Fotolia **587,** Fotolia **592,** Clive Streeter/Dorling Kindersley, Ltd. **597,** Fotolia **603,** Adam Przezak/Shutterstock **607,** Shutterstock **619,** PJF/Alamy **620,** Planet5D, LLC/Shutterstock **632,** Fotolia **643,** Fotolia **660,** Shutterstock **670,** Fotolia **681,** Courtesy of Wendy Rockswold **697,** Gregory Sams/ScienceSource/Photo Researchers, Inc. **700,** Pixelbully/Alamy **701,** Fotolia **719,** Shutterstock **731,** Alex Segre/Alamy **738,** Kristoffer Tripplaar/Alamy **754,** Everett Collection **755,** Cyberstock/Alamy **768,** MIRA/Alamy **781,** Aardvark/Alamy **796,** NASA **797,** Mark Williamson/Fotolia **800,** Visual & Written SL/Alamy **806,** Mark Williamson/Fotolia **807,** Andrea Danti/Shutterstock **822,** Matt McPhee/Fotolia **826,** Ed Young/AG Stock Images, Inc./Alamy **836,** Fotolia **837,** Fotolia **839,** Fotolia **841,** TBK Media/Alamy **850,** Fotolia **864,** Shutterstock **879,** Fotolia **885,** Fotolia **886,** STILLFX/Shutterstock **889,** Dave Allen Photography/Shutterstock

Index of Applications

Profit
maximizing, 729, 730
maximum, 723
revenue and cost and, 352–353, 362
Revenue
cost and profit and, 352–353, 362
iPhone, 82
maximizing, 169, 229, 730
of technology companies, 31
Salaries and wages, 394
increases in, 415, 849, AP-36
Sales
of baseball game tickets, 736
of cars, 5–9, 83
of CDs, 101
of CRT and LCD screens, 102
of iPads, 753
of iPods, 90, 187, 704
of music in United States, 83
of plate glass, 780
of play tickets, 733, 736, 753
sale price, 101
of tablet computers, 117, 848
of tires, 779–780
of vinyl records, 101
Savings, 394
for retirement, 396
Student loans, 717, 718, 794
Walmart employees, 187, 335

COMBINATORICS AND PROBABILITY
Antibiotic resistance, 902–903
Area, 884
ATM access codes, 872
Baseball positions, 873
Batting orders, 873
Birthdays, 867, 873
Books on a shelf, 872, 873
Car designs, 873
Card hands, 873
College courses, 869, 873
Committee makeup, 870, 902
Computer packages, 872
Defective automobile parts, 896
Dinner choices, 872
Disease probability, 897
Drawing cards, 885–886, 889, 890, 891, 896
Electronic waste, 897
Exam questions, 901, 902
Exam responses, 865
Eye color probability, 887
Falling objects, 902
Flower samples, 873
Garage door opener codes, 872, 896
Handshakes, 884

Height of a ball, 902
Introductions, 872
Keys on a ring, 872
License plates, 865, 871, 901
Lock combinations, 872, 902
Lottery, 870, 872, 873, 896
Marble color, 873, 896, 902, 906
Musical chairs seating, 873
Organ transplant probability, 886
Peach samples, 873
Perimeter, 884
Polygraph test analysis, 892
Quality control, 902
Radio station call letters, 872
Rolling dice, 888–889, 891, 896, 902
Sides of a polygon, 884
Sitting at a round table, 873
Speeches in class, 901
Standing in line, 872, 901
Strings of letters, 871
Student characteristics, 897
Team selection, 873
Telephone numbers, 872, 873
Tennis serves, 896
Test questions, 873
Toll-free telephone numbers, 866
Tossing coins, 890, 896
Tower of Hanoi, 884
Traveling salesmen, 867, 872
Weather, 896

DESIGN/CONSTRUCTION
Angle of depression of a floodlight, 477
Arch bridges, 820, 835
Box construction, 185, 186, 229, 319, 320, 347, 699
Construction zones, 305
Green building material, 84
Height of a building, 477, 564
Height of an antenna, 478
Height of a pyramid, 478
Height of a tower, 477, 632
Height of the Gateway Arch, 632
Highway design, 439, 473–474, 479, 483–484, 495, 496–497, 508, 512, 536, 548, 549, 581, 585, 612, 631, 642
grade resistance and, 542, 548
Length of a guy wire, 477
Lumber costs, 131
Relative error in measurement, 151
Robotic arms
angle of, 542
design, 480
distance between hand and shoulder of, 641
distance of hand from origin, 659, 696

locating using vectors, 650
position of hand, 658, 696
spray painting using, 535
work space of, 460–461
Roman Coliseum, 820
Roof pitch, 542
Roof trusses, 710–711, 717
construction, 630, 641
design, 635
Safe distance for a tree, 548
Shrub placement, 543
Step design, 542
Suspension bridge, 170
Whispering gallery, 820

EARTH AND LIFE SCIENCE
Acid rain, 412–413
Antarctic ozone layer, 131
Archaeology, 152
Atom structure, 831
Bacterial populations, 394, 434, 449, 848
of E. coli, 396
E. coli concentration, 433
E. coli growth, 389
growth of, 396, 414, 552, AP-36
Biological equation, 422
Biological rhythms, 492, 496, 497
Birds
diversity of, 414
life span of, 434
populations of, 281, 408, 443
survival rates for song sparrows, 65
wing size of, 327–328, 330–331, 334, 442–443
Body temperature, 526
Daylight hours, 527, 528, 542, 579, 585, 586, 617
Depth of a lake, 11
Discharge of water, 10
Distance
across a canyon, 630
across a lake, 640
across a river, 630
between two cities, 458, 464, 548
Dog years, 282
Earthquakes, 412–413
Endangered species, 66
Estimating populations, 133
e-waste, 717
Eye color probability, 887
Fertilizer usage, 443
Fiddler crab growth, 321, 335
Filtering water, 397, 863
Fish
growth of, 450
length of, 292–293

Index

Formulas from Geometry

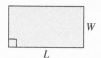

Rectangle

$A = LW$

$P = 2L + 2W$

Triangle

$A = \frac{1}{2}bh$

$P = a + b + c$

Pythagorean Theorem

$c^2 = a^2 + b^2$

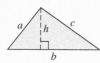

Circle

$C = 2\pi r$

$A = \pi r^2$

Equilateral Triangle

$A = \frac{\sqrt{3}}{4} s^2$

$P = 3s$

Parallelogram

$A = bh$

$P = 2a + 2b$

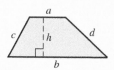

Trapezoid

$A = \frac{1}{2}(a + b)h$

$P = a + b + c + d$

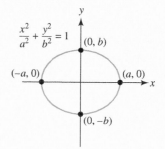

Ellipse

$A = \pi ab$

$P \approx 2\pi \sqrt{\dfrac{a^2 + b^2}{2}}$

$$\frac{x^2}{a^2} + \frac{y^2}{b^2} = 1$$

Sum of the Angles in a Triangle

$A + B + C = 180°$

Sum of the Angles in a Quadrilateral

$A + B + C + D = 360°$

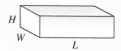

Rectangular (Parallelepiped) Box

$V = LWH$

$S = 2LW + 2LH + 2WH$

Cylinder

$V = \pi r^2 h$

$S = 2\pi rh + 2\pi r^2$

Sphere

$V = \frac{4}{3}\pi r^3$

$S = 4\pi r^2$

Cone

$V = \frac{1}{3}\pi r^2 h$

$S = \pi r^2 + \pi r \sqrt{r^2 + h^2}$